T3-BVC-472

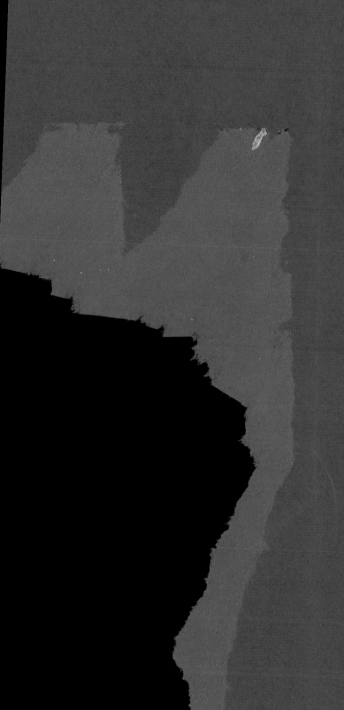

Biology of the Reptilia

Volume 19, Morphology G

Visceral Organs

Biology of the Reptilia

Edited by
Carl Gans

Volume 19, Morphology G
Visceral Organs

Co-editor for this volume
Abbot S. Gaunt

WITHDRAWN

Society for the Study of Amphibians and Reptiles
1998

SERIES EDITOR'S NOTE

This is the first volume in this celebrated series to be published under the imprint of the Society for the Study of Amphibians and Reptiles. A complete list of the previous volumes is provided at the end of this book. This list gives the names of the various publishers and other details of publication.

SSAR is pleased to be entrusted by Professor Carl Gans with the publication of this series and acknowledge his cooperation, and that of his co-editor, Abbot S. Gaunt, in producing this volume. We also thank Susan Abrams, biology editor at the University of Chicago Press, for her help in making the transition from Chicago's sponsorship.

CONTRIBUTIONS TO HERPETOLOGY, VOLUME 14

KRAIG ADLER, *Editor*   TIMOTHY D. PERRY, *Associate Editor*

Volumes in the *Contributions to Herpetology* series can be purchased from the Publications Secretary, Robert D. Aldridge, Department of Biology, Saint Louis University, 3507 Laclede, Saint Louis, Missouri 63103, USA (*telephone*: area code 314, 977–3916 or 977–1710; *fax*: area code 314, 977–3658; *e-mail*: ssar@slu.edu). A list of all Society publications, including those of The Ohio Herpetological Society and the *Catalogue of American Amphibians and Reptiles*, is printed at the end of this book; additional copies of this list are available from Dr. Aldridge. Volumes in the *Contributions* series are published irregularly and ordered by separate subscription, although Society members receive a substantial pre-publication discount. Authors who wish to have manuscripts considered for publication in the *Contributions* series should contact the Editor: Kraig Adler, Cornell University, Section of Neurobiology and Behavior, Seeley G. Mudd Hall, Ithaca, New York 14853–2702, USA.

Members of the Society receive a quarterly technical journal (*Journal of Herpetology*) and a quarterly news-journal (*Herpetological Review*). Currently, dues are US$30.00 for students, $40.00 for all others, world-wide; institutional subscriptions are $70.00. Additional $35.00 for airmail delivery outside the USA. Society members receive substantial discounts on *Herpetological Circulars* and *Facsimile Reprints* and on books in the *Contributions* and *Herpetological Conservation* series. The *Catalogue* is available by separate subscription. Apply to the Society's Treasurer, Robert D. Aldridge (address above). Overseas customers can make payments in USA funds or by International Money Order. All persons may charge to MasterCard or VISA (include account number and expiration date).

Contents

Contributors

WARREN W. BURGGREN
Department of Biological Sciences
University of Nevada, Las Vegas,
4505 Maryland Parkway
Las Vegas, Nevada 89154–4004
U.S.A.

ANTHONY P. FARRELL
Department of Biological Sciences
Simon Fraser University
Burnaby, British Columbia V5A 1S6
Canada

E. T. B. FRANCIS (deceased)
University of Sheffield
Western Bank
Sheffield S10 2TN
U.K.

A. K. GAMPERL
Department of Biological Sciences
Simon Fraser University
Burnaby, British Columbia V5A 1S6
Canada

JAMES W. HICKS
The Evolutionary and Comparative
   Physiology Group
Department of Ecology and Evolu-
   tionary Biology
University of California, Irvine
Irvine, California 92697
U.S.A.

STEVEN F. PERRY
Abteilung Morphologie und Systematik
Zoologisches Institut
Universität Bonn, 53115 Bonn
Germany

FENTON SCHAFFNER
Mount Sinai School of Medicine
City University of New York
Box 1101, 1 Gustave L. Levy Place
New York, New York 10029
U.S.A.

ALLAN W. SMITS
Department of Biology
University of Texas at Arlington
P.O. Box 19498
Arlington, Texas 76019
U.S.A.

YASUKAZU TANAKA
Department of Clinical Pathology
Ohme Municipal General Hospital
4–16–5 Higashi-ohme
Ohme, Tokyo 198
Japan

VAN WALLACH
Center for Vertebrate Studies
Department of Biology
Northeastern University
Boston, Massachusetts 02138
U.S.A.

TOBIAS WANG
Department of Biological Sciences
University of Odense
Campusvej 55
Odense
Denmark

Preface

The *Biology of the Reptilia* was designed to provide a reference to all aspects of reptilian biology independent of the kinds of specialists who had generated the information and independent of their workplace, institution, and geographical site. Initially we sorted things by classical subdivisions such as morphology, physiology, and behavior, because most of the available literature had been assembled in this fashion.

Consequently, the morphological subsection of the *Biology of the Reptilia* aimed to generate a guide to the major organ systems, to their phylogenetic diversity, and to other topics pertaining thereto. More recently, it is becoming clear that investigators are no longer restricting themselves to such classical subdivisions. More commonly, descriptive morphology is being combined with discussions of the way structures are used in terms of simple function and of the ecological and evolutionary implications of their use.

The reptilian visceral system incorporates several critical structures occupying the coelomic cavity. Some support metabolism; others are involved with endocrine and reproductive aspects. All occupy adjacent positions in the coelomic space, most are associated by placement adjacent to the gut and the circulatory pathways. Some of these visceral organs have been covered in previous volumes. However, we had major difficulty in assembling accounts of certain important organs, such as the heart, the lungs, the spleen, and the liver, which are finally covered here.

A major problem has been that the amount of information now available on these organ systems differs drastically for the several groups of reptiles. Thus, there are only some 24 species of crocodylians, some 250 of testudinians, and perhaps 5000 sphenodontids and lepidosaurians, yet, we do not have 200 times as much literature for the latter as for the former group. Furthermore, the available literature is even more skewed within each major group, and the reasons for species selection have reflected convenience and historical accidents more than biological reasoning. The largest extant reptiles continue to be represented by juveniles, although we know that allometric growth is common. However, practical reasons have forced us to compromise in the ways these issues are treated and the amount of detail that is included and presented.

The present volume is designed to deal with the major organs housed in the coelomic space. Some of the structures here placed have already been dealt with in past volumes of this series (urinogenital system, volume 6: Fox, 1977; digestive tract, 6: Parsons and Cameron, 1977; 6: Luppa, 1977; 8: Skoszylas, 1978; immunology, 14: Cooper et al., 1985). However, the present accounts concentrate on the morphology of the major organs placed here, namely the lungs, the heart, the liver, and the spleen.

As part of the developmental history of the series, some functional aspects have already been noted in earlier volumes. Here we deal with the structure of these systems; however, for lungs and heart we benefit from a diversity of approaches and include further functional information. We have also taken advantage of a very extensive analysis of snake lungs being generated by Van Wallach. Whereas he provides far more detail in the database for this assemblage of 2500 species than we can report for the remaining reptiles, his analysis, although admittedly preliminary, provides an excellent indication of the extent of structural and by implication of ecological and functional diversity to be expected.

Much of the work here reported derives from studies carried out since the *Biology of the Reptilia* first started to be organized. This documents that the limited amount of material available at various earlier times was insufficient then to comprise a cohesive volume. For instance, an account on the reptilian heart by my long-term friend, E. T. B. Francis, arrived decades ago just after accounts of some related structures could be published; consequently, it had to be put aside for lack of companionship. I am happy that, with the approval of Dr. Francis, it finally could serve as the basis for the present chapter on the heart organized by Anthony Farrell. While the material for this volume was being assembled in 1994, we received the sad news of Dr. Francis's demise. It appears appropriate to dedicate this volume to his memory.

I am grateful to Abbot Gaunt for agreeing to assist with the planning and editorial process on this volume. Advice and specific reviews were obtained from Nancy Anderson, Warren W. Burggren, David Cannatella, David Carrier, Bobby R. Collins, Anthony P. Farrell, Fredric Frye, Keith Henley, James Hicks, Donald C. Jackson, David R. Jones, Edmond Malnate, Scott Moodie, Thomas S. Parsons, Steven F. Perry, Rebecca Pyles, Herbert I. Rosenberg, Allan Smits, Van Wallach, Tobias Wang, and Fred White, and we appreciate the assistance of the colleagues providing them. Ernie Liner kindly reviewed the lists of references and helped to standardize these, and George Zug once again checked the taxonomic names for appropriateness and orthography. I remain in their debt. The Society for the Study of Amphibians and Reptiles came forward at a critical moment with the decision to publish this volume. I express my appreciation to Kraig Adler, who facilitated the shift of the series to publication by the Society. He and his associate, Timothy Perry, also helped us profoundly with checking of obscure literature, systematic terminology, indexing procedures, and general herpetological information.

The Department of Biology of The University of Michigan and the Department of Zoology of the University of Texas at Austin assisted with the costs of postage and e-mail.

Austin, Texas   CARL GANS

Dedication

IN HONOR OF ERIC THOMAS BRAZIL FRANCIS

Dr. Francis, known to generations of herpetologists as the author of the book *The Anatomy of the Salamander*, was born in Reading, England, on 3 October 1900. A colleague notes that he was of Berkshire origins and that his family may have been in the provision trade. After completing his training at the local Reading University College in 1926, he obtained pre-degree certification and an external degree from the University of London in 1929. He was an early research student of F. J. Cole and N. Eales, who held his work in great esteem. He joined the Zoology Department of Sheffield University as Lecturer in October 1933 and retired in 1973. He died in 1996. It has proven very difficult to obtain personal data from the institutions concerned, and much that has been learned was anecdotal commentary from past acquaintances, friends, and students, whose comments are much appreciated.

The comments provided indicate a very different academic world from that to which most present students are likely accustomed. Reference is made to Reading and Sheffield being "redbrick" institutions. Mention is made that there were no archivists or departmental secretaries, hence few records of past faculty or students. Upon arrival at Sheffield, Francis found a replica of the institution he had left: one professor, the entomologist L. E. S. Eastham, himself as filling the vertebrate side of teaching and research, one museum curator, and from time to time a research student. In 1935 the faculty changed by the shift to an assistant lecturer as substitute for the curator. The facility has been described as containing two teaching labs, two research rooms, a museum room and a stretch of corridor. During his tenure, Dr. Francis saw the transformation of the administrative and faculty pattern as well as of the kinds of research and training to the kind "nowadays accepted as proper." Some students of the last decades will appreciate a reference in one letter to a dichotomy between the old and the new that is almost unbridged and unbridgeable.

The scientific demands on such faculty members were for the production of monographic works and some supervision of student projects. The tradition of independent publication by the students complicates reconstruction of the research and supervisory influence. Collaboration was mainly with Francis Davies, Professor and Head of the Department of Anatomy. References were to Francis as a caring and enthusiastic supervisor, and to an appreciated lecturer and highly respected zoologist.

I initially knew of Francis as a distinguished morphologist on sala-manders and discussed his efforts with Dr. Angus Bellairs, who was very supportive of his studies. I had been reminded of Francis's earlier studies when I noted his very stimulating, indeed pathbreaking, report on the nature of amphibian salivary secretions. We first started corre-spondence in the early 1960s, and he then agreed to provide a chapter on the anatomy of the reptilian heart. He appeared to lack both secre-tarial assistance and laboratory space, and his letters contained much incidental comment on other difficulties such as intermittent hospitali-zation. Yet his enthusiasm for research always shone though. We met twice in London. One of the visits was made memorable to Mrs. Gans by his arranging to take us to a high tea and energetically explaining many of its customs to us colonials.

The difficulties he faced during retirement were never fully known to me during his life. Only comments by various students noted prob-lems due to the chronic illness of his wife and the suicide of his only son. These sad events explain the repeated delays and the missing of several schedules. Yet even the latest letters commenting on the modi-fied manuscript and its imminent publication stressed his courtesy and interest in scholarship.

I am deeply appreciative of the biographical information provided by Dr. and Mrs. Alastair Graham, Dr. Peter Holland, Dr. R. Presley, Dr. F. Seagrove, and Dr. Graham Twigg. Also several U.S. colleagues kindly checked the references.

LIST OF DR. FRANCIS'S PUBLICATIONS

1931. Francis, E. T. B. A case of an abnormal hyobranchial skeleton in *Salamandra maculosa* (Laur.). *J. Anat.* 65, 358–391.

1934. Francis, E. T. B. *The Anatomy of the Salamander.* Oxford University Press, Oxford, xxxi + 381 pp. (25 pls. and color frontispiece)

1941. Davies, F., Francis, E. T. B., and Winter, L. B. The glycogen content of the frog's heart. *J. Physiol.* 100, 329–336.

1941. Davies, F., and Francis, E. T. B. The heart of the salamander (*Salamandra salamandra* L.), with special reference to the conducting (connecting) system and its bearing on the phylogeny of the conducting systems of mammalian and avian hearts. *Phil. Transact. Royal Society London*, Ser. B, 231, 99–134.

1946. Davies, F., and Francis, E. T. B. The conducting system of the vertebrate heart. *Biol. Reviews, Cambridge Philos. Soc.* 21, 173–188.

1947. Davies, F., Francis, E. T. B., and Stoner, H. B. The distribution of nucleotide, phosphocreatine and glycogen in the heart. *J. Physiol.* 106, 154–166.

1951. Davies, F., Francis, E. T. B., and King, T. S. The conducting (connecting) system of the crocodilian heart. *J. Anat.* 86, 152–161.

1951. Davies, F., Francis, E. T. B., and King, T. S. Electrocardiogram of the crocodilian heart. *Nature* 167, 146.

1951. Francis, E. T. B., and Eisa, E. A. Salivary diastases of the frog and toad. *Nature* 167, 281.

1952. Francis, E. T. B. Various articles on vertebrate topics for Chamber's encyclopedia.

1952. Davies, F., and Francis, E. T. B. The conduction of the impulse for cardiac contraction. *J. Anat.* 86, 302–309.

1956. Davies, F., Francis, E. T. B., Wood, D. R., and Johnson, E. A. The atrioventricular pathway for conduction of the impulse for cardiac contraction in the dog. *Transact. Royal Soc. Edinburgh* 63, 71–85.

1956. Francis, E. T. B. The vertebrate heart—I & II. *School Sci. Rev.* 132, 73–85, 226–233.

1961. Francis, E. T. B. The sources and nature of salivary secretions in Amphibia. *Proc. Zool. Soc. London* 136, 453–476.

1977. Francis, E. T. B. Amphisbaenia: heart and arterial arches. *British J. Herpetol.* 5, 607–610.

1998. Farrell, A., Gamperl, A. K., and Francis, E. T. B. Comparative Aspects of Heart Morphology. In *Biology of the Reptilia*, vol. 19 (Morphology G) (C. Gans and A. S. Gaunt, eds.). Society for the Study of Amphibians and Reptiles, Ithaca, New York, Contrib. Herpetol., vol. 14, 375–424.

1

Lungs: Comparative Anatomy, Functional Morphology, and Evolution

Steven F. Perry

CONTENTS

I. INTRODUCTION

Reptiles are characterized by the great diversity of their pulmonary structure. Two lungs is the plesiomorphic state, although reduction or loss of a lung is common in elongate and/or limbless species. Non-platynotan lepidosaurs have lungs of relatively simple, primary structure. These lungs typically lack intrapulmonary airways and show little tendency toward internal compartmentalization of the central lumen. Testudines, platynotan lizards, and crocodylians possess multichambered lungs in which between 8 and 40 groups of air spaces are connected separately to an unbranched, intrapulmonary airway.

Although the structural diversity of reptilian lungs has been known for more than 175 years, the use of the lung in taxonomic/systematic studies is not widespread. One factor retarding the use of pulmonary morphology in reptilian systematics is the lack of a standard terminology. Furthermore, the descriptive literature on lung anatomy in various reptilian groups is widely scattered. One aim of the present chapter is to provide a terminological consensus for comparing lungs of different structural types as well as to summarize the structural types of lungs present in testudines, lizards, amphisbaenians, and crocodylians. Snake lungs are described in detail in the chapter by Wallach (this volume).

For most reptiles, the lungs provide the only gas exchange surface of significance. The degree to which lung structure may determine the ability of a reptile to exploit an aerobically demanding niche can be appreciated if the functional correlates of lung structure are known. Thus, a further aim is to summarize these correlates as they relate to the oxygen diffusing capacity and to breathing mechanics in reptiles.

Finally, I indulge in some speculation on the evolution of reptilian lungs and the origin of the high-performance lung types of birds and mammals. It is clear that the morphological and physiological properties of all organ systems, as well as the complex ethology of a given species, are interdependent and that the environment in which a species has existed also must be considered before one can attempt to retrace the path of evolution of its lungs. In this context, the evolution of the lung cannot be considered in isolation, but only as part of the evolution of the species. For the sake of argumentation in reconstructing the origin and evolution of pulmonary structural types, however, the lung will be regarded as the principal constraining factor in the evolution of reptiles (including birds) and synapsids (including mammals).

II. STRUCTURAL PRINCIPLES AND TERMINOLOGY
A. Introduction

For purposes of description and analysis, three independent structural variables of the lung must be characterized. These are the structural type

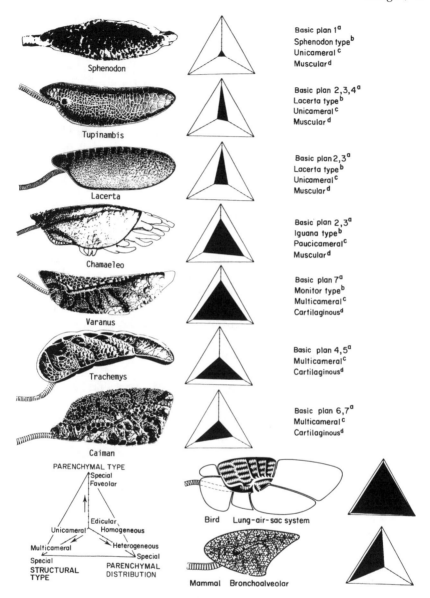

Fig. 1.1. Types of lungs seen in amniotes. Schemata show the internal surface of the medial half of the left lung, together with the classification systems of previous authors: [a]numbered "Grundbaupläne" of Wolf (1933) (see also Table 1.1), [b]Milani (1894), [c]Duncker (1978b), [d]Marcus (1937). Triangular diagrams indicate the degree of anatomical diversion of three variables from the condition in a hypothetical ancestral reptilian lung. Reptilian species are *Sphenodon punctatus, Tupinambis teguixin (=merianae), Lacerta viridis, Chamaeleo chamaeleon, Varanus exanthematicus, Trachemys scripta,* and *Caiman crocodilus.* (From Duncker 1978b, 1981.)

(Bauplan), the characteristic parenchymal type, and the pattern of intrapulmonary distribution of the gas-exchange tissue. In addition to these characters, the location of the lungs with respect to intracoelomic septa, such as the post-pulmonary or post-hepatic septum, the pattern of attachment of the dorsal and ventral pulmonary ligaments (mesopneumonia) to the lungs and the surrounding viscera, broad adherence of the lungs to the wall of the pleuroperitoneal cavity as well as size and shape differences between right and left lungs should be noted during dissection (Fig. 1.17). This additional information has proved be valuable in the use of the respiratory system in reptilian systematics (Broman, 1904; Becker et al., 1989; Becker, 1993; Wallach, 1985).

B. Structural Types of Lungs

The lungs of frogs and lizards were included in the studies of the founder of comparative vertebrate anatomy, Volcher Cöiter, and it was observations of the lungs of frogs and tortoises that led to the discovery by Malpighi that blood and air were separated in the lung (see Cole, 1975). In spite of these early observations, reptilian lungs received only cursory attention (Cuvier, 1805) until the systematic comparative anatomical study of Meckel (1818), which, employing the taxonomy of his time, included 24 reptilian and 8 amphibian genera with up to 16 species per genus. Meckel focused on the establishment of an anatomical series leading to the mammalian bronchoalveolar lung type.

Subsequent investigators attempted to classify reptilian lungs on the basis of their structural type, as summarized in Figure 1.1. The number of recognized lung types ranges from two (muscular and cartilaginous; Marcus, 1937) to seven (Wolf, 1933), with three (Duncker, 1978b) or four (Milani, 1894, 1897) having proved most useful. As did Meckel (1818), Wolf (1933) viewed reptilian lungs as forming a series leading to a more perfect lung type: in this case the avian rather than the mammalian lung. His seven basic designs (Grundbaupläne) stress the location of thin-walled "mechanical regions," which lack respiratory septa, as well the presence of perforations in respiratory septa (Table 1.1).

A purely descriptive approach to lung classification led to the recognition of four groups of reptilian lungs (Milani, 1894, 1897), whereby the names applied to the groups designate one typical representative rather than clades. The *Sphenodon* type is single-chambered, with coarse, homogeneous partitioning and lacks an intrapulmonary airway. The *Lacerta* type is also single-chambered but has fine, often heterogeneous, partitioning and a row of coarse niches. The *Iguana* type is like the *Lacerta* type, except that the single chamber is subdivided into separate chambers and/or lobes. Finally, the *Varanus* type is multichambered and possesses an intrapulmonary airway. The multichambered lungs of

Table 1.1. Summary of Wolf's (1933) classification system for reptilian lungs.

Grundbauplan	Characterization
1	Intrapulmonary airway absent. Respiratory septa present in all parts of lung. Amphibians.
2	Intrapulmonary airway absent. Mechanical regions for storage and pumping of gas caudal only. Lizards e.g., *Anguis*, and some snakes, e.g., *Boa*.
3	Intrapulmonary airway absent. Mechanical regions both caudal and cranial. Snakes, e.g., *Typhobis* (=*Typhlops*), and some lizards, e.g., *Iguana*.
4	Intrapulmonary airway present. Mechanical areas caudal only. Septa not perforated. Some turtles, e.g., *Emys*, and snakes, e.g., *Vipera*.
5	Intrapulmonary airway present. Mechanical areas both caudal and cranial. Septa not perforated. Snakes.
6	Intrapulmonary airway present. Respiratory septa present cranially but lacking caudally. Septa perforated. Some lizards and snakes, e.g., *Eunectes*.
7	Intrapulmonary airway present. Mechanical areas both caudal and cranial. Septa perforated. *Varanus*.

Examples include only those given by Wolf (1933).

testudines and crocodylians are included in the *Varanus* type. Duncker (1978b) combined Milani's *Sphenodon* type and *Lacerta* type into a single "unicameral" group and assigned the names "paucicameral" and "multicameral," respectively, to Milani's (1894, 1897) *Iguana* and *Varanus* types (Fig. 1.1).

Crucial to the above classification is the definition of the lung chamber as a lung region that is connected by a single, narrow opening to an intrapulmonary airway, to the central lumen, or at the hilus to the bronchial orifice of the lung (Fig. 1.2). The subdivision of structural types of lungs employed in the present chapter is similar to that of Duncker (1978b) but employs more easily understood English language terms: "single-chambered," for unicameral, "multichambered" for multicameral. In addition, the term "transitional" is proposed to replace "paucicameral," because the critical difference between this type of lung and the single- and multichambered types is not the number but the confluent character of the pulmonary subdivisions. The term is not meant to imply that the lungs themselves are in transition, but rather that the category covers the morphological intermediate between single-chambered and multichambered stages. Unlike the systems of Duncker (1978b) and Milani (1894, 1897), the present one does not exclude the possibility of a cartilaginously reinforced airway in single-chambered and transitional lungs. The major structural types of lungs are defined as follows:

Single-chambered: Uniform central lumen of lung not subdivided by major septa. One or more rows of niches may be present.

Transitional: Central lumen dissected by large septa. All subdivisions confluent within lung via the central lumen (Fig. 1.2).

Multichambered: Subdivisions (chambers) within lung connect separately to an intrapulmonary airway.

C. Parenchymal Types

1. Historical Background Although there is no consensus regarding the terminology for structural types of lungs, there is also little confusion because the definition of a chamber (see above) is not ambiguous. The designation of the parenchyma, i.e., of surface elaborations within a chamber or lung, however, does not fare as well.

In testudine and iguanian lungs, the chambers are commonly lobed: i.e., invaded by large septa that do not reach the bronchial orifice. Similar subdivisions of the central lumen are termed niches (in German, Nische) whenever arranged in one or more rows, as in a *Lacerta* type lung (Milani, 1894). However, the term "Nische" earlier had been proposed (Wiedersheim, 1883 as quoted in Milani, 1894) for a nest of small

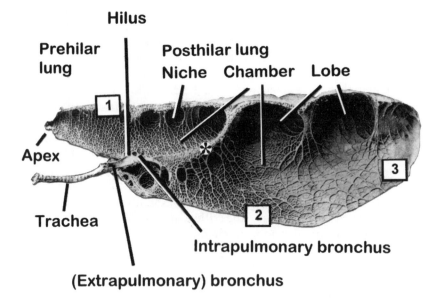

Fig. 1.2. *Iguana iguana*. Lung of transitional type. Medial half of the left lung, illustrating descriptive terminology for macroscopic structure employed in this chapter. Labels: *, Intercameral septum; 1, Faveolar parenchyma; 2, Edicular parenchyma; 3, Trabecular parenchyma. (Adapted from Milani, 1894.)

cubicles (crypts), much as an alveolar sack is a nest of alveoli: chamber > niche > crypt. The similarity with the terminal units of the mammalian lung is particularly evident in testudine lungs (Fleetwood and Munnell, 1996) but is less evident in the single-chambered lungs of lizards and snakes.

Milani (1894) complicated matters by employing the term "alveolus" in place of "Nische": chamber > alveolus > crypt, thus making a reptilian alveolus the analogue of a mammalian alveolar sac and a reptilian crypt the analogue of a mammalian alveolus. This confusion led later investigators (e.g., Moser, 1902; Gräper, 1931) to employ the original (Wiedersheim, 1883) definition of "Nische."

Based on the position of the air spaces in the branching hierarchy of the airway system, airspaces in the multichambered lungs of varanid lizards (Kirschfeld, 1970) can be designated numerically. Although appealing because of its apparent precision and independence of terminology for mammalian lungs, this method has serious limitations because the relative height of all septa within the lung must be determined before any given airspace can be named, which, in turn, requires tedious and reproducible three-dimensional reconstruction of the lung.

The reptilian analogues of mammalian alveoli (i.e., the terminal subdivisions of the air spaces) are termed "alveoli" (Schulze, 1871; Königstein, 1903; Marcus, 1937), "air sacs" (Meban, 1978a, 1978b), "cells" (Meckel, 1818; Lereboullet, 1838; Cuvier, 1840; Günther, 1861; Owen, 1866), and "crypts" (Wiedersheim, 1883; Milani, 1894; Moser, 1902; Gräper, 1931). The terms "faveolus(i)," (derived from "favus" = Latin for honeycomb) and "edicula(ae)" (derived from "aedicula" = Latin for small wall recess) have been introduced recently to describe parenchymal gas exchange units that are deeper than they are wide or wider than they are deep, respectively (Duncker, 1978b). Most recent workers have tended to adhere to Duncker's terminology (Fleetwood and Munnell, 1996). For the lungs of snakes, however, the term "vascular portion" (VP) has been used to designate parenchymal regions, as opposed to "avascular portion" (AP), which contains neither parenchyma nor a pulmonary blood supply (Wallach, 1985). The VP is further subdivided into a "dense" (DVP) region, which contains faveolar parenchyma and a more caudally located, "sparse" (SVP) region, which consists of edicular and trabecular parenchyma (Wallach, 1985).

The tissue structures that separate adjacent parenchymal air spaces are "septa" (singular, "septum") or "partitions." Some authors (Stannius, 1856; Perry, 1983; Becker et al., 1989) have restricted the term "septum" to large structures, such as those separating adjacent chambers, in analogy to major structures that subdivide the body cavity (septum transversum, septum postpulmonale, septum post-hepaticum). Others

(Moser, 1902; Gräper, 1931) used "septum" for all structures that separate air spaces within the chambers, and employ "partitions" (Scheidewände, Trennwände) for the larger structures. Thus, in recent publications (Perry, 1988, 1989a; Perry et al., 1989b, 1994), the terms "partition" or "partitioned" are used only in a descriptive sense to designate the degree of subdivision of the parenchyma (e.g., densely partitioned), whereas the separating structure itself, regardless of its size, is termed "septum," accompanied by a qualifying adjective: e.g., intercameral, interlobular, interedicular, or interfaveolar septum. This avoids terminological confusion whenever comparing mammalian interalveolar septa and analogous structures in reptilian lungs. The latter usage is employed here.

The system of polygonal openings to the parenchymal air spaces is variously referred to as "mailles" (Lereboullet, 1838; Cuvier, 1840) in the old French literature or "Maschen" and "Nischennetz" (Stannius, 1856; Gräper, 1931) in the German. To my knowledge, no equivalent English word is available. Instead, cumbersome circumscriptions (e.g., "strong rings around the mouth of small and large evagination") are used (Engel, 1962).

2. Proposed Terminology

The following terminology for lung structure, including that of lung parenchyma, is proposed:

I. Extrapulmonary structures

  A. (Extrapulmonary) trachea(ae): Cartilage-reinforced tube connecting the glottal (laryngeal) apparatus with the bronchi or, when bronchi are lacking, with the lung(s).

  B. (Extrapulmonary) bronchus(i): Cartilage-reinforced tube connecting trachea with lung. It can be surrounded by pulmonary tissue but is considered "extrapulmonary" until its serosa merges with the pleural surface of the lung.

  C. Accessory structures, e.g., glottal or laryngeal apparatus, vocal sacs.

II. Lung(s)

  A. External features (Fig. 1.2)

    1. Hilus(i) [also Hilum(i)]: Place at which airways (bronchial hilus, tracheal hilus) or great vessels (vascular hilus) penetrate the pleural surface of the lungs. The terms "proximal" and "distal" are with reference to the hilus unless otherwise specified.

    2. Prehilar lung [also apical region]: Portion of the lung that extends cranially from the hilus. Terminates cranially in the apex of the lung.

    3. Posthilar lung: Portion of the lung that extends caudally from the hilus.

4. Lung surface: Flat or gently curved portion of the outer aspect of the lung. Designated as dorsal, ventral, etc. surface depending on location.

5. Lung margin: Sharply curved portion of the outer aspect of the lung, i.e., the dorsomedial margin lies between the dorsal surface and the medial surface.

B. Internal features

1. Supraparenchymal structures (Fig. 1.2).

  a. Intrapulmonary airway(s): Typically cartilage-reinforced, tubes or troughs. They are lined with clearance-type epithelium, that contains ciliated cells and goblet cells or serous secretory cells.

    (1). Intrapulmonary trachea(ae): Tubular or troughlike portion of the trachea that opens directly to the central lumen or to faveoli in snake lungs.

    (2). Intrapulmonary bronchus(i): Tubular or troughlike extension of the bronchus into the lung, supplying individually the chambers of transitional (Fig. 1.2) or multichambered lungs (Fig. 1.15). Unbranched except in varanid lizards, which have a cranial intrapulmonary branch (Fig. 1.14a).

    (3). Intrapulmonary duct: Like (1) or (2) above but lacking cartilage.

  b. Chamber (Fig. 1.2): Pulmonary subdivision, separately connected by a narrow orifice to the intrapulmonary airway in multichambered lungs, or to the bronchial orifice or to the central lumen in single-chambered and transitional lungs, respectively. Separated from other chambers by intercameral septa (Fig. 1.2). Supports interlobular septa and parenchyma.

  c. Lobe (Fig. 1.2): Subdivision of a chamber in multichambered lungs or of the entire lung in transitional and single-chambered lungs. Does not open separately into the intrapulmonary airway; opens broadly into the central lumen of the chamber or lung.

  d. Niche (Fig. 1.2): Smallest supraparenchymal structure. Raised trabeculae surround a subordinate group of parenchymal units (see ediculae and faveoli, below), all of which have the same anatomical orientation as the niche itself. The parenchyma within a niche may occur in levels or "tiers." In analogy to the numerical terminology for branching of mammalian airways, the niche is here defined as constituting level 1 (compare trabecula, below).

e. Central lumen: The general, unstructured air space enclosed by b, c, and d above.

2. Parenchyma: Gas-exchange tissue and the air spaces that it immediately encloses. Three different systems are employed to define parenchyma: type characterization, descriptive characterization and morphometric characterization. None of these takes into account the hierarchical subdivision of the air spaces; rather, they are based on either the shape characteristics of the smallest parenchymal subunits (type and descriptive characterization) or on numerical analysis of all gas-exchange tissue (morphometric characterization). Parenchyma, whether of the same or of different types, is contiguous within a given lung: one type merges with another without forming distinct boundaries.

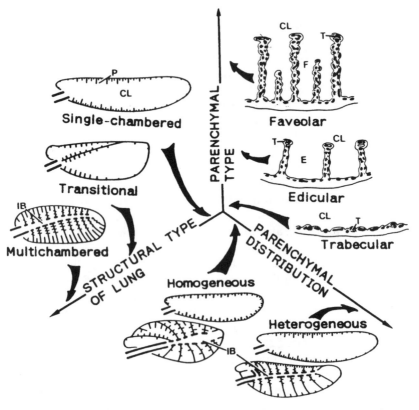

Fig. 1.3. Schema of three independent variables in reptilian lungs: Structural type, parenchymal type, and parenchymal distribution. Abbreviations: CL, central lumen; E, edicula; F, faveolus; IB, intrapulmonary bronchus; P, parenchyma; T, trabecula. (From Perry, 1992.)

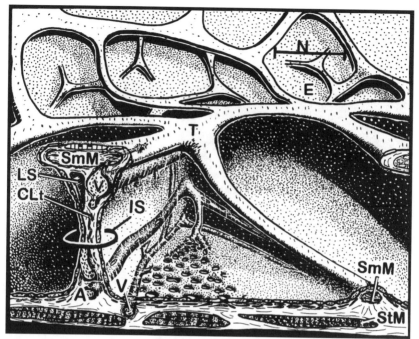

Fig. 1.4. Structure of edicular parenchyma illustrating terminology employed in this chapter. Abbreviations: A, branch of pulmonary artery; CLt, central leaflet; E, edicula; IS, interedicular septum; LS, lymphatic space; N, niche; SmM, trabecular smooth muscle; StM, striated muscle sometimes found in the outer wall of the lung in snakes and testudines; T, trabecula; V, branch of pulmonary vein. (Adapted from Perry, 1993.)

a. Type characterization (Figs. 1.2 and 1.3.)

(1). Faveolar parenchyma (Duncker, 1978b): Terminal air spaces deeper than they are wide. This type is typical of scincomorph lizards and of most snakes and is also present in the lungs of iguanid and agamid lizards. In some snakes, the proximal regions of the faveoli are permanently folded (Fig. 1.6b). The thus formed "secondary faveoli" open perpendicularly to the long axis of the primary faveoli in contrast to faveoli of high order (see "trabecula(ea)," which are nested within the primary faveoli and open in the same direction as the latter.

(2). Edicular parenchyma (Duncker, 1978b): Terminal air spaces raised from inner lung wall. Air spaces at least as wide as they are deep; typical of testudines, *Sphenodon*, varanid, chamaeleonid, and some gekkonid lizards and crocodylians but also present in distal pulmonary regions in iguanid and agamid lizards.

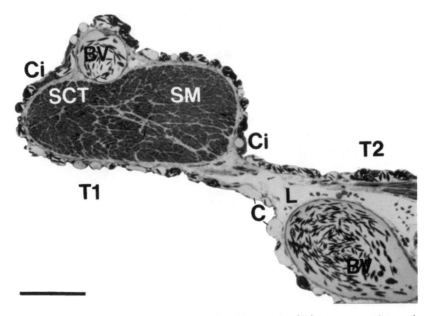

Fig. 1.5. *Rhacodactylus leachianus*. Trabecula of first order (T1) in cross section and subjacently an obliquely sectioned second-order trabecula (T2). Both ciliated epithelium (Ci) and a respiratory capillary net (C) are present on the trabeculae. The smooth muscle (SM) is enveloped by connective tissue (SCT) that extends into the central leaflet of the interedicular septum, surrounding the large blood vessel (BV) and the lymphatic space (L) found there. Scale bar is 100 microns. (Adapted from Perry et al., 1989b.)

(3). Trabecular parenchyma (Perry, 1983): Trabeculae are fused with the inner wall of the lung and do not support free septa. This type is typical of the sac-like portions of the lungs of many testudines and lizards. Snakes tend to possess aparenchymal regions (see below) rather than trabecular parenchyma.

b. Descriptive characterization (Perry, 1983)

(1). Deep versus shallow partitioning: Height of the intraparenchymal septa is great or small, respectively, relative to that of other septa in the same lungs.

(2). Dense versus sparse partitioning: Diameter of the intra-parenchymal air spaces is large or small, respectively, relative to that of other air spaces in the same lung.

c. Morphometric characterization (Perry, 1978, 1983)

(1). Percent (or volumetric proportion) of parenchyma, where parenchymal volume is expressed as percent or volume proportion of the lung inflated to ¾ total pulmonary capacity.

(2). Surface area-to-volume ratio (A/V) in parenchyma. Also called "surface density" and expressed in cm^{-1} (=$cm^2\,cm^{-3}$).

(3). Parenchymal surface area.

(a). Surface area of nonrespiratory surfaces: Airways and large trabeculae that have clearance-type epithelium.

(b). Surface area of potential respiratory surfaces: Total surface area of the lung, excluding (a) above.

(c). Respiratory surface area: Restricted to (b) above and excluding that portion of the potential respiratory surface that lies between gas exchange capillaries (Perry, 1976, 1978, 1981, 1983).

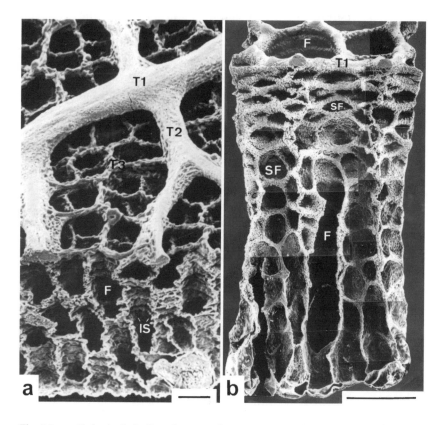

Fig. 1.6. a. *Podarcis sicula.* Faveolar parenchyma; scanning electron micrographs. Three levels of trabeculae (T1, T2, T3) have been labeled. Note reversible pleating of the interfaveolar septa (IS), which form the walls of the faveoli (F). b. *Nerodia sipedon*; Scanning electron micrographs. Note the secondary faveoli (SF) oriented at right angles to the main axis of the primary faveoli (F). Two levels of trabeculae exist, of which the upper (T1) has been labeled. b is a mosaic, shown in part in Fig. 1.18a. Scale bars indicate 500 microns.

3. Subparenchymal structures.
   a. Trabecula(ae) (Figs. 1.4 and 1.5): Structure that dynamically supports the free end of a septum. Characteristically composed of a core of longitudinally oriented smooth muscle and elastic tissue (myoelastic or elasticomyal; Engel, 1962) surrounded by a sheath of dense collagenous connective and/or elastic tissue. Gas-exchange epithelium can occur on trabeculae (Figs. 1.4–1.7), but clearance-type epithelium (Figs. 1.5 and 1.6) is also common, often forming a contiguous mucociliatory band that conveys particles onto larger trabeculae and eventually onto the surface of the extrapulmonary airways. Trabeculae are of first, second, third, or greater order, depending on their position in the hierarchy of the faveoli or ediculae (Klemm et al., 1979; Figs. 1.6 and 1.7). In analogy to the numerical designation of branching of mammalian airways, the largest trabeculae (i.e., those of the niches) compose the first level; higher-order trabeculae lie successively deeper in the parenchyma and support shorter tiers of septa. High-order trabeculae often lack smooth muscle and clearance-type epithelium.
   b. Septal components
      (1). Central leaflet (Figs. 1.4 and 1.9): A sheet of connective tissue that connects the trabeculae via the intraparenchymal septa with the subpleural connective tissue of the lung. Composed of collagen, elastic tissue and smooth muscle, the latter sometimes in bundles (Ogawa, 1920, Klemm et al., 1979; Perry, 1983).
      (2). Capillary net: Gas exchange capillaries disposed in a net-like arrangement on the central leaflet and covered by gas-exchange epithelium, which in all amniotes consists of squamous type 1 cells and cuboidal type 2 cells (Fig. 1.8.). In reptilian lungs, the latter produce surfactant and lie primarily in intercapillary spaces (Figs. 1.8 and 1.19).
         (a). Double capillary net (Fig. 1.9): Network of capillaries covering both sides of a septum and completely separated from each other by the central leaflet. Only one side of each capillary net is available for gas exchange.
         (b). Pseudo-single capillary net (Fig. 1.9): Double capillary net communicating through occasional perforations in the central leaflet. Except for the communicating vessels, only one side of the capillaries is available for gas exchange, as in the double capillary net.

(c). Single capillary net (Fig. 1.9): Capillaries communicate freely through multiple perforations in the central leaflet. As a rule, both sides of a given capillary have a thin air-blood barrier for gas exchange.

(3). Air-blood diffusion (tissue) barrier (Fig. 1.8b): Tissue lying between the capillary surface and the nearest respiratory surface of the lung. The thickness of this barrier for purposes of estimating the diffusing capacity is measured as the harmonic mean, abbreviated as τ_{ht}.

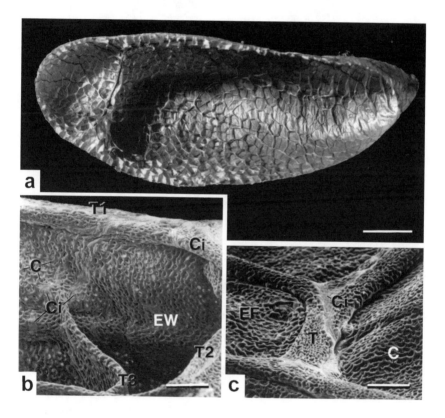

Fig. 1.7. *Rhacodactylus leachianus.* a. Medial half of the left lung; apex to left. Prehilar and posthilar lobes are separated medially by a stout septum. The ventromedial bronchial entrance is hidden in shadows. Edicular parenchyma becomes trabecular at the caudal end of the lung. b. Detail of edicular parenchyma; scanning electron micrograph. c. Detail of trabecular parenchyma; scanning electron micrograph. Abbreviations: C, capillary; Ci, ciliated epithelium; EF, edicular floor; EW, edicular wall; T, trabecula; T1, T2, T3, trabeculae of first, second, and third order, respectively. Scale bars indicate 1 cm in part a and 100 microns in parts b and c. (Modified from Perry et al., 1989b.)

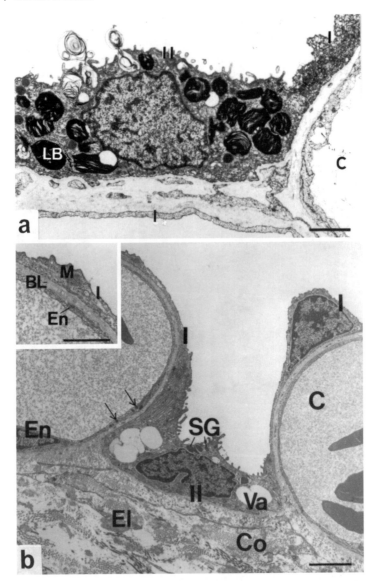

Fig. 1.8. a. *Crotalus viridis oreganus*. Type 1 (I) and type 2 epithelial cells (II), the latter showing prominent lamellar bodies (LB). b. *Rhacodactylus leachianus*. Type 2 epithelium contains small homogeneously contrasted secretion granules (SG) and empty vacuoles (Va). The relatively smooth surface of the type 1 epithelium contrasts with the microvilli-rich surface of the type 2 cells. Inset shows a detail of the air-blood barrier. Additional abbreviations: BL, fused epithelial-endothelial basement lamina; C, capillary; Co, collagen; El, elastic tissue; En, endothelium; M, mitochondrion. Scale bars indicate 2 microns in a and b, and 1 micron in the inset. Arrows indicate dense bodies in endothelial cells. (a: adapted from Luchtel and Kardong, 1981; b: from Perry et al., 1989b.)

4. Aparenchymal regions: Saccular lung regions lacking gas exchange capillaries (Luchtel and Kardong, 1981). Smooth muscle, if present, does not form trabeculae.

D. Parenchymal Distribution

Although Milani (1894) and other earlier workers noted the unequal distribution of respiratory septa in many reptilian lungs, Wolf (1933) was the first to provide a functional interpretation. He assumed that the thin-walled, parenchyma-poor lung regions, later termed "dilatations" (Duncker, 1978b; Becker et al., 1989; Becker, 1991), serve in storage and distribution of gas rather than directly in gas exchange. The presence of highly flexible and relatively rigid regions within the same lung is energetically advantageous for the animal, because, in the calculation of the work of breathing, only the mechanical resistance of the most flexible parts is important (Perry and Duncker, 1978, 1980).

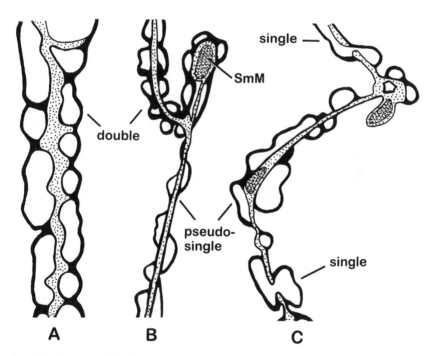

Fig. 1.9. Patterns of distribution of capillaries on respiratory surfaces of reptilian lungs. A. *Trachemys scripta* shows a double capillary net. B. *Varanus exanthematicus* shows both a double and an alternating, pseudo-single pattern. C. *Tupinambis teguixin* (=*merianae*) has a pseudo-single and a single capillary net. In the latter pattern the capillaries cross the central leaflet, indicated by stippling. Black indicates endothelial and epithelial tissue; cross hatching, smooth muscle bundles (SmM). (Adapted from Perry, 1983.)

Thus, the regional distribution of internal partitioning within a lung can be of strategic importance to reptiles; it also serves as a convenient method for classifying lungs.

Lungs are characterized as "homogeneously" or "heterogeneously" partitioned. In the first case, the height of the first order septa that define the entrances to faveolar or edicular air spaces is similar in all parts of the lung (Perry, 1983), whereas in "heterogeneously partitioned" lungs, the height of first order septa differs greatly among regions (Figs. 1.2, 3, 7). Note that the word "heterogeneous" here has a limited application rather than its more global use in respiratory physiology (Hughes, 1973). The height of septa and depth of the parenchymal layer have proved useful in reptilian systematics (Klaver, 1973, 1977, 1979); whereas more physiologically oriented morphometric studies (Cragg, 1975, 1978; Perry 1978, 1983, 1990; Perry et al., 1994; Stinner, 1982; Tenney and Tenney, 1970) tend to favor volume as a measure of parenchymal distribution, either as a proportion of the regional lung volumes or in absolute terms.

III. WHO HAS WHAT?
A. Testudines

All testudines have multichambered lungs (Fig. 1.10), with an unbranched, intrapulmonary bronchus that is reinforced by cartilage over its entire length. Each bronchus gives rise to between three and eleven groups of chambers (Gräper, 1931). In most species, each group consists of a medial and a lateral chamber. Embryological studies (Hesser, 1905; Moser, 1902; Broman, 1939) disclose that not two but three chambers per group bud off the tubular anlage of the intrapulmonary bronchus in a counterclockwise spiral for the right lung (clockwise for the left) in the order dorsomedial, ventromedial, lateral. During later development, the orifices of the two medial chambers of a given group fuse; this reduces the number of chambers per group to a single medial chamber with dorsal and ventral lobes separated by a longitudinal septum, and a lateral chamber. As the intrapulmonary bronchus tends to lie closer to the midline of the body than to the margin of the carapace, the medial chamber tends to be high and narrow and the lateral chamber broad and flat. The lateral chamber may encroach dorsally upon the medial chamber, forcing the medial chamber ventrally under the intrapulmonary bronchus. Secondary rotation of the chambers (clockwise in the right lung, counterclockwise in the left) about the intrapulmonary bronchus is most pronounced in the cranial portion of the lung in emydines and testudinines (Gräper, 1931). In *Testudo*, this rotation has resulted in a complete dislocation of the chambers; consequently, the "lateral" chambers lie not only laterad but also dorsad to the intrapulmonary bronchus, and the small "medial" chambers lie ventrad to it.

Similarities in testudine lung structure allowed Gräper (1931) to describe a typical lung for each of the five families recognized at the time: "Testudinidae," (present Testudininae), "Emydidae" (includes present Emydinae and Chelydridae), "Chelydae" (includes present Chelidae and Pelomedusidae), "Trionychidae" (present Trionychidae), and "Cheloniidae" (present Cheloniidae and Dermochelyidae). Given the improbable mixture of present phyletic groups combined in Gräper's analysis, it is surprising that familial similarities were observed. Convergence is likely. Like his contemporaries (Moser, 1902; Hesser, 1905; Marcus, 1927), Gräper envisions a successive increase in lung complexity from types with few, cavernous chambers (*Testudo*; four groups of dorsal and ventral chambers) through intermediate forms (*Trionyx*; seven groups of medial and lateral chambers) to the parenchyma-rich, almost mammal-like lungs of sea turtles with 10 or 11 groups of dichotomously bifurcating medial and lateral chambers (Fleetwood and Munnell, 1996). Given the otherwise highly derived condition of *Testudo*, however, it is

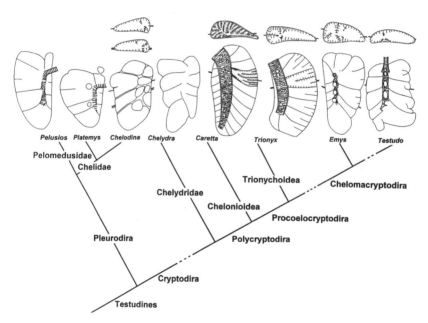

Fig. 1.10. Abbreviated cladogram of Recent testudines, showing lung types in the major groups. Upper drawings are schematic cross sections, levels indicated on margin of lower drawings. *Chelodina longicollis*, *Platemys* sp., *Pelusios* (= *Sternothaerus*) *subniger* ventral view of dorsal half of right lung; *Caretta caretta*, *Trionyx* sp. ventral view of dorsal half of left lung; *Emys orbicularis*, *Testudo graeca* dorsal view of ventral half of right lung; *Chelydra serpentina* dorsal view of left lung. (Schemata of lungs: adapted from Gräper, 1931, except *Chelydra serpentina*: adapted from Gaunt and Gans, 1969; cladogram: adapted from Gaffney and Meylan, 1988.)

more likely that the ancestral testudine lung was more similar to that of sea turtles or soft-shelled turtles. A reanalysis of the structural types of lungs in light of more recent testudine systematics (Gaffney and Meylan, 1988) is long overdue.

In sea turtles (Gräper, 1931; Broman, 1939) and in trionychid turtles (Gräper, 1931), the intrapulmonary bronchus is broad cranially and tapers caudally. It is supported by cartilaginous rings, and cartilage in the form of rings, as a network or as islands (in trionychid turtles) extends into the chambers (Gräper, 1931). In other testudines the intrapulmonary bronchus tends to be narrow and does not taper, and cartilage forms a network rather than rings.

Histologically, the intrapulmonary bronchus and major trabeculae within the chambers of testudine lungs support a clearance-type epithelium. It is composed of ciliated and goblet cells, the latter bearing greater similarity to the goblet cells of the mammalian tracheal epithelium than to the serous secretory cells of other reptiles (Klemm et al., 1979; Tesik, 1978, 1982; Perry, 1971; Plopper et al., 1983; Perry et al., 1989b; Fleetwood and Munnell, 1996).

The development of the post-pulmonary septum varies among testudine groups. In *Chelydra serpentina*, the post-pulmonary septum is lacking, and the lungs are attached dorsomedially by means of broadened mesopneumonia to the vertebral column (Duncker, 1978a). In emydids (Duncker, 1978a), *Chelonia* (Duncker, 1978a), and *Caretta* (S. F. Perry, unpublished), the lungs are covered completely by the post-pulmonary septum. They are appressed to the carapace, with the exception of the posterior chamber in *Trachemys* and the lateral margin in *Chelonia*. These regions of the lungs extend into the peritoneal cavity, carrying their post-pulmonary septal covering with them. Thus, the retroperitoneal appearance of the lungs in these testudine groups is deceiving: the lungs are covered not only by peritoneum as in the case of the kidneys but also secondarily by the post-pulmonary septum (Duncker, 1978a).

As mentioned above, all testudine lungs are multichambered. In general, all intrapulmonary septa, from the intercameral to the interedicular level, lack perforations, and most species possess a complete double capillary net (Meban, 1977; Perry, 1978, Perry et al., 1989c). The single capillary net reported for *Caretta* (Perry et al., 1989c) appears to be an unusual occurrence (Fleetwood and Munnell, 1996). The lamellar bodies of the type 2 epithelial cells withstand dehydration for electron microscopy, and in this respect are similar to those of mammals, birds, and crocodylians but are unlike those of many lizards and snakes. A further similarity to non-lepidosaurian amniotes is the presence of goblet cells rather than of serous secretory cells on the trabeculae and the intrapulmonary bronchus (Tesik, 1982)

B. Lepidosaurs (Figs. 1.1 and 1.11)

1. RHYNCHOCEPHALIANS The lungs of *Sphenodon punctatus* are characterized in the older (Milani, 1894) and newer (Duncker, 1978b) literature as "froglike." Unlike anuran amphibians (e.g., *Rana* or *Xenopus*; Marcus, 1937), *Sphenodon* possesses a trachea but lacks bronchi. The nearly apical hilus is typical of amphibian lungs; reptilian lungs usually have a well-developed prehilar region. The lungs of *Sphenodon* are single-chambered, with homogeneously distributed, edicular parenchyma. No microscopic or ultrastructural details are available.

2. SAURIA: IGUANIA

The families Iguanidae, Agamidae, and Chamaeleonidae together occupy the infraorder Iguania (Dowling and Duellman, 1978; Estes et al., 1988). At least some lungs in each of the three families have been described as "transitional" (Milani, 1894; Perry, 1989b), although few iguanid and agamid species have been studied.

Among lizards with lungs of the transitional type, those of iguanids (Fig. 1.2) are most similar to multichambered lungs. A short, troughlike intrapulmonary bronchus typically extends from the hilus to the base of a septum that divides the lung into a small, anterior chamber and a larger,

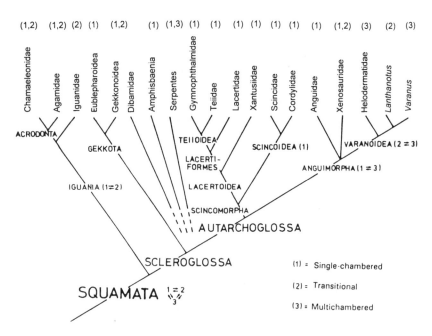

Fig. 1.11. Cladogram of lizard families. Numbers represent lung types. (Modified from Perry, 1989b; cladogram adapted from Estes et al., 1988, and Kluge, 1987.)

posterior one. The anterior chamber is densely partitioned, and the posterior chamber becomes increasingly sparsely partitioned as one progresses caudad. In *Iguana iguana*, two or three large septa subdivide the ventral chamber into lobes (Lereboullet, 1838; Milani, 1894; Becker, 1993) reminiscent of the situation in the lungs of *Lanthanotus* (see "Varanoidea" below). The lungs of *Anolis carolinensis, Ctenosaura acanthura, C. hemilopha,* and *Brachylophus fasciatus* conform to the general iguanid Bauplan (Milani, 1894; Becker, 1993). In *Brachylophus,* however, five large, caudo-cranially oriented septa subdivide the anterior chamber. *Phrynosoma cornutum* and *P. orbiculare* (Milani, 1894) possess ventral and dorsal subdivisions of the anterior chamber. Both of the subchambers flank the intrapulmonary bronchus, which lies against the medial surface of the lung, and originate with caudad facing orifices at the level of the hilus. A larger, lateral division of the anterior chamber separates the dorsal and ventral subchambers and is contiguous with the voluminous posterior chamber. The latter is subdivided by two or three large septa, as in other iguanid lungs.

The lungs of agamid lizards lack the intrapulmonary bronchus. In *Laudakia stellio, Uromastyx acanthinurus, U. hardwickii, Pogona barbata, Draco volans,* and *Leiolepis belliana,* a small anterior chamber extends dorso-craniad from the point of bronchial entry. The large posterior chamber typically contains a row of dorsomedial niches and may be divided into lobes by large septa. In *Physignathus cocincinus,* the large anterior chamber also contains niches, and the posterior chamber is divided by two large septa into three lobes (Becker, 1993). *Calotes* is exceptional among agamids in lacking the anterior pulmonary chamber (Tiedemann, 1811; Meckel, 1818; Milani, 1894). Like other agamid lungs, however, the main part is internally lobed and displays two distinct septal orders. First order septa form niches that, in turn, contain ediculae bounded by the second order septa.

Pulmonary ultrastructure has been studied in the agamid *Ctenophorus nuchalis* (McGregor et al., 1993). The lungs differ microscopically from those of scincomorph lizards such as *Tupinambis* or *Lacerta* in two respects: hyaline cartilage is present in some large trabeculae, and the lamellar bodies of the type 2 cells appear to resist extraction upon dehydration.

The early literature on chameleon lungs is limited to marginal comments and a small number of developmental studies (Milani, 1894; Moser, 1902; Hesser, 1905; Beddard, 1907; Methuen and Hewitt, 1914; Meckel, 1818; Marcus, 1937; Broman, 1942). Hollow, tentacular diverticula attracted the attention of these investigators, and the possible structural or functional relationship of these appendages to avian air sacs became and remains the subject of discussion (Wolf, 1933; Klaver, 1973).

Recently, lung structure has been used as a trait complex in the systematics of 46 species of *Chamaeleo* and 22 species of *Brookesia* (Klaver, 1977, 1979). The diverticula represent one of four lung traits analyzed: septal arrangement, diverticula, "alveolar" network, and terminal sac (Fig. 1.12a). Of particular interest from the point of view of comparison with other reptilian lungs is the trait "septal arrangement."

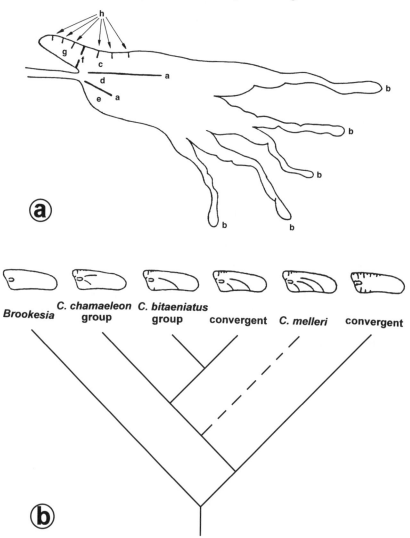

Fig. 1.12. a. *Chamaeleo africanus*. Schema of right lung in medial view showing the characters (a–h) that Klaver (1981) used in order to construct the hypothetical cladogram shown in part b.

Based on the assumption that the ancestral chameleons most closely resembled *Chamaeleo chamaeleon* (Klaver, 1973), the lung of ancestral chameleons is essentially an agamid lung with diverticula. Just as in the lungs of *Laudakia stellio*, the apical portion is isolated from the remainder of the lung by a septal ring ("diaphragm"), effectively dividing it into chambers (Klaver, 1973). The main, caudal, part of the lung possesses two major septa that extend from the middorsal and midventral margin of the lung toward the bronchial orifice. Dorsad and caudad to the "diaphragm," lies a row of niches. The partitioning is heterogeneous, being most dense in the cranial third of the lung. In all of these respects, the lungs of *Chamaeleo chamaeleon* and of agamids are similar. In keeping with the laterally flattened body form of most chameleons, however, the lungs are also laterally compressed, and the major septa lie in the frontal or transverse planes. It is significant to note that the major septa develop very early in lung ontogeny (Broman, 1942), suggesting that they may represent relics of ancient segmentation of the lung rather than a phylogenetically new development.

In a revised interpretation (Fig. 1.12b), the septate lung is derived from a nonseptate progenitor (Klaver, 1980). In general, the pattern of lung septation correlates well with the anatomy of the hemipenis in chameleons and brookesians; among the more highly derived African groups, the lung morphology allows better resolution and reveals three groups that correspond to a single type of hemipenis (Klaver and Böhme, 1986). The lung Bauplan of chameleons and brookesians is derived from a Southeast African group without major septa but possessing small diverticula; the Malagasy brookesians possess neither diverticula nor septa (Klaver, 1980). Whether the diverticula were lost before or after the invasion of Madagascar is not known (Klaver, 1979). The implications of this interpretation for the evolution of iguanian lungs is discussed in Section VII.C.1.

3. GEKKOTA (Fig. 1.13)

The Gekkota are represented by more than 90 genera and nearly 950 species, and are found in a circumpolar distribution throughout tropical and subtropical regions. The lungs of common or especially bizarre geckos have received some attention, even in the older anatomical literature: *"Gecko aegypticus"* (=*Tarentola annularis*) (Meckel, 1818), *Phyllodactylus* and *Tarentola* (Wiedersheim, 1906), *Uroplatus* (Tiedemann, 1818; Werner, 1912), and *Hemidactylus* (Mahendra, 1947).

More recent investigations have concentrated on the respiratory epithelium and lung innervation in *Hemidactylus*, the gross and microscopic structure of the lungs in *Rhacodactylus*, including electron microscopy, and the morphometrics of the lungs of *Gekko* (Welsch and

Müller, 1980a, 1980b; Perry et al., 1989b, 1994). Taken together, these studies provide a picture of gecko lungs as single-chambered but possessing a row of dorsomedial niches. The parenchyma is faveolar to edicular; that of *Rhacodactylus* is trabecular caudally. Unlike iguanian lungs, gecko lungs are not lobed. Ultrastructurally, they do not differ in any significant way from those of other lizards (Meban, 1978a, 1978b; Klemm et al., 1979), except perhaps in the absence of conserved lamellar bodies in the type 2 cells of *Rhacodactylus*. This feature does not necessarily reflect the lack of surfactant, but rather the high solubility of its lung lipids in nonpolar solvents used for dehydration in preparation for electron microscopy.

The structure of the lungs and the extrapulmonary airways has been compared in 39 species, representing four major subgroups: Eublepharinae, Diplodactylinae, Gekkonini, and Sphaerodactylini. Fifteen traits have been examined. Whereas individual or closely related species have very similar tracheo-pulmonary attributes, and one can identify "types"

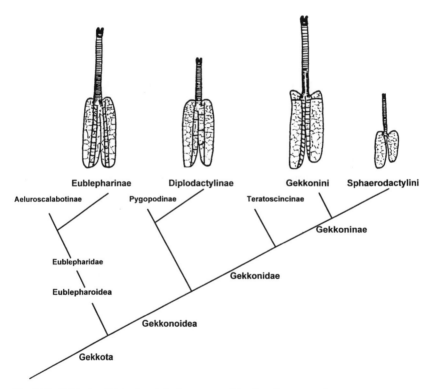

Fig. 1.13. Gekkota. Abbreviated cladogram combined with "type" schemata of lungs and extrapulmonary airways in four groups. (Cladogram adapted from Kluge, 1987; schemata adapted from Büsing, 1990.)

characterizing the subgroups (Fig. 1.13), trends within these groups cannot be discerned with certainty. In general, the above characterization of a gekkonid lung remains valid, but the work of Büsing (1990) and Becker (1993) allows its further refinement for the subfamilies as summarized below.

Eublepharines possess a relatively long trachea that tends to increase in diameter in the caudal direction. The frequency of cartilage rings increases caudally and usually exceeds 50 in total. Long "pseudobronchi" are present (Mauelshagen, 1997). Right and left lungs are of approximately equal size and contain dorsomedial niches less than 0.5 mm in diameter.

Gekkonines share 11 to 13 (depending on the species) of the 15 traits examined for eublepharines. The trachea tends to be of uniform diameter, "pseudobronchi" are present, and the left lung tends to be larger than the right. *Cyrtodactylus pulchellus* has not only dorsomedial but also ventromedial niches, and some species have an intrapulmonary septum similar to that of iguanians. The latter structure divides the lung into two chambers, either medially (*Rhacodactylus leachianus*, Perry et al., 1989b) or completely (*Chondrodactylus angulifer*, Büsing, 1990). *Chondrodactylus* also shows a reduction in tracheal width from 3.9 mm to less than 1 mm (outside diameter) as one proceeds from the glottis to the lungs.

In *Uroplatus fimbriatus* and *U. sikorae*, the width of the trachea varies due to a membranous postlaryngeal dilatation (Werner, 1912; Rittenhouse, 1995). The distal portion of the trachea is divided mediosagittally by a membrane, thus creating two "pseudobronchi" (Becker, 1993). A similar structure also occurs in the anguid *Barisia imbricata*, and in the teiid *Neusticurus bicarinatus*. The lungs of *U. fimbriatus* also differ from those of other gekkonines by having fingerlike protuberances similar to those of many chameleon lungs as well as by lacking dorsomedial niches. Further similarities to chameleons are the presence of a post-pulmonary septum and the reduction of the ventral mesopneumonia. This species also displays an unusual pattern of attachment of the lung to surrounding structures. In most geckos, the dorsal mesopneumonia of both lungs are complete. Ventrally, the right mesopneumonium attaches the lung over most of its length to the liver, and a left ventral mesopneumonium attaches the proximal posthilar region to the mediastinum. *Uroplatus fimbriatus* has only the dorsal mesopneumonia; the medial aspect of the right lung is attached directly to a protuberance of the liver, and a fingerlike extension of the left lung makes contact with the gut.

Diplodactyline lungs resemble a simplified version of gekkonine lungs. The trachea and "pseudobronchi" are short and broad. Left and right lungs tend to be of similar size; dorsomedial niches are large (greater than 5 mm in diameter) and relatively few in number, and intrapulmonary septa are absent. *Diplodactylus williamsi* has both dorsomedial and ventromedial niches (Büsing, 1990; Mauelshagen, 1997).

The Spherodactylinae are probably the most highly derived group of geckos (Kluge, 1987; Russell, 1979). The animals are small, which could explain the extremely simplified lung structure. The right lung is usually larger than is the left; both lungs lack intrapulmonary septa and dorsomedial niches. The trachea is relatively short, and separate bronchi are present (Büsing, 1990).

The lung structure in the nearly limbless, gecko-like Pygopodidae is poorly known. Becker (1993) finds the right lung of *Pygopus lepidopodus* to be twice as long as the left. Only dorsal mesopneumonia are present; the medial surface of each lung is fused broadly with the esophagus. Internally, a septum separates the apical region from the rest of the lung, as occurs in *Chondrodactylus*.

4. SCINCOMORPHA (Fig. 1.1)

Lung anatomy in the taxonomically diverse scincomorphs has been poorly studied. Except for the presence of small bronchi, the lungs of the lacertids *Lacerta viridis*, *Podarcis sicula*, and *Gallotia stehlini* are similar to those of gekkonid geckos. The development of the right ventral mesopneumonium is also similar to that of geckos, but in *Gallotia*, the caudal portion of the left ventral mesopneumonium attaches the lung to the lateral body wall (Becker, 1993).

The lungs of the teiids *Anadia bogotensis*, *Ameiva ameiva*, *Neusticurus bicarinatus*, and *Tupinambis teguixin* (=*merianae*) differ from gekkonid lungs in the complete absence of dorsomedial niches (Becker, 1993). Short bronchi occur in *Tupinambis*, but *Neusticurus* has "pseudobronchi," and bronchi may be lacking in *Ameiva* and in *Anadia* (Becker, 1993). Right and left lungs are of similar size in strongly quadrupedal teiid species. In *Bachia*, a genus characterized by an elongate body form and reduced appendages, the right lung is reduced (Böhme, 1989), a rare trait shared with only amphisbaenians and some species of *Diploglossus* (Becker, 1993).

A surprising apomorphy of teiids is the presence of a well-developed, post-hepatic septum that is not connected to the ventral hepatic mesentery (Broman, 1904; Becker, 1993). This septum is particularly well developed in *Tupinambis teguixin* (=*merianae*) (Broman, 1904, 1937; Duncker, 1978a). On the right side, it completely separates the liver and the lung from the rest of the body cavity; on the left side, a narrow communication connects anterior and posterior coelomic compartments. In general, ventral mesopneumonia are poorly developed in macroteiids, but in one microteiid (*Neusticurus bicarinatus*), the ventral mesopneumonium of the right lung is developed as in geckos.

The lungs of scincid lizards are very similar to those of teiids. Cordylid and gerrhosaurid lungs, on the other hand, may possess a row of dorsomedial niches (*Gerrhosaurus major*; Becker, 1993). A post-hepatic septum is lacking, and the right ventral mesopneumonium is well developed. Further studies of lung anatomy and lung suspension in the scincomorph radiation could help to clarify some of the unresolved questions within and among families (Rieppel, 1988).

5. ANGUIMORPHA (Fig. 1.14b)

The division of the anguimorphs into two subgroups, Anguioidea and Varanoidea, is supported by lung anatomy. Within the Anguioidea, the quadrupedal *Celestus occiduus* has bronchi and small lungs of approximately equal size. The bronchi are short. The apical region makes up one-third of the total lung length. The postapical region is single-chambered and bears a homogeneous layer of finely partitioned parenchyma. Niches are lacking (Becker, 1993). Only the dorsal mesopneumonium is developed; the ventral mesopneumonium and the intracoelomic septa are lacking.

In *Diploglossus warreni*, *D. fasciatus*, and *D. tenuifasciatus*, the right lung is shorter than the left lung by 17%, 18%, and 20%, respectively (Becker, 1993). In this respect, diploglossid lungs are similar to those of amphisbaenians and of the teiid *Bachia* (see Sections 4. above and 6. below). The three above-mentioned diploglossids also show a tendency toward reduction of the lung parenchyma caudally. Like *D. warreni*, *Celestus occiduus* possesses short bronchi; in *D. fasciatus* and *D. tenuifasciatus*, they are lacking (Becker, 1993). *Diploglossus fasciatus* has rows of intrapulmonary niches dorsally and ventrally, as does the gekkonine gecko, *Cyrtodactylus*.

In the elongate, legless anguid lizard *Anguis fragilis*, the right lung extends about two-thirds of the body length; the left lung approximately half as far (Meban, 1978b). Both lungs are sausage-shaped and are connected to the trachea nearly apically by short bronchi. Internally, the edicular parenchyma is more densely partitioned cranially than caudally, and the lung appears to lack a distinct row of niches. A small apical protuberance, the ventral wall of which continues as an intrapulmonary septum, separates the region of the lung lying anterior to the hilus into a dorsal and a ventral portion (Milani, 1894). This septum is reminiscent of that separating off the apical bronchus and its subchambers in the lung of varanids (see below).

The respiratory epithelium in *Anguis* is composed of pneumocytes of types 1 and 2, typical of amniote lungs (Meban, 1978b). Osmiophilic inclusion bodies in the type 2 pneumocytes appear more electron dense than in the same cell type of mammals, and the contents appear more floccular than lamellar. The microvilli of these cells are often concentrated on hillocks in the perinuclear region. Both types of pneumocytes have mitochondria not only in the perinuclear region but also in the flanges that form the thin air-blood barrier. In this respect, the lungs of *Anguis* are similar to those of testudines and crocodylians (Perry, 1978, 1988).

Some confusion exists as to which of the lungs is reduced in *Ophisaurus*. Although early reports state that the left lung is 20% longer than the right in *O. apodus* (Pallas, 1775) and in *O. ventralis* (Meckel, 1818), later studies report the reduction of the left lung in this genus, ranging from "slight" reduction in *O. apodus* (Milani, 1894) to a reduction of from 27%

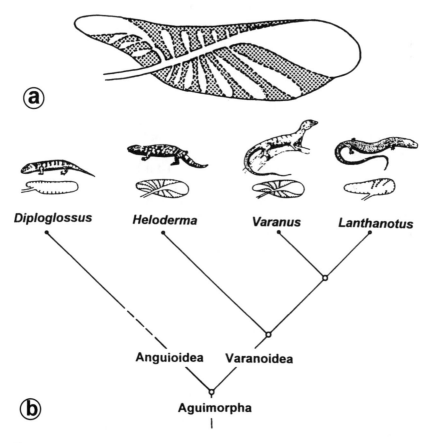

Fig. 1.14. a. *Varanus* sp., schema of right lung in medial view, showing multichambered structure and branched intrapulmonary bronchus typical of the genus. b. Anguimorph lizards and schemata of lungs representative of representative genera. (a: adapted from Milani, 1894; b: modified from Becker, 1989.)

in *O. apodus* to 56% in *O. harti* (Becker, 1993) relative to the length of the right lung. In light of these new data, it is probable that the observations of Pallas (1775) and Meckel (1818) are erroneous.

The bronchi of *Ophisaurus* are short. Internally the lungs lack parenchyma at their caudal end; otherwise they are very similar to those of *Anguis* (Milani, 1894). Ventral mesopneumonia are very short, but dorsal mesopneumonia are fully developed (Becker, 1993).

The lungs in Xenosauridae, as represented by *Shinisaurus crocodilurus* and *Xenosaurus grandis*, differ from those of other anguinoid lizards in the presence of a single, dorsal intrapulmonary septum and of well-developed ventral mesopneumonia and are, thus, strongly reminiscent of agamid lungs (Becker, 1993). Right and left lungs are of approximately equal size and have short bronchi. An affinity to the internal septation and degree of development of the ventral mesopneumonia in *Lanthanotus* is also possible. Xenosaurid and lanthanotid lungs differ, however, in the length of the bronchi, which are long in *Lanthanotus*, as well as in the presence of a weakly developed post-pulmonary septum in *Lanthanotus* and its absence in xenosaurids.

Varanoidea (Platynota). Varanids and helodermatids are unique among lizards in having multichambered lungs (Milani, 1894; Figs. 1.14 and 1.15). The lungs of *Lanthanotus* (Lanthanotidae), however, have a very simple structure (Becker et al., 1989) and are somewhat reminiscent of those of *Diploglossus* (Fig. 1.14b). The cranial portion of the lanthanotid lung is undivided, whereas the saccular, caudal portion contains three or four large septa, which bear gas-exchange tissue and extend from the lateral surface toward the hilus. The bronchus enters the middle of the ventromedial surface of the lung. Although the right bronchus is longer and the right lung is larger than the left, both lungs demonstrate a similar structure. The dorsal and ventral mesopneumonia are well developed on both lungs, and a weakly developed post-pulmonary septum covers the cranial half of the lungs and liver. As no cartilage-reinforced intrapulmonary bronchus has been demonstrated, the term "transitional" rather than "multichambered" should be applied to the lanthanotid lung. However, helodermatid and varanid lungs are clearly multichambered (Milani, 1894; Becker et al., 1989).

The lungs in the beaded lizard and the Gila monster, *Heloderma horridum* and *H. suspectum* (Fig. 1.15), respectively, are similar (Becker, 1993) and have been characterized as follows: "The right lung is much larger than the left. [...] The internal structure is multichambered as in *Varanus* and the proportion of parenchyma is high. The intrapulmonary bronchus is closed and a secondary bronchus [typical of varanid lizards] is lacking. The lung vessels enter cranial to the bronchus" (Becker et al., 1989). Pulmonary asymmetry and the lack of a cranially oriented secondary bronchus are traits shared with *Lanthanotus*, whereas the closed intrapulmonary bronchus, the cranial location of the pulmonary blood vessels relative to the bronchial entrance and the presence of more than 10 chamber groups (in *Heloderma* 12–13) is plesiomorphic with varanid lungs (Becker, 1991). Thus, in terms of lung structure, helodermatids lie between lanthanotids and varanids, sharing more traits with the latter.

A descriptive anatomical study of the lungs of the seven species of *Varanus* — *V. bengalensis, V. exanthematicus, V. flavescens, V. griseus, V. niloticus, V. salvator,* and *V. storri*—provides a firm morphological basis for further studies (Kirschfeld, 1970), not only of varanid lungs, but also of multichambered lungs in general. Varanid lungs are large, heterogeneously partitioned and possess a cartilage-reinforced, secondary bronchus that supplies the apical chamber group (Kirschfeld, 1970) or groups (Becker et al., 1989; Fig. 1.14a). Although the left lung tends to be longer and thinner than the right, the volume of both lungs is similar. The intrapulmonary bronchus possesses typically complete cartilage rings, which become more netlike and eventually disappear as one proceeds caudad. At the same time, the intrapulmonary bronchus widens into a terminal sac, and the orifices of its chambers become increasingly cavernous. Craniad, as in testudine lungs, there are three chambers per group: dorsal, ventromedial and broad, thin-walled lateral chambers. This structural plan is clearest at the level of the second chamber group, just caudal to the hilus, and becomes unclear through dovetailing of the chambers and the caudal formation of accessory bronchial niches. Again as in testudines, the chamber orifices

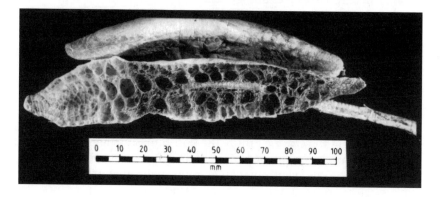

Fig. 1.15. *Heloderma suspectum.* Medial half of right lung showing multichambered structure and unbranched intrapulmonary bronchus. Shorter left lung in background. Scale bar is 10 cm.

tend to spiral about the intrapulmonary bronchus. The septa at all levels can show perforations; intercameral septal perforations are most common in the ventral, caudal, and cranial regions (Kirschfeld, 1970).

Recent examination of the lungs of 25 varanid species suggests progressive anatomical changes in the anatomy of the respiratory system that correlate with the westward migration of varanids from an Australo-New Guinean origin (Becker, 1991, 1993; Becker et al., 1989). Sack-like lobes appear to be characteristic of primitive varanids of the Indo-Australian radiation, such as *Varanus salvadorii*, *V. varius*, *V. indicus*, and *V. glebopalma*. In such species, the bronchial hilus lies near the middle of the lung, well caudad of the first rib. However, species of the Afro-Asiatic radiation, such as *V. niloticus*, *V. yemenensis*, and *V. exanthematicus* have the hilus positioned well within the cranial quarter of the lung and anterior to the first rib. On the other hand, in species inhabiting the middle of these ranges (*V. mertensi*, *V. acanthurus*, *V. timorensis*, *V. prasinus*, and *V. mitchelli*), the lung vessels exit caudad to the bronchus, a property shared with only the most primitive varanids (*V. salvadorii* and *V. varius*).

In platynotan and diploglossan lizards, the cartilage rings of the trachea are incomplete dorsally. The shape of the free ends of these open rings appears to be of great taxonomic significance, as this character is independent of the size of the animal. Thus, the lungs of the *Odatria* group (dwarf monitors) bear a similarity to those of the giant *V. salvadorii* in this trait. *Heloderma* and *Diploglossus* are similar, and *Lanthanotus* occupies a position of its own between *Heloderma / Diploglossus* and *Varanus*.

All platynotans possess a post-pulmonary septum, but its degree of development varies characteristically. In *Lanthanotus*, it is incomplete, separating part of the liver and gut from the pericardium, but does not envelop the lung (Becker, 1993). In *Heloderma*, the septum covers the ventral aspect of the lungs almost completely, beginning at the caudal margin of the pericardium and extending caudally; here it fuses with the cranial nephric fold. It is attached to the lateral margin of the liver, thus effectively separating the liver and gut from the heart and lungs. The post-pulmonary septum of varanids is very similar to that of *Heloderma*, except that the lateral margin is attached to the lateral body wall near the free ends of the ribs (Becker, 1993).

In varanids of the *Odatria* group, the dorsal mesopneumonia of both lungs and ventral mesopneumonium of the left one connect the respective dorsomedial and ventromedial margins of the lung with the gut. In the *Empagusia* group, the right ventral mesopneumonium is reduced to a remnant at the level of the pericardium, and the mechanical stability of the right lung is assumed by direct adhesion to the pericardium and liver (Becker, 1993).

6. AMPHISBAENIANS

Descriptions of amphisbaenian lungs date back to Meckel (1818), Cuvier (1840), and Stannius (1856). Bedriaga (1884, as quoted in Milani, 1894) and Smalian (1885) provide the first detailed descriptions. All amphisbaenians have a left lung. The degree of development of the right lung, however, ranges from "not very different: right lung possible larger than left" (*Leposternon* sp.; Stannius, 1856), through "rudimentary" (*Bipes canaliculatus, Amphisbaena fuliginosa, A. alba*; Meckel, 1818; Cuvier, 1840) to completely lacking (*Blanus strauchi, B. cinereus, Anops kingii*; Bedriaga, 1884; Smalian, 1885). The following description of the lungs of *A. alba* is typical for amphisbaenians with a reduced right lung (Milani, 1894): the trachea divides directly into two orifices, one of which opens into the tiny, lobe-like right lung and the other into the long, cylindrical left one. The right lung is homogeneous and has densely partitioned parenchyma, whereas the left lung has such parenchyma only in the cranial third. Caudally the parenchyma becomes coarse and shallow, and finally trabecular. Niches and intrapulmonary septa are lacking. A tracheal lung, typical of snakes, is also lacking.

7. SNAKES

In snakes, two lungs represents the plesiomorphic state, but the left lung is always reduced or lacking (see Wallach, this volume). In the families Xenopeltidae, Loxocemidae, Pythonidae, and Boidae, the length of the left lung is generally ⅓ to ⅔ that of the right lung; when present in other groups, the left lung is vestigial (V. Wallach, pers. comm.). The bronchial bifurcation lies just caudad to the apex of the heart. Accordingly, the cartilage-reinforced airways in snakes are divided into three regions: the precardiac trachea, the cardiac trachea, and the bronchus. Unlike lizards, most snakes have gas exchange tissue surrounding the trachea, thus forming the so-called tracheal and cardiac lungs.

A tracheal lung appears to have arisen several times in the evolution of snakes. It can be present or absent both in primitive groups and in highly derived ones (see chapter by Wallach, this volume). The hypothesis that the tracheal lung in primitive, single-lunged snakes in fact may be the rudimentary left lung (Robb, 1960) has been refuted, in particular by the simultaneous presence of both a tracheal right lung and a rudimentary left lung in such genera as *Typhlops, Ungaliophis, Homalopsis,* and *Trimeresurus* (Brongersma, 1960; Wallach, 1993).

In families Anomalepididae, Typhlopidae, and Acrochordidae (*Acrochordus*), the lung is multichambered, and the parenchyma is edicular and homogeneously distributed. The saccular structure of these chambers, the medial location of the intrapulmonary bronchus, and the presence of a non-subdivided, sack-like caudal chamber that contains edicular parenchyma are strongly reminiscent of lungs of *Heloderma*. Also, the number of sequential chamber groups present in the lung proper (i.e., excluding the tracheal and cardiac lung) in those typhlopids that have a multichambered lung ranges from 11 to 15, just as in *Heloderma*.

In other snake families, the lungs are single-chambered. Typically, the faveolar parenchyma is heterogeneously distributed: deep cranially, becoming shallow and eventually disappearing caudally. In most snakes the caudal region of the lung is aparenchymal and lacks pulmonary vascularization. The faveolar parenchyma is deepest near the hilus; here its upper portion may contain secondary faveoli (Fig. 1.6b). The single-chambered lung of snakes often contains an intrapulmonary bronchus; the tracheal lung generally contains an intrapulmonary trachea. In these respects, snake lungs differ from the single-chambered lungs of lizards, suggesting the separate or even multiple origin of single-chambered lungs in snakes and lizards.

C. Crocodylians (Figs. 1.1 and 1.16)

Prior to 1900, descriptive accounts of lung anatomy in *Crocodylus niloticus* (Lereboullet, 1838; Cuvier, 1840), *C. acutus* (Owen, 1866) "*C. americanus*" (=*C. acutus*; Milani, 1897), and *Alligator mississippiensis* (Milani, 1897) are recorded. The lungs of unnamed species of crocodile (Schulze, 1871; Miller, 1893), alligator (Miller, 1893), or caiman (Meckel, 1818) are also described, and "Bronn's Klassen und Ordnungen des Thier-Reichs" includes comparative data on the number of cartilage rings in the extrapulmonary and intrapulmonary airways of *Caiman crocodilus*, *C. latirostris*, *Crocodylus porosus*, *C. acutus*, *Gavialis gangeticus*, "*Alligator punctulatus*," and *Paleosuchus palpebrosus* (Hoffmann, 1890). More recent anatomical studies of the lungs of *Alligator mississippiensis*, *Caiman crocodilus*, and *Crocodylus niloticus* (Marcus, 1928b, 1937; Duncker, 1978b; Perry 1988, 1990) are not comparative in nature, although some provide detailed, quantitative data (Marcus, 1928b; Perry, 1988, 1990).

Like those of testudines, the lungs of all crocodylians are multichambered; beyond this they are very different (Fig. 1.16). The cranial half of the intrapulmonary bronchus is cartilage-reinforced and gives rise sequentially to four series of radially disposed chambers, each series potentially consisting of dorsal, ventral, medial, and lateral ones (Broman, 1939; Perry, 1988). During lung development, the cranial half of the future intrapulmonary bronchus fails to form ventral chamber buds in alligators (Broman, 1939). The embryologically ventral surface has rotated to lie against the medial surface of the lung in the adult *Crocodylus niloticus*, and medial chambers are lacking in the cartilaginous portion of the intrapulmonary bronchus (Perry, 1988). As in chelomacryptodirid turtles (Fig. 1.10), the most cranial chambers demonstrate the greatest degree of rotation from their embryological locations, but crocodylian lung chambers migrate from lateral to ventral (i.e., counterclockwise in the right lung), rather than from lateral to dorsal as in testudines.

The individual chambers of crocodylian lungs tend to be tubular; the most cranial chambers arch craniad, thus extending the apex of the lung far beyond the hilus (Fig. 1.16). The more caudal chambers extend caudad, flanking the intrapulmonary bronchus. The three major ventral chambers extend at first ventrad from the intrapulmonary bronchus, then fold back dorsad upon themselves and end near the dorsal margin of the lung (Perry, 1988). This complicated chamber structure and the

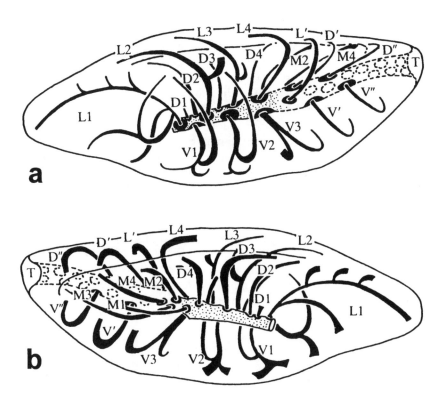

Fig. 1.16. *Crocodylus niloticus.* Left lung in lateral view (a), medial view (b); apex left in a, right in b. Abbreviations: D, dorsal chambers; L, lateral chambers; M, medial chambers; V, ventral chambers; T, terminal chamber. Numbers indicate the chamber group, beginning with 1 as the most cranial. Letters with hash marks indicate chambers that lie caudad to the cartilage-reinforced (stippled) portion of the intrapulmonary bronchus. (Adapted from Perry, 1988.)

monopodial branching system appear to be similar in all crocodylian lungs. They are quite different from the essentially dichotomously branched testudine lungs (Milani, 1897; Broman, 1939).

Unlike testudines, *Crocodylus niloticus, C. acutus*, and *Caiman crocodilus* have perforations of intrapulmonary septa at all levels, from intercameral to interedicular (Perry, 1988, 1990). The presence of a complete double capillary network and the persistence of lamellar bodies in type 2 pneumocytes following dehydration for electron microscopy are similar in the lungs of crocodylians and those of testudines (Meban, 1977; Perry, 1983).

Little can be said about species differences in crocodylian lung structure. The number of cartilaginous rings in the trachea and extrapulmonary bronchi appears to be relatively constant within a species and does not increase with growth of individuals. The number is least in *Gavialis*, and greatest in *Crocodylus* (Hoffmann, 1890). Like tracheal length, the number of cartilaginous rings in the intrapulmonary bronchus (Hoffmann, 1890) also is greatest in crocodiles (*Crocodylus porosus*, 19; *C. acutus*, 22–25), but is intermediate in *Gavialis gangeticus* (16) and is least in caimans and alligators (*Caiman crocodilus*, 15; *C. latirostris*, 13; *Alligator mississippiensis*, 9; "*A. punctulatus*," 16; *Paleosuchus palpebrosus*, 13).

The lungs of crocodiles have between 11 and 13 chambers; gharials and the alligators (species not identified) have 9 and 7, respectively (Gegenbaur, 1901). The intrapulmonary bronchus also appears to differ among the three major crocodylian groups. In crocodiles, it is straight and ends in a terminal sac, whereas it swings laterally in gharials. In alligators and caimans, it bends medially and terminates against the medial surface of the lung (Hoffmann, 1890; Milani, 1897; Perry, 1988, and S. F. Perry, unpub. obs.).

The lung parenchyma appears to be more densely partitioned in the lungs of alligators than in those of crocodiles (Milani (1897). Morphometric comparison of juvenile specimens of *Alligator mississippiensis* (Marcus, 1928b) and *Crocodilus niloticus* (Perry, 1990) showed the former to have 3.6 times as much pulmonary surface area per kilogram of body mass as the latter.

D. Summary

Reptilian groups possess lungs of characteristic structural types. Based upon recent detailed studies of chameleons, geckos, and varanids, characteristic differences begin to crystallize at a level between genus and family. The accuracy of the method might be improved by adopting a standard nomenclature and by further establishment of standard allometric methods. The physiological and behavioral correlates of different structural types of lungs are known only in part, and will be discussed in Sections V and VI.

Because all testudines, members of the most ancient group of extant reptiles, have multichambered lungs and well-developed bronchi, it is tempting to surmise that "turtle-like" lungs are a plesiomorphic trait for reptiles. However, the different rotation of chambers about the intrapulmonary bronchus as well as the different branching pattern within the intrapulmonary chambers of testudines, platynotan lizards, and crocodylians suggest that the multichambered lung structure with a well developed intrapulmonary bronchus is apomorphic in each group.

The degree of differentiation of the bronchi also appears to bear little relationship to lung structure. On the contrary, well-developed bronchi may be associated with the differentiation of the neck and with the caudal displacement of the heart (descensus cordis) and of the lung hilus (Duncker, 1978a). For example, *Lanthanotus* has a long neck, decensus cordis, and long bronchi, but its lungs are of the transitional type. If the lack of bronchi in *Sphenodon* reflects the primitive lepidosaurian condition, the long bronchi of platynotan lizards would be a derived trait. The presence of long, fused "pseudobronchi" in primitive groups of geckos is consistent with the hypothesis that long bronchi are plesiomorphic in squamates.

The internal pulmonary structure in non-platynotan lizards displays two common features that merit further discussion: dorsomedial niches and interlobular septa. Although the homology of the dorsomedial niches in all species remains to be established, it is possible that they represent the remnant of metameric intrapulmonary segmentation that dates back to the tubular lungs common to lobe-finned fishes. In the South American *Lepidosiren paradoxa* and the African *Protopterus amphibius*, small metamerically arranged chambers emanate from an acentric air duct (Hughes and Weibel, 1976; Duncker, 1978b). Increasing the diameter of the lung by broadening the lumen of the duct reduces the chambers to niches, whereas reinforcing the duct with cartilage and deepening the chambers would result in a multichambered lung. In this scenario, the dorsomedial niches are homologous to the dorsomedial row of chambers (see description of the testudine lung, above), and the metamery of the reptilian lung, if not the actual structure of the chambers and niches themselves, is a plesiomorphic trait shared by all vertebrate lungs. The widespread occurrence of these niches among the major groups of lizards, their number (commonly 7–15) being similar to the maximal number of chamber groups in multichambered lungs and their appearance early in embryological development (Moser, 1902) are consistent with the above hypothesis.

The interlobular and intercameral septa of transitional lung types are more problematic. A particular pattern of such major septa appears to be characteristic of closely related groups of lizards: e.g., the septum separating dorsal and ventral chambers of iguanid lungs, or the "diaphragm" of chameleon lungs and the anterior interlobular septum in agamids. In addition, their appearance very early in embryological development of the lung (Broman, 1942) suggests their antiquity. On the other hand, the location of these septa can be extremely variable even within a monophyletic group such as chamaeleonids, or it can be similar in some very widely separated groups such as lanthanotids, xenosaurids, and iguanids. The most parsimonious conclusion is that the specific location of interlobular and intercameral septa may confirm the relationship among genera within a family, but its value above the family level is questionable.

It is unlikely that the intercameral septa of transitional lungs represent the remnants of intercameral septa of a multichambered lung, because (except in iguanids) they are not associated with an intrapulmonary bronchus. In addition, they can coexist with dorsomedial niches, which may be the remnants in question. Nevertheless, it is interesting that they occur in the most basal groups of lizards and tend to become less prominent in more highly derived forms. One direction of lung evolution appears to be the total elimination of major intrapulmonary septa, achieved separately in brookesians, teiids, skinks, and snakes. The other direction is possibly the evolution of a multichambered lung, exemplified in anguimorph lizards by the morphotypic series: *Diploglossus* → *Heloderma* → *Varanus* (Fig. 1.14b).

The above analysis keeps unclear the position of the *Sphenodon* lung. This lung possesses neither interlobular septa nor dorsomedial niches, but consists entirely of a coarse, homogeneously distributed, edicular parenchyma. It remains to be clarified whether this structure represents a primitive reptilian lung or the further simplification of a relatively undifferentiated stage of squamate lung evolution concomitant with low metabolic needs.

IV. DYNAMIC SUSPENSION AND MECHANICAL PROPERTIES
A. External Suspensory Structures (Fig. 1.17)

The internal compartmentalization of the body cavity as it relates to the ventilation and suspension of reptilian lungs is a long-neglected topic that has only recently received renewed attention. Duncker (1978a, 1978b) summarized older works of Broman (1937), Goodrich (1930), and Nelsen (1953), enhancing them with new, well-illustrated dissections and reorienting them to the respiratory system of tetrapods. These results were later summarized in English (Perry, 1985) and are shown here in Fig. 1.17. Becker (1993) used coelomic compartmentalization together with characters of the lungs and rib cage in a cladistic analysis of anguimorph lizards.

Two different types of intracoelomic membranes are relevant to the lungs, namely intracoelomic septa and pulmonary ligaments called "mesopneumonia" (Broman, 1904; Duncker, 1978a, 1978b). The septa result in a transverse (albeit often highly modified) division of the body cavity into subcompartments, whereas the mesopneumonia attach the lung directly to the surrounding viscera or to the dorsomedial body wall in a predominantly cranio-caudal direction.

Two different intracoelomic septa are identified, the post-pulmonary septum and the post-hepatic septum. The post-pulmonary septum arises from the transverse septum in connection with the ductus cuvieri and extends ventrad to the lung, separating it from the liver. It divides the pleuroperitoneal cavity into pleuro-pericardial and hepato-visceral compartments. A post-pulmonary septum has been described in such diverse groups as the testudine *Trachemys scripta*, chameleons including *Brookesia*, "some agamid species" (Broman, 1937), one species of gecko (*Uroplatus fimbriatus*), and varanoid lizards, as well as in mammals, where it forms the sternocostal part of the diaphragm (Duncker, 1978a; Becker, 1993).

The post-hepatic septum, on the other hand, originates caudad to the liver and divides the body cavity into a pleuro-hepato-pericardial compartment and a visceral one that contains only the gut, pancreas, spleen, urogenital organs, and, in crocodylians, the gall bladder. The septum is characteristic of teiid lizards, in which it separates the liver, lungs, and heart from the rest of the body cavity, completely on the right side and incompletely on the left.

Most other groups of lizards lack both septal types; annielline lizards have developed a transversely oriented intracoelomic septum that is neither post-hepatic nor post-pulmonary and lies caudad to the reduced left lung (Becker, 1993). Crocodylians (e.g., *Caiman crocodilus*) and birds have both a post-pulmonary and a post-hepatic septum (Duncker, 1978a).

Functionally, these septa appear to increase the efficiency of aspiration breathing. In the case of lizards that engage in costal breathing, the septa may prevent free shifting of the viscera and the accompanying paradoxical movement of the abdominal wall (Perry, 1983, 1985). Groups that are characterized by delicate, sack-like or fingerlike caudo-ventral pulmonary elaborations (many chameleons, *Uroplatus fimbriatus*, *Heloderma*, and *Varanus*) also possess a post-pulmonary septum. In *Varanus* this septum is attached to the body wall in a line connecting the free ends of the ribs, suggesting a direct function in breathing mechanics. In some testudines, the post-pulmonary septum attaches the liver and stomach to the ventral surface of the lung, thus aiding in the direct transmission of the movement of the body wall and shoulder muscles through the visceral mass to the lung (Gans and Hughes, 1967; Gaunt and Gans, 1969).

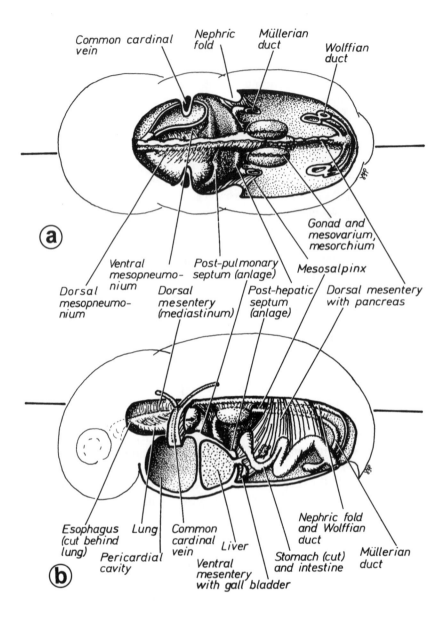

Common cardinal vein

Nephric fold

Müllerian duct

Wolffian duct

(a)

Gonad and mesovarium, mesorchium

Ventral mesopneumo-nium

Post-pulmonary septum (anlage)

Mesosalpinx

Dorsal mesopneumo-nium

Dorsal mesentery (mediastinum)

Post-hepatic septum (anlage)

Dorsal mesentery with pancreas

Esophagus (cut behind lung)

Lung

Common cardinal vein

Liver

Nephric fold and Wolffian duct

Müllerian duct

Pericardial cavity

Ventral mesentery with gall bladder

Stomach (cut) and intestine

(b)

Fig. 1.17. Generalized amniote embryo showing the relative location of the dorsal and ventral mesopneumonia, as well as the anlagen of the postpulmonary and posthepatic septa. a. Ventral half following frontal sectioning in plane indicated in part b. b. Right half following parasagittal sectioning in plane indicated in part a. (From Perry, 1985.)

Attachment of the post-pulmonary septum to the large liver in *Heloderma* may imply the participation of the liver in breathing in members of this genus. The role of the crocodylian liver, and thus of the post-pulmonary and post-hepatic septa that encase it, in piston-like ventilatory movement has been demonstrated in *Caiman crocodilus* (Gans and Clark, 1976).

The mesopneumonia have received only limited attention in reptilian systematics. These delicate structures extend caudally from the lung hilus. The dorsal mesopneumonium connects the dorsomedial margin of lung to the dorsal midline, and the ventral mesopneumonium connects the ventromedial margin to the gut or to the liver (Fig. 1.17).

For lizards, a correlation may exist between the spaces bounded by mesopneumonia of the right lung (Broman, 1904) and Camp's division of squamates into two groups: "Ascalabota" and "Autarchoglossa" (Camp, 1923). The type A intracoelomic recess (pulmo-enteric recess present as cranial extension of hepato-mesenterico-enteric recess; i.e., the right mesopneumonium extends from the bronchial hilus on the lung to the gut and liver) is present in iguanids, agamids, chamaelonids, gekkonids, lacertids, and cordylids. Type B (pulmo-enteric recess separate; i.e., right mesopneumonium short and/or does not extend onto liver) is seen in teiids, anguids, scincids, gerrhonotids, and amphisbaenians. Broman (1904) also describes a type C recess in which both A and B are present. Type C was reported only in two species of agamids (*Laudakia stellio* and *Ctenophorus nuchalis*) and could not be confirmed by later studies (Becker, 1993).

The mesopneumonia guide the lung during inflation. In contrast to intracoelomic septa, the mesopneumonia are easily identified in most lungs and, therefore, can be a valuable tool in reptilian systematics. The condition of the mesopneumonia and of the intracoelomic septa (if known) is given below along with the characteristic lung structure.

B. Internal Suspension of Respiratory Surfaces
(Figs. 1.4–1.7, and 1.9)

Following forced expiration, mammalian lungs remain suspended in the concavity of the closed, pleural cavities in a state of partial inflation. The amount of air thus contained is defined as the "residual volume" of the lung. The lungs of some reptiles are similarly protected from complete atelectasis by their partial (in crocodylians) or complete (e.g., in many testudines, most snakes, all varanid lizards) attachment of the lung to the body wall and to surrounding viscera. The single-chambered and transitional lungs of most lizards, however, can collapse completely on expiration, and thus have a residual volume that approaches zero.

Between breathing episodes, reptiles rarely maintain the lungs in the collapsed state. Instead, they close the glottis and maintain the lungs under positive pressure in a partially inflated state. A system of trabeculae, each containing a bundle of longitudinally oriented myoelastic or elasticomyal tissue (Engel, 1962), is embedded in the free edge of the interfaveolar or interedicular septa. In a single-chambered lung, the trabecular network forms a false floor, raised above the lung wall but running parallel to the latter, and connected to it by the septa (Figs. 1.4, 1.6, and 1.7). Tension within the trabeculae tends to decrease the area of the trabecular false floor by narrowing the entrances to the parenchymal ediculae and faveoli. The tension created by the reduction of the area of the trabecular false floor is transmitted from the trabeculae, along the septa to the lung wall. In a submaximally inflated lung with the glottis closed, the septa thus are maintained in dynamic equilibrium at the center of a tug-of-war: positive intrapulmonary air pressure causes the lung to expand further, but trabecular tension causes it to contract. These opposing forces are balanced exactly by the contractile force of surface tension at the air-lung interface of the septa and lung wall, as in the mammalian lung (Wilson and Bachofen, 1982; Weibel, 1984). Thus, the connective tissue leaflet of the septa may prevent overdistention and rupture of the septa, but in the normal, resting state does not actually transmit tension from the trabeculae to the pleural surface. The suspension model for a multichambered lung is the same as above for each chamber.

The dynamic mechanical model of the reptilian lung presented above differs from the suspension bridge model (Perry and Duncker, 1978), in that surfactant now plays a central role in mediating the transmission of force between the trabecular false floor (analog of suspension cables) and the subpleural connective tissue (analog of the roadway). The lung wall and each side of the septa support a contiguous network of gas-exchange capillaries, although in some species (e.g., *Caretta caretta*, Perry et al., 1989b; *Tupinambis nigropunctatus* (*=teguixin*), Perry, 1983) the double septal network partially merges into a single net. These capillaries are covered by a gas-exchange epithelium similar to that of the mammalian lung, consisting of type 1 squamous cells and type 2 cuboidal cells (Okada et al., 1964; Klika, et al., 1976; Meban, 1977, 1978a, 1978b; Klemm et al., 1979; Welsch and Müller, 1980a, 1980b; Perry, 1983, 1988; Perry et al., 1989c; Fleetwood and Munnell, 1996). The latter cells secrete a phospholipid-rich surfactant, which reduces the surface tension at the lung-air interface and allows the septa to be stretched and perfused at intrapulmonary pressures of less than 10 cm H_2O. Reduction of the surface tension also allows capillary bulging, which, in the *Tupinambis* lung, increases the surface area by

Table 1.2. Smooth muscle (SM) in reptilian and human lungs in relation to body mass (Mb).

Species*	Trabecular SM[a] ml kg Mb^{-1}	Septal SM[a] ml kg Mb^{-1}	Total volume of lung tissue[b] ml kg Mb^{-1}	Trabec./Septal SM ratio[c] Dimensionless	Reference
Crocodylus	0.30 (7%)	0.18 (4%)	4.14 (11%)	1.7 (63%)	Perry, 1988
Varanus	0.71 (8%)	0.09 (1%)	9.12 (9%)	7.9 (89%)	Perry, 1983
Tupinambis	0.25 (7.3%)	0.25 (7.3%)	3.39 (14.6%)	1.0 (50%)	Perry, 1983
Gekko	0.40 (17%)	0.05 (2%)	2.30 (19%)	8.0 (89%)	Perry et al., 1994
Mean of values	0.41 (9.8%)	0.14 (3.6%)	4.73 (13.4%)	4.65 (72.8)	
Homo	Airway wall 0.15 (1.16%)		Lung tissue 12.9** (1.16%)		Gehr et al., 1978

Crocodylus niloticus, Varanus exanthematicus, Tupinambis nigropunctatus (=teguixin), Gekko gecko, Homo sapiens. **Assuming airway wall in man to be 3.4% smooth muscle (F. H. Y. Green, pers. comm.), [a]percent of lung tissue, [b]percent of total lung volume, [c]percent SM in trabeculae.

one third compared with a non-bulging surface (Perry, 1983). Perhaps more important in many reptiles, surfactant functions as an antiglue, preventing the adhesion of surfaces during local atelectasis (Daniels et al., 1995). For more information on reptilian surfactants, see Wang et al., this volume.

To continue the analogy, the modified suspension bridge model would require that the support cables that connect the roadway to the suspension cables be flanked by spring-loaded ones that normally hold the support cables in a folded state, thus adjusting the position of the roadway according to the traffic load: the springs represent the surface tension at the lung-air surface, and surfactant reduces the stiffness of the springs. The degree of folding of the support cables is inversely proportional to the traffic load on the bridge, and only at peak loads would the support cables be fully extended. In the lung, the degree of folding of the lung septa is inversely proportional to the intrapulmonary pressure. Unlike a suspension bridge, a reptilian lung contains an active component: antagonistic smooth muscle bundles (see below). Both the trabeculae and the septa contain copious smooth muscle. As shown in Table 1.2, in a reptilian lung, the total amount of nonvascular smooth muscle per unit volume of lung tissue (roughly 10% of the tissue volume) is an order of magnitude greater than it is in man. In general, for a given lung the trabeculae contain more smooth muscle than do the septa, although the relative volumes of smooth muscle are equal in *Tupinambis nigropunctatus* (=*teguixin*). In lungs with faveolar parenchyma, the septal smooth muscle tends to be disposed in bundles that run parallel to the trabeculae. Whenever contracted, the septal muscles pleat the septa, reducing both the height and the exposure of the capillaries of the latter (Perry et al., 1989a; Daniels et al., 1994; Figs. 1.6 and 1.9). In *Crocodylus niloticus*, the septal musculature runs perpendicular to the trabeculae (Perry, 1988), but can still reduce the height of septa by compressing them.

The epithelium of the small trabeculae constitutes a continuation of the gas-exchange epithelium of the parenchyma, but that of the larger trabeculae is basically similar to the clearance epithelium of mammalian airways. It consists primarily of ciliated cells and secretory cells. The secretory cells are serous in lepidosaurs (Tesik, 1984a, 1984b; Fig. 1.18b), but in crocodylians and in testudines, they are more similar to the goblet cells of mammals (Perry, 1971, 1988; Tesik 1982; Fleetwood and Munnell, 1996).

In lizards (*Rhacodactylus leachianus*, Perry et al., 1989c; *Tupinambis nigropunctatus* [=*teguixin*], Perry, 1989a) and in *Caretta caretta* (Fleetwood and Munnell, 1996), the clearance-type epithelium is separated from the gas-exchange epithelium by a row of microvilli- or microridge-containing "hedge cells" (Fig. 1.19b–c). Cytologically, hedge cells are most similar to mammalian Clara cells and may be active in resorption of lung surface fluid. Testudine lungs have a large quantity of lung surface fluid due to leaky pulmonary vasculature (Burggren, 1982). If reptiles have the same clearance mechanism as do anurans, fluid moves across the edicular surface; from there it is swept up onto the ciliated conveyor belt of the trabeculae and thence out of the lung (Kilburn, 1969; Daniels et al., 1995). The hedge cells may be instrumental in causing a change in viscosity of this fluid, thus allowing the cilia to work at high efficiency while maintaining contiguity of trabecular and edicular fluid layers. In *Crotalus viridis*, serous cells lie in this position (Luchtel and Kardong, 1981; Fig. 1.19a). Their function may be similar to that of the hedge cells in conditioning the faveolar lining layer for ciliary transport.

Fig. 1.18. *Nerodia sipedon.* a. Dome-like structures (D) are located predominantly at the junction of first-order trabeculae (T1) that delimit the mouths of faveoli (F). Scanning electron micrograph (see also Fig. 1.6b). Scale bar is 100 μm. b. Capillaries (C) are embedded in loose connective tissue (LCT) between a sheath of dense connective tissue (DCT), which envelops the trabecular smooth muscle (SmM) and the epithelium, which consists of secretory cells (S) and ciliated cells (Ci). Cell processes (CP) approach the base of neuroendocrine cells (NC), which lie basal to the epithelium. Scale bar is 10 μm. c. Portions of three neuroendocrine cells (NC1,2,3) lie basal to two secretory cells (S1,2). The rectangular area including portions of two cell processes (CP) are shown in below. Scale bar is 1 μm. d. Dense core vesicles in various stages of development (DCV1,2,3) abound basally. Cell processes (CP) lie in close proximity to the neuroendocrine cell basally. Scale bar is 0.2 μm.

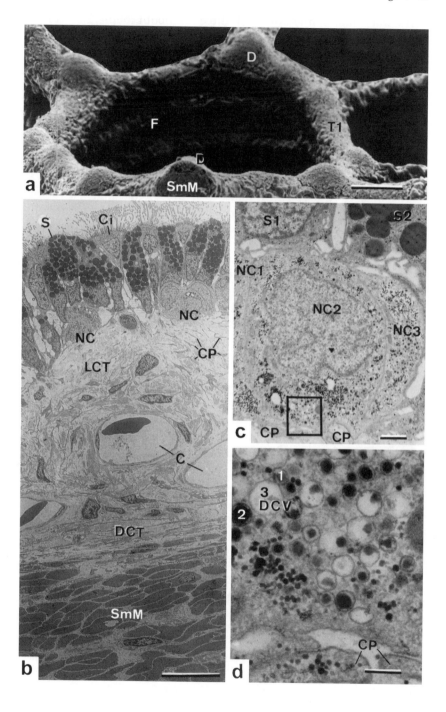

The trabecular epithelium of all three reptilian groups also contains neuroendocrine cells (Fig. 1.18a, 1.18b, and 1.18c). These cells occur singly or form dome-like neuroepithelial bodies (Scheuermann et al., 1983; Pastor et al., 1987; Scheuermann, 1987; Perry, 1988; Fleetwood and Munnell, 1996). The exact role of the neuroepithelial bodies is not known. They have been shown to contain serotonin and other neuroactive substances, and their predominance in reptilian lungs could be correlated functionally with the abundance of smooth muscle in reptilian as opposed to mammalian lungs. In mammals (Lauwreyns et al., 1978), dense-core vesicles suspected to contain serotonin are released from neuroepithelial bodies in response to hypoxia but not in response to hypoxemia. It is, thus, possible that local hypoxia could trigger serotonin release and local contraction of the trabecular smooth muscle in reptilian lungs, raising the trabecular net and exposing the capillaries (Perry et al., 1989b; Daniels et al., 1994).

C. Mechanism of Breathing in the First Amniotes

Aspiration breathing is characteristic of amniotes but may have originated among ancient amphibians (Perry, 1989) or even in crossopterygian fishes (Gans, 1970, 1971). Thus, aspiration breathing may have been a prerequisite for, rather than a consequence of, the xeric adaptation strategy of amniotes. The shift from a buccal pump mechanism and predomination of aspiration breathing are not mutually exclusive processes. Buccal pumping is commonly used for olfaction in crocodylians and turtles (Vos, 1936). Lizards that inhabit rock crevices also use buccal pumping to overdistend the lungs (Saalfeld, 1934). All of these groups, however, habitually ventilate by aspiration breathing.

Extant amphibians are characterized by poor differentiation or absence of ribs, thus making lung inflation by costal movement unlikely. Those Paleozoic amphibian groups (e.g., anthracosaurs and diadectomorphs) that lie close to the first amniotes (Panchen, 1972; Olson, 1976; Gauthier et al., 1988; Panchen and Smithson, 1988), however, have well-developed pleurocentral vertebral elements and long, broad-headed ribs.

Based upon the similarity in layering of hypaxial trunk musculature in extant urodele amphibians and in reptiles (Maurer, 1891, 1896), it is highly probable that the first amniotes retained the well-differentiated intercostal musculature of their reptiliomorph ancestors. This musculature probably consisted of two external intercostal, one internal intercostal and one transverse muscle group(s), as well as a well differentiated rectus group. The belly wall of anthracosaurs typically was stiffened by dermal skeletal elements called gastralia (Panchen, 1970), which may have prevented paradoxical belly wall movement and, thus, abetted the origin and evolution of aspiration breathing.

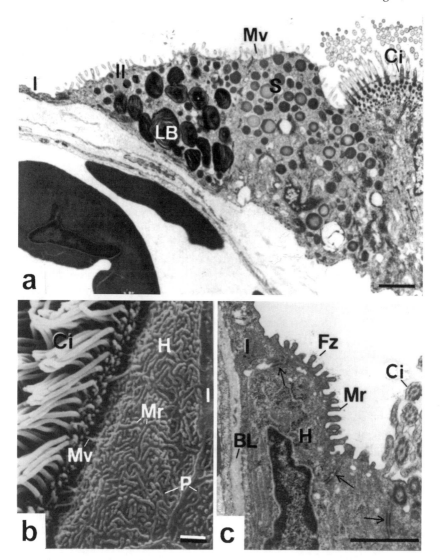

Fig. 1.19. *Crotalus viridis oreganus.* a. Sequence of type 1 (I), type 2 (II), serous secretory (S), and ciliated (Ci) epithelial cells on a trabecula. LB indicates lamellar bodies of type 2 cells. Scale bar is 1 μm. b. *Rhacodactylus leachianus.* Similar sequence of cells as in a and c. Scanning electron micrograph shows microridges (Mr) and pits (P) on hedge cells (H) and microvilli (Mv) on the ciliated cells (Ci). Scale bar is 1 μm. c. *Rhacodactylus leachianus.* Section similar to a. Hedge cells lack secretory granules. Fuzzy coat (Fz) is present on microridges (Mr). BL indicates fused basal laminae of capillary endothelium and epithelial cells, I is a type 1 cell and arrows show desmosomal connections of hedge cells and other epithelial cells. Scale bar is 1 μm. (a: adapted from Luchtel and Kardong, 1981; b–c: adapted from Perry et al., 1989b.)

D. Mechanics of Breathing in Recent Reptiles

Prior to 1978 studies on the mechanics of breathing in reptiles were scattered and few, and no system existed for comparing the results from animals of different size or structural type of lung (Gans and Clark, 1976; Wood and Lenfant, 1976). The first attempts at comparative static lung mechanics showed that, compared with mammalian lungs, reptilian lungs have high compliance values, and hence are easy to inflate (Tenney et al., 1974; Perry and Duncker, 1978, 1980; Perry, 1988). The compliance correlates positively both with the size of the lung (Leith, 1976) and with the presence of the thin-walled, sack-like regions (Perry and Duncker, 1978). Thus, for example, even when normalized against residual lung volume, the heterogeneously partitioned, single-chambered lungs of Gekko gecko are twice as compliant as are the homogeneously partitioned, single-chambered lungs of Lacerta viridis. The degree of partitioning in the most densely partitioned lung region, on the other hand, appears to correlate positively with the hysteresis of the volume-pressure diagram, estimated as the perpendicular distance between the inflation and deflation curves at mid-inflation in a volume-standardized diagram (Perry and Duncker, 1978). This observation was later substantiated by Dupré et al. (1985), who used the change in hysteresis as an indicator of increasing lung complexity in amphibian lung development. The Bauplan of the lung appears to be unimportant in determining compliance or hysteresis (Perry and Duncker, 1978). Later comparative studies of static lung mechanics use opening pressure as an indicator of compliance (Daniels et al., 1994)

The elastic work of breathing is inversely proportional to compliance (i.e., the greater the compliance the lower the work of breathing), but directly proportional to the square of the volume of air moved (Perry and Duncker, 1980). It is, therefore, not surprising that most reptiles increase their respiratory minute volume by increasing breathing frequency whenever faced with the potentially long term metabolic stress induced by temperature increase; however, they increase tidal volume following strenuous exercise (Perry and Duncker, 1980). An interesting exception that verifies the rule is that Iguana iguana breathes both faster and deeper, increasing its minute volume when warmed from 25°C to 30°C, but it adopts a fast and shallow breathing pattern and reduces its ventilation when further warmed from 30°C to 35°C (Perry, 1989a). In the latter case, the percent O_2 extracted from the inspired air increases, in some cases more than doubling. A similar response has been reported in Ctenophorus nuchalis, which increases its breathing frequency with increasing temperature, whereas tidal volume remains constant and the oxygen extraction increases (Frappell and Daniels, 1991).

Although not measured in the above-mentioned long-term experiment, it is likely that the apparent increase in breathing frequency was achieved by decreasing the length of nonventilatory periods rather than by increasing the breathing frequency during breathing episodes. This response has been observed many times, but the mechanical correlates were most elegantly demonstrated by Milsom and coworkers (Milsom, 1984; Milsom and Vitalis, 1984; Milsom and Chan, 1986). In these studies, both the lung compliance and that of the body wall are taken into account. The compliance of the body wall is much smaller than that of the lung and, therefore, is more important in determining the total resistance of the respiratory system to volume change. The total dynamic compliance, which reflects changes actually experienced by the animal, decreases at high breathing frequencies. The combination of frequency and tidal volume chosen by the animal during a breathing episode is that which yields the lowest work of breathing. This observation provides at least a teleological explanation of the energetic advantage of increasing overall breathing frequency by closing the gap between breathing episodes while maintaining the optimal pattern during the breathing episode.

In the above studies, it is important to note that the body wall compliance is so much lower than the lung compliance that the latter has a nearly negligible effect on the work of breathing. The implication for the evolution of high-compliance lungs is that the structures that result in high compliance (large lungs, heterogeneous partitioning, sacklike regions) may have been selected by factors such as efficiency of ventilation or mechanics of locomotion, thus making the high compliance merely a nondetrimental side effect. In lungs of extremely high compliance, such as in chameleons or varanids, the flexible regions are covered by the post-pulmonary septum that increases their stability but reduces the compliance.

V. GAS EXCHANGE
A. Morphometry of the Lung

1. GENERAL Because of its time-consuming nature, stereological determinations of the respiratory surface area and of the air-blood barrier thickness have been performed in only seven reptilian genera: one testudine (*Trachemys scripta*), four lizards (*Gekko gecko, Lacerta* spp., *Tupinambis nigropunctatus* [=*teguixin*], and *Varanus exanthematicus*), one snake (*Pituophis melanoleucus*), and one crocodilian (*Crocodylus niloticus*) (Cragg, 1975, 1978; Perry, 1978, 1983, 1990; Stinner, 1982; Perry et al., 1994).

2. Volume of the Lung

In order to compare pulmonary volumes among reptiles or between the Reptilia and members of other vertebrate groups, one must first establish a uniform definition of "volume of lung." As most reptiles are intermittent breathers, one possibility would be to define "volume of lung" as the volume maintained by the animal during the nonventilatory period. Although attractive physiologically, this definition presents two major obstacles: living animals and relatively sophisticated apparatus must be available, and at best the values are not constant, even in the same animal (François-Franck, 1908; Gans and Hughes, 1967; Jackson, 1969).

For purposes of comparative lung morphometry and static mechanics, Perry and Duncker (1978) constructed simple closed-chest, volume-pressure diagrams on freshly killed animals and established three volumes: zero volume (V_{Lo}), which is equivalent to the volume of the totally collapsed mammalian lung, resting or residual lung volume (V_{Lr}), which is roughly equivalent to functional residual capacity (FRC) in mammals, and maximal lung volume (V_{Lmax}), which is equivalent to total lung capacity (TLC) in mammals. The volumes are determined by inflating the lungs of a freshly killed animal to near the estimated V_{Lmax} and letting them deflate spontaneously. The remaining air is then extracted to a pressure of -10 cm H_2O, and its volume measured. That volume is defined as V_{Lr}. Next, the lungs are inflated stepwise through V_{Lr} until the upper inflection point of the diagram is reached, then stepwise deflated to V_{Lr}. The determination of the upper inflection point is somewhat arbitrary, as also noted by Daniels et al. (1994), who employed a similar technique. The volumes determined in this way (Fig. 1.20) show that, compared with mammals, reptiles have relatively large lungs and that the volume of their lungs appears to be independent of the structural type.

For purposes of stereological morphometry, a single volume rather than a range of volumes is necessary, and this reference volume must also contain the volume of lung tissue. The reference volume is determined by glutaraldehyde fixation of the lungs at 0.75 V_{Lmax} (Weibel, 1970–1971). The lungs are then carefully removed from the body, and their volume (including tissue volume) is determined by buffer displacement (Scherle, 1970). Comparison of displacement volumes in juvenile and adult *Gekko gecko* shows that the lungs of juvenile animals can be twice as large as those of adults (Perry et al., 1994) on a gram-body weight basis, and preliminary studies indicate that adults that have been exposed to 12% O_2 (rather than to 20% for control animals) for six months also have significantly larger lungs than do controls of the same age (Hein, 1989). Thus, the lung volumes given in Fig. 1.20 could represent the high end of the spectrum for *Crocodylus niloticus* (juvenile animals) and the low end for other species, of which measurements have been made of presumably well-nourished adult specimens.

3. RESPIRATORY SURFACE AREA

It is a reasonable assumption that the entire inner surface area of the mammalian lung, from the respiratory bronchioles to the alveoli, is potentially capable of gas exchange. However, this assumption does not hold for reptilian lungs. In addition to many snakes, in which the posterior saccular region is devoid of pulmonary capillaries, the lungs of testudines, crocodylians, and lizards often display a very coarse capillary network: i.e., large intercapillary spaces. Thus, there is a discrepancy between the "potential" respiratory surface area (S_A, the total surface area of the lung minus that proportion bearing clearance epithelium or having no pulmonary capillaries whatsoever) and the "effective" respiratory surface area (S_{AR}, that proportion of the lung surface in electron micrographs that can be connected to a capillary surface by a straight line).

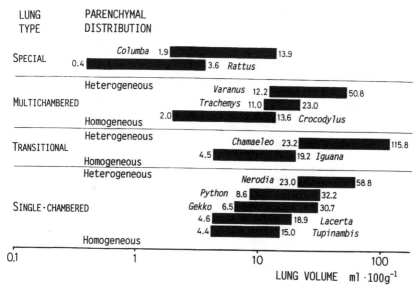

Fig. 1.20. Lung volumes in various reptiles (grouped according to lung type), rat, and pigeon (lung and air sacs). Lower values indicate functional residual capacity; higher values, vital capacity. Species are (from top to bottom): *Columba livia domestica, Rattus norvegicus, Varanus exanthematicus, Trachemys scripta, Crocodylus niloticus, Chamaeleo chamaeleon, Nerodia sipedon, Python reticulatus, Gekko gecko, Tupinambis nigropunctatus (=teguixin).* (Adapted from Perry, 1983.)

As shown in Table 1.3, for those reptiles measured to date, S_{AR} represents roughly 73% of S_A. The variation within the lungs of a given species, however, can be substantial. Thus, in *Crocodylus niloticus*, S_{AR} is 71% of S_A near the intrapulmonary bronchus but only 26% of S_A distally (Perry, 1990a). Similarly, in *Gekko gecko*, extreme values of 92% on the septa and 29% on the lung wall have been reported (Perry et al., 1994). *Trachemys scripta*, *Varanus exanthematicus*, and *Tupinambis nigropunctatus* (=*teguixin*) have equivalent trends that are not as extreme (Perry, 1978, 1983).

In general, reptiles have approximately 10% to 20% as much respiratory surface area as do mammals of similar body mass (Table 1.3; Fig. 1.21). The single (right) lung of the colubrid snake, *Pituophis melanoleucus*, has as much surface area per unit body mass as do two lizard lungs (Stinner, 1982). In addition to faveolar parenchymal structure, colubrid lungs also possess permanent polygonal folds in the interfaveolar septa, resulting in "secondary faveoli" (Fig. 1.6b). In light of the relatively large volume of reptilian lungs, their small surface area is surprising and leads to the hypothesis that the lungs may have important nonrespiratory functions. On the other hand, and as shown below, surface area is only one of several factors that influence the gas exchange function of the lung.

Fick's first law (Equation 1.1) states that the quantity (M) of a certain gas (x) transferred per unit time ($\dot{M}x$) by a lung is directly proportional to the surface area (S) available for gas exchange in the lung. It also states that the quantity of $\dot{M}$ is directly proportional to the diffusivity (Dx) and solubility (βx) of gas x in lung tissue as well as to the partial pressure difference (ΔP) of gas x across the diffusion barrier. Thus,

$$\dot{M}x = Dx \times \beta x \, (S \div \tau) \, \Delta Px \qquad \text{(Eq. 1.1)}$$

It will probably be intuitively clear to the reader that ΔPx is a complex entity in and of itself that depends on the partial pressure of gas x in the inspired air, the efficiency of convection in the lung, the perfusion rate of the pulmonary vasculature, the hematocrit and binding capacity of hemoglobin for gas x (if oxygen), the presence of other gases that may influence the properties of gas x, the pH, and the temperature (which also effects the Dx and βx). The above variables constitute the respiratory "software," as opposed to "hardware," which consists of such structural entities as the gas exchange surfaces, vasculature, airways, nerves, and intrinsic muscles of the lung (Perry, 1992).

The respiratory surface area can be measured morphometrically. It consists of the respiratory surface area of the lung on one side and that of the pulmonary capillaries on the other. Together with the thickness

Table 1.3. Morphometric comparison of reptilian lungs with those of selected vertebrates.

Parameter	Symbol	Units	A	B	C	D	E	F	G	H	I	J
Body weight	W	kg	0.72	0.02	0.197	1.00	0.44	1	3.59	0.5	0.14	0.45
Total lung volume	VL	ml kg^{-1}	84.4	94.8	164.6	97.5	306.7	262.3	113.1	46.8	45	27.1
												(178.7)
Parenchymal volume	%P	% of VL	26.0	34.6	11.7	—	28.7	44.9	42.0	44.1	81	48.8
												(7.4)
Parenchymal volume	VP	ml kg^{-1}	22.0	32.8	19.3	—	83.2	117.8	39.7	20.6	36	13.2
Total parenchymal surface area	SA	$\times 10^3$ cm^2 kg^{-1}	3.76	6.07	1.38	2.00	6.13	2.49	1.38	0.88	(27.7)	—
Respiratory surface area	%AR	% of SA	78.2	70.0	69.3	—	88.6	82.7	50.0	96.5	(100.0)	—
Respiratory surface area	SAR	$\times 10^3$ cm^2 kg^{-1}	2.94	4.25	0.95	—	5.43	2.06	0.66	0.85	27.70	40.3
Harmonic mean thickness of tissue barrier	τht	$\times 10^{-4}$ cm (= μm)	0.46	0.53	1.08	0.46	0.65	0.50	1.4	0.86	0.38	0.12
Anatomical diffusion factor	ADF	$\times 10^3$ cm^2 μm^{-1} kg^{-1}	6.39	8.01	0.90	4.4	8.35	4.12	0.63	0.99	72.89	335.83
Oxygen diffusing capacity of tissue barrier*	DtO$_2$	ml min^{-1} kg^{-1} Torr^{-1}	1.9	2.5	0.28	1.36	2.6	1.3	0.33	0.3	24.0	114.1
Effective surface-to-volume ratio in parenchyma	SAR/VP	cm^2 cm^{-3}	133.6	129.6	36.4	101	65.3	18.0	15.3	41.2	750	3053.0

A: *Tupinambis nigropunctatus* (=*teguixin*) (Perry, 1983); B: *Lacerta* spp. (Cragg, 1975, 1978); C: *Gekko gecko* (Perry et al., 1994); D: *Pituophis melanoleucus* (Stinner, 1982); E: *Varanus exanthematicus* (Perry, 1983); F: *Trachemys scripta* (Perry, 1978a); G: *Crocodylus niloticus* (Perry, 1990); H: *Lepidosiren paradoxa* (Hughes and Weibel, 1976); I: *Rattus norvegicus* (Burri and Weibel, 1971), numbers in parentheses indicate values assuming %AR = 100%; J: *Columba livia domestica* (Otten, 1973), barrier thickness calculated by the author from electron micrographs by H.-R. Duncker, numbers in parentheses indicate values for entire lung-air-sac system; *Calculated using KO$_2$ for rat lung tissue (Grote, 1967): at 20°C for geckos, at 30°C for other reptiles and the lungfish and at 37°C for rat, KO$_2$ is 2.8, 3.1, and 3.3 $\times 10^{-8}$ cm^2 min^{-1} Torr^{-1}, respectively.

of air-blood diffusion barrier (τ), discussed below, it participates in the anatomical diffusion factor (ADF): the "hardware" of pulmonary gas exchange.

4. Air-Blood Barrier Thickness

Because of its small dimension (often less than $1\mu m$ in reptiles) compared with that of the surface area (measured in thousands of cm^2 per kilogram body mass in reptiles), the importance of diffusion barrier is often underestimated. Inspection of Figure 1.22 and Table 1.3 reveals a

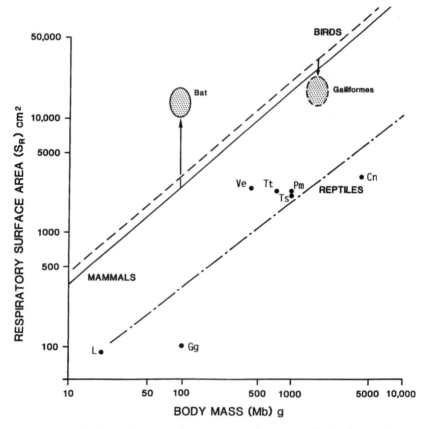

Fig. 1.21. Double logarithmic plot of respiratory surface area against body mass in reptiles as compared with birds and mammals. Reptiles are: Cn, *Crocodylus niloticus*; Gg, *Gekko gecko*; L, *Lacerta* spp.; Pm, *Pituophis melanoleucus*; Ts, *Trachemys scripta*; Tt, *Tupinambis nigropunctatus* (=*teguixin*); Ve, *Varanus exanthematicus*. Note the extreme variation in reptiles: *Varanus exanthematicus* has approximately the same respiratory surface area as *Crocodylus niloticus* of 10 times its body mass. Bat is *Epomophorus wahlbergi* (Maina et al., 1982). (Adapted from Perry, 1990b.)

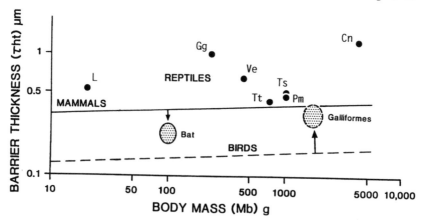

Fig. 1.22. Double logarithmic plot of air-blood barrier thickness against body mass in reptiles as compared with birds and mammals. Reptiles are: Cn, *Crocodylus niloticus*; Gg, *Gekko gecko*; L, *Lacerta* spp.; Pm, *Pituophis melanoleucus*; Ts, *Trachemys scripta*; Tt, *Tupinambis nigropunctatus* (=*teguixin*); Ve, *Varanus exanthematicus*. Bat is *Epomophorus wahlbergi* (Maina et al., 1982). (Adapted from Perry, 1990b.)

threefold difference among reptilian species measured thus far. As Mx is inversely proportional to the barrier thickness (given as the harmonic mean thickness of the tissue barrier, τ_{ht}), it has the same physiological impact as a threefold difference in surface area. It should be noted that the barrier thickness bears no obvious relationship to the structural type of lung: *Trachemys scripta* and *Varanus exanthematicus* show overall τ_{ht} values similar to those of *Lacerta* and *Pituophis*, which have single-chambered lungs, whereas *Crocodylus niloticus* (multichambered lungs) has the thickest, and *Tupinambis nigropunctatus* (=*teguixin*) (single-chambered lungs) the thinnest overall τ_{ht}. The barrier thickness in *Gekko gecko* (single-chambered lungs) varies considerably within the lung, but the overall value is similar to that of *Crocodylus* (Perry et al., 1994).

Like the respiratory surface area, the barrier thickness tends to show a characteristic distribution within lungs. In the multichambered lungs of *Trachemys scripta* and *Crocodylus niloticus*, τ_{ht} is thinner near the intrapulmonary bronchus than peripherally, and in the single-chambered lung of *Tupinambis nigropunctatus* (=*teguixin*), it is thinner near the mouths of the faveoli than at their bases (Perry, 1978, 1990a; Perry et al., 1994). However, these tendencies could not be demonstrated in the multichambered lungs of *Varanus exanthematicus* and single-chambered lungs of *Gekko gecko*; instead *Gekko gecko* shows an inverse relationship between the thickness of the parenchymal layer and τ_{ht} (Perry, 1983; Perry et al., 1994).

5. Anatomical Diffusion Factor and Morphometric Diffusing Capacity of Pulmonary Tissue

Combination of the two physical constants Dx and βx in Equation 1.1 yields a single value called Krogh's diffusion constant (Kx) for gas x in pulmonary tissue. Rearrangement gives the following relationship:

$$\dot{M}x \div \Delta Px = Kx \, (S \div \tau_{ht}) \qquad \text{(Eq. 1.2)}$$

This new relationship has the units of rate of gas transfer per unit partial pressure difference across the diffusion membrane and is called the "diffusing capacity" (Dx). It is a product of Krogh's diffusion constant and a combined term for the "hardware" of gas exchange: the "anatomical diffusion factor" (ADF).

$$Dx = Kx \times ADF \qquad \text{(Eq. 1.3)}$$

Because the interspecies differences in Kx at temperatures between 25°C and 35°C are small (actually 1% per °C; Bartels, 1971), we can use ADF as an indicator of diffusing capacity.

Inspection of Figure 1.23 reveals how different reptiles combine S and τ_{ht} to achieve their characteristic ADF values and also how reptiles as a group compare with birds and mammals. *Tupinambis nigropunctatus* (=*teguixin*) and *Varanus exanthematicus* achieve similar ADF values and diffusing capacities per unit body mass, but do so by two different avenues. Thus, the lungs of *V. exanthematicus* have nearly twice as much surface area as do those of *T. nigropunctatus* (=*teguixin*), but their diffusion barrier is also nearly twice as thick.

Compared with mammals, reptiles show considerable overlap in τ_{ht} but no overlap in surface area. Mammals have a larger ADF than do reptiles because they have more respiratory surface area, but birds have both a greater surface area and a thinner τ_{ht} than do reptiles. The reason that birds are able to achieve extremely thin τ_{ht} values could be that their virtually constant-volume lungs do not have to retain a membrane reserve to allow stretching during inflation. In addition, the constant-volume lung may be the key to the maintenance of extremely small-bore air capillaries, an extremely high surface-to-volume ratio in the parenchyma, and a very low surface tension. This hypothesis can be tested by reexamination of heterogeneously partitioned reptilian lungs, in which one can assume that the thin-walled, sack-like regions are more highly mobile than are the more densely partitioned regions. As discussed above (Section V.A.4), data from *Trachemys*, *Gekko*, and *Crocodylus* are consistent with this hypothesis, and those from the *Varanus* do not refute it. The functional significance of heterogeneous partitioning in the reptilian lung may lie in the optimization of regional gas exchange.

B. Functional Implications of Morphometric Data

1. GENERAL The morphometric data presented above show that a single-chambered lung should provide adequate gas exchange for most reptiles. Inspection of Figure 1.24 suggests that this is indeed the case. Although two orders of magnitude separate the maximal oxygen consumption rates of reptiles and birds, this difference is matched by differences in the diffusing capacity of the pulmonary "hardware." Consequently, the mean ΔP_{O_2} values necessary to maintain adequate oxygen

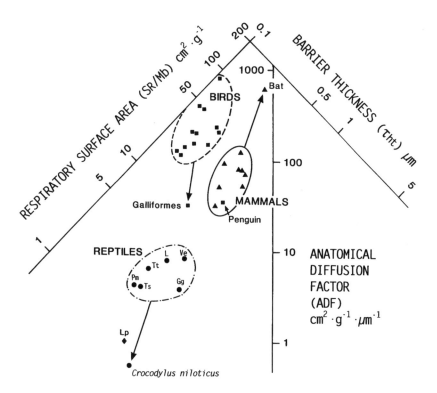

Fig. 1.23. Double logarithmic plot of respiratory surface area against air-blood barrier thickness in reptiles as compared with birds and mammals. Each point can be read off perpendicularly against each of the three axes. The vertical middle axis gives the anatomical diffusion factor (ADF); respiratory surface area divided by barrier thickness. Reptiles are: *Crocodylus niloticus*; Gg, *Gekko gecko*; L, *Lacerta* spp.; Pm, *Pituophis melanoleucus*; Ts, *Trachemys scripta*; Tt, *Tupinambis nigropuntatus* (=*teguixin*); Ve, *Varanus exanthematicus*. Lp is the lungfish *Lepidosiren paradoxa*. Bat is *Epomophorus wahlbergi* (Maina et al., 1982). (Adapted from Perry, 1990b.)

consumption in a reptile or a bird often differ by less than a factor of two. Comparison of reptiles and mammals yields similar results and leads one to the conclusion that the pulmonary diffusion capacity in each group of animals reflects the ecological life style characteristic in that group. This observation cannot disclose, however, the possible advantage of the often radically distinct and taxonomically associated differences in lung structure among reptiles, nor the key variables that might have resulted in the evolution of high-performance lungs from less highly derived structural types.

2. GAS EXCHANGE STRATEGIES

Physiological measurement of the diffusing capacity of the lung for oxygen (D_{LO_2}) and its comparison with the morphometrically derived oxygen diffusing capacity of the air-blood tissue barrier (D_{tO_2}) indicates that D_{tO_2} is 10 to 30 times greater than D_{LO_2}. This difference is attributable only in part to resistance to diffusion within the blood plasma and blood

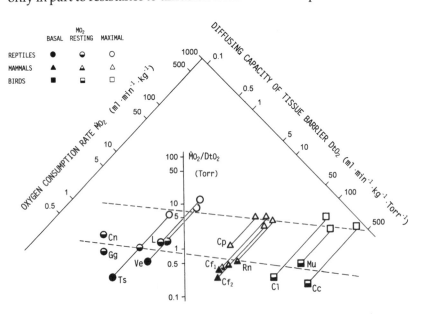

Fig. 1.24. Double logarithmic plot of oxygen consumption rate against the morphometric diffusing capacity of the air-blood tissue barrier in reptiles as compared with selected birds and mammals. Each point can be read off perpendicularly against each of the three axes. The vertical middle axis gives the driving pressure. Reptiles are: Cn, *Crocodylus niloticus*; Gg, *Gekko gecko*; L, *Lacerta* spp.; Ts, *Trachemys scripta*; Ve, *Varanus exanthematicus*. Mammals are: Cf₁, *Canis lupus familiaris* (11 kg); Cf₂, *Canis lupus familiaris* (23 kg); Cp, *Cavia aperea porcellus*; Rn, *Rattus norvegicus*. Birds are: Cc, *Colibri coruscans*; Cl, *Columba livia domestica*; Mu, *Melopsittacus undulatus*. Values for *Gekko gecko* from Perry et al. (1994) and Nielsen (1961). (Adapted from Perry, 1993.)

Table 1.4. Comparison of morphometric (DtO_2) and physiological (DO_2) values for pulmonary diffusing capacity.

	DtO_2 Mb^{-1} $ml\ min^{-1}\ kg^{-1}\ Torr^{-1}$	DO_2 Mb^{-1} $ml\ min^{-1}\ kg^{-1}\ Torr^{-1}$		DtO_2/DO_2	
Tupinambis	0.84[a]	*0.049[a,b]*		*17.1*	
Varanus	0.86[a]	*0.073[a,b]*		*11.8*	
Trachemys	1.18[c]	*0.041[d]*	*0.081[e]*	*28.8*	*14.6*
Canis	24.30	*0.96*	*2.06[f]*	*25.3*	*11.8*
Homo	9.05[h]	*0.36*	*0.64[g]*	*25.1*	*14.1*

Italics indicate resting animals. Species are: *Tupinambis nigropunctatus* (=*teguixin*), *Varanus exanthematicus, Trachemys scripta elegans, Canis lupus familiaris, Homo sapiens.* [a]Mb = 2.2 kg; [b]Converted from DCO using factor 1.23; [c]Mb = 1 kg; [d]1.5 kg, 30 s rebreathing, high value; [e]1.5 kg, 120 s rebreathing; [f]Maximal $\dot{M}O_2$; [g]Exercise. For data sources references, see Perry, 1983.

cells. At increased levels of oxygen consumption, the discrepancy decreases but never completely disappears. The remainder (approximately a factor of 2 in mammals) is attributed to a layer of undisturbed gas on the alveolar surface, which produces effective diffusion distances longer than those morphometrically measured (Piiper and Scheid, 1971; Weibel et al., 1983). In simple systems, such as the skin of salamanders or the unperfused pleural membrane of dog lungs, the morphometrically calculated and physiologically measured values are very close (Magnussen et al., 1974; Piiper and Scheid, 1986); however, the more inaccessible the gas exchange surfaces are to ventilation, the greater is the discrepancy between calculated and measured diffusing capacity (Table 1.4).

Recalling that most reptiles increase the overall breathing frequency in response to an increase in ambient temperature, one would expect that species with trabecular or edicular parenchyma would be able to increase their oxygen extraction when warmed up. Such a gas exchange strategy has been characterized as "convection dominated" (Perry, 1992). On the other hand, those species with faveolar parenchyma would experience less of a rise in oxygen extraction, and their gas exchange strategy is "diffusion dominated." Figure 1.25 indicates that this hypothesis holds in a general way for literature values from 15 different reptilian genera. A more detailed comparison of two species (*Nerodia sipedon*, which has faveolar parenchyma, and *Iguana iguana*, in which the parenchyma ranges from trabecular to faveolar), is given in Figure 1.26. In response to a temperature rise from 25°C to 35°C, the snake tends to increase its minute ventilation (entirely by increasing frequency) and to keep its oxygen extraction constant, whereas the iguana keeps its ventilation rate constant (by decreasing tidal volume in proportion to the increase in frequency) and increases its oxygen extraction.

3. FUNCTIONAL ADVANTAGES OF MULTICHAMBERED LUNGS

Compared with birds and mammals, reptiles have a relatively large lung volume in which to distribute a relatively small respiratory surface area. Multichambered lungs provide an advantageous starting point for sur-

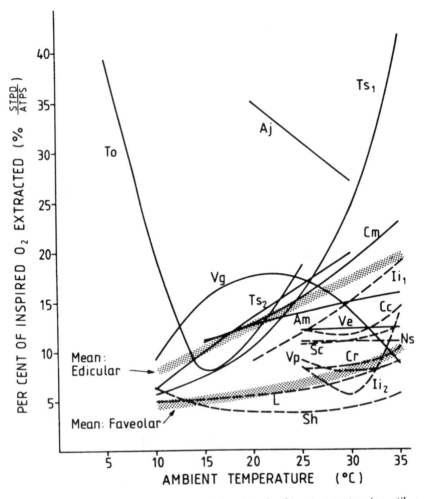

Fig. 1.25. Percentage of inspired oxygen as a function of ambient temperature in reptiles. Solid lines represent species with primarily edicular parenchyma; dashed lines, those with primarily faveolar parenchyma. *Iguana iguana* (Ii) has a transitional lung type with both edicular and faveolar parenchyma (see Fig. 1.2). Primarily edicular: Aj, *Acrochordus javanicus*; Am, *Alligator mississippiensis*; Cm, *Chelonia mydas*; To, *Terrapene ornata*; Ts, *Trachemys scripta*; Ve, *Varanus exanthematicus*; Vg, *V. gouldii*. Primarily faveolar: Cc, *Cerastes cerastes*; Cr, *Coluber ravergieri*; L, *Lacerta viridis* and *Podarcis sicula*; Ns, *Nerodia sipedon*; Sc, *Spalerosophis diadema cliffordi*; Sh, *Sauromalus hispidus*; Vp, *Vipera palaestinae*. (Adapted from Perry, 1992.)

Table 1.5. Comparison of lung parenchyma in similarly sized lizards with different lung types: single-chambered, *Tupinambis*; multichambered, *Varanus*.

Species (Mean body mass in kg)	Lung volume (ml kg^{-1})	Parenchymal volume (cm^3 kg^{-1})	S/V in parenchyma (cm^{-1})	Surface area (cm^2 kg^{-1})
*Tupinambis** (512)	87.7	21.9	189.4	4151
*Varanus** (437)	306.7	83.2	75.7	6127
Tupinambis /*Varanus* (dimensionless)	3.5	3.8	0.4	1.5

Tupinambis nigropunctatus (=*teguixin*); *Varanus exanthematicus*. All values from Perry, 1983.

face elaboration. The intercameral septa of *Trachemys scripta*, for example, have 38% more surface area than does the outer wall of the lung (Perry, 1992). This species can, therefore, satisfy its gas-exchange requirements with a very coarsely partitioned (surface-to-volume ratio 18 cm^2 cm^{-3}) parenchyma (Table 1.3). This combination of coarse parenchyma and large surface area in a multichambered lung is best illustrated by the comparison of similarly sized *Varanus exanthematicus* and *Tupinambis nigropunctatus* (=*teguixin*), lizards with similar life styles but very different lungs. In the following comparison only the generic names are used.

The parenchymal volume of the multichambered lung of *Varanus* is approximately the same as the total volume of the single-chambered lung of *Tupinambis*, but the surface-to-volume ratio is only 40% of that of *Tupinambis* (Table 1.5). If the lungs of each species were converted to cylinders based on their actual volume and length, the parenchymal thickness in *Varanus* would be almost twice that of *Tupinambis* (2.2 mm versus 1.3 mm; Perry, 1983). Stereological methods do not allow a direct measurement of parenchymal thickness, but the species dedicate a similar proportion of lung volume to parenchyma: *Tupinambis*, 25%; *Varanus*, 27%.

One functional consequence of a multichambered lung is that the surface area in part of the lung can be exposed to flowing air, thus allowing the rest of the lung to be used for gas storage and propulsion. Furthermore, the heterogeneously partitioned, multichambered lung of *Varanus* is twice as compliant per unit V$_{Lr}$ as is the homogeneously partitioned, single-chambered lung of *Tupinambis* (S. F. Perry and R. M. Jones, unpubl. data). This difference in compliance results in a relatively low work of breathing in *Varanus* and in the possibility of effective ventilation of gas exchange surfaces due to locomotor body movements alone (Carrier, 1987). The mass movement of air between left and right lungs during locomotion together with the large lung volume in this species could explain the reported ability of *V. exanthematicus* to sustain a high level of aerobic activity (Wood et al., 1978), although the animals tend to breathhold while walking (Carrier, 1987). Gular pumping in conjunction with locomotion may also increase the aerobic scope of this species (Owerkowicz and Brainerd, 1997). Most of the diffusing capacity in *Varanus* is located in the dorsal half of the lung (Perry, 1983), and pre-

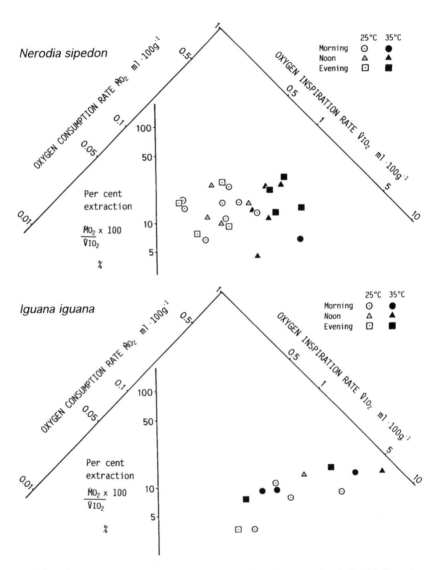

Fig. 1.26. Pattern of oxygen extraction at 25°C and 35°C in *Nerodia sipedon* (a) (faveolar parenchyma; compare Fig. 1.6b) and in *Iguana iguana* (b) (all parenchymal types, compare Fig. 1.2). Values for oxygen consumption rate and oxygen inspiration rate are read off perpendicularly against the respective logarithmic axes, and the per cent oxygen extraction, against the middle axis. (Adapted from Perry, 1989a.)

cisely this region is held relatively immobile by its suspension in the dorsal concavity of the body cavity. In *Trachemys scripta*, the similarly immobile medial chambers are ventilated indirectly by movement of air across the intrapulmonary bronchus from the large, flexible lateral chambers (Perry, 1992). This phenomenon could apply also to the varanid lung and may have been instrumental in the evolution of the avian lung-airsac system from an ancestral lung similar to that of present-day crocodylians (See Section VII.D).

4. ADVANTAGES OF SINGLE-CHAMBERED LUNGS

If multichambered lungs and the convection-oriented gas-exchange strategy provide efficient ventilation at low cost, why do single-chambered lungs and the diffusion-oriented strategy persist? To answer this question we must first recognize (1) that the volume of air in the central lumen is usually greater than that in the parenchyma, (2) that faveolar parenchyma is mobile, due to its large fraction of nonvascular smooth muscle, and (3) that faveolar, edicular, and trabecular parenchyma often occur in the same lung.

The single-chambered structure provides the resting animal with a mechanism for matching oxygen supply and demand that is elegant in its simplicity. The following scenario illustrates this principle. At the beginning of the nonventilatory period in a resting lizard, air convection in the lung ceases, and the pulmonary circulation quickly removes the oxygen contained in the parenchyma. Because diffusion time is proportional to the square of the diffusion distance (Schmidt-Nielsen, 1975), a significant concentration gradient of oxygen is established at the mouths of the faveoli. Oxygen flux decreases because the surface area for gas exchange (S in Equation 1.1) now has been reduced to that of the "false floor" at the level of the first-order trabeculae. As this scenario was defined to include no convection in the parenchyma, the conditions of diffusion apply in the faveolar air spaces: τ increases to the mean half-depth of the faveolar layer, to which applies the K value (Equations 1.1–1.3) for oxygen in water vapor-saturated air. During this period of inactivity, oxygen uptake is reduced quickly and effectively by a simple, self-regulating mechanism that decreases the surface area and increases the diffusion distance.

The trabeculae and intraparenchymal septa, however, are dynamic structures that possess smooth muscle. Rhythmic intrapulmonary pressure changes that occur independently of heart beat were reported first by Fano and Fasola (1894) and later studied by François-Franck (1906a, 1906b).Transection of the spinal cord exacerbates this rhythmic contraction of intrinsic pulmonary smooth muscle, whereas vagotomy eliminates it.

Although the response of intrinsic pulmonary smooth muscle to CO_2 in reptiles has been known since the early 20th century (see Babák, 1924; Gans and Hughes, 1967), direct observation of trabecular contraction in intact animals appears to be lacking. However, the exposed lungs of anesthetized *Lacerta viridis* show wavelike contraction in response to manual stimulation of the lung surface (S. F. Perry, unpubl. observ.). Also, a transient post-inflation pressure rise at middle volume levels is normally seen in reptiles during recording of open-chest volume-pressure curves (Perry and Duncker 1978, 1980; Daniels et al., 1993). This activity could be attributed either to the raising or to the lowering of trabecular network by the antagonistic smooth muscle groups in the trabeculae and in the interfaveolar septa. Such a self-regulatory movement of the faveoli, which could expose more or less faveolar surface or even refill the faveolar air spaces and possibly involve neuroepithelial cells as local paracrine regulators, is a fascinating concept that needs further study.

One would expect that the exposed surfaces of edicular and trabecular parenchyma in heterogeneously partitioned, single-chambered lungs would participate rapidly in gas exchange even during periods of low pulmonary ventilation. In *Gekko gecko*, only 61% of the ADF lies on the septa, and far from being an inert sac, the posterior region of the lung can make up 55% of the total ADF (Perry et al., 1994). In many snake lungs, however, the deep faveoli combined with a complete lack of gas exchange capillaries in the posterior two-thirds of the lung speak for a complete functional separation into gas exchange and gas storage portions (Wolf, 1933). Studies using radioactive xenon gas or a mixture of helium and sulphur hexafluoride gases demonstrate the lack of ventilation of the saccular lung region in *Morelia spilota* and *Vipera palaestinae*, respectively, and note stratification of gas along the length of the lung (Donnelly and Woolcock, 1977; Gratz et al., 1981). During elevated activity in the python, however, the stratification in the faveolar lung is destroyed, and perfusion of the lung also increases (Donnelly and Woolcock, 1977; Read and Donnelly, 1972). Breath-by-breath analysis in a flow-through preparation of *V. palaestinae* shows a fall in P_{O_2} and a more gradual rise in P_{CO_2} of lung air (Gratz et al., 1981) during breathing activity. However, no vertical stratification in the faveoli of the single-chambered lung of *Tupinambis teguixin* (=*merianae*) has been demonstrated (Hlastala et al., 1985)

The single-chambered lung thus appears to be well suited for long-term, low-to-medium levels of oxygen demand such as would occur under temperature stress, moderate activity, or repayment of oxygen debt following a burst of strenuous, anaerobic activity (Gleeson, 1980; Carrier, 1987). The dual function of the single-chambered lung in gas storage and oxygen uptake during sustained activity is demonstrated in sea snakes, which draw on their pulmonary oxygen reserves during the entire period of a 30-min dive (Seymour and Webster, 1975). In *Vipera*, the oxygen reserves also have been shown to last approximately one half hour (Gratz et al., 1981). The question remains: does the presence of single-chambered lungs dictate the life style or does the life style determine the optimal lung type?

The single-chambered lung is not well suited for sustaining high levels of activity, because the surface area available for elaboration of easily ventilatable parenchyma (convection strategy) is relatively small compared with that of a multichambered lung. Increasing the surface area at the expense of the sack-like region results in a stiff lung and increases the work of breathing (Perry and Duncker, 1978). For snakes or elongated lizards, however, the single-chambered lung is particularly well suited, not only because the long, cylindrical form offers an advantageous starting point for the elaboration of respiratory surfaces, but also because the lung forms a light-weight, deformable mass that smooths the body contour and, thus, may aid in maintaining contact with the substrate during locomotion.

VI. NONRESPIRATORY FUNCTIONS OF THE LUNG AND THEIR MORPHOLOGICAL CORRELATES

A. Locomotion

Lungs are not a prerequisite for terrestrial locomotion, as proved by the success of lungless plethodontid salamanders. If present, however, the lungs must be calculated into the physiology and biomechanics of locomotion. To my knowledge there have been no studies on the effect of intrapulmonary pressure on the efficiency of locomotion in reptiles. Lillywhite (1987), however, noted a positive correlation between the development of the avascular lung regions in snakes and their propensity to climb vertically. Because of their low blood pressure, snakes with homogeneously distributed lung parenchyma would accumulate blood in the caudal lung regions while climbing. The same cardiovascular restraints could set an upper limit on the maximum intrapulmonary pressure that is compatible with pulmonary perfusion, and could also in part explain the propensity of ventral lung lobes in varanid lizards to contain little parenchyma (Becker et al., 1989). In terrestrial testudines, the resting intrapulmonary pressure is commonly 2 cm H_2O but varies between 5 cm H_2O and slightly subatmospheric levels (Gans and Hughes, 1967).

Possibly more important than the resting pulmonary air pressure is the mechanical resistance to air flow during serpentine locomotion. If the lungs are elongate, portions thereof would become alternately compressed and expanded during lateral undulation, thus tending to move air between left and right lungs. The importance of transpulmonary ventilation could explain the presence of broad and direct interpulmonary communication and the lack of bronchi in such distantly related groups as rhynchocephalians and geckos, and could also provide an argument for regarding the lack of bronchi as an apomorphic trait in these groups rather than as a plesiomorphic trait among lepidosaurians. The factors that speak for long, narrow bronchi are neck development and thoracic spatial constraints (Duncker, 1978b).

B. Behavior

With such a large gas bladder in the body, it is not surprising that reptiles use the lungs for more than breathing. The most physically compelling use is as a hydrostatic organ. Sea turtles not only can adjust the entire lung volume, as does *Trachemys*, but also can regulate the left and right lungs separately (Jacobs, 1939; Milsom, 1975; Jackson, 1969). A recent review on the role of the lungs in diving reptiles is that of Seymour (1989).

Another interesting use of large lungs, apparently developed independently in several groups, i.e., in agamid, iguanid, and varanid lizards, is the use of gular pumping either as a supplement to normal, costal breathing (Saalfeld, 1934a, 1934b; Owerkowicz and Brainerd, 1997) or to increase the lung volume in excess of that which can be achieved by costal inspiration alone (Salt, 1943). The latter behavior helps prevent extraction of an animal that has wedged itself into a rock crevice. Such behavior, however, is not universal among reptiles. In spite of its thin, flexible shell, the pancake tortoise, *Malacochersus tornieri*, does not increase intrapulmonary pressure in response to attempts to extract it from a crevice (Ireland and Gans, 1972).

Sound production by hissing (snakes), snorting (varanid and teiid lizards), roaring (crocodiles, alligators), grunting and humming (tortoises), calling (geckos and at least one lacertid lizard), barking and clicking (geckos) all involve the lungs as a source of forced air. The purpose of sound production in reptiles ranges from warning or threat displays (snakes, varanids, teiids, geckos) to social or sexual signals (geckos and possibly tortoises) (Gans and Maderson, 1973; Paulsen, 1967; Marcellini, 1977). Probably the most bizarre use of the lungs in sound production is "hissing mimicry" in the egg-eating snake, *Dasypeltis* (Gans and Richmond, 1957; Gans and Maderson, 1973; Gans, 1974). The snake coils itself such that two adjacent slings rub against one another in opposite directions. Stridulation of a row of diagonally oriented, sawtooth-keeled scales produces the sound, which is amplified by the lung as a sounding chamber.

The lungs are also involved in silent displays, particularly well developed in those chameleons that straighten the ribs and display the flank. Similar activity can be involved in camouflage, making the animal high, flat, and more leaflike. Chameleons also engage in gular pumping that further inflates the lungs (Marcus, 1937). The extremely high compliance of the lungs and body wall in *Chamaeleo chamaeleon* allows it to achieve a lung volume of more than 4 times the resting volume at a pressure of 3 cm H_2O (Perry and Duncker, 1978).

VII. ADAPTATION AND EVOLUTION IN REPTILIAN LUNGS
A. Lung Structure of Primitive Reptiles

The only vertebrate lungs that have been preserved in fossils are those of the Devonian placoderm, *Bothriolepis* (Denison, 1941). For reconstructing the origin of reptilian lungs, one could hardly have chosen an animal that is less well-suited for the task. Lacking direct fossil evidence of lung structure in early reptiles, we use comparative anatomy, embryology, and functional morphology. The type of information provided by these three sources is qualitatively different and can, by mutual enlightenment, provide a general picture of the lungs of extinct reptiles and (outgroup) synapsids.

Classical comparative anatomical studies (Milani, 1894, 1897; Marcus, 1937; Gräper, 1931) show that the lungs of testudines, the oldest surviving group of reptiles, to be without exception multichambered. Developmental studies of testudine lungs (Hesser, 1905; Moser, 1902; Broman, 1939) reveal sequential groups of chambers developing along slender, unbranched intrapulmonary bronchi. Thus, at an early stage in their ontogenetic development, these multichambered lungs resemble the single-chambered lungs of lungfish, gymnophionians, or urodele amphibians (Hughes and Weibel, 1976; Marcus, 1923, 1928a; Goniakowska-Witalinska, 1980) with their rows of pouch-like niches. The large intrapulmonary septa in the transitional lungs of chameleons develop at an early ontogenetic stage (Broman, 1942). Similar septa are common among other iguanian lizards as well as among anguinomorphs. The hypothesis that these septa, because of their early development, might be a remnants of an ancestral multichambered lung is in contradiction to their absence in the most primitive chameleons (Klaver, 1980).

The main contribution of functional morphology to the reconstruction of lung structure in the first reptiles is to emphasize that not all lung types effectively function in all body types: e.g., plump animals tend to have plump lungs. In addition, the pulmonary volume of reptiles increases in direct proportion to body mass, whereas the surface area increases at a lower rate: (body mass) $^{0.75}$ (Tenney and Tenney, 1970). The combination of these two observations leads to the hypothesis that if the lungs of large, short-bodied animals are to maintain a high metabolic rate, and the packing of gas exchange surfaces must yield effective gas exchange, then the lungs will be multichambered.

Primitive representatives of advanced "reptiliomorph amphibians" such as *Solenodonsaurus* or primitive diadectomorphs (Panchen and Smithson, 1988; Gauthier et al., 1988) tended to be of modest size and to have an elongated trunk. These properties indicate that a simple lung structure would have sufficed to meet their respiratory demand. On the other hand, the "reptiliomorph amphibian" lineage also includes highly derived, plump, large-bodied species (e.g., *Eryops*), and giant forms have repeatedly evolved in all major synapsid and reptilian groups. Thus, not only the first reptiles but also the first amniotes (reptiles plus synapsids) may have possessed unspecialized, multichambered lungs. The closest modern analogue would lie between the coarse, single-chambered lungs of *Sphenodon* and the simple, multichambered lungs of *Heloderma* or *Typhlops* (Milani, 1894; Duncker, 1978b; Becker et al., 1989; Perry, 1983; Wallach, this volume).

As discussed in Section II, for early amniotes the bulk of comparative anatomical and embryological evidence speaks for a strictly metameric lung in which a broad, noncartilaginous intrapulmonary duct opens into a series of niche groups, each group consisting of three (or possibly four) radially disposed niches. With the development of cartilage reinforcement, the duct evolves into an intrapulmonary bronchus; the niches evolve into chambers. Based on the maximum number of chamber groups in sea turtles, varanids, helodermatids, and typhlopids (11 to 15) or dorsomedial niches in single-chambered lungs of lizards (approximately 15), the lungs of the first amniote must have had between 11 and 15 groups of three niche-like chambers. As the monopodial branching pattern in archosaurians (including birds) is fundamentally different from the dichotomous pattern in the chambers and airways of testudines and mammals, it is reasonable to assume that branching within the chambers evolved separately in synapsids (either separately or together with testudines) and in diapsids. Thus, the niche-like chambers in first amniotes were probably not further subdivided, but ended in edicular parenchyma.

Both faveolar parenchyma and heterogeneous parenchymal distribution appear to be derived traits that correlate with high metabolic oxygen demand. The former provides a large, if not easily ventilated, surface area, and the latter efficiently couples biomechanics and gas exchange.

B. Testudines and Synapsids

The large number of chamber groups with a dichotomous intracameral branching pattern in soft-shelled turtles (Trionychoidea) is consistent with the presumed central position of this group within the Cryptodira

(Gräper, 1931; Gaffney and Meylan, 1988). The basic trionychoid pattern appears to have been modified either by reducing the number of chambers in the less active testudine groups or by maintaining the number of chambers while increasing the complexity of their internal structure in the highly aerobically active sea turtles (Gräper, 1931; Gaunt and Gans, 1969; Lutcavage et al., 1987; Tenney et al., 1974; Fleetwood and Munnell, 1996).

The similarity between the basic structure of the lung of sea turtles and that of diving mammals (Perry et al., 1989c; Wislocki, 1935; Wislocki and Belanger, 1940; Kooyman, 1973; Fleetwood and Munnell, 1996) has been noted. These similarities include a proximally wide, caudally tapering main bronchus and relatively short secondary bronchi. These traits are probably convergent and favor rapid expulsion and inspiration of air on surfacing. The similarity to marsupial lungs (Marcus, 1937), however, is of greater interest, particularly in light of studies in progress on the echidna lung (S. F. Perry and S. Nicol, unpublished). Echidna lungs show a reduced number of bronchial groups as opposed to those of *Caretta*, but otherwise share a large number of structural similarities, such as a tapering main bronchus, node-like secondary bronchial groups, and three levels of dichotomous branching in secondary bronchi.

Structurally speaking, the mammalian lung could have evolved from a testudine lung-like predecessor. The ultrastructure of the bronchial epithelium, including the presence of goblet cells rather than of serous secretory cells, also speaks for a closer affinity of testudines to mammals than to lepidosaurs (Tesik, 1978, 1980, 1982, 1984a, 1984b). Mechanically, however, the mammalian lung shows a much lower compliance than even the complex lung of sea turtles (Lutcavage et al., 1989; Tenney et al., 1974), because the small alveoli must be inflated with each breath. The development of the diaphragm was, thus, the key to the further evolution of bronchoalveolar mammalian lungs as high-performance, gas-exchange organs (Perry and Duncker, 1980).

C. Lepidosaurs
1. RHYNCHOCEPHALIANS AND NON-PLATYNOTAN LIZARDS
Much more research is necessary on the pattern of structural diversity in the lungs of lepidosaurs before evolutionary trends can be recognized. For example, it is unclear whether the status of the bronchi is plesiomorphic for all lepidosaurs or apomorphic among the various groups. Archosaurs, the diapsid sister group of lepidosaurs, have well developed bronchi, but these structures are lacking in rhynchocephalians, the sister group to all other lepidosaurs. In iguanians, the most archetypal group of lizards, bronchi are again present. They are generally lacking or modestly developed among scincomorphs and non-platynotan

anguimorphs, but are well developed in platynotan lizards. In geckos, separate bronchi are present in the Sphaerodactylinae, a group that exhibits a large number of derived traits, but other groups possess long "pseudobronchi" (Mauelshagen, 1997).

Functionally, a direct connection between left and right lungs results in a low resistance to the transfer of gas between lungs during locomotory swinging of the body in lizards, and thus in ventilation of the respiratory surfaces during locomotion. Therefore, the lack of bronchi is not without functional significance in animals with single-chambered or transitional lung types. As discussed above, these structural types present less primary surface area for the elaboration of gas-exchange surfaces than do multichambered lungs, and passive air movement could be of critical importance in ventilation during extended periods of elevated aerobic activity. Thus, the bronchi could have been lost separately in various lepidosaurian groups including rhynchocephalians. Small lizards and/or those that do not swing the body during locomotion would then represent exceptions to the rule.

Similarly, the presence of large intrapulmonary septa in chameleon lungs is now considered to be a derived trait (Klaver, 1980). Thus, the transitional lung type may be a convergent feature in the lungs of chamaeleonids, agamids, and iguanids rather than a synapomorphy of these groups. The presence of a major dorsal septum that effectively divides the lung into two chambers in the anguimorph lizards *Xenosaurus* and *Shinisaurus* and in *Lanthanotus*, as well as the presence of a ventral septum of similar magnitude in anguid and anniellid lizards (Becker, 1993; Milani, 1984), demonstrates that the transitional lung type has developed many times. Until the compelling constraints that lead to the development of a transitional lung and the mechanisms of its formation are clarified, the relationship between lung structure, lung function, and systematics in lizards with single-chambered and transitional lung types remains difficult to interpret. A challenging field of future research is to determine if there are genetically determined paths for apparently convergent lung structures or if similar structures in distantly related species arise truly independently.

2. Platynotan Lizards

As shown in Figure 1.14b, the increasing complexity of lung structure in lizards from single-chambered (Anguidae) through transitional (Lanthanotidae) to multichambered (Helodermatidae) and highly derived, multichambered (other Varanoidea) is not consistent with the concept that the Varanidae and the Lanthanotidae together represent a sister group to the Helodermatidae. In *Lanthanotus*, not only the structure of the lungs but also their caudal location in the body cavity and the well-developed ventral mesopneumonia speak for the primitiveness rather than for the secondary simplification of the respiratory apparatus. Thus, multichambered lungs appear to have originated independently in *Heloderma* and *Varanus* (Becker, 1993).

The implication of the multiple origin of the multichambered lung from a transitional lung within a single monophyletic taxon (Varanoidea) is far reaching. It emphasizes the phylogenetic adaptability of the transitional lung type as the possible structural ancestor of multichambered testudine and archosaurian lungs and suggests that multichambered lungs are not an unlikely occurrence. Thus, they may have been present in extinct groups of amphibians such as seymouriamorphs and diadectomorphs and in non-reptilian amniotes such as "pelycosaurs" and "therapsids" as well as in extinct and extant reptilian groups. At the same time, the repeated appearance of multichambered lungs is not in conflict with the multiple origin of the nonseptate, single-chambered lung as presented in Section V.B.3, but it is consistent with the hypothesis that single-chambered lungs are not ancestral but derived among reptiles.

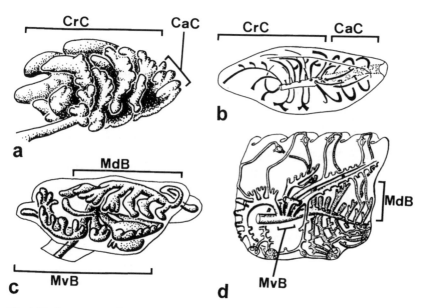

Fig. 1.27. Comparison of branching pattern in embryonic (a,c) and adult (b,d) crocodylian (a, b) and avian (c, d) lungs. Abbreviations: CrC, cranial chambers; CaC, caudal chambers; MdB, mediodorsal bronchi; MvB, medioventral bronchi. Parts a, b, and d show the right lung of embryonic *Alligator* sp., adult *Crocodylus niloticus*, and adult *Gallus* sp. in medial view and c of embryonic *Gallus* in dorsal view, respectively. (a: adapted from Broman, 1939); b: adapted from Perry, 1988; c: adapted from Locy and Larsell, 1916a; d: adapted from King, 1966.)

D. Archosaurs

It is perhaps not surprising that recent studies support older reports of a basic similarity in lung structure in all crocodylian groups (Broman, 1939; Locy and Larsell, 1916a, 1916b; Perry, 1988, 1989b). In the embryonic avian lung, as in that of crocodylians, four or five highly ordered chamber groups emerge from the anterior part of the bronchus, whereas several chambers emerge distally in a less strictly organized fashion (Fig. 1.27). Lereboullet (1838) did not even recognize the latter as separate chambers, but counted them as a single, posterior chamber. Perhaps more surprising in light of the highly specialized nature of the avian lung-airsac system is that an affinity to the adult crocodylian lung can be recognized. The number of chambers per group (maximally four) as well as the lateral-to-ventral direction of migration of the chamber rows as one proceeds caudally along the bronchus is the same as in birds. Furthermore, the branching pattern in the crocodylian lung consists of a system of main airways that give rise to subsidiary passages of smaller diameter. This monopodial pattern is also characteristic of the avian lung.

It is possible to envision the stepwise evolution of the avian lung-airsac system from a crocodylian-like precursor (Perry, 1992, Fig. 1.28). The first step is to construct a minimum-consensus lung and to assign it to a primitive archosaur, such as *Euparkeria*, the presumed common ancestor of crocodylians and birds (Figs. 1.28 and 1.29). The presumptive "euparkerian" lung is similar to a crocodylian lung, except that, unlike the condition in Recent crocodylians, the posterior chambers do not radiate caudally. The next step is to assume that the posterior chambers radiate craniad and establish contact with the anterior chambers. As in crocodylians, the intercameral septa are perforated. This first stage, in which an extrabronchial circulation is possible, is called the "early coelurosaurian" stage, as birds probably originated from coelurosaurian-like, saurischian dinosaurs (Weishampel et al., 1990). Later, as the extrabronchial circulation becomes established, the most anterior, ventral and posterior chambers evolve into airsacs. The perforations become the main path of air movement, and gas exchange tissue becomes established there. From this "late coelurosaurian" stage, it is not difficult to visualize the development of secondary bronchi from the chambers and the evolution of parabronchi from the perforations.

Physiologically, this model makes sense because the crocodylian lung already possesses the prerequisites for the cross-current gas-exchange model (Piiper and Scheid, 1986; Perry, 1990a): tubular structures in which the distal regions have a lower diffusing capacity than do the proximal ones. The above evolutionary model of the avian lung developing from a crocodylian-like predecessor involves a linked sequence

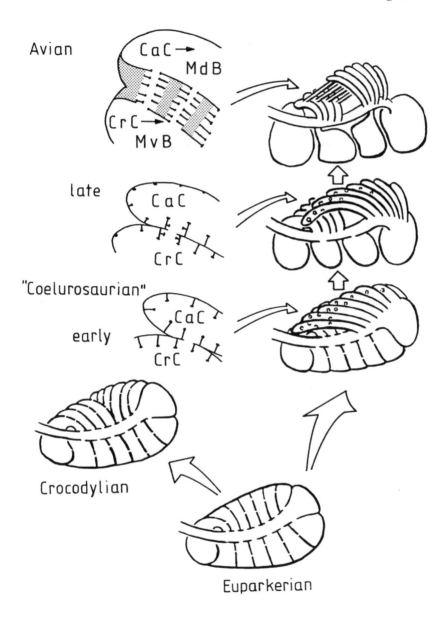

Avian

CaC→
MdB
CrC→
MvB

late

CaC

CrC

"Coelurosaurian"

CaC

early

CrC

Crocodylian

Euparkerian

Fig. 1.28. Proposed pathway of the evolution of the crocodylian lung and the avian lung-airsac system from a consensus structural type, tentatively assigned to *Euparkeria*. Transitional types, here assigned to small "coelurosaurian" theropods envision contact between cranial and caudal chamber groups and the development of connecting foramina to parabronchi. Abbreviations: CrC, cranial chambers; CaC, caudal chambers; MdB, mediodorsal bronchi; MvB, medioventral bronchi. (Adapted from Perry, 1992.)

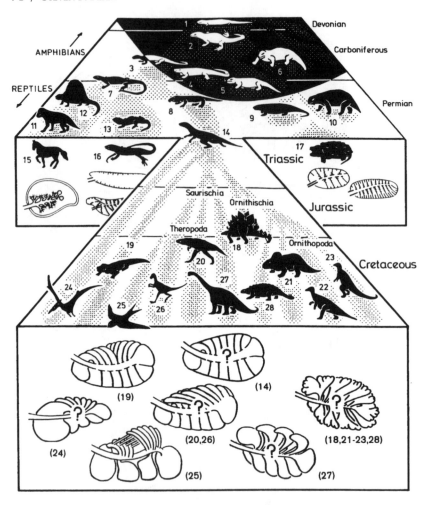

Fig. 1.29. Paleozoic and Mesozoic tetrapods and their lungs, including postulated types for extinct groups. White profiles indicate suspected amphibians. Testudines (17) are now believed to originate close to captorhinomorphs (3) (Gaffney and Meylan, 1988). Labels: 1, Anthracosauria; 2, Gephyrostegidae; 3, Captorhinomorpha; 4, Limno-scelidae; 5, Seymouriamorpha; 6, Diadectidae; 7, Romeriidae; 8, Captorhinidae; 9, Procolophonia; 10, Pareiasauria; 11, Therapsida; 12, "Pelycosauria"; 13, Lepidosauria; 14, Euparkeria; 15, Mammalia with bronchoalveolar lung type; 16, Squamata with sin-gle-chambered and multichambered lungs depicted; 17, Testudines with multi-chambered lungs; 18, Stegosauria; 19, Crocodylia; 20, Carnosauria; 21, Ceratopsia; 22, Hadrosauridae; 23, Iguanodontidae; 24, Pterosauria; 25, Aves; 26, "Coelurosauria"; 27, Sauropoda; 28, Ankylosauria. Numbers in parentheses indicate lung types for the numbered animal groups. Note bronchoalveolar-like lung postulated for ornithischians, multisaccular lung for sauropods and avian-like lung with airsacs postulated for theropods. (From Perry, 1992.)

of anatomical steps, each of which represents a physiological advance for an active endotherm with a high, constant metabolic rate. By considering such anatomical constraints as the presence or absence of excavated vertebrae and hollow humeri with pneumatic foramina together with phylogenetic relationships and known lung structures, it is possible to propose a tentative lung structure for archosaurs and pterosaurs (Fig. 1.29).

VIII. SUMMARY

There are many structural possibilities for constructing a reptilian lung, all of which provide an adequate anatomical diffusion factor for gas exchange. The resulting anatomical variety has made the lung and extrapulmonary airways valuable tools in reptilian systematics. In order to use the lung in cladistic analysis, one must be able to recognize convergence, and thus understand the sequence of structural evolution of lung types. Table 1.6 summarizes the consequences of various structural properties for the gas-exchange and the mechanical (passive pump) functions of the lung.

Before one can compare structures, a common terminology must exist for all reptilian lungs. Accordingly, the first half of this chapter has concentrated on establishing such a vocabulary. A description of lung types typical of the major reptilian groups and the mode of suspension of the lungs in the body cavity follows. The second half of this chapter takes a close look at the functional morphology of reptilian lungs without delving too deeply into the anatomy of snake lungs or into respiratory physiology, which are the subjects of separate chapters in this volume (see chapters by Wallach and Wang et al., this volume). Finally, I have attempted to make some plausible arguments for the evolution from reptilian progenitors to the high-performance lungs of mammals and birds.

Reptiles present an extremely broad spectrum of lung structure, but lack the highly specialized pulmonary types seen in homeotherms. Single-chambered lungs appear to be well suited for maintaining a low metabolic rate but have severe physiological and mechanical limitations whenever high levels of aerobic metabolism must be maintained. The multichambered lungs combine a large surface area, easily ventilatable, edicular parenchyma, and high compliance, and thus represent a starting point for the further evolution of high-performance lungs such as those seen in birds and mammals.

ACKNOWLEDGMENTS

I am indebted to Anke Schmitz for uncompromizing proofreading and for assistance in production of the final illustrations and tables and to Marion Schlich for photography and reprographic work.

Table 1.6. Structure/function correlations in the respiratory system of reptiles

Key	Lung morphology	Exchanger	Passive pump
1.	**STRUCTURAL TYPE**		
1.1	Single-chambered	Small primary surface area; surface/volume ratio greatest when lung is elongate.	—
1.2	Transitional	Greater primary surface area than single-chambered.	—
1.3	Multichambered	Potentially greater primary surface area than transitional; ventilation of surfaces by intrapulmonary bronchus.	—
2.	**PARENCHYMA**		
2.1	Distribution		
2.1.1	Homogeneous	Gas exchange in all lung parts; tendency towards small lungs.	Trabeculae necessary for maintenance of lung shape; lung equally flexible in all parts; relatively low compliance; high work of breathing.
2.1.2	Heterogenous	Regional distribution of gas exchange surfaces; tendency towards large lungs.	Lung shape maintained by attachment to body wall and intracoelomic septa; trabeculae for support of partitions; regions of high compliance; highly kinetic with low work of breathing.
2.2	Parenchymal type		
2.2.1	Atrabecular	Minimal surface area/volume ratio; no hindrance of convection.	Potentially extremely flexible; if smooth muscle lacking, poor potential for maintenance of lung shape.
2.2.2	Trabecular	Small surface/volume ratio; little hindrance of convection.	Potentially very flexible; full potential for maintenance of lung shape.
2.2.3	Edicular (shallow, sparse-dense)	Potentially large surface/volume ratio; convection possible.	Potentially less flexible than above; full potential for maintenance of lung shape.
2.2.4	Faveolar (deep, dense)	Potentially very large surface/volume ratio; convection in deep portions only during breathing movements.	Least flexible of reptilian parenchymal types; full potential for maintenance of lung shape.
3.	**CAPILLARY NET**		
3.1	Disposition		
3.1.1	Double	Large blood volume; low %CR*; diffusion barrier thick on one side of each net.	—

(Continued on next page)

Table 1.6. (Continued)

3.1.2	Pseudo-single	Small blood volume; high %CR*, but diffusion barrier thick on one side of net.	—
3.1.3	Single	Small blood volume, high %CR* and diffusion barrier potentially thin on both sides of net.	—
3.2	Bulging		
3.2.1	Steep sided	Potentially large proportion of surface area with uniform, thin diffusion barrier; enlargement of pulmonary surface area due to bulging.	Potentially large surface tension due to steep-sided concavities in lung surface; potentially low compliance and high work of breathing.
3.2.2	Embedded	Potentially small proportion of surface area with uniform, thin diffusion barrier; little enlargement of pulmonary surface area.	Gradual concavities; potentially little decrease in compliance due to surface tension factors.
3.3	Barrier thickness (harmonic mean)		
3.3.1	Thick	Small diffusing capacity per unit pulmonary surface area.	Large mechanical stability.
3.3.2	Thin	Large diffusing capacity per unit pulmonary surface area.	Small mechanical stability.

*%CR per cent of capillary surface that participates in a thin air-blood barrier.

APPENDIX: REPTILIAN SPECIES DISCUSSED

TESTUDINES

Caretta caretta
  Gräper, 1931
  Broman, 1939
  Jacobs, 1939
  Milsom, 1975
  Lutcavage et al., 1987
  Lutcavage et al., 1989
  Perry, 1989b
  Perry et al., 1989c
  Fleetwood and Munnell, 1996
  S. F. Perry, unpubl. obs.
Chelodina longicollis
  Gräper, 1931
Chelonia mydas
  Tenney et al., 1974

Duncker, 1978a
Perry, 1992
Chelydra serpentina
  Gaunt and Gans, 1969
  Duncker, 1978a
Emys orbicularis
  Hesser, 1905
  Gräper, 1931
Malacochersus tornieri
  Ireland and Gans, 1972
Pelusios (as *Sternothaerus*) *subniger*
  Gräper, 1931
Platemys sp.
  Gräper, 1931

Terrapene ornata
  Perry, 1882
Testudo graeca
  Gräper, 1931
  Gans and Hughes, 1967
  Perry, 1976
  Meban, 1977
Trachemys (as *Pseudemys*) *scripta*
  Jackson, 1969
  Duncker, 1978a

  Perry, 1978
  Perry, 1983
  Scheuermann et al., 1983
  Scheuermann, 1987
  Perry, 1989b
  Perry, 1990b
  Perry, 1992
  Perry, 1993
Trionyx sp.
  Gräper, 1931

RHYNCHOCEPHALIA

Sphenodon punctatus
  Dunker, 1978b
  Marcus, 1987

  Perry, 1989b
  Milani, 1894

SAURIA

Anadia bogotensis
  Becker, 1993
Ameiva ameiva
  Becker, 1993
Anguis sp.
  Milani, 1894
Anguis fragilis
  Meban, 1978
Anolis carolinensis
  Becker, 1993
Bachia sp.
  Böhme, 1989
Barisia imbricata
  Becker, 1993
Brachylophus fasciatus
  Becker, 1993
Brookesia sp.
  Klaver, 1977
  Klaver, 1979
  Becker, 1993
Calotes sp.
  Tiedemann, 1811
  Meckel, 1818
  Milani, 1894
Celestus (as *Diploglossus*) *occiduus*
  Becker, 1993
Chamaeleo sp.
  Klaver, 1977
  Klaver, 1979

Chamaeleo africanus (as *basiliscus*)
  Klaver, 1980
Chamaeleo chamaeleon
  Klaver, 1973
  Perry and Dunker, 1978b
  Perry and Dunker, 1980
  Perry, 1983
  Perry, 1989b
Chondrodactylus angulifer
  Büsing, 1990
Ctenophorus nuchalis
  Broman, 1904
  Frappell and Daniels, 1991
  Becker, 1993
  Daniels et al., 1993
  McGregor et al., 1993
  Daniels et al., 1994
Ctenosaura acanthura
  Becker, 1993
Ctenosaura hemilopha
  Becker, 1993
Cyrtodactylus pulchellus
  Büsing, 1990
Diplodactylus williamsi
  Büsing, 1990
Diploglossus sp.
  Becker, 1993
Diploglossus tenuifasciatus
  Becker, 1993

Diploglossus warreni
Becker, 1993
Draco volans
Becker, 1993
Gallotia stehlini
Becker, 1993
Gekko gecko
Welsch and Müller, 1980a
Welsch and Müller, 1980b
Perry et al., 1989b
Büsing, 1990
Becker, 1993
Perry et al., 1994
Gerrhosaurus major
Becker, 1993
Heloderma horridum
Becker, 1993
Heloderma suspectum
Becker et al., 1989
Becker, 1993
Hemidactylus sp.
Mahendra, 1947
Welsch and Müller, 1980a
Welsch and Müller, 1980b
Iguana iguana
Lereboullet, 1838
Milani, 1894
Perry, 1989a
Perry, 1992
Becker, 1993
Lacerta sp.
Milani, 1894
Perry, 1990b
Perry, 1993
Lacerta agilis
Tesik, 1984a
Lacerta viridis
Cragg, 1975
Cragg, 1978
Duncker, 1978b
Meban, 1978a
Perry and Duncker, 1978
Duncker, 1981
Perry, 1992
Becker, 1993
S. F. Perry, unpubl. obs.

Lacerta vivipara
Tesik, 1984a
Lanthanotus borneensis
Becker et al., 1989
Becker, 1993
Laudakia (as Agama) stellio
Becker et al. 1989
Becker, 1993
Leiolepis belliana
Becker, 1993
Neusticurus bicarinatus
Becker, 1993
Ophisaurus apodus
Pallas, 1775
Milani, 1894
Becker, 1993
Ophisaurus harti
Becker, 1993
Ophisaurus ventralis
Meckel, 1818
Physignathus cocincinus
Becker, 1993
Phrynosoma cornutum
Milani, 1894
Phrynosoma orbiculare
Milani, 1894
Phyllodactylus sp.
Wiedersheim, 1906
Podarcis (as Lacerta) sicula
Cragg, 1975
Cragg, 1978
Perry, 1992
Becker, 1993
Pogona (as Amphibolurus) barbata
Becker, 1993
Rhacodactylus leachianus
Perry et al., 1989b
Sauromalus hispidus
Perry, 1992
Sauromalus obesus
Salt, 1943
Shinisaurus crocodilurus
Becker, 1993
Tarentola sp.
Wiedersheim, 1906
Tarentola annularis
Meckel, 1818

Tupinambis merianae (as *tequixin*)
  Broman, 1904
  Broman, 1937
  Duncker, 1978a
  Hlastala et al., 1985
  Perry, 1989b
  Becker, 1993
Tupinambis teguixin (as *nigropunctatus*)
  Klemm et al., 1979
  Perry, 1983
  Hlastala et al., 1985
  Perry et al., 1989a
Uromastyx acanthinurus
  Becker, 1993
Uromastyx hardwickii
  Saalfeld, 1934a
  Saalfeld, 1934b
  Becker, 1993
Uroplatus fimbriatus
  Tiedemann, 1818
  Werner, 1912
  Büsing, 1990
  Becker, 1993
  Rittenhouse, 1995
Uroplatus sikorae
  Rittenhouse, 1995
Varanus acanthurus
  Becker et al., 1989
  Becker, 1993
Varanus bengalensis
  Kirschfeld, 1970
  Becker et al., 1989
  Becker, 1993
Varanus exanthematicus
  Perry, 1990b
  Kirschfeld, 1970
  Wood et al., 1978
  Perry, 1983
  Becker et al., 1989
  Perry, 1989b
  Becker, 1991
  Becker, 1993
  Perry, 1993
Varanus flavescens
  Kirschfeld, 1970
Varanus glebopalma
  Becker, 1993

Varanus gouldii
  Perry, 1992
Varanus griseus
  Kirschfeld, 1970
Varanus indicus
  Becker et al., 1989
  Becker, 1991
  Becker, 1993
Varanus mertensi
  Becker et al., 1989
  Becker, 1991
  Becker, 1993
Varanus mitchelli
  Becker et al., 1989
  Becker, 1991
  Becker, 1993
Varanus niloticus
  Kirschfeld, 1970
  Becker et al., 1989
  Becker, 1993
Varanus prasinus
  Becker et al., 1989
  Becker, 1991
  Becker, 1993
Varanus salvadorii
  Becker et al., 1989
  Becker, 1991
  Becker, 1993
Varanus salvator
  Kirschfeld, 1970
  Becker et al., 1989
  Becker, 1991
  Becker, 1993
Varanus storri
  Kirschfeld, 1970
  Becker et al., 1989
  Becker, 1991
  Becker, 1993
Varanus timorensis
  Becker et al., 1989
  Becker, 1991
  Becker, 1993
Varanus varius
  Becker et al., 1989
  Becker, 1991
  Becker, 1993

Varanus yemenensis
  Becker, 1991

Xenosaurus grandis
  Becker, 1993

AMPHISBAENIA

Amphisbaena alba
  Meckel, 1818
  Cuvier, 1840
  Milani, 1894
Amphisbaena fuliginosa
  Meckel, 1818
  Cuvier, 1840
Anops kingii
  Smalian, 1885
  Bedriaga, 1884

Bipes canaliculatus
  Meckel, 1818
  Cuvier, 1840
Blanus cinereus
  Smalian, 1885
  Bedriaga, 1884
Blanus strauchi
  Smalian, 1885
  Bedriaga, 1884
Leposternon sp.
  Stannius, 1856

SERPENTES

Acrochordus javanicus
  Perry, 1992
  V. Wallach, pers. comm.
Cerastes (as *Aspis*) *cerastes*
  Perry, 1992
Coluber ravergieri
  Perry, 1992
Crotalus viridis oreganus
  Luchtel and Kardong, 1981
Dasypeltis sp.
  Gans and Richmond, 1957
  Gans, 1974
Homalopsis sp.
  Wallach, 1993
Nerodia sipedon
  Perry, 1983
  Perry, 1989a
  Perry, 1992

Pituophis melanoleucus
  Stinner, 1982
  Perry, 1983
  Perry, 1989a
Python reticulatus
  Perry, 1983
Spalerosophis diadema cliffordi
  Perry, 1992
Trimeresurus sp.
  Wallach, 1993
Typhlops sp.
  Brongersma, 1960
  Wallach, 1993
Ungaliophis sp.
  Wallach, 1993
Vipera (*xanthina*) *palaestinae*
  Gratz et al., 1981

CROCODYLIA

Alligator sp.
  Schulze, 1871
  Miller, 1893
  Broman, 1939
Alligator mississippiensis
  Hoffmann, 1890
  Milani, 1897
  Marcus, 1928b
  Perry, 1992

"Alligator punctulatus"
  Hoffmann, 1890
Caiman sp.
  Meckel, 1818
Caiman crocodilus
  Hoffmann, 1890
  Gans and Clark, 1976
  Duncker, 1978a
  Duncker, 1978b
  Perry, 1989b

Caiman latirostris
Hoffmann, 1890
Crocodylus sp.
Schulze, 1871
Miller, 1893
Crocodylus acutus
Owen, 1866
Hoffmann, 1890
Milani, 1897
Crocodylus niloticus
Lereboullet, 1838

Cuvier, 1840
Perry, 1983
Perry, 1988
Perry, 1990b
Perry, 1993
Crocodylus porosus
Hoffmann, 1890
Gavialis gangeticus
Hoffmann, 1890
Paleosuchus palpebrosus
Hoffmann, 1890

REFERENCES

Babák, E. (1921). Die Mechanik und Innervierung der Atmung. In *Handbuch der vergleichenden Physiologie* (H. Winterstein, ed.). Gustav Fischer, Jena, vol. 1/2, pp. 584–1052.

Bartels, H. (1971). Diffusion coefficients and Krogh's diffusion constants. Diffusion coefficients of gases in water. In *Respiration and Circulation* (P. L. Altman and D. S. Dittmer, eds.), Federation of American Societies for Experimental Biology, Bethesda, Maryland, pp. 21–24.

Becker, H. O. (1991). The lung morphology of *Varanus yemenensis* Böhme, Joger & Schätti, 1989, and its bearing on the systematics of the Afro-Asian monitor radiation. *Mertensiella* 2, 29–37.

Becker, H. O. (1993). "Vergleichende Untersuchungen am respiratorischen Apparat anguimorpher Eidechsen: Eine stammesgeschichtliche Deutung." Dissertation. Rheinische Friedrich-Wilhelms-Universität, Bonn.

Becker, H. O., Böhme, W., and Perry, S. F. (1989). Die Lungenmorphometrie der Warane (Reptilia: Varanidae) und ihre systematisch-stammesgeschichtliche Bedeutung. *Bonn. Zool. Beitr.* 40, 27–56.

Beddard, F. E. (1907). Contributions to the knowledge of the systematic arrangement and anatomy of certain genera and species of Squamata. *Proc. Zool. Soc. London* 1907, 35–45.

Bedriaga, J. von (1884). *Amphisbaena cinerea* Vand. und *A. Strauchi* v. Bedr., erster Beitrag zur Kenntnis der Doppelschleichen. *Arch. Naturgesch.* 50, 23–77.

Böhme, W. (1989). Zur systematischen Stellung der Amphisbänen (Reptilia: Squamata), mit besonderer Berücksichtigung der Morphologie des Hemipenis. *Z. Zool. Syst. Evol.-forsch.* 27, 330–337.

Broman, I. (1904). *Die Entwicklungsgeschichte der Bursa omentalis und ähnlicher Rezessenbildung bei den Wirbeltieren*. Bergmann, Wiesbaden.

Broman, I. (1937). Cölom. In *Handbuch der vergleichenden Anatomie der Wirbeltiere* (L. Bolk, E. Göppert, E. Kallius, and W. Lubosch, eds.). Urban und Schwarzenberg, Berlin, vol. 3, pp. 989–1018.

Broman, I. (1939). Die Embryonalentwicklung der Lungen bei Krokodilen und Seeschildkröten. *Jb. Morph. Mikr. Anat.* 84, 244–306.

Broman, I. (1942). Über die Embryonalentwicklung der Chamäleonlungen. *Gegenbaurs Morphol. Jahrb.* 87, 490–535.

Brongersma, L. D. (1960). Tracheale long of linker long? *Proc. Kon. Ned. Akad. Wetenschapp. Afd. Natuurkunde* 69, 125–128.

Burggren, W. W. (1982). Pulmonary blood plasma filtration in reptiles: a "wet" vertebrate lung. *Science* 215, 77–78.

Burri, P., and Weibel, E. R. (1971). Morphometric estimation of pulmonary diffusion capacity. II. Effect of PO_2 on the growing lung. Adaptation of the growing rat lung to hypoxia and hyperoxia. *Respir. Physiol.* 11, 247–264.

Büsing, M. G. (1990). "Untersuchungen zur Morphologie der Trachea und der Lungen in der Systematik der Gekkonidae (Reptilia)." Diplomarbeit, Universität Oldenburg, Germany.

Camp, C. L. (1923). Classification of the lizards. *Bull. Am. Mus. Nat. Hist.* 48, 289–481.

Carrier, D. R. (1987). Lung ventilation during walking and running in four species of lizards. *Exp. Biol.* 47, 33–42.

Cole, F. J. (1975). *A History of Comparative Anatomy from Aristotle to the Eighteenth Century.* Reprinted by Dover Publications, New York.

Cragg, P. A. (1975). "Respiration and Body Weight in the Reptilian Genus *Lacerta*, a Physiological, Anatomical and Morphometric Study." Dissertation, University of Bristol, UK.

Cragg, P. A. (1978). Oxygen consumption in the lizard genus *Lacerta* in relation to diel variation, maximum activity and body weight. *J. Exp. Biol.* 77, 33–56.

Cuvier, G. L. C. F. D. (1805). *Leçons d'Anatomie Comparée, Recueillies et Publiées par G.-L. Duvernoy*, vol. 4. Baudouin, Paris.

Cuvier, G. L. C. F. D. (1840). *Leçons d'Anatomie Comparée, Rédigées et Publiées par G.-L. Duvernoy*, vol. 7, 2nd ed. Fortin, Masson et Cie., Paris.

Daniels, C. B., Eskandari-Marandi, B. D., and Nicholas, T. E. (1993). The role of surfactant in the static lung mechanics of the lizard *Ctenophorus nuchalis*. *Respir. Physiol.* 94, 11–23.

Daniels, C. B., McGregor, L. K., and Nicholas, T. E. (1994). The dragon's breath: a model for the dynamics of breathing and faveolar ventilation in agamid lizards. *Herpetologica* 50, 251–261.

Daniels, C. B., Orgeig, S., and Smits, A. W. (1995). The evolution of the vertebrate pulmonary surfactant system. *Physiol. Zool.* 68, 539–566.

Denison, R. H. (1941). The soft anatomy of *Bothriolepis*. *J. Paleont.* 15, 553–561.

Donnelly, P. M., and Woolcock, A. J. (1977). Ventilation and gas exchange in the carpet python, *Morelia spilotes variegata*. *J. Comp. Physiol.* 122, 403–418.

Dowling, H. G., and Duellman, W. E. (1978). *Systematic Herpetology: A Synopsis of Families and Higher Categories.* HISS Publications, New York.

Duncker, H. R. (1978a). Coelom-Gliederung der Wirbeltiere—Funktionelle Aspekte. *Verh. Anat. Ges., Jena* 72, 91–112.

Duncker, H. R. (1978b). Funktionsmorphologie des Atemapparates und Coelomgliederung bei Reptilien, Vögeln und Säugetieren. *Verh. Deutsch. Zool. Ges.* 1978, 99–132.

Duncker, H. R. (1981). Stammesgeschichte der Struktur- und Funktionsprinzipien der Wirbeltierlungen. *Verh. Anat. Ges., Jena* 75, 279–303.

Dupré, R. K., Taylor, R. F., and Frazier, D. T. (1985). Static compliance during the development of the bullfrog, *Rana catesbeiana*. *Respir. Physiol.* 59, 231–238.

Engel, S. (1962). *Lung Structure*. Charles C. Thomas, Springfield, Illinois.

Estes, R., de Queiroz, K., and Gauthier, J. A. (1988). Phylogenetic relationships within Squamata. In *Phylogenetic Relationships in Lizard Families* (R. Estes and G. Pregill, eds.). Stanford University Press, Stanford, California, pp. 119–281.

Fano, G., and Fasola, G. (1894). Sur la contractilité pulmonaire. *Arch. Ital. Biol.* 21, 338.

Fleetwood, J. N., and Munnell, J. F. (1996). Morphology of the airways and lung parenchyma in hatchlings of the loggerhead sea turtle, *Caretta caretta*. *J. Morphol.* 227, 289–304.

François-Franck, C. E. (1906a). Études de mécanique respiratoire comparée. I. Rapport entre la structure muscularie et de la contractilité du poumon de la tortue terrestre. *Comptes Rendus Soc. Biol.* 60, 1126–1127.

François-Franck, C. E. (1906b). La mécanique respiratoire des chéloniens. I. Contractilité de l'appareil pulmonaire de la tortue terrestre. *Comptes Rendus Soc. Biol.* 60, 968–970.

François-Franck, C. E. (1908). Études critiques et expérimentales sur la mécanique respiratoire comparée des reptiles. I. Cheloniens (Tortue greque). *Arch. Zool. Exp. Gen.* 9, 31–187.

Frappell, P. B., and Daniels, C. B. (1991). Temperature effects on ventilation and metabolism in the lizard, *Ctenophorus nuchalis*. *Respir. Physiol.* 86, 257–270.

Gaffney, E. S., and Meylan, P. A. (1988). A phylogeny of turtles. In *The Phylogeny and Classification of Tetrapods* (M. J. Benton, ed.). Clarendon Press, Oxford, UK, vol. 1, pp. 157–219.

Gans, C. (1970). Respiration in early tetrapods—the frog is a red herring. *Evolution* 24, 723–734.

Gans, C. (1971). Strategy and sequence in the evolution of external gas exchangers of ectothermal vertebrates. *Forma et Functio* 3, 61–104.

Gans, C. (1974). *Biomechanics: An Approach to Vertebrate Biology*. J. B. Lippincott, Philadelphia, Toronto.

Gans, C., and Clark, B. D. (1976). Studies in ventilation of *Caiman crocodilus* (Crocodilia: Reptilia). *Respir. Physiol.* 26, 285–301.

Gans, C., and Hughes, G. M. (1967). The mechanism of lung ventilation in the tortoise, *Testudo graeca* Linné. *J. Exp. Biol.* 47, 1–20.

Gans, C., and Maderson, P. F. A. (1973). Sound producing mechanisms in recent reptiles: review and comment. *Amer. Zool.* 13, 1195–1203.

Gans, C., and Richmond, N. D. (1957). Some notes on warning reactions in snakes of the genus *Dasypeltis*. *Copeia* 1957, 269–274.

Gaunt, A. S., and Gans, C. (1969). Mechanics of respiration in the snapping turtle, *Chelydra serpentina* (Linné). *J. Morphol.* 128, 195–228.

Gauthier, J. A., Kluge, A. G., and Rowe, T. (1988). The early evolution of the Amniota. In *The Phylogeny and Classification of Tetrapods* (M.J. Benton, ed.). Clarendon Press, Oxford, UK, vol. 1, pp. 103–155.

Gegenbaur, C. (1901). *Vergleichende Anatomie der Wirbeltiere mit Berücksichtigung der Wirbellosen, vol. 2.* Engelmann, Leipzig, pp. 300–324.

Gehr, P., Bachofen, M., and Weibel, E. R. (1978). The normal human lung. Ultractructure and morphometric estimation of diffusion capacity. *Respir. Physiol.* 32, 112–140.

Gleeson, T. T. (1980). Metabolic recovery from exhausting exercise by a large lizard. *J. App. Physiol.* 48, 689–694.

Goniakowska-Witalinska, L. (1980). Ultrastructural and morphometric changes in the lung of the newt *Triturus crisatus carnifex* Laur. during ontogeny. *J. Anat.* 130, 571–583.

Goodrich, E. S. (1930). *Studies on the Structure and Development of Vertebrates,* vols. 1–2. Macmillan, London.

Gräper, L. (1931). Zur vergleichenden Anatomie der Schildkrötenlunge. *Gegenbaurs Morphol. Jb.* 68, 323–375.

Gratz, R. K., Ar, A., and Geiser, J. (1981). Gas tension profile of the lung of the viper, *Vipera xanthina palestinae. Respir. Physiol.* 44, 165–176.

Grote, J. (1967). Die Sauerstoffdiffusionskonstanten im Lungengewebe und Wasser und ihre Temperaturabhängigkeit. *Pflügers Arch.* 295, 245–254

Günther, A. C. L. G. (1861). Contribution to the anatomy of *Hatteria. Phil. Trans. Roy. Soc. London* 157, 595–629.

Hein, J. (1989). "Der Einfluss chronischer Hypoxie auf die Lungenstruktur des Geckos, *Gekko gecko.*" Diplomarbeit, Universität Oldenburg, Germany.

Hesser, K. (1905). Entwicklung der Reptilienlungen. *Anat. Hefte* 29, 215–310.

Hlastala, M. P., Standaert, T. A., Pierson, D. J., and Luchtel, D. L. (1985). The matching of ventilation and perfusion in the lung of the tegu lizard, *Tupinambis nigropunctatus. Respir. Physiol.* 60, 277–294.

Hoffmann, C. K., ed. (1890). *Dr. H. G. Bronn's Klassen und Ordnungen des Thier-Reichs,* vol. 6, sect. 3. C. F. Winter'sche Verlagshandlung, Leipzig, pp. 1025–1037.

Hughes, G. M. (1973). Comparative vertebrate ventilation and heterogeneity. In *Comparative Physiology* (L. Bolis, K. Schmidt-Nielsen, and S. H. P. Maddrell, eds.). North Holland, Amsterdam, pp. 187–220.

Hughes, G. M., and Weibel, E. R. (1976). Morphometry of fish lungs. In *Respiration of Amphibious Vertebrates* (G. M. Hughes, ed.). Academic Press, London and New York, pp. 213–231.

Ireland, L. C., and Gans, C. (1972). The adaptive significance of the flexible shell of the tortoise *Malacochersus tornieri. Anim. Behav.* 20, 778–781.

Jackson, D. C. (1969). Buoyancy control in the freshwater turtle, *Pseudemys scripta elegans. Science* 166, 1649–1651.

Jacobs, W. (1939). Die Lunge der Seeschildkröte *Caretta caretta* (L.) als Schwebeorgan. *Z. Vergl. Physiol.* 27, 1–28.

Kilburn, K. H. (1969). Alveolar clearance of particles. A bullfrog lung model. *Arch. Environ. Health* 18, 556–563.

King, A. S. (1966). Structural and functional aspects of the avian lung and air sacs. *Int. Rev. Gen. Exp. Zool.* 2, 171–267.

Kirschfeld, U. (1970). Eine Bauplananalyse der Waranlunge. *Zool. Beitr. Neue Folge.* 16, 401–440.

Klaver, C. J. J. (1973). Lung anatomy: aid in chameleon taxonomy. *Beaufortia* 269, 155–177.

Klaver, C. J. J. (1977). Comparative lung morphology in the genus *Chamaeleo* Laurenti, 1768 (Sauria: Chamaeleonidae) with a discussion of taxonomic and zoogeographic implications. *Beaufortia* 327, 167–199.

Klaver, C. J. J. (1979). A review of *Brookesia* systematics with a special reference to lung-morphology (Reptilia: Sauria: Chamaeleonidae). *Bonn. Zool. Beitr.* 30, 16–175.

Klaver, C. J. J. (1980). Lung-morphology in the Chamaeleonidae (Sauria) and its bearing upon phylogeny, systematics and zoogeography. *Z. Zool. Systematik Evolutionsforsch.* 19, 36–58.

Klaver, C. J. J., and Böhme, W. (1986). Phylogeny and classification of the Chamaeleonidae (Sauria) with special reference to hemipenis morphology. *Bonn. Zool. Monogr.* 22, 1–64.

Klemm, R. D., Gatz, R. N., Westfall, J. A., and Fedde, M. R. (1979). Microanatomy of the lung parenchyma of a tegu lizard *Tupinambis nigropunctatus*. *J. Morphol.* 161, 257–280.

Klika, E., Tesik, I., and Nedved, J. (1976). Ultrastructure of the air-blood barrier in the great house gecko or tokay (*Gekko gecko*). *Folia Morphol.* 24, 29–34.

Kluge, A. G. (1987). Cladistic relationships in the Gekkonoidea (Squamata, Sauria). *Misc. Publ. Mus. Zool. Univ. Michigan* 173, 1–54.

Königstein, H. (1903). Die Funktion der Muskulatur in der Amphibienlunge. I. Anatomischer Teil. *Arch. Ges. Physiol.* 95, 616–624.

Kooyman, G. L. (1973). Respiratory adaptations in marine mammals. *Amer. Zool.* 13, 457–468.

Lauwreyns, J. M., Cokelaere, M., Lerut, T., and Theunynck, P. (1978). Cross-circulation studies on the influence of hypoxia and hypoxaemia on neuro-epithelial bodies in young rabbits. *Cell Tiss. Res.* 193, 373–386.

Leith, D. E. (1976). Comparative mammalian respiratory mechanics. *Physiologist* 19, 485–510.

Lereboullet, A. (1838). *Anatomie comparée de l'appareil respiratoire dans les animaux vertébrés*. Derivaux, Strasbourg and Germer-Baillère, Paris.

Lillywhite, H. B. (1987). Circulatory adaptations of snakes to gravity. *Amer. Zool.* 27, 81–95.

Locy, W. A., and Larsell, O. (1916a). The embryology of the bird's lung based on observations of the domestic fowl. Part 1. *Am. J. Anat.* 19, 447–504.

Locy, W. A., and Larsell, O. (1916b). The embryology of the bird's lung based on observations of the domestic fowl. Part 2. *Am. J. Anat.* 29, 1–44.

Luchtel, D. L., and Kardong, K. V. (1981). Ultrastructure of the lung of the rattle-snake, *Crotalus viridis oreganus*. *J. Morphol.* 169, 29–47.

Lutcavage, M., Lutz, P. L., and Baier, H. (1987). Gas exchange in the loggerhead sea turtle, *Caretta caretta*. *J. Exp. Biol.* 131, 365–372.

Lutcavage, M., Lutz, P. L., and Baier, H. (1989). Respiratory mechanics in the loggerhead sea turtle, *Caretta caretta*. *Respir. Physiol.* 76, 13–24.

Magnussen, H., Perry, S. F., Willmer, H., and Piiper, J. (1974). Transpleural diffusion of inert gases in excised lung lobes of the dog. *Respir. Physiol.* 20, 1–15.

Mahendra, B. C. (1947). Contributions to the bionomics, anatomy, reproduction and development of the Indian house-gecko, *Hemidactylus flaviviridis* Rüppell. Part IV. The respiratory and vocal organs. *Proc. Indian Acad. Sci.* 2, 29–42.

Maina, J. N., King, A. S., and King, D. Z. (1982). A morphometric analysis of the lung of a species of bat. *Respir. Physiol.* 50, 1–11.

Marcellini, D. (1977). Acoustic and visual display behavior in gekkonid lizards. *Amer. Zool.* 17, 251–260.

Marcus, H. (1923). Beitrag zur Kenntnis der Gymnophionen. VI. Über den Übergang von der Wasser- zur Luftatmung mit besonderer Berücksichtigung des Atemmechanismus von *Hypogeophis. Z. Anat. Entw.* 69, 328–343.

Marcus, H. (1927). Lungenstudien. *Morphol. Jahrb.* 58, 100–127.

Marcus, H. (1928a). Lungenstudien III und IV. *Morphol. Jahrb.* 59, 297–342.

Marcus, H. (1928b). Lungenstudie V. Vergleichende Untersuchungen über die respiratorische Oberfläche und ihr Verhältnis zum Körpergewicht. *Morphol. Jahrb.* 59, 561–566.

Marcus, H. (1937). Lungen. In *Handbuch der vergleichenden Anatomie der Wirbeltiere* (L. Bolk, E. Göppert, E. Kallius, and W. Lubosch, eds.). Urban and Schwarzenberg, Berlin, vol. 3, pp. 909–988.

Mauelshagen, N. M. P. (1997). "Die phylogenetische Bedeutung des Luftweg-Lungen-komplexes der Gekkota." Diplomarbeit, Universität Bonn, Bonn, Germany.

Maurer, F. (1891). Der Aufbau und die Entwicklung der ventralen Rumpfmuskulatur bei den urodelen Amphibien und deren Beziehung zu den gleichen Muskeln der Selachier und Teleostier. *Morph. Jb.* 2, 76–179.

Maurer, F. (1896). Die ventrale Rumpfmuskulatur einiger Reptilien. In *Festschrift zum siebenzigsten Geburtstage von Carl Gegenbaur am 21. August 1896.* W. Engelmann, Leipzig, pp. 181–256.

McGregor, L. K., Daniels, C. B., and Nicholas, T. E. (1993). Lung structure and the surfactant-like system of the central netted dragon, *Ctenophorus nuchalis. Copeia* 1993, 326–333.

Meban, C. (1977). Ultrastructure of the respiratory epithelium in the lungs of the tortoise, *Testudo graeca. Cell Tiss. Res.* 181, 267–275.

Meban, C. (1978a). Functional anatomy of the lungs of the green lizard, *Lacerta viridis. J. Anat.* 125, 421–431.

Meban, C. (1978b). The respiratory epithelium of the lungs of the slow-worm, *Anguis fragilis. Cell Tiss. Res.* 190, 337–347.

Meckel, J. F. (1818). Ueber das Respirationssystem der Reptilien. *Arch. Physiol.* 4, 60–89.

Methuen, P. A., and Hewitt, J. (1914). Contributions to our knowledge of the anatomy of chameleons. *Trans. Roy. Soc. South Africa* 7, 545–592.

Milani, A. (1894). Beiträge zur Kenntnis der Reptilienlunge. I. Lacertilia. *Zool. Jb. Abt. Anat. Ont.* 7, 545–592.

Milani, A. (1897). Beiträge zur Kenntnis der Reptilienlunge. II. *Zool. Jb. Abt. Anat. Ont.* 10, 93–153.

Miller, W. S. (1893). The structure of the lung. *J. Morphol.* 8, 165–188.

Milsom, W. K. (1975). Development of buoyancy control in juvenile Atlantic loggerhead turtles, *Caretta c. caretta. Copeia* 1975, 758–762.

Milsom, W. K. (1984). The interrelationship between pulmonary mechanics and spontaneous breathing in the tokay lizard, *Gekko gecko*. *J. Exp. Biol.* 113. 203–214.

Milsom, W. K., and Vitalis, T. Z. (1984). Pulmonary mechanics and work of breathing in the tokay lizard, *Gekko gecko*. *J. Exp. Biol.* 113, 187–202.

Milsom, W. K., and Chan, P. (1986). The interrelationship between lung volume, respiratory drive and breathing pattern in the turtle, *Chrysemys picta*. *J. Exp. Biol.* 120, 233–247.

Moser, F. (1902). Beiträge zur vergleichenden Entwicklungsgeschichte der Wirbeltierlunge. (Amphibien, Reptilien, Vögel, Säuger). *Arch. Mikrosk. Anat. Entw.* 60, 587–668.

Nelsen, D. E. (1953). *Comparative Embryology of the Vertebrates.* Blakiston, New York, Toronto.

Nielsen, B. (1961). On the regulation of respiration in reptiles. II. The effect of hypoxia with and without moderate hypercapnia on the respiration and metabolism of lizards. *J. Exp. Biol.* 39, 107–117.

Ogawa, C. (1920). Contributions to the histology of the respiratory spaces of the vertebrate lungs. *Am. J. Anat.* 27, 333–393.

Okada, Y., Ishiko, S., Daido, S., Kim, J., and Ikeda, S. (1964). Comparative morphology of the lung with special reference to the alveolar lining cells. 2. Lung of the Reptilia. *Acta Tuberc. Japonica* 12, 1–10.

Olson, E. C. (1976). The exploitation of land by early tetrapods. In *Morphology and Biology of Reptiles* (A. d'A. Bellairs and C. B. Cox, eds.). Academic Press, London and New York, pp. 1–30.

Otten, G. (1973). "Volumetrie des Lungen-Luftsacksystems von Haustaube, Blässhuhn und Höckerschwann." Inaugural Dissertation, Hamburg, Germany.

Owen, R. (1866). *On the Anatomy of Vertebrates*, vol. 1. Longmans, Green and Co., London, pp. 520–651.

Owerkowicz, T., and Brainerd, E. L. (1997). How to circumvent a mechanical constraint: ventilatory strategy of *Varanus exanthematicus* during locomotion. *J. Morphol.* 232, 305.

Pallas, P. S. (1775). *Lacerta apoda* descripta. *Novi Comment. Acad. Scient. Imperial. Petropolit.* 19, 435–454.

Panchen, A. L. (1970). Batrachosauria, Part A, Anthracosauria. In *Encyclopedia of Paleoherpetology* (O. Kuhn, ed.). Gustav Fischer, Stuttgart, pp. 1–84.

Panchen, A. L. (1972). The interrelationships of the earliest tetrapods. In *Studies in Vertebrate Evolution: Essays Presented to Dr. F. R. Parrington FRS* (K. A. Josey and T. S. Kemp, eds.). Boyd and Oliver, Edinburgh, pp. 65–78.

Panchen, A. L., and Smithson, T. R. (1988). In *The Phylogeny and Classification of Tetrapods* (M. J. Benton, ed.). Clarendon Press, Oxford, vol. 1, pp. 1–32.

Pastor, L. M., Ballesta, J., Perez-Tomas, R., Marin, J. A., Hernandez, F., and Madrid, J. F. (1987). Immunocytochemical localization of serotonin in the reptilian lung. *Cell Tiss. Res.* 248, 713–715.

Paulsen, K. (1967). *Das Prinzip der Stimmbildung in der Wirbeltierreihe und beim Menschen.* Akademische Verlagsgesellschaft, Munich.

Perry, S. F. (1971). Alcian blue as an en bloc stain for turtle lung goblet cells with and without prior periodate oxidation. *Stain Technol.* 46, 191–194.

Perry, S. F. (1976). Model of exchange barrier and respiratory surface area in the lung of the tortoise (*Testudo graeca*) and its practical application. *Mikroskopie* 32, 282–293.

Perry, S. F. (1978). Quantitative anatomy of the lungs of the red-eared turtle, *Pseudemys scripta elegans. Respir. Physiol.* 35, 245–262.

Perry, S. F. (1981). Morphometric analysis of pulmonary structure: methods for evaluation and comparison of unicameral and multicameral lungs. *Mikroskopie* 38, 278–293.

Perry, S. F. (1983). *Reptilian Lungs. Functional Anatomy and Evolution.* Springer-Verlag, Berlin and Heidelberg.

Perry, S. F. (1985). Evolution of the mammalian chest wall. In *Lung Biology in Health and Disease* (C. Lenfant, C. Roussos, and P. T. Macklem, eds.). Marcel Dekker, New York, Basel, vol. 29, pp. 187–198.

Perry, S. F. (1988). Functional morphology of the lungs of the Nile crocodile, *Crocodylus niloticus*: non-respiratory parameters. *J. Exp. Biol.* 134, 99–117.

Perry, S. F. (1989a). Structure and function of the reptilian respiratory system. In *Lung Biology in Health and Disease* (C. Lenfant and S. C. Wood, eds.). Marcel Dekker, New York, Basel, vol. 39, pp. 193–236.

Perry, S. F. (1989b). Mainstreams in the evolution of vertebrate respiratory structures. In *Form and Function in Birds* (A. S. King and J. McLelland, eds.). Academic Press, London, vol. 4, pp. 1–67.

Perry, S. F. (1990a). Gas exchange strategy in the Nile crocodile: a morphometric study. *Comp. Physiol,* ser. B, 159, 761–769.

Perry, S. F. (1990b). Recent advances and trends in the comparative morphometry of vertebrate gas exchange organs. In *Advances in Comparative and Environmental Physiology* (R. G. Boutilier, ed.). Springer-Verlag, Berlin, Heidelberg, vol. 6, pp. 45–71.

Perry, S. F. (1992). Gas exchange strategies in reptiles and the origin of the avian lung. In *Physiological Adaptations in Vertebrates. Respiration, Circulation, and Metabolism* (S. C. Wood, R. E. Weber, A. R Hargens, and R. W. Millard, eds.). Marcel Dekker, New York, pp. 149–167.

Perry, S.F. (1993). Evolution of the lung and its diffusing capacity. In *The Vertebrate Gas Transport Cascade. Adaptations to Environment and Mode of Life* (J. E. P. W. Bicudo, ed.). CRC Press, Boca Raton, Ann Arbor, London, Tokyo, pp. 142–153.

Perry S. F., and Duncker, H. R. (1978). Lung architecture, volume and static mechanics in five species of lizards. *Respir. Physiol.* 34, 61–81.

Perry S. F., and Duncker, H. R. (1980). Interrelationships of static mechanical factors and anatomical structure in lung evolution. *J. Comp. Physiol.* 138, 321–334.

Perry, S. F., Aumann, U., and Maloney, J. E. (1989a). Intrinsic lung musculature and associated ganglion cells in a teiid lizard, *Tupinambis nigropunctatus* Spix. *Herpetologica* 45, 217–227.

Perry, S. F., Bauer, A. M., Russell, A. P., Alston, J. T., and Maloney, J. E. (1989b). Lungs of the gecko *Rhacodactylus leachianus* (Reptilia: Gekkonidae): a correlative gross anatomical light and electron microscopic study. *J. Morphol.* 199, 23–40.

Perry, S. F., Darian-Smith, C., Alston, J.T., Limpus, C., and Maloney, J. E. (1989c). Histological structure of the lungs of the loggerhead turtle, *Caretta caretta*, before and after hatching. *Copeia* 1989, 1000–1010.

Perry, S. F., Hein, J., and Dieken, E. van (1994). Gas exchange morphometry of the lungs of the tokay, *Gekko gecko* L. (Reptilia: Squamata: Gekkonidae). *J. Comp. Physiol.*, ser. B, 164, 196–206.

Piiper, J., and Scheid, P. (1971). Respiration: alveolar gas exchange. *Ann. Rev. Physiol.* 33, 131–154.

Piiper, J., and Scheid, P. (1986). Models for comparative functional analysis of gas exchange organs in vertebrates. *J. Appl. Physiol.* 53, 1321–1329.

Plopper, C. G., Mariassy, A. T., Wilson, D. W., Alley, J. L., Nishio, S. J., and Nettesheim, P. (1983). Comparison of nonciliated tracheal epithelial cells in six mammalian species: ultrastructure and population densities. *Exper. Lung Res.* 5, 281–294.

Read, J., and Donnelly, P. M. (1972). Stratification of blood flow in the elongated lungs of the carpet python. *J. Appl. Physiol.* 32, 842–846.

Rieppel, O. (1988). The classification of the Squamata. In *The Phylogeny and Classification of Tetrapods* (M. J. Benton, ed.). The Systematics Association Special Volume No. 35A. Clarendon Press, Oxford, vol. 1, pp. 261–293.

Rittenhouse, D. R. (1995). "Laryngeal Morphology of Afro-Madagascan Gekkonine Lizards (Gekkonidae: Reptilia)." Master's Thesis, University of Calgary, Alberta, Canada.

Robb, J. S. (1960). The internal anatomy of *Typhlops* Schneider (Reptilia). *Aust. J. Zool.* 8, 181–216.

Russell, A. P. (1979). Parallelism and integrated design in the foot structure of the gekkonine and diplodactyline geckos. *Copeia* 1979, 1–21.

Saalfeld, E. von (1934a). Die Mechanik der Atmung bei *Uromastix* (Lacertilia). *Pflügers Arch. Ges. Physiol.* 223, 431–448.

Saalfeld, E. von (1934b). Die nervöse Regulierung der Atembewegung bei *Uromastix* (Lacertilia). *Pflügers Arch. Ges. Physiol.* 223, 431–448.

Salt, G. W. (1943). The lungs and inflation mechanism of *Sauromalus obesus. Copeia* 1943, 193.

Scherle, W. F. (1970). A simple method for volumetry in quantitative stereology. *Mikroskopie* 26, 57–60.

Scheuermann, D. W. (1987). Morphology and cytochemistry of the endocrine epithelial system in the lung. *Int. Rev. Cytol.* 106, 35–88.

Scheuermann, D. W., Groodt-Lasseel, M. H. A. de, Stilman, C., and Meisters, M. L. (1983). A correlative light-, fluorescence- and electron-microscopic study of neuroepithelial bodies in the lung of the red-eared turtle, *Pseudemys scripta elegans. Cell Tiss. Res.* 234, 249–269.

Schmidt-Nielsen, K. (1975). *Animal Physiology*. Cambridge University Press, London.

Schulze, F. E. (1871). Die Lungen. In *Handbuch der Lehre von Geweben des Menschen und der Thiere* (S. Stricker, ed.). Wilhelm Engelmann, Leipzig, pp. 465–488.

Seymour, R. S. (1989). Diving physiology. Reptiles. In *Comparative Pulmonary Physiology. Current Concepts* (S. C. Wood, ed.). Marcel Dekker, New York, pp. 697–720.

Seymour, R. S., and Webster, M. E. D. (1975). Gas transport and blood acid-base balance in diving sea snakes. *J. Exp. Zool.* 191, 169–182.

Smalian, C. (1885). Beiträge zur Anatomie der Amphisbaeniden. *Z. Wiss. Zool.* 42, 126–202.

Stannius, H. (1856). *Handbuch der Zootomie von v. Siebold und Stannius,* 2nd ed. Veit & Co., Berlin, 271 pp.

Stinner, J. N. (1982). Functional anatomy of the lung of the snake *Pituophis melanoleucus. Am. J. Physiol.* 243, R251–R257.

Tenney, S. M., and Tenney, J. B. (1970). Quantitative morphology of cold-blooded lungs: Amphibia and Reptilia. *Respir. Physiol.* 9, 197–215.

Tenney, S. M., Bartlett, D., Jr., Farber, J. P., and Remmers, J. E. (1974). Mechanics of the respiratory cycle in the green turtle (*Chelonia mydas*). *Respir. Physiol.* 22, 361–368.

Tesik, I. (1978). Comparative morphological study on the tracheal epithelium of reptiles. Symposia, Ninth Morphological Congress. Charles University, Prague, pp. 412–414.

Tesik, I. (1980). Ultrastructure of the ciliated cells of the tracheal epithelium in reptiles. *Folia Morphol.* 28, 181–183.

Tesik, I. (1982). Ultrastructural morphology of the tracheal epithelium of some species of testudinates. *Folia Morphol.* 30, 412–414.

Tesik, I. (1984a). The ultrastructure of the tracheal epithelium in European common lizard (*Lacerta agilis* L.) and in sand lizard (*Lacerta vivipara* Jacq.). *Anat. Anz.* 155, 329–340.

Tesik, I. (1984b). Morphological study of the functional cycle of the secretory cells of the upper respiratory tract epithelium of amphibians and reptiles. *Folia Morphol.* 32, 391–394.

Tiedemann, F. (1811). *Anatomie und Naturgeschichte des Drachens.* Schrag, Nürnberg.

Tiedemann, F. (1818). Ueber einen beim gefranzten Gecko oder Wanderkletterer entdeckten Luftbehälter. *Arch. Physiol.* 6, 549–592.

Vos, H. J. (1936). "Over ademhaling en reukzin bij reptielen en amphibien." Dissertation, Rijkuniversiteit te Groningen, Netherlands.

Wallach, V. (1985). A cladistic analysis of the terrestrial Australian Elapidae. In *Biology of Australasian Frogs and Reptiles* (G. Grigg, R. Shine, and H. Ehmann, eds.). Royal Zoological Society of New South Wales, Chipping Norton, NSW, Australia, pp. 223–253.

Wallach, V. (1993). Presence of a left lung in the Typhlopidae (Reptilia: Serpentes). *J. Herpetol. Assoc. Africa* 42, 32–33.

Weibel, E. R. (1970–1971). Morphometric estimation of pulmonary diffusion capacity. I. Model and method. *Respir. Physiol.* 11, 54–75.

Weibel, E. R. (1984). *The Pathway for Oxygen.* Harvard Univ. Press, Cambridge, Massachusetts.

Weibel, E. R, Taylor, C. R., O'Neill, J. J., Leith, D. E., Gehr, P., and Baudinette, R. V. (1983). Maximal oxygen consumption and diffusing capacity: a direct comparison of physiologic and morphometric measurements in canids. *Respir. Physiol.* 54, 173–188.

Weishampel, D. B., Dodson, P., and Osmolska, H. (1990). *The Dinosauria*. University of California Press, Berkeley and Los Angeles.

Welsch, U., and Müller, W. (1980a). Elektronenmikroskopische Beobachtungen zur Innervationen der Reptilienlunge. *Z. Mikrosk.-Anat. Forsch*. 94, 435–444.

Welsch, U., and Müller, W. (1980b). Feinstrukturelle Beobachtungen am Alveolarepithel von Reptilien unterschiedlicher Lebensweise. *Z. Mikrosk.-Anat. Forsch*. 94, 479–503.

Werner, F. (1912). Beiträge zur Anatomie einiger seltener Reptilien, mit besonderer Berücksichtigung der Atmungsorgane. *Arb. Zool. Inst. Univ. Wien* 19, 373–424.

Wiedersheim, R. E. E. (1883). *Lehrbuch der vergleichenden Anatomie der Wirbeltiere*. Gustav Fischer, Jena.

Wiedersheim, R. E. E. (1906). *Lehrbuch der vergleichenden Anatomie der Wirbeltiere*. Gustav Fischer, Jena.

Wilson, T. A., and Bachofen, H. (1982). A model for mechanical structure of the alveolar duct. *J. Appl. Physiol*. 52, 1064–1070.

Wislocki, G. B. (1935). The lungs of the manatee (*Trichechus latirostris*) compared with those of other aquatic mammals. *Biol. Bull*. 68, 385–396.

Wislocki, G. B., and Belanger, L. F. (1940). The lungs of the larger Cetacea compared to those of smaller species. *Biol. Bull*. 78, 289–297.

Wolf, S. (1933). Zur Kenntnis von Bau und Funktion der Reptilienlungen. *Zool. Jb*. 57, 139–190.

Wood, S. C., and Lenfant, C. J. M. (1976). Respiration: Mechanics, control and gas exchange. In *Biology of the Reptilia* (C. Gans and W. D. Dawson, eds.). Academic Press, New York, vol. 5, pp. 225–274.

Wood, S. C., Johansen, K., Glass, M. L., and Maloiy, G. M. O. (1978). Aerobic metabolism of the lizard *Varanus exanthematicus*: effects of activity, temperature, and size. *J. Comp. Physiol*. 127, 331–336.

Perry, S. F. (1998). Lungs: Comparative Anatomy, Functional Morphology, and Evolution. In *Biology of the Reptilia*, vol. 19 (Morphology G) (C. Gans and A. S. Gaunt, eds.). Society for the Study of Amphibians and Reptiles, Ithaca, New York, Contrib. Herpetol., vol. 14, pp. 1–92.

2

The Lungs of Snakes

VAN WALLACH

I. INTRODUCTION

A. General

"Snakes are limbless musculoskeletal tubes housed in a casing of integument and containing a core of viscera" (Cundall, 1987). Among the viscera of snakes, the most variable in size and complexity is the respiratory system. Several features distinguish this system, making it unique among vertebrates. No snake has the more or less equally sized and symmetrical left and right lungs present in other tetrapods. The left lung in snakes is much smaller than the right, usually vestigial, and sometimes lost. Additionally, members of half of the extant snake families show a tracheal lung, a third lung, in the precardiac region, which often functions as the main respiratory organ. Whereas the left lung is commonly reduced, the right lung and tracheal lung have become greatly elongated in many species, with the lungs occupying more than half of the body length. The lengthened caudal portion of the right lung may even act as an air reservoir.

B. Application to Systematics

The approximately 2750 recognized species of extant snakes may be placed in some 460 genera (K. L. Williams and Wallach, 1989), of unclear phylogenetic relationships. In spite of considerable interest and research, the systematics of snakes remain poorly understood, although some improvement has been made upon Boulenger's pioneering classification (1893–1896). Alternative systematic arrangements pertain to specific taxonomic groups or geographical regions; none satisfactorily treats the Serpentes as a whole.

The characters emphasized by the taxonomist have strongly influenced the resulting classification. Beyond lepidosis, Boulenger (1893, 1894, 1896) emphasized cranial osteology, including dentition, in his classification of the world's ophiofauna. Cope (1894a–1900) expanded the character analysis to include vertebral hypapophyses, hemipenes, and lungs. Only four workers since Boulenger and Cope have reclassified the Serpentes as a whole, although F. Werner (1917–1922a, 1923–1929) listed the world's species but without a new classification. Romer (1956) reassessed the Serpentes based on osteology and introduced the superfamilial taxon. Underwood (1967) initiated a revolution in snake systematics by considering novel characters of the cranium, jaw musculature, retinal cells, and visceral anatomy. His brilliant work generated new avenues of investigation and cast doubt upon some traditional theories of snake phylogeny and evolution. Dowling (*in* Dowling and Duellman, 1978) used traditional characters in presenting the most recent listing of all genera and higher taxa; he initiated the use of the hierarchical level of tribe- to group-related genera—a system both practical and utilitarian, especially among the Colubridae. McDowell (1974a, 1975, 1979, 1987) considered cranial osteology, cranial myology, and hemipenial morphology to produce his system of classification. Others have worked mostly on primitive snakes (i.e., Rieppel, 1979; Kluge, 1991, 1993a, 1933b) or proposed higher taxonomic classifications (i.e., H. M. Smith et al., 1977; Rasmussen, 1985). However, the four classification schemes of Romer, Underwood, Dowling, and McDowell differ substantially; only the generic content of certain well-defined tribes or subfamilies is similar, and major incongruence exists from the tribal to infraordinal levels. This disparity is attributable to individual philosophies, different analytical approaches, and emphasis on different characters.

Why has a universally acceptable hypothesis of snake phylogeny been so difficult to achieve on a worldwide basis? One major obstacle is the general morphological similarity of all snakes; their structure seems trimmed to an anatomical minimum through reduction and loss of features such as appendages and supporting girdles. However, the elongation of the body has provided an opportunity for increased variation within the soft anatomy. The attenuation of the serpentine body form resulted in three derived visceral effects in relation to other tetrapods (Gans, 1975a): (1) all of the internal organs have elongated and become more linear in aspect; (2) the paired organs have developed an asymmetry, with the right member positioned more craniad and the left more caudad; and (3) there has also been a nearly universal reduction in the left-sided member in comparison with the right. To my knowledge, the only exception to the latter occurs with the aortic arches, in which the right systemic arch is always reduced (and rarely lost, fide Malnate and Underwood, 1988) in comparison with the left. The asymmetry of many of the paired organs is least among the most primitive snakes (Anilioidea and Scolecophidia) and greatest among the most derived forms (Colubroidea).

The variability and importance of the respiratory organs were recognized by early researchers (Meckel, 1818, 1833; Schlegel, 1837a; Cuvier, 1840; Cope, 1894a–1900). Cope (1895b) claimed that the "diversity of lung structure" warranted "according it a high systematic value." He further remarked that for classifying the Ophidia, "It seemed probable to me that an organ which presents so much variation must furnish some important clues" (Cope, 1894a). More recent authors have commented on the potential taxonomic value of lung characters. Brongersma (1957a) noted: "Although many authors have already dealt with the respiratory system in snakes, relatively little is yet known about the great diversity shown by this group." That statement remains valid, in spite of Underwood's (1967) claim that "in relation to the amount of information which may be obtained, visceral dissection is not very time consuming." Dowling (1959) expressed the view that "most species are still known only by their external features," a remark that provoked Underwood's comment (1967) that the external anatomy of only two species of snakes had been adequately described, these being *Rhinophis* (Baumeister, 1908) and *Dasypeltis* (Gans, 1959). Bullock and Tanner (1966) stated that "snake anatomy has been generally neglected." Thorpe (1975) suggested that the viscera "could be used in ophidian systematics to a far greater extent than they are at present" because they are easy to observe with a mid-ventral incision. He claimed that "the large number of possibly diagnostic features that the visceral anatomy of ophidians may provide are largely ignored." Maina (1989) stated that "extensive and detailed comparative studies on the ophidian lungs are essential for any meaningful systematic use" of the variation in lung morphology in snakes.

Relative length of the viscera is expressed as a ratio scaled to the body or snout-vent length (SVL). As an example of the visceral variation present in the Serpentes (all values representing % SVL), the distance from the snout to the posterior tip of hyoid ranges from 3–25%, the length of the tracheal lung (when present) ranges from 3–44%, the tip of the snout to the posterior tip of heart from 15–57%, junction of systemic arches from 5% craniad of the heart tip to 12% caudad of the tip, length of the right lung from 8–82%, the length of the right bronchus from 0.5–54%, the tip of the snout to the posterior tip of right lung from 33–100%, the length of the left lung (when present) from 1–31%, the gap between heart and liver from −5% to 16%, length of the liver from 8–42%, the gap between liver and gall bladder from −5% to 44%, the liver-gall bladder interval from 11–59%, length of the testis from 1–10%, length of the kidney from 2–20%, gap between the kidney and the vent from 1–18%, and distance from the anterior margin of the left kidney to the vent (kidney plus gap) from 6–28%. The number of tracheal rings varies from 70–1120, and the tracheal lung, left lung, left bronchus, left orifice, right saccular lung, and right bronchus may be present or absent.

All snake lungs (whether a vestigial left lung < 1% or an elongated right lung 75%) vary in degree of vascularization from a thick-walled, multilayered faveola parenchyma to single-layered edicular and trabecular parenchyma and even thin-walled avascular membranes. Often a single organ exhibits a graded series of two or more types. The lungs of most snakes occupy a major portion of the body cavity. They vary in relative width from 0.1–1.0 body diameter and in relative length from 8–94%. The magnitude of interspecific and intergeneric variation, in conjunction with low intraspecific variability of individual characters (Bergman 1949–1962; Rossman et al., 1982; Wallach, 1991; Keogh, 1993, Wong, 1994) makes the viscera a prime but neglected source of taxonomic information.

Comparisons of juveniles versus adults, males versus females, and fresh versus preserved specimens in *Crotalus viridis* yielded low standard deviations for organ positions and failed to reveal significant differences. Results suggested considerable stability in the visceral topography of particular species and its appropriateness as a source of phylogenetically useful characters (Reyes et al., 1989; J. S. Keogh and V. Wallach, submitted).

Some of the literature is based partly or wholly on the soft anatomy of snakes. However, much of the earlier information, and even certain recent material, is inaccurate or fallacious. Whereas there are many works dealing with particular systems, organs, or tissues in a variety of snakes, only a few studies have described in detail the viscera of a single species (see Section I.D). No comparative studies have dealt with snake lungs or snake viscera in general. In spite of the numerous publications cited in this chapter, the study of the internal morphology of snakes remains at a rather primitive level (Brongersma, 1957a; Bullock and Tanner, 1966; Thorpe, 1975).

C. Historical Review

Aristotle made the first description of the respiratory system of a snake; he reported that the trachea is very long and that only a single lung is present, also very long and extending beyond the thoracic region (Aristotle, 1513, 1862 [Cresswell translation]). Other early references to the ophidian respiratory system, or illustrations depicting it, are found in Cöiter (1573), Abbatius (1589, 1603, 1660), Topsell (1608, 1658), Aldrovandi (1640), Severinus (1645), Jonstonus (1653, 1657), Redi (1664, 1670, 1684), Frenzelius (1665), Worm (1665), Charas (1669–1694), Blasius (1674, 1681), Jacobaeus (1680), Tyson (1683), Mead (1702, 1708), Sloane (1725), Seba (1735), and Sonnini and Latreille (1801). In the early Nineteenth Century, snake lungs were referred to by Cuvier (1798–1840), Blumenbach (1805), Westphal (1806), Nitzsch (1808), Méhes (1810), G. Fischer (1813), Meckel (1818–1833), Fleming (1822), Frivaldszky (1823), Broderip (1825a, 1825b), Dugès (1827), Retzius (1830, 1832), Duvernoy (1832), Schlegel (1837–1843), Roberton (1838), Henle (1839), Rathke (1839), Vogt (1839, 1851), Cantor (1841), Holbrook (1842), Duméril and Bibron (1844), Gosse (1850), Stannius (1850, 1856), van der Hoeven (1853–1859), Jacquart (1855–1864), Milne-Edwards and Compte (1855), Milne-Edwards (1855, 1857a, 1871), Lamare-Picquot (1858), Rufz (1859), and Hering (1860). Later works included Peters (1861, 1882), Brandt (1865), R. Owen (1866), Bert (1869), Lataste (1876), Lataste and Blanchard (1879), Hopley (1882), Garman (1883), Leunis and Ludwig (1883), Bedriaga (1884), Hatch (1890), and Canton (1895).

Early encyclopedias or natural history texts referring to or illustrating snake lungs include Daubenton (1784), Lacepède (1790, 1802), Bonnaterre (1790, 1795), Ruschenberger (1852), Dallas (1855), Chenu and Desmarest (1857), W. B. Carpenter (1844), W. B. Carpenter and Dallas (1866), Gervais (1866, 1869), MacAlister (1878), Orton (1883), Brehm (1878, 1885), Günther (1886), Railliet (1895), and Kingsley (1908).

The first comparative studies of snake lungs are attributable to Meckel (1818, 1833), Schlegel (1837b), Cuvier (1840), and Stannius (1850, 1856). Meckel (1818) was the first to report on the variability of lung types in snakes and dispell the reports that snakes had only a single lung. He cites five characters by which snake lungs can be classified, namely: (1) size, (2) location in body, (3) shape, (4) structure, and (5) the relationships between the lungs. He later (1833) summarized three characteristic lung types: (1) a single lung (composed of the tracheal lung, which he did not recognize as distinct, plus the right lung) as in *Pelamis* and *Vipera*, (2) paired lungs with a relatively large left lung as in *Python*, and (3) paired lungs with only a rudiment of the left lung as in *Anilius*, *Coluber*, and *Natrix*. Cope (1894a–1900) examined 150 species from all major taxa and mapped the presence or absence of a left lung and tracheal lung. Wolf (1933) classified lung types based on morphology and provided the basis for the present system as elucidated by Duncker (1978a). Antipchuk (1966b) characterized 12 pulmonary types in snakes (each occurring in a family) based upon: (1) presence or absence of a vascular or avascular tracheal lung, (2) presence or absence of a large or small left lung, (3) presence or absence of a saccular lung, and (4) presence or absence of a thoraconuchal lung.

Most authors observe that the lungs of snakes are asymmetrical in that the left is smaller than the right, often rudimentary or even absent (Blumenbach, 1803–1824; Carus, 1827–1838; W. B. Carpenter, 1839–1859, 1867; Duméril and Bibron, 1844; Milne-Edwards, 1845, 1855, 1857a, 1871; Gervais, 1847, 1848; Stannius, 1850; van Beneden, 1852–1854; van der Hoeven, 1855, 1858; W. B. Carpenter and Dallas, 1857, 1866; Chenu and Desmarest, 1857; Knight, 1858; Claus, 1868–1897; Gegenbaur, 1870–1878b; H. A. Nicholson, 1872–1887; E. Nicholson, 1874; Orton, 1876–1888; MacAlister, 1878; Packard, 1879–1889; Garman, 1883; Leunis and Ludwig, 1883; Wiedersheim, 1883–1909; Brehm, 1885; Günther, 1886; Boas, 1888, 1890; Hoffmann, 1890; Röse, 1890; J. A. Thomson, 1892–1929; Colton, 1894, 1903a, 1903b; Railliet, 1895; Kingsley 1897, 1908, P. Martin, 1902; Wilder, 1902; Orton and Dodge, 1903; Sedgwick, 1905; Wiedersheim and Parker, 1907; Schimkewitsch et al., 1910, 1921; Werner, 1910, 1922; Hilzheimer, 1912; G. A. Boulenger, 1913; Brehm and Werner, 1913, 1920; Waite, 1918; Shipley and MacBride, 1920; Steche, 1922; Ihle et al., 1924, 1927; Remane, 1924; Dowsett, 1928; T. J. Parker et al., 1928–1962; Perrier,

1928; Walter, 1929; Stefanelli, 1943; Cole, 1944; D. F. Thomson, 1946; Ihle, 1947; Portmann, 1948; Quirling, 1950; Villiers, 1950; Bellairs, 1957; Dowling, 1959; Fuhn and Vancea, 1961; Guibé, 1962; de Witte, 1962; Dottrens and Aellen, 1963; Padoa, 1963; Donoso-Barros, 1965; Bellairs and Carrington, 1966; Inger, 1966; Pisano and Barbieri, 1967; Rietschel, 1968; van den Eeckhoudt, 1968; Kent, 1969–1983; Patt and Patt, 1969; Pirlot, 1969; Leviton, 1970; Dunson, 1971, 1975a; Appleby, 1971; Waterman et al., 1971; Roots, 1974; Saint Girons and Saint Girons, 1974; Hediger, 1975; Ziswiler, 1976; Kluge et al., 1977; H. W. Parker and Grandison, 1977; Cihar, 1979, 1990; Gavrilov, 1979; L. C. Marcus, 1981; Orr, 1982; J. D. Wallach and Boever, 1983; Hackbarth, 1985; Lanka and Vit, 1985; Lawrence, 1985; Walker, 1987; Jessop, 1988; Obst et al., 1988; Chaves-Mora et al., 1990; Shea et al., 1993; G. R. Zug, 1993; Hildebrand, 1995; Mutschmann, 1995). Somewhat more detailed and accurate descriptions are found in Rufz (1859), T. Williams (1859), R. Owen (1866), Baudrimont (1929), Bellairs (1969), Guibé (1970b), Porter (1972), Russell (1980, 1983), and Ernst and Zug (1996).

Detailed anatomical studies on the respiratory system of snakes can be found in Hoffmann (1890), Göppert (1899, 1937), Beddard (1903–1909), H. Marcus (1927–1937), Rothley (1930a, 1930b, 1931), Brongersma (1938–1969), and Lüdicke (1964). More general comparative anatomy works include P. Martin (1902), Wiedersheim (1909), Schimkewitsch et al. (1910), Thäter (1910), Hilzheimer (1912), Ihle et al. (1924), Little (1932), Böker (1937), Boué and Chanton (1959), Ballard (1964), Rietschel (1968), Saint Girons and Saint Girons (1974), and Wurmbach (1985).

General dissection guides to the snake include Colton (1894, 1903b), Atwood (1923), P. H. Fischer (1942), Oldham (1968), Oldham et al. (1970), and Meneghel (1991). More detailed guides to specific taxa include: *Typhlops vermicularis* (Heyder, 1966), *Boa constrictor* (Gomes et al., 1989), *Eryx conicus* (Folk, 1971), *Bothrops jararaca* (Gomes and Puorto, 1994), *Vipera aspis* (Lécuru-Renous and Platel, 1970a, 1970b; Sparing, 1976), *V. berus* (Sparing, 1976), and *V. palaestinae* (Frenkel and Kochva, 1970; Barnard, 1996), *Pseudechis porphyriacus* (Rosenzweig, 1981), *Coluber constrictor* (Atwood, 1916), *Heterodon platyrhinos* (Kellicott, 1898), *Lampropeltis triangulum* and *Nerodia sipedon* (Chiodini et al. 1982), *Natrix natrix* (Röseler and Lamprecht, 1914; J. T. Saunders and Manton, 1931–1959; J. T. Saunders et al., 1969), and *Thamnophis sirtalis* (Kellogg, 1901; Atwood, 1918). Comparative visceral studies include those on the Colubrini (Twerenbold, 1987), *Elaphe* (Helfenberger, 1989), and the Thamnophiini (Rossman et al., 1982). Organ position based upon ventral scute number has been reported in the following snakes: *Nerodia sipedon* (Bragdon, 1953), seven species from Kansas (Toland and Dehne, 1960), 22 species from Kansas (Garrigues, 1962), *Agkistrodon piscivorus* (Collins and Carpenter, 1970), and the Thamnophiini (Rossman et al., 1982).

Studies specializing upon the ophidian respiratory system include those on the Acrochordidae, Homalopsinae, and Hydrophiinae of Australia (Ramsay, 1979), *Nerodia taxispilota* and *Thamnophis sirtalis* (Karlstrom, 1952), and *Pseudechis porphyriacus* (Rosenzweig, 1981). The respiratory system has provided characters for various systematic studies of snakes, including recognition of a new family, several genera, and numerous species, and specific analyses have dealt with: various respiratory system characters (*Helminthophis flavoterminatus* versus *Typhlops mutilatus*; Wallach and Günther, 1997a); tracheal rings, tracheal lung, right lung, and foramina (*Ramphotyphlops depressus* versus *R. flaviventer*; Wallach, 1996b); tracheal lung, cardiac lung, and right lung (*Rhinotyphlops acutus* versus *Typhlops acutus*; Wallach, 1994b); various respiratory system characters (*Typhlops marxi*; Wallach, 1993b; *Typhlops fredparkeri*, *T. mcdowelli*; Wallach, 1997a); absence of tracheal lung (*Xenotyphlops* versus *Typhlops*; Wallach and Ineich, 1996); various characters of the respiratory system (*Leptotyphlops macrops*, *L. pungwensis*, *L. sylvicolus*; Broadley and Wallach, 1996–1997b); various characters of the respiratory system (*Leptotyphlops drewesi*; Wallach, 1996c; *L. broadleyi*; Wallach, 1997b; *L. meszoelyi*; Wallach, 1997c); large left lung and absence of tracheal lung (*Epicrates inornatus* versus *Boella tenella*; Wallach and Smith, 1992); tracheal lung and absence of left lung (Tropidophiidae versus Boidae; Brongersma, 1951b); tracheal lung and absence of left lung (Xenophidiidae; Wallach and Günther, 1997b); five pulmonary artery patterns (Viperidae; Brongersma, 1949); seven pulmonary artery and lung patterns (Viperinae; Groombridge, 1980); variation in numerous characters of the respiratory system (Atractaspididae; Wallach, 1991; *Aparallactus lineatus* versus *A. niger*; Wallach, 1994a; Hydrophiidae; Wallach, 1985); left lung, tracheal lung, and saccular lung (*Laticauda* and related Elapidae and Hydrophiidae; McCarthy, 1986); left lung, right lung, and tracheal lung (Hydrophiidae; McDowell, 1969a, 1972a, 1972b, 1974b; Mao and Chen, 1980); tracheal entry (*Pliocercus* versus *Urotheca*; H. M. Smith et al., 1995); absence of tracheal lung (*Tropidodipsas* versus *Sibon*; Wallach, 1995a); right bronchus and left lung (*Crotaphopeltis* and *Dipsadoboa*; Rasmussen, 1979, 1989a–1993b); left lung and length of trachea-bronchus (*Dipsadoboa shrevei*; Rasmussen, 1986); tracheal lung and right lung (*Gonyosoma* versus *Elaphe*; Thompson, 1914b; Brongersma, 1957a, 1957b); intrapulmonary bronchus (Lampropeltini; Keogh, 1996); position of the left orifice, left lung length, bronchus, and position of right lung tip (*Natrix natrix*; Thorpe, 1975–1987); position of the posterior tip of the left lung (*Thamnophis sirtalis*; Benton, 1980); tracheal lung, tracheal entry, left lung, right bronchus, and vascularization of the right lung (*Tropidonophis*; Malnate and Underwood, 1988); and the left lung and tracheal lung (Natricinae, Revkin, 1977).

D. Terminology and Approaches

This account calls the precardiac cavity of the body in which the trachea and tracheal lung are found a nuchal cavity, whereas the postcardiac cavity, generally known as the pleuroperitoneal, is referred to as the visceral cavity. Measurements are recorded in mm rather than by number of ventral scutes, and an index to visceral size and position is provided based on snout-vent length (see Wallach, 1991). All percentages, unless specifically stated to be percent ventral scutes (% VS), refer to percent snout-vent length (% SVL) and are cited as % with the SVL omitted. Except for the above, all ratios involving two characters are presented in the text as decimals. The coefficient of variation (CV) for visceral characters is rounded off to the nearest percent. Table 2.1 lists definitions and abbreviations of characters analyzed in this chapter. Text figures are denoted with upper case F as opposed to figures cited in references with lower case f. Museum acronyms follow Leviton et al. (1985), with the exception of these additions: BH (Berry Hughes, private coll.), GVP (George V. Pickwell, private coll.), IRSL (Institut de Recherche Scientifique, Lwiro), JV (John Visser, private coll.), KUHS (Klamath Union High School, Klamath Falls, Oregon), MNN (Museo Nacional de Nicaragua, Managua), TNRC (Thailand National Reference Collection, Bangkok), UCA (Universidad de Centro América, Managua), UG (University of Ghana, Legon), UNAZA (Université Nacional de Zaire, Kisangani), and VW (Van Wallach field number).

All data presented in Appendix C are derived from my studies, and most of the values represent % SVL. This avoids confusion due to possible differences in observation and measurement of the lungs, and due to the use of % VS terminology. Whenever literature reports exceed the range of variation as given in Appendix C, those data are cited in the text with the proper authority. Data in the tables of Appendix C are listed systematically by genus. Representatives of almost all genera are included. The exceptions are the typhlopid *Cyclotyphlops*, the pythonids *Apodora* and *Leiopython*, and the colubrids *Anoplohydrus, Brygophis, Buhoma, Cercophis, Calamodontophis, Compsophis, Cryptophidion, Ditaxodon, Emmochliophis, Heurnia, Iguanognathus, Leioheterodon, Lycodryas, Parahelicops, Pararhabdophis,* and *Thalesius,* most of which are known from the type specimen only. Representatives of some recently established genera (*Libertadictus, Nuchisulcophis, Paranatrix, Leioselasma,* and *Pseudolaticauda*) have been examined and determined not to warrant separate generic status based upon the viscera.

The general classifications followed in recognizing genera and assigning them to higher taxa include: Underwood (1967, 1979), H. M. Smith et al. (1977), Dowling (*in* Dowling and Duellman, 1978), Rieppel (1979), Rasmussen (1985), McDowell (1987), and Cundall et al. (1994). Other

Table 2.1. Abbreviations and definitions of characters referred to in text and Appendix C!

Abbrev.	Character	Definition
CF	cardiac foramina	total number of cardiac lung foramina
CL	cardiac lung length	distance between anterior and posterior margins of heart (as % SVL)
CLT	cardiac lung type	U = unicameral, P = paucicameral, M = multicameral
FT	foramina type	classification type (A–H) of pulmonary foramina
HT	heart tip	posterior tip of heart (as % SVL)
L	total lung length	tracheal, cardiac, and / or right lungs (as % SVL)
LAL	left anterior lobe length	anterior tip of anterior lobe of left lung to orifice (as % SVL)
LB	left bronchus	+ = present, 0 = absent
LBL	left bronchus length	left orifice to terminal bronchial cartilage (as % SVL)
LBR	left bronchus rings	number of bronchial rings in left bronchus
LL	left lung	+ = present, 0 = absent
LLL	left lung length	anterior to posterior tips of left lung
LL/RL	left lung / right lung	left lung as percent of right lung
LO	left orifice	+ = present, 0 = absent
LOM	left orifice midpoint	midpoint position of left orifice (as % SVL)
LPT	left lung posterior tip	posterior tip of left lung (as % SVL)
LSL	left saccular lung	presence (and length) or absence (0) of saccular portion of left lung
NTR	number of tracheal rings	estimated number of tracheal rings per 10% SVL
RAL	right anterior lobe length	anterior tip of anterior lobe of right lung to orifice (as % SVL)
RB	right bronchus	+ = present, 0 = absent
RBL	right bronchus length	posterior heart tip to last bronchial cartilage (as % SVL)
RB/RL	right bronchus / right lung	right bronchus as percent of right lung
RF	right lung foramina	number of total right lung foramina
RL	right lung length	posterior heart tip to posterior tip of lung (as % SVL)
RLT	right lung type	U = unicameral, P = paucicameral, M = multicameral
RPT	right lung posterior tip	posterior tip of right lung (as % SVL)
RSL	right saccular lung	presence (and length) or absence (0) of saccular portion of right lung
SL	saccular lung length	caudalmost point of parenchyma to posterior tip of right lung (as % SVL)
S/N	species / sample size	number of species examined / total number of individuals in generic sample
T	trachea length	anterior edge of orbitonasal trough to the posterior tip of heart (as % SVL)
TE	tracheal entry into lung	subterminal (S), paraterminal (P), or terminal (T)
TF	tracheal foramina	total tracheal lung foramina number
TL	tracheal lung	moderately to strongly developed lung with tracheal artery (+), absent (0)

Table 2.1. (continued)

Abbrev.	Character	Definition
TLF	total lung foramina	total number of tracheal, cardiac, and right lung foramina
TLL	tracheal lung length	anteriormost point of parenchyma to anterior edge of heart (as % SVL)
TLT	tracheal lung type	U = unicameral, P = paucicameral, M = multicameral (2M = biserial, 4M = quadriserial)
TTR	total tracheal rings	total number of tracheal rings estimated from count of a short mid-trachea segment

[1] In Appendix C, data are included for both juveniles and adults but not for embryos or neonates. A moderately to strongly developed tracheal lung (TL), as defined by presence of a tracheal artery, is coded as present or absent, whereas weakly developed tracheal parenchyma, because presence of a tracheal artery is suspect, is coded as absent and its length is combined with that of the cardiac lung (CL), which normally is 3–4%, rarely 2–5% SVL. Therefore, any CL value > 4–5% suggests an incipient or weakly developed tracheal lung that would be confirmed if served by pulmonary vessels. When polymorphic states occur in a qualitative character (i.e., TE, TL, RB, LL, LB, LO), one of three symbols separates the states with the most common condition appearing first or to the left. A colon ":" separates two conditions of approximately equal occurrence (less common condition occurring in 40–50% of samples); parentheses "( )" enclose a state of rare occurrence (present in 1-10% of samples); a slash "/" separates intermediate ranges of occurrence (less common condition occurring in 11–39% of samples). Thus, with a sample of n=4 and the formula S/P:T for TE, two specimens exhibit an S entry and one each a P and T entry; a sample of n=7 with S:T means four specimens have an S entry, three have a T entry; a sample of n=15 with S:T(P) is seven each with S and T entry and one with P entry. Whenever two states are equal or nearly equal, the more primitive is given first. Taxa are listed consecutively as follows: family number first; if subfamilies are present, they are numbered and separated from the family number by a dash; if tribes are recognized, they are listed alphabetically with letters. Thus, "14–9d" is the fourteenth family (Colubridae), ninth subfamily (Dipsadinae), and the fourth tribe (Leptodeirini).

less-inclusive classifications relied upon for the following taxa include: Anilioidea and Henophidia (McDowell, 1975), Booidea (Kluge, 1991–1993b), Viperidae (Hoge and Romano-Hoge, 1981), Atractaspididae (Bourgeois, 1968; B. Hughes, 1983; Wallach, 1991; Underwood and Kochva, 1993; A. Resetar, in manuscript), Australian Elapidae (Scanlon, 1985; Wallach, 1985; Hutchinson, 1990), marine Hydrophiidae (Burger and Natsuno, 1974; Voris, 1977), Nothopsini (Savitzky, 1974), Xenodontinae (Greene and McDiarmid, 1981; Cadle, 1984a, 1984b; Ferrarezzi, 1994), Lampropeltini (Keogh, 1993), and Natricinae (Rossman and Eberle, 1977). The taxonomic arrangement of caenophidian families in the text and appendices follows current ideas on the subject (McDowell, 1987; Underwood, 1993; Dowling et al., 1996), with the Viperidae as the most basal colubroid clade, followed by the Atractaspididae, Elapidae, Hydrophiidae, and Colubridae. Certain genera are problematical with respect to content and assignment to a higher taxon. When one or several species differs remarkably from their congeners, data for those particular taxa are given separately, either in the same table or different tables (such as the natricines *Amphiesma*, *Macropisthodon*, and *Rhabdophis*, which can be found in Appendix C1 and C4). Also, some controversial genera are listed separately from the genera to which they are usually referred. This is designed to facilitate comparison; listing such genera does not necessarily suggest their recognition. Examples include such forms as *Pseudoplectrurus* (Mahendra, 1984), *Acrantophis* and *Sanzinia* (Kluge, 1991), *Calabaria* (Kluge, 1993a), *Gongylophis* (Rage, 1972; Tokar, 1989), *Chilopoma* (D. A. Rossman, pers. comm.), *Gastropyxis* (Broadley, 1966; K. L. Williams and Wallach, 1989), *Lielaphis* (Leviton, 1959), *Liochlorophis* (Oldham and Smith, 1992), *Toxicodryas* (Underwood, 1967; Welch 1982), *Elapops* (D. G. Broadley, pers. comm.), *Hemibungarus* (McDowell, 1986), and *Unechis* (Wallach, 1985). I have followed traditional classifications whenever the lung data do not suggest otherwise, and certain poorly known genera have been grouped with others displaying similar lung features (which does not imply that the groups are monophyletic). The visceral anatomy of *Azemiops* does not suggest even a distant relationship to the Viperidae; its only qualification for viperid status is the solenoglyphous condition, which, if it were an atractaspid-grade serpent, it would be considered independently derived. The arrangement of genera in Appendix C should not be considered a classification but only a listing of genera; each genus had to be placed somewhere, and I questionably allocated some based upon little evidence of relationship. I do not favor grouping certain problematic taxa as *incertae sedis* as the implication is then that all the remaining taxa are correctly arranged in monophyletic groups, which is certainly not the case.

II. MORPHOLOGY OF THE TRACHEAE, BRONCHI, AND LUNGS
A. Classification of Lung Types

The ophidian respiratory system consists of a tracheal/bronchial air-conducting system and a pulmonary gaseous exchange system. It can be conveniently divided into three parts: (1) a tracheal complex anterior to the heart including the larynx, trachea, tracheal membrane, tracheal lung, cardiac lung, and tracheal vessels (Fig. 2.1); (2) a right lung complex posterior to the heart including the right lung with its tracheal entry, anterior lobe, right bronchus, vascular portion, semi-saccular portion, saccular portion, and pulmonary vessels (Fig. 2.2); and (3) a left lung complex including a left lung, left bronchus, left orifice and pulmonary vessels (Fig. 2.3). Snake lungs are elongate and membranous; the viper lung was described as a "vesicula oblonga membranosa" (Aldrovandi, 1640) and the lung of *Epicrates subflavus* as "very membranaceous, being nothing but blood vessels and air bladders" (Sloane, 1725; C. Owen, 1742).

Snake lungs are fusiform and have a voluminous tissue-free central axial lumen; their luminal surfaces are lined by a thin layer of vascularized tissue or parenchyma less than 3–4 mm in thickness (Perry, 1983). They were long known to be relatively larger than the lungs of other animals, occupying up to three-fourths of the body length (Browne, 1756; Sonnini and Latreille, 1801). Total length of the lung (tracheal, cardiac, and right) ranges from 16% (*Uropeltis*) to 94% (*Acrochordus granulatus*); most snakes have values between 40–80% (see Appendix C). Lung volume in snakes can be very large (Tables 2–3), comprising as much as 30% of the total body volume (Duncker, 1978a). In *Pelamis platurus*, mean lung volume ranges from 9.7–11.8% of the wet body weight (in which 1 ml gas = 1 g tissue; Graham, 1973; Graham et al., 1975), which allows the species to spend 80% of its time underwater (Gee, 1987). In *Laticauda colubrina*, the volume of the tracheal lung as a percent of total lung volume ranges from 27–42%, the vascularized por-

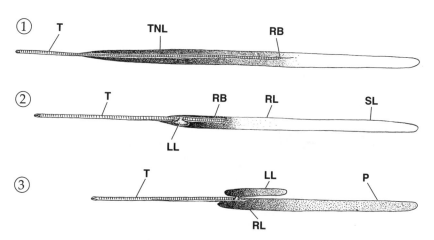

Fig. 2.1. *Crotalus viridis.* Diagram of ventral view of the thoraconuchal lung (TNL) showing trachea (T) entering the lung terminally and a short right bronchus (RB); anterior is to the left. (Adapted from Kardong, 1972b.)

Fig. 2.2. *Elaphe obsoleta.* Diagram of ventral view of the right lung (RL) and vestigial left lung (LL) showing trachea (T), long right bronchus (RB), and long saccular lung (SL); anterior is to the left. (Adapted from Kardong, 1972b.)

Fig. 2.3. *Charina bottae.* Diagram of ventral view of the right lung (RL) and relatively large left lung (LL) showing trachea (T) entering lungs subterminally and parenchyma (P) extending to termination of both lungs; anterior is to the left. (Adapted from Kardong, 1972b.)

Table 2.2. Total lung volumes of snakes.

Species	n	Mean ± SE	Reference
Boa constrictor	13	72.5 ± 59.0 ml kg⁻¹	Standaert and Johansen, 1974
Acrochordus javanicus	10	66.0 ± 31.0 ml kg⁻¹	Standaert and Johansen, 1974
Pelamis platurus	12	11.1 ± 1.8 ml g⁻¹	Graham et al., 1975
Pelamis platurus	8	13.0 ± 2.7 ml g⁻¹	Graham et al., 1975
Nerodia erythrogaster	10	64.0 ± 12.2 ml kg⁻¹	Baeyens et al., 1980
Nerodia fasciata	5	61.4 ± 9.2 ml kg⁻¹	Baeyens et al., 1980
Nerodia rhombifer	8	75.1 ± 11.0 ml kg⁻¹	Gratz, 1978
Nerodia rhombifer	12	51.0 ± 11.1 ml kg⁻¹	Baeyens et al., 1978
Nerodia rhombifer	12	51.7 ± 11.1 ml kg⁻¹	Baeyens et al., 1980
Elaphe obsoleta	3	80.3 ± 12.5 ml kg⁻¹	Baeyens et al., 1978
Elaphe obsoleta	6	80.2 ± 12.7 ml kg⁻¹	Baeyens et al., 1980

tion of the right lung from 32–63%, and the saccular lung from 10–26% (Heatwole, 1981). In *Pelamis platurus*, the mean tracheal lung volume ranges from 29–32%, the vascular lung 33–37%, and the saccular lung 31–38% and represents 23%, 65%, and 12% of the total lung length, respectively (Graham et al., 1975; Seymour, 1981). In *Vipera aspis* and *V. berus*, total lung volume represents 30–53% of body volume (mean = 36%), lung surface in cm² g⁻¹ body weight ranges from 2.3–5.7 (mean = 4.2), and vascular surface area/total lung area ranges from 49–68% (mean = 58%) (Sparing, 1976). Snout-vent length (SVL) and lung surface/body weight (r = 0.98), SVL and lung volume (r = 0.91), SVL and lung surface (r = 0.90), lung volume and body volume (r = 0.90), lung volume and body weight (r = 0.85), and SVL and lung length (r = 0.83) are strongly correlated (Sparing, 1976). In *V. berus*, the volume of the lumen of the vascularized lung increases posteriorly, as reflected by the length of the region and its corresponding volume as follows: tracheal lung (100 mm, 4.14 cm³), cardiac lung (20 mm, 1.03 cm³), and right lung (30 mm, 3.67 cm³). The tracheal lung is twice the length of the cardiac and right lungs but contains only 0.9 the

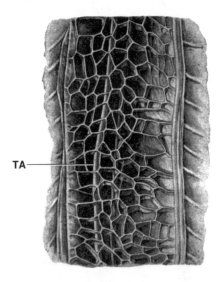

Fig. 2.4. *Dipsas indica*. Internal view of unicameral tracheal lung showing edicular parenchyma; tracheal artery (TA) visible beneath the ediculae. (Adapted from Werner, 1911.)

volume (Sparing, 1976). In *Vipera aspis* and *V. berus*, the saccular lung comprises 63% of the total lung volume, the tracheal lung lumen 24%, and the vascular lung wall 13% (Sparing, 1976). However, the inner surface of the vascular lung comprises 58% of its total area, the saccular lung 37%, and the tracheal rings 5% (Sparing, 1976). Tracheal volume in *Nerodia rhombifer* also represents 5% (4 ml kg^{-1}) of lung volume (75 ml kg^{-1} body weight) (Gratz, 1978).

The lungs of amniote vertebrates are separated into three increasingly complex, internal structural types (Duncker, 1978a): (1) a single chambered or unicameral organ that lacks any partitions or chambers, being tubular with a large hollow central cavity, (2) a transitional or paucicameral organ with transverse septa forming more or less distinct dextrolateral pockets or niches, and (3) a multiple chambered or multicameral organ composed of separate chambers with lumina that connect solely with the tracheal lumen by way of individual foramina that pierce the tracheal membrane. It has been claimed that all snake lungs are unicameral (Duncker, 1978a; Perry, 1983; but see Perry, 1989a). However, certain snakes have paucicameral and multicameral lungs, and the Acrochordidae have both biserial and quadriserial multicameral lungs.

Duncker (1978a) pointed out that, as the units of reptilian parenchyma are not homologous with mammalian alveoli, a more appropriate term is faveoli (singular faveolus). Reptiles have three general types of parenchyma: (1) trabecular parenchyma, consisting of a single layer of low-relief branching muscular structures (trabeculae) that lie in a polygonal

Table 2.3. Relative lung volumes of snakes.

Species	n	Mean	Range
Acrochordus granulatus	4	0.30 ml g^{-1}	0.22–0.39 ml g^{-1}
Laticauda colubrina	2	0.32 ml g^{-1}	0.32–0.32 ml g^{-1}
Aipysurus apraefrontalis	1	0.19 ml g^{-1}	—
Aipysurus duboisii	15	0.31 ml g^{-1}	0.18–0.53 ml g^{-1}
Aipyurus fuscus	1	0.26 ml g^{-1}	
Aipysurus laevis	20	0.26 ml g^{-1}	0.10–0.38 ml g^{-1}
Emydocephalus annulatus	21	0.36 ml g^{-1}	0.15–0.52 ml g^{-1}
Astrotia stokesii	3	0.55 ml g^{-1}	0.29–0.89 ml g^{-1}
Hydrophis melanocephalus	4	0.42 ml g^{-1}	0.33–0.53 ml g^{-1}
Hydrophis elegans	3	0.32 ml g^{-1}	0.23–0.50 ml g^{-1}
Hydrophis semperi	2	0.45 ml g^{-1}	0.45–0.45ml g^{-1}
Lapemis curtus	9	0.36 ml g^{-1}	0.25–0.44 ml g^{-1}
Disteira kingii	2	0.20 ml g^{-1}	0.17–0.22 ml g^{-1}
Pelamis platurus	4	0.58 ml g^{-1}	0.31–0.68 ml g^{-1}

Data from Heatwole and Seymour, 1975b.

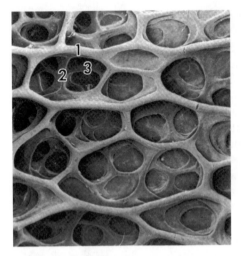

Fig. 2.5. *Crotalus viridis.* Scanning electron micrograph (×240) of faveoli of tracheal lung depicting primary (1), secondary (2), and tertiary (3) trabeculae. (Adapted from Luchtel and Kardong, 1981, reprinted by permission of Wiley-Liss, Inc.)

pattern directly on the lung wall, (2) edicular parenchyma, composed of a single layer of trabeculae with raised walls or septa that form cubicles (ediculae) that are wider than they are deep (Fig. 2.4), and (3) single- or multiple-layered faviform parenchyma, the compartments (faveoli) of which are deeper than wide and often present a honeycomb appearance (Fig. 2.5) (Perry, 1983, 1989a, 1989c; Duncker, 1978a, 1978c, 1981). See Perry (this volume) for a detailed description of the microscopic anatomy and terminology of reptilian lungs.

In snakes, faveolar parenchyma consists of up to four levels of subdividing septa that commence on the free or luminal surface and lead to the faveoli that extend radially from the pleural surface. The inner circumference of the luminal surface of the lung is covered by large primary septa with trabeculae that give rise to smaller secondary septa (that can be seen through the openings between the trabeculae), which in turn give rise to even smaller tertiary septa (Fig. 2.6). The tertiary partitions or interfaveolar septa enclose the faveoli and continue to the pleural surface of the lung. The interfaveolar septa are supported by connective tissue composed primarily of fibrocytes, collagen, and elastic fibers and contain capillaries on both sides of the partition, whereas capillaries cover only one side of the trabecular septa (Maina, 1989).

The openings of the primary trabeculae on the luminal surface of faviform parenchyma have a maximum diameter of 1–2 mm, whereas those of single-layered polygonal trabeculae may, in some forms, reach a diameter of 7 mm (i.e., *Atheris, Causus*). In *Elaphe obsoleta,* the mean diameter of the faveolus is 182 μm, whereas in *Nerodia rhombifer,* it is 84 μm (Baeyens et al., 1978). The basal or abluminal interfaveolar partitions are held in shape by the luminally located system of interconnecting trabeculae, which are composed of bundles of smooth muscle and elastic tissue. The bundles adjust to the state of inflation of the lung, hold the partitions taut under tension as suspension cables do with a bridge; their contraction simultaneously pulls the partitions taut and

Fig. 2.6. *Coluber constrictor.* Faveolar parenchyma of right lung showing oval interfaveolar openings. (Adapted from W. S. Miller, 1893.)

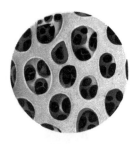

increases the intrapulmonary air pressure (Gans, 1978; Perry and Duncker, 1978; Perry, 1989b). In *Pituophis sayi*, the smooth muscle fibers are arranged both radially (in relation to the lumen of the lung) and circumferentially (in relation to the faveoli) (Larson and van de Velde, 1969). Structural integrity of the lung is maintained mostly by collagen, not elastin (Pohunková, 1986).

A major challenge in classifying snake lung types is the categorization of the patterns of parenchymal tissue. The definitions of Perry and Duncker (1978) categorize two simple parenchymal types (trabecular and edicular) and one complex type (faviform). However, shapes of the trabeculae (and their resulting openings) of the parenchyma in snakes exhibit various patterns, and the septa are arranged into one to three tiers. With faviform parenchyma, the septa form at least a dozen recognizable patterns, but to date they have defied objective description or quantification. TEM ultrastructure in various snakes needs to be studied and compared with the parenchymal patterns. To complicate matters, individuals usually exhibit several patterns, although a single pattern generally predominates in any given lung region. The pattern in the vascular lung is normally different from that in the semisaccular lung, tracheal lung, and left lung. The openings of the primary trabeculae have been noted as generally rounded (Fig. 2.7; Tourneux and Herrmann, 1876; W. S. Miller, 1893, fig. 4; F. Werner, 1911; Ramsay, 1979, plate 7; Kang et al., 1986, fig. 1), transversely oval (Fig. 2.7; Tourneux and Herrmann, 1876; Ramsay, 1979,

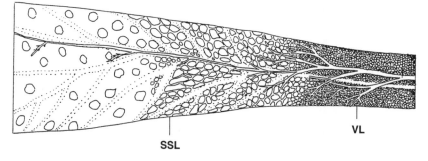

Fig. 2.7. *Pseudechis porphyriacus.* Diagram of internal surface of right lung depicting transition from caudal portion of vascular lung (VL) into semisaccular lung (SSL). (Adapted from Rosenzweig, 1981.)

T

AL

VL

SSL

SL

pls. 6c, 8; Luchtel and Kardong, 1981, fig. 1a), triangular and quadrangular (Gravier, 1994), diamond-shaped, polygonal (Fig. 2.8; Tourneux and Herrmann, 1876; Werner, 1911, Fig. 2.11; Wolf, 1933, fig. 14; Kang et al., 1986, fig. 3; Twerenbold, 1987, fig. 3), pentagonal and hexagonal (Plate 2.1B; Pohunková and Hughes, 1985, fig. 1), irregular but nonangular (Ramsay, 1979, plate 6b; Maina, 1989, fig. 4), or transversely elongated (Plate 2.1C; Wolf, 1933, fig. 13; Graham et al., 1975, fig. 2; Kang et al., 1986, fig. 2). The patterns made by the secondary septa (visible through the primary openings) include further symmetrical and geometrical arrangements. Tertiary patterns may be evident through the openings of the secondary septa whenever three tiers are present. Sometimes the openings of the multiple tiers are arranged in tubular radial columns that line up with the faveoli so that the secondary and tertiary septa are hidden beneath the primary trabeculae and the faveoli are visible at the distal end; in other forms, the layers alternate, and the septa of the layer beneath, which form smaller openings, are visible through the opening of the trabeculae above (Luchtel and Kardong, 1981, fig. 1a).

A common pattern is the arrangement of primary trabeculae in transversely-oriented, more-or-less parallel rows around the lung with secondary septa extending at right angles to the primary ones (Fig. 2.4). In the Booidea, the primary trabeculae course irregularly in a slightly zigzag pattern (Read and Donnelly, 1972, fig. 7; Kang et al., 1986, figs. 1–2), but many Colubridae have straight, transverse rows, with the secondary septa also straight and longitudinal, and the tertiary septa arranged in pairs with rounded openings between the adjoining primary trabeculae.

Fig. 2.8. *Coluber constrictor.* Ventral cutaway view of right lung showing anterior lobe (AL), subterminal entry of the trachea (T) into lung, and differentiation of parenchyma from dense, thick-walled vascular lung (VL) through sparse, thin-walled semisaccular lung (SSL) to membranous saccular lung (SL). (Adapted from W. S. Miller, 1893.)

The distribution of parenchyma in snake lungs is generally heterogenous; the parenchyma is deepest and most densely partitioned near the cardiac region and more sparsely partitioned and shallow towards both the head and tail (i.e., the tracheal lung is best developed caudally, whereas the right and left lungs exhibit their strongest development cranially). Because of this heterogeneity, regions with shallow, sparsely partitioned or no parenchyma would theoretically be overinflated at the expense of densely partitioned areas. This situation would be especially true of the saccular lung in snakes. Snakes, therefore, tend to have the lungs attached to the body wall or surrounded by the intracoelomic septa (Perry, 1983). The vascularity of the respiratory system of snakes can be conveniently categorized into three levels of increasingly complex organization based upon the definitions of Duncker (1978a) and Perry (1983). The heterogenous distribution of parenchyma in snake lungs consists of a gradual transition from avascular through weakly vascular to highly vascular tissue, usually resulting in two or three different conditions in a single lung. The three general types may be defined as follows. Each lung of a snake, or portion thereof, may lack any grossly observable parenchymal development, and the lung wall may appear as a semitransparent, atrabecular membrane devoid of muscular tissue or blood vessels. This condition represents the primary structural type and is called avascular or saccular. The tracheal membrane, tracheal lung, right lung, and left lung may be partly or entirely avascular. The secondary structural arrangement is a nonfaviform organization in which the vascularity consists of: (1) transverse, parallel branches from the pulmonary or tracheal vessels or (2) a criss-crossing network of low-relief, referred to as edicular or trabecular parenchyma. This sparse vascular or semisaccular tissue is found in the tracheal lung, right lung, and left lung, particularly as a transition zone between the densely vascular and avascular portions of the lung. The most common type of vascular arrangement, the tertiary type or dense vascular tissue, consists of a honeycomb-like structure composed of faviform parenchyma or faveoli.

Except those of the Acrochordidae, all snake lungs, whether unicameral, paucicameral, or multicameral, are arranged in a single longitudinal unit (uniserial). *Acrochordus*, however, is unique among serpents in possessing either two (biserial) or four (quadriserial) longitudinal, multicameral lungs fused into a single organ with either two or four corresponding air chambers in each transverse row.

B. Histology and Ultrastructure
The histology of the ophidian respiratory system, although briefly mentioned in *Python* and *Natrix* (Leydig, 1857), was first described in *Natrix natrix* (Eberth, 1863; Elenz, 1864; Tourneux and Herrmann, 1876;

Baumann, 1902). Several taxa were later reviewed (Oppel, 1905; Varde, 1951; Lüdicke 1964; Antipchuk and Sobolieva, 1971). More detailed cytological descriptions of the pulmonary tissue are available for *Eunectes murinus* (Phleger et al., 1978), *Elaphe obsoleta* (Brooks, 1970), *E. quadrivirgata* (Ogawa, 1920; Gomi, 1982), *E. obsoleta* and *Nerodia rhombifer* (Morgans et al., 1978), *Natrix natrix* (Wenslaw, 1926; Baudrimont, 1929), *Vipera aspis* (Baudrimont, 1929), and *V. berus* (Bazantová, 1986). There is a report of carbohydrate, fat and water content of lung tissue for *Psammophis sibilans* (Hanna, 1963), and one on the trace elements present in the respiratory system of *Gloydius blomhoffii* (Lin et al., 1995).

The ultrastructure of snake lungs was first examined in *Elaphe climacophora* (Okada et al., 1962) and *E. quadrivirgata* (Okada et al., 1962; Nagaishi et al., 1964). More recent studies have dealt with *Coronella austriaca* (Meban, 1980), *E. quadrivirgata* (Gomi, 1982; Iwahori et al., 1987), *Natrix maura* (Pastor, 1990), *N. natrix* (Meban, 1980), *Thamnophis sirtalis* (Pohunková and Hughes, 1982, 1985), *Dendroaspis polylepis* (Maina, 1989), *Hydrophis cyanocinctus* (Liu and Chen, 1983), *Agkistrodon contortrix* (Jacobs and Coons, 1981), and *Crotalus viridis* (Luchtel and Kardong, 1981). Reviews of the histology and ultrastructure of snake lungs are provided by Pattle (1976, 1978), Stratton and Wetzstein (1979), Perry (1989a), and Pastor and Pallares (1995).

C. Embryology of Snake Lungs

The embryological development of snake lungs has been discussed by various authors (Wiedersheim, 1884, 1909; Heilmann, 1914; H. Marcus, 1927; Goodrich, 1930; Hilber, 1933; Oidumi, 1940; Risley, 1941; Rensch, 1946; Portmann, 1948; Baer, 1964; J. W. Saunders, 1970; Heine, 1976). Several studies have examined the asymmetrical development of the lungs in *Natrix natrix* (Rathke, 1839; Hoffmann, 1890; Baumann, 1902; Weber and Buvignier, 1903; Broman, 1904; Schmalhausen, 1905). In an embryo with a 3 mm head length, the right lung bud is 3.5 times the size of the left. By the 3.5 mm head stage the right lung is 10.4 times the size of the left, and in the 5 mm head stage it is 43.3 times as large as the left. By the 5.5 mm head stage the right lung has rotated 90° and is 59.0 times the length of the left, which has become attached to it and shifted to a nearly ventral position. In the near-term 7 mm head stage, the left lung is directly ventrad of the right (Baumann, 1902).

In *Natrix natrix*, the respiratory organs develop from a bulbous outpocketing from the ventral wall of the endodermal tube near the point of crossing of the pharynx and the esophagus. This pulmonary bulb is broader than the portion of the intestine from which it arises; its cross-section is pear-like. The pulmonary bulb fuses with the pharynx cranially; caudally, the outpocketing stops abruptly and swells into a clublike shape. The two lateral ridges that caused the initial separation of the bulb from the gut thin ever further. A pair of small lateral outpockets develops (Fig. 2.9a). These lateral chambers will eventually form the lungs, whereas the median chamber connecting the lung buds to the pharynx will become the trachea. Shortly after the lung buds develop, the pulmonary bulb with its primitive lung sacs separates from the esophagus by a narrowing and pinching off of its sections from the caudal end in the cranial direction; this separated section will eventually form the lungs and trachea. A progressive narrowing occurs cranially to form the larynx at the anterior end of the primitive tracheal tube. The lateral ridges bordering the slit-like pulmonary groove, which originally occurred caudally, migrate cranially and fuse at the anterior end; the larynx will develop here, with the groove becoming the glottis (Schmalhausen, 1905).

Two lung buds of equal size originate, either simultaneously or shortly after one another (Fig. 2.9b). Whenever the lung buds do not appear simultaneously, the right bud always develops first. They develop at different rates, the right lung growing more rapidly than the left (Fig. 2.9c), ending with a diameter four times that of the left. The right lung also shows more rapid histological differentiation. Whereas the growth rate of the right lung is constant, that of the left lung is subject to significant variation from the earliest stages, although it continues to grow

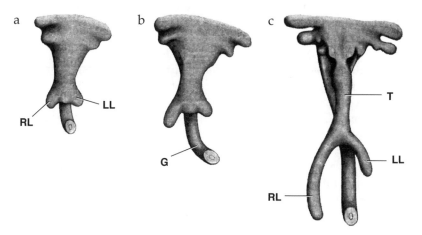

Fig. 2.9. *Natrix natrix.* a. Ventral view of left lung (LL) and right lung (RL) buds in an early embryo depicting symmetrical early budding. b. Ventral view of lung buds in a later stage embryo showing asymmetrical growth beginning to occur; G = gut. c. Ventral view of lung buds after further development of embryo, illustrating increased growth of right lung (RL) in comparison with left lung (LL). Abbreviation: T, trachea. (Adapted from Schmalhausen, 1905.)

throughout the period. The differential growth rate of the lungs continues in the postembryonic period (Schmalhausen, 1905). A primary asymmetry affects distribution of primordial germ cells of *Thamnophis* embryos, with most cells occurring on the right side (Risley, 1941). Thus, the reduction and more caudal placement of the left-sided organs are apparently genetic.

In *Thamnophis radix*, the respiratory anlage arises as a median evagination of the midpharyngeal floor between the first and second pairs of pharyngeal pouches. Neither the groove's length nor its position changes throughout subsequent embryonic development. This laryngotracheal groove immediately gives rise to the laryngotracheal tube that develops posteriorly as a free structure in the surrounding mesenchyme. Thus, the tracheal anlage arises as a direct outgrowth from the caudal portion of the laryngotracheal groove (Harrison and Denning, 1930). As the lungs originally extend to the glottis and the trachea develops secondarily from the lung buds, the tracheal lung is a novel development of evolution (H. Marcus, 1927).

The asymmetrical development of the lungs disturbs the order of the other viscera. The esophagus is pushed to the left side, and the left lung assumes a more ventral position in relation to the right. Later, the esophagus is gradually forced toward the left side and eventually to a ventral position, whereas the right lung, which rotates about its axis, assumes a central position. The liver is pushed to the right side. At earliest development, the lungs are adjacent to the heart, which is pushed to the right in the latest developmental stage. The rapid growth of the trachea in later stages shifts the lungs so that the left lung comes to lie just posterior to the heart (Schmalhausen, 1905). In snakes lacking a left lung as adults, the organ is apparently arrested genetically, prior to embryological development, as no trace of a left lung bud is found in the earliest stages of *Typhlops lumbricalis* or *Vipera aspis* (Butler, 1895).

Developmental anomalies include two-headed snakes. Although numerous cases are recorded, very little is known of the internal anatomy of such specimens (Brongersma, 1952a). However, it is known that part or all of the respiratory system may also be duplicated. The earliest reference to the internal anatomy of a dicephalic snake is that of *Vipera aspis* possessing two tracheae and two lungs (Redi, 1684; Lacepède, 1790, 1802; Tiedemann, 1831). Duplicated tracheae and/or lungs have also been reported in dicephalic specimens of other species, *Boa constrictor* (de Cunha, 1968), *Crotalus adamanteus* (J. B. Murphy and Shadduck, 1977), *Gloydius blomhoffii* (Nakamura, 1938), *Trimeresurus flavoviridis* (misidentified as *Hemibungarus japonicus*; Nakamura, 1938), *Vipera berus* (Dorner, 1873; Borgert, 1897), *V. russellii* (Khaire and Khaire, 1984), and *Vipera* sp. (Dutrochet, 1830a, 1830b), *Coluber florulentus* (Heasman, 1933),

Elaphe climacophora (Nakamura, 1938; Niimi, 1965, 1971), *E. conspicillata* (Nakamura, 1938), *Homalopsis buccata* (Rayer, 1850; Brongersma, 1952a), *Lampropeltis getulus* (Wallach 1995b), *Natrix natrix* (Vsevolojsky, 1812; Cantoni, 1921; Ladeiro, 1935, 1944), *Nerodia clarkii* (List, 1954), *Rhabdophis tigrinus* (Nakamura, 1938).

III. TRACHEAL COMPLEX
A. General

A long, flexible tracheal air duct conducts air into the pulmonary system, via the snake's glottis (Fig. 2.10), through the tracheal lung (if present), directly into the right lung; air passes into the left lung (if present) via an orifice or short left bronchus. Air normally reaches the trachea after passage through the external nares, the nasal sinuses, and the internal nares, which open into the buccal cavity. From there it passes through the anterior buccal cavity and then the glottal opening; whenever the mouth is open, air can enter the glottis directly from the atmosphere. The nasal passages of *Elaphe quadrivirgata* are lined with pseudo-stratified epithelium containing cylindrical columnar, globlet-like mucous, and triangular basal cells (Iwahori et al., 1987). The ophidian nasal cavity conducts inspired air from the atmosphere to the glottis and consists of three sections. The anterior portion is a small tubular vestibulum nasi leading from the external naris to the anterior end of the cavum nasi proprium, a large chamber with its greatest volume near its caudal end. The posterior end of the cavum nasi proprium is connected to the internal naris or choana by a short, wide ductus nasopharyngeus (Parsons, 1959, 1970). In *Thamnophis*, the vestibulum is lined by one or two layers of stratified columnar cells. The remaining portions are lined by two epithelial cell types that are not distinct but merge

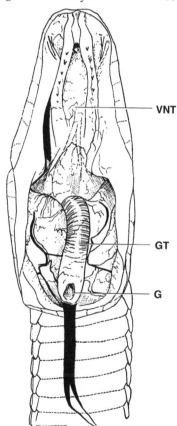

VNT

GT

G

Fig. 2.10. *Vipera aspis.* Buccal cavity showing glottis (G), glottal tube (GT), and vomeronasal trough (VNT). (Adapted from Lécuru-Renous and Platel, 1970b.)

along their boundaries: sensory epithelium and low columnar epithelium (Parsons, 1959). In *E. quadrivirgata*, the nasal cavity of embryos is slightly wavy, that of adults deeply folded; both are lined by compound, non-ciliated columnar mucous epithelium. The respiratory epithelium may also warm, humidify, and filter inspired air (Iwahori et al., 1987).

B. Larynx

The larynxes of 29 species of snakes from ten families (Typhlopidae, Aniliidae, Cylindrophiidae, Pythonidae, Boidae, Viperidae, Atractaspididae, Colubridae, Elapidae, Hydrophiidae) were described and illustrated by Henle (1839). Later descriptions include those of *Charina bottae* (Kardong, 1972b), *Crotalus viridis* (Kardong, 1972a), *Elaphe obsoleta* (Kardong, 1972a), *Natrix natrix* (Göppert, 1899; Edgeworth, 1935), *Nerodia taxispilota* (Karlstrom, 1952), and *Thamnophis sirtalis* (Karlstrom, 1952).

Located at the anterior end of the trachea, the larynx consists of two small, vertical arytenoid cartilages on either side, connected by a large azygous and a rounded, ventral cricoid cartilage (Fig. 2.11). The glottis is the vertical, slit-like anterior opening or laryngeal valve between the arytenoids; it is obliquely angled, in lateral view, with an anteroventral slope of 60°–75° to the tracheal axis. It controls air flow and permits hissing. The preglottal keel (Saiff, 1975) was initially termed an epiglottis (in *Pituophis*; C. A. White, 1884; Cope, 1891), but it is not homologous to the epiglottis of mammals. The preglottal keel is a vertical, longitudinal laminiform body (Fig. 2.12a). It lies immediately anterior to the glottis in the median sagittal plane and bisects the air streaming from the larynx during exhalant hissing (Lockwood, 1875; Shufeldt, 1885; Dugès, 1888; C. B. Perkins, 1938; Klauber, 1947, 1956; Gans and Maderson, 1973). Numerous colubrids show two other types of preglottal structures, low horizontal ridges and small rounded projections (Figs. 2.12b, 2.12c; Cope, 1891; G. A. Boulenger, 1913; Saiff, 1975).

In a snake resting horizontally with the jaws closed, the larynx lies far craniad in the buccal cavity, being slightly elevated above

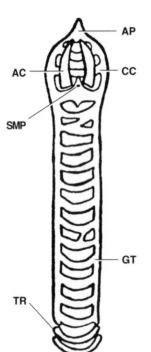

Fig. 2.11. *Nerodia taxispilota.* Diagram of dorsal view of larynx and glottal tube (GT) depicting arytenoid cartilage (AC), cricoid cartilage (CC), anterior process of cricoid (AP), superior median process (SMP), and tracheal rings (TR). (Adapted from Karlstrom, 1952.)

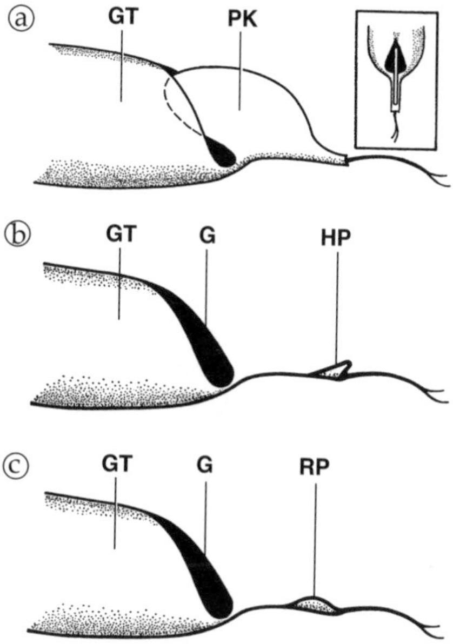

Fig. 2.12. a. *Pituophis melanoleucus.* Diagram of lateral view of glottal region depicting preglottal keel (PK) with its posterior border projecting through glottis into glottal tube (GT); inset shows dorsal view. b. Colubridae sp. Diagram of lateral view of glottal region showing preglottal horizontal ridge (HR), glottis (G), and glottal tube (GT) c. Colubridae sp. Diagram of lateral view of glottal region showing preglottal rounded projection (RP), glottis (G), and glottal tube (GT). (a: adapted from W. F. Martin and Huey, 1971; b–c: adapted from Saiff, 1975.)

the floor of the mouth. It is opposite the orbitonasal trough, a median longitudinal excavation in the roof of the mouth (Fig. 2.10). This trough lies between the palatine and pterygoid bones, just caudad of the choanal arc of the subchoanal shield, deep to which open the internal nares. The orbitonasal trough and the glottis abut these openings in the relaxed position (Göppert, 1937; Thäter, 1910; Frazzetta, 1966; Heyder, 1966; Parsons, 1970; Groombridge, 1979), allowing for the normal method of narial ventilation in snakes with the mouth closed. However, snakes can also breathe with the mouth open. A snake that is excited or in a defensive situation may open its mouth and inspire directly from the environment (via mouth and glottis). Some snakes have buccal epithelial flaps that border the internal nares posteriorly and may act as nasal valves (Karlstrom, 1952).

The processus epiglotticus represents the anterior apex of the laryngeal floor and is formed from the convergence of two flattened bars along the midline. The glottal tube is a cartilaginous bridge formed from dorsal extensions on both sides of the posterior cricoid cartilage, the anterior extension of which is the superior median process of the cricoid (Fig. 2.13). This glottal tube is formed from two longitudinal bars of cartilage that connect the dorsal tips of the first few tracheal rings. The number of rings involved varies. *Charina bottae* has 12, *Crotalus viridis* and *Deinagkistrodon acutus* have 6, *Elaphe obsoleta* has 3, *Natrix natrix* has 14, and *Nerodia taxispilota* and *Thamnophis sirtalis* have 12–16 (MacAlister, 1878; Edgeworth, 1935; Karlstrom, 1952; Kardong, 1972a; Ma, 1982b). The glottal tube is reported to be extremely long in some snakes such as the dipsadines (G. A. Boulenger, 1913). A survey of 22 species from seven families has revealed significant interspecific variation in the morphology of the laryngeal cartlages and the number of tracheal rings fused to the glottal tube (B. A. Young, pers. comm.)

During deglutition of large prey the larynx can be thrust forward between the tips of the mandibles or anterolaterally to the side of the mouth and the glottis opened to permit ventilation (Hopley, 1882; Gadow, 1901, 1923; Leighton, 1901; Burt, 1944; Karlstrom, 1952; Huang and Tsu, 1983). This process was first reported in *Boa constrictor* (Broderip, 1825a, 1925b, 1828; Dillon, 1831; Roberton, 1838), *Python reticulatus* (Bingley, 1829), and *P. molurus* (Hatch, 1890), although many other species employ this technique, i.e., *Agkistrodon, Nerodia, Pituophis, Thamnophis* (Karlstrom, 1952) and *Bitis* (C. Gans, 16mm film). The glottis is opened by the M. dilatator laryngis (Fig. 2.14), which originates from the lateral surface of the first few tracheal rings and inserts upon the anterolateral edge of the arytenoid cartilage. It is closed by a muscle having both superficial and deep fibers, the M. sphincter laryngis (Figs. 2.15, 2.16), that compress the arytenoid cartilages towards the midline (Kardong, 1972a, 1972b). Depending upon the species, the muscle originates from the dorsal surface of the arytenoid cartilage, its superior median process, or the dorsomedial surface of the first tracheal ring, and inserts upon the processus epiglotticus of the cricoid cartilage or on the glottal fascia on the lateral side of the cricoid at the base of the processus epiglotticus (Kardong, 1972a, 1972b). Earlier authors considered the M. sphincter laryngis to be composed of the M. laryngis dorsalis (located dorsal to the arytenoid cartilage) and of the more ventral M. laryngis ventralis (Henle, 1839; Göppert, 1899).

The trachea was early believed to be pressed flat when a snake was swallowing its prey, and the resulting protrusion of the glottis was due to pressure in the mouth (R. Owen, 1866). However, the larynx is protruded in the buccal cavity by the M.

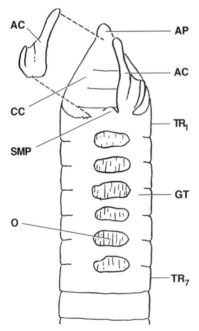

Fig. 2.13. *Crotalus viridis*. Dorsal view of larynx and glottal tube (GT) with the left arytenoid cartilage (AC) displaced from its attachment with the first tracheal ring (TR$_1$) and illustrating the anterior process of cricoid (AP), the cricoid cartilage (CC), orifices between cartilage elements (O), superior median process (SMP), and the seventh tracheal ring (TR$_7$). (Adapted from Kardong, 1972a.)

Fig. 2.14. *Natrix natrix.* Dorsal view of intrinsic musculature of larynx, depicting the M. geniotrachealis (MGT), M. hyotrachealis (MHT), M. laryngis ventralis (MLV), M. laryngis dorsalis (MLD), M. dilatator laryngis (MDL), arytenoid cartilage (AC), and glottal tube (GT). (Adapted from Göppert, 1899.)

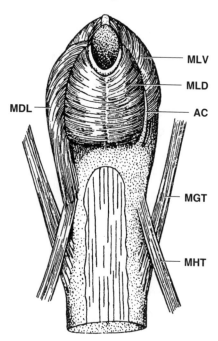

geniotrachealis, which originates on the midventral surface of the dentary and inserts on the anterior trachea. Caenophidians also have an M. protractor laryngis, which originates from the sublingual gland and fascia of the intermandibular symphysis; it inserts on the fascia at the ventrolateral margin of the anterior larynx and assists in the protraction of the larynx by the M. geniotrachealis. The larynx is retracted into the mouth by the M. hyotrachealis, which originates on the hyoid cornua or the fascia of the throat and inserts on the first few tracheal rings caudad of the larynx or on the fascia of the lateral surface of the larynx (Fig. 2.14) (Karlstrom, 1952; Gibson, 1966; Kardong, 1972a). In *Pituophis*, the unique M. tensor laryngis originates from supporting cartilage of the cricoid and inserts on the midline of the laryngeal septum, playing a role in the production of the bellow (Young et al., 1995).

Snakes can hiss by prolonged expulsion of air from fully inflated lungs (Carus, 1827; W. B. Carpenter, 1839; Hopley, 1882; Dugès, 1888). Although known in many boid, pythonid, colubrid, elapid, and viperid species (Holbrook, 1840, 1842; Ditmars, 1936; Linzey, 1979), the phenomenon of snake hissing was first reported in *Pituophis melanoleucus*, which was claimed to produce "a terrible hiss, resembling distant thunder" that can be heard over a distance of 50–150 feet (Bartram, 1791). The hiss of *P. melanoleucus* has also been described as a loud whistling sound (Kelly et al., 1936) and is composed of two distinct acoustic profiles: a hiss and a bellow (Young et al., 1995). However, *Pituophis* produces sound by vibration of the horizontal laryngeal septum, which originates from the cricoid that subdivides the anterior portion of the laryngeal lumen (Young et al., 1995).

Most snakes hiss through an open mouth. Hissing may occur either on inspiration or exhalation, although usually during the latter (Bellairs, 1969). Some snakes, such as *Vipera russellii* and *Bitis arietans*, can hiss as loudly

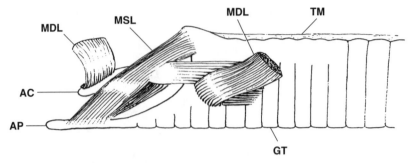

Fig. 2.15. *Charina bottae.* Lateral view of intrinsic musculature of the larynx with M. dilatator laryngis (MDL) bisected and reflected to expose M. sphinctor laryngis (MSL) showing arytenoid cartilage (AC), anterior process of cricoid (AP), glottal tube (GT), and tracheal membrane (TM); anterior is to the left. (Adapted from Kardong, 1972b.)

upon inspiration as upon exhalation (Pope, 1946). In *Heterodon platyrhinos*, a loud hiss or guttural whistle is produced upon expiration, but a weak snoring sound is produced during inspiration (Lönnberg, 1894; Kellicott, 1898), and the hiss of *Notechis scutatus* has been termed a shrill call of high-pitched staccato notes (Bushman, 1944). Hissing in *Boa constrictor* lasts 11–16 seconds with 3-second rest intervals (Stebbins, 1954). A nearly asphyxiated boa constrictor (more likely an anaconda), was allowed to breathe, and then hissed for several hours at a rate of 4.5 hisses per minute (13.3 second cycles); the exhalations resembled "high-pressure steam escaping from a great Western locomotive" (Wallace, 1853).

Other sounds are collectively termed growls (Young, 1991) and appear to be functionally related to the presence of multicameral, avascular tracheal lungs. *Acrochordus* has been reported to make a "plop-plop-plop" sound while swimming on the surface of the water (R. Mackay *in* Kinghorn, 1964). *Ptyas mucosus* produces a deep resonant or sibilant hiss; other sounds have been described for it are that of a vibrating tuning fork, a groaning sound, a deep prolonged snore, the deep growl of a big dog, and a mewing cat at bay (Cantor, 1847; Flower, 1899; Wall, 1905a, 1906, 1909, 1921; Herklots, 1934; Deoras, 1965–1978; Soderberg, 1973; A. de Silva, 1990). *Ophiophagus hannah* also produces a loud bellowing sound or deep guttural growl (R. Mertens, 1946; T. Harrisson, 1950; Soderberg, 1973; Young, 1981).

C. Trachea

It was early obvious that the trachea of snakes is very long (Veslingi, 1664; Charas, 1669; Tyson, 1683), consisting of a large number of incomplete cartilaginous rings that are separated dorsally by a thin membrane (Westphal, 1806; Meckel, 1829a; Cuvier 1829; Lereboullet, 1838). The larynx and trachea in snakes were reviewed by Göppert (1937). The internal anatomy and histology of the trachea has been studied in *Python molurus* and *Boa constrictor* (M. M. Grant et al., 1981; Kang et al., 1986), *Crotalus viridis* (Luchtel and Kardong, 1981), *Vipera aspis* (Livini, 1896), *Coluber viridiflavus* (Livini, 1896a, 1986b), *Natrix natrix* (Rothley, 1930a, 1930b), and *N. maura* (Pastor, 1990). Early studies noted that the tracheal membrane of most snakes lacked muscle fibers (Meckel, 1833; Cuvier, 1840), although they occur in booids such as *Python molurus* (Retzius, 1830). In addition to its major function as a respiratory duct, the trachea also allows for the expulsion of foreign particulate matters from the lungs (Gillian and Conklin, 1938; M. M. Grant et al., 1979, 1981).

The ophidian trachea is composed of about 100–1000 rings of hyaline cartilage joined by connective tissue interspaces (Kellicott, 1898). Estimates for the numbers of rings in the trachea vary from 70 (*Thamnophis*) to 1120 (*Microcephalophis*); most species have between 150–300 rings. The estimated number of rings per 10% SVL varies from 34 (*Thamnophis*) to 234 (*Python*), with the majority of species exhibiting from 50–100 (see Appendix C). The rings are incomplete throughout the length of the trachea, as observed by early authors (Tyson, 1683; Cuvier, 1805, 1840; Berthold, 1827; Meckel, 1833; Hopkinson and Pancoast, 1837; Holbrook, 1842), except at the cranial end where they form the glottal tube. However, *Python molurus* has 30 complete rings (Cuvier, 1840), and *Crotalus viridis* has 20–25 complete rings following the glottal tube (Kardong, 1972a). All of the remaining rings are incomplete, and in

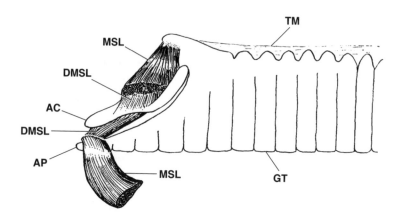

Fig. 2.16. *Elaphe obsoleta.* Lateral view of intrinsic musculature of the larynx with superficial fibers of M. sphinctor laryngis (MSL) bisected and deflected to expose the deep fibers of the M. sphinctor laryngis (DMSL), showing arytenoid cartilage (AC), anterior process of cricoid (AP), glottal tube (GT), and tracheal membrane (TM); anterior is to the left. (Adapted from Kardong, 1972a.)

the primitive state, their tips are truncated, not projecting beyond the junction of the border of the trachea with the tracheal membrane. Certain snakes (some Typhlopidae, Tropidophiidae, Viperidae, some Colubridae) have developed variously shaped free tips or extensions that project beyond the tracheal border into the tracheal lung lumen (Brongersma, 1951b; Klauber, 1956; Frenkel and Kochva, 1970; Kardong, 1972a). These tips, which usually also occur in a long intrapulmonary bronchus, as first observed in *Bitis arietans* by Lereboullet (1838) and Cuvier (1840), can interdigitate with one another to form a closed tube, possibly to transfer inspired air towards the rear of the lung or to hold the trachea in a tubular configuration whenever pressure is applied, as during deglutition. Whenever the trachea of *Chrysopelea ornata* is relaxed, the opposing tips form a closed tube separate from the tracheal membrane lumen, but whenever the trachea dilates, the tips separate and the lumen of the tracheal membrane then joins the lumen of the trachea (Thompson, 1913c).

The length of the trachea, or its midpoint value, is useful in systematics, as it combines high interspecific variation with low intraspecific variation (Wallach, 1991; Wong, 1994). Length of the trachea ranges from a minimum of 14% (*Leptotyphlops*) to a maximum of 57% (*Microcephalophis*), with 25–35% found in most species (see Appendix C). The CV for the midpoint of the trachea in *Typhlops lumbricalis* (n = 30) is 3.1, in *Rhinotyphlops schlegelii* (n = 30) is 4.7, and in *Acutotyphlops kunuaensis* (n = 40) is 5.4 (Wong, 1994). These species reveal no significant sexual dimorphism in this character. Among 17 atractaspid species for which large samples (n = 15–30) are available, the tracheal midpoint CV has a mean of 4 (range = 2–10). The majority of species show no significant sexual dimorphism in the midpoint value, although females always have lower values than males. All four tested species of *Amblyodipsas* show a significant difference (*P* < 0.05) between males and females; in *Aparallactus*, six of the eight species tested differ significantly in sex; in *Atractaspis*, only three of seven show significant sexual differences; in *Xenocalamus*, one of three is significantly different; and in *Polemon*, only one of seven is sexually dimorphic. Among all species tested (n = 4 or more for each sex), 16 exhibit significant dimorphism and 17 show no statistical difference between the sexes (Wallach, 1991, 1994a). The trachea plus right bronchus length and midpoint are both sexually dimorphic and exhibit moderate variability in *Acutotyphlops kunuaensis*. Mean length and CV in 20 males and 20 females are 52.6% and 4, 50.9% and 6, whereas the midpoint data are 27.0% and 4 and 26.2% and 6, respectively. In *Typhlops lumbricalis* there is no sexual difference and the female values for both characters are larger than those for the males, with CV = 5–6 (Wong, 1994).

The individual cartilaginous units of the trachea are more accurately termed tracheal cartilages in snakes, as very few of them actually form complete rings; however, they generally assume a ½–¾ ring shape in cross-section so the term "rings" is retained for tracheal elements and cartilages and bronchial elements. In snakes, the number of tracheal rings ranges from 100 in *Natrix natrix* to more than 350 in *Python molurus*. *Typhlops, Anilius, Naja,* and *Vipera* have about 200 rings, *Acrochordus* has about 260, and *Laticauda laticaudata, Crotalus durissus,* and *Bothrops lanceolatus* have about 300 (Meckel, 1833). Values reported for other species are 280–310 in *Typhlops vermicularis* (Heyder, 1966), 200–250 in *C. viridis* (Kardong, 1972a), and 200 in *Deinagkistrodon acutus* (Huang and Tsu, 1983), 200–250 in *Elaphe obsoleta* (Kardong, 1972a), 150–200 in *Nerodia taxispilota* (Karlstrom, 1952), 425 in *Ptyas mucosus* (D. Singh, 1971), and 150–200 in *Thamnophis sirtalis* (Karlstrom, 1952). The variable length of the trachea in snakes makes the number of rings per 10% SVL a more useful comparative statistic. Among atractaspidids, the number of rings/10% SVL ranges from 42 (male *Brachyophis krameri*) to 130 (male *Xenocalamus mechowii*) with most species ranging between 70–100. Only six out of 32 species (*Aparallactus lunulatus, A. werneri, Atractaspis bibronii, Polemon collaris, P. neuwiedi,* and *Xenocalamus mechowii*) exhibit significant sexual dimorphism in ring number, with the females having more rings than the males (Wallach, 1991). The CV for this character is high, averaging about 10 (range = 4–20). See Appendix C for data on other genera.

The width of the tracheal rings is variable, as indicated by the cartilaginous ring/interspace (CR/IS) ratio, which measures the width of the rings along the longitudinal midline (opposite the tracheal membrane) divided by the width of the membraneous or fibrous interspaces between them. Primitive snakes and burrowers have broad rings with narrow interspaces, the cartilages at least three times the width of the interspaces (CR/IS = 3.0–10.0). Rings of moderate width have interspaces approximately equal to or half the width of the ring (CR/IS = 1.0–2.0). Thin rings, in which the interspaces are wider than the rings, occur mainly in arboreal species (CR/IS = 0.3–0.9).

Ring shape is variable, but three major kinds are observable. Type I rings are wide with parallel edges, exhibit the

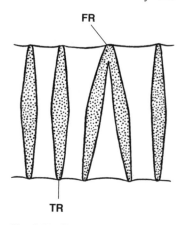

Fig. 2.17. *Dasypeltis inornata*. Diagram of trachea spread flat to illustrate single tracheal rings (TR) and one pair of fused rings (FR); tracheal membrane not shown. (Adapted from Gans and Richmond, 1957.)

same width from tip to tip, have squared-off or truncated tips, and are separated by narrow interspaces. Type II rings are moderate in width, having arms that taper towards their tips with the widest portion along the tracheal midline (Fig. 2.17). Thin rings, Type III, may have tapered or parallel arms but much wider interspaces than rings. Free tips occur in either Type II or III. In most snakes the tracheal rings are separate from one another, an arrangement referred to as regular. In contrast, in the irregular arrangement (Weichert, 1951, 1965), the tips of successive tracheal rings have fused through branching spurs (as first noted by Tyson, 1683, in *Crotalus horridus*); this occurs in both Type II and III rings. Most species show a gradual craniocaudal reduction in ring width, with a concomitant decrease in the CR/IS ratio; examples are *Bungarus multicinctus, Naja atra, Deinagkistrodon acutus, Protobothrops mucrosquamatus, Trimeresurus stejnegeri,* and *Vipera russellii* (Mao, 1993). The tracheal rings of *V. berus* are widest and present the greatest surface area cranially, their width showing a gradual reduction towards the saccular lung (Sparing, 1976).

The trachea assumes numerous cross-sectional shapes, the primitive condition being circular (Carus, 1835). Various degrees of openness are found from nearly closed (Rothley, 1930a, 1930b; Gans, 1974), horseshoe-shaped (Heyder, 1968; Larson and van de Velde, 1969), semicircular (Rothley, 1930a, 1930b; Robb, 1960; Heatwole and Seymour, 1975b; Stinner, 1980, 1982b; Mao, 1993), oval (Sparing, 1976), half-hooped (J. C. George and Shah, 1956), C-shaped (Fig. 2.18; Kellicott, 1898; Gans and Richmond, 1957; Luchtel and Kardong, 1981; Huang and Tsu, 1983; Lillywhite and Smits, 1992), U-shaped (Thompson, 1914b; Rothley, 1930a, 1930b; Suomalainen, 1939; Folk, 1971; Ruben, 1976b; Luchtel and Kardong, 1981), V-shaped, often with a median crease or fold

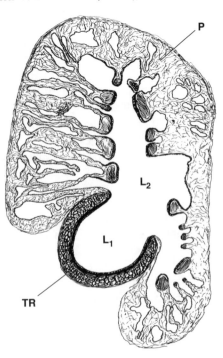

Fig. 2.18. *Crotalus viridis.* Cross-section of unicameral tracheal lung showing the C-shaped tracheal ring (TR), faveolar parenchyma (P), and lumen of trachea (L_1) continuous with that of the lung (L_2). (Adapted from Kardong, 1972a.)

(Fig. 2.19; Gans and Richmond, 1957), and trough- or gutter-shaped (Suomalainen, 1939; Stinner, 1980; Luchtel and Kardong, 1981; Ma, 1982a). The trachea in *Morelia spilota* encompasses only 2% of the total volume of the respiratory system (Donnelly and Woolcock, 1977).

The position of the tracheal membrane and distal ring tips varies from ventral to dorsal of the longitudinal axis of the trachea and all positions in between, mainly towards the right side (Brongersma, 1957a; Young, 1992). Normally, the distal tips and the intervening membrane of the trachea are directed dorsad (i.e., Booidea, Hydrophiidae, Viperidae) or dextrolaterad (i.e., Colubridae), although they can be oriented ventrad, as in *Calabaria* and *Dasypeltis* (Gans and Richmond, 1957).

The trachea normally lies ventrad to the esophagus, but it may lie dextroventrolaterad or dextrolaterad with respect to the latter. It may extend along the left or right side of the nuchal cavity or, in those forms with a well-developed tracheal lung, along the midventral line (Plate 2.1C). Upon reaching the cardiac region, the trachea follows one of three courses. In all snakes except the scolecophidians, the trachea reportedly passes to the left side of the heart (Cope, 1894a–1895b, 1900). More precisely, in the most primitive snakes (Scolecophidia and Anilioidea), the trachea curves dextrodorsad such that it passes dorsad to the atria of the heart and lies along the right lateral side of the ventricle. Among the Booidea, the trachea passes middorsal to the heart. In all other snakes, the trachea curves sinistrodorsad, sinistrodorsolaterad, or sinistrolaterad of the heart such that it lies along the left side of the body in the cardiac region (Plate 2.1D). In most snakes with a well-developed tracheal lung, it secondarily has a middorsal course above the heart.

Whenever a tracheal lung is present, the trachea can be divided into three different regions. That portion of the trachea craniad of the vascular tissue of the lung is considered a nonpulmonary trachea (NPT), the portion adjacent to the lung and exposed is the extrapulmonary trachea (EPT), and the portion (if any) completely embedded in the tissue of the lung is termed an intrapulmonary trachea (IPT) (Suomalainen, 1939). In *Ramphotyphlops*, the entire trachea is extrapulmonary (Robb, 1960), whereas the caudal 0.40–0.50 part of the trachea is intrapulmonary in *Typhlops bibronii* and *T. fornasinii.*

Branches of the left and right common carotid and the anterior vertebral artery supply blood to the trachea; the left and right common jugular veins drain it in *Ptyas mucosus* (Ray, 1934, 1936). Branches of the left common carotid artery serve the trachea in the viperids *Agkistrodon, Crotalus, Lachesis, Sistrurus,* and *Vipera* (Bothner, 1959; Bourgondien and Bothner, 1969; Lécuru-Renous and Platel, 1970). The left carotid supplies the trachea in *Coluber constrictor, Natrix natrix, Naja naja, Thamnophis sirtalis,* and *Xenochrophis piscator* (O'Donoghue, 1912; Atwood, 1916, 1918;

Kurtz, 1953; P. H. D. H. de Silva, 1953, 1955; Kashyap and Velankar, 1959). In addition to systemic vessels, small anterior branches of the pulmonary artery also serve the trachea and cardiac lung region in *Erythrolamprus aesculapii*, *Nerodia taxispilota*, and *Thamnophis sirtalis* (Beddard, 1906b; Karlstrom, 1952).

D. Tracheal Membrane

In the typical ophidian condition, a thin, smooth, narrow membrane of collagenous and elastic connective tissue, lacking muscle fibers, connects the tips of the tracheal rings (Lereboullet, 1838; Beddard, 1903; Gans and Richmond, 1957). Literature reports maintain that this membrane lies dorsad of the trachea (Meckel, 1833; Beddard, 1903, 1906a; Wiedersheim, 1909; H. Marcus, 1937; Kurtz, 1953) but, except in tracheal lungs, it is most commonly laterad to the right or dorsolaterad (Thompson, 1913c). Only occasionally is the membrane ventrolaterad or ventrad as in *Dasypeltis* (Gans and Richmond, 1957) or *Calabaria*. In nearly all species, the anterior trachea in the gular region is oriented laterad to the right; it torques around the tracheal axis in many species from the nuchal to the cardiac region, whereupon the orientation then changes. The composition of the atrabecular tracheal membrane varies; in arboreal colubrids, it is a thin, transparent membrane capable of considerable expansion, but in the Booidea it is a thickened membrane of elastic tissue with longitudinal rugosities or striations (Retzius, 1830). In *Acrochordus*, it is entirely fibrous or cartilaginous. The tracheal membrane may also be variously vascularized (i.e., trabecular, edicular, or faveolar).

In snakes, tracheal cartilages constitute only 0.3–0.9 of the tracheal circumference, and the tracheal membrane often possesses a diameter equal to or larger than that of the rings (Rees, 1820; Lereboullet, 1838). Expansion of the tracheal membrane relative to its circumference is de-

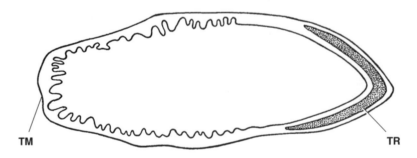

TM   TR

Fig. 2.19. *Dasypeltis inornata.* Cross-section of trachea illustrating V-shaped tracheal ring (TR) and expanded tracheal membrane (TM). (Adapted from Gans and Richmond, 1957.)

Table 2.4. Species reported to exhibit inflation of neck or body via trachea or lungs[1]

Boidae	Colubridae (continued)	Colubridae (continued)
Epicrates inornatus	*A. nasuta*	*Heterodon nasicus*
Viperidae	*A. prasina*	*H. platyrhinos*
Bitis arietans	*Boiga cyanea*	*Leptodeira annulata*
B. caudalis	*B. dendrophila*	*Leptophis ahaetulla*
Causus rhombeatus	*B. trigonata*	*Natrix natrix*
Crotalus atrox	*Chironius carinatus*	*Oligodon bitorquatus*
C. cerastes	*C. scurrulus*	*Philothamnus angolensis*
C. enyo	*Clonophis kirtlandii*	*P. dorsalis*
C. mitchelli	*Coluber constrictor*	*P. hoplogaster*
C. ruber	*Dasypeltis scabra*	*P. irregularis*
C. scutulatus	*Dendrelaphis cyanochloris*	*P. natalensis*
C. viridis	*D. formosus*	*P. ornatus*
Vipera berus	*D. pictus*	*P. semivariegatus*
Elapidae	*D. punctulatus*	*Pituophis catenifer*
Aspidelaps scutatus	*D. tristis*	*P. melanoleucus*
Bungarus caeruleus	*Dispholidus typus*	*P. sayi*
Dendroaspis angusticeps	*Drymarchon corais*	*Psammophis aegypticus*
Ophiophagus hannah	*Elaphe guttata*	*Pseustes poecilonotus*
Hydrophiidae	*E. helena*	*P. shropshirei*
Denisonia maculata	*E. quadrivirgata*	*P. sulphureus*
Oxyuranus scutellatus	*E. radiata*	*Ptyas mucosus*
Pseudechis porphyriacus	*E. subradiata*	*Spilotes pullatus*
Suta suta	*E. taeniura*	*Thamnophis sirtalis*
Colubridae	*Gonyosoma jansenii*	*Thelotornis capensis*
Ahaetulla mycterizans	*G. oxycephalum*	*T. kirtlandii*

[1]Reports summarized in C. C. Carpenter and Ferguson (1977) and Greene (1988); see Appendix B for references.

noted by the ratio of tracheal membrane/cartilaginous ring (TM/CR). This ratio is calculated as the maximal width of the tracheal membrane divided by the width of the tracheal rings when measured in a plane or along their inner circumference from tip to tip. Membrane expansion has three general states: narrow, moderate, and wide. In the primitive condition, occuring in most Leptotyphlopidae, Anilioidea, and Booidea, the membrane is narrow (TM/CR <0.25). In the Leptotyphlopidae and Uropeltidae, the mean value is <0.10, and the rings are nearly circular with only a narrow strip of membrane separating their opposing tips. Membranes with a moderate expansion exhibit a TM/CR ratio between 0.25 and 1.0. *Toxicocalamus* has a value of 1.0 (McDowell, 1969b). Ratios greater than 1.0 indicate a wide or greatly expanded tracheal membrane (Fig. 2.19), with the ultimate expansion of 5.0 as seen in some arboreal colubrids that inflate their necks defensively (i.e., *Dispholidus, Pseustes, Spilotes*). This enlarged tracheal membrane was first recorded in *Thrasops flavigularis* (Cope, 1894b). Its association with neck inflation was reported in *Ptyas korros* (Lamare-Picquot, 1858) and *Thelotornis kirtlandii* (L. Müller, 1910). Arboreal snakes commonly inflate the anterior trunk region as a defensive display (Greene, 1979). It occurs in no fewer than 15 genera (14 colubrids, one boid, and possibly an elapid or two) and nearly 40 species (Table 2.4; C. C. Carpenter and Ferguson, 1977). In *Dasypeltis*, and presumably other species, the neck region is inflated by filling the lungs, closing the glottis, and forcing the air forward into the trachea (Gans and Richmond, 1957). Hypotheses concerning the functional role of an expandable tracheal membrane (and consequent neck inflation) include: (1) defensive intimidation of predators through increased apparent size (R. Mertens, 1946; Gans and Richmond, 1957; H. W. Parker, 1963; H. W. Parker and Grandison, 1977), (2) defensive warning by display of startling coloration (H. W. Parker, 1963, 1965; H. W. Parker and Grandison, 1977), (3) mimicry of avian fledgings that make them vulnerable to predation (Goodman and Goodman, 1976), (4) an air reservoir like the saccular right lung (Werner, 1911), and (5) mimicry of the pattern in various small vipers (Gans, 1974).

Some literature confuses tracheal inflation of the neck or anterior body in the vertical plane and spreading or flattening a hood in the horizontal plane. The latter, as exemplified by cobras, is performed by extending the cervical ribs laterally; it lacks a functional connection with the respiratory system, and is responsible for erroneous reports of lung inflation in *Waglerophis merremii* and *Dendroaspis polylepis* (E. G. Boulenger, 1914; Noble, 1921; Rose, 1950–1962; Shaw, 1956; H. W. Parker, 1963; Roze, 1966; H. W. Parker and Grandison, 1977; Freiberg, 1982).

In snakes with multicameral lungs, the tracheal membrane is pierced with foramina that lead to the separate respiratory chambers,

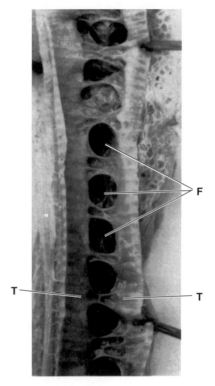

Fig. 2.20. *Typhlops punctatus*. Internal view of tracheal lumen of multicameral lung after bisection and deflection of trachea (T), showing large type A foramina (F) that lead to air chambers. (Adapted from Brongersma, 1958a.)

typically one foramen per chamber. Relative foramen size is indicated by the ratio of foramen diameter/tracheal membrane (FD/TM), which varies from 0.2–1.0. Six of the eight foraminal types of snakes occur in typhlopoids (Wallach, 1993b). Type A foramina are large, have their borders contacting both edges of the trachea, and have diameters equal to those of the membrane (FD/TM = 1.0). Many scolecophidians possess type A foramina (Fig. 2.20; Plate 2.1E), as does *Ophiophagus hannah* (Beddard, 1903; Young, 1991). Whenever rings have free tips, these project into the foramina beyond the tracheal border. More commonly, the diameters of the foramina are small (FD/TM = 0.25–0.50), centered along the longitudinal midline of the membrane, and are out of contact with either tracheal border (type C). Type C foramina occur in typhlopoids and colubroids. Foramina may have moderate size (FD/TM = 0.50–0.75), and their position may let them contact only a single edge of the trachea, either the ventral border (type B) or the dorsal (type D). Types B and D occur in the Typhlopoidea; type B foramina were first reported in *Gonyosoma oxycephalum* (Thompson, 1914b). The type E arrangement, which occurs in only a few typhlopids (i.e., *Typhlops lineolatus*, *T. koekkoeki*), consists of transversely paired foramina (and chambers) with a large primary median foramen and a smaller secondary one positioned between the tracheal border and the primary foramen. The secondary foramen, leading to the small air chamber, lies either ventrad or sinistrad of the primary foramen (E_1), or else dorsad or dextrad of it (E_2). Type F contains small, intercalary foramina wedged irregularly between foraminal types A–D. The foramina lead to minor niches located between the major chambers and occur only in some typhlopids, such as *Acutotyphlops kunuaensis*, *Typhlops muelleri*, and *T. punctatus* (Fig. 2.20). Type G are small and not located along the tracheal membrane but between the tips of the rings in the trachea itself or on the right bronchus; these foramina occur only in the Leptotyphlopidae and Acrochordidae. Type H pattern consists of two to four small foramina (FD/TM = 0.15–0.25) arranged out of contact the tracheal border but in transverse rows along the membranes; they occur only in *Acrochordus* and correspond to the two or four longitudinally arranged chambers in the tracheal lung, known respectively as biserial (*A. arafurae* and *A. javanicus*) or quadriserial (*A. granulatus*). The total number of foramina (hence, chambers) in the tracheal, cardiac, and right lung varies from 34–50 (21–33 in tracheal lung, mean = 29) in *Acutotyphlops kunuaensis*, 37–59 (30–48 in tracheal lung, mean = 39) in *Rhinotyphlops schlegelii* (Plate 2.5), and 32–49 (26–38 in tracheal lung, mean = 31) in *Typhlops lumbricalis* (Wong, 1994). Foraminal number exhibits moderate variability (CV = 8–12) and lacks sexual dimorphism.

E. Tracheal Lung

Vascularized respiratory tissue (i.e., a tracheal lung) along an expanded tracheal membrane is a derived condition in snakes; there is substantial morphological variation among diverse snakes. A tracheal lung was first illustrated in *Crotalus horridus* (Tyson, 1683), *Typhlops reticulatus* (Fig. 2.21; Meckel, 1818), and *Enhydrina schistosa* (Cantor, 1841). Early authors noted the presence of an expanded tracheal membrane with parenchyma extending from the heart to the throat but considered this to be an extension of the right lung (Cuvier, 1805; Schlegel, 1837b; Lereboullet, 1838; Milne-Edwards, 1857b). It was initially suggested that the vascularized structure anterior to the heart in *Crotalus* and *Vipera* was a lung, possibly one that had migrated cranially (Meckel, 1818, 1833). However, only after its use as a systematic character was it recognized as a unique respiratory organ (Cope, 1894a). In view of Cope's (1894a, 1894b, 1895b, 1900) extensive survey of 150 species from all major groups, including both *Typhlops* and *Acrochordus*, it is surprising that he concluded that the tracheal lung lacked a lumen and did not communicate with the lumen of the trachea; he speculated that it might be a gland lacking respiratory function. I attribute this error to poorly preserved material; early in my studies I recorded a partially dessicated, multicameral lung of *Ramphotyphlops acuticaudus* as unicameral. A tracheal lung is absent in the Leptotyphlopidae but present in the Anomalepididae and Typhlopidae (Brongersma, 1958a).

Members of such snake families as the Anomalepididae, Typhlopidae, Xenophidiidae, Tropidophiidae, Acrochordidae, Viperidae, Atractaspididae, and marine Hydrophiidae have a well developed, vascularized tracheal lung (see

Fig. 2.21. *Typhlops reticulatus.* Ventral cutaway view of the tracheal lung (TL), cardiac lung (CL), and right lung (RL) showing the multicameral aspect, trachea (T), and long right bronchus (RB). (Adapted from Meckel, 1818.)

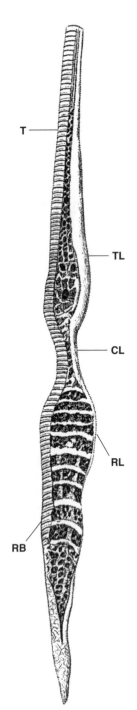

Appendix C). So do all members of certain colubrid subfamilies and tribes (i.e., Xenodermatini, Nothopsini, Dipsadini, Homalopsinae, Lycophidini) plus a few diverse colubrid genera. Many colubrid groups have a moderately or weakly developed tracheal lung. A criterion for the presence of a tracheal lung is vascularization of the tracheal membrane supported by a tracheal artery and vein (Brongersma, 1957c; Underwood, 1967). Many species of snakes have a cardiac lung, i.e., parenchyma extending craniad of the right lung along the tracheal membrane adjacent to the heart (Plate 2.1F). This parenchyma differs from that of the right lung, and its extent is usually shorter than 5% SVL. Several Colubridae and a few Atractaspididae and Elapidae have moderately developed tracheal lungs. The Booidea lack tracheal lungs but may rarely have cardiac lungs. The tracheal lungs reported in *Corallus caninus* and *C. hortulanus* (Beddard, 1908), *Charina bottae* (Kardong, 1972b), *Rhinoplocephalus gouldii* (Brongersma, 1958b) and *R. bicolor* (McDowell, 1972b), are considered cardiac lungs, as is also the vascularized strip in many other terrestrial Australian hydrophiids that presumably lack a tracheal artery.

A weakly developed or incipient tracheal lung (Lereboullet, 1838; Cuvier, 1840) occurs in numerous Colubroidea, usually in the form of a narrow membrane supporting sparse ediculae or trabeculae that extend along the trachea into the cardiac region, or perhaps one heart length anterior to the heart, before disappearing. Whether these are supplied by the pulmonary circulation is questionable. This uncertainty leads me to include such organs with the cardiac lung measurements in Appendix C until tracheal blood supply can be demonstrated. This approach seems preferable to listing all snakes with parenchyma craniad of the heart as possessing a tracheal lung.

The length of the tracheal lung is limited by the position of the heart. In species with a strongly developed tracheal lung, the heart appears to have been caudally displaced, as evidenced by the reduction and loss of the heart-liver gap (Underwood, 1967). The tracheal lung ranges from 3% (*Cerastes cerastes*) to 44% (*Acrochordus granulatus*); typical values are 10–20% (see Appendix C). The length of the tracheal lung varies from 21–24% (CV = 5–6) in three typhlopid species. The length of the tracheal lung shows no sexual dimorphism in *Acutotyphlops kunuaensis* or *Typhlops lumbricalis*, but there is a significant dimorphism in *Rhinotyphlops schlegelii* (Wong, 1994). On the other hand, the midpoint of the tracheal lung of *Acutotyphlops kunuaensis* has a CV = 3–6 and exhibits highly significant sexual dimorphism. This is absent in *Typhlops lumbricalis* and *Rhinotyphlops schlegelii*. Only four of the 13 genera of Atractaspididae have a well developed tracheal lung (*Brachyophis, Chlorhinophis, Elapotinus,* and *Micrelaps*). Length of the tracheal lung plus the right lung ranges from

50–70%, averaging 60–65% in most species. This character exhibits moderate variability (CV = 5–10) and lacks sexual dimorphism (Wallach, 1991). Tracheal lung volume relative to right lung volume ranges from 5% (*Emydocephalus annulatus*) to 43% (*Hydrophis elegans*) in the Hydrophiidae (Heatwole and Seymour, 1975b).

The atrabecular multicameral tracheal organ of *Ophiophagus* was early described (Beddard, 1903) as were the tracheal lungs of *Laticauda* and *Pelamis* (Beddard, 1904b). Variation in the tracheal lung of the Pareatinae and Dipsadini (including *Aplopeltura*, *Pareas*, *Dipsas*, *Sibon*, and *Sibynomorphus*) was discussed by F. Werner (1911) and the tracheal lung in *Vipera berus* was described by Suomalainen (1939). Tracheal lungs were also mentioned in *Ramphotyphlops braminus*, *Lycodon aulicus*, *Cerberus rynchops*, *Gerarda prevostiana*, *Enhydrina schistosa*, *Hydrophis cyanocinctus*, *Vipera russellii*, and *Echis carinatus* (J. C. George and Varde, 1941; J. C. George and Shah, 1956, 1965).

The most detailed study of the tracheal lung was on *Ramphotyphlops australis*, *R. ligatus*, *R. polygrammicus*, and *R. proximus* (Robb, 1960). It assumed that the left pulmonary artery and vein (=tracheal artery and vein) serve the anterior lung. This led to the conclusion that a left lung has rotated cranially, whereas the heart and other viscera have migrated caudally so that the trachea is the original left bronchus remaining embedded in pulmonary tissue. A similar conclusion in *Typhlops vermicularis* has been based on analysis of the pulmonary vessels, similarity of vascular tissue craniad and caudad of the heart, absence of a rudimentary paries membranaceus connecting the tips of the cartilaginous rings, caudal placement of the heart, and the difference in the development of the lung and trachea (Heyder, 1966, 1968). Both studies concluded that the typhlopid tracheal lung is homologous with the saurian left lung. However, this hypothesis is untenable on several grounds. Two species of *Rhinotyphlops* and 11 species of *Typhlops* from Africa and Asia have a

---

Plate 2.1. A. *Boiga cynodon*. Internal view of cranial right lung (RL) depicting sparse parenchyma of cardiac lung (CL) adjacent to heart (H), trachea (T), left orifice (LO), and short right bronchus (RB). B. *Enhydris enhydris*. Interior of narrow, moderately developed unicameral tracheal lung (TL) as viewed through bisected and reflected trachea (T). C. *Pelamis platurus*. Interior of wide, well developed unicameral tracheal lung (TL) as viewed through bisected and reflected trachea (T). D. *Heterodon platyrhinos*. External view of heart (H) region with viscera in natural position showing enormous anterior lobe (AL), trachea (T), esophagus (E), anterior right lung (RL), and small sparsely vascularized left lung (LL). E. *Rhinotyphlops schlegelii*. Internal view of tracheal lumen in multicameral lung after bisecting the trachea (T) to reveal type A foramina (F) piercing the tracheal membrane (TM); foramina lead to separate air chambers. F. *Boiga cynodon*. Internal view of cardiac pulmonary region showing cranialmost right lung (RL), heart (H), bisected and deflected trachea (T), and sparse parenchyma of cardiac lung (CL) merging with aparenchymal tracheal membrane (TM).

PLATE 2.1

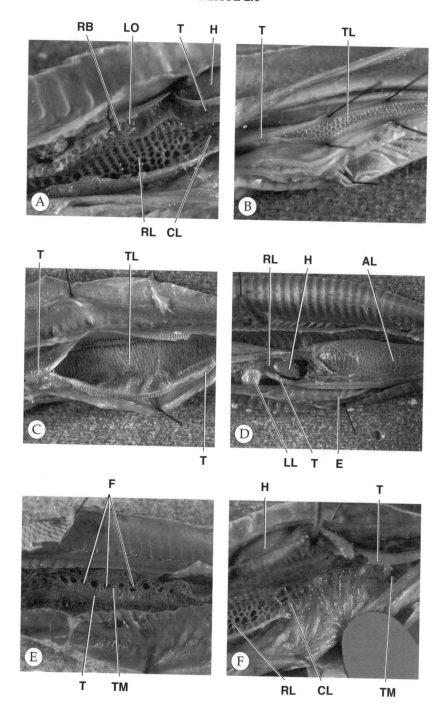

PLATE 2.2

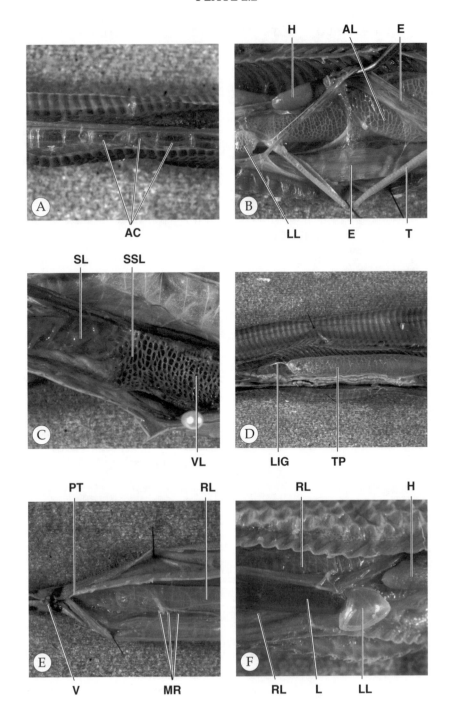

vestigial left lung positioned just caudad to the ventricular apex of the heart; here lies the left lung of all other snakes (Brongersma, 1958a; Wallach, 1993a). Many other groups of snakes exhibit tracheal lungs, although only the Anomalepididae and Acrochordidae possess a multi-cameral organ as do the Typhlopidae. A distinct left lung, right lung, and tracheal lung was first reported in *Gerarda prevostiana* (Varde, 1951). All three organs occur simultaneously in other widely divergent genera from different families, subfamilies, and tribes (Tropidophiidae, Viperinae, Crotalinae, Atractaspididae, Elapidae, Hydrophiidae, Xeno-dermatini, Nothopsini, Pareatini, Dipsadini, Calamariini, Hydra-ethiopsini, Homalopsinae, Alsophiini, Elapomorphini, Philodryadini, Geophiini, Sonorini; see Appendix C). The heart tip in typhlopids (at 24–42%) does not lie as far caudad as in some other taxa such as the Anomalepididae (29–43%), Acrochordidae (44–53%), Viperidae (25–49%), Hydrophiidae (29–57%), Homalopsinae (20–43%), Nothopsini (24–39%), and Dipsadini (22–44%); consequently, the caudal migration of viscera postulated by Robb (1960) to explain the separation of the right lung from the left is meaningless. The parenchyma of the tracheal lung and right lung are significantly different in the majority of typhlopid species (those possessing a unicameral right lung). The vascular tissue of forms in which the multicameral chambers extend into the cardiac lung and the anterior portion of the right lung has a similar structure and organization. If the tracheal lung were indeed the homologue of the left lung, the organ would be unicameral (as are all left lungs, regard-less of size), and the trachea would be divided into bronchi (as in all snakes) at the cranial and not at the caudal end of the lung (Brongersma, 1960). Also, snakes with only a right lung and a well developed right pulmonary artery have the stem of the pulmonary trunk lying in the same position as that of snakes with two pulmonary arteries. The ligamentum arteriosum connects a small diverticulum of the pulmo-nary artery to the left aortic arch in *Typhlops* and other snakes. This

---

Plate 2.2. A. *Gonyosoma oxycephalum*. External view of aparenchymal multicameral tra-cheal organ showing individual air chambers (AC). B. *Heterodon platyrhinos*. External view of heart (H) region with trachea (T) and portion of esophagus (E) displaced to show subterminal tracheal entry, anterior lobe (AL) independent of the trachea, and small left lung (LL). C. *Boiga cynodon*. Internal view of right lung illustrating the dense parenchyma of the vascular lung (VL) and the aparenchymal saccular lung (SL) separated by a very short transitional semisaccular lung (SSL). D. *Heterodon platyrhinos*. External view of cau-dal portion of right lung (RL) showing trabecular parenchyma (TP) and ligament (LIG) attached to posterior tip. E. *Pelamis platurus*. External view of caudal portion of right lung (RL) showing internal transverse muscular ridges (MR) and posterior tip (PT) near vent (V). F. *Trimeresurus stejnegeri*. External view of the heart-liver region showing the small aparenchymal left lung (LL), heart (H), anterior liver (L), and right lung (RL).

diverticulum is the remnant of the ductus arteriosus Botalli, which, in the embryological state, connects the pulmonary and systemic circulatory systems (Brongersma, 1958a, 1960). The ductus arteriosus stems from the base of the left pulmonary artery; hence, presence of the ductus in some snakes indicates that the artery running craniad along the tracheal lung is unlikely to be the homologue of the left pulmonary artery (as maintained by Robb, 1960), but rather is a branch of the right pulmonary or the tracheal artery. The tracheal lung of snakes is an accessory breathing organ; it is not the left lung nor an extension of the right lung (G. A. Boulenger, 1913). Also, neither the position nor the vascularization of the tracheal lung in *Vipera palaestinae* (Frenkel and Kochva, 1970) support the earlier hypothesis (Robb, 1960).

The hypothesis that the tracheal lung of typhlopids is the homologue of the left lung of lizards requires the origination of another lung of similar dimensions, structure, and placement as the original ophidian left lung. It is more parsimonious to accept the left lung of typhlopids as the true vestige of the saurian left lung and the tracheal lung as a novel respiratory organ developed along the pre-existing trachea. After all, embryologically the lungs extended up to the glottis and the trachea developed secondarily out of the lungs; hence, the tracheal lung must be a novel evolutionary development (Marcus, 1927).

The tracheal lung is sometimes narrow, even when extensively developed, as in the Homalopsinae (Plate 2.1B) or Hydrophiidae, in which it may occupy only ¼ of the nuchal cavity (Fig. 2.22). In other groups, it may be greatly expanded to occupy the entire nuchal cavity, as in the Viperidae, in which case TM/CR = 8.0. Parenchyma may reach only halfway to the head (i.e., *Hydrelaps, Bitis*) or extend to the gular region (i.e., *Acrochordus, Crotalus*). In *Vipera berus*, the relative faveolar surface area reaches a maximum near the midlung region and then decreases towards the saccular lung, with the tracheal lung averaging 114 cm², the cardiac lung 14 cm², and the right lung 12 cm² (Sparing, 1976). The volume of the vascularized region, on the other hand, is fairly constant throughout the length of the tracheal lung, with averages of 2.86 cm³ for the total tracheal lung, 0.46 cm³ for the cardiac lung, and 0.30 cm³ for the right lung (Sparing, 1976). Often, when the tracheal lung is extensive, the entire right lung may be aparenchymal, as in *Sibon* (Underwood, 1967).

Variability in the development of the tracheal lung in congeneric species is rare, but has been documented in *Pareas* (Brongersma, 1957c), *Laticauda* (McDowell, 1972a), *Bitis* (Groombridge, 1980), and *Xenodon* (V. Wallach, pers. obs.), although such variation may reflect different phylogenetic histories. For example, *Bitis worthingtoni* of Kenya and the three large species of widely distributed African *Bitis* possess a tracheal lung and have the heart lung and tip located at 31–45% SVL, whereas all of the small species of "*Bitis*" (seven of the eight species examined), which are restricted to southern Africa, lack a tracheal lung, and have the heart tip located at 29–33% SVL (V. Wallach, pers. obs.). It is possible that these two groups are not monophyletic and that their current placement as congeners is based on primitive features. Consequently, I here employ the available name *Calechidna* for the small South African species of *Bitis* (which are currently under investigation by W. R. Branch) in Appendix C. A small tracheal lung was reported to be served by a branch of the pulmonary artery in *Erythrolamprus aesculapii* (Beddard, 1906b). Because three species of *Erythrolamprus* (including *E. aesculapii*) examined by me lacked obvious blood vessels and parenchyma extending craniad of the heart, Appendix C lists *Erythrolamprus* as lacking a tracheal lung.

The tracheal lung possessed by the overwhelming majority of snakes, and the right and left lung of all Serpentes, comprises a single longitudinal organ that could be termed a uniserial structure. Only the three species of the Acrochordidae show two different arrangements (biserial and quadriserial) of the tracheal lung. The biserial structure of the paired chambers in the tracheal lung of *Acrochordus* was first described by Stannius (1856). The organs of *A. arafurae* and *A. javanicus* consist of 90–150 transversely paired parenchymal chambers in a longitudinal series (200–300 total chambers); this is essentially a left and right multicameral arrangement in which each chamber is served by a single foramen located

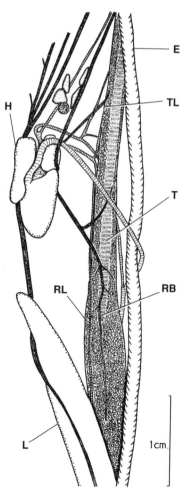

Fig. 2.22. *Hypsiglena torquata.* Ventral view of heart-liver region illustrating narrow tracheal lung (TL), barely wider than trachea (T), terminal entry of trachea into right lung (RL) with absence of anterior lobe, short right bronchus (RB), and absence of left lung complex. The esophagus (E), heart (H), and liver (L) have been displaced to reveal the lung complex. In the natural position, liver tip nearly contacts heart. (Adapted from Underwood, 1967, by courtesy of the Natural History Museum, London.)

along the tracheal membrane or between the ring tips. The quadriserial lung of *A. granulatus* is a double biserial structure with more than 200 longitudinal chambers that are transversely arranged in groups of four, the medial pair of spaces communicating with the tracheal lumen by foramina along the tracheal membrane, the lateral pair by foramina wedged between the tips of the tracheal rings. The tracheal lung of *A. granulatus* thus possesses about 840 total chambers. Consequently, *Acrochordus* possesses the most extensive vascular respiratory system of all snakes (Bergman, 1958a; McDowell, 1979; Shine and Houston, 1993).

The tracheae of unicameral and paucicameral lungs are essentially identical to those of snakes lacking a tracheal lung and having the outer wall of the lung formed by the membrane. However, multicameral lungs vary in the number, size, and position of the tracheal foramina. The number of chambers and corresponding foramina in avascular multicameral tracheal organs varies from 1 (*Elaphe hodgsonii*) to 41 (*Ophiophagus hannah*) (Plate 2.2A; Beddard, 1903; Thompson, 1914b; Brongersma, 1957a; Underwood, 1967; Young, 1992). Vascularized multicameral tracheal lungs of the Typhlopoidea exhibit from 11 (*Ramphotyphlops becki*) to 80 (*Acutotyphlops infralabialis*) total foramina and of the Acrochordidae from 200 (*Acrochordus arafurae*) to 840 (*A. granulatus*) total foramina. However, most species have 20–40 foramina and an equivalent number of chambers in their tracheal lungs (see Appendix C).

The tracheal lung is hypothesized to be a derived condition in snakes (Cope, 1894b) and also a primitive feature that has sometimes been lost (Beddard, 1906b; Underwood, 1967). Both ideas are likely valid as the tracheal lung probably arose quite early in snake history, evolved variously in different phyletic lines, and has been lost in certain groups. One hypothesis suggests that the tracheal lung originated from the fusion of the trachea with the anterior lobe of the right lung (Rietschel, 1968), leading to the transition from a subterminal to terminal tracheal entry; the enormous anterior lobe of *Heterodon* may represent an intermediate stage in such a transition and could be a precursor of the tracheal lung of the viperids. Another hypothesis suggests arid zone viperids lost the tracheal lung as it involved an undesirable source of water loss during respiration (Groombridge, 1980). Avascular tracheal chambers may function as a (1) cranial air reservoir like the saccular lung, useful during digestion of prey, (2) accessory site of gas exchange, (3) cranial buoyancy enhancer, (4) device for inflation of neck as a defensive display, or (5) device for acoustical amplification of the hiss (Young, 1991, 1992). Possible origins of parenchymal chambers include: (1) a simplified, vascularized multicameral lung, (2) a partitioned, expanded tracheal membrane, and (3) de novo structures (Young, 1992). Because multicameral lungs are primitive for reptiles and snakes (Perry, this volume), it is likely that the avascular tracheal lung is not a de novo structure but rather a simplification or degeneration of a vascularized structure present in ancestral forms.

Hypotheses that have attempted to explain the origin of tracheal lungs in snakes include: (1) need for increased buoyancy as a hydrostatic organ (Schlegel, 1837b; Cope, 1894b, 1895b; Thompson, 1913b), (2) compensation for respiration needed during deglutition and digestion after filling of the stomach with a large prey item and compression of the right lung (Bumpus, 1888; Cope, 1894b, 1895b; J. C. George and Varde, 1941; Bellairs and Underwood, 1951; Kardong, 1972a; Heatwole and Seymour, 1975b), (3) inflation of the anterior part of the body in a defensive display (Cope, 1894b, 1895b; Noble, 1921), (4) flexibility of the trachea during the constriction and swallowing of large prey items (Thompson, 1913b; Werner, 1911), (5) replacement for the missing left lung and saccularized right lung in vipers (Werner, 1911), (6) increase of the respiratory surface area permitting aquatic snakes to remain submerged (Thompson, 1913b), (7) crowding of the right lung by an enlarged liver due to acquisition of venom (Thompson, 1913b), (8) crowding due to retention of embryos (Varde, 1951), (9) evolution of organs with functional safety margins, useful under times of stress but unnecessary under normal conditions (Bellairs, 1969), (10) compensation for poor ventilation in the caudal region of the lung (Stinner, 1980), and (11) requirement for an anterior respiratory organ for more efficient ventilation when underground and with limited ventilatory body movements (V. Wallach, pers. obs.).

Some of the above hypotheses may explain the development of the tracheal lung in certain taxa, but none have good evidence to support them. The origin of the tracheal lung remains a mystery. Consider the following comments on the above hypotheses. (1) The tracheal lung serves as a hydrostatic organ in swimming vipers such as *Agkistrodon* and *Crotalus*, which swim with the anterior third or half of the body floating high on the water. (2) This hypothesis is weak and fails to explain away the large number of snakes lacking a tracheal lung that eat large prey items and have their right lungs compressed. (3) Undoubtedly a tracheal lung allows a snake to inflate its forebody, yet many snakes can inflate their necks with a much simpler tracheal membrane. (4) A weak hypothesis with no visible support. (5) This hypothesis also seems implausible. (6) At least in marine snakes (Acrochordidae, marine Hydrophiidae, Homalopsinae, etc.), this seems to be partly true, although the extended right lung probably also plays a role equal to the tracheal lung in the ability to remain submerged. (7) The enlargement of the liver has possibly played a role in the development of the tracheal lung. (8) This seems unlikely as developing embryos compress, at most, only the terminal right or saccular lung. (9) Mother Nature's safety valve? The evolutionary cost of developing such an organ, without selective pressure to do so, seems uneconomical. (10) A weak argument since the caudal region of most snake lungs is actually an enlargement over the primitively short lung. (11) It appears to me that the tracheal lung in the Scolecophidia developed in response to a need for an efficient method of ventilation when the quantity and oxygenation of environmental air was limited (as when underground).

F. Cardiac Lung

Most snakes possessing a tracheal lung tend to have a discontinuity or pulmonary constriction between the caudal portion of the tracheal lung and the cranial portion of the right lung (Wallach, 1993b). The two organs are generally clearly distinct as the lung is greatly reduced in diameter in the cardiac region, occasionally only the trachea connecting the two lungs (i.e., *Acrochordus*). That portion of the lung between the caudal end of the tracheal lung (i.e., anterior edge of heart) and the cranial end of the right lung (i.e., posterior tip of heart) is termed the cardiac lung. It is always less than half (usually 0.20–0.25) the diameter of the visceral cavity (i.e., *Typhlops reticulatus, fide* Meckel, 1818; *Laticauda colubrina, fide* Seymour, 1978). As the diameter of the tracheal lung is usually 0.7–1.0 that of the nuchal cavity, the cardiac lung is not comparable to the tracheal lung in ventilatory power per unit length. The cardiac lung typically exhibits reduced parenchyma along the membrane (Plate 2.1F), sometimes to a single layer of faveoli as in *Cerberus rynchops* (Ramsay, 1979), more often of the type present in the tracheal lung rather than the right lung. In *Boiga ceylonensis*, parenchyma extends only adjacent to the heart, although the tracheal membrane is itself expanded, and cranially directed branches from the pulmonary artery are lacking (Werner, 1911).

The cardiac lung represents an important morphological structure, but its length does not exhibit much variation because it is, by definition, equal to that of the heart (3–5%). However, as the presence of a pulmonary blood supply to the tracheal membrane or incipient tracheal lung has not yet been verified for many species, the length of parenchymal tissue along the tracheal membrane is listed with that of the cardiac lung in Appendix C rather than under the tracheal lung. The length of parenchyma craniad of the heart can be deduced by subtracting 3–5% from the cardiac figure.

The cardiac lung is unicameral in alethinophidians, but in scolecophidians, it may also be paucicameral or multicameral. As a discrete pulmonary structure, it is significant in typhlopoid systematics. The number of foramina range from two (*Rhinotyphlops pallidus*) to 15

(*R. praeocularis*) in the cardiac lung. The cardiac lung in *Acrochordus granulatus*, which was first described by Stannius (1856) as a narrowing of the lung to cartilaginous rings lacking vascular tissue over the heart, has since been analyzed by Bergman (1958a). Unpublished data of R. A. M. Bergman (pers. comm. to H. MacDonald) show the relative length of the cardiac lung in *Cerberus rynchops* to range from 2.6–7.6%, and in *A. granulatus* to range 1.2–4.7% in males, and 0.9–4.2% in females.

G. Thoraconuchal Lung

Relatively few snakes possess a tracheal lung that is indistinguishable from the right lung. These snakes lack a discernible cardiac lung and a constriction or tapering of the lung in the cardiac region, and the parenchyma is uniform throughout (Fig. 2.1). This single, continuous tube may be referred to as a thoraconuchal lung. Usually most of the parenchyma lies craniad of the heart, and that portion corresponding to the right lung is mostly avascular. Three of the taxa in the lung classification of Antipchuk (1966b) were considered to possess a thoraconuchal lung (marine Hydrophiidae, Viperinae, and Crotalinae). However, certain representatives of each of those groups exhibit a cardiac constriction, so the diagnosis is not true for all members. The thoraconuchal lung appears to be the most derived type of unicameral lung and is found mainly in the Viperidae, marine Hydrophiidae, and some colubrids (i.e., *Dipsas*).

IV. RIGHT LUNG COMPLEX
A. General

All snakes have a right lung, located dorsal to the liver and lateral to the stomach on the right side of the visceral cavity, usually long and extending caudad of the gall bladder; sometimes it is the only lung present (Blumenbach, 1805; Cuvier, 1805). Numerous early researchers confused the identity of the left and right lungs (W. B. Carpenter, 1854; Brehm, 1878; Cope, 1894a–1900; Gadow, 1901–1923; Atwood, 1916; Kingsley, 1917, 1926), believing the vestigial organ to be the right. However, whenever a left lung is present, it is always reduced in size in comparison with the right (Butler, 1895).

The typical serpentine right lung (and the left lung in the Booidea) is divisible into two major structural and functional regions, a cranial portion that is thick-walled, highly vascularized and respiratory in nature and a caudal portion that is thin-walled, transparent, avascular and nonrespiratory (Blasius, 1674; Valentini, 1720; Tyson, 1683; Westphal, 1806). Previous authors have commented that it is impossible to determine objectively the precise demarcation between the vascular and saccular regions because the former gradually diminishes and eventually disappears into the latter (Werner, 1911; Bergman, 1950; Karlstrom,

1952; Klauber, 1956; Ramsay, 1979). This is perhaps one reason why the study of snake lungs has not been popular. The two clearly defined regions are separated by a transitional zone of varying magnitude in which the parenchyma gradually (or sometimes abruptly) becomes less concentrated, and the faveoli exhibit larger diameters, lower and thinner walls, and fewer horizontal tiers. About three-fourths of the blood in *Morelia spilota* perfuses the cranial half of the vascularized region of the lung (Read and Donnelly, 1972). This great disparity in the parenchyma of the anterior and posterior regions of the vascular lung allows division of the typical snake lung into three regions: the cranial densely vascularized portion (DVP or vascular lung), the caudal avascular portion (SAC or saccular lung), and the intermediate, sparsely vascularized portion (SVP or semisaccular lung).

Length of the right lung varies from 8% (*Ramphotyphlops*) to 82% (*Dasypeltis*), most species having values from 25–60% (see Appendix C). Among most of the Booidea, the right lung measures 30–45%. The Philothamnini possess the longest right lungs, averaging 70%, whereas the Anomalepididae possess the shortest, averaging 15%. Among atractaspids, the right lung length varies from 35–55% with little sexual dimorphism (only four out of 23 species) and moderate to high intraspecific variation (CV = 3–18). The midpoint of the right lung, a more stable character with CVs ranging from 1–10 (mean = 4), is sexually dimorphic in nine of 32 species (*Amblyodipsas* and *Aparallactus*) and generally occurs at 45–50% (Wallach, 1991, 1994a). The midpoint of the right lung is sexually dimorphic in *Acutotyphlops kunuaensis* but not in *Rhinotyphlops schlegelii* or *Typhlops lumbricalis* (Wong, 1994). The length of the right lung displays no significant difference between the sexes and is very short, 16.7% in *A. kunuaensis*, 17.2% in *T. lumbricalis*, and 21.1% in *R. schlegelii*. The midpoint of the right lung is much more stable than its length as evidenced by the mean CV values for *Acutotyphlops*, *Rhinotyphlops*, and *Typhlops*, respectively, for the midpoint (4.7, 6.6, 3.6) and length (15.3, 10.4, 15.1).

In all snakes except some typhlopids, the right lung is unicameral and generally composed of three longitudinally differentiated sections, a highly vascular thick-walled cranial portion and a thin-walled avascular caudal portion, separated from one another by an intermediate transition zone (Fig. 2.7). The ancestral length of the right lung appears to be about 25%, as observed in *Anilius* and other primitive taxa. Fossorial species generally have a right lung that is relatively short and reduced to 10–25%, whereas it is somewhat longer (30–40%) in the Booidea. A sample of 25 *Charina bottae* and 23 *Lichanura roseofusca* has a mean right lung length of 38% VS (Kaban, 1978). The longest organs are found in the Caenophidia with values of 50–80%.

B. Tracheal Entry and Anterior Lobe

The trachea may enter the right lung in several ways. In the primitive condition, known as the subterminal (S) entry (Thompson, 1913a), the trachea enters the mesial side of the right lung ventrad and caudad of its anterior tip; a small cranial apex or lobe projects freely laterad of the trachea (Fig. 2.8). The lumen of this free apex or lobe comunicates with that of the right lung by way of an orifice. The orifice may be very large, as wide as the lung at that point, or the approximate size of a single faveolus; normally, its diameter is equivalent to the width of 4–6 faveoli. The dimension of the lumen varies with the size of the orifice. In snakes with a relatively large left lung, the left bronchus enters the left lung subterminally in a manner similar to the entry into the right (Fig. 2.23).

The anterior lobe is measured from its cranial tip to the internal orifice, this length ranging from 0.1% (*Aparallactus* and *Drymobius*) to 17% (*Heterodon*; Plate 2.1D); in most snakes it is less than 2% (see Appendix C). Interestingly, the length of the anterior lobe is often equal to the length of the left bronchus and also of the right or intrapulmonary bronchus. *Heterodon* is the only genus having a hypertrophied (12–17%), vascularized anterior lobe that fills the nuchal cavity and extends to the gular region (Lereboullet, 1838). The cranial end of the anterior lobe of *H. platyrhinos* is anchored by a mesentery. Upon first glance, the anterior lobe appears to be a tracheal lung, however, it originates from the right lung and lacks direct communication with the trachea (Plate 2.2B; Lereboullet, 1838; Cuvier, 1840; Cope, 1894b). This structure might be a precursor of the unicameral tracheal lung of the Viperidae.

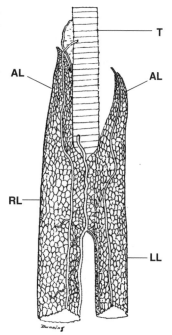

The anterior lobe typically is vascularized to the same extent as the cranial portion of the vascular lung (Fig. 2.8). Occasionally, in some individuals of a species, the anterior lobe is avascular, as in some aberrant Colubridae (*Dasypeltis atra*, *Elaphe erythrura*, *Mehelya crossii*, *M. poensis*, *Gonionotophis klingi*, *Ficimia publia*, *Polemon gabonensis*, Dispholidini),

Fig. 2.23. *Xenopeltis unicolor*. Ventral view of the cranial portion of left lung (LL) and right lung (RL) depicting mesial lung attachment, subterminal entry of tracheal (T), and anterior lobes (AL). (Adapted from Thompson, 1913a.)

Elapidae (*Dendroaspis polylepis, Naja melanoleuca, N. mossambica, Paranaja multifasciata, Pseudohaje goldii*), and Viperidae (*Crotalus horridus, C. molossus, C. tigris, Deinagkistrodon acutus, Lachesis muta, Sistrurus catenatus*). In one *Dendroaspis jamesoni*, the cranial half of the anterior lobe is saccular, and the caudal half vascular. Occasionally, two orifices and lumina lie in a single lobe (*Drymoluber brazili, Ficimia streckeri, Fordonia leucobalia, Leptodrymus pulcherrimus, Liopholidophis lateralis, Polemon fulvicollis, P. notatus, Pseustes sulphureus, Toluca conica, Xenocalamus bicolor*). Rarely there are two anterior lobes, each with a separate orifice and lumen, at the cranial end of the lung (*Dasypeltis fasciata, Grayia tholloni, Philothamnus occidentalis, Salvadora intermedia, Senticolis triaspis, Sibynophis sagittarius, Demansia psammophis, Naja melanoleuca, Pseudohaje goldii*); one atypical *Polemon neuwiedi* has a paraterminal entry and two lobes, but no orifices.

The most derived condition of tracheal entry is terminal (T) (Underwood, 1967, 1976b). This condition occurs whenever the trachea enters the most cranial portion of the right lung (Fig. 2.22); by definition an anterior lobe is absent. Although many snakes lacking a tracheal lung exhibit a terminal tracheal entry, this type is also characteristic of most species possessing an extensive tracheal lung.

Several states intermediate between subterminal and terminal are also recognizable. They are grouped together under the heading of paraterminal (P) tracheal entry (see Appendix C). Paraterminal tracheal entry involves either: (1) the absence of a lumen of the anterior lobe (i.e., it being completely filled with parenchyma) with the lobe free externally from attachment to the lung or trachea (i.e., *Lycodon muelleri*), or (2) fusion of the lobe to the trachea or lung with internal persistence of the orifice and lumen of the lobe (i.e., *Coluber ventromaculatus, Leptodeira annulata, Leptophis mexicanus, Opisthotropis andersoni, Philothamnus heterolepidotus, Atractaspis irregularis, Hypnale hypnale*). The paraterminal condition, which appears to represent a stage in the transition from subterminal to terminal entry, is found only rarely or occasionally in many different groups. A few examples should suffice to illustrate the transitory nature of paraterminal entry. In *Oligodon chinensis* (MCZ 28825), the anterior lobe is fused to the trachea along its caudal edge. This intermediate condition is 50% S (cranially) and 50% P (caudally). In *Dryocalamus nympha* (MCZ 18384), the caudal 75% of the anterior lobe is fused with only the cranial tip free. In *Lycodon travancoricus* (MCZ 47887), fusion is nearly complete, and only the apical tip (about 10%) is free; although this lung is technically subterminal, it is essentially paraterminal. The above three cases display an internal orifice leading to a lumen that inflates under pressure. In two female *Coluber ventromaculatus* from Pakistan, one specimen (SDSNH 63287) exhibits subterminal entry with a diminutive anterior lobe shorter than 0.2%, whereas the other specimen (SDSNH 63288) has complete fusion of the lobe (with its open lumen) to the lung, so that the condition is paraterminal. In most species, a large series will reveal that most individuals have exclusively one condition or the other (S or T). However, a few species are quite variable and exhibit equal percentages of two or more conditions (see Appendix C).

C. Right Bronchus

By definition, the trachea becomes a bronchus upon entrance into the right lung. Technically, however, the trachea terminates and the right bronchus commences at the left orifice in those snakes possessing a left lung (Plate 2.1A). As perhaps half of all species of snakes lack a left orifice, it is difficult to determine the actual point of division between the trachea and bronchus. The matter is complicated even further as the position of the left orifice varies both intraspecifically and interspecifically with respect to the ventricular apex of the heart. However, the left orifice always occurs at the level of, or within 1–2 mm of, the posterior tip of the heart (Brongersma, 1957c). Personal examination of hundreds of specimens from many different taxa supports this conclusion: occasionally the left orifice occurs at the cardiac apex; more often it lies just craniad or less than 0.5% SVL (snout-to-vent length) caudad thereof. Thus, comparison among snakes is facilitated by using the level of the tip of the heart to represent the division between the trachea and bronchus. Although most snakes possess at least a very short right bronchus (see Appendix C), in certain snakes lacking a left lung, there is no bronchus whenever the trachea terminates anterior to the ventricular apex of the heart (i.e., *Bitis arietans*). The length of the right bronchus varies interspecifically, ranging from 0.1% (*Salomonelaps par*) to 54% (*Rhinocheilus lecontei*); in most species it is short, i.e. less than 5% (see Appendix C).

Only in some members of the Booidea is the trachea of snakes divided into bronchi (Rees, 1820; Fleming, 1822; Lereboullet, 1838; Cuvier, 1840). No external bronchi appear, as the separate bronchi are embedded in the mesial walls of the right and left lungs (Fig. 2.23). Only one specimen (of *Python molurus*) had a Y-shaped bifurcation of the trachea into two external bronchi, the left bronchus 0.5% with 4 rings, the right bronchus 0.7% with 10 rings; this specimen was unusual in that the trachea also lay lateral to the heart on the left side instead of middorsally and may represent a more primitive stage in the transition from the Anilioidea to the Booidea. Normally in the Booidea, the trachea continues directly into the right lung as the intrapulmonary bronchus, and the left bronchus splits off to the left lung at an angle of 30–60°.

The continuation of cartilaginous rings or bronchial cartilages into the right lung caudad of the heart tip forms the right bronchus, which may be either intrapulmonary (IPB) (Beddard, 1908; J. C. George and Shah, 1956; Underwood, 1976b) or extrapulmonary (EPB). An intrapulmonary route, embedded in the lung parenchyma and not visible externally, is the most common; in the Scolecophidia and some other snakes, the bronchus is extrapulmonary. Like the trachea, the right bronchus exhibits various degrees of development and cross-sectional shape, including everything from a trachea-like circular configuration with interdigitating free tips (i.e., Lampropeltini), to a series of small flat cartilages joined by connective tissue and embedded in the lung parenchyma in a linear series (i.e., Booidea). Most commonly the bronchus flattens out into a broad shallow trough caudad of the left orifice or heart (Fig. 2.24; Milne-Edwards, 1857b; Karlstrom, 1952). Some species have a fibrous "seam" continuing caudally from the termination of the bronchus (Retzius, 1830; Beddard, 1908; Kang et al., 1986); this "seam" is believed to be a vestigial remnant of a previous bronchus (Beddard, 1906b). The Booidea usually have several complete rings forming a tube through the mesial lung wall, followed by a flat bronchus of several of cartilages along the inner wall of the lung. In most snakes, the right bronchus is positioned sinistrolaterally along the medial wall of the lung, but in forms with a tracheal lung it may lie midventrally.

Normally, a moderate bronchus terminates around the level of the transition from the vascularized lung to the saccular lung (Fig. 2.2), often at the level of the anterior end of the liver, but a long bronchus may continue into the saccular lung (e.g., *Bitis arietans*, Lereboullet, 1838) or even to the posterior tip of the lung (e.g., *Leptotyphlops*, *Typhlops*, and *Tropidophis*). The bronchus extends nearly the length of the right lung in *Arizona* (Karlstrom, 1952); in *Elaphe guttata*, it extends the entire

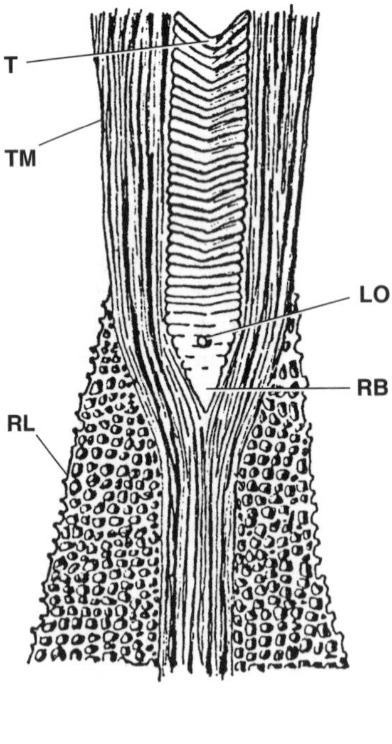

Fig. 2.24. *Naja naja*. Internal view of the trachea (T) with V-shaped cartilages, tracheal membrane (TM) with longitudinal rugosities, and right lung (RL) showing left orifice (LO) and short right bronchus (RB). (Adapted from Wolf, 1933.)

length of the saccular lung (Brongersma, 1957b). Relative length of the bronchus is determined by the ratio of right bronchus/right lung (RB/RL), ranging from 0.1% (*Boiga* and *Philothamnus*) to 100% (*Leptotyphlops*), with most species having values less than 10% (see Appendix C). In the primitive condition, as represented by the Anilioidea and most Booidea, the bronchus is short (RB/RL < 0.5%) and consists of only a few flat cartilages connected by fibrous connective tissue. A bronchus of moderate length (RB/RL = 10–50%), representing a more derived condition, is found in some Erycinae, Tropidophiidae, Viperidae, and marine Hydrophiidae. Here the cartilages may be connected in the form of a grooved seam or longitudinal band, or semicircular rings may form a nearly closed bronchus. In the most derived state, the bronchus is long (RB/RL > 50%), circular in cross-section, and forms a closed tube with interdigitating free tips. Many Scolecophidia and Lampropeltini have a long right bronchus. The number of rings and cartilages varies widely and is related to the length of the bronchus; *Elaphe guttata* has 296 bronchial cartilages compared with 65 in *E. obsoleta* and 13 in *E. scalaris* (Brongersma, 1957b). The intrapulmonary bronchus within the Lampropeltini is long, varying from 5–7% in *E. flavirufa* to 41–55% in *Rhinocheilus lecontei*, and all lampropeltine genera except *Elaphe* and *Pituophis* have mean lengths greater than 35% SVL (Keogh, 1993). Relative length of the IPB in this group is moderately variable with the CV ranging from 3–14 (mean = 9%). The midpoint of the IPB is more stable with CV ranging from 2–8 (mean = 6%) (Keogh, 1993).

Termination of the bronchus is either abrupt, with the last bronchial cartilage similar in size to the preceding ones, or gradual, with the width of the cartilages tapering to a terminal point (Plate 2.1A). In the latter case, the last three or four cartilages usually fuse with irregular branches. As mentioned above, a rudimentary elastic seam or narrow fibrous band that lacks cartilaginous elements may continue beyond this point (Beddard, 1906b).

D. Vascular Lung

The vascular lung (DVP or dense vascular portion) is defined as the region extending from the cranial tip of the right lung (or posterior tip of the heart) to a point along the middorsal surface of the lung at which the size of the faveoli first changes noticeably. This point is characterized by a reduction in: (1) the thickness of the septal walls, (2) the number of faveoli per unit area, and (3) the number of tiers of parenchyma, with the transition from faveoli to ediculae or trabeculae. In *Morelia spilota*, the vascular lung occupies only 8% of the total lung volume (Donnelly and Woolcock, 1977).

Within the Lampropeltini, the length of the dense vascular lung is typically 8–14% with means between 9–13% and CV = 6–15. The midpoint of the dense vascular lung ranges from 23–33% with means between 26–31% and low variability (CV = 2–7). The position of the posterior edge of the DVP is also stable (CV = 1–6) with mean values between 31–37% (range = 29–40%) (Keogh, 1993). In *Pseudechis porphyriacus*, the relative length of the vascular lung, which is 40 times the thickness of the saccular lung, is constant in embryos, juveniles, and adults at 15–16% SVL, although the length of the saccular lung increases proportionately with age and size (Rosenzweig, 1981). In *Boa constrictor*, the right lung is oval in cross-section. It has a horizontal diameter of 35 mm, a vertical diameter of 20 mm, and a lung wall thickness of 5 mm (Kang et al., 1986).

The faviform parenchyma of *Nerodia taxispilota* and *Thamnophis sirtalis* has primary septa that are 1.5–2.0 mm deep and have maximum diameters of 1.0 mm, whereas the secondary septa are 0.5–1.0 mm deep (Karlstrom, 1952). In *Aplopeltura boa*, the luminal openings of the parenchyma range in diameter from 0.5 mm cranially to 4.0 mm caudally (Werner, 1911). The maximal thickness of the lung wall theoretically is 4.0 mm and affects the diffusion of gases into the parenchyma (Duncker, 1978c). The right lung wall of *Python sebae* (Lataste and Blanchard, 1879) and *Boa constrictor* (Kang et al., 1986) is claimed to be 5.0 mm thick; however, the maximum thickness of lung walls that I have observed is 3.5–4.0 mm.

A characteristic pattern in the Acrochordidae, Homalopsinae, marine Hydrophiidae, and several mainly aquatic genera (i.e., *Eunectes, Amphiesma, Nerodia, Xenochrophis*) is the presence of smooth muscle knobs at the junctions of all first-order trabeculae throughout the vascular lung; these spherical knobs are about twice the diameter of the trabeculae. They presumably have a ventilatory function when the snake is submerged (during apnea).

In most snakes, the entire inner circumference of the right lung is lined with parenchyma. As first noted in *Naja naja* (Meckel, 1818) and *Hemachatus haemachatus* (Lereboullet, 1838), some Colubridae (i.e., *Boiga, Chrysopelea, Dispholidus, Drymarchon, Dryophiops, Ptyas, Rhamnophis, Stegonotus, Thelotornis, Thrasops, Tropidonophis*), Elapidae (*Boulengerina, Dendroaspis, Laticauda, Ophiophagus, Paranaja, Pseudohaje*), and Viperidae (*Bitis, Lachesis*) have an avascular midventral strip (AMS) in the vascular and semisaccular lung (Thompson, 1913c; J. C. George and Shah, 1956; Malnate and Underwood, 1988). Although a feature of terrestrial snakes (J. C. George and Shah, 1956), the strip occurs also in arboreal forms but not in aquatic or fossorial species. In *Drymarchon corais*, this surface is serous and lined by ciliated columnar epithelium (Gillian and

Conklin, 1938). The relative width of the strip may be noted by dividing the width the lung diameter (AMS/LD). Reports of the AMS/LD ratio in snakes include 0.25 in *Naja naja* (Meckel, 1818) and 0.50 in *Chrysopelea ornata* (Thompson, 1913c), with values for this index ranging from 0.25 (*Boulengerina christyi*) to 0.67 (*Stegonotus muelleri*) to 1.0 (Dispholidini, *Lachesis muta*).

The right lung of all snakes is, at least in part, unicameral caudally. Within the Typhlopidae and Anomalepididae, the cranial portion of the right lung may be multicameral or paucicameral and have from one to 21 foramina and air chambers or niches. A multicameral right lung occurs in some West Indian *Typhlops*, most African *Rhinotyphlops*, and all Solomon Island *Acutotyphlops*.

The ultrastructure of the respiratory epithelium has been examined in *Python molurus* and *Boa constrictor* (Kang et al., 1986), *Dendroaspis polylepis* (Maina, 1989), *Hydrophis cyanocinctus* (Liu and Chen, 1983), *Elaphe obsoleta* (Brooks, 1970), *E. quadrivirgata* (Nagaishi et al., 1964), *E. scalaris* and *Natrix maura* (Castells et al., 1985), *Thamnophis sirtalis* (Pohunková and Hughes, 1985), and *Crotalus viridis* (Luchtel and Kardong, 1981). The minimal thickness of the air-blood barrier is 0.25 μm in *Coronella austriaca* (Meban, 1980), 0.1 μm in *Elaphe climacophora* and *E. quadrivirgata* (Okada et al., 1962), 0.2 μm in *Natrix natrix* (Meban, 1980), 0.45 μm in *Pituophis catenifer* (Stinner, 1982b), 0.55 μm in *Dendroaspis polylepis* (Maina, 1989), and 0.4–0.6 μm in *Crotalus viridis* (Luchtel and Kardong, 1981).

E. Semisaccular Lung

A semisaccular lung (SVP or sparse vascular portion) was first described in *Anilius scytale* as the middle third of the lung in which the cells suddenly become wider and shallower until finally disappearing (Meckel, 1818). It is defined as continuing from the posterior edge of the vascular lung to the point along the middorsal line at which the last ediculae or trabeculae are visible. Sometimes the lateral walls of the lung have ediculae or trabeculae extending obliquely caudad (or rarely craniad) from that point (Fig. 2.7), but the line of demarcation is often perpendicular to the body axis (Plate 2.2C). Typically, the right bronchus and branches of the pulmonary vessels terminate at the caudal edge of the semisaccular lung (Karlstrom, 1952). The length of this transition zone in relation to the vascular lung, defined as SVP/DVP, is variable and may range from 0.05 (*Boiga cyanea*) to more than 3.0 (*Boa constrictor*), although it averages from 0.25–0.33 in most snakes (Twerenbold, 1987: fig. 6). In *Xenochrophis vittatus* the transition zone covers 5–10 mm or 1–2% (Bergman, 1950). Only rarely is the transition from the vascular lung to the saccular lung abrupt, as first reported in *Gonyosoma oxycephalum* (Thompson, 1914b) but also known in *Naja atra* (Mao, 1993) and other arboreal colubrids such as *Boiga, Dendrelaphis,* and *Philothamnus* (V. Wallach, pers. obs.). In *Eunectes murinus,* the semisaccular lung section comprises 10% of the lung's length (SVP/DVP = 0.22; Phleger et al., 1978), with the cranial 45% vascular and caudal 45% saccular.

F. Saccular Lung

The distal portion of the right lung of most snakes is termed the saccular lung (Fig. 2.8). It was early recognized as a distinct entity, the "posterior vesicam oblongam" (Valentini, 1720). The saccular lung is generally mesentery-like with a thin, transparent or translucent wall, making it difficult to recognize (Thompson, 1913c). It has even been claimed that the right lung "has no abrupt termination, but becomes constantly less and less vascular until it merges into the connective tissues of the body cavity" Atwood (1916). Examination of the visceral topography of large series of many different Indonesian snake species by Bergman did not permit him to determine the termination of the saccular lung except in species such as *Xenopeltis unicolor* or *Cerberus rynchops,* where the lung is thick and vascularized to its tip (Bergman, 1955b, 1955c). Inflation of an undamaged lung with a pipette reveals the contours and tip of the lung (Kellicott, 1898). An example of the thinness of the saccular lung is an ectopic pregnancy in *Corallus annulatus* in which a perforation in the saccular lung had allowed entry to a 300 mm fetus (Griner, 1983). Also, an emaciated 587 mm SVL *Philothamnus angolensis* (UF 52485), collected in Zaire on 20 October 1979, contained five large eggs (28–30 × 10–12 mm) in the oral and gular portions of the trachea (one pair side by side), blocking the esophagus and obviously preventing the animal from feeding. Apparently, these entered the respiratory system through the saccular lung and somehow worked their way forward to the buccal region.

Typically, the saccular lung represents most of the right lung (75–90%), but in some species, particularly those with a well-developed tracheal lung, the entire right lung may be atrabecular. In other snakes, it may be entirely vascular. A saccular lung, when present, exhibits considerable interspecific variation; its length ranges from 3% (*Uropeltis* and *Laticauda semifasciata*) to 74% (*Dasypeltis*) with most species having a length of 30–60% (see Appendix C). Certain species with an extensive tracheal lung (i.e., *Crotalus, Enhydris, Lycophidion, Xylophis*) show an entirely atrabecular right lung with the parenchyma terminating in the cardiac region. The length of the saccular lung in atractaspidid snakes is highly variable interspecifically, ranging from 20–50%; in a few species, its CV ranges from 3–5, but for most species it ranges from 10–20 (Wallach, 1991, 1994a). Sexual dimorphism is rare, but females of three species of *Amblyodipsas* (*katangensis, polylepis, ventrimaculata*) and *Atractaspis corpulenta* have significantly shorter saccular lungs than do males. However, the position of the posterior tip is more stable and shows a CV of 1–8 for most species, with a mean near 4. The position of the lung tip is sexually dimorphic in eight of 33 aparallactine or atractaspidid species (3 *Ambylodipsas*, 3 *Aparallactus*, 1 *Atractaspis*, 1 *Xenocalamus*). In all cases, the male value is larger than that of the female. The lung tip ranges from 55–85% in most species, averaging about 65–70% (Wallach, 1991).

In some species, the saccular lung contains a network of smooth muscle ridges, but the few blood vessels located beneath the smooth muscle bundles are not in contact with the chambers (Grant et al., 1981). The saccular lung of *Natrix natrix* contains circular bands of muscle, 0.08 mm in diameter (Eberth, 1863); these bands are better developed in *Nerodia* than they are in *Thamnophis* (Karlstrom, 1952). The saccular lung of *Elaphe obsoleta* and *Nerodia rhombifer* is composed primarily of connective tissue and a muscle layer containing smooth muscle cells is interspersed with connective tissue (Baeyens et al., 1978). In *T. sirtalis*, the wall of the saccular lung contains no smooth muscle, and its connective tissue is reduced in comparison with that of the vascular lung. Capillaries are absent below the epithelium, and only a few larger branches of the blood vessels occur in the thin layer of connective tissue (Pohunková and Hughes, 1985). In *Pseudechis porphyriacus*, an Australian elapid basal to the hydrophiid radiation, the saccular lung is composed of smooth muscle fibers lined internally with ciliated columnar epithelium; the thickness of the entire lung wall is only 2.5% that of the vascular lung (Rosenzweig, 1981).

Most of the Scolecophidia and Henophidia, plus certain aquatic Colubroidea (e.g., Homalopsinae), lack a true saccular lung and have instead a trabecular network extending to the caudal tip (Plate 2.2D; Meckel 1818; Thompson, 1914b; H. Marcus, 1937; Bergman, 1960; Guibé, 1970b). In the Acrochordidae and many marine Hydrophiidae, the parenchyma of the right lung continues evenly to the caudal tip, and the pulmonary artery and vein serve the entire region (Donald and Lillywhite, 1989b; V. Wallach, pers. obs.). The lumen of the caudal lung in marine hydrophiids is lined with ciliated epithelium, which overlies a continuous layer of muscle (Varde, 1951). In *Acrochordus* and the marine Hydrophiidae, the right pulmonary artery sends branches along the entire length of the right lung (Kashyap and Sohoni, 1973; Ramsay, 1979). Among 12 species of seven genera of marine Hydrophiidae, the vascularized lung, consisting of the tracheal lung and right lung, comprises 80–100% of the total lung volume, and the saccular lung consists of 0–20% (Heatwole and Seymour, 1975b). The caudal lung has a thickened elastic wall of circularly arranged smooth muscle fibers or "ribs" in hydrophiids such as *Pelamis platurus* (Plate 2.2E; also in *Acrochordus* and *Laticauda*). These muscles may circulate air throughout the lung while the snake is submerged; preserved specimens often have this region constricted sufficiently to occlude the lumen (Beddard, 1904b; Volsøe, 1939). Also, as a snake dives, the lung collapses regionally, starting at the posterior end and progressing anteriorly (Seymour, 1978). The caudal portion of the right lung rarely shows heavy investment of smooth muscle except in marine snakes, the lung wall of which appears thick, opaque, and elastic (Fig. 2.25). A thickened, opaque distal right lung also occurs in some colubrid genera such as *Hydromorphus*, *Hydrodynastes*, *Rhabdops*, and *Trachischium*. Both *Hydrodynastes bicinctus* and *H. gigas* even contain grossly observable circular ridges of smooth muscle that overlie the caudal end of the right lung. This synapomorphy separates *Hydrodynastes* from other Xenodontinae and suggests that the muscularized region may constrict to circulate air from the caudal dead space into the more cranial vascular region.

The position of the posterior tip of the right lung is a good systematic character, exhibiting high interspecific variation yet with low intraspecific variation. The position of the lung tip varies from 34% (*Leptotyphlops*) to 100% (*Acrochordus*, most Hydrophiidae, and most arboreal Colubridae), although in most species the average is between 50–90% (see Appendix C). Ancestrally, the right lung appears to have terminated near the level of the gall bladder and pylorus near midbody. Among the Scolecophidia the right lung is reduced, and its posterior tip is generally located between 40–50%. The convoluted and multisegmented liver of this group completely surrounds the right lung. Many species show a 180° reversal of the distalmost 1–5% of the right lung, this being adpressed to the more anterior portion of the lung and pointed cranially. In some specimens, the distal portion of the lung is folded several times in a zigzag manner. An extreme example, with the lung tip nearly reaching the apex of the heart, was reported in *Typhlops reticulatus* (Brongersma, 1958a). Possibly

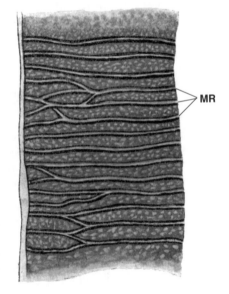

Fig. 2.25. *Pelamis platurus*. Inner surface of caudal right lung diagramming the transverse smooth muscle ridges (MR). (Adapted from Beddard, 1904b.)

this represents an artifact due to injection of preservative from the caudal region of the animal. In the Henophidia, the posterior tip of the lung generally lies at 55–75%. The right lung is best developed in the Caenophidia; its caudal tip may reach 90–95% in certain species, although the tip usually ranges from 70–85%. Early authors noted that the lung extends clear to the vent in arboreal species like *Dendrelaphis pictus* and *Leptophis ahaetulla* and marine forms such as *Acrochordus, Disteira major, Enhydrina schistosa,* and *Pelamis bicolor* (Plate 2.2E; Schlegel, 1837b; Lereboullet, 1838; Cuvier, 1840).

The position of the lung tip is sexually dimorphic in most species of snakes, with the tip more caudally placed in males than in females, as in the following taxa: Typhlopidae (Wong, 1994), *Cylindrophis ruffus* (Bergman, 1953), *Acrochordus javanicus* (Bergman, 1958a), *Cerberus rynchops* (Bergman, 1955b), *Enhydris alternans* and *E. plumbea* (Bergman, 1960), *Rhabdophis subminiatus* (Bergman, 1956), *Xenochrophis piscator* (Bergman, 1958b), Aparallactinae (Wallach, 1991), and *Bungarus candidus* and *Naja naja* (Bergman, 1962). A caudal ontogenetic shift in both sexes in the position of the posterior tip of the right lung is known in *C. ruffus* (Bergman, 1953). The length of the saccular lung increases proportionately with age and size in *Pseudechis porphyriacus* (Rosenzweig, 1981). Geographic variation in increasing lung length in *Thamnophis sirtalis* was noted in a north-south cline by Atwood (1918), who attributed it to different metabolic needs.

A peculiar feature of many saccular lungs is an abruptly tapered caudal portion (Table 2.5). Typically, the lung constricts to 10–20% of its cranial diameter and continues to its tip as a very slender "tail." This tail of the saccular lung, varying in length from 1% to 37% of the right lung, has been observed in the Typhlopidae, Leptotyphlopidae, Cylindrophiidae, Uropeltidae, Pythonidae, Boidae, Tropidophiidae, Viperidae, Atractaspididae, Elapidae, Hydrophiidae, and Colubridae. In those individuals possessing a pulmonary tail, the point of constriction occurs at or near the mean value of the lung tip's position for the entire sample, suggesting that the pulmonary tail may represent a stage in either the progressive lengthening or shortening of the lung. If lengthening, then the pulmonary tail is a precursor of the longer lung of descendant forms; if shortening, it represents a regression or ancestral remnant. The tip of the lung may or may not be attached to the coelomic wall by strands of connective tissue as in *Pseudechis porphyriacus* (Ramsay, 1979).

Recent physiological studies do not provide evidence for any significant gaseous exchange in the saccular lung (Read and Donnelly, 1972; Donnelly and Woolcock, 1977, 1978; Grant et al., 1979, 1981; Gratz et al., 1981; Stinner, 1982a). However, several genera of small-sized snakes

Table 2.5. Length of right lung tails in families (% SVL).

Typhlopidae		*C. japonicus*	37
Typhlops angolensis	1–5	*C. macclellandi*	8
Leptotyphlopidae		*Naja melanoleuca*	1–6
Leptotyphlops anthracinus	3	*Walterinnesia aegyptia*	6
L. macrolepis	3	Hydrophiidae	
Cylindrophiidae		*Cacophis harriettae*	4
Cylindrophis maculatus	7	*Demansia atra*	2
Uropeltidae		*D. torquata*	7
Rhinophis philippinus	3	*Denisonia devisii*	8
Pythonidae		*Drysdalia coronoides*	3
Aspidites melanocephalus	1	*Ephalophis greyi*	2
Python sebae	3	*Glyphodon barnardi*	3
Boidae		*Hoplocephalus bitorquatus*	9–14
Epicrates monensis	5	*H. bungaroides*	24
Tropidophiidae		*Pseudonaja textilis*	20–22
Tropidophis wrighti	6	*Rhinoplocephalus nigrostriatus*	4
Viperidae		*Simoselaps fasciolatus*	12
Atheris nitschei	10	*Vermicella annulata*	4–25
A. squamiger	6–8	Colubridae	
Atropoides nummifer	6	*Ahaetulla nasuta*	6
Azemiops feae	10	*Alsophis portoricensis*	9
Bitis peringueyi	4	*A. dorsalis*	10
Bothrops atrox	8	*Amphiesma beddomei*	9
Causus maculatus	5–18	*A. deschauenseei*	4
Crotalus atrox	3	*A. platyceps*	15
C. basiliscus	17	*Antillophis parvifrons*	8
C. horridus	4	*Aplopeltura boa*	1
Hypnale hypnale	4	*Atractus resplendens*	19
Protobothrops mucrosquamatus	7	*Bogertophis subocularis*	15
Tropidolaemus wagleri	3	*Calamaria bicolor*	3
Vipera ammodytes	7	*C. muelleri*	2
Atractaspididae		*C. virgulata*	2
Aparallactus lineatus	5	*Cercaspis carinatus*	11
A. lunulatus	3	*Chilomeniscus stramineus*	17
A. niger	4	*Chrysopelea paradisi*	1
A. werneri	5	*Clelia rustica*	1
Atractaspis aterrima	13	*Coluber algirus*	15
A. boulengeri	6	*C. caspius*	17
A. dahomeyensis	14	*Coniophanes bipunctatus*	1
Chilorhinophis butleri	5–15	*C. fissidens*	5
Polemon bocourti	12	*C. frangivirgatus*	10
P. christyi	1–8	*Coronella austriaca*	6
P. collaris	9	*Crotaphopeltis hippocrepis*	14
Xenocalamus mechowii	3–13	*C. hotamboeia*	3–21
X. transvaalensis	2	*C. tornieri*	5
Elapidae		*Dasypeltis palmarum*	5
Calliophis calligaster	12	*D. scabra*	27
C. gracilis	23	*Dendrophidion bivittatus*	4

(Continued on next page)

Table 2.5. (continued)

Dinodon orientale	10	O. octolineatus	8
Dipsina multimaculata	9	O. perkinsi	2
Dispholidus typus	7	O. purpurascens	18
Dromophis lineatus	14–21	O. quadrilineatus	4
D. praeornatus	21	O. sublineatus	24
Dryadophis pulchriceps	18	O. taeniolatus	2
Dryocalamus davisonii	7	O. waandersi	6
D. nympha	18	Oxyrhopus leucomelas	3
Elaphe helena	16	O. trigeminus	2
E. flavolineata	7	Pareas carinatus	1
Elapomorphus quinquelineatus	4	P. stanleyi	3
Enulius flavitorques	12	Philodryas psammophideus	10
Ficimia olivacea	12	Philothamnus angolensis	4–30
F. publia	6	P. bequaerti	6
Geagras redimitus	1	P. dorsalis	4–21
Grayia ornata	1–11	P. hoplogaster	31
Helicops trivittatus	6	P. neglectus	3
Helophis schoutedeni	6	Phyllorhynchus browni	5
Hemirhagerrhis kelleri	15	Prosymna ambigua	4–5
Hydrodynastes gigas	1	Psammophis leightoni	25
Lampropeltis calligaster	14	P. lineolatus	10
L. mexicana	17	P. notostictus	22
L. triangulum	4	P. phillipsii	2–23
Lamprophis fuliginosus	1–3	P. subtaeniatus	16
L. lineatus	5	Pseudorabdion collaris	5
L. olivaceus	1–4	P. montanum	10
Leptodeira annulata	5	Psomophis joberti	1
Leptophis diplotropis	20	Ptyas luzonensis	3
Lielaphis parvus	9	Pythonodipsas carinata	3
Liopeltis rappi	20	Rhabdophis auriculatus	13
Liophidium vaillanti	4	R. chrysargus	10
Liophis almadensis	9	R. chrysargoides	7
Lycodon laoensis	23	R. lineatus	4
L. travancoricus	16	R. subminiatus	9
Lycodonomorphus bicolor	2	Rhadinophanes monticola	7
Lycophidion capense	23	Rhamphiophis rubropunctatus	27
L. laterale	3	Rhynchocalamus satunini	9
L. meleagris	14	Scaphiodontophis annulatus	5
Manolepis putnami	9	Scaphiophis albopunctatus	8–29
Mehelya capensis	7–12	Scolecophis atrocinctus	3
M. crossii	3	Senticolis triaspis	24
M. poensis	4–19	Sibynomorphus mikanii	3
Natriciteres olivacea	3–12	S. turgidus	9
N. variegata	3	Sibynophis sagittarius	2
Oligodon arnensis	6	Simophis rhinostoma	7–16
O. cinereus	6	Sonora semiannulata	3
O. cyclurus	19	Storeria occipitomaculata	14
O. modestus	24	Sympholis lippiens	10

(Continued on next page)

Table 2.5. (continued)

Colubridae (continued)		Trimorphodon biscutatus	15
Telescopus dhara	14	Tropidonophis dendrophiops	3
T. fallax	4	T. doriae	11
T. variegatus	27	Waglerophis merremii	6
Thamnophis elegans	5	Xenochrophis maculatus	10
T. eques	6	X. trianguligerus	21
Thelotornis kirtlandii	6	X. vittatus	1

(*Achalinus, Aplopeltura, Chersodromus, Maticora, Ninia, Xenodermus*) lack visible parenchyma in either the tracheal lung or right lung; both lungs appear atrabecular. It cannot be doubted that these snakes respire and that gas exchange occurs across the pulmonary wall. It is possible that oxygen and carbon dioxide diffuse across the thin membrane of the lung wall into the systemic circulation. The pulmonary artery normally terminates at the end of the vascular lung, with the saccular lung receiving its blood supply from the posterior dorsal aorta, the vertebral arteries, and the hepatic artery; the saccular lung is drained by the inferior vena cava and hepatic portal vein (Rees, 1820; van der Hoeven, 1855, 1858; Bert, 1869; Atwood, 1916, 1918; Suomalainen, 1939; Brongersma, 1952b; Luchtel and Kardong, 1981). Branches of the aorta serving the saccular lung in snakes have long been known (Cuvier, 1805), with accessory pulmonary supply also including branches from the esophageal, gastric, and hepatic arteries (W. C. George, 1923). However, at least in some snakes, the pulmonary circulation serves the saccular lung. Whereas branches of the aorta serve the caudal portion of the lung in *Python reticulatus* (Brongersma, 1952b), the posterior pulmonary artery serves the saccular lung in *Echis carinatus* (Deoras and Vad, 1966). The right vagus nerve serves the terminal portion of the lung in *Natrix* (Hofmeister, 1889), and both the vascular lung and saccular lung are innervated by the vagus nerve in *Thamnophis* (Carlson and Luckhardt, 1920; D. G. Smith and Macintyre, 1979).

The ability of snakes to undergo apnea for long periods of time is well known and is probably associated partly with the presence of a saccular lung. Times reported for submergence of various species of snakes include 20–45 min by *Liasis mackloti*, *L. olivaceus*, *Morelia amethistina*, and *M. spilota* (Ehmann, 1993a), 8–32 min by *Acrochordus arafurae* (Pough, 1973; Seymour et al., 1981a), 16–53 min in *A. granulatus* (Glass and Johansen, 1976), 7–55 min by *Cerberus rynchops* (Heatwole, 1977), 30–120 min by the Hydrophiidae (Heatwole, 1958; Graham et al., 1987a; Heatwole and Cogger, 1993), 15–50 min by *Laticauda* (Heatwole et al., 1978; Heatwole, 1981; Heatwole and Guinea, 1993), and 20–30 min by *Tropidonophis mairii* (Lyon, 1973, cited in Ehmann, 1993b).

Possible functions of the ophidian saccular lung, some of which are similar to those mentioned above for the tracheal lung, have been a topic of much discussion (Brattstrom, 1959; McDonald, 1959a; Heatwole, 1981). Among the hypotheses proposed are that it functions as: (1) an air reservoir or oxygen storage chamber (Tyson, 1683; Cantor, 1841; Gervais, 1866; C. A. White, 1878; Lataste and Blanchard, 1879; Bumpus, 1888; Baudrimont, 1929; Wolf, 1933; Curran and Kauffeld, 1937; J. C. George and Varde, 1941, Varde, 1951; Karlstrom, 1952; J. C. George and Shah, 1956; Brattstrom, 1959; Deoras and Vad, 1966; G. M. Hughes, 1973; Lillywhite and Smits, 1992), (2) a hydrostatic organ, buoyancy device, or aid in attitude control in the water or during subsurface swimming (Cantor, 1841; Pagenstecher, 1878; Beddard, 1904b, 1906a; Wolf, 1933; Bellairs and Underwood, 1951; Klauber, 1956; Brattstrom, 1959; Bellairs, 1969; Graham et al., 1987b), (3) a chamber for storage of deoxygenated air containing a high concentration of CO_2, so that the vascular lung will not be contaminated (T. Williams, 1859), (4) a caudal bellows or ventilation substitute whenever normal lung function is hindered as (a) during constriction or (b) ingestion of prey whenever the trachea is compressed and the anterior ribs cannot produce thoracic expansion and contraction, or (c) in submerged aquatic snakes, whenever contraction of smooth muscle may force air forward into the vascular lung (R. Owen, 1866; C. A. White, 1878; Brehm, 1885; Werner, 1911; Wolf, 1933; J. C. George and Varde, 1941; Bellairs and Underwood, 1951; Klauber, 1956; McDonald, 1959a), (5) a mechanism for exposing the vascular lung to inspired air twice during each biphasic cycle (C. A. White, 1878; Brattstrom, 1959; McDonald, 1959a), (6) an intimidation device that permits inflation of the tracheal membrane of the neck, prolongation of a defensive hiss, or body inflation increasing size and enhancing threatening posture (Beddard, 1906a; Klauber 1956; Gans and Richmond, 1957; Deoras and Vad, 1966; Gans and Maderson, 1973; Duncker, 1978a; Russell, 1983), (7) a mechanism for lowering the breathing pattern index and reducing the large dead space of the lumina of the trachea and vascular lung, through increased tidal flow and volume, to compensate for small body-wall expansion during ventilation and lung volume deficit due to body elongation and reduction or loss of the left lung (H. Marcus, 1927; McDonald, 1959a; Kardong, 1972b; Perry and Duncker, 1980; Heatwole, 1987; Milsom, 1989), (8) a mechanism for thermoregulatory or evaporative cooling in an overheated snake or, during the breeding season, for gonadal (testicular) cooling through inspiration of cool air (Klauber, 1956; Brattstrom, 1959; J. C. George and Shah, 1965; Pohunková and Hughes, 1985), (9) a mechanism for maintaining posterior body form when the intestines are empty, especially in arboreal snakes (Brattstrom, 1959; Duncker, 1978a), (10) a remnant of a previously existing hydrostatic organ in extinct aquatic and marine snakes (Terent'ev, 1961, 1965), (11) a sound resonation chamber for detecting airborne vibrations as a means of hearing (Hartline and Campbell, 1969; Hartline, 1971), (12) a correlate of development of serous cells and toxicity of salivary glands (Deoras and Vad, 1973), (13) a mechanism for producing greater aerobic capacity by increasing V_T during exercise (Ruben, 1976b), (14) a mechanism for better ventilation in larger snakes, being a correlate of the low oxygen affinity and high hematocrit in large snakes versus high oxygen affinity and low hematocrit in small snakes (Pough, 1977a, 1977b), (15) a mechanism for retaining highly saturated blood and insuring the maximum partial pressure gradient for gas diffusion during the breath-holding period, via metabolic acidosis through storage of CO_2 in the blood and greater unloading of O_2 to the tissues, when most respiration takes place (Gratz et al., 1981), (16) an aid in locomotion by ensuring optimal contact of the belly wall with the substrate in terrestrial forms (Perry, 1983), and (17) a mechanism to compensate for the loss of the left lung (Weidensaul, 1991).

Probably most of the above hypotheses hold true for at least some taxa at certain periods of their life cycles; comments on the above hypotheses are listed below with corresponding numerals. (1) Laboratory and field studies on *Vipera* (Gratz et al., 1981), *Laticauda* (Heatwole, 1981), and *Pituophis* (Stinner, 1982b, 1987a) demonstrate the role of the saccular lung as an air reservoir. (2) Likewise, both types of studies have shown that *Laticauda* (Heatwole, 1981), *Pelamis* (Graham et al., 1975, 1987a, 1987b), and other marine Hydrophiidae (Seymour, 1982) use the hydrostatic function of the lung. (3) Support for the idea that the saccular lung acts as a storage site for air with a high concentration of CO_2 is seen in studies of *Morelia* (Donnelly and Woolcock, 1978) and *Pituophis* (Stinner, 1987a). (4) The caudal bellows hypothesis has been demonstrated in such taxa as *Vipera* (Gratz et al., 1981), *Pseudechis* (Rosenzweig, 1981), many marine Hydrophiidae (Heatwole, 1987), *Pituophis* (Stinner, 1987c), and *Thamnophis* (Rosenberg, 1973), and is inferred for all species (i.e., *Hydrodynastes*, V. Wallach, pers. obs.) that possess considerable smooth muscle in the wall of the saccular lung. (5) Double exposure of the vascular lung to inspired air has been demonstrated in the laboratory in *Morelia* (Donnelly and Woolcock, 1977) and *Thamnophis* (Rosenberg, 1973). (6) That the saccular lung is instrumental in the inflation of the neck and/or body of certain species, as well as having a role in prolonged hissing, is inferred from anatomy and empirical observations. (7) Lung volume deficit, large dead space, and limited body-wall expansion during ventilation have been compensated by an increased tidal flow and volume with a lowered breathing pattern index in snakes, as shown by studies of *Morelia* (Donnelly and Woolcock, 1977), *Crotalus* and *Coluber* (Ruben, 1976b), *Pituophis* (Stinner, 1980, 1982b), and *Thamnophis* (Bartlett et al., 1986). (8) The possible role of the saccular lung for cooling overheated snakes may pertain especially to desert inhabitants (Bogert and Cowles, 1947) although no snakes seem to pant. (9) In at least two groups, arboreal colubrids (i.e., *Oxybelis, Philothamnus*) and heavy-bodied vipers (i.e., *Bitis*), I have observed the maintenance of posterior body form through inflation of the saccular lung; with forceful expiration of air the posterior body cavity collapses. (10) Terent'ev's (1961, 1965) hypothesis seems unlikely even though extinct marine snakes probably had a long vascularized right lung (as do extant forms); the saccular lung appears at a much earlier stage in the ophidian phylogenetic tree and is, thus, probably not inherited as a degenerative structure from ancestral marine snakes. (11) Observations of *Dendrelaphis* support the contention that the saccular lung aids in detecting airborne vibrations (Yahya, 1978). (12) The hypothesis of Deoras and Vad (1973) seems implausible, and their correlation is probably spurious and due in part to inadequate sample size; most Colubridae have a large saccular lung, yet not all have serous supralabial glands (Taub, 1967). (13) Comparison of aerobic metabolism in *Lichanura* and *Crotalus* (with short or nonexistent saccular lungs) with that of *Coluber* and *Masticophis* (with long saccular lungs) suggests that the saccular lung is involved in increasing aerobic capacity (Ruben, 1976a). (14) Studies on *Thamnophis* and *Nerodia* show an ontogenetic shift in hematocrit and oxygen affinity that results in increased ventilation in adult snakes (Pough, 1977c, 1978). (15) Laboratory experiments on *Pseudechis* support the hypothesis that the saccular lung maintains a maximal partial pressure gradient for gas diffusion during apnea (Rosenzweig, 1981). (16) It is possible that the inflation of the saccular lung helps to ensure optimal contact of the ventrals with the substrate. (17) The development of the saccular lung, to compensate for the loss of the left lung is not supported by any evidence; the left lung is absent in many groups lacking a saccular lung, and it most likely was reduced to a vestige in the earliest snakes or their ancestors.

V. LEFT LUNG COMPLEX
A. General

The left lung complex in snakes, when complete, consists of a left lung, a left bronchus or single bronchial ring, and a left orifice. As discussed below, any or all of these elements may be absent in a particular taxon or specimen (see Appendix C). Asymmetry in the size of the left and right lungs has long been known (Figs. 2.2, 2.26; Meckel, 1818; Fleming, 1822). The left lung of snakes displays the greatest asymmetry of any of the viscera; the minimal pulmonary asymmetry is an order of magnitude greater than the maximal asymmetry present in any of the other paired viscera.

Hypotheses attempting to explain the suppression or extreme reduction and/or loss of the left lung, in relation to the right, include: (1) lack
of space due to the lengthening of the body and narrowing of the body
cavity (Wiedersheim, 1886; Latter, 1923; M. A. Smith, 1954; Klauber, 1956;
Eaton, 1960; Bellairs and Carrington, 1966; Vesey-FitzGerald, 1968; Orr,
1982), (2) a result of cramping due to the position of the esophagus and
stomach on the left side of the body (Butler, 1895), (3) elongation of the
body and loss of limbs with development of a new type of locomotion
that placed a premium on internal body space for lung development
(Schmalhausen, 1905), (4) selection pressure on the side of the body from
torquing during constriction of prey items (Willard, 1977; Greene and
Burghardt, 1978; Heinrich and Klaassen, 1985), and (5) coiling of the
snake during embryological development (V. Wallach, pers. obs.).

B. Left Lung

A vestigial left lung was first described in *Natrix natrix* (Nitzsch, 1808),
although controversy existed over whether it was the left or right lung
that was reduced. Subsequent investigators supported Nitzsch's view that
the left lung was vestigial in *Anilius scytale* and *Crotalus horridus* (Meckel,
1818), *Telescopus fallax* (Fleischmann, 1831), *Coronella austriaca* (Carus, 1827,
1835), *Hemachatus haemachatus* and *Naja naja* (Lereboullet, 1838), and *Eryx
jaculus*, *Heterodon platyrhinos*, and *Pseudechis porphyriacus* (Cuvier, 1840).
Absence of a left lung was first reported in *Malpolon monspessulana*
(Fleischmann, 1831) and *Vipera* and *Pelamis* (Meckel, 1833; Cuvier, 1840).
The left lung may be absent in both the most primitive and the most derived snake families; it is lacking in all species of the Anomalepididae,
Leptotyphlopidae, Anomochilidae, Xenophidiidae, Acrochordidae, and
several colubrid tribes (i.e., Lycophidini, Sibynophiini). It is absent in most
species of the Typhlopidae, Tropidophiidae, Viperidae, marine Hydrophiidae, and other colubrid tribes (i.e., Xenodermatini, Nothopsini, Alsophiini, Psammophiini). Numerous genera and species within the
Colubridae also lack a left lung (see Appendix C). Among 23 Colubridae
studied by Meckel (1818), 16 species were reported to have a left lung and
seven to lack it; one year later, he reported 21 species with a left lung and
only five without it from a sample of 26 species (Meckel, 1819), suggesting that the left lung was previously overlooked in several species. Among
the 43 species of Colubridae examined by H. Marcus (1927, 1937), 31 possessed a small left lung and 12 lacked this organ.

The literature probably contains more errors about the ophidian left
lung than about any of the other viscera. As noted above, many early
authors confused the vestigial left lung with the right, or declared the
left to be larger of the two. Cope's (1894a–1900) erroneous statements
became well entrenched in the literature and were often repeated. In

snakes with two lungs, he mistook the vestigial left lung for the right and even thought that the right lung of the Typhlopidae and Lepto-typhlopidae was homologous to the rudimentary left lung of the Colubroidea. However, the left lung is always reduced in comparison with the right (Butler, 1895; Brongersma, 1957a; Bellairs, 1972) and, when the left lung is relatively large, its cranial apex is symmetrically oppo-site that of the right lung. Additionally, the left lung in many species is difficult to observe and often overlooked, as in *Anilius scytale* (Cuvier, 1829), *Rhinophis oxyrhynchus* (Stannius, 1856; Bedriaga, 1884), *Dendroaspis polylepis* (Cope, 1894a; Maina, 1989), *Ahaetulla prasina* (Butler, 1895), *Drymarchon corais* (Gillian and Conklin, 1938), and *Elaphe obsoleta* and *Nerodia rhombifer* (Baeyens et al., 1978).

The left lung is situated sinistrad and ventrolaterad of the right lung, just caudad of the ventricular apex of the heart. In most species, it ex-tends caudally from its bronchus or orifice (Fig. 2.26). Whenever a left bronchus is present connecting the left lung to the trachea, it is usually extrapulmonary. Some snakes, such as the Aniliidae, Uropeltidae, Atractaspididae, and Calamariini, possess a left lung with a body di-rected cranially along the left lateral surface of the heart. This condition resembles the retention of only the anterior lobe (of a previously much larger lung). In most species, the direction of the unattached portion of the left lung is variable. The lung usually points caudally in most spe-

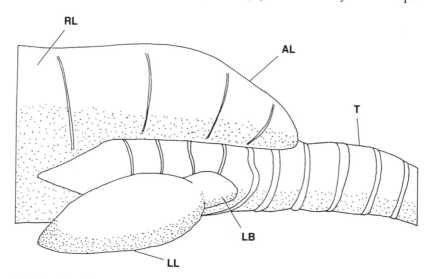

Fig. 2. 26. *Pseudechis porphyriacus*. Diagram of lateral view of the left lung region illustrat-ing paraterminal tracheal entry with anterior lobe (AL) of the right lung (RL) fused to trachea (T), short tapering right bronchus (RB), short left bronchus (LB), and vestigial left lung (LL). (Adapted from Rosenzweig, 1981.)

cies but is directed cranially in *Anilius* (Meckel, 1833). This type of lung is normally tear-drop shaped with the rounded base near the orifice and an anteriorly tapered end. In these lungs, there is no free bronchus, and the left bronchus is entirely enclosed within the lung parenchyma (similar to the condition of the left bronchus in the Booidea), further supporting the notion that the left lung is the homologue of an anterior lobe.

When present, the left lung (LL) exhibits considerable variation both in relative size and morphological shape. Its length ranges from 0.1% in many species to as much as 30% (*Aspidites melanocephalus*). Early researchers noted that the left lung in *Python reticulatus* (Hopkinson and Pancoast, 1837) and *Boa constrictor* (Hering, 1860) is about half the size of the right lung, although Meckel (1833) reported them to be nearly the same size, with *Python* having the largest left lung (Fig. 2.27), *Boa* intermediate, and with *Eryx* having the smallest left lung. The Booidea have a relatively large left lung, ranging from 11% (*Boa*) to 30% (*Aspidites*), but in *Epicrates gracilis* and several species of *Eryx* the left lung is reduced to only 3–10%. Mean left lung length in *Charina bottae* (n = 25) is 13% VS (ventral scutes) and in *Lichanura roseofusca* (n = 23) it is 16% VS (Kaban, 1978). In the Booidea, the position of the posterior tip of the left lung varies from 31% (*Charina* and *Eryx*) to 59% (*Python*), although in most species it occurs at 40–55% (see Appendix C).

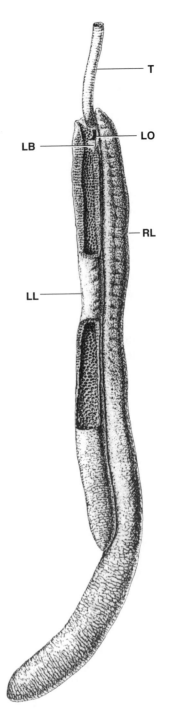

Fig. 2.27. *Python* sp. Dorsal view of lungs showing trachea (T) with subterminal entry, left orifice (LO) and short left bronchus (LB) of relative large left lung (LL) with dense faveoli cranially and sparse faveoli caudally, and right lung (RL) lacking a caudal aparenchymal (saccular) region. (Adapted from Marcus, 1937.)

A more revealing index is the length of the left lung relative to the right (LL/RL). In snakes, this ranges from 0.01 (*Lamprophis*) to 0.85 (*Morelia*) (see Appendix C). Except for some Erycini and *Epicrates gracilis* with LL/RL values as low as 0.09–0.21, most of the Booidea average 0.30–0.65, with the largest value (0.85) reported in *Morelia amethistina* and *M. viridis* (Underwood, 1976b; Withers and O'Shea, 1993). In *Charina* and *Lichanura*, mean LL/RL values are 0.34 and 0.43, respectively (Fig. 2.3; Kaban, 1978). A report on 15 specimens of *M. spilota variegata* (Read and Donnelly, 1972; and repeated in Donnelly and Woolcock, 1977, 1978) shows values for the left lung length (29.6%) greater than those for the right (17.4%), with an RL/LL ratio of 0.59; unless this entire sample was anomalous, this may be a mistaken observation. Examination of their figures suggests that the identities of the lungs were reversed; thus, their fig. 1 shows the right lung (labelled as the left) in ventral view being longer than the left, and their fig. 7 depicts a medial view of the right lung (based on orientation of the bronchus) rather than the left. In two individuals examined by me, the right lung was longer than the left (LL/RL=0.50–0.57), a conclusion confirmed by Underwood (1976b). However, the specimens I examined had the lungs rotated dextrodorsad by 90°, with the effect that the right lung was dorsal and the left lung ventral in the postcardiac region. Such rotation of the lungs along the body axis is common (Brongersma, 1957a). In my specimens, the caudal portion of the right lung also crossed the midline and terminated on the left side of the body (as in many Booidea); this could account for the error if only the posterior portion of the lung is observed. I have observed only one specimen (*Corallus caninus*) in which the right lung (14%) was smaller than the left (23%). This right lung was clearly aberrantly short, as the normal length of the right lung in *Corallus* is 36–39%, whereas the left is 23–27%.

A more moderate-sized left lung occurs in a few lower and higher snakes (see Appendix C). Among the lower snakes, 13 species of the Typhlopidae exhibit a left lung of 1–4% (LL/RL = 0.03–0.25) (Wallach, 1993a), *Cylindrophis* exhibits a left lung of 2–4% (LL/RL = 0.06–0.14), and five genera of the Uropeltidae have left lungs of 3–6% (LL/RL = 0.11–0.27). Some arboreal colubrids have what appears to be a secondarily enlarged left lung, the largest (6–8%; LL/RL = 0.09–0.11) occurring in *Gonyosoma oxycephalum* (Thompson, 1914b). Other relatively large left lungs occur in *Boiga cynodon* (5%, LL/RL = 0.08, three species of *Pseustes* (5–8%, LL/RL = 0.06–0.10), *Spilotes pullatus* (3–6%, LL/RL = 0.04–0.08), two species of *Thrasops* (2–5%, LL/RL = 0.02–0.09), and two species of *Toxicodryas* (4–8%, LL/RL = 0.02–0.12). An exceptionally long left lung occurs in *T. blandingii* (12 VS or 4–5% VS), and Rasmussen (1979) presumes it to be primitive; this seems unlikely in view of the above discussion and the taxonomic position of *Toxicodryas*.

However, in the overwhelming majority of snakes possessing a left lung, it is reduced to a minute vestige ranging from 0.1–2.0% (LL/RL = 0.01–0.03) (Fig. 2.2). Although quite variable (CV = 17–25), the LL/RL ratios are significantly larger in *Aparallactus niger* (0.03–0.05) than in *A. lineatus* (0.01–0.02) (Wallach, 1994a). Even when it is shorter than 1%, the left lung is usually vascularized and served by a small branch of the pulmonary artery. Some species (e.g., *Hoplocephalus bungaroides*, *Atractus badius*, *Boiga multifasciata*, *Gonyosoma frenata*, and *Pseudoxenodon stejnegeri*) exhibit a left lung that is sparsely vascularized along the cranial half and saccular along the caudal half as first reported in *Hemachatus haemachatus* and *Naja naja* (Lereboullet, 1838; Cuvier, 1840). One specimen of *Boiga cynodon* has the cranial four-fifths trabecular and the caudal one-fifth edicular. In other species, the cranial half may be faviolar and the caudal half trabecular (e.g., *Pseudotyphlops philippinus*). A few taxa, such as the Viperidae (Plate 2.2F), *Mehelya*, and some arboreal colubrids (Dispholidini, *Ahaetulla*, *Boiga*, *Gonyosoma*, *Philothamnus*, *Spilotes*), possess an avascular or saccular left lung. In *Dipsas indica*, the left lung is avascular and lacks any blood vessels as well as a bronchus (Werner, 1911). Normally, the left lung is translucent and reticulated with a network of trabeculae; it may also be lined with dense faveoli.

The midpoint of the left lung is moderately variable, with CVs ranging from 2–8 among the Lampropeltini (Keogh, 1993). Among 30 atractaspidid species, 15 exhibit sexual dimorphism in the lung midpoint position with the male means larger than those of the female. Sample CVs range from 2–13, and fall between 5 and 8 in most species (Wallach, 1991, 1994a).

The rudimentary left lung not only varies in size but also in shape, most commonly it is oval, spherical, or teardrop-shaped, with its length nearly equal to or slightly longer than its width (Kurtz, 1953; Parsons and Djatschenko, 1983). It may also appear roughly triangular-shaped (Plate 2.2F; Uropeltidae, Atractaspididae), diamond-shaped, or mushroom-shaped, with its length up to twice as long as wide. In *Pseudotyphlops philippinus*, *Naja melanoleuca*, *Mehelya capensis*, and *Pseudoficimia frontalis*, the left lung may be trilobed, T-shaped, or Y-shaped. An unusual *M. capensis* from Zaire exhibits a trilobed left lung in which the axes of all three lobes, which originate at the junction of the bronchus, are perpendicular to one another when inflated. The primary lobe is avascular and 10% SVL, whereas the secondary and tertiary lobes are vascular and 0.4% and 0.2% long. In a series of *Naja melanoleuca* (n = 48), the shape of the left lung shows sexual variation. One class of lungs includes oval or elongate lungs, the other is T-shaped, Y-shaped, or trilobed. Three types of vascularization are evident: (1) entirely vascular, (2) vascular cranially and saccular caudally, and (3) entirely saccular. Males exhibit a significantly higher percentage of vascular lungs and females a significantly higher proportion of saccular lungs, with an equal percentage of vascular/saccular lungs. Males predominate in the oval-to-elongate shape, and females show a significantly greater percentage of T- or Y-shaped lungs. One Y-shaped lung is completely vascular, two trilobed lungs have the distal portion of each lobe vascular and the proximal portion saccular, one trilobed lung has the two cranial lobes vascular and the caudad lobe saccular, and one trilobed lung has the cranial lobe vascular, the caudal lobe saccular, and the medial lobe with a vascular distal portion and saccular base.

The presence or absence of a left lung is not as good a systematic character as the occurrence of a tracheal lung (Beddard, 1906b). In most species, the left lung is either present or absent, but it appears variable in a few species, especially if the left lung is very small and may be in the process of being lost. The left lung in *Homalopsis buccata* has been reported both present (Schlegel, 1837b) and absent (Butler, 1895). I examined two specimens; one of these (SDSU) had a left lung, but the other (LSUMZ 48373) lacked a left lung, bronchus, and orifice. Brongersma (1957b) reports no trace of a left lung complex in *Elaphe porphyracea*; his specimen was likely a female, because a male I examined (FMNH 15828) possesses an orifice (23%), a short bronchus (0.3%) with 7 rings, and a tiny trabecular lung (0.1%). Absence of a left lung complex is also reported in *Elaphe guttata* (Brongersma, 1957b), but a female I examined (SDSU) has an orifice (24%), a short 3-ring bronchus (0.1%) with 6-pointed crown, and a small left lung (0.3%). The left lung appears to be disappearing in these species, but only examination of a large series can determine which state is most representative.

Some genera display, among their various species, the transition from forms with a left lung complex to those without any trace. For example, reduction in the size of the left lung is documented in three species of *Elaphe*, with *E. climacophora* having a long left lung, *E. quadrivirgata* a moderate organ, and *E. conspicilliata* a short left lung (Oidumi, 1940). Within *Crotalus*, four species usually possess a small, avascular left lung (*basiliscus, durissus, horridus, molossus*) and five others sometimes exhibit a left lung (*atrox, cerastes, enyo, exsul, lepidus*), whereas 11 species lack a left lung (*adamanteus, intermedius, mitchelli, pricei, ruber, scutulatus, tigris, tortugensis, triseriatus, viridis, willardi*) (Schwenkmeyer *in* Klauber, 1956). The species of *Helicops* show the following arrangement (presence [+] or absence [0] of left lung, left bronchus and left orifice, respectively): *H. carinicaudus, H. hagmanni, H. leopardinus, H. modestus, H. pictiventris, H. scalaris* (all +, +, +), *H. angulatus* (+, 0, +), *H. danieli, H. pastazae* (0, +, +), *H. polylepis* (0, 0, +), and *H. petersi, H. trivittatus* (0, 0, 0). Likewise, in *Lamprophis* the left lung complex varies as follows: *L. virgatus* (+, +, +), *L. inornatus* (+, 0, +), *L. fuliginosus, L. geometricus, L. olivaceus* (0, +, +), *L. aurora* (0, 0, +), and *L. fiskii, L. fuscus, L. guttatus, L. lineatus* (0, 0, 0,).

Variation in the left lung complex consists of sexual dimorphism in both relative and absolute length of left lung (males >> females) in *Thamnophis sirtalis* (Parsons and Djatschenko, 1983) and the Atractaspididae (Wallach, 1991). Sexual dimorphism is evident in *Atractaspis microlepidota*, in which significantly more females than males lack the lung and bronchus. In a sample of 33 individuals (18 ♂♂, 15 ♀♀), 56% of the males and 13% of the females have a left lung, 72% and 33% respectively have a left bronchus, and 72% and 40% respectively have a left orifice (Wallach, 1991). Variation also occurs in a larger sample (n = 239, 87 ♂♂, 152 ♀♀) of *Natriciteres olivacea*; a left lung is lacking in 1.1% of males and 7.2% of females. However, sexual dimorphism is not always present in the left lung complex. Only 15 of 30 atractaspidid species exhibit significant sexual dimorphism in the position of the left lung midpoint, and only four species show a significant difference in left lung length (Wallach, 1991, 1994a). Both a left lung and left bronchus occur, but the size of the left lung shows no sexual dimorphism in a sample of 49 specimens of three species of *Elaphe* or 47 specimens of *Rhabdophis tigrinus* (Oidumi, 1940).

The left lung has occasionally reappeared in individuals of genera that have supposedly lost it. Examples include *Lycophidion ornatum* (in which the left lung is present in one specimen out of a sample of 20), *Dasypeltis scabra* (left lung present in three of 19), *Atheris nitschei* (left lung present in one out of 19), and *A. squamiger* (left lung present in three out of 85).

A rare condition is the retention of a rigid, transparent, noninflatable clear cap or blind sac covering the orifice or bronchus like a tiny dome (Underwood, 1967). This appears to be the last stage in the reduction of the left lung before its loss. Possibly this is the structure reported in *Natrix natrix* and *Coronella austriaca* as a "small blind depression" by Nitzsch (1808) and Carus (1827) or the left lung sac in *Amphiesma vibakari* (Thompson, 1914b) and the blind sac in *Crotalus viridis* (Kardong, 1972a). A blind sac has been observed in single individuals of the following species (sample size in parentheses): *Boulengerina christyi* (9), *Micrurus lemniscatus* (1), *Suta punctata* (1), *Atheris squamiger* (85), *Echis coloratus* (2), *Chilopoma rufipunctatus* (1), *Chionactis occipitalis* (7), *Coluber jugularis* (1), *Dasypeltis scabra* (20), *Drepanoides anomalus* (1), *Gerarda prevostiana* (2), *Grayia smythii* (63), *Lamprophis fuliginosus* (128), *L. olivaceus* (24), *Liophis poecilogyrus* (2), *Lycodonomorphus whytii* (2), *Lystrophis histricus* (1), *Mehelya capensis* (32), *Natriciteres olivacea* (241), *Oligodon calamarius* (1), *O. ocellatus* (1), *Pseudotomodon trigonatus* (1), *Sibon sanniola* (1), *Sonora aemula* (2), *Toluca lineata* (1), *Trachischium guentheri* (1), *Tropidodryas serra* (1), and *Umbrivaga mertensi* (1). It is less common among the Elapidae and terrestrial Hydrophiidae, most of which possess a left lung, and the Viperidae, most of which lack a left lung.

Previous researchers have claimed that a relatively large left lung represents the ancestral condition in snakes (Bellairs and Underwood, 1951; Dowling, 1959; Terent'ev, 1961, 1965; Butner, 1963a; Underwood, 1967; Bellairs, 1969; Ramsay, 1979). However, McDowell (1987) suggested that the relatively large left lung of the Booidea may be derived. I judge that McDowell is correct and further suggest that the moderate-sized left lungs of *Epicrates gracilis* and some species of *Eryx* are secondarily reduced. No other snakes have a large left lung, and because the Scolecophidia and Anilioidea represent more primitive groups than the Booidea (Rage, 1984, 1987; McDowell, 1987; Rieppel, 1988a, 1988b; Kluge, 1991), parsimony dictates that the large left lung is a synapomorphy originating within the Booidea. Circumstantial evidence supporting this hypothesis includes, first, the intuitive fact that the first true snakes (i.e., *Pachyrachis* or possibly even its immediate ancestors) must have possessed elongated and asymmetrically arranged viscera (left organs shorter than the right) and left lung markedly reduced, perhaps even to a mere vestige. Second, there are no intermediate-sized left lungs among primitive snakes; one might expect these if the organ was in the process of degenerating. The largest non-Booidean left lungs are 6% in some Uropeltidae, less than half the size of the smallest left lungs of the Booidea. Third, with the reduction and loss of the left lung, the left pulmonary artery and vein have also disappeared. However, even though the left lung is relatively large in the Booidea, only a single pulmonary vein persists, and the left lung is supplied by branches of the right pulmonary artery (Jacquart, 1855; Brongersma, 1951a). This suggests that the left lung was reduced in the ancestral lineage, the pulmonary vein then lost, and the left lung re-enlarged with a new vascular source.

Also, there appears to be some physiological selection pressure for lengthening of both lungs in arboreal snakes. Regardless of taxonomic affinity, the right lungs of all arboreal species usually reach the vent and are longer than those in the most closely related non-arboreal species. As most arboreal snakes are lighter in build than their terrestrial counterparts, the long right lung may aid in supporting the posterior body form or increasing the lung volume to support a higher metabolism. The left lung also may show this effect, as certain arboreal Colubridae have it enlarged to greater than 3%. If the ancestral booids were arboreal (as are most extant species), this effect may explain why their left lungs are hypertrophied.

C. Left Bronchus

A left bronchus may occur in various species (see Appendix C). The Booidae often have very short tubular bronchus, containing from 1–6 rings, normally entirely embedded in the parenchyma of the medial lung wall. Only rarely does the trachea bifurcate into a pair of external tubular bronchi (R. Singh and Kar, 1982), in the form of an inverted "Y," before entering the right and left lungs (*Python molurus*). More normally, the trachea enters the right lung and continues in a straight line as the intrapulmonary bronchus and the left bronchus, branches off at an oblique angle to enter the left lung, with or without several complete rings, continuing along the mesial wall as a band of flattened cartilages the length of which is usually less than 2%. The number of rings and/or cartilages in the left bronchus of the Booidea ranges from one (*Xenopeltis*) to 57 (*Eryx*) (see Appendix C). *Python molurus* has 12 rings in the right lung and four half-rings in the left (Meckel, 1833). In the Booidea, the trachea often communicates directly with the left lung via the left orifice (Folk, 1971).

Whenever non-booid snakes have a left lung, they may have a left bronchus or a single bronchial ring, or the lung may communicate directly via the orifice (Meckel, 1833). The number of rings or cartilages in the bronchus ranges from one in many species to 13 (*Boulengerina*), although most species have an average between 2–5 (see Appendix C). The left bronchus of *Heterodon platyrhinos* contains four rings (Lereboullet, 1838). The left bronchus is usually parallel with and fused to the trachea (Parsons and Djatschenko, 1983), often completely surrounded and enclosed by the left lung (as in the Atractaspididae), and always has a much smaller diameter than the trachea. Among the Colubridae, instead of running parallel to the trachea and fused to it, the left bronchus is occasionally free distally and projecting obliquely caudad at an angle of 30°–90° to the tracheal axis, presumably a derived condition at that level. In such cases the bronchus may contain as few as two rings (*Adelphicos quadrivirgatus*) or as many as 10 (*Philodryas psammophideus*). Species exhibiting a left bronchus inclined at 30° include *Elaphe climacophora* and *E. quadrivirgata* (Oidumi, 1940), *Philodryas nattereri*, and *Ptyas carinatus*. *Typhlops angolensis*, *Calabaria reinhardtii*, *Eunectes murinus*, *Eryx conicus*, *Lichanura trivirgata*, *Laticauda laticaudata*, *Hoplocephalus bitorquatus*, *Drymarchon corais*, *Elaphe moellendorffi*, *Helicops carinicaudus*, *Mehelya crossii*, *Rhachidelus brazilii*, and *Uromacer frenatus* have a 45°-angled bronchus. *Bothrops alternatus*, *Crotalus molossus*, *Aparallactus modestus*, *Atractaspis dahomeyensis*, *Rhinoplocephalus nigrescens*, *Adelphicos quadrivirgatus*, *Diadophis punctatus*, *Farancia erytrogramma*, *Helicops modestus*, *Heterodon platyrhinos*, *Liopholidophis lateralis*, *Tantalophis discolor*, *Trimorphodon biscutatus*, and *Xenochrophis piscator* show a bronchus extending at a 90° angle. The presence of a 90° bronchus appears to be a synapomorphy defining the Heterodontini. The presence of a cranially oriented left lung is paralleled in *Polemon christyi* by a cranially directed bronchus at an angle of 60°.

Among non-booid snakes, the length of the left bronchus is very short, ranging from 0.1% in many species to 1.4% (*Lycodonomorphus*) (see Appendix C). In most species the left bronchus is shorter than the lung, although it is twice the length of the lung in *Pituophis catenifer* and *Boulengerina annulata* (Cope, 1900; Brongersma, 1957a; V. Wallach, pers. obs.). *Pseudoficimia frontalis* (CAS 142447) has a peculiar L-shaped left bronchus, the base with four complete rings and a perpendicular arm with five incomplete cartilages.

The terminal ring in the bronchus is often crown-like with from 3–8 points that project perpendicularly from the last ring. In *Thamnophis sirtalis*, the rings of the left bronchus are difficult to perceive without staining (Parsons and Djatschenko, 1983). However, rings are easily detectable in an opened left lung, even in small specimens.

Some snakes that have lost the left lung still retain a left bronchus, the terminus of which is covered with tissue, and has an orifice (*Lamprophis fuliginosus*). Occasionally, a bronchus lacks apparent rings, being a stiff but flexible, transparent tube, possibly composed of cartilage.

D. Left Orifice

The orifice (LO) of the left lung may be present or absent in different species (see Appendix C). When present, it may be large to small and variously shaped (usually round, oval, or figure-eight shaped). The width of the orifice divided by the diameter of the trachea (LO/TD) indicates the relative size of the orifice. It varies from 1.0 in the Booidea to about 0.1 in some Colubridae, although most higher snakes have values between 0.25–0.50. The position of the orifice may primitively have lain along the midline of the trachea or along its left lateral edge (sinistrolaterad). Although there may or may not be a bronchus associated with a left lung, normally an orifice will occur whenever a lung is present. However, some species may retain an orifice, even if the lung and bronchus are absent; it is then covered by a thin layer of tissue (in *Enuliophis*, *Limnophis*, *Mimophis*, *Taeniophallus*).

The midpoint position of the left orifice is a relatively stable character that exhibits large interspecific variation. It varies from 16% (*Dasypeltis*) to 46% (*Enhydrina schistosa*), although it lies between 25% and 35% in most species (see Appendix C). Among 14 species of the Lampropeltini, the CV for left orifice position averages 4 (range = 1–8) (Keogh, 1993). Among 31 atractaspidid species, the position of the left orifice is sexually dimorphic in 17 species, with the value for females averaging less than that for males. The CV for this character ranges from 2–8, with an average of 5 (Wallach, 1991).

A few forms that have lost the entire left lung complex sometimes have either a minute concavity or indentation in the trachea or an irregularity in the ring structure (with the normally transverse cartilages replaced by a median circular ring); this modification lies just caudad of the heart at the position at which an orifice would be located if present.

Such a structure is mentioned in *Sistrurus ravus* (Bourgondien and Bothner, 1969). It has been observed as well in *Bothrops neuwiedi, Protobothrops flavoviridis, Aspidelaps scutatus, Chrysopelea paradisi, Diadophis punctatus, Lamprophis fuliginosus, L. olivaceus, Natriciteres olivacea, Psammophis condanarus,* and *Thamnodynastes strigatus.* It seems that this indentation in the trachea marks the ancestral position of the left orifice in lineages that previously had a left lung complex.

Only rarely do snakes have a left bronchus or left lung but no left orifice. A specimen of *Ficimia olivacea* had a left lung without a left bronchus or orifice (Cope, 1894a–1900), undoubtedly an anomalous condition; two females of *F. olivacea* (FMNH 208165, SDSNH 57044), examined by me, both have a left orifice. A left lung without an orifice has been reported in *Coluber florulentus* (Thompson, 1914b); a male *C. florulentus* (FMNH 171894), examined by me, lacks the entire left lung complex. Several other similar, isolated aberrant cases have a lung but no orifice. *Sibon sanniola* (FMNH 153582) has a tiny noninflatable blind sac (0.2%) and a left bronchus (0.5%) but no left orifice; similarly, *Gongylosoma baliodeira* (FMNH 158614) exhibits a left lung but no left bronchus or orifice. A single *Natriciteres olivacea* (out of a sample of 239) has a left lung and left bronchus with only a tracheal indentation; likewise, a specimen of *Chrysopelea paradisi* (FMNH 131757) retains a minute left lung (0.3%) but has no left bronchus and only an indentation.

VI. SUMMARY

By the early 1800's, it had become clear that the ophidian respiratory system shows much variation, and this has been used in taxonomy and systematics for the past century. Numerous morphological characters differ, providing characters useful in systematic studies and phylogenetic analyses. Certain characters, such as the presence of a tracheal lung or absence of a left lung complex, define taxa at the family level. Others, such as the intrapulmonary bronchus or length of saccular lung, are diagnostic at the tribal level. Still others, such as absence of a left lung or the type of tracheal entry, are characteristic of genera or species. However, the pulmonary characters of each species of snake are at least partially independent from those of related forms, so that broad generalizations are impossible. The type and amount of intraspecific variation is species-specific: characters may be ontogenetically, sexually, or geographically variable in one taxon, but invariable in other, closely related ones. Likewise, characters may be relatively stable in one species (CV < 5), yet be moderately or highly variable (CV 10 or more) in another. The soft viscera provide numerous systematic characters that are as stable and reliable as traditionally employed characters of osteology and scutellation.

Investigations to date suggest that the respiratory system of snakes evolved from an ancestral form that exhibited the following generalized features: (1) a trachea with cartilaginous rings lacking free tips and a CR/IS ratio > 1.0, (2) a trachea lying ventral to the esophagus with a dorsad orientation of the tracheal membrane (tracheal membrane abutting the ventral surface of esophagus), (3) a narrow tracheal membrane with a TM/CR ratio of 1.0, (4) tracheal rings with a circular cross-section, (5) an unmodified and avascular tracheal membrane, lacking a tracheal lung, (6) a dextrodorsally curving trachea adjacent to the heart, (7) a trachea entering the right lung subterminally, (8) a moderate-sized, unicameral right lung measuring 30–35% SVL and half the diameter of the body (LD/VC = 0.5), lacking a saccular portion, (9) a small vascularized anterior lobe on the right lung, (10) a heterogenous right lung exhibiting faviform parenchyma cranially and trabecular parenchyma caudally, (11) a right lung terminating near the pancreas, spleen, gall bladder, and pylorus near midbody, (12) a vestigial but vascularized left lung less than 5% SVL, (13) a left bronchus with 2–3 rings, (14) a left orifice, (15) a very short right bronchus in the right lung (< 2% SVL), (16) two pulmonary arteries, of which the left is reduced, and (17) a single pulmonary vein (V. Wallach, pers. obs.).

Various changes and developments can be hypothesized to have occurred among different phyletic lines and among differing habitats. (1) Projecting free tips on tracheal rings developed in some groups. Except in most burrowing forms, the tracheal rings became thinner, and the CR/IS ratio increased to 2.0–3.0. (2) The tracheal membrane expanded in many lines, with a TM/CR > 1.0. Extreme expansion occurred in some arboreal snakes; ratios of 3.0–6.0 resulted in an avascular neck inflation mechanism. (3) Both unicameral and multicameral tracheal lungs evolved early in snake history, probably several times independently, and likely were lost in many groups. The tracheal lung consists of parenchyma extending cranially from the cardiac region or right lung along the tracheal membrane. Unicameral tracheal lungs exist in all stages of development from short and trabecular to extensive faviform organs that reach the gular region. Some taxa developed paucicameral lungs with transverse septation of the tracheal lumen forming niches. Multicameral lungs with separate air chambers developed in several groups. Loss of parenchyma may have resulted in avascular multicameral organs. (4) The trachea was primitively located on the right side relative to the heart; it changed from the right to the left side in advanced snakes. In those forms with a large left lung (Booidea) or an extensive tracheal lung, the trachea became middorsal. Tracheal entry shifted from subterminal to terminal in many groups, probably first going through a paraterminal stage. (5) With the acquisition of a tracheal lung, the size and vascularity of the right lung became modified in various ways. In most snakes, the right lung lengthened as a caudal, avascular section developed. Only among the Scolecophidia and certain aquatic forms did the right lung become shorter or retain its vascularity to its tip. (6) The small left lung was further reduced to a vestige less than 2% SVL or lost altogether. Only among the Booidea and certain arboreal colubrids has the left lung increased in size. The left bronchus became reduced to a single ring surrounding the orifice, or was lost completely. The left orifice, although enlarged to the diameter of the trachea in the Booidea, became progressively smaller in most snakes; it was lost repeatedly. (7) Some taxa developed a moderate-to-long right bronchus, with interdigitating, free tips, probably as an aid to circulation of inspired air within the saccular lung.

It is important to establish the extent to which the variation observed in lung morphology results from (1) environmental or behavioral selection pressures, (2) ancestry, or (3) both. The ability to recognize the effects of ecological influences is critical, as phylogenetic hypotheses are commonly confounded by environmentally influenced characteristics. Habitat specialization has had a great influence on the anatomy of the respiratory system, perhaps even more so than its influence on other organ systems. Some patterns are readily apparent, such as the greatly elongated right (and left) lung in arboreal snakes. Irrespective of taxonomic affinity, all arboreal species exhibit relatively longer right lungs, with the posterior tip located near the vent, than do their closest non-arboreal relatives. Except for the Viperidae, tracheal lungs are rare among arboreal snakes. A vestigial left lung and subterminal tracheal entry characterize most arboreal species.

The opposite trend is observed in many fossorial snakes. These usually lack a left lung complex, have a terminal tracheal entry, and often develop a tracheal lung. Whenever a tracheal lung is present, the right lung is reduced in size and vascularity. Fossorial snakes often have a long right bronchus.

Fully aquatic snakes present two contrasting conditions. The Acrochordidae and marine Hydrophiidae have tracheal lungs and possess very long but narrow right lungs that, although vascularized to their caudal tip, have a small volume. The hydrostatic implications are obvious for snakes that spend much of their time underwater; a large lung volume would complicate diving. Aquatic Colubridae and Elapidae, lacking tracheal lungs, exhibit short but wide and heavily vascularized right lungs.

Many derived characters define groups from the species level up to that of the family or superfamily. A terminal tracheal entry defines many genera, tribes, and families. A unicameral tracheal lung is characteristic of the Xenophiidae, Tropidophiidae, Viperidae, marine Hydrophiidae, Homalopsinae, Laticaudinae, Xenodermatini, Nothopsini, and Lycophidini. The entire left lung complex has been lost in the Anomalepididae, Leptotyphlopidae, Anomochilidae, Xenophidiidae, Lycophidini, Sibynophiini, and Psammophiini. A long right bronchus defines the Tropidophiinae and Lampropeltini.

Some snakes show associated character complexes. For example, an extensive tracheal lung is associated with a heart that lies far caudad in the body, meeting or overlapping the anterior tip of the liver, with a terminal tracheal entry, lack of a left lung complex and right bronchus, and vascular parenchyma longer than 35% SVL. Conversely, the lack of a tracheal lung is usually associated with a distinct heart-liver gap, a subterminal tracheal entry, a left lung complex that is present, and parenchyma shorter than 20% SVL.

The large amount of morphological variation exhibited by the respiratory system of snakes warrants further study from a phylogenetic standpoint. Knowledge of the lungs and other viscera should increase our understanding of the systematic relationships of snakes. Species descriptions cannot be considered adequate until they include characterization of the visceral anatomy. The topography of an internal organ can easily be summarized with a limited number of variables: its total length and the position of its midpoint in the body, as well as its diameter. These data allow reconstruction of the entire topographical relationships of the viscera, including anterior and posterior points along with gaps and intervals between organs or points. It is hoped that future researchers will stress these aspects of the soft anatomy, as science will benefit from these observations.

ACKNOWLEDGMENTS

It is impossible to acknowledge everyone who has contributed in some way to this review over the past two decades. Data on specimens have been acquired via loans, exchanges, gifts, and purchases of specimens. I am grateful to all who allowed me to dissect material, especially the curators and collection managers of the museums I visited. The collections of the CAS (R. C. Drewes, A. E. Leviton, and J. V. Vindum), FMNH (R. F. Inger, H. Marx, A. Resetar, and H. K. Voris), and MCZ (P. Alberch, J. E. Cadle, J. P. Rosado, and E. E. Williams) have provided the majority of my data base. I thank them as well for financial support. The following institutions also loaned material used in the tables of Appendix C: AMNH (R. G. Zweifel and C. W. Myers), AMS (H. G. Cogger, A. Greer, and R. A. Sadlier), ANSP (E. V. Malnate), BMNH (E. N. Arnold, C. J. McCarthy, and A. F. Stimson), BNHM (J. C. Daniel), BPBM (C. Kishinami), BYU (J. W. Sites, Jr., and S. Skidmore), CIB (E.-M. Zhao),

CIEZAH (A. Mijares), CM (C. J. McCoy and E. J. Censky), CSIRO (J. Wombey), FML (R. F. Laurent and G. Scrocchi), IFAN (A. Seck), IRSNB (G. Lenglet and M. Lang), KU (W. E. Duellman), LACM (R. L. Bezy and J. W. Wright), LIVCM (M. Largen), LSUMZ (D. A. Rossman), MHNG (V. Mahnert and J.-L. Perret), MNHN (I. Ineich), MPM (R. W. Henderson), MRAC (M. Louette), MSNM (L. Capocaccia), MSP (R. Whitaker), MVZ (H. W. Greene), MZUF (B. Lanza and M. Poggesi), MZUSP (A. M. Costa and P. E. Vanzolini), NHRM (S. O. Kullander), NMV (A. J. Coventry), NMBA (E. Kramer and A. Schätti), NMW (H. Grillitsch), NMZB (D. G. Broadley and R. Chidavaenzi), NTM (P. G. Horner), NUVC (G. S. Jones), PEM (W. R. Branch), PNGM (I. Bigilale), QM (P. Couper and J. Covacevich), QVMT (R. Green), RMNH (M. S. Hoogmoed), ROM (R. W. Murphy), SAM (M. N. Hutchinson and T. Schwaner), SDSNH (G. K. Pregill), SDSU (R. E. Etheridge), SIU (R. A. Young), SMNS (A. Schlüter), TAU (H. Mendelssohn), TCWC (J. R. Dixon), TM (W. D. Haacke), TNRC (M. J. Cox and J. Nabhitabhata), UCM (H. M. Smith and S.-K. Wu), UF (W. A. Auffenberg, D. Auth, and P. A. Meylan), UG (B. Hughes), UIMNH (L. Maxson), UMMZ (A. G. Kluge and R. A. Nussbaum), UPNG (J. I. Menzies), USNM (R. Crombie, K. de Queiroz, A. H. Wynn, and G. R. Zug), UTA (J. A. Campbell), WAM (L. Smith and G. M. Storr), ZFMK (W. Böhme), ZIL (N. B. Ananjeva and N. L. Orlov), ZMA (L. van Tuijl), ZMB (R. Günther), ZMH (H.-W. Koepcke), ZMUC (J. B. Rasmussen), ZMUZ (A. Schätti), ZRC (M. C. Yang), and ZSI (R. Mathew). I owe special thanks to native collectors in the Philippines, Nicaragua, and Zaire for snakes, especially Christof from Kinsuka, Zaire. Specimens were also provided from the private collections of Joseph Copp, Barry Hughes, James Lazell, Gerald Marzec, Albert Schwartz, Richard Thomas, and John Visser.

Grants and fellowships that have aided my research include: a grant from Banco Nacional de Nicaragua, Managua (1977–1978), a grant from the Institut de Recherche Scientifique, Kinshasa, Zaire (now Congo) (1980–1981), a Thomas J. Dee fellowship from Field Museum of Natural History, Chicago (1982), three NSF Visiting Scholar fund stipends from the California Academy of Sciences, San Francisco (1983–1985), a Harold A. Dundee herpetological research grant from Louisiana State University, Baton Rouge (1986), a national and local (Louisiana) Sigma Xi Grant-in-Aid (1987), an Ernst Mayr grant from Harvard University, Cambridge (1988), a Zoology and Physiology Graduate Student Organization travel grant from Louisiana State University (1989), a grant from the Chicago Herpetological Society, Chicago (1993), a Stearns Grant from the California Academy of Sciences (1994), a grant from the New England Herpetological Society, Boston (1994), and a Thomas J. Dee fellowship from the Field Museum of Natural History, Chicago (1996).

Numerous individuals kindly provided published literature and shared unpublished manuscripts, including W. Böhme, D. G. Broadley, J. S. Keogh, E. V. Malnate, H. Marx, H. S. McDonald, S. B. McDowell, J. B. Rasmussen, A. Resetar, G. Underwood, J. Visser, K. L. Williams, and A. H. Wynn. Numerous libraries (public, private, and personal), librarians, and colleagues provided access to much-needed and often rare and valuable references. Translations were provided by Herman in den Bosch (Dutch), Ingela Chef-Johansson (Swedish), Roxane Coombs (French), Katharina Hespe (German), Shoko Kushinara (Japanese), Mathias Lang (Dutch, Flemish, German), Angela Lim (Chinese), Shiu-Ping Osborn (Chinese), Andrea Schwartz (German), and Marina Werbeloff (Russian). Kraig Adler and Timothy Perry (Cornell University) helped prepare the figures.

This review is dedicated to Richard Etheridge, my mentor and undergraduate advisor at San Diego State University, who enabled me to focus my research interests on the tracheal lung of snakes, subsequently upon the ophidian respiratory system, and finally upon the visceral anatomy. My studies on snake lungs began in 1974 under his guidance, and the results thus far are attributable to his encouragement, inspiration, and creativity.

APPENDIX A: SYNONYMY OF OPHIDIAN PULMONARY TERMINOLOGY

FAVEOLAR, EDICULAR, OR TRABECULAR PARENCHYMA

Reticular compages of valvulae conniventes (Tyson, 1683), Zellenbildungs und tiefen Zellen (Meckel, 1818); fine lattice-like net-work of vessels (Carus, 1827); luftcellulernes (Retzius, 1830); mailles (Lereboullet, 1838); réseau vasculaire à larges ou mailles polygones (Cuvier, 1840); cancelli or cancellated structure of the parietes (Cantor, 1841); blaseformiga med grofva celler (Nilsson, 1842); mailles celluleuses (Duméril and Bibron, 1844); Maschenbildung (Stannius, 1846); Maschen (Stannius, 1856); vascular rete (T. Williams, 1859); réticules vasculaires (Gervais, 1866); honeycombed parietes (R. Owen, 1866); lacework of air-cells (E. Nicholson, 1874), trabécules pulmonaires et alvéoles pulmonaires (Tourneux and Herrmann, 1876); Nische (Wiedersheim, 1883), respiratory air-cells (Carus and Otto, 1885); sacs or air-sacs (W. S. Miller, 1893); trabeculae and reticulate structure (Cope, 1894a); reticulate bars and laminae (Cope, 1900); Nischen (Moser, 1902), alveoli (Beddard, 1906b); honey-comb cells (Lydekker et al., 1912); pulmonary pleura (Thompson, 1913c); air-cells (Thompson, 1914b); infundibula (Kingsley, 1917); respiratory cells (Dowsett, 1928), sacs pulmonaires complique (Perrier, 1928); respiratorische Lungenteile (Lüdicke, 1939); tracheoles and bronchioles (J. C. George and Varde, 1941); poumon acineux (Lacoste and Baudrimont, 1942); alveolar septa (Karlstrom, 1952); trabecular tissue (Bergman, 1950); zone trabéculaire (Bergman, 1952);

infundibulae (Varde, 1951); calyculated epithelium (Kurtz, 1953); trabekulärens Lungengewebe (Bergman, 1962); lacework of air-cells (Gharpurey, 1962); primitive alveoli (Okada et al., 1962); bronchial air tubes (Ballard, 1964); alvéolos pulmonares (Pisano and Barbieri, 1967); fluted surface (Barme, 1968), alveolar ostia (Larson and van de Velde, 1969); areolae (McDowell, 1972b); alveolar ridges (Graham et al., 1975); Ductus und Sacculi alveolares (Sparing, 1976); air sac (Meban, 1978); faveoli or faveolar parenchyma (Duncker, 1978c); shallow pits (Seymour, 1978); ediculae or edicular parenchyma (Duncker, 1981); primary and secondary infundibulae (Rosenzweig, 1981); alveolus pulmonis (Ma, 1982a); reticular plicae (Griner, 1983); trabeculae or trabecular parenchyma (Perry, 1983); reticulated, open-end sacs (Frye, 1984); radial chambers (Gratz et al., 1981); septa (Donald and Lillywhite, 1989b), areolae (Mao, 1993), sacculae (Pastor, 1995).

LUMEN OF LUNG

Vesicule (Tyson, 1683); central cavity (Wiedersheim and Parker, 1886); Mesobronchus (Moser, 1902); main bronchus (Wiedersheim and Parker, 1907); Vorbronchus (H. Marcus, 1927); atrium (Walter, 1929); Lungenraum (Oidumi, 1940); central canal (Brongersma 1952c); canal spacieux (Brongersma, 1958a); central cavity (Jollie, 1962); zentraler Raum (Sparing, 1976); axial chamber (Luchtel and Kardong, 1981); large axial chamber (Lillywhite 1987a).

ORBITONASAL TROUGH

Mundhöhle (Meckel, 1818); Rima glottidis (Carus, 1827); choanae, internal nares, choanal openings (Frazzetta, 1966); ductus nasopharyngeus (McDowell, 1972b); orbitonasal trough (Groombridge, 1979); "inner nostrils" (Liu and Chen, 1983).

LARYNX

Kehlkopf (Henle, 1839); processus arytaenoideus (Henle, 1839); cartilago arytaenoidea (Henle, 1839); cartilago cricothyroidea (Henle, 1839); processus epiglotticus (Henle, 1839); cartilago cricoidea (Henle, 1839); processus arytaenoïdei (Stannius, 1846); larynx (Stannius, 1850); laryngeal septum (Young et al., 1995).

EPIGLOTTAL KEEL

Epiglottis (C. A. White, 1884); vertical epiglottis (Cope, 1900); small tubercle of glottis (Cope, 1900); filament of cartilaginous flesh (Ditmars, 1907); processus medianus (Lüdicke, 1962); preglottal keel (Saiff, 1975); low horizontal ridge (Saiff, 1975); small rounded projection (Saiff, 1975); epiglottal keel (Young et al., 1995).

GLOTTAL TUBE

Anneaux cartiligineux joints les uns aux autres (Lacepède, 1790); tube cartilagineux flexible (Lereboullet, 1838); ring-like fenestrated cartilage (MacAlister, 1878); crico-tracheal cartilages (Karlstrom, 1952); glottal tube (Kardong, 1972a).

TRACHEA

Aspera arteria (Aldrovandi, 1640); trachée-artère (Lacepède, 1790); tracheae... longam, cartilaginibus semiannularibus distinctam (Nitzsch, 1808); trachée-artère extrêmement longue (Cuvier, 1840); Luftröhre (Stannius, 1846); trachea (R. Owen, 1866); windpipe (Beddard, 1906a); gutter (Beddard, 1904b); oral mechanischer Teil (Wolf, 1933); kraniale extrapulmonäre Trachea (Suomalainen, 1939); kaudale pulmonäre Trachea (Suomalainen, 1939); tracheal tube (Deoras and Vad, 1966); traquéia (Gomes et al., 1989); ventral canal or intrapulmonary trachea (Pastor, 1995).

TRACHEAL RINGS

Semi-annular cartilages (Tyson, 1683); demi-anneaux (Lacepède, 1790); Knorpel-ringe der Luftröhre (Meckel, 1818); Luftrohrenringe (Meckel, 1833); demi-anneaux cartilagineux (Schlegel, 1837a); Kehlkopfknorpel (Henle, 1839); anneaux incomplets et cerceaux complets (Cuvier, 1840); cartilaginous half rings (Cope, 1895b); cartilaginous rings (Beddard, 1903); tracheal rings (Beddard, 1903); incomplete rings (Beddard, 1906a); tracheal semirings (Beddard, 1906b); cartilaginous hoops (Beddard, 1906b); semi-rings (Thompson, 1913c); tracheal cartilages (Thompson, 1914b); crico-tracheal bars (Karlstrom, 1952); Halbringe (Sparing, 1976); tracheal arms (Ramsay, 1979); semilunate rings (Rosenzweig, 1981).

RIGHT BRONCHUS

Trachée intrapulmonaire (Cuvier, 1840); cerceaux dans la paroi du sac droit (Cuvier, 1840); demi-canal des plaques cartilagineuse transversales (Milne-Edwards, 1857b); narrow and shallow kind of air-canal (R. Owen, 1866); intrapulmonary bronchus (Moser, 1902); extrapulmonary bronchus (Moser, 1902); median, thin fibrous wall of trachea (Beddard, 1903); bronchus (Beddard, 1904b); tracheal gutter (Beddard, 1906a); bronchial semirings (Beddard, 1906b); flat band (Beddard, 1906b); tracheal extension (Beddard, 1906b); bronchial extension (Beddard, 1906b); intrapulmonary bronchus (Beddard, 1908); narrow fibrous intrapulmonary band (Thompson, 1914b); intrapulmonary streak (Thompson, 1914b); Bronchialrinne (Wolf, 1933); Hauptbronchus (Oidumi, 1940); bronche intra-pulmonaire (Lacoste and Baudrimont, 1942); intrapulmonary trachea, bronchus and trough (Kardong, 1972b); intrapulmonary extension (Underwood, 1976a); single bronchus (Stinner, 1982b).

BRONCHIAL FORAMINA

Small perforations (Beddard, 1908).

POST-BRONCHIAL EXTENSION

Une bande ligamenteuse (Cuvier, 1840); white seam (Beddard, 1903); fibrous band (Beddard, 1906b); seam (Beddard, 1906b); rudimentary seam (Beddard, 1906b); longitudinal seam (Beddard, 1908).

FREE TIPS

Les bords libres de ses anneaux sont dentelés (Lereboullet, 1838); cerceaux plus forts ayant leurs extrémités libres (Cuvier, 1840); cartilage-ends or free extremities (Thompson, 1914b); dorsal ends of the cartilages or free tips (Kardong, 1972a); dorsally directed horns (Heatwole and Seymour, 1975b).

TRACHEAL MEMBRANE

Sac pulmonaire très large et spacieaux (Schlegel, 1837a); trachée . . . partie membraneuse (Cuvier, 1840); portion membraneuse de la trachée (Rufz, 1859); dilatation of the membranous part of the tracheal tube (R. Owen, 1866); membranous interspace (Beddard, 1903); fibrous fold (Beddard, 1906a); air sac (Beddard, 1906b); dorsal membranous interval (Beddard, 1906b); interannular membrane (Beddard, 1906b); erweiterte Trachea (F. Werner, 1911); tracheal membrane (Thompson, 1913c); tracheales Bindegewebe (Suomalainen, 1939); dorsal ligament or wall (Brongersma, 1949); extensive sac or tracheal expansion (Gans and Richmond, 1957); tracheal wall (Robb, 1960); paries membranaceus (Heyder, 1968); strip of membrane (McDowell, 1969b); dorsal zone of trachea . . . without cartilaginous semirings (McDowell, 1970); membranous dorsal wall of trachea (McDowell, 1972a); wide and flat sac of connective tissue (Gans, 1974); roof of the trachea (Underwood, 1976b); soft membrane (Groombridge, 1980); dorsal membranous surface (Stinner, 1980); post-dorsal part of the trachea (Russell, 1980); tracheal muscle (Frye, 1984).

TRACHEAL LUNG

Partie supérieure de poumons (Bonnaterre, 1790); anterior pulmonis (Westphal, 1806); vorwärts gerückte Lunge (Meckel, 1833); poumon . . . cellules . . . en avant du coeur sur les membranes de la trachée (Schlegel, 1837a); la partie celluleuse du poumon . . . soit en avant du coeur (Cuvier, 1840); sac pulmonaire (Cuvier, 1840); trachée . . . réticulée, celluleuse et vasculeuse (Cuvier, 1840); cellular trachea (Cantor, 1841); vesicular cavity (Gray, 1842); poumon accessoire (Milne-Edwards, 1857b); le poumon . . . deux cotés de la trachée (Rufz, 1859); dilatation of the membranous part of the tracheal tube (R. Owen, 1866); einzige Lunge (Peters, 1882); accessory lung (Günther, 1886); tracheal lung and tracheal gland (Cope, 1894a); precardiac diverticulum (Beddard, 1906b); accessory breathing organ (G. A. Boulenger, 1913); extrapulmonary respiratory organ (Karlstrom, 1952); poumon-trachéal (Brongersma, 1958b); anterior lung (Klauber, 1956); annexe du poumon (Dottrens and Aellen, 1963); vordere Lunge (Heyder, 1968); poumon trachéen (Saint Girons and Saint Girons, 1974); vascular lung (Heatwole and Seymour, 1975b); right anterior lung (Russell, 1980); "right lung front part" (Ma, 1982a); compound tracheal lung (McDowell, 1987); lobular lung (Heatwole and Guinea, 1993); pulmão (Gomes and Puorto, 1994).

VASCULAR TRACHEAL AIR CHAMBERS

Stärkere vertiefungen Säcken (Meckel, 1818); coarse cells (Cope, 1894a); air-cells (Kingsley, 1888); respiratory chambers (Kingsley, 1888); tracheal air sacs (Kingsley, 1888); two rows of sacs (Brongersma, 1952c); central pulmonary chamber (J. C. George and Shah, 1956); tracheal appendages (Brongersma, 1958a); sacs aériens (Brongersma, 1958b); appendices ont une structure alvéolaire (Brongersma, 1958b); petit poumon accessoiré (Brongersma, 1958b); compartmentized parenchyma (Standaert and Johansen, 1974); small lobules (Heatwole and Seymour, 1975b); lateral vascularized diverticulae (Gans, 1978); air spaces (Perry, 1981); large, rounded cavities or bronchioles (Robb, 1960); tracheal air-sacs (Underwood, 1967); Kammerbildung (Heyder, 1968); lobular lung (Heatwole and Guinea, 1993).

AVASCULAR TRACHEAL AIR CHAMBERS
Poches latérales (Cuvier, 1840); diverticula (Beddard, 1906a); air sacs (Beddard, 1906b); membranous sacs (Beddard, 1903); intercalary sacs (Beddard, 1903); cervical set of air-chambers (Thompson, 1914b); compartments with transverse partitions (Thompson, 1914b); imperforate compartments (Thompson, 1914b); poumon . . . cloisonnement transversal incomplet (Perrier, 1928); atrium (Walter, 1929); auxiliary air-sacs (Pooley, 1946); anangious air-sacs (Brongersma, 1957a); tracheal air sac (Gans and Richmond, 1957); smooth-walled anangious air-sacs (Brongersma, 1958a); separate membranous sacs (McDowell, 1972a); air space (Perry, 1981).

TRACHEAL FORAMINA
Foramina (Cope, 1894a); symmetrical pores (Cope, 1894a); oval foramina (Beddard, 1903); apertures (Thompson, 1914b); pores (Brongersma, 1952c); perforations de la membrane dorsale de la trachée-artère (Brongersma, 1958b); tracheal perforations or apertures (Robb, 1960); dorsal tracheal perforations (McDowell, 1972a).

CARDIAC LUNG
Einschnürung zwischen vorderer Theil der Lunge und dem hintern Theile (Meckel, 1818); Einschnürung in der Gegend des Herzens (Meckel, 1818); partie membraneuse du poumon (Carus, 1827); interstitial trachea (Bergman, 1958a); intercalated trachea (Bergman, 1958a); narrow, canalized constriction (Robb, 1960); verengte Zone (Heyder, 1968); cardiac flexure (Graham et al., 1975); cardiac constriction (Heatwole and Seymour, 1975b); Einnischung der Herzregion (Sparing, 1976); conspicuous constriction (Seymour et al., 1981b); "heart pressure indentation" (Liu and Chen, 1983).

RIGHT LUNG
Vesicula oblonga membranosa (Aldrovandi, 1640); membranaceous . . . air bladder (Sloane, 1725); saccum pulmonalem, celluleuse et membraneuse (Seba, 1735); partie inférieur de poumons (Bonnaterre, 1790); major pulmonis (Westphal, 1806); pulmone dextrum contra maximum, longissimum (Nitzsch, 1808); Hauptlunge (Meckel, 1833); vesicles (Hopkinson and Pancoast, 1837); un seul sac (Schlegel, 1837); poumon principal (Lereboullet, 1838); sac pulmonaire développé (Cuvier, 1840); poumon développé (Cuvier, 1840); active lung (Dallas, 1855); pneumatischer Sack (Stannius, 1856); sacs à parois minces (Chenu and

Desmarest, 1857); grand poumon (Milne-Edwards, 1857b); grand sac pulmonaire (Gervais, 1869); functional lung (R. Owen, 1866); poumon principal (Milne-Edwards, 1871); single lung (Cope, 1894a); dorsal lung (Cope, 1894a); left lung (Cope, 1894a); true lung (Cope, 1894a); normal lung (Cope, 1894a); principal normal lung (Cope, 1895b); pulmonary lung (Cope, 1895b); posttracheal lung (Cope, 1894a); fully-developed lung (Beddard, 1903); thoracic lung, bronchial lung (Beddard, 1904b); air sac (Beddard, 1906a); principal lung (Beddard, 1906b); large lung (Beddard, 1906b); rechten Pectorallunge (Werner, 1911); posterior lung (Robb, 1960); hintere Lunge (Heyder, 1968); proper lung (Bellairs, 1969); saccular lung (Kashyap and Sohoni, 1973); "middle lung" (Liu and Chen, 1983); central lung (Russell, 1980); right lobe (Deoras and Vad, 1973); principal respiratory unit (Heatwole and Seymour, 1975b); "right lung back part" (Ma, 1982a); pulmão direito (Gomes et al., 1989).

RIGHT ORIFICE
Large orifice (Rees, 1820); grand orifice (Cuvier, 1840); larger perforation (Thompson, 1913c); larger aperture (Underwood, 1976a).

ANTERIOR LOBE
Cul de sac (Hopkinson and Pancoast, 1837); appendice conique (Lereboullet, 1838); cul-de-sac antérieur (Cuvier, 1840); small pouch (R. Owen, 1866); pulmonary sac (Günther, 1886); proximal auricle (Cope, 1894a); proximal pocket (Cope, 1894a); proximal diverticulum (Cope, 1894b); pyramidal caecum (Beddard, 1906b); forward pocket (Beddard, 1906b); anterior diverticulum (Beddard, 1906b); anterior lobe (Beddard, 1906b); headward extension of lung (Beddard, 1906b); forward caecal extension (Beddard, 1908); anterior process (Beddard, 1908); free apex (Thompson, 1913c); apical lobe (Karlstrom, 1952); apex (Thompson, 1914b); forward pocket or extension (Underwood, 1967), Apicallappen (Rietschel, 1968); antero-lateral pocket (Groombridge, 1980); diverticulum (Luchtel and Kardong, 1981).

VASCULAR LUNG
Pulmonis pars superior (Valentini, 1720); partis superioris pulmonis interna superficies cellulosa (Seba, 1735); poumon proprement (Lereboullet, 1838); superior vascular portion (Jones, 1856); portion respiratoire (Baudrimont, 1929); respiratorischer Teil (Wolf, 1933); bronchial lung (J. C. George and Shah, 1956); central lung (Klauber, 1956); vascular region (McDonald, 1959a); alveolar lung (J. C. George and Shah, 1965); faveolar region (M. M. Grant et al., 1981); respiratory region (Luchtel and Kardong, 1981); faveolar gas exchange region (Maina, 1989).

AVASCULAR MIDVENTRAL STRIP
Streifen herabläuft (Meckel, 1818); face inférieure purement membraneuse sans aucune trace de cellules (Cuvier, 1840); membraneous sheath on ventral side of bronchial lung (J. C. George and Shah, 1956); non-vascular membrane (Malnate and Underwood, 1988); smooth strip (Malnate and Underwood, 1988).

SEMISACCULAR LUNG

Semisaccular lung (J. C. George and Shah, 1965); zone of transition (Phleger et al., 1978); semi-saccular transition zone (Read and Donnelly, 1972); transition zone (Gratz et al., 1981).

SACCULAR LUNG

Large bladder without any cells (Tyson, 1683); pulmonis pars inferior, vesicularis (Valentini, 1720); pulmonis pars inferior, intus laevis (Seba, 1735); partie inférieur des poumons . . . est purement membraneuse . . . sans vésicules (Bonnaterre, 1790); grand sac pulmonaire . . . perdoit les cellules . . . absolument simple (Cuvier, 1805); saccus pulmonis (Westphal, 1806); simple thin membranous bladder (Rees, 1820); posterior pulmonis . . . minor vesicae membranaceae (Westphal, 1806); membranous bag, simple membranous cavity (Blumenbach et al., 1827); organe simplement membraneuses . . . vessie natatoire (Carus, 1835); une poche membraneuse (Schlegel, 1837a); une poche à air extrêmement volumineuse (Schlegel, 1837b); poumon membraneuse (Lereboullet, 1838); sac pulmonaire ou réservoir aérien (Cuvier, 1840); avascular sac (Cantor, 1841); Lungensack (Stannius, 1856); pneumatischer Sack (Stannius, 1856); non-cellulated portion (T. Williams, 1859); simple sac sans cellules pulmonaires et sans cils vibratiles (Bert, 1869); vesicular air-reservoir (Carus, 1835); transparent air sac (Colton, 1903a); anangious region (Beddard, 1904b); swim bladder (Beddard, 1904b); Luftsack (Oppel, 1905); air-sac (Thompson, 1913c); anangious air-sac (Thompson, 1914b); air reservoir (Atwood, 1918); sac aérien postérieur (Baudrimont, 1929); kaudal mechanischer Teil (Wolf, 1933); Luftsäcke (Marcus, 1937); anangious air sac (Brongersma, 1949); air sack (Bergman, 1950); saccular lung (Varde, 1951); sac pulmonaire (Bergman, 1952); lung sac (Bergman, 1956b); saccular chamber (J. C. George and Shah, 1956); nonvascular lung (Klauber, 1956); posterior lung (Klauber, 1956); caudal smooth-walled air-sac (Brongersma, 1957b); air sac (Brattstrom, 1959); Lungensack (Bergman, 1962); Sacklunge (Heyder, 1968); simple air-sac (Bellairs, 1969), sac aérifère (Lécuru-Renous and Platel, 1970b); gas bag (Read and Donnelly, 1972); Luftsackregion (Sparing, 1976); sac (Donnelly and Woolcock, 1977); caudal dilatation (Duncker, 1978a); posterior nonvascular sac (Russell, 1980); bladder-like tube (Russell, 1980); membranous caudal air sac (Stinner, 1980); avascular dilatation (Duncker, 1981); posterior nonfaveolar region (Luchtel and Kardong, 1981); saccular region (Luchtel and Kardong, 1981); "storage air sack" (Liu and Chen, 1983); blind-ending sac (Lillywhite, 1987a); saco aéreo (Gomes and Puorto, 1994); aparenchymal region (Perry, this volume).

THORACONUCHAL LUNG

Single lung (Cantor, 1841); solitary lung (Deoras, 1965); vascular lung (Heatwole and Seymour, 1975b); faveolar region (Gratz et al., 1981).

LEFT LUNG

Pulmone sinistrum liberum, minimum (Nitzsch, 1808); Nebenlunge (Meckel, 1833); rudiment du poumon gauche (Carus, 1835); petit poumon accessoire (Schlegel, 1837a); lobe pulmonaire accessoire (Schlegel, 1837a); sac accessoire

(Lereboullet, 1838); poumon rudimentaire (Lereboullet, 1838); petite vésicule (Cuvier, 1840); rudiment du second poumon (Cuvier, 1840); sac pulmonaire rudimentaire (Cuvier, 1840); second sac pulmonaire (Cuvier, 1840); poumon accessoire (Cuvier, 1840); "accessory pulmonary lobe" (Schlegel, 1843); linke Lunge unbedeutender (Stannius, 1846); kleines Lungenrudiment (Stannius, 1856); obliterated appendage (T. Williams, 1859); atrophied lung or small pouch (R. Owen, 1866); petit poumon (Milne-Edwards, 1871); right lung (Cope, 1894a); posttracheal lung (Cope, 1894a); rudimental lung (Cope, 1894a); second lung (Cope, 1894a); ventral lung (Cope, 1894a); pulmonary lung (Cope, 1894a); petit sac (Jammes, 1904); rudimentary lung (Beddard, 1903); thoracic lung (Beddard, 1906a); pulmonary appendage (Beddard, 1906b); vesicle . . . without pulmonary tissue (Thompson, 1913c); poumon appendiculaire (Bergman, 1952); secondary lung (Bergman, 1955a); accessory lung (Bergman, 1958b); rudimentary left lung (Klauber, 1956); poumon gauche rudimentaire (Brongersma, 1958b); left lobe (Deoras and Vad, 1973); ovoid diverticulum (McDowell, 1974b); pulmão esquerdo (Gomes et al., 1989).

LEFT LUNG BLIND SAC
Blind sac (Cope, 1894a); fibrous sac (Thompson, 1914b); ventral blind sac (Bergman, 1950); small bulb (Deoras and Vad, 1973).

LEFT BRONCHUS
Halbe Knorpelringe (Meckel, 1833); cerceaux extra-pulmonaires (Cuvier, 1840); cerceaux intra-pulmonaires (Cuvier, 1840); terminal whole-ring (R. Owen, 1866); cartilaginous half rings (Cope, 1894a), short tube (Cope, 1894a); cartilaginous semirings (Beddard, 1906b); Hauptbronchus (Oidumi, 1940); "branch of trachea" (Ma, 1982a), left bronchus (Wallach, 1985).

LEFT ORIFICE
Enfoncement en cul-de-sac (Carus, 1827); orifice du sac accessoire (Lereboullet, 1838); orifice (Cuvier, 1840); grand orifice (Cuvier, 1840); orifice (R. Owen, 1866); foramen (Cope, 1894a); foramen bronchiale (Cope, 1894a); bronchial foramen (Cope, 1894a); minute orifice of 2nd bronchus (Beddard, 1906a); tracheal gutter perforation (Beddard, 1906b); aperture (Beddard, 1906b); smaller perforation (Thompson, 1913c); pore (Atwood, 1916); ouverture du poumon appendiculaire (Bergman, 1952); ouverture du poumon accessoire (Bergman, 1955b); smaller aperture (Underwood, 1976a); left orifice (Wallach, 1991).

APPENDIX B: SYSTEMATIC LIST OF SPECIMENS AND ILLUSTRATIONS

Key to superscripts, indicating illustrations of the following: 1 = viscera, 2 = orbitonasal trough, 3 = glottis, 4 = larynx, 5 = trachea and inflation of tracheal membrane, 6 = lungs and lung interiors, 7 = cross-sections, diagrams, and schematics of lungs, 8 = ultrastructure of respiratory system, 9 = pulmonary vessels.

"SNAKE"

Snake (Seba, 1735[1]; Gegenbaur, 1870[9], 1878b[9]; Mojsvár, 1885[9]; Brehm, 1885[6]; W. S. Miller, 1893[7]; Colton, 1903a[7]; Oppel, 1905[7]; Shipley and MacBride, 1920[9]; Lacoste and Baudrimont, 1942[7]; Boué and Chanton, 1959[7]; F. N. White, 1959[9]; Alvarez del Toro, 1960[1]; Toland and Dehne, 1960[1,9]; Villa, 1962[1]; Ballard, 1964[7]; Inger, 1966[9]; Huntington, 1973[1]; Webster and Webster, 1974[7]; Underwood, 1976a[6]; Frank, 1978[1], 1979[1]; M. E. Fowler, 1980[7]; Haast and Anderson, 1981[6]; Chiodini et al., 1982[1,7]; Griner, 1983[8]; Hackbarth, 1985[1]; Mattison, 1986[1], 1991[1]; Patterson, 1986[1]; Coborn, 1987[1]; Hilf et al., 1990[5,6]; Ross and Marzec, 1990[3]; R. Walker, 1990[1]; J. A. Burton, 1991[1]; Cox, 1991[3,5]; Shine, 1991[1]; Weidensaul, 1991[1]; Brazaitis and Watanabe, 1992[1]; S. Parker, 1993[1]; Withers and O'Shea, 1993[1]; Bauchot, 1994[1]; Mattison, 1995[1]).

ANOMALEPIDIDAE

Anomalepis mexicanus (Underwood, 1967; McDowell, 1972c[2,5]; LSUMZ 19450–51; NUVC 944), *Helminthophis flavoterminatus* (Brongersma, 1958a; BMNH 1886.7.27.7; MCZ 5129–30; ZMB 6708, 15872), *H. frontalis* (MCZ 55117), *Helminthophis* sp. A (USNM 286925), *H. praeocularis* (FMNH 30814; MCZ 19196), *Liotyphlops albirostris* (Brongersma, 1958a; CAS 94620; CIEZAH 392–93; FMNH 216257; KU 116887–88, 116891; MCZ 165197; USNM 306188), *L. anops* (MCZ 67937, 150203), *L. argaleus* (MCZ 66383), *L. beui* (MCZ 16702, 17842, 142557, 142576), *L. ternetzii* (LSUMZ 46268), *Typhlophis squamosus* (KU 69819; MCZ 145403; ZMB 48044).

TYPHLOPIDAE

Typhlopid (Stannius, 1856; McDowell, 1974a), *Acutotyphlops infralabialis* (Wallach, 1995c; MCZ 65991, MVZ 40753), *A. kunuaensis* (Wong, 1994[7]; Wallach 1995c; MCZ 66012–13, 72132, 76206, 76682–87, 76690–95, 76697, 76705, 76707–08, 76710, 76712, 76718, 76720, 76722–23, 76724, 76726, 76926, 76930, 76959–61, 76967, 76969, 76971, 76980, 76990, 76699–01, 77005, 77007, 77016, 77021, 124473, 175099), *A. solomonis* (MCZ 65996, 145955, 175090, 175099), *A. subocularis* (MCZ 175091; NMBA 11706, 11710), *Ramphotyphlops acuticaudus* (CAS-SU 19079–80; FMNH 42453; SDSNH 68437), *R. affinis* (FMNH 97878, 97880; MCZ 35020; QM 11631, 46706), *R. albiceps* (MCZ 177983, 181196; SLS 196; ZMUC 52204), *R. angusticeps* (FMNH 41354, 41968; ZMUC 52220), *R. australis* (Robb, 1960[5,6,9]; BYU 38834; FMNH 97876; SAM 39175, 40981, 41666, 42472; WAM 36567, 49164), *R. becki* (Wallach, 1995c; MCZ 110252, 110256, 110258), *R. bituberculatus* (CAS 74317; NMV 12160, 12723, 61739, 66876; SAM 12796, 29513, 38082, 38362, 42321), *R. braminus* (Nakamura, 1941[7,9]; Kashyap, 19507; J. C. George and Shah, 19566,7, 19656; Brongersma, 1958a; Wallach, 1993b; CAS 94443; FMNH 18283, 53251; MCZ 172796, 175924; UMMZ 167976–77, 3 uncat.), *R. broomi* (AMS 128848; MCZ 175104; QM 20315), *R. centralis* (SAM 40480), *R. chamodracaena* (MCZ 175101; QM 31963), *R. cumingii* (Wallach, 1993b; CAS 169878; CAS-SU 25483; FMNH 41092, 53221), *R. depressus* (Wallach, 1996b; MCZ 92508, 90994, 90998, 140722, 153106–07; ZMH 4167), *R. diversus* (WAM 54027, 75828), *R. endoterus* (SAM 18868, 26647, 38481, 39746), *R. erycinus* (MCZ 49619, 49396), *R. exocoeti* (MCZ 28643), *R. flaviventer* (Brongersma, 1958a; Wallach, 1995c, 1996b; BPBM 3127; FMNH 42352, 73846; MCZ 7571, 171562–63; USNM 216003),

R. *grypus* (MCZ 35019; QM 27510, 39487; WAM 44820), R. *guentheri* (MCZ 48843; NMV 10777), R. *hamatus* (WAM 66323, 69242), R. *leptosomus* (MCZ 32809), R. *ligatus* (Robb, 1960[5,6,9]; CAS 135108), R. *lineatus* (Brongersma, 1958a; FMNH 131235, 158645, 197951; RMNH 5788), R. *minimus* (AMS 40918); R. *multilineatus* (ZMA 17765), R. *nigrescens* (CAS 84090; FMNH 97892; MCZ 129883; NMV 55375, 60871, 129883; 1 SDSU uncat.), R. *nigroterminatus* (MCZ 67926; WAM 47784), R. *olivaceus* (Brongersma, 1958a; Wallach, 1993b; FMNH 131588; MCZ 45757), R. *pinguis* (MCZ 32813; NMV 7173), R. *polygrammicus* (Robb, 1960[5,6,9]; FMNH 97892, 154852; MCZ 25289, 74162, 135506), R. *proximus* (Robb, 1960[5,6,9]; CAS 84075; NMV 61647, 61667, 64910), R. *silvia* (QM 27386), R. *tovelli* (MCZ 48845), R. *unguirostris* (FMNH 97884–85; NMV 4515; QM 29747), R. *waitii* (NMV 7196; WAM 89295, 104279), R. *wiedii* (CAS 84079, 84086; FMNH 73853, 97882–83; MCZ 10224; QM 23329, 36914, 43373), *Ramphotyphlops* sp. A (FMNH 180003–07; ZMUC 52174), *Ramphotyphlops* sp. B (MCZ 72108, 92527), *Rhinotyphlops acutus* (Kashyap, 1950[9]; Deoras and Vad, 1973; Wallach, 1994b; CAS-SU 12515; FMNH 8651; UF 19900), R. *anomalus* (Wallach, 1993a; MCZ 25870), R. *ataeniatus* (CAS 151200), R. *boylei* (NMZB 15184), R. *caecus* (Brongersma, 1958a; BMNH 1980.28; CM 90395; FMNH 212324; MCZ 13600; 2 SDSU uncat.; 1 USNM uncat.), R. *crossii* (FMNH 25055; MCZ 49012; PEM 4901), R. *debilis* (MNHN 1991.378), R. *feae* (ZMUC 257), R. *gracilis* (MCZ 42896, 54051–52, 54054, 1 MCZ uncat.), R. *graueri* (MCZ 48052–54; 1 SDSU uncat.), R. *kibarae* (MCZ 54379), R. *lalandei* (CAS 160747; MCZ 29418, 43020; PEM 702, 7819, 8227, 8550, 8868, 9822–25, 9827), R. *lumbriciformis* (MCZ 46115, 48045, 48047), R. *newtoni* (UMMZ 187932), R. *pallidus* (FMNH 62344–46; MCZ 53324, 53332), R. *praeocularis* (FMNH 75088; ZMUC 52197), R. *rufescens* (MNHN 1995.9606), R. *schinzi* (FMNH 187111, 233343; TM 48347, 48928), R. *schlegelii* (Stannius, 1856; Butner, 1963a; Wallach, 1993a; Wong, 1994[7]; FMNH 224413; MCZ 12626, 44457, 52549, 52551, 52554–60, 52562, 52565, 52568–69, 52572, 52575, 52578–79, 52584, 52587, 52594–95, 52609, 52612–14, 52616–22; 1 SDSU uncat.; ZMUC 52198), R. *scorteccii* (MCZ 74456, 74458), R. *simoni* (FMNH 69219; MCZ 22083; USNM 336231), R. *somalicus* (ANSP 4692–93; MCZ 126236), R. *stejnegeri* (BMNH 1980.32), R. *sudanensis* (MCZ 13599), R. *unitaeniatus* (MCZ 18175, 40080; ZMB 21154a–b, 29080), *Rhinotyphlops* sp. A (MNHN 1992.4621), *Rhinotyphlops* sp. B (PEM 4643), *Rhinotyphlops* sp. (Pagenstecher, 1881), *Typhlops albanalis* (NHRM 351), T. *angolensis* (McDowell, 1972c[2]; BMNH 1980.27; 9 IRSL uncat.; MCZ 57454, 170384–85; MZUSP 8165; ZMUC 96061), T. *arenarius* (MNHN 1933.83; 1 UMMZ uncat.), T. *ater* (FMNH 142108, MCZ 33505, ZMA 17737), T. *beddomii* (MCZ 3913, 3929, 175867; FMNH 217694), T. *bibronii* (Wallach, 1993a; FMNH 224414; MCZ 21438; TM 33718, 68956, 71072, 75744–45), T. *biminiensis* (KU 269656–57; MCZ 68944), T. *bisubocularis* (USNM 43455), T. *blanfordi* (MCZ 84329), T. *boettgeri* (FMNH 73112, 73114–15; MNHN 1901.177; UMMZ 41092, 129031–32, 197245), T. *brongersmianus* (FMNH 35590–91, 161601, 195928), T. *caecatus* (MCZ 55381), T. *capitulatus* (KU 269674–75; MCZ 121901), T. *castanotus* (Wallach, 1993a; CAS 127973; CAS-SU 27942; MCZ 25594), T. *catapontus* (KU 269705), T. *caymanensis* (KU 269714; MCZ 79177), T. *collaris* (Wallach, 1993a; UF 54186, 68443), T. *congestus* (BMNH 1980.31; CAS 16954; 7 IRSL uncat.; MHNG 1453.13–14), T. *cuneirostris* (CAS 131682, 131687; MCZ 74451–52, 74464), T.

decorosus (MCZ 14996), *T. decorsei* (MNHN 1950.210; 1 UMMZ uncat.), *T. depressiceps* (MCZ 145954), *T. diardii* (Wallach, 1993a; CAS-SU 13982; FMNH 180008, 252064; MCZ 2284b), *T. domerguei* (UMMZ 197249), *T. dominicanus* (KU 269715; MCZ 10694, 57815), *T. elegans* (Wallach, 1993a; MCZ 25871; UMMZ 187897), *T. epactius* (KU 269726), *T. exiguus* (ZMB 50030), *T. floweri* (MCZ 181198; NMBA 328), *T. fornasinii* (Wallach, 1993a; MCZ 41947; TM 4836, 46001, 46022; PEM 12119–21, 12123, 12173–77), *T. fredparkeri* (MCZ 142651), *T. gierrai* (MCZ 23084, 23088–89; ZMUC 52191), *T. gonavensis* (KU 269773–75), *T. granti* (KU 269780; MCZ 38301), *T. hectus* (KU 288542, 288544, 288553; MCZ 167775), *T. hedraeus* (Wallach, 1993b; MCZ 17578; USNM 229285, 1 USNM uncat.), *T. humboldti* n. sp. (MNHN 1889.25), *T. hypomethes* (KU 269851–52; MCZ 78762), *T. inornatus* (MCZ 140724, 140728, 175100), *T. jamaicensis* (Evans, 1955[5]; Underwood, 1967[1]; KU 269898, 269900, 269917; MCZ 7372, 26669, 127852; USNM 252320), *T. jerdoni* (ZMUC 52121), *T. khoratensis* (FMNH 189933; 1 TNRC uncat.), *T. koekkoeki* (FMNH 71579), *T. kraalii* (Brongersma, 1958a; ZMA 14225), *T. lankaensis* (FMNH 100134), *T. lehneri* (MCZ 48923–25), *T. leucostictus* (MHNG 722.93), *T. lineolatus* (BMNH 1980.29–30; CAS 148005; MCZ 84331), *T. lumbricalis* (Meckel, 1818, 1833; J. Müller, 1832; Lereboullet, 1838; Cuvier, 1840; Butler, 1895; Brongersma, 1958a; Underwood, 1976a; Wong, 1994[7]; CAS 71689; FMNH 22854; KU 288502; MCZ 10824, 10826, 10828–29, 10831–32, 18116, 19924, 21826, 22279–80, 22283–85, 22676, 22678, 22854, 32607, 32613, 32615–16, 32619–21, 32624, 32626–29, 32631, 32637, 71689, 84953–54, 84957, 84959), *T. malcolmi* (ZMH 3967), *T. marxi* (Wallach, 1993b; FMNH 96520), *T. mcdowelli* (PNGM 24604; UPNG 5978), *T. microcephalus* (4 UMMZ uncat.), *T. microstomus* (CM 45287; FMNH 26975–76, 36346), *T. minuisquamus* (TCWC 42791), *T. mirus* (FMNH 123533–34; MCZ 18377–78), *T. monastus* (KU 274089, 274094; MCZ 12641; USNM 236411), *T. monensis* (MCZ 38307–08), *T. mucronatus* (MCZ 33504; 2 UMMZ uncat.; ZMB 9877; ZMH 3970, 3972), *T. muelleri* (Antipchuk, 1966b[7]; Antipchuk and Sobolieva, 1976[7]; Brongersma, 1958a[6,7,9]; Wallach, 1993a; FMNH 161275; TNRC 3788, 7336–37, 3 TNRC uncat.), *T. obtusus* (FMNH 203728; NMZB-UM 23667), *T. ocularis* (UMMZ 197250, 1 UMMZ uncat?), *T. pammeces* (MCZ 5229), *T. platycephalus* (KU 273816–17; MCZ 38333), *T. platyrhynchus* (MCZ 39798), *T. porrectus* (FMNH 60645; MCZ 3702, 4802, 165023–24), *T. punctatus* (Cope, 1894a[1], 1900[1]; Brongersma, 1958a[6]; Butner, 1963a; Wallach, 1993a; CAS 125541, 136316, 147663; FMNH 212323), *T. pusillus* (KU 272805, 272807–11, 288567–69; MCZ 123716, 176367), *T. reticulatus* (Meckel, 1818[6], 1833; J. Müller, 1832; Lereboullet, 1838; Cuvier, 1840; Stannius, 1846; Milne-Edwards, 1857b; Cope, 1894a, 1900; Brongersma, 1958a[6]; Butner, 1963a; FMNH 5699, 11174, 165551; MCZ 48962; RMNH 3725), *T. richardii* (MCZ 166983, 176827), *T. rondoensis* (Wallach, 1993a; MCZ 48067, 57184–85), *T. rostellatus* (MCZ 38357, 38362, 165036), *T. ruber* (Wallach, 1993b; CAS 182566; FMNH 53223; MCZ 79698), *T. ruficaudus* (Wallach, 1993b; CAS 135667; CAS-SU 19517, 21066, 26815; MCZ 25594; UF 54652), *T. schmidti* (Wallach, 1993a; MCZ 57462; NMZB-UM 9445), *T. schmutzi* (UF 29452, 29528), *T. schwartzi* (KU 273852; MCZ 176367), *T. siamensis* (Wallach, 1993a; MCZ 16655; TCWC 29356), *T. steinhausi* (FMNH 4034; ZMB 30686b), *T. sulcatus* (KU 273920, 273936–37; MCZ 121897), *T. syntherus* (CM 39610; KU 274048–50; TCWC 51296), *T. tenebrarum* (FMNH 120237, 167012),

T. tenuis (FMNH 70687, 105181–82), *T. tetrathyreus* (KU 208798–800; MCZ 81150), *T. titanops* (MCZ 68571), *T. trinitatus* (MCZ 55670), *T. uluguruensis* (MCZ 23081), *T. vermicularis* (Antipchuk, 1966b[7], 1966c[9]; Antipchuk and Sobolieva, 1976[7]; Heyder, 1966[7,9], 1968[6,7,9], 1973[9], 1974[2]; Antipchuk and Sobolieva, 1971[9]; CAS 185206, 185210, 185218, 185220, 185225; FMNH 74392, 233386),*T. violaceus* (FMNH 124231), *T. zenkeri* (MCZ 13242), *T. "amphixanthus"* (=sp. indet.) (Henle, 1839[4]; Hoffmann, 1890[4]; Lüdicke, 1964[4]), *Typhlops* sp. undet. (Meckel, 1818, 1831, 1833; Stannius, 1846, 1850; T. Williams, 1859; E. O. Schmidt, 1865, 1872; Pagenstecher, 1881; Peters, 1882; Günther, 1886; Hoffmann, 1890; Gadow, 1911; Perrier, 1928; Marcus, 1937; de Saint-Aubain, 1984[7]), *Typhlops* sp. A (UMMZ 192037, 202049), *Typhlops* sp. B (FMNH 191888–89),*Typhlops* sp. C (1 UMMZ uncat.), *Typhlops* sp. D (2 UMMZ uncat.), *Typhlops* sp. E (CAS 66188), *Typhlops* sp. F (MHNG 1326.62), *Typhlops* sp. G (MCZ 177982), *Typhlops* sp. H (CAS 142915), *Typhlops* sp. I (CAS-SU 16099), *Typhlops* sp. J (MCZ 173290, 1 uncat.), *Typhlops* sp. K (MCZ 72108, 92527), *Typhlops* sp. L (TM 69018), *Typhlops* sp. M (KU 288580), *Xenotyphlops grandidieri* (MNHN 1905.272).

LEPTOTYPHLOPIDAE

Leptotyphlops affinis (Butner, 1963a), *L. albifrons* (Butler, 1895; Brongersma, 1958a; Antipchuk, 1966c[9]; FMNH 39405, 40626, 105183; MCZ 17393), *L. albipunctus* (FML 1228; MCZ 163240), *L. albiventer* (SMNS 8454.1), *L. algeriensis* (CAS 84215), *L. anthracinus* (FMNH 34353), *L. australis* (FML 1400), *L. bicolor* (BH LIB 150, 163, 233, 274, 397, 499, 595, 747; CAS 103292, 136146, 146008–09; CM 92651; FMNH 42565; MCZ 53655), *L. bilineatus* (MCZ 10693), *L. blanfordii* (CAS 120486, 121054), *L. borapeliotes* (MZUSP 8261), *L. borrichianus* (MCZ 15900), *L. boueti* (MCZ 53273; MNHN 1983.474), *L. boulengeri* (MCZ 40085), *L. brasiliensis* (Wallach, 1996a; UMMZ 108817), *L. cairi* (CAS 18148; FMNH 64030, 64038, 129894, 130459, 133573, USNM 130459), *L. collaris* (MCZ 149550), *L. columbi* (CM 72262), *L. conjunctus* (MCZ 55831; NMZB 11399; NMZB-UM 7563, 7603, 12522, 20579, 20698, 23924, 28498, 31422–23; TM 76130, 76153), *L. cupinensis* (MCZ 3728, 142652, 149551), *L. diaplocius* (KU 212594), *L. dimidiatus* (FMNH 189352; MCZ 115573), *L. distanti* (MCZ 21304; NMZB-UM 31602; TM 5059, 12720, 12772, 54016), *L. drewesi* (CAS 85756), *L. dugandi* (MCZ 58785), *L. dulcis* (Cope, 1894a, 1900; Varde, 1951; Brongersma, 1958a; Antipchuk, 1966c; FMNH 95209, 105218, 105220; MCZ 127408), *L. emini* (FMNH 56371–73; MCZ 48038–40; NMZB 4971, 10598, 10622; NMZB-UM 5410; ZMUC 5317), *L. goudotii* (CAS 78688; FMNH 153535, 153542; MCZ 9624; TCWC 7411, 9452; 2 UCA uncat.), *L. gracilior* (TM 48343), *L. humilis* (Butner, 1963a; Underwood, 1967[1]; McDowell, 1972c[2,5]; FMNH 19905, 26616; SDSNH 20411, 28839, 39275), *L. joshuai* (UMMZ 84093), *L. labialis* (CAS 173390; TM 57050), *L. latifrons* (MCZ 38248), *L. latirostris* (MCZ 53261, 57459), *L. leptepileptus* (KU 275559–60; USNM 236669), *L. longicaudus* (Peters, 1882[1]; CAS 85839; MCZ 51038; NMZB 1400, 2967; TM 57956, 62060), *L. macrolepis* (MCZ 39705, 48918, 140118; ZMUC 5316), *L. macrops* (Broadley and Wallach, 1996; NMZB-UM 11352; ZMUC 5315), *L. macrorhynchus* (CAS 105926, 105930; FMNH 21033, 26355, 105094), *L. macrurus* (BMNH 1957.1.10.26), *L. maximus* (CAS 134444, 137769; FMNH 1263; MCZ 160088; MVZ 45026; TCWC 17167), *L. melanotermus*

(FML 699, 998, 1421, 2592; FMNH 161503, 229948; MCZ 120055), *L. merkeri* (MCZ 52629, 52631; NMZB 8089, 9938, 11371–72, 14101, 14109; ZMB 21172, 29081c), *L. munaoi* (FMNH 216398, 216402, 216409; LSUMZ 27752), *L. narirostris* (CAS 104555; FMNH 25056; MCZ 76631; UMMZ 182250), *L. nigricans* (FMNH 205836–40, 205848, 205850, 233252–53, 233255, 233280, 233283, 233285, 234041, 234043–45, 234048, 234050, 234052; PEM 58, 1728, 3040, 3046, 3308, 3439–40, 3045, 6381, 7180, 7182, 11299, 12439), *L. nursii* (CAS 135251; FMNH 66157–59), *L. occidentalis* (FMNH 187108; TM 57057), *L. pembae* (MCZ 19111, 46118), *L. perreti* (MHNG 1453.10), *L. peruvianus* (ZFMK 41475), *L. phillipsi* (MCZ 9641–42; UMMZ 51761), *L. pungwensis* (Broadley and Wallach, 1997a; NMZB-UM 7251), *L. reticulatus* (BMNH 1954.1.12.77), *L. rufidorsus* (FMNH 34305), *L. scutifrons* (Renous, 1985[5,9]; CAS 85761; FMNH 80015; MCZ 52630, 54515, 54813; NMZB-UM 28264, 31233; TM 5068, 24629, 25576, 44732), *L. septemstriatus* (Meckel, 1819, 1833; FMNH 26660), *L. striatulus* (FML 1287a–b; FMNH 40210, 59169, 62125, 81509–10), *L. subcrotillus* (MCZ 48936, 160520), *L. sundewalli* (FMNH 196258; MCZ 55396; 2 MNHN uncat.), *L. sylvicolus* (NMZB-UM 11903; TM 29975, 54602), *L. telloi* (NMZB-UM 30635), *L. tenellus* (CAS-SU 12510; FMNH 217237–38; MCZ 160088), *L. tesselatus* (FMNH 36726, 134464; ZMB 26256), *L. tricolor* (KU 135177), *L. unguirostris* (CM 89638; FMNH 44174; LSUMZ 48194), *L. weyrauchi* (FML 603, 921, 2334, 2584, 2617; FMNH 229949; MCZ 126659), *Leptotyphlops* sp. A (NMZB-UM 14334), *Leptotyphlops* sp. B (1 MNHN uncat.), *Leptotyphlops* sp.C (MNHG 1464.2), *Leptotyphlops* sp. D (KU 172930; MCZ 52634, 54813), *Leptotyphlops* sp. (Gadow, 1911), *Rhinoleptus koniagui* (MNHN 1902.10).

ANOMOCHILIDAE
Anomochilus weberi (Brongersma and Helle, 1951; P. H. D. H. de Silva, 1955; Cundall et al., 1994; RMNH 9507).

ANILIIDAE
Anilius scytale (Meckel, 1818, 1819, 1829a, 1831, 1833; Cuvier, 1829, 1831, 1836, 1840; Duvernoy, 1832[5], 1833[5]; J. Müller, 1832; Schlegel, 1837b; Lereboullet, 1838; Stannius, 1846, 1850, 1856; Milne-Edwards, 1857b; Hoffmann, 1890; Cope, 1894a, 1894b, 1895b, 1900; Butler, 1895; Beddard, 1906a; Gadow, 1911; Thompson, 1914a; H. Marcus, 1937; Brongersma, 1951a[7], 1951b, 1951c[9], 1954; Brongersma and Helle, 1951; P. H. D. H. de Silva, 1955; Butner, 1963a; Underwood, 1967, 1976a[5,6]; Rieppel, 1977[2], 1983[2]; Groombridge, 1979[2]; McDowell, 1975[2]; ANSP 3251, 3253, 3255; FMNH 74045; LSUMZ 11819, 41301, 46263; MCZ 1207a–b, 2986; TCWC 44582; UIMNH 54649; UMMZ 53923–24).

CYLINDROPHIIDAE
Cylindrophis boulengeri (Brongersma, 1951a[7]), *C. isolepis* (Brongersma, 1951a[7,9]), *C. lineatus* (Butner, 1963a), *C. maculatus* (Schlegel, 1837b; Henle, 1839[4]; Hoffmann, 1890[4]; Cope, 1894a, 1900; Thompson, 1914a; Brongersma, 1951a; Lüdicke, 1964[4]; Groombridge, 1979[2]; FMNH 121489; MCZ 15797; SDSU uncat.), *C. ruffus* (Schlegel, 1837b; Butler, 1895; Thompson, 1914a; Bergman, 1953; Brongersma, 1951a[7],c[9], 1954; Brongersma and Helle, 1951; P. H. D. H. de Silva, 1955; Antipchuk,

1966a[9], 1966b[7], 1966c; Antipchuk and Sobolieva, 1976[7]; Underwood, 1967; McDowell, 1975[2]; Rieppel, 1977[9], 1980[9], 1983[9]; de Saint-Aubain, 1984[7]; FMNH 129412, 129415–16, 129418; LSUMZ 9639, 46846; MCZ 4076), *Cylindrophis* sp. (Stannius, 1846, 1850).

UROPELTIDAE

Uropeltid (Gans, 1974[7]); *Brachyophidium rhodogaster* (BMNH 1923.10.13.35; CAS 104256), *Melanophidium wynaudense* (Butner, 1963a; Underwood, 1967; CAS 39633), *Platyplectrurus madurensis* (Butner, 1963a; Underwood, 1967; CAS 9114), *Plectrurus aureus* (CAS 17176), *P. perroteti* (Underwood, 1967; FMNH 171566; MCZ 3867), *Pseudoplectrurus canaricus* (MCZ 24737), *Pseudotyphlops philippinus* (Underwood, 1967; Rieppel, 1983[2]; BMNH 1968.871; KU 31249–51), *Rhinophis blythii* (Butler, 1895), *R. drummondhayi* (Underwood, 1967; AMNH 85076), *R. homolepis* (CM 20484), *R. oxyrhynchus* (Meckel, 1819; Cope, 1894a, 1900), *R. philippinus* (SDSNH 25464), *R. trevelyanus* (Butner, 1963a; Antipchuk, 1966b[7], 1966c[9]; Antipchuk and Sobolieva, 1976[7]), *Rhinophis* sp. (Stannius, 1856; Gadow, 1911), *Teretrurus rhodogaster* (Underwood, 1967), *T. sanguineus* (BMNH 1868.8.12.3; MCZ 6203), *Uropeltis arcticeps* (FMNH 217697; MCZ 22389), *U. brevis* (Rieppel, 1977[2]), *U. broughmani* (CAS 9113), *U. ceylanicus* (Butner, 1963a; MCZ 3868), *U. ellioti* (FMNH 16110), *U. grandis* (MCZ 6200), *U. liura* (CM 90216), *U. macrolepis* (MCZ 28644), *U. madurensis* (Underwood, 1967), *U. melanogaster* (Butner, 1963a; UMMZ 96275), *U. myhendrae* (CAS 39632), *U. nitidus* (MCZ 47292), *U. ocellatus* (MCZ 3873), *U. petersi* (MCZ 6201), *U. phipsoni* (Kashyap, 1960a[9]), *U. pulneyensis* (MCZ 1335), *U. rubrolineatus* (MCZ 47040), *U. rubromaculata* (MCZ 6199), *U. woodmasoni* (MCZ 18040).

XENOPELTIDAE

Xenopeltis unicolor (Schlegel, 1837b; Cuvier, 1840; Stannius, 1856; Pagenstecher, 1881; Cope, 1894a, 1894b, 1895b, 1900; Butler, 1895; Thompson, 1913c[6,9]; Fürbringer, 1922[5]; Brongersma, 1951a[7], 1951b, 1951c[9], 1954, 1958b; Bergman, 1955c; P. H. D. H. de Silva, 1955; Butner, 1963a; Antipchuk, 1966b[7], 1966c[9]; Antipchuk and Sobolieva, 1976[7]; Underwood, 1967, 1976b; McDowell, 1975[2]; Rieppel, 1977[2]; CAS 15801; FMNH 180278; MCZ 173225).

LOXOCEMIDAE

Loxocemus bicolor (Cope, 1894a, 1900; Underwood, 1967, 1976b; McDowell, 1972c[2,4,5], 1975[2]; CAS 145210; MNN 100, 107; SDSNH 42312).

PYTHONIDAE

Antaresia childreni (Underwood, 1976b; MCZ 118703), *A. stimsoni* (Shine, 1991[3]), *Apodora papuana* (Brongersma, 1951a), *Aspidites melanocephalus* (Underwood, 1967, 1976b; FMNH 97054), *Bothrochilus boa* (Brongersma, 1951a[7]; Underwood, 1967, 1976b; FMNH 21730), *Leiopython albertisii* (Brongersma, 1951a), *Liasis fuscus* (MCZ 53754), *L. mackloti* (Brongersma, 1951a[7], 1951b, 1951c[9]; Kardong, 1972b; Ramsay, 1979; SDSU uncat.), *Liasis* sp. (Henle, 1839[4]; Hoffmann, 1890[4]), *Morelia amethistina* (Schlegel, 1837b; Brongersma, 1951a[7], 1951b, 1951c[9];

Antipchuk, 1966b[7], 1966c[9]; Antipchuk and Sobolieva, 1976[7]; Underwood, 1967, 1976b; Kardong, 1972b; Webb et al., 1974[7]; Ramsay, 1979; Engelmann and Obst, 1981[3]; SDSU uncat.), *M. boeleni* (Brongersma, 1956a[9]), *M. carinata* (Barker and Barker, 1994[3]), *M. spilota* (Schlegel, 1837b; Cope, 1894a, 1900; Beddard, 1908[6]; Brongersma, 1951a[7],c[7,9]; Underwood, 1967, 1976b; Kardong, 1972b; Donnelly and Woolcock, 1972, 1977[6,7], 1978[6]; Webb, 1972[9]; Read and Donnelly, 1972[6,7]; Ramsay, 1979; Barker and Barker, 1994[7]; 2 SDSU uncat.), *M. viridis* (Brongersma, 1951a[7], 1951b, 1951c[9]; Butner, 1963a; Underwood, 1967, 1976b; Griner, 1983[8]; FMNH 14075), *Python curtus* (Brongersma, 1951a[7], 1951b, 1951c[9]; Underwood, 1967, 1976b; Kardong, 1972b; Ramsay, 1979; Divers, 1995[6]; FMNH 71588), *P. molurus* (Meckel, 1833; d'Alton, 1834[5]; Hopkinson and Pancoast, 1837[6]; Schlegel, 1837b; Lereboullet, 1838; Henle, 1839[4]; Vogt, 1839[9]; Stannius, 1850; Jacquart, 1855[6,9], 1856, 1864[6]; Milne-Edwards, 1857b; R. Owen, 1866; Fritsch, 1869[9]; Gegenbaur, 1870[4], 1874[4], 1878a[4], 1878b[4]; Pagenstecher, 1881; Hoffmann, 1890[4,5,9]; Cope, 1894a, 1900; Butler, 1895; Broman, 1904[1], 1937[1]; Oppel, 1905; Thäter, 1910[2]; Goodrich, 1919[9]; Fürbringer, 1922[5]; Wolf, 1933[6]; Edgeworth, 1935[4,5]; Gnanamuthu, 1937; Göppert, 1937[2]; Brongersma, 1951a[7], 1951b, 1951c[9]; Varde, 1951[6,8,9]; Lüdicke, 1964[1]; Underwood, 1967; Kardong, 1972b; Deoras and Vad, 1973; Ramsay, 1979; Cole, 1981[3]; Kundert, 1984[3]; Kang et al., 1986; Bargar and Johnson, 1987b[3]; Barker and Barker, 1995[7]; Divers, 1995[3]), *P. molurus* (3 SDSNH uncat.; 2 SDSU uncat.; VW 3683–84), *P. regius* (Cope, 1894a, 1900; Brongersma, 1951a[7], 1951b, 1951c[7,9]; Kardong, 1972b; Underwood, 1976; Ramsay, 1979; Divers, 1995 SDSNH; VW 268–79), *P. reticulatus* (Meckel, 1818; Hopkinson and Pancoast, 1837[9]; Schlegel, 1837b; Pagenstecher, 1881; Butler, 1895[7]; Göppert, 1899[5]; Göppert, 1937[7]; Brongersma, 1951a–1951c, 1952b[9], 1954, 1958b; Butner, 1963a; Kardong, 1972b; Underwood, 1976b; Duncker, 1978c[6]; Ramsay, 1979; Perry and Duncker, 1980; Bargar and Johnson, 1987b[3]; SDSNH; VW 223, 238, 282, 3685–86), *P. sebae* (Lataste and Blanchard, 1879; Brongersma, 1951a[7], 1951b, 1951c[7,9]; Frazzetta, 1966[2,5]; Kardong, 1972b; Groombridge, 1979[2]; Ramsay, 1979; Patterson, 1987[3]; MZUSP 8122; NMV 55561; TM uncat.; UF 52481, 80352–57; VW 866, 945–46, 1738, 1870, 2202; ZRC 2.3452), *P. timorensis* (Brongersma, 1951a), "*Python*" sp. (Meckel, 1831, 1833; Cuvier, 1840; Stannius, 1846–1856; Leydig, 1857, 1866; T. Williams, 1859; Gegenbaur, 1878a; Wiedersheim, 1883[9]; Günther, 1886; Marcus, 1928a, 1928b, 1937[6,7]; Perrier, 1928; Walter, 1929; Benninghoff, 1931[9]; Lüdicke, 1964[6]; Dulzetto, 1968[6]; Guibé, 1970b[6]; de Saint-Aubain, 1984[7]).

BOIDAE

Boid (Orton, 1876[6], 1883[6], 1888[6], 1894[6]; Butler, 1895[7]; Orton and Dodge, 1903[6]), *Acrantophis dumerilii* (Underwood, 1967; FMNH 73107), *A. madagascariensis* (Mocquard, 1888; Hoffmann, 1890[9]; Beddard, 1909; F. Werner, 1911; Brongersma, 1951a, 1951b, 1951c[9]; Kardong, 1972b; Ramsay, 1979; CAS 13945), *Acrantophis* sp. (Underwood, 1976b), *Boa constrictor* (Blumenbach, 1803[2]; Meckel, 1818; Schlemm, 1827; Dillon, 1831; Schlegel, 1837b; Roberton, 1838; Henle, 1839[4]; Jacquart, 1855[9], 1864[9]; Milne-Edwards, 1857b; Hering, 1860; Fritsch, 1869; Gegenbaur, 1878b[9]; Hopley, 1882; Hoffmann, 1890[4]; Cope, 1894a, 1900; Butler, 1895; Couvreur, 1901[9]; Greil, 1903[9]; Oppel, 1905; Beddard, 1909[6]; Schimkewitsch et al., 1910, 1921; Benninghoff, 1922[9], 1931[9], 1933[9]; Walter, 1929; Leene and Vorstman, 1930[7]; Bütschli, 1933[4]; Hafferl, 1933[9]; Wolf, 1933[6]; Acolat, 1943[9]; Bellairs and Underwood, 1951[9]; Brongersma, 1951a[7], 1951b, 1951c[7,9]; P. H. D. H. de Silva, 1955; Willnow, 1961; Butner, 1963a; Antipchuk, 1966b[7],c[9]; Antipchuk and Sobolieva, 1976[7]; Underwood, 1967, 1976a, 1976b; Guibé, 1970a[9]; Tenney and Tenney, 1970; Antipchuk and Sobolieva, 1971[8]; Kardong, 1972b; Groombridge, 1979[2]; Ramsay, 1979; Grant et al., 1981[6,7,8]; de Saint-Aubain, 1984[7]; Wurmbach, 1985; Kang et al., 1986; Gomes et al., 1989[1,5,9]; Frye, 1991[8]; Kardong and Haverly, 1993[5]; Coborn, 1994[2]), "Boa" sp. (Meckel, 1818, 1819, 1831, 1833; Cuvier, 1840; Stannius, 1846, 1856; Wyman, 1849a[6], 1849b[6]; van der Hoeven, 1855, 1858; Milne-Edwards, 1857b; T. Williams, 1859; Gegenbaur, 1878b[9]; Günther, 1886; H. Marcus, 1928a, 1937; Wolf, 1933[7]; 2 SDSNH; SDSU uncat.; 23 UCA uncat; VW 206, 321, 324, 385–86, 504–05, 616, 618), Calabaria reinhardtii (Brongersma, 1951a[7],c[9], 1954, 1958b; Butner, 1963a; Antipchuk, 1966c[9]; Underwood, 1967, 1976b; Groombridge, 1979[2]; 4 IRSL uncat.; SDSU uncat.; 2 UNAZA uncat.), Candoia aspera (Brongersma, 1951a, 1951b, 1951c[9]; Kardong, 1972b; Underwood, 1976b; Ramsay, 1979; FMNH 13915), C. bibroni (Brongersma, 1951a[7], 1951b, 1951c[7]; Butner, 1963a; Underwood, 1967, 1976b; FMNH 13633), C. carinata (Meckel, 1818; Schlegel, 1837b; Butler, 1895; Brongersma, 1951a; Kardong, 1972b; Underwood, 1976b; SDSU uncat.), Charina bottae (Cope, 1894a[1], 1900[1]; Brongersma, 1951a, 1951b, 1951c[9]; Underwood, 1967, 1976b; Kardong, 1972b[6]; Kaban, 1978[7]; Ramsay, 1979; SDSNH 38053; SDSU uncat.), Corallus annulatus (MCZ 76678), C. caninus (Schlegel, 1837b; Cope, 1894a, 1900; Beddard, 1908; Brongersma, 1951a, 1951b, 1951c[7,9]; Underwood, 1967; Kardong, 1972b; Ramsay, 1979; Divers, 1995; SDSU uncat.), C. hortulanus (Schlegel, 1837b; Beddard, 1908; Brongersma, 1951a, 1951b, 1951c[9]; Butner, 1963a; Underwood, 1967; Kardong, 1972b; Ramsay, 1979; SDSU uncat.), Corallus sp. (Underwood, 1976b), Epicrates angulifer (Antipchuk, 1966b[7], 1966c[9]; Antipchuk and Sobolieva, 1976[7]; Antipchuk and Sobolieva, 1971[8]; SDSNH 43749), E. cenchria (Meckel, 1818; Schlegel, 1837b; Hopley, 1882; Cope, 1894a, 1900; Butler, 1895; Brongersma, 1951a[7], 1951b, 1951c[7,9]; Butner, 1963a; Underwood, 1967, 1976b; Kardong, 1972b; Ramsay, 1979), E. chrysogaster (UMMZ 117027), E. exsul (UMMZ 176881), E. fordii (UMMZ 173419), E. gracilis (UMMZ 173432), E. inornatus (Cope, 1894a, 1900; Grant, 1933[5]; Angel, 1950[5]; Brongersma, 1951a; Wallach, 1992; UCM 56508; UMMZ 74415), E. monensis (MCZ 37300), E. striatus (Brongersma, 1951a; SDSU uncat.; VW 2861), E. subflavus (Sloane, 1725; Underwood, 1967; UMMZ 173471), Epicrates sp. (Underwood, 1976b), Epicrates angulifer × Python sebae (SDSNH 39311), Eryx colubrinus (MCZ 39008, 39010, 96924), E. conicus (Schlegel, 1837b; Beddard, 1908; Butner, 1963a; Folk, 1971[1,6]; Kardong, 1972b; Underwood, 1976b; Ramsay, 1979; R. Singh and Kar, 1982[6,9]; MCZ 3885; SDSU uncat.), E. jaculus (Schlegel, 1837b; Lereboullet, 1838; Cuvier, 1840; Stannius, 1846; Milne-Edwards, 1857b; Hoffmann, 1890; Butler, 1895; Brongersma, 1951a[7], 1951b, 1951c[9]; Underwood, 1967, 1976b; Kardong, 1972b; Groombridge, 1979[2]; Ramsay, 1979; MCZ 56871), E. jayakari (MCZ 56887), E. johnii (Cope, 1894a, 1900; Butler, 1895; Beddard, 1908; Brongersma, 1951a; Kashyap, 1960a[9]; J. C. George and Shah, 1965[6]; Bellairs, 1969[6], 1970; Kardong, 1972b; Underwood, 1976b; Ramsay,

1979; R. Singh and Kar, 1982[6,9]; SDSU uncat.), *E. miliaris* (Antipchuk, 1966b[7], 1966c[9]; Antipchuk and Sobolieva, 1971[9], 1976[7]; Yao, 1985[1,9]; MCZ 34042), *E. tataricus* (SDSU uncat.), *Eryx* sp. (Meckel, 1833; Schlegel, 1837b; Cuvier, 1840; Stannius, 1846, 1850, 1856; Günther, 1886), *Eunectes murinus* (Meckel, 1818[6]; Schlegel, 1837b; Milne-Edwards, 1857b; Cope, 1894a, 1900; Brehm and Werner, 1920; Rau, 1924; Bütschli, 1933[6]; Wolf, 1933[7]; Brongersma, 1951a[7], 1951b, 1951c[9]; Bellairs and Boyd, 1957[2]; Antipchuk, 1966b[7],c[9]; Antipchuk and Sobolieva, 1976[7]; Rietschel, 1968; Bellairs, 1969[2], 1970; Phleger et al., 1978; Petzold, 1984; Wurmbach, 1985[6]), *Eunectes* sp. (Bütschli, 1933[6]; Wolf, 1933[7]; Rietschel, 1968[6]; Underwood, 1976b; Wurmbach, 1985[6]), *Lichanura trivirgata* (Brongersma, 1951a; Kaban, 1978[7]; Underwood, 1976b; Stinner, 1980[6,7]; SDSU uncat.; VW 3835), *Sanzinia madagascariensis* (Beddard, 1908; Brongersma, 1951a; Underwood, 1967, 1976b; SDSU uncat.).

BOLYERIIDAE

Bolyeria multocarinata (Underwood, 1967, 1976b; Groombridge, 1979[2]; BMNH 1896.3.25.2), *Casarea dusssumieri* (Schlegel, 1837b; Underwood, 1967, 1976b; Groombridge, 1979[2]; BMNH R.170/2; MCZ 49135).

XENOPHIDIIDAE

Xenophidion acanthognathus (FMNH 235170).

TROPIDOPHIIDAE

Exiliboa placata (Bogert, 1968; FMNH 202685, 207669; UTA 4716–20, 8474, 8505–06, 8508, 8510), *Trachyboa boulengeri* (FMNH 78106; LSUMZ 46847), *T. gularis* (Brongersma, 1951c[7]; Butner, 1963a; Kardong, 1972b; Ramsay, 1979), *Trachyboa* sp. (Brongersma, 1954; Underwood, 1976b), *Tropidophis canus* (FMNH 233), *T. caymanensis* (Groombridge, 1979[2]; CAS 111091; LSUMZ 24917), *T. haetianus* (Brongersma, 1951c[7]; Underwood, 1976b; FMNH 42118; MCZ uncat.), *T. maculatus* (Cope, 1894a, 1900; MCZ 10836), *T. melanurus* (Schlegel, 1837b; Cope, 1894a, 1900; Brongersma, 1951c[7]; Butner, 1963a; Kardong, 1972b; Ramsay, 1979; MCZ 38173), *T. nigriventris* (UMMZ 70887), *T. pardalis* (Brongersma, 1951c[7,9]; FMNH 22583; LSUMZ 11831), *T. paucisquamis* (UMMZ 115651), *T. pilsbryi* (UMMZ 65043), *T. semicinctus* (CAS 14900), *T. taczanowskyi* (Underwood, 1976b; MCZ 93584), *T. wrighti* (FMNH 71789), *Tropidophis* sp. (Gadow, 1911; F. Werner, 1911; H. Marcus, 1937; Brongersma, 1954), *Ungaliophis continentalis* (UTA 6392, 7917), *U. panamensis* (Butner, 1963a, 1963b[7,9]; Kardong, 1972b; Ramsay, 1979; CAS 7150; FMNH 19397).

ACROCHORDIDAE

Acrochordus arafurae (Ramsay, 1979[6,7,8]; CAS 121093; CSIRO 827; QM 11033; SDSU uncat.), *A. granulatus* (Schlegel, 1837b; Cuvier, 1840; Cantor, 1841, 1847; Stannius, 1856; Cope, 1894a[1], 1894b, 1900[1]; Butler, 1895; Beddard, 1903; Gadow, 1911; Brongersma, 1938, 1952c; Bergman, 1958a; Kashyap, 1960a[9]; Antipchuk, 1966b[7], 1966c[9]; Antipchuk and Sobolieva, 1976[7]; Underwood, 1967; Kashyap and Sohoni, 1973[6,7,9]; Heatwole and Seymour, 1975a; Ramsay, 1979[7]; Lillywhite, 1987a[7], 1987b[7]; Lillywhite and Donald, 1987; Donald and Lillywhite, 1989a, 1989b[9]; FMNH 13806,

43693, 97032, 121472, 135189, 179302, 179307, 213189, 213198, 213200, 213202–03; MCZ 146128; SDSU uncat.), *A. javanicus* (Schlegel, 1837b; Cuvier, 1840; Cantor, 1841, 1847; Stannius, 1846; Brongersma, 1938, 1952c; Bergman, 1958a[1]; Underwood, 1967; Standaert and Johansen, 1974; Groombridge, 1979[2]; Ramsay, 1979; Coborn, 1991[2]; 3 SDSU uncat.), *Acrochordus* sp. (Meckel, 1833; Stannius, 1846, 1850; Pagenstecher, 1881; Wiedersheim, 1883, 1886; Günther, 1886; Perrier, 1928; H. Marcus, 1937; Wolf, 1933; Brongersma, 1938, 1952c, 1958b).

VIPERIDAE

Viperid (Charas, 1669[1,2,3,6], 1670[1,2,3,6], 1672[1,2,3,6], 1673[1,2,3,6], 1693[1,2,3,6], 1694[1,2,3,6]; Mead, 1702[3], 1708[3], 1747[3]; Valentini, 1720[5,6]; Seba, 1735[1,6]; Bellairs and Underwood, 1951[7,9]; Lillywhite and Smits, 1992[9]), *Adenorhinos barbouri* (Groombridge, 1980; ZMUC 68258, 68260), *Agkistrodon bilineatus* (FMNH 42147), *A. contortrix* (Cope, 1894a, 1900; Noble, 1921; Reese, 1926[7]; Bothner, 1959[9]; Butner, 1963a; Bourgondien and Bothner, 1969[9]; Kardong, 1972b; Ramsay, 1979; Cleave, 1994[2]; 3 SDSU uncat.; VW 2895), *A. piscivorus* (Cope, 1894a, 1900; Reese, 1926[7]; Brongersma, 1949; Collins and Carpenter, 1970[7]; Kardong, 1972b; Bourgondien and Bothner, 1969; Kardong, 1977[2,3]; Linzey, 1979[2]; Ramsay, 1979; Levy, 1983[2]; Bargar and Johnson, 1986b[3]; Gloyd and Conant, 1990[2,3]; J. A. Burton, 1991[2]; Weidensaul, 1991[3]; FMNH 194470; 3 SDSU uncat.), *Atheris chlorechis* (Brongersma, 1949; FMNH 214737), *A. desaixi* (CAS 122705), *A. hispidus* (FMNH 154900, 167058), *A. nitschei* (13 IRSL uncat.; LSUMZ 40703; MCZ 170386–88; VW 2513, 2561), *A. rungweensis* (SDSU uncat.), *A. squamiger* (CAS 156702; FMNH 214816–25; NMV 55555, 55559; MZUSP 8161; 9 PEM; SDSNH 63841; 2 SDSU uncat.; TAU 12621, 12623, 12625; UF 52902, 80384–89, 80406–19, 80676–79; UMMZ 172978; VW 1342, 1395, 1469, 1493, 1574, 1591, 1615, 1706–15, 1783–84, 1948, 2001–04, 2007, 2009–10, 2012–13, 2111–16, 2118, 2140–42, 2145–46, 2361, 2708, 2778; ZRC 2.3422–23; ZMUC), *Atropoides nummifer* (Brongersma, 1949; FMNH 35517), *Azemiops feae* (Liem et al., 1971; Groombridge, 1980[6,7,9]; FMNH 170643, 152987, 218627; MHNG 2270.40), *Bitis arietans* (Lereboullet, 1838; Cuvier, 1840; Milne-Edwards, 1857b; R. Owen, 1866; Hopley, 1882; Cope, 1894a, 1900; Roman, 1980; Butler, 1895; F. W. FitzSimons, 1912[1,3,6], 1921[1,3,6]; Brongersma, 1949[7,9]; Butner, 1963a; Boltt and Ewer, 1964[5]; Isemonger, 1962[3], 1968[3]; M. Burton, 1973a[3], 1978[2]; Broadley and Cock, 1975[1]; Honders, 1975[2]; Groombridge, 1980[7,9]; Roman, 1980[2]; Freiberg and Walls, 1984[2]; Auerbach, 1985[3], 1987; McCarthy, 1987[3]; Patterson, 1987[3]; Coborn, 1991[3]; Leetz, 1991[2]; Gravier, 1994[6]; MCZ 170357; MZUSP 8157, 8162; PEM; SDSU uncat.; TAU 12606; UF 101242; VW 1437, 2157, 2322, 2352–53; ZRC 2.3436), *B. gabonica* (Wolf, 1933[6]; Brongersma, 1949; Mehrtens, 1987[3]; Coborn, 1991[3]; A. Fowler, 1992[3]; 8 IRSL uncat.; SDSU uncat.; UF 80680; VW 975, 991, 1042, 1250, 1775, 1886), *B. nasicornis* (Hopley, 1882; Butler, 1895; Butner, 1963a; Griner, 1983[6]; SDSNH; 2 SDSU uncat.; 9 IRSL uncat.; 41 PEM; 4 UNAZA uncat.; VW 1076, 1251–53, 1296, 1397, 2812; ZRC 2.3437), *B. worthingtoni* (Groombridge, 1980[7,9]; FMNH 58141), *Bitis* sp. (Brongersma, 1958b), *B. gabonica* × *B. nasicornis* (VW 1774), *Bothriechis bicolor* (LSUMZ 11638), *B. lateralis* (SDSU uncat.), *B. schlegelii* (Cope, 1894a, 1900; Brongersma, 1949; 3 UCA uncat.), *Bothriopsis bilineatus* (Brongersma, 1949; FMNH 81466), *B. peruvianus* (FMNH 68597), *Bothrops alternatus* (Brongersma, 1949; SDSU uncat.), *B. ammodytoides* (Brongersma, 1949; Cei, 1993), *B. asper* (Shine, 1991[3]; MNN 146; UCA uncat.; UF 13857, 13865), *B. atrox* (Cuvier, 1840; Milne-Edwards, 1857b; Butler, 1895; Noble, 1921; Brongersma, 1949[9], 1958b; 2 SDSU uncat.), *B. cotiara* (SDSU uncat.), *B. erythrurus* (Kardong, 1972b; Ramsay, 1979), *B. fonsecai* (SDSU uncat.), *B. itapetiningae* (MCZ 20915), *B. jararaca* (Gomes and Puorto, 1994[1,3,5,6,9]; SDSU uncat.), *B. jararacussu* (Brongersma, 1949; SDSNH 29866), *B. lanceolatus* (Meckel, 1819, 1833; Rufz, 1859[3]; Cope, 1894a, 1900; Wolf, 1933[6,7]; Kardong, 1972b; Ramsay, 1979), *B. neuwiedi* (Phelps, 1981[2,3], 1989[2,3]; SDSU uncat.), *B. picadoi* (Villa et al., 1988[2]), *B. pictus* (Cope, 1894a, 1900; Kardong, 1972b; Ramsay, 1979), *B. pradoi* (SDSU uncat.), *Bothrops* sp. (Mavridis et al., 1994[3]), *Calechidna atropos* (Hopley, 1882; Groombridge, 1980; SDSU uncat.), *C. caudalis* (Groombridge, 1980; SDSU uncat.), *C. cornuta* (Groombridge, 1980[7,9]; FMNH 187145), *C. heraldica* (Groombridge, 1980; MCZ 32489), *C. inornata* (FMNH 206278), *C. peringueyi* (Groombridge, 1980; 2 SDSU uncat.), *C. schneideri* (Groombridge, 1980; MCZ 159176), *C. xeropaga* (Groombridge, 1980), *Calloselasma rhodostoma* (Brongersma, 1949; Bergman, 1961c; FMNH 180026), *Causus bilineatus* (Groombridge, 1980), *C. defilippii* (Groombridge, 1980; FMNH 152591; MCZ 53063, 53073), *C. lichtensteini* (Groombridge, 1980; 5 IRSL uncat.; LSUMZ 40784; 3 SDSU uncat.; UNAZA uncat.; VW 2245), *C. maculatus* (Groombridge, 1980[7,9]; BMNH 1979.215–1979.220; CAS 156695; 10 LSUMZ; LSUMZ 40769–72, 48450; MCZ; MCZ 170347–55; 7 MZUSP 8152–55, 8158, 8163–64; NMV 55552–53; 10 PEM; SDSNH 63871–72; 8 SDSU uncat.; TAU 12607, 12609–10; UF 80400–05, 80448–72; 2 UMMZ; 4 UNAZA uncat.; VW 1122, 1130, 1143, 1220, 1302, 1315, 1318, 1321, 1326, 1352, 1388, 1412–13, 1508, 1576, 1639, 1653, 1669–70, 1675–76, 1681, 1684, 1686, 1688, 1696, 1759–62, 1773, 1809, 1846–47, 1854, 1880–81, 1958, 1971, 2119, 2187, 2190, 2192, 2198, 2207, 2215–16, 2220, 2229, 2237, 2243, 2334; ZRC 2.3454–57), *C. resimus* (Groombridge, 1980; FMNH 58374; MCZ 97240), *C. rhombeatus* (Cope, 1894a, 1900; Thompson, 1914b; Brongersma, 1949[7,9], 1958b; Underwood, 1967; IRSL uncat.), *Causus* sp. (Underwood, 1976a), *Cerastes cerastes* (Meckel, 1819; Butler, 1895; Brongersma, 1949[9]; Groombridge, 1980; Staniszewski, 1990[2]; SDSU uncat.), *C. vipera* (Hochstetter, 1901; P. H. D. H. de Silva, 1955; Groombridge, 1980; FMNH 23542), *Cerrophidion barbouri* (CAS 134466), *C. godmani* (2 SDSU uncat.), *Crotalus adamanteus* (Cope, 1894a, 1900; Klauber, 1956; Kardong, 1972b; Ramsay, 1979; McCarthy, 1987[3]; Carmichael and Williams, 1991[3,4]; UF 46223–26, 48984–85), *C. atrox* (Noble, 1921; Oldham, 1968[7]; Bourgondien and Bothner, 1969; Haller, 1971[1]; Green and Sanford, 1984[3]; Daniels et al., 1995a, 1995b; FMNH 27158; UF 42585–87; VW 2875; ZIL), *C. basiliscus* (Klauber, 1956; Kardong, 1972b; Ramsay, 1979; SDSNH), *C. catalinensis* (SDSNH 44352), *C. cerastes* (Butner, 1963a; Kardong, 1972b; Ramsay, 1979; Tropea, 1987; SDSNH 39297; 2 SDSU uncat.; VW 200–01), *C. durissus* (Meckel, 1833; Carus and Otto, 1835[3,5]; Henle, 1839[4]; Hoffmann, 1890[4]; Butler, 1895; Noble, 1921; Brongersma, 1949, 1951a, c[9]; Klauber, 1956; Antipchuk, 1966b[7], 1966c[9]; Antipchuk and Sobolieva, 1976[7]; Kardong, 1972b; Ramsay, 1979; SDSU uncat.), *C. enyo* (Klauber, 1956; Kardong, 1972b; Ramsay, 1979; SDSU uncat.), *C. horridus* (Tyson, 1683[1,2,6]; Bonnaterre, 1790[1,2,6], 1795[1,2,6]; Blumenbach, 1803[2]; Meckel, 1818, 1831; Henle, 1839[4]; Stannius, 1846; Pagenstecher, 1881; Hopley, 1882; Cope, 1894a, 1900; Butler, 1895; F. Cole,

1944; Ahrenfeldt, 1955; Bourgondien and Bothner, 1969[9]; Kardong, 1972b; Ramsay, 1979; Larousse, 1980[2]; Lavies, 1990[2]; Frye, 1991[8]; FMNH 204081; UF 10849.6, 10855.1, 10855.3), *C. intermedius* (Klauber, 1956; Kardong, 1972b; Ramsay, 1979; SDSNH 44467), *C. lepidus* (Klauber, 1956; Kardong, 1972b; Ramsay, 1979; VW 2863), *C. mitchelli* (SDSNH; VW 2894), *C. molossus* (Klauber, 1956; Kardong, 1972b; Ramsay, 1979; FMNH 27772; VW 2876, 2884), *C. polystictus* (SDSNH 49979), *C. pricei* (SDSNH 35600), *C. pusillus* (SDSNH 42904), *C. ruber* (Klauber, 1956; Kardong, 1972b; Oulahan, 1977[2,3]; Ramsay, 1979; Weidensaul, 1990[4]; SDSNH; SDSU uncat.), *C. scutulatus* (Brongersma, 1949[7]; Butner, 1963a; SDSNH 3400; VW 3953), *C. stejnegeri* (SDSNH 41120), *C. tigris* (VW 2874. 2877), *C. triseriatus* (J. A. Burton, 1991[3]; FMNH 39125; SDSNH 46795), *C. unicolor* (SDSNH 60980), *C. viridis* (Cope, 1894a[1], 1900[1]; Thompson, 1913c; Pope, 1955[3]; Oliver, 1958[2,3]; Butner, 1963a; Bourgondien and Bothner, 1969; Kardong, 1972a[4,7], 1972b[6]; Ruben, 1976b[7]; Ramsay, 1979; Stinner, 1980[6,7]; Luchtel and Kardong, 1981[5–8]; Lillywhite, 1987a[7], 1987b[7]; Milsom, 1989[1]; Lillywhite and Smits, 1992[7]; SDSNH 3588, 3589, 3596–97, 3600, 3604–09, 3611–14, 3619–21, 3670, 3717–19, 4521, 4527–28, 4537, 4542, 6157–58, 6160, 6162, 6165–67, 6169–73, 6175–76, 6178, 6180–82, 6184, 6186–87, 6193, 6195–96, 6202–19, 6221–32, 6235, 6237, 6239–41, 6256, 6266, 6268, 6272, 6289, 6300, 6302–03, 6312, 6344, 6349–50, 6352, 6358–61, 6363, 6366, 6411–13, 6415–20, 6428, 6430–31, 6433, 6436–37, 8129, 8131, 8138, 8140, 8144–45, 8147, 8149, 8152, 8157, 8162, 8164, 8166–68, 8217, 8257–59, 8295–97, 8299–300, 8302–05, 8309–14, 8316, 8319–22, 8447, 8751, 29568; 5 SDSU uncat.; VW 4239–40), *C. willardi* (SDSU uncat.), *Crotalus* sp. (Meckel, 1818, 1819, 1831, 1833; Stannius, 1846, 1850, 1856; T. Williams, 1859; R. Owen, 1866[1,5]; Pagenstecher, 1881; Hoffmann, 1890[9]; Perrier, 1928; H. Marcus, 1937; J. R. Miller, 1963[1]; Gibbons, 1983[3]; Griner, 1983[8]; Schroeder and Radcliffe, 1989[1]), *C. scutulatus × unicolor* (SDSNH 43963), *C. viridis × ruber* (SDSNH 41829), *Deinagkistrodon acutus* (Ma, 1982a[4,6], 1982b[9]; Huang and Tsu, 1983[6,9]; Mao, 1993; FMNH 140109), *Echis carinatus* (J. C. George and Varde, 1941[6,7]; Brongersma, 1949; Varde, 1951[6]; J. C. George and Shah, 1956[6], 1965[6]; Deoras, 1965[6,7,9], 1970[6,7,9], 1978[6,7]; Antipchuk, 1966b[7], 1966c[9]; Antipchuk and Sobolieva 1976[7]; Deoras and Vad, 1966[3,6,9], 1973; Guibé, 1970b[7]; R. Singh and Kar, 1982; UF 48989–90), *E. coloratus* (CAS 139532; SDSU uncat.), *E. ocellatus* (UG V5P65), *Eristicophis macmahonii* (Groombridge, 1980; SDSU uncat.), *Gloydius blomhoffii* (Nakamura, 1938[6]; Lin et al., 1995; 2 SDSU uncat.), *G. halys* (Antipchuk, 1966b[7], 1966c[9]; Antipchuk and Sobolieva, 1971[9], 1976[7]; SDSU uncat.), *Hypnale hypnale* (2 SDSU uncat.), *H. nepa* (SDSU uncat.), *Lachesis muta* (Schlemm, 1826, 1827; Meckel, 1831, 1833; Noble, 1921; Brongersma, 1949; Butner, 1963a; Bourgondien and Bothner, 1969[9]; Moonen et al., 1979[2,3]; FMNH 49991, 49995), *"Lachesis"* sp. (Stannius, 1846, 1850; Pagenstecher, 1881; Hoffmann, 1890), *Montatheris hindii* (Groombridge, 1980; FMNH 142082), *Ophryacus undulatus* (UCM 41214), *Ovophis chaseni* (FMNH 71860), *O. monticola* (Brongersma, 1949; FMNH 204508), *O. okinavensis* (FMNH 45709), *Porthidium hyoprorum* (2 SDSU uncat.), *P. lansbergii* (Brongersma, 1949), *P. nasutum* (SDSU uncat.; UTA), *P. ophryomegas* (UTA), *Proatheris superciliaris* (Groombridge, 1980; FMNH 191337), *Protobothrops flavoviridis* (Brongersma, 1949; CAS 21968; MCZ 55967–68; UF 48987), *P. jerdoni* (MCZ 46905), *P. mucrosquamatus* (Mao, 1993; CAS 18921), *Pseudocerastes persica* (Groombridge, 1980; FMNH

166969), *Sistrurus catenatus* (Cope, 1894a, 1900; Brongersma, 1949; Bourgondien and Bothner, 1969[9]; Froom, 1972[3]; SDSU uncat.), *S. miliarius* (Bourgondien and Bothner, 1969; Young et al., 1994[6]; UF 17258–60), *S. ravus* (Bourgondien and Bothner, 1969; FMNH 113016), *Sistrurus* sp. (Butner, 1963a), *"Trigonocephalus"* sp. (Stannius, 1846), *Trimeresurus albolabris* (SDSNH), *T. elegans* (CAS 21970), *T. gramineus* (Cope, 1894a, 1900; Noble, 1921; Kashyap, 1960a[9]; SDSU uncat.), *T. popeorum* (FMNH 180273), *T. puniceus* (Brongersma, 1949[7]), *T. purpureomaculatus* (Brongersma, 1949), *T. stejnegeri* (Mao, 1993; FMNH 25203), *T. trigonocephalus* (SDSU uncat.), *Tropidolaemus wagleri* (Brongersma, 1949, 1951a; Antipchuk, 1966b[7]; Antipchuk and Sobolieva, 1976[7]; Kardong, 1972b; Ramsay, 1979; CAS 15359; FMNH 124297), *Vipera ammodytes* (Meckel, 1819; F. Werner, 1910[5,6]; Rothley, 1930a[7,8], 1930b[7,8]; Wolf, 1933[7]; Morris and Morris, 1965[3]; UF 48988), *V. aspis* (Abbatius, 1589[1], 1660[1]; Aldrovandi, 1640[1]; Severinus, 1645; Blasius, 1681[1]; Valentini, 1720[1]; Tiedemann, 1831; Butler, 1895; Livini, 1896; Oppel, 1905; Phisalix, 1922[5]; Baudrimont, 1929, 1952, 1956; Butner, 1963a; Luce, 1963[5,6,9]; Lécuru-Renous and Platel, 1970a[1,6,9], 1970b[1,5,6,9]; Kardong, 1972b; Sparing, 1976[6,7]; Underwood, 1976a; Ramsay, 1979; Renous, 1985[5,6,9]; Schnieper, 1995), *V. berus* (Cöiter, 1573; Severinus, 1645, 1651; Lacepède, 1790; Sonnini and Latreille, 1801[2,3]; Meckel, 1818, 1819, 1831; Schlemm, 1826, 1827; Henle, 1839[4]; Cuvier, 1840; A. Calori, 1842[5,6]; van der Hoeven, 1855, 1858; Stannius, 1846, 1856; Milne-Edwards, 1857b; Wahlström, 1868[3]; Lütken, 1882[6]; Hoffmann, 1890[4]; Butler, 1895[7]; Hochstetter, 1901; Leighton, 1901[1]; O'Donoghue, 1917[9]; Wolf, 1933[6,7]; Böker, 1937[1]; Suomalainen, 1939[7,8]; Boyd, 1942[9]; Brongersma, 1949; Bellairs and Boyd, 1950[2]; M. A. Smith, 1951[3]; H. M. Smith, 1954[3]; P. H. D. H. de Silva, 1955; Johansen and Hol, 1960[9]; Fuhn and Vancea, 1961[3]; Antipchuk, 1966b[7], 1966c[9], 1969a, 1969b; Antipchuk and Sobolieva, 1976[7]; Appleby, 1971[2]; Kardong, 1972b; Sparing, 1976[6,9]; Ramsay, 1979; Bazantová, 1986[8]; Mara, 1993; VW 2249–52), *V. bornmulleri* (MCZ 33576), *V. kaznakovi* (FMNH 153105), *V. lebetina* (Antipchuk, 1966b[7], 1966c[9]; Antipchuk and Sobolieva, 1971[9], 1976[7]), *V. palaestinae* (Frenkel and Kochva, 1970[1,6,7,9]; Kochva, 1974[1]; Saint Girons and Saint Girons, 1974[1]; Sparing, 1976; Gratz et al., 1981[7]; Barnard, 1996[1]; SDSNH 63874), *V. russelii* (J. C. George and Varde, 1941[7]; Brongersma, 1949[9]; Varde, 1951[6]; Deraniyagala, 1955[2]; J. C. George and Shah, 1956[6,7], 1965[6]; Bergman, 1961b; Bellairs, 1969[6], 1970; Deoras and Vad, 1973; Whitaker, 1978[3]; Mao, 1993; Mara, 1993[2]; FMNH 169380), *V. ursinii* (Kashyap, 1960a[9]; Antipchuk, 1966b[7], 1966c[9], 1969a, 1969b; Antipchuk and Sobolieva, 1971[8], 1976[7]; SDSU uncat.), *Vipera* sp.(Jacobaeus, 1680; Meckel, 1818, 1819, 1831, 1833; Stannius, 1846, 1850, 1856; E. O. Schmidt, 1865, 1872; Günther, 1886; Schimkewitsch et al., 1910, 1921; Perrier, 1928; H. Marcus, 1937; Underwood, 1976a; Bruno, 1985[2]).

ATRACTASPIDIDAE

Amblyodipsas concolor (Wallach, 1991; CM 68835; FMNH 205859, 218636; MCZ 16163; TM 56371), *A. dimidiata* (Wallach, 1991; MCZ 30400), *A. katangensis* (Wallach, 1985, 1991; FMNH 129584; MCZ 52852–53, 52855, 52857, 52859, 52864–66, 54535, 54538, 54542, 54572, 55474, 55834), *A. microphthalma* (Wallach, 1991; TM 55880), *A. polylepis* (Wallach, 1985, 1991; MCZ 48949, 52837, 52840–41, 54531–

32, 54833–36, 55475–76, 55833, 67889–92; SDSU uncat.; TM 52398, 56970), *A. rodhaini* (Wallach, 1991; MRAC 3067), *A. unicolor* (Wallach, 1985, 1991; FMNH 58315, 74821;LSUMZ 30600; MCZ 49725, 53734–36, 55242–43; UG C5U41), *A. ventrimaculata* (Wallach, 1991; FMNH 134261, 206407; NMZB 4843, 22823, 22849, 23998, 24176–77, 24179, 28089, 29619, 29664), *Aparallactus capensis* (Wallach, 1985, 1991; FMNH 78201, 83493, 134564, 154725, 191186, 205918–20, 206410, 206412–13; MCZ 52912, 52916–17, 52928, 80991; NMZB 3413; PEM 8; SDSNH 63882; TM 62890–91), *A. guentheri* (Underwood, 1967; Wallach, 1985, 1991; FMNH 78194, 81038–40, 81696; MCZ 51735, 51738, 51744, 51887–88, 51893–94, 51897, 54006; NMZB 20612), *A. jacksoni* (Wallach, 1991; CAS 113518; FMNH 62221–22, 62224–25; MCZ 11484, 56934, 59176; MHNG 1356.30, 1356.33), *A. lineatus* (Wallach, 1991, 1994a; IFAN 1953.8.60; MCZ 5826, 52129, 52219; NHMB 2132–33; ZMB 7745a–b), *A. lunulatus* (Wallach, 1985, 1991; CAS 153178; FMNH 58325, 58411, 58413, 58501, 62226–28, 62230–31, 78191–92, 81046–47, 81697, 187425; MCZ 51745, 51748, 52885, 52903, 53474, 53476–77, 53481, 53484, 69042, 80978, 96883; NMZB 7689), *A. modestus* (Cope, 1894a, 1900; Brongersma, 1957a; Wallach, 1985, 1991; BMNH 1979.209; FMNH 4024, 119665, 154727, 178384, 179355; 4 IRSL uncat.; LACM 39024, 39236; MCZ 7847, 9253, 49455; SDSNH; SDSU uncat.; 3 UNAZA uncat.), *A. moeruensis* (Wallach, 1991; IRSNB 9670, 9672), *A. niger* (Wallach, 1985, 1991, 1994a; IFAN 1946.1.1, 1946.1.5–6, 1953.8.37, 1953.8.64; MCZ 43206–07, 46986), *A. werneri* (Wallach, 1991; FMNH 81048; MCZ 51701, 51704–06, 51709, 51713, 51717–18, 54837–39, 172620–26; ZFMK 29792), *Atractaspis aterrima* (Wallach, 1991; CAS 103738; FMNH 53637, 62201; IFAN 1953.10.137, 1956.4.39, 1961.1.5; MCZ 23466, 49609; MHNG 1464.24; ZFMK 17571), *A. bibronii* (Brongersma, 1949; Wallach, 1991; FMNH 214819; MCZ 52951–53, 52955–56, 52959, 52961–62, 52966, 52975–76, 52978–84, 52986, 52989, 53003–05, 53007, 55133; NMZB 8400; SDSU uncat.; TM 36098), *A. boulengeri* (Wallach, 1991; MCZ 9247; MHNG 1323.20, 1323.22, 1464.21, 1464.23; ZMH 2848), *A. congica* (Wallach, 1991; FMNH 133038; ZMB 10046; ZMH 2839, 2842–46), *A. corpulenta* (Wallach, 1991; FMNH 122506, 178608, 178882; MCZ 4826, 7852, 22850, 53998; MHNG 1323.29, 1323.33), *A. dahomeyensis* (Wallach, 1991; CAS 146025; FMNH 154663–64, 170712, 196247; MCZ 55288, 55290, 55294; UG V2D141), *A. duerdeni* (Wallach, 1991; NMZB 8817; TM 45003; ZFMK 44916), *A. engdahli* (Wallach, 1991; CAS 140347, 153421), *A. fallax* (Wallach, 1991; CM 53633, 53639), *A. irregularis* (Brongersma, 1949[7]; Underwood, 1967; Wallach, 1991; CAS 156701, 156708; FMNH 34487, 48092, 58393, 58410, 62203–04, 214771, 219916; LSUMZ 40704–06; MCZ 80985, 170358, 170400–01; MHNG 975.65; MZUSP 8156, 8160, 8166; 2 SDSU uncat.; TAU 12608; UF 52894–95, 75993, 101198; VW 555, 1939, 1959, 5320), *A. leucomelas* (Wallach, 1991; ZMH 2847), *A. microlepidota* (Wallach, 1991; CAS 153176; FMNH 375, 48091, 48094, 58324, 58391, 58396, 58398–401, 62192, 62197–200, 144000; MCZ 53536, 53539, 53554, 53556; MHNG 1155.81; NHMB 21640; ZFMK 68208; ZMH 2849), *A. micropholis* (Wallach, 1991; IFAN 1948.4.29–30, 1954.4.20, 1955.4.18, 1955.5.20, 1955.6.24), *A. reticulata* (Wallach, 1991; FMNH 58958, 212306; MCZ 42976; MHNG 1464.16, 1464.18, 1464.48; SDSNH 63850; 2 SDSU uncat.; ZMB 14724), *A. scorteccii* (Wallach, 1991; BMNH 1949.2.3.13), *Brachyophis krameri* (Wallach, 1991; MZUF 3902), *B. revoili* (Wallach, 1991; MCZ 38692, 71850, 74307; MZUF 2794–95), *Chilorhinophis butleri*

(Wallach, 1991; FMNH 78179–81, 81024–27, 81031, 81037; MCZ 52829–34), *C. gerardi* (Wallach, 1991; IRSNB 9697–98; NMZB 1611, 4020, 5551, 10708, 11294, 20294, 22796, 23098, 30212, 32642), *Elapotinus picteti* (Wallach, 1991; MHNG 1246.76), *Hypoptophis wilsoni* (Wallach, 1985, 1991; FMNH 173037), *Macrelaps microlepidotus* (Cope, 1894a, 1900; Wallach, 1985, 1991; FMNH 187164–65, 191164–65, 205858, 205860–61, 205863; LSUMZ 30181; MCZ 21440, 42649; TM 53489, 56981), *Micrelaps boettgeri* (Wallach, 1991; CAS 130641; FMNH 58415, 58495; MCZ 20948, 40708, 51350, 53462, 97276; MSNG 46363; MZUF 27154), *M. muelleri* (Wallach, 1985, 1991; FMNH 34942, 48520, 74389; LACM 35822, 56495; MCZ 54392; ZMH 2900), *Pararhadinaea albignaci* (UMMZ 200065) *Poecilopholis cameronensis* (Wallach, 1985, 1991; ZMH 1252–53), *Polemon acanthias* (Brongersma, 1957a; Wallach, 1991; CAS 123527, 125538; FMNH 19836, 178375, 178386, 178894–95; IFAN 1945.1.3, 1953.8.50, 1953.8.101; MCZ 22524, 22527, 22529, 51814; ZMFK 30688), *P. barthii* (Wallach, 1991; MCZ 52222), *P. bocourti* (Wallach, 1991; LACM 49523–24; MHNG 1511.65; NHMB 2130; MRAC 5668; ZMB 20282; ZMH 1248–49, 1251), *P. christyi* (Wallach, 1985, 1991; CAS 147905; FMNH 58444, 219913–15, 219917–18; 7 IRSL uncat.; IRSNB 12808, 13337; LSUMZ 48374; VW 1735, 1802), *P. collaris* (Wallach, 1985, 1991; BMNH 1979.210; FMNH 212310, 219909; 2 IRSL uncat.; MCZ 29356, 32593, 42957; MHNG 1511.36, 1511.38–39; PEM; SDSU uncat.; ZMB 27744; ZMH 2903), *P. fulvicollis* (Wallach, 1991; FMNH 214834; 218997–99, 219905–08; MCZ 54737; ZMH 2901), *P. gabonensis* (Wallach, 1985, 1991; FMNH 59000; 4 IRSL uncat.; MCZ 9254; VW 836; ZMB 20307; ZMH 2902, 2904–05, 2909), *P. gracilis* (Wallach, 1991; FMNH 190751), *P. griseiceps* (Wallach, 1991; MCZ 7846; MHNG 1511.30; ZMB 28828), *P. neuwiedi* (Wallach, 1991; CAS 97511, 136270, 136416; FMNH 74833, 196267; MCZ 53737–38, 55258–59; ZMB 14150), *P. notatus* (Wallach, 1991; FMNH 212309; MCZ 14995; MHNG 1511.44; NHMB 13460; ZMB 28051; ZMH 2899), *P. robustus* (Wallach, 1991; MRAC 14916, 20229), *Xenocalamus bicolor* (Wallach, 1985, 1991; FMNH 72587, 73477, 190741; MCZ 21247, 159172; NMZB 8624, 8672, 12378, 22405, 22480, 29068; TM 33277, 42829, 42832, 46130), *X. mechowii* (Wallach, 1985, 1991; BMNH 1979.207–1979.208; FMNH 134239, 214831; LSUMZ 40711; MCZ 159173; NMZB 21282, 21284–85, 22828–29, 22854; PEM; SDSNH 63843; SDSU uncat.; TM 39387, 39389; VW 503, 1173, 2133), *X. micheli* (Wallach, 1991; IRSNB 9581), *X. sabiensis* (Wallach, 1991; CAS 159102; NMZB 3827, 6985, 19912, 21670, 23870, 31295), *X. transvaalensis* (Wallach, 1991; TM 28772).

ELAPIDAE

Aspidelaps lubricus (FMNH 187167, 224423–24), *A. scutatus* (PEM 12), *Boulengerina annulata* (Brongersma, 1957a; Wallach, 1985; FMNH 214754–59; SDSNH 63854; SDSU uncat.; UF 80444; 2 UNAZA uncat.; VW 1808, 1860, 2856), *B. christyi* (Wallach, 1985; FMNH 214833; LSUMZ 40826; SDSNH 63892; 3 SDSU uncat.; UF 52720, 75997, 101243), *Bungarus caeruleus* (Cuvier, 1840; Deoras and Vad, 1973; R. Singh and Kar, 1982, 1984[5,9]; Wallach, 1985; FMNH 121508; SDSU uncat.), *B. candidus* (Cope, 1894a, 1900; Butler, 1895; Brongersma, 1951a; Bergman, 1962; Wallach, 1985; FMNH 191117), *B. ceylonicus* (CM 67817), *B. fasciatus* (Fürbringer, 1922[5]; Brongersma, 1951a, 1957a; Bergman, 1962; Butner, 1963a; Ramsay, 1979;

FMNH 229812), *B. flaviceps* (Brongersma, 1957a; Ramsay, 1979; Wallach, 1985; FMNH 138691, 233158), *B. multicinctus* (Mao, 1993; FMNH 140150), *Bungarus* sp. (Stannius, 1846, 1850), *Calliophis calligaster* (Butner, 1963a; FMNH 15009; MCZ 25844a–b, 25848), *C. gracilis* (FMNH 178400; MCZ 82899a–b), *C. japonicus* (Nakamura, 1938[6,9]; Wallach, 1985; FMNH 43632, 45070; MCZ 55958; UMMZ 183709) *C. macclellandi* (Wallach, 1985; FMNH 6659, 109761, 170646), *C. maculiceps* (Wallach, 1985; FMNH 178379, 178426, 180060), *C. nigrescens* (MCZ 3837), *Dendroaspis angusticeps* (Noble, 1921[5]; Angel, 1950[5]; FMNH 68752), *D. jamesoni* (BMNH 1979.211; 4 IRSL uncat.; 2 UNAZA uncat.; VW 1048, 1223–24,1324, 1367), *D. polylepis* (Cope, 1894a, 1900; Rose, 1955[5]; Sweeney, 1961[5]; Pitman, 1974[5]; Spawls, 1979[3]; Marais, 1985[2], 1992[2]; Capula and Behler, 1989[5]; Maina, 1989[8]; SDSU uncat.), *D. viridis* (Bargar and Johnson, 1986c[2,3]; UG E1V53), *Elapsoidea laticincta* (Wallach, 1985; FMNH 95837; MCZ 53494), *E. loveridgei* (MCZ 49511, 96852), *E. nigra* (MCZ 23412), *E. semiannulata* (Wallach, 1985; BMNH 1979.212; FMNH uncat.; MCZ 21439, 42968, 52941, 54844; PEM; SDSU uncat.), *E. sundevallii* (FMNH 224422; MCZ 21439), *Hemachatus haemachatus* (Lereboullet, 1838; Cuvier, 1840; Milne-Edwards, 1857b; Beddard, 1906b; L. Perkins, 1974[2]; Patterson, 1987[3]; Coborn, 1991[3]; FMNH 212979), *Homoroselaps dorsalis* (Wallach, 1991; NMZB 6581; TM 55792, 55826), *H. lacteus* (Henle, 1839[4]; Stannius, 1856; Hoffmann, 1890[4]; Butler, 1895; Brongersma, 1957a; Ramsay, 1979; Wallach, 1985, 1991; FMNH 16037, 17717, 204890–92, 206414–15; IRSNB 2999, 3001; MCZ 6037, 11922–23, 21353; NMZB 6348, 12932; PEM 10; TM 27277, 55070), *Homoroselaps* spp. (Wallach, 1988), *Laticauda colubrina* (Schlegel, 1837a, 1837b; Pagenstecher, 1881; Beddard, 1904b[6]; Brongersma, 1956b; McDowell, 1969b; Dunson, 1975b[3]; Heatwole and Seymour, 1975a; Seymour, 1978[7,9]; Ramsay, 1979[7]; Mao and Chen, 1980; Heatwole, 1981; Lillywhite, 1987a[7], 1987b GVP 38, 40; SDSNH 39195; VW 135), *L. laticaudata* (Meckel, 1819, 1833; Cope, 1894a, 1900; Butler, 1895[7]; Antipchuk, 1966b[7]; Antipchuk and Sobolieva, 1976[7]; McDowell, 1969b; Ramsay, 1979[7]; Mao and Chen, 1980; GVP 76, 85–86), *L. semifasciata* (McDowell, 1969b; Mao and Chen, 1980; GVP 81; VW 151), *Laticauda* sp. (Meckel, 1833), Stannius, 1846), *Leptomicrurus collaris* (MCZ 865), *L. narduccii* (FMNH 35576, 152318; MCZ 36980), *Maticora bivirgata* (Thompson, 1914b; Brongersma, 1957a; Butner, 1963a; Ramsay, 1979; FMNH 147660), *M. intestinalis* (MCZ 43596–97), *Micruroides euryxanthus* (FMNH 74972; SDSU uncat.), *Micrurus corallinus* (Cope, 1894a, 1900; MCZ 27682; 2 SDSU uncat.), *M. diastema* (SDSU uncat.), *M. fulvius* (Meckel, 1833; Cope, 1894a, 1900; Butler, 1895; Brongersma, 1957a; Ramsay, 1979; Bargar and Johnson, 1987a[3]; VW 662), *M. lemniscatus* (Lereboullet, 1838; Henle, 1839[4]; Stannius, 1856; Milne-Edwards, 1857b; Hoffmann, 1890[4]; Cope, 1894a, 1900; SDSU uncat.), *M. mipartitus* (VW 388), *M. multifasciatus* (Cope, 1894a, 1900), *M. nigrocinctus* (VW 235), *Micrurus* sp. (Meckel, 1831; Stannius, 1846, 1850; Pagenstecher, 1881), *Naja atra* (Kundert, 1984[3]; Mao, 1993), *N. haje* (Meckel, 1819; Stannius, 1856; Brongersma, 1957a; Broadley and Cock, 1975[1]; Ramsay, 1979; FMNH 206233), *N. katiensis* (Roman, 1980[2]; MCZ 49566), *N. melanoleuca* (Berridge, 1935[3]; Brongersma, 1957a; Bellairs and Carrington, 1966[3]; Honders, 1975[2]; Ramsay, 1979; Wallach, 1985; Mara, 1993[3]; Coborn, 1994[2]; BMNH 1979.213–14; 15 IRSL uncat.; LSUMZ 40708–09; MCZ 170391; MZUSP 8151; NMV 55558; PEM; SDSU uncat.; TAU 12633; UF

52479, 80362–65, 80668–69, 101244; UMMZ; 4 UNAZA uncat.; VW 1768, 2324–30; ZRC 2.3431–32), *N. mossambica* (SDSU uncat.), *N. naja* (Meckel, 1818, 1819; Lereboullet, 1838; Henle, 1839[4]; Cuvier, 1840; Stannius, 1846, 1850, 1856; Milne-Edwards, 1857b; R. Owen, 1866; Hoffmann, 1890[4]; Cope, 1894a, 1900; Wolf, 1933[6,7]; Fraser, 1937[5]; J. C. George and Varde, 1941[7]; Varde, 1951[6,8]; P. H. D. H. de Silva, 1953[5,9], 1955; J. C. George and Shah, 1956[6,7], 1965[6]; Brongersma, 1957a; Kashyap, 1960a[7,9], 1960b[7,9]; Bergman, 1962; Antipchuk, 1966b[7], 1966c[9]; Bellairs and Carrington, 1966; Guibé, 1970a; Deoras and Vad, 1973; Agarwal and Sharma, 1979[5,9]; Ramsay, 1979; Bargar and Johnson, 1986a[3]), *N. nigricollis* (Brongersma, 1957a; Bellairs and Carrington, 1966[3]; Bellairs, 1969[3], 1970; Ramsay, 1979; Rage, 1994[3]; FMNH 224418, 224415; TAU; UNAZA uncat.), *N. nivea* (Brongersma, 1957a; Ramsay, 1979; Buys and Buys, 1981[3]; PEM 11), *N. oxiana* (SDSU uncat.), *N. samarensis* (VW 215–16, 218, 227–28, 231–32, 234, 236, 240, 242, 245–46, 249–50, 255, 260, 262), *N. sputatrix* (Bergman, 1962; Bellairs, 1972[7]), "*Naja*" sp. (Meckel, 1818, 1819, 1831, 1833; Cuvier, 1840; Stannius, 1846, 1850; van der Hoeven, 1855, 1858), *Ophiophagus hannah* (Beddard, 1903[5,6]; Oppel, 1905; Thompson, 1914b; Brongersma, 1957a, 1958b; Butner, 1963a; Carr, 1963[3], 1979[3]; Leen, 1963[3], 1978[3]; Ramsay, 1979; Pinney, 1981[3]; Young, 1991[5,6], 1992; FMNH 180215; VW 40), *Paranaja multifasciata* (Wallach, 1985; CM 6797; IRSL uncat.; MCZ 22380, 55408), *Pseudohaje goldii* (2 IRSL uncat.), *P. nigra* (FMNH 191090), *Walterinnesia aegyptia* (FMNH 74025, 109991).

HYDROPHIIDAE

Acanthophis antarcticus (Meckel, 1819; Lereboullet, 1838; Cuvier, 1840; Stannius, 1846, 1850; Milne-Edwards, 1857b; Brongersma, 1957a; Butner, 1963a; Ramsay, 1979; CAS 121225; SDSU uncat.), *A. pyrrhus* (SDSU uncat.), *Acanthophis* sp. (Meckel, 1833; Stannius, 1846; Hoffmann, 1890), *Aspidomorphus lineaticollis* (McDowell, 1967); *A. muelleri* (Brongersma, 1957a; McDowell, 1967; Ramsay, 1979; CAS 132222), *A. schlegelii* (Brongersma, 1957a; FMNH 14200), *Austrelaps superbus* (FMNH 216286, 216288; SDSNH 41997; 8 SDSU uncat.), *Cacophis harriettae* (CSIRO 3112; FMNH 97013), *C. krefftii* (SDSU uncat.), *C. squamulosus* (SDSU uncat.), *Demansia atra* (CSIRO 814; FMNH 97169), *D. olivacea* (CAS 133797), *D. psammophis* (Cope, 1894a, 1900; Brongersma, 1957a; 3 SDSU uncat.), *D. torquata* (CSIRO 797; FMNH 97161), *Denisonia devisii* (FMNH 216292; SDSU uncat.), *D. maculata* (Brongersma, 1957a, 1958b; Ramsay, 1979; CAS 77751; SDSU uncat.), *Drysdalia coronata* (SDSU uncat.), *D. coronoides* (6 SDSU uncat.), *D. mastersi* (SDSU uncat.), *D. rhodogaster* (CSIRO 2596; SDSU uncat.), *Echiopsis curta* (Butner, 1963a; CSIRO 268; FMNH 202668), *Elapognathus minor* (WAM 34112), *Furina barnardi* (CAS 121102), *F. diadema* (CSIRO 360; FMNH 97028), *F. dunmalli* (SDSU uncat.), *F. ornata* (FMNH 202662; MCZ 140178), *F. tristis* (CAS 121229, 132198), *Hemiaspis damelii* (SDSU uncat.), *H. signata* (Brongersma, 1957a, 1958b; Ramsay, 1979; FMNH 216290; SDSU uncat.), *Hoplocephalus bitorquatus* (CAS 77739–40; FMNH 216289; SDSU uncat.), *H. bungaroides* (Brongersma, 1957a; Ramsay, 1979; SDSU uncat.), *H. stephensii* (FMNH 97315), *Loveridgelaps elapoides* (CAS 135209), *Micropechis ikaheka* (Brongersma, 1957a; Ramsay, 1979; FMNH 13937), *Notechis ater* (FMNH 216283–84; 6 SDSU uncat.), *Ogmodon vitianus* (FMNH 22999; MCZ 76633), *Oxyuranus microlepidotus* (QM 3729, 28778, 36749), *O. scutellatus* (Masci and Kendall, 1995[2,3]; CAS 103391; QM 22454, 24391, 32975, 34317; SDSU uncat.), *Parapistocalamus hedigeri* (FMNH 44842), *Pseudechis australis* (Gow, 1989[2]; CSIRO 2634; FMNH 97707), *P. guttatus* (SDSU uncat.), *P. papuanus* (CAS 121228), *P. porphyriacus* (Cope, 1894a, 1900; Ramsay, 1979[6–8]; Rosenzweig, 1981[5–9]; FMNH 216285; SDSU uncat.), *Pseudonaja affinis* (CSIRO 1827; FMNH 202670), *P. guttata* (CSIRO 2701; FMNH 97158), *P. modesta* (CSIRO 169; FMNH 97172), *P. nuchalis* (CSIRO 1688; FMNH 202667), *P. textilis* (3 SDSU uncat.), *Rhinoplocephalus bicolor* (WAM 68140), *R. boschmai* (CAS 77755; FMNH 97188), *R. nigrescens* (Brongersma, 1957a, 1958b; Ramsay, 1979; CAS 44128; FMNH 216291; 2 SDSU uncat.), *R. nigrostriatus* (CAS 127353; CSIRO 2712; FMNH 97175), *R. pallidiceps* (FMNH 97910), *Rhinoplocephalus* sp. (Ramsay, 1979), *Salomonelaps par* (FMNH 13807, 13834), *Simoselaps australis* (SDSU uncat.), *S. bertholdi* (FMNH 152148), *S. bimaculatus* (FMNH 202658), *S. calonotus* (CSIRO 2245; FMNH 202659), *S. fasciolatus* (FMNH 202660), *S. roperi* (FMNH 97084), *S. semifasciatus* (FMNH 152145), *S. warro* (FMNH 97753), *Suta fasciata* (FMNH 202663), *S. flagellum* (SDSU uncat.), *S. gouldii* (Brongersma, 1957a, 1958b; CAS 77781; SDSU uncat.), *S. monachus* (FMNH 202664), *S. nigriceps* (SDSU uncat.), *S. punctata* (CSIRO 2073), *S. suta* (3 SDSU uncat.), *Toxicocalamus holopelturus* (MCZ 156548), *T. loriae* (Butner, 1963a; CAS 139584; MCZ 121546), *T. preussi* (FMNH 43030), *T. stanleyanus* (Underwood, 1967; CAS 118943), *Tropidechis carinatus* (SDSU uncat.), *Vermicella annulata* (CAS 77728; FMNH 216287; 2 SDSU uncat.).

Hydrophiid (MacLeish, 1972[6]), *Acalyptophis peronii* (Brongersma, 1956b; Ramsay, 1979[6,7]; FMNH 213057), *Aipysurus apraefrontalis* (Heatwole and Seymour, 1975a; Ramsay, 1979), *A. duboisii* (Heatwole and Seymour, 1975a; Ramsay, 1979[6,7]; MCZ 142297), *A. eydouxi* (FMNH 213235), *A. fuscus* (Heatwole and Seymour, 1975a; Ramsay, 1979; MCZ 23482), *A. laevis* (Heatwole and Seymour, 1975a, 1975b[6]; Ramsay, 1979[7]; Heatwole, 1987[2,6]; Lillywhite, 1987a; LSUMZ 48190), *Astrotia stokesii* (Heatwole and Seymour, 1975a; Ramsay, 1979; AMNH 86174; FMNH 213063), *Disteira kingii* (Heatwole and Seymour, 1975a; Ramsay, 1979; AMNH 111818), *D. major* (Cuvier, 1840; AMNH 115067), *Disteira* sp. (Ziswiler, 1976[7]), *Emydocephalus annulatus* (Heatwole and Seymour, 1975a; Ramsay, 1979; FMNH 213674), *E. ijimae* (Mao and Chen, 1980; FMNH 120878), *Enhydrina schistosa* (Lereboullet, 1838; Cuvier, 1840; Cantor, 1841[6]; Stannius, 1846, 1850; Milne-Edwards, 1857b; J. C. George and Varde, 1941[7]; Varde, 1951[6,8]; Deoras and Vad, 1973; FMNH 197982), *Ephalophis greyi* (Ramsay, 1979; FMNH 212365), *Hydrelaps darwiniensis* (McDowell, 1972b; Ramsay, 1979; FMNH 97316), *Hydrophis caerulescens* (Bal and Navathe, 1949[9]; Heatwole and Seymour, 1975b[9]), *H. cyanocinctus* (J. C. George and Varde, 1941[6,7]; Guibé, 1970[7]; Varde, 1951[6,8]; Ramsay, 1979; Liu and Chen, 1983[4,6,8]; Mao and Chen, 1980), *H. elegans* (Heatwole and Seymour, 1975a; Ramsay, 1979[7]; MCZ 153112), *H. fasciatus* (Lereboullet, 1838; Butler, 1895; FMNH 166242), *H. melanocephalus* (Heatwole and Seymour, 1975a; Ramsay, 1979; Mao and Chen, 1980; SDSU uncat.), *H. melanosoma* (FMNH 206681), *H. ornatus* (Cope, 1894a; Ramsay, 1979), *H. semperi* (Heatwole and Seymour, 1975a; Ramsay, 1979), *H. spiralis* (Minton, 1966), *H. "trigonocephalus"* (=sp. indet.) (Henle, 1839[4]; Pagenstecher, 1881; Hoffmann, 1890[4]; Bütschli, 1933[4]), *Hydrophis* sp. (Schlegel, 1837b; Stannius, 1846, 1850, 1856; Pagenstecher, 1881; Günther,

1886; Schimkewitsch et al., 1910, 1921; Perrier, 1928; H. Marcus, 1937), *Kerilia jerdoni* (FMNH 178774), *Kolpophis annandalei* (FMNH 179041), *Lapemis curtus* (Cope, 1894a, 1900; Bergman, 1949; Antipchuk, 1966b[7], 1966c[9]; Antipchuk and Sobolieva, 1976[7]; Heatwole and Seymour, 1975a; Ramsay, 1979[7]; FMNH 199697; MCZ 25980), *Microcephalophis cantoris* (MCZ 5206), *M. gracilis* (FMNH 201934), *Parahydrophis mertoni* (AMS 54955), *Pelamis platurus* (Meckel, 1818; Schlegel, 1837a, 1837b; Lereboullet, 1838; Cuvier, 1840; Stannius, 1846, 1850, 1856; Milne-Edwards, 1857b; R. Owen, 1866; Pagenstecher, 1881; Hoffmann, 1890; Cope, 1894a, 1900; Butler, 1895; Beddard, 1904b[6]; Wolf, 1933; Kropach, 1972; Graham et al., 1975[6]; Heatwole and Seymour, 1975a; Ramsay, 1979[6-8]; Mao and Chen, 1980; Seymour, 1981; Seymour et al., 1981b[7]; VW 1612), *Praescutata viperina* (FMNH 213059), *Thalassophis anomalus* (Bergman, 1954; BMNH 1926.11.1.14).

COLUBRIDAE

Colubrid (McDowell, 1972c[4,5]; Gans, 1974[7]; Roman, 1980[2]; Stoops and Wright, 1992[5]; Keogh, 1996[6]), *Achalinus braconnieri* (CAS 64222), *A. niger* (UMMZ 183251), *A. rufescens* (MCZ 172686, 172808), *A. spinalis* (Butner, 1963a; FMNH 170639), *A. werneri* (Underwood, 1967; Saiff, 1975; FMNH 75198; MCZ 48875), *Adelophis copei* (USNM 110335), *A. foxi* (LSUMZ 16411; UCM 36413), *Adelphicos nigrilatus* (CAS 145203), *A. quadrivirgatus* (CAS 101393; FMNH 20421; UCM 34344, 34348, 34353), *Adelphicos* sp. (Wallach, 1988), *Aeluroglena cucullata* (BMNH 1905.10.30.127), *Afronatrix anoscopus* (Brongersma, 1957a; CAS 123666; UG C23A27), *Ahaetulla fasciolata* (FMNH 131669), *A. mycterizans* (Cope, 1894a, 1900; Hochstetter, 1901; Wall, 1905b[5]; P. H. D. H. de Silva, 1955; FMNH 27266), *A. nasuta* (H. W. Parker, 1965[3]; Goin and Goin, 1971[3]; Kardong, 1972b; Soderberg, 1972[5]; Deoras and Vad, 1973; A. de Silva, 1976[5], 1990[5]; Goin et al., 1978[3]; Whitaker, 1978[5]; Ramsay, 1979; Henderson and Binder, 1980[5]; Rajendran, 1986[5;] Nutaphand, 1988[5]; Young et al., 1994[6]; Greene, 1997[5]; VW 2264–68), *A. prasina* (Henle, 1839[4]; Pagenstecher, 1881; Hoffmann, 1890[4]; Butler, 1895[7]; Mell, 1928[5], 1929[5]; van Hoesel, 1959[5]; R. Mertens, 1930[5], 1959, 1960[5]; Nutaphand and Tumwipart, 1982[5]; Mehrtens, 1987[5]; VW 2259–63), *A. pulverulenta* (FMNH 122572), *A. xanthozona* (FMNH 131238), *Ahaetulla* sp. (Pagenstecher, 1881; Angel, 1950[5]; Black and Woodward, 1989[5]), *Alluaudina bellyi* (NMV 26836), *Alsophis angulifer* (Cope, 1894a, 1900), *A. antillensis* (Schlegel, 1837b; Cope, 1894a, 1900), *A. cantherigerus* (MCZ 7947a–b), *A. portoricensis* (FMNH 51982), *A. rufiventris* (Henle, 1839[4]), *A. vudii* (Cope, 1894a, 1900), "*A.*" *dorsalis* (FMNH 37273), "*A.*" *hoodensis* (MCZ 9880), "*A.*" *slevini* (FMNH 57601), "*A.*" *steinbachi* (MCZ 160097), *Amastridium veliferum* (Underwood, 1967; Wallach, 1988; FMNH 37140), *Amphiesma beddomei* (Underwood, 1967; CAS 17182), *A. bitaeniata* (Underwood, 1967), *A. celebica* (Brongersma, 1957a; Underwood, 1967), *A. conspicillata* (Brongersma, 1957a), *A. craspedogaster* (Underwood, 1967; FMNH 170641), *A. doriae* (Brongersma, 1957a), *A. flavifrons* (Underwood, 1967; FMNH 148852), *A. frenata* (FMNH 138600), *A. inas* (Underwood, 1967; FMNH 180154), *A. johannis* (FMNH 170635), *A. khasiensis* (Brongersma, 1957a; CAS 105028), *A. modesta* (CAS 73737; MCZ 16648), *A. monticola* (Underwood, 1967; CAS 17184), *A. octolineata* (FMNH 18722), *A. parallela* (Underwood, 1967; UMMZ 138282), *A. petersi* (Underwood, 1967; MCZ 11233), *A. picturata* (Brongersma, 1957a), *A.*

platyceps (Brongersma, 1957a; CAS 90690; FMNH 204502), *A. popei* (Underwood, 1967; FMNH 6658), *A. pryeri* (Underwood, 1967; LSUMZ 24710), *A. sarawacensis* (Brongersma, 1957a; MCZ 22642), *A. sauteri* (Thompson, 1914b; Underwood, 1967; LSUMZ 20056), *A. stolata* (Meckel, 1819; Brongersma, 1957a; FMNH 171766; VW 2957), *A. venningi* (Underwood, 1967), *A. vibakari* (Thompson, 1914b; Brongersma, 1957a; CAS 15859), *A. xenura* (Underwood, 1967), *Amphiesmoides ornaticeps* (MVZ 23627), *Amplorhinus multimaculatus* (FMNH 205909–10), *Antillophis andreae* (FMNH 67422), *A. parvifrons* (Cope, 1894a, 1900; FMNH 100, 42557), *Aplopeltura boa* (Butler, 1895; Brongersma, 1957c[7]; Antipchuk, 1966c[9]; FMNH 148814; MCZ 9025), *Apostolepis ambiniger* (FMNH 69934), *A. assimilis* (LSUMZ 46269; MVZ 176334), *A. dorbignyi* (MVZ 110991), *A. erythronota* (MCZ 27660), *A. niceforoi* (FMNH 121828), *A. nigroterminata* (FMNH 39646), *A. quinquelineata* (FMNH 26665), *Argyrogena fasciolata* (Padgaonkar and Warbhuwan, 1991[5]; CAS 17216), *Arizona elegans* (Underwood, 1967; Kardong, 1972b; Saiff, 1975; Ramsay, 1979; Keogh, 1993[7]; SDSU uncat.; 2 ZIL), *Arrhyton callilaemus* (Underwood, 1967; MCZ 69079–80), *A. funereum* (SDSNH 64242), *A. vittatum* (MCZ 68943), *Aspidura brachyorrhos* (FMNH 125015), *A. guentheri* (MCZ 15803), *A. trachyprocta* (Butler, 1895; FMNH 131367), *Aspidura* sp. (Wallach, 1988), *Atractus badius* (Cope, 1894a, 1900; MCZ 166571), *A. bocourti* (MCZ 42427), *A. carrioni* (MCZ 93585), *A. collaris* (MCZ 29298, LSUMZ 44597), *A. crassicaudatus* (SDSU uncat.), *A. duboisi* (USNM 232552), *A. elaps* (MCZ 61158), *A. emmeli* (ZMH 2850), *A. erythromelas* (MCZ 19206), *A. favae* (MCZ 5196), *A. fuliginosus* (MCZ 119470), *A. guentheri* (ZMH 2851), *A. lasallei* (MCZ 32799), *A. latifrons* (LSUMZ 43795), *A. lehmanni* (FMNH 54880), *A. longimaculatus* (FMNH 82024), *A. loveridgei* (SDSU uncat.; USNM 86817), *A. maculatus* (ZMH 2852), *A. major* (MCZ 53220, 96674, 166523; SDSU uncat.), *A. manizalesensis* (FMNH 54872), *A. modestus* (MCZ 166569), *A. multicinctus* (FMNH 11588), *A. nicefori* (USNM 86816), *A. occidentalis* (MCZ 17084), *A. occipitoalbus* (MCZ 29293), *A. orcesi* (USNM 232712), *A. pamplonensis* (FMNH 39485), *A. paucidens* (MCZ 164423), *A. peruvianus* (MCZ 8837), *A. poeppigi* (MCZ 48977), *A. punctiventris* (MCZ 150190), *A. resplendens* (MCZ 29295), *A. reticulatus* (MCZ 142563), *A. sanctaemartae* (MCZ 6533), *A. trilineatus* (Underwood, 1967; MCZ 49065), *A. torquatus* (MCZ 152702), *A. ventrimaculatus* (MCZ 112442), *A. werneri* (MCZ 150191), *Atractus* sp. (Wallach, 1988; MCZ 36990, 37701, 152593, 166570), *Atretium schistosum* (Gnanamuthu, 1937; Underwood, 1967; FMNH 121480), *A. yunnanensis* (FMNH 169366), *Balanophis ceylonensis* (Underwood, 1967; BMNH 1864.7.11.40), *Bitia hydroides* (FMNH 198701, 229568), *Blythia reticulata* (Wallach, 1988; ZSI 1408), *Bogertophis rosaliae* (Keogh, 1993[7]; CAS 144063, 147202), *B. subocularis* (Saiff, 1975; Keogh, 1993[7]; CAS 169715; SDSNH 57043; VW 2882), *Boiga angulata* (CAS 154175), *B. ceylonensis* (Butler, 1895; F. Werner, 1911; SDSU uncat.), *B. cyanea* (Meckel, 1818; pers. obs.[5]; FMNH 180282), *B. cynodon* (Lim, 1958[5]; SDSU uncat.), *B. dendrophila* (Schlegel, 1837b; Greene, 1977[6]; de Saint-Aubain, 1984[7]; Coburn, 1991[3], 1994[3]; Cleave, 1994[3]; FMNH 145841; VW 16), *B. dightoni* (FMNH 217699), *B. drapiezii* (Brongersma, 1957a; FMNH 196806), *B. forsteni* (FMNH 119688), *B. gokool* (MCZ 58261), *B. irregularis* (Berkhoudt et al., 1995[2]; SDSU uncat.), *B. jaspidea* (Brongersma, 1957a; Lim and Lee, 1989[5]; MCZ 5174), *B. kraepelini* (LSUMZ 19344), *B. multifasciata* (MCZ 3228), *B. multomaculata*

(Schlegel, 1837b; Stannius, 1856; Cope, 1894a, 1895b, 1900; Brongersma, 1957a; CAS 8321), *B. nigriceps* (FMNH 158646), *B. nuchalis* (MCZ 3876), *B. ochracea* (CAS 12365), *B. philippina* (FMNH 161637), *B. schultzei* (FMNH 105498), *B. trigonata* (Noble, 1921[5]; LSUMZ 24702), *Bothrolycus ater* (FMNH 4002), *Bothrophthalmus lineatus* (BMNH 1979.155–56; 10 IRSL uncat.; SDSU uncat.; TAU 12614; 4 UNAZA uncat.), *Brachyorrhos albus* (Wallach, 1988; FMNH 134323), *Calamaria acutirostris* (MCZ 25292), *C. albiventer* (CAS 14940), *C. bicolor* (FMNH 131595), *C. bitorques* (CAS 15295), *C. borneensis* (CAS 8569), *C. ceramensis* (FMNH 83464), *C. crassa* (FMNH 134230), *C. curta* (MCZ 25301), *C. everetti* (MCZ 22649), *C. gervaisii* (Underwood, 1967; CAS 23148), *C. grabowskyi* (MCZ 43573), *C. griswoldi* (SDSNH 63753), *C. javanica* (FMNH 109791), *C. lateralis* (MCZ 43582), *C. leucogaster* (MCZ 43576), *C. linnaei* (Schlegel, 1837b; FMNH 83077), *C. lovii* (CAS 8525), *C. lumbricoidea* (FMNH 72374; MCZ 43566), *C. melanota* (FMNH 109964), *C. modesta* (FMNH 83164; MCZ 7525), *C. muelleri* (MCZ 25328–30), *C. multipunctata* (Bergman, 1965), *C. nuchalis* (MCZ 45486), *C. pavimentata* (FMNH 178567), *C. schlegeli* (FMNH 147648, 178408; MCZ 8008), *C. septentrionalis* (MCZ 32419), *C. virgulata* (CAS 23167), *Calamaria* sp. (Wallach, 1988), *Calamorhabdium* sp. (Wallach, 1988; ANSP 21951), *Cantoria annulata* (CAS 133812), *C. violacea* (FMNH 206912), *Carphophis amoenus* (Saiff, 1975; Wallach, 1988; MCZ 32369; MZUSP 8183), *Cemophora coccinea* (Schlegel, 1837b; Cope, 1894a, 1900; Underwood, 1967; Kardong, 1972b; Saiff, 1975; Ramsay, 1979[7]; Keogh, 1993[7]; FMNH 427; SDSU uncat.), *Cerberus australis* (MCZ 48846), *C. microlepis* (MCZ 25683), *C. rynchops* (Meckel, 1819; Cantor, 1841; Cope, 1894a, 1900; Thompson, 1914b; J. C. George and Varde, 1941[7]; Varde, 1951[6]; Bergman, 1955b; Ramsay, 1979[6,7]; FMNH 203431; SDSNH; VW 46–47), *Cercaspis carinatus* (Schlegel, 1837b; CAS 17211; FMNH 197955; MCZ 4188), *Chamaelycus christyi* (IRSNB 8269, 13029), *C. fasciatus* (FMNH 26337), *C. parkeri* (MCZ 42687), *Chersodromus liebmanni* (FMNH 111985; MCZ 162830), *Chilomeniscus cinctus* (Saiff, 1975; FMNH 131978), *C. savagei* (SDSNH 44394), *C. stramineus* (Underwood, 1967; Saiff, 1975; SDSNH 30369), *Chilomeniscus* sp. (Wallach, 1988), *Chilopoma nigronuchalis* (LSUMZ 24541; SDSU uncat.), *C. rufipunctatus* (SDSU uncat.), *Chionactis occipitalis* (4 SDSNH; SDSU uncat.; 2 ZIL), *C. palarostris* (SDSU uncat.), *Chironius bicarinatus* (SDSU uncat.), *C. carinatus* (Meckel, 1819; Henle, 1839[4]; Hoffmann, 1890[4]; Cope, 1894a; Mole, 1924[5]; Brongersma, 1957a; Test et al., 1966[5]; Saiff, 1975; Greene, 1988[5]; SDSU uncat.), *C. exoletus* (Meckel, 1819;), *C. flavolineatus* (Saiff, 1975; SDSU uncat.), *C. fuscus* (Meckel, 1833; Saiff, 1975), *C. grandisquamis* (Saiff, 1975; 2 UCA uncat.), *C. monticola* (Saiff, 1975; LSUMZ 44769), *C. quadricarinatus* (MCZ 17939), *C. scurrulus* (Dixson et al., 1995[5]; SDSNH), *Chionactis occipitalis* (Saiff, 1975), *Chrysopelea ornata* (Cope, 1894a, 1900; Thompson, 1913c; VW 2254–58), *C. paradisi* (FMNH 131757; USNM 497052; VW 39, 2253), *C. pelias* (FMNH 158610; SDSNH 64294), *C. rhodopleuron* (FMNH 134320), *C. taprobanica* (FMNH 123760), *Clelia bicolor* (UMMZ 62822), *C. clelia* (Meckel, 1819; Schlegel, 1837b; Cope, 1894a, 1900; Brongersma, 1957a; MCZ 32715–16), *C. equatoriana* (FMNH 54863), *C. occipitolutea* (FMNH 140203), *C. rustica* (SDSU uncat.), *C. scytalina* (VW 631), *Clonophis kirtlandii* (SDSU uncat.), *Collorhabdium williamsoni* (Wallach, 1988; ZRC 2.2171), *Coluber algirus* (CAS 132824; MCZ 25883), *C. caspius* (Twerenbold, 1987[6]; MCZ 38524), *C. constrictor*

(Meckel, 1818; Miller, 1893[6,7]; Cope, 1894a, 1900; Thompson, 1914b; Atwood, 1916[5,6,9]; F. N. White, 1959; Kardong, 1972b; Saiff, 1975[7]; Ruben, 1976b[7]; Ramsay, 1979; Stinner, 1980[6,7]; Twerenbold, 1987; Keogh, 1993[7]; LSUMZ 16133; SDSU uncat.), *C. cypriniensis* (Twerenbold, 1987), *C. dahli* (Lüdicke, 1939, 1940[2, 5]), *C. dorri* (MCZ 67900), *C. elegantissimus* (CAS 139796), *C. florulentus* (Thompson, 1914b; Heasman, 1933[9]; Twerenbold, 1987; FMNH 171894), *C. gemonensis* (Meckel, 1819, 1833; Twerenbold, 1987; FMNH 25758; LSUMZ 34393), *C. hippocrepis* (Meckel, 1818; Cuvier, 1840; Hopley, 1882; Twerenbold, 1987; FMNH 83653), *C. jugularis* (Twerenbold, 1987; FMNH 67369), *C. karelini* (Saiff, 1975; CAS 120540), *C. keniensis* (CAS 11904), *C. najadum* (Schlegel, 1837b; Lüdicke, 1964[2,5]; Twerenbold, 1987; FMNH 22811), *C. nummifer* (MCZ 56480; NHMB SS6), *C. ravergieri* (Antipchuk, 1966b[7], 1966c[9]; Antipchuk and Sobolieva, 1976[7]; Twerenbold, 1987), *C. rhodorachis* (Thompson, 1914b; CAS 149437; MCZ 167015), *C. rogersi* (FMNH 171895; NHMB 16443), *C. socotrae* (MCZ 25884), *C. smithi* (MCZ 96964), *C. spinalis* (FMNH 24843), *C. variabilis* (Stannius, 1856; Perrier, 1928; CAS 143990), *C. ventromaculatus* (SDSNH 63287–88), *C. viridiflavus* (Cope, 1894a, 1900; Butler, 1895; Livini, 1896; Oppel, 1905; Jullien et al., 1960[9]; Twerenbold, 1987; CAS 94245), *C. "obscurus"* (=sp. indet.) (Meckel, 1819,1833), *C. "rudis"* (=sp. indet.) (Meckel, 1819), *C. "strictor"* (=sp. indet.) (Meckel, 1833), *C. "trilineatus"* (=sp. indet.) (Meckel, 1819, 1833), *"Coluber"* sp. (Meckel, 1818, 1819, 1831, 1833; Stannius, 1846, 1850; van der Hoeven, 1855, 1858; T. Williams, 1859; E. O. Schmidt, 1865, 1872; Pagenstecher, 1881; H. Marcus, 1937; Dulzetto, 1968[6]), *Coniophanes bipunctatus* (Cope, 1894a, 1900; Saiff, 1975), *C. fissidens* (Cope, 1894a, 1900; Underwood, 1967; CAS 143174, uncat.; FMNH 20459, 36317; UCA uncat.), *C. frangivirgatus* (LSUMZ 7841), *C. piceivittis* (FMNH 36365), *C. quinquevittatus* (Cope, 1894a, 1900; LSUMZ 8330), *C. schmidti* (SDSNH 45224), *Conophis lineatus* (Cope, 1894a, 1894b, 1900; Saiff, 1975; MNN 136; 19 UCA uncat.), *C. vittatus* (Cope, 1894a, 1894b, 1900; FMNH 104948), *Conopsis biseriatus* (Saiff, 1975; FMNH 40815), *C. nasus* (Saiff, 1975; FMNH 102843), *Contia tenuis* (Saiff, 1975; SDSU uncat.), *Coronella austriaca* (Meckel, 1818, 1831; Schlemm, 1826; Dugès, 1827[4]; Carus, 1827, 1835[5,6], 1838; Henle, 1839[4]; Cuvier, 1840; Leydig, 1857, 1866; Hoffmann, 1890[4]; Göppert, 1899[4,5]; Hochstetter, 1901; Böker, 1937[1]; P. H. D. H. de Silva, 1955; Trutnau, 1975[3]; Meban, 1980; Twerenbold, 1987; SDSU uncat.), *C. girondica* (Cope, 1894a, 1900; Lüdicke, 1939; CAS 92367a–b), *Coronella* sp. (Stannius, 1856), *Crisantophis nevermanni* (UCA uncat.), *Cryophis hallbergi* (LSUMZ 39532; UCM 41161), *Cryptolycus nanus* (NMZB-UM 20337), *Crotaphopeltis braestrupi* (CAS 153383), *C. degeni* (CAS 141748), *C. hippocrepis* (CAS 97515, 154290), *C. hotamboeia* (Schlegel, 1837b; Cuvier, 1840; Hoffmann, 1890; Butler, 1895; Beddard, 1906b; Thompson, 1914b; BMNH 1979.196–1979.204; CAS 156693–94; FMNH 214781, 214806–15; MZUSP 8125; NMV 55551; SDSNH 63851; TAU 12611, 12616–17; UF 52477; UMMZ 172976; VW 861, 873, 875–76, 903, 951, 971, 1021, 1023, 1029, 1038, 1052, 1055, 1063, 1118–19, 1125, 1133–34, 1138, 1147, 1153, 1155, 1162, 1172, 1190, 1210, 1249, 1312–13, 1346, 1378, 1409, 1419, 1506, 1518, 1641–42, 1650, 1671–72, 1687, 1723–24, 1748, 1763–65, 1813, 1863, 1967, 2120; ZMUC 631048–75; ZRC 2.3453), *C. tornieri* (MCZ 23320, 23332), *Cyclocorus lineatus* (Thompson, 1913c; FMNH 161639), *C. nuchalis* (FMNH 106933), *Cyclophiops doriae* (MCZ 44714), *C.*

major (FMNH 120858), *C. semicarinatus* (Saiff, 1975; 75175), *Darlingtonia haetiana* (UMMZ 123097), *Dasypeltis atra* (6 IRSL uncat.; LSUMZ 40775–76; MZUSP 8171; VW 2418, 2650), *D. fasciata* (LSUMZ 40707; VW 869), *D. inornata* (Gans and Richmond, 1957[5]; Gans, 1974[3]; FMNH 206377), *D. medici* (SDSU uncat.), *D. palmarum* (Cope, 1894a, 1900; BMNH 1979.192; UNAZA uncat.; VW 1006), *D. scabra* (Meckel, 1819; Stannius, 1856; Weale, 1871; Cope, 1894a, 1895b, 1900; Butler, 1895; Kathariner, 1898[5]; Böker, 1937[5]; R. Mertens, 1946[5], 1955; Gans and Richmond, 1957[5]; Sweeney, 1961[5]; V. F. M. FitzSimons, 1962[5]; Lüdicke, 1964[5]; Underwood, 1967; Gans, 1974[3]; Kalmus, 1984[5]; Staniszewski, 1990[3]; Geus, 1992[3]; BMNH 1979.193–194; CAS 156700; FMNH 214832; LSUMZ 40774, 40787; TAU 12612, 12618, 12620; UF 101199; VW 931, 1039, 1109–10, 1112, 1199, 1241, 1421, 1812, 1966, 2416; ZRC 2.3446), *Dasypeltis* sp. (Weale, 1871[5]; Gans, 1974[2,3,7]; Honders, 1975[3]; S. A. Johnson, 1986[3]), *Dendrelaphis caudolineatus* (VW 54, 118), *D. cyanochloris* (Kundert, 1974[5], 1984[5]; Manthey and Grossmann, 1997[5]), *D. formosus* (Lim and Lee, 1989[5]; Manthey and Grossmann, 1997[5]), *D. pictus* (Cuvier, 1840; Cope, 1894a, 1900; Butler, 1895; R. Mertens, 1930[5]; Bergman, 1955a; Brongersma, 1957a; Kardong, 1972b; Reitinger and Lee, 1978[5]; Ramsay, 1979; Mara, 1993[5]; Coborn, 1994[5]; VW 31, 36, 53, 63, 142), *D. punctulatus* (C. R. Johnson, 1975[5]; Mehrtens, 1987[5]; Wilson and Knowles, 1988[5]; Gow, 1989[5]; Shine, 1991[5]; Coborn, 1994[5]; SDSU uncat.), *D. subocularis* (FMNH 180041), *D. tristis* (Wall, 1910[5]; Whitaker, 1978[5]; SDSU uncat.), *Dendrelaphis* sp. (Schlegel, 1837b; Pagenstecher, 1881), *Dendrolycus elapoides* (BMNH 1907.5.22.35), *Dendrophidion bivittatus* (SDSU uncat.), *D. brunneus* (MCZ 156328), *D. dendrophis* (FMNH 45571), *D. nuchalis* (MCZ 22210), *D. paucicarinatum* (MCZ 34319), *D. percarinatum* (SDSU uncat.), *D. vinitor* (FMNH 154039), *Diadophis punctatus* (F. N. White, 1959[9]; McDowell, 1972c[3]; LSUMZ 22723; MZUSP 8184–85; SDSNH), *Diaphorolepis laevis* (MCZ 143839), *D. wagneri* (KU 75682), *Dinodon flavozonatum* (McDowell, 1972a), *D. orientale* (McDowell, 1972a; MCZ 7400, 25882), *D. rufozonatum* (McDowell, 1972a; FMNH 18758), *D. semicarinatum* (Cope, 1894a, 1900; McDowell, 1972a; FMNH 45093), *D. septentrionale* (FMNH 140168), *Dipsadoboa aulica* (MCZ 159164), *D. duchesnei* (IRSL uncat.), *D. shrevei* (MCZ 55487), *D. unicolor* (Underwood, 1967; IRSL uncat.), *D. viridis* (MZUSP 8126; VW 1394; ZMUC 631045–46), *D. weileri* (IRSL uncat.; 2 UNAZA uncat.), *Dipsas albifrons* (Werner, 1911; Brongersma, 1957c[7]; Wallach, 1995; MCZ 20855), *D. annulata* (Henle, 1839[4]), *D. boettgeri* (Wallach, 1995; LSUMZ 27371–72), *D. catesbyi* (Werner, 1911; Brongersma, 1957c[7]; Wallach, 1995; LSUMZ 45543), *D. gaigeae* (Wallach, 1995; LSUMZ 37112), *D. gracilis* (Wallach, 1995; MCZ 156894), *D. indica* (Werner, 1911[6]; Brongersma, 1957c[7]; Wallach, 1995; MCZ 153972), *D. latifasciata* (Wallach, 1995; MCZ 166589), *D. latifrontalis* (Wallach, 1995; MCZ 51477), *D. oreas* (Wallach, 1995; MCZ 8431, 17083), *D. pavonina* (Brongersma, 1957c[7]; Wallach, 1995; UMMZ 47747), *D. peruana* (Wallach, 1995; LSUMZ 27369), *D. sanctijoannis* (Wallach, 1995; FMNH 54905), *D. schunkii* (Wallach, 1995; FMNH 188757), *D. variegata* (Brongersma, 1957c[7]; Wallach, 1995; FMNH 204479), *D. vermiculata* (Wallach, 1995; MCZ 147184), *D. viguieri* (Wallach, 1995; MCZ 34376), "*Dipsas*" sp.(Stannius, 1846, 1850, 1856; Pagenstecher, 1881; Hoffmann, 1890; Perrier, 1928; Brongersma, 1958b), *Dipsina multimaculata* (SDSU uncat.), *Dispholidus typus* (Schlegel, 1837b; Lereboullet, 1838; Henle, 1839[4]; Cuvier, 1840; Stannius, 1856; Milne-Edwards,

1857b; Hoffmann, 1890[4]; Cope, 1894a, 1894b, 1895b, 1900; E. G. Boulenger, 1914[5]; Noble, 1921[5]; Barbour, 1926[5]; Loveridge, 1928[5]; Rose, 1929a[5], 1929b[5], 1955[5], 1962[5]; Pitman, 1938[5], 1974[5]; Scortecci, 1939[5]; Cansdale, 1948[5]; Angel, 1950[5]; Villiers, 1950[5], 1975[5]; Pringle, 1954[5]; Isemonger, 1955[5], 1962[5], 1968[5]; K. P. Schmidt and Inger, 1957[5]; Vesey-FitzGerald, 1958[5], 1975[5]; Broadley, 1957a, 1959[5], 1983[5], 1990[5]; R. Mertens, 1959[5], 1960; Hoesch, 1960[5]; Cansdale, 1961[5]; Sweeney, 1961[5]; V. F. M. FitzSimons, 1962[5], 1970[5]; Bellairs and Carrington, 1966; Zingg, 1968[5]; Bellairs, 1969[5], 1970; Stidworthy, 1971[5]; Visser, 1972[5]; Burton, 1973b; Skinner, 1973[5]; Broadley and Cock, 1975[5]; Gans, 1975b[5]; H. W. Parker and Grandison, 1977[5]; Visser and Chapman, 1978[5]; Stucki-Stirn, 1979[5]; Buys and Buys, 1981[5]; Phelps, 1981[5], 1989[5]; Hedges, 1983[5]; Marais, 1985[5]; Patterson, 1986[5], 1987[3]; Mehrtens, 1987[5]; Jaroniewski, 1992[5]; BMNH 1979.205; FMNH 58379; 2 IRSL uncat.), *Ditypophis vivax* (BMNH 1957.1.10.30; MCZ 100292), *Drepanoides anomalus* (Wallach, 1988; FMNH 81525), *Dromicodryas bernieri* (Henle, 1839[4]; Hoffmann, 1890[4]; Lüdicke, 1964[4]; FMNH 75599, 75603), *D. quadrilineatus* (FMNH 60893), *Dromophis lineatus* (TAU 12615; UF 52478, 80445, 101200; UMMZ 172974; VW 1807, 2269; ZRC 2.3424), *D. praeornatus* (UG C12P38), *Dryadophis bifossatus* (Cope, 1894a, 1900; SDSU uncat.), *D. boddaerti* (Cope, 1894a, 1900; Brongersma, 1957a; Saiff, 1975; FMNH 49328), *D. dorsalis* (Saiff, 1975; MNN 127), *D. melanolomus* (Saiff, 1975; 2 SDSU uncat.), *D. pleei* (Saiff, 1975; SDSNH 31803), *D. pulchriceps* (Saiff, 1975; MCZ 164517), *Drymarchon corais* (Cope, 1894a, 1900; Beddard, 1906b; Mole, 1924[5]; Gillian and Conklin, 1938[7]; Angel, 1950[5]; Saiff, 1975; SDSNH; UCA uncat.; VW 205, 2896, 3831–34), *Drymobius chloroticus* (CAS 143170), *D. margaritiferus* (Cope, 1894a, 1900; Saiff, 1975; 5 UCA uncat.), *D. melanotropis* (Cope, 1894a, 1900; UMMZ 79762), *D. rhombifer* (Saiff, 1975; FMNH 81310), *Drymoluber brazili* (SDSU uncat.), *D. dichrous* (Saiff, 1975; FMNH 152306), *Dryocalamus davisoni* (FMNH 180074), *D. nympha* (Schlegel, 1837b; MCZ 18384), *D. subannulatus* (FMNH 183797), *D. tristrigatus* (FMNH 147659), *Dryophiops philippina* (CAS 60953), *D. rubescens* (FMNH 178385), *Duberria lutrix* (Schlegel, 1837b; VW 1606), *D. variegatum* (FMNH 224425), *Duberria* sp. (Wallach, 1988), *Echinanthera melanostigma* (MCZ 39436), *E. undulata* (MCZ 20739), *Eirenis collaris* (SDSU uncat.), *E. coronelloides* (FMNH 72114), *E. decemlineata* (FMNH 74397), *E. lineomaculata* (FMNH 48510), *E. meda* (FMNH 153109), *E. modesta* (FMNH 83964), *E. persica* (CAS 86530), *E. punctatolineata* (FMNH 83963), *E. rothi* (CAS 87423), *Elachistodon westermanni* (Underwood, 1967; FMNH 152140), *Elaphe bairdi* (Keogh, 1993[7]; SDSNH 46178), *E. bimaculata* (Saiff, 1975; FMNH 108657), *E. cantoris* (FMNH 204509), *E. carinata* (Saiff, 1975; Helfenberger, 1989; LSUMZ 36789), *E. climacophora* (Nakamura, 1938[6,9]; Oidumi, 1940[6]; Brongersma, 1957b; Niimi, 1965[6], 1971[6]; Helfenberger, 1989; LSUMZ 7381), *E. conspicillata* (Oidumi, 1940[6,7]; Brongersma, 1957b; Helfenberger, 1989; CAS 13228), *E. dione* (Meckel, 1833; Acolat, 1955; Brongersma, 1957b; Antipchuk, 1966b[7], 1966c[9]; Antipchuk and Sobolieva, 1976[7]; Saiff, 1975; Helfenberger, 1989; BYU 11282; SDSU uncat.), *E. erythrura* (Brongersma, 1957b; Saiff, 1975; Helfenberger, 1989; FMNH 15055; MCZ; 173307; VW 27, 29, 41–42, 44, 70, 75, 77, 87, 95–96, 102–03, 105, 114), *E. flavirufa* (Underwood, 1967; Saiff, 1975; Keogh, 1993[7]; USNM 110302), *E. flavolineata* (Brongersma, 1951a, 1957b; Lim and Lee, 1989[3]; Helfenberger, 1989; FMNH 67309; MCZ 15211), *E. frenata*

(Brongersma, 1957b; Saiff, 1975; FMNH 172322), *E. grabowskyi* (MCZ 45319), *E. guttata* (Meckel, 1819; J. Jones, 1856[5,6,9]; Beddard, 1906b; Brongersma, 1957b; Saiff, 1975; Helfenberger, 1989; Keogh, 1993[7]; SDSU uncat.), *E. helena* (Wall, 1913[5]; Brongersma, 1957b; Bröer and Engelhardt, 1981[5]; Schulz, 1996[5]; SDSU uncat.), *E. hodgsonii* (Brongersma, 1957b; Saiff, 1975; Helfenberger, 1989; CAS 90675), *E. hohenackeri* (Helfenberger, 1989; CAS 105951), *E. jansenii* (Brongersma, 1957b; Young, 1992; Schulz, 1996[5]), *E. japonica* (UMMZ 130089), *E. leopardina* (Meckel, 1818; Cope, 1894a, 1900; Beddard, 1906b; Lüdicke, 1939; Saiff, 1975), *E. longissima* (Panizza, 1833[1]; Hyrtl, 1837[6]; Henle, 1839[4]; Pagenstecher, 1881; Hoffmann, 1890[4]; Butler, 1895; Hochstetter, 1901[9]; Greil, 1903[7]; Beddard, 1906b; Acolat, 1955[7,9]; P. H. D. H. de Silva, 1955; Brongersma, 1957b; Jullien et al., 1960[6,9]; Kardong, 1972b; Saiff, 1975; Ramsay, 1979; Twerenbold, 1987; Helfenberger, 1989; CAS 17107), *E. mandarina* (Brongersma, 1957b; Saiff, 1975; Helfenberger, 1989; FMNH 18695), *E. melanura* (Butler, 1895; Bergman, 1961a; Saiff, 1975), *E. moellendorffi* (Helfenberger, 1989; SDSU uncat.), *E. obsoleta* (Cope, 1894a[1], 1900[1]; Beddard, 1906b; Atwood, 1916; Brongersma, 1957b; Albright and Nelson, 1959[3]; Brooks, 1970[8]; Kardong, 1972a[4], 1972b[6]; Saiff, 1975; Pattle, 1976; Baeyens et al., 1978, 1979b, 1980; Ramsay, 1979; Lillywhite and Gallagher, 1985[9]; Lillywhite, 1987a[7], 1987b[7]; Donald et al., 1990[9]; Coborn, 1991[3]; Keogh, 1993[7]; LSUMZ 64020; MZUSP 8186; SDSNH; 2 SDSU uncat.), *E. porphyracea* (Brongersma, 1957b; Saiff, 1975; Helfenberger, 1989; FMNH 15828), *E. prasina* (FMNH 128282), *E. quadrivirgata* (Ogawa, 1920[8]; Oidumi, 1940[6,7]; Brongersma, 1957b; Nagaishi et al., 1964[8]; Saiff, 1975; Yoshihara et al., 1979[5]; Gomi, 1982[8]; Iwahori et al., 1987[8]; Helfenberger, 1989; SDSU uncat.), *E. quatuorlineata* (Meckel, 1831; Butler, 1892[7], 1895; Broman, 1904[7]; Wolf, 1933; Saiff, 1975; Twerenbold, 1987; Helfenberger, 1989; SDSU uncat.), *E. radiata* (M. A. Smith, 1914[5]; Wall, 1914[5]; Noble, 1921[5]; Heurn, 1929[5]; Brongersma, 1951a, c[9], 1957b; van Hoesel, 1959[5]; Antipchuk, 1966c[9], 1967b; Campden-Main, 1970[5]; Antipchuk and Sobolieva, 1971; Kardong, 1972b; Saiff, 1975; Ramsay, 1979; Karsen et al., 1986[3,5]; Schulz, 1986[5], 1988[5]; Twerenbold, 1987[6]; Lim and Lee, 1989[5]; Coborn, 1991[5]; Cox, 1991[5]; Leetz, 1991[5]; Boilstone, 1994[5]; Staszko and Walls, 1994[5]; Schulz, 1996[5]; SDSU uncat.; Manthey and Grossmann, 1997[5]), *E. rufodorsata* (Brongersma, 1957b; Saiff, 1975; FMNH 24915), *E. scalaris* (Brongersma, 1957b; Saiff, 1975; Lanka and Vit, 1985a[1], 1985b[1]; Helfenberger, 1989; Castells et al., 1990; SDSU uncat.), *E. schrenckii* (Antipchuk, 1966b[7], 1966c[9], 1967b[9]; Antipchuk and Sobolieva, 1971[9], 1976[7]; Saiff, 1975; Helfenberger, 1989; FMNH 7066), *E. situla* (Brongersma, 1957b; Helfenberger, 1989; LSUMZ 34394), *E. subradiata* (Brongersma, 1957b; Saiff, 1975; MCZ 26986), *E. taeniura* (Mell, 1928[5], 1929[5]; Saiff, 1975; Schulz, 1996[5]; CAS 22061; 31363; SDSNH 52839), *E. vulpina* (Kellicott, 1898[9]; Underwood, 1967; Saiff, 1975; Keogh, 1993[7]; MZUSP 8187–88), *Elaphe* sp. (Angel, 1950[5]; Okada et al., 1962[7,8]; H. W. Parker, 1977[5]; Ramsay, 1979), *Elapoidis fuscus* (Brongersma, 1957a; Wallach, 1988; FMNH 134231), *Elapomorphus lepidus* (FMNH 9028), *E. quinquelineatus* (MCZ 20768; 2 SDSU uncat.), *Enhydris albomaculata* (MCZ 27104), *E. alternans* (Bergman, 1960; FMNH 11092), *E. bennettii* (Gray, 1842), *E. bocourti* (FMNH 11549), *E. chinensis* (K. P. Schmidt, 1927; MCZ 166898), *E. doriae* (MCZ 5240), *E. enhydris* (Bergman, 1955d; MCZ 58248–49), *E. jagorii* (LSUMZ 29602), *E. maculosa* (MCZ 18390), *E. pakistanica* (MCZ 84090), *E.*

plumbea (Bergman, 1960; MCZ 16687), *E. polylepis* (MCZ 121562), *E. sieboldi* (MCZ 22384), *E. smithi* (FMNH 179114), *Enuliophis sclateri* (FMNH 101006), *Enulius flavitorques* (CAS 94256; 2 UCA uncat.), *Enulius* sp. (Stannius, 1856; Wallach, 1988), *Eridiphas slevini* (BYU 37416; CAS 86093), *Erpeton tentaculatus* (SDSU uncat.), *Erythrolamprus aesculapii* (Meckel, 1819, 1833; Schlegel, 1837b; Cuvier, 1840; Cope, 1894a, 1900; Beddard, 1906b[6,9]; SDSU uncat.), *E. bizona* (FMNH 165380), *E. mimus* (UCA uncat.), *Etheridgeum pulchrum* (Wallach, 1988; NHW 23449), *Farancia abacura* (Cope, 1894a, 1900; Underwood, 1967; Saiff, 1975; LSUMZ 19177; SDSU uncat.), *F. erytrogramma* (Meckel, 1819; Cope, 1894a, 1900; Saiff, 1975; FMNH 38114), *Ficimia olivacea* (Cope, 1894a, 1894b, 1900; Saiff, 1975; FMNH 208165; SDSNH 57044), *F. publia* (Saiff, 1975; SDSU uncat.), *F. ruspator* (Saiff, 1975), *F. streckeri* (FMNH 67430), *Fimbrios klossi* (FMNH 71699), *Fordonia leucobalia* (Butler, 1895; Bergman, 1960; MCZ 137470), *Geagras redimitus* (Wallach, 1988; FMNH 105140), *Geodipsas depressiceps* (AMNH 12205), *G. procterae* (Underwood, 1967; MCZ 23277), *G. vauerocegae* (ZMUC 63906), *Geophis blanchardi* (LSUMZ 28708), *G. brachycephalus* (MCZ 15321), *G. carinosus* (LSUMZ 37138), *G. dubius* (ZMH 2853–54), *G. hoffmanni* (MCZ 15301; UCA uncat.), *G. latifrontalis* (MCZ 19045), *G. mutitorques* (LSUMZ 11015; MCZ 78584), *G. nasalis* (MCZ 22111), *G. rhodogaster* (MCZ 22441), *G. semidoliatus* (FMNH 70741), *Geophis* sp. (Wallach, 1988), *Gerarda prevostiana* (J. C. George and Varde, 1941[7]; Varde, 1951[6]; FMNH 179108; MCZ 74092), *Gongylosoma baliodeira* (Schlegel, 1837b; Brongersma, 1957a; Bergman, 1963; FMNH 158614), *G. longicauda* (FMNH 73841), *G. scripta* (FMNH 180114), *Gonionotophis brussauxi* (MCZ 9252), *G. granti* (CAS 126393), *G. klingi* (UG C14K2), *Gonyophis margaritatus* (FMNH 138677), *Gonyosoma oxycephalum* (Thompson, 1914b; Angel, 1950[5]; Tweedie, 1953[5], 1983[5]; Brongersma, 1957b, 1958b; van Hoesel, 1959[5]; Klynstra, 1959[5]; Bröer, 1978[5]; Ramsay, 1979; Pickersgill and Meek, 1988[5]; Young, 1991, 1992; Lillywhite, 1993[5,6]; Young et al., 1993[9]; Schulz, 1996[5]; FMNH 180107; 2 SDSU uncat.; Manthey and Grossmann, 1997[5]), *Grayia caesar* (4 IRSL uncat.), *G. ornata* (BMNH 1979.160–1979.161; CAS 156697–98; FMNH 214742–53; LSUMZ 40728, 40773; MZUSP 8128; NMV 55565–66; SDSNH 63887; TAU 12619, 12622; UF 53619, 56009, 63440–42; UMMZ 172975; VW 968, 1019, 1061, 1106, 1203, 1303, 1393, 1460, 1480, 1597–98, 1662, 1693, 1833,–34, 1842, 1885, 2020, 2041, 2204, 2316, 2319, 2851–52; ZRC 2.3433–35), *G. smythii* (BMNH 1979.162–1979.163; CAS 156704–05; FMNH 214760–70; LSUMZ 40780, 48408; NMV 55557; SDSNH 63857; TAU 12624, 12626; UF 63443–48, 80377; UMMZ 172977; VW 885, 1185, 1212, 1215, 1353, 1398–99, 1422, 1461, 1592, 1594, 1596, 1617–18, 1661, 1674, 1841, 1843, 1862, 1872, 1884, 1892, 1913, 1924, 1964, 2023, 2027, 2029–31, 2136–37, 2139, 2153–55, 2310, 2313, 2838; ZRC 2.3447–48), *G. tholloni* (BMNH 1979.164; FMNH 214793–805; LSUMZ 40777, 40783; NMV 55556; TAU 12630, 12637; MZUSP 8132–33, 8135; UF 63450–54; UMMZ 172979–80; VW 917, 1098, 1142, 1216, 1310, 1343–44, 1400, 1423, 1425–26, 1458, 1462–63, 1494, 1511–12, 1540–41, 1694, 1911, 2033, 2035, 2038, 2040–42, 2044–45, 2047, 2133, 2152, 2165, 2304; ZRC 2.3449–51), *Gyalopion canum* (FMNH 30429), *G. quadrangularis* (Saiff, 1975; BYU 41445), *Haplocercus ceylonensis* (Wallach, 1988; FMNH 16699), *Hapsidophrys lineatus* (BMNH 1979.165–1979.167; 15 IRSL uncat.; 4 UNAZA uncat.; VW 921, 1010), *H. smaragdinus* (Cope, 1894a, 1900; BMNH 1979.157–1979.159; FMNH 214773; 14

IRSL uncat.; MZUSP 8159; 4 UNAZA uncat.; VW 907, 1012, 1026, 1068, 1099, 1308, 1414), *Helicops angulatus* (Hoffmann, 1890; Cope, 1894a, 1900; Underwood, 1967; SDSU uncat.), *H. carinicaudus* (Cope, 1894a, 1900; LSUMZ 35272), *H. danieli* (FMNH 165276), *H. hagmanni* (LSUMZ 20000), *H. leopardinus* (LSUMZ 35289), *H. modestus* (SDSU uncat.), *H. pastazae* (LSUMZ 29385; MCZ 150202), *H. petersi* (LSUMZ 29386), *H. pictiventris* (UMMZ 108781), *H. polylepis* (LSUMZ 29572), *H. scalaris* (LSUMZ 29573), *H. trivittatus* (LSUMZ 36608), *Helophis schoutedeni* (VW 913), *Hemirhagerrhis kelleri* (FMNH 62240), *H. nototaenia* (SDSU uncat.), *Heterodon nasicus* (Cope, 1894a[1]–b[1], 1900[1]; Platt, 1969[5]; LSUMZ 47477; SDSU uncat.), *H. platyrhinos* (Meckel, 1818, 1833; Stannius, 1856; Milne-Edwards, 1857b; Hopley, 1882; Cope, 1894a, 1894b, 1895b, 1900; Lönnberg, 1894; Butler, 1895; Beddard, 1906a; Brongersma, 1957a; Platt, 1969[5]; Kardong, 1972b; Saiff, 1975; Linzey, 1979; Ramsay, 1979; Vogt, 1981[2]; Weidensaul, 1991[3]; Coborn, 1991[2], 1994[2]; Keogh, 1993[7]; 2 SDSU uncat.), *H. simus* (Stannius, 1856; Saiff, 1975; SDSU uncat.), *Heterodon* sp. (Cuvier, 1840; Stannius, 1846, 1850, 1856; Pagenstecher, 1881; Günther, 1886; Baskett and Ditmars, 1902; F. Werner, 1911; Bütschli, 1933), *Heteroliodon occipitalis* (UMMZ 209339), *Hologerrhum philippinum* (FMNH 116770), *Homalopsis buccata* (Schlegel, 1837b; Henle, 1839[4]; Stannius, 1856; Pagenstecher, 1881; Hoffmann, 1890[4]; Butler, 1895; Bergman, 1951; Brongersma, 1952a[9]; Underwood, 1967; LSUMZ 48373; SDSU uncat.), "*Homalopsis*" sp. (Cantor, 1841, 1847), *Hormonotus modestus* (Brongersma, 1957a; MCZ 5649; SDSU uncat.), *Hydrablabes periops* (FMNH 146230), *Hydraethiops laevis* (FMNH 59002), *H. melanogaster* (Saiff, 1975; FMNH 58967), *Hydrodynastes bicinctus* (FMNH 128444), *H. gigas* (FMNH 27583), *Hydromorphus concolor* (FMNH 178716; LSUMZ 15654), *Hydrops martii* (LSUMZ 8457; MCZ 2963), *H. triangularis* (FMNH 170764; MCZ 5614), *Hypsiglena torquata* (Underwood, 1967[6,9], 1976a[6]; Kardong, 1972b; Saiff, 1975; Ramsay, 1979; LSUMZ 29917; VW 2868, 2883), *Hypsirhynchus ferox* (Cope, 1894a, 1900; CM 38866), *Ialtris dorsalis* (Cope, 1894a, 1900; KU 268613, 268620), *I. parishi* (MCZ 126214), *Imantodes cenchoa* (Meckel, 1818; F. Werner, 1911; Underwood, 1967; SDSU uncat.), *I. gemmistratus* (Cope, 1894a, 1900; FMNH 20601), *I. inornatus* (FMNH 178710), *I. lentiferus* (SDSU uncat.), *I. tenuissimus* (FMNH 153506), *Imantodes* n. sp. (SDSNH 64405), *Ithycyphus goudoti* (FMNH 60890), *I. miniatus* (FMNH 18294), *I. oursi* (FMNH 75584; MCZ 21890), *Lampropeltis calligaster* (Kardong, 1972b; Saiff, 1975; Ramsay, 1979; Keogh, 1993[7]; SDSNH; SDSU uncat.), *L. getulus* (Cope, 1894a, 1900; Butler, 1895; Butner, 1963a; Underwood, 1967; Kardong, 1972b; Saiff, 1975; Ramsay, 1979; Keogh, 1993[7]; SDSNH; SDSU uncat.; VW 1739, 2869, 2890, 2897), *L. mexicana* (Keogh, 1993[7]; MCZ 162063; SDSU uncat.), *L. pyromelana* (Saiff, 1975; Keogh, 1993[7]; MCZ 31924), *L. ruthveni* (MCZ 161011), *L. triangulum* (Meckel, 1833; Cope, 1894a, 1900; Underwood, 1967; Saiff, 1975; Chiodini et al., 1982[6]; Keogh, 1993[7]; SDSNH; 5 UCA uncat.; VW 2889), *L. zonata* (Saiff, 1975; Keogh, 1993[7]; VW 2878, 2893), *Lamprophis aurora* (Schlegel, 1837b; CAS 156734; PEM 4), *L. fiskii* (FMNH 224426; JV 2051), *L. fuliginosus* (Underwood, 1967, 1976a; 4 BMNH 1979.149–1979.152; CAS 85747, 111686, 111856, 123511, 135185, 146024, 146371, 148014, 150973, 153337–39, 153451, 154790, 154801; FMNH 214774–80; 42 IRSL uncat.; LSUMZ 40761–65, 48417–18, 55398–99; MCZ 170393–99; MZUSP 8123, 8168–70; NMV 55550; PEM 6; 7 PEM; 2 SDSNH 63860; 3 SDSU uncat.; UF 52482,

60657–62, 80370–75; UMMZ; VW 877, 1075, 1449, 1504, 1628, 1638, 1660, 2121, 2214, 2242; ZRC 2.3428–29, 2.3445), *L. fuscus* (FMNH 187170), *L. geometricus* (Schlegel, 1837b; MCZ 3075), *L. guttatus* (CAS 126071; FMNH 206269), *L. inornatus* (Cope, 1894a, 1900; CAS 111677; PEM 5), *L. lineatus* (Beddard, 1906b; Underwood, 1976a[6]; CAS 103308–09, 125432, 125456, 130069, 148008), *L. olivaceus* (Brongersma, 1957a; 2 BMNH 1979.153–1979.154; 4 IRSL uncat.; MZUSP 8124; NMV 55562; PEM; 3 SDSU uncat.; UF 80376; 9 UNAZA uncat.; VW 924; ZRC 2.3440), *L.virgatus* (CAS 103184, 146116; FMNH 179006), *Langaha nasuta* (Underwood, 1967; FMNH 60892; MCZ 18017), *Leioheterodon geayi* (FMNH 75583), *L. madagascariensis* (Underwood, 1967; Saiff, 1975; FMNH 18292), *L. modestus* (FMNH 75589), *Leptodeira annulata* (Meckel, 1819; Schlegel, 1837b; Stannius, 1856; Hoffmann, 1890; Underwood, 1967[6,9], 1976a[6]; Saiff, 1975; IRSNB 77821; MNN 101; SDSU uncat.; VW 2888), *L. bakeri* (Brongersma, 1959; Saiff, 1975), *L. frenata* (SDSU uncat.), *L. maculata* (VW 2881), *L. nigrofasciata* (MNN 151; 6 UCA uncat.), *L. punctata* (Saiff, 1975; SDSU uncat.), *L. splendida* (SDSNH 41181), *L. septentrionalis* (Cope, 1894a, 1900; Saiff, 1975), *Leptodeira* sp.(Underwood, 1976a), *Leptodrymus pulcherrimus* (FMNH 102683; MNN 102), *Leptophis ahaetulla* (Meckel, 1818; Henle, 1839[4]; Cuvier, 1840; Hoffmann, 1890[4]; Cope, 1894a, 1900; Mole, 1924[5]; Oliver, 1948[5]; Pope, 1955[3]; Kundert, 1984[3]; Mattison, 1986[3]; Coborn, 1991[3]; Leetz, 1991[3]; Geus, 1992[2]; Bauchot, 1994[3]; Mattison, 1995[5]; Ernst and Zug, 1996[3]; SDSU uncat.; 2 UCA uncat.; J. C. Murphy, 1997[3,5]), *L. cupreus* (MCZ 166586), *L. depressirostris* (Halliday and Adler, 1986[3]; UCA uncat.), *L. diplotropis* (Butner, 1963a; SDSU uncat.), *L. mexicanus* (Cope, 1894a, 1900; R. Mertens, 1946[5]; Coborn, 1991[2], 1994[2]; Geus, 1992[2]; VW 2887), *L. modestus* (LSUMZ 38829), *L. nebulosus* (UMMZ 117655), *L. riveti* (MCZ 154613), *Leptophis* sp. (Hoffman, 1988[3]; Baker, 1990[3]), *Lepturophis borneensis* (FMNH 148894), *Limnophis bicolor* (Saiff, 1975; FMNH 74247), *Liochlorophis vernalis* (Saiff, 1975; FMNH 155231), *Liopeltis calamaria* (FMNH 179246), *L. frenatus* (FMNH 14427), *L. philippinus* (FMNH 53372), *L. rappi* (MCZ 3147), *L. tricolor* (Brongersma, 1957a; FMNH 15054), *Liophidium torquatum* (FMNH 18285), *L. vaillanti* (FMNH 73104), *Liophidium* sp. (Wallach, 1988), *Liophis almadensis* (4 SDSU uncat.), *L. andinus* (SDSU uncat.), *L. cobella* (Meckel, 1833; Schlegel, 1837b; Henle, 1839[4]; Cuvier, 1840; Hoffmann, 1890; MCZ 154820), *L. epinephelus* (SDSU uncat.), *L. jaegeri* (SDSU uncat.), *L. melanotus* (FMNH 165645), *L. miliaris* (Cope, 1894a, 1900; SDSU uncat.), *L. poecilogyrus* (Schlegel, 1837b; Butler, 1895; 2 SDSU uncat.), *L. reginae* (Meckel, 1819, 1833; Schlegel, 1837b; MCZ 2952), *L. sagittifer* (SDSU uncat.), *L. taeniurus* (Saiff, 1975), *L. typhlus* (Saiff, 1975), *L. viridis* (MCZ 146947), *Liopholidophis lateralis* (MCZ 11679–81), *L. pinguis* (UMMZ 126090), *L. pseudolateralis* (MCZ 11682–83), *L. sexlineatus* (Underwood, 1967; SDSU uncat.), *Lycodon aulicus* (Schlegel, 1837b; Cope, 1894a, 1900; J. C. George and Varde, 1941[7]; Varde, 1951[6]; J. C. George and Shah, 1956[6]), *L. capucinus* (CAS 137253; SDSNH; VW 25, 101, 115, 117, 147), *L. dumerilii* (FMNH 53424; LSUMZ 24818), *L. effraensis* (FMNH 148902), *L. fasciatus* (FMNH 180145), *L. jara* (Schlegel, 1837b; MCZ 190854), *L. laoensis* (MCZ 16651), *L. muelleri* (MCZ 25705), *L. ruhstrati* (FMNH 140168), *L. striatus* (SDSNH 63305), *L. subcinctus* (Schlegel, 1837b; Brongersma, 1957a; SDSU uncat.), *L. travancoricus* (MCZ 47887), *Lycodon* sp. (Stannius, 1856; Pagenstecher, 1881), *Lycodonomorphus bicolor* (Underwood, 1967;

MCZ 54944), *L. laevissimus* (MCZ 6038), *L. rufulus* (Schlegel, 1837b; Butler, 1895; FMNH 205906), *L. whytii* (FMNH 224419–20), *Lycognathophis seychellensis* (Schlegel, 1837b; Underwood, 1967; FMNH 213903), *Lycophidion capense* (Schlegel, 1837b; Butler, 1895; Brongersma, 1957a; BMNH 1979.168–1979.169; 2 IRSL uncat.; MZUSP 8136; 2 SDSU uncat.; TAU 12631; UF 52725; ZRC 2.3425), *L. depressirostre* (CAS 153329), *L. irroratum* (CAS 123530), *L. laterale* (BMNH 1979.170–1979.172; IRSL uncat.; LSUMZ 40710; PEM; 2 SDSU uncat.; 2 UNAZA uncat.), *L. meleagris* (MCZ 5627), *L. nigromaculatum* (UG C18N9), *L. ornatum* (CAS 156707; LSUMZ 40778, 40785–86; MCZ 170390; MZUSP 8173; VW 2395, 2428, 2520, 2539, 2593–40, 2546–47, 2634, 2638, 2658, 2666, 2726–27), *L. semiannule* (FMNH 81084), *L. semicinctum* (UG C18S26), *Lystrophis dorbignyi* (Cope, 1894a, 1900; Butler, 1895; Brongersma, 1957a; SDSU uncat.), *L. histricus* (SDSU uncat.), *L. semicinctus* (Thompson, 1913b; FMNH 195849), *Lytorhynchus diadema* (FMNH 67245), *L. gaddi* (FMNH 20859), *L. maynardi* (CAS 101406), *L. ridgewayi* (CAS 120495), *Macrocalamus lateralis* (Wallach, 1988; FMNH 10994), *Macropisthodon flaviceps* (Brongersma, 1957a[5,6]; Young, 1992; FMNH 131631), *M. plumbicolor*;(Brongersma, 1957a; FMNH 122262), *M. rhodomelas* (Brongersma, 1957a; FMNH 198378), *M. rudis* (Underwood, 1967; Young, 1992; FMNH 24955), *Macropisthodon* sp. (Brongersma, 1958b), *Macroprotodon cucullatus* (Schlegel, 1837b; FMNH 109884), *Madagascarophis colubrinus* (MCZ 11566), *M. meridionalis* (FMNH 73090), *Malpolon moilensis* (CAS 145343; FMNH 82963), *M. monspessulana* (Fleischmann, 1831; Schlegel, 1837b; Henle, 1839[4]; Pagenstecher, 1881; Hoffmann, 1890[4]; Cope, 1894a, 1900; Butler, 1895; Göppert, 1899[7], 1937[7]; Lüdicke, 1939; SDSU uncat.), *M. moilensis* (Hochstetter, 1901; P. H. D. H. de Silva, 1955), *Manolepis putnami* (Cope, 1894a, 1900; FMNH 103805), *Masticophis anthonyi* (SDSNH 28499), *M. aurigulus* (CAS 145170), *M. bilineatus* (Saiff, 1975; SDSNH 22859), *M. flagellum* (Meckel, 1818[6], 1833; Milne-Edwards, 1857b; Cope, 1894a, 1900; Atwood, 1916; Kardong, 1972b; Saiff, 1975; Ramsay, 1979; Stinner, 1980[6,7]; Twerenbold, 1987; SDSNH; VW 2866), *M. lateralis* (Butner, 1963a; Lillywhite, 1987a; SDSU uncat.; ZIL), *M. mentovarius* (Cope, 1894a, 1900; Butner, 1963a; 9 UCA uncat.), *M. taeniatus* (Saiff, 1975; SDSNH; SDSU uncat.), *Mastigodryas danieli* (KU 169953), *Mehelya capensis* (Underwood, 1967; Ramsay, 1979; BMNH 1979.173–1979.175; CAS 156706; 2 IRSL uncat.; LSUMZ 40712; NMV 55560; 4 PEM; SDSNH; 7 SDSU uncat.; TAU 12632; UF 52719, 75998; UNAZA uncat.; VW 881, 1137, 1861, 1873, 1902, 2197, 2203; ZRC 2.3438), *M. crossii* (CAS 125462; UG C19C48), *M. guirali* (CAS 103190; FMNH 191127), *M. nyassae* (FMNH 77612), *M. poensis* (Saiff, 1975; BMNH 1979.176; CAS 156696; 3 IRSL uncat.; 2 SDSU; 6 UNAZA uncat.; ZRC 2.3439), *M. stenophthalmus* (BMNH 1979.177–1979.179; CAS 156715; FMNH 214826; SDSNH 63853; 2 SDSU uncat.), *Meizodon coronatus* (UG C20C21), *M. plumbiceps* (CAS 153344), *M. regularis* (FMNH 62306), *M. semiornatus* (FMNH 78235, 224421), *Mimophis mahfalensis* (FMNH 73086), *Montaspis gilvomaculata* (TM 68088), *Myersophis alpestris* (Wallach, 1988; KU 203013), *Myron richardsoni* (FMNH 97649), *Natriciteres fuliginoides* (FMNH 4030), *N. olivacea* (Lambiris, 1965[5]; BMNH 1979.145–1979.148; FMNH 214782–92; LSUMZ 40758–60, 40766–68; MZUSP 8139–44, 8146–47, 8149; NMV 55567; SDSNH 63844–46; TAU 12627–29; UF 75994–96, 80420–43, 80674, 80682, 101201–40; UMMZ 172981; VW 958–59, 1066, 1102, 1156, 1159, 1161, 1175, 1213,

1322, 1362, 1380–81, 1383, 1386–87, 1390–92, 1403–05, 1432–35, 1446–48, 1452–
53, 1471, 1474–76, 1481–82, 1497–98, 1501, 1503, 1513, 1515, 1526–31, 1533–35,
1544, 1553–55, 1564–70, 1578, 1581–88, 1621–22, 1625, 1648, 1666, 1791–92, 1801,
1824, 1837–39, 1848–50, 1853, 1878, 1895, 1898–99, 1904–05, 1938–39, 1941–42,
1960–61, 2049–50, 2052–56, 2060, 2062–63, 2065–66, 2067–69, 2071–72, 2074, 2078–
80, 2082, 2084, 2089–98, 2100–02, 2104–07, 2122–30, 2148–51, 2166–68, 2200, 2232–
35, 2244, 2305–06, 2308, 2311, 2317; ZRC 2.3441–44), *N. variegata* (Brongersma,
1957a; FMNH 170716), *Natrix maura* (Brongersma, 1957a; Castells et al., 1990;
Pastor, 1990[8], 1995[8]; Pastor and Pallares, 1995[5]; FMNH 83655), *N. natrix* (Blasius,
1674; Nitzsch, 1808; Meckel, 1818, 1831, 1833; Rees, 1820; Cloquet, 1821[2,3];
Schlemm, 1826, 1827[5,9]; Carus, 1827, 1835, 1838; Henle, 1839[4]; Rathke, 1839[6,9];
Cuvier, 1840; W. B. Carpenter, 1844[1], 1848[1], 1851[1], 1854[6,9], 1859[1], 1867[1]; Stannius,
1846, 1850, 1856; Vogt, 1851[1]; Leydig, 1857, 1866; Dallas, 1855[1]; W. B. Carpenter
and Dallas, 1857[1], 1866[1]; Milne-Edwards, 1845[1], 1855[1], 1857a[1], 1857b, 1871[1]; Eberth,
1863[8]; Elenz, 1864[8]; R. Owen, 1866; Schulze, 1871; S. Tenney, 1875[1], 1876[1];
Tourneux and Herrmann, 1876; Hopley, 1882; Brenner, 1883[9]; Strahl, 1883;
Wiedersheim, 1883, 1886; Bemmelen, 1886[5], 1888[5]; Hoffmann, 1890[4,9]; Hochstetter,
1892, 1901[9]; Cope, 1894a, 1894b, 1895b, 1900; Butler, 1895[7]; Railliet, 1895[1]; Göppert,
1899[4,7], 1937[4,7]; Baumann, 1902[7]; Greil, 1903[7]; Broman, 1904[7]; Jammes, 1904[1,9];
Oppel, 1905[8]; Schmalhausen, 1905[6,8]; Thäter, 1910; O'Donoghue, 1912[9]; Röseler
and Lamprecht, 1914[1,9]; Brehm and Werner, 1920[1]; Shipley and MacBride, 1920[9];
Cantoni, 1921[5]; Steche, 1922; Wenslaw, 1926; Perrier, 1928; Baudrimont, 1929[8,9],
1952, 1956[8]; Goodrich, 1930[9]; Rothley, 1930a[7,8], 1930b[7,8]; Saunders and Manton,
1931[1,9], 1949[1,9], 1959[1,9]; Gelderen, 1933[9]; Wolf, 1933[7]; H. Marcus, 1937[7]; Pischinger,
1937[5]; Siwe, 1937[6]; Lüdicke, 1939[8], 1940[2], 1964[2,4,5,8]; P. H. Fischer, 1942[9]; Witte,
1948[1]; P. H. D. H. de Silva, 1953, 1955; Terent'ev, 1956[1,6,9]; Brongersma, 1957a;
Frommhold, 1959[1]; Johansen and Hol, 1960[9]; Willinow, 1961; Luce, 1963[5,6,9];
Sledz et al., 1963; Antipchuk, 1966b[7], 1966c[9], 1969a, 1969b; Antipchuk and
Sobolieva, 1976[7]; Heyder, 1966[7], 1968[7]; Bellairs, 1969[1,6,7], 1970[6]; Saunders et al.,
1969[1,9]; Guibé, 1970a[9], 1970b[4]; Lécuru-Renous and Platel, 1970b[1,6]; Kardong,
1972b; Kabish, 1974[1], 1990[1]; Ramsay, 1979; Zinyakova and Rudenko, 1979;
Meban, 1980; Davies, 1981[1,6]; Engelmann and Obst, 1981[1]; Bruno, 1984[1]; Rogers,
1986[1]; Bruno and Maugeri, 1990[1]; Schnieper, 1995[3]; SDSU uncat.; VW 2246–
48), *N. tessellata* (Hochstetter, 1901; Lüdicke, 1939; P. H. D. H. de Silva, 1955;
Brongersma, 1957a; Antipchuk, 1966b[7], 1966c[9]; Antipchuk and Sobolieva, 1971[8],
1976[7]; Zinyakova and Rudenko, 1979; Saint-Aubain, 1984[7]; Saint Girons, 1994[2];
SDSU uncat.), "*Natrix*" sp. (Jacobaeus, 1680; Stannius, 1856; Schimkewitsch et
al., 1910, 1921; Bütschli, 1933; Scott and Kendall, 1935[7]; J. C. George and Shah,
1956[6,7], 1965[6]; Brongersma, 1958b; Tanara, 1975[1], 1978[1]; Rogers, 1986[1]), *Nerodia
clarkii* (Brongersma, 1957a; SDSU uncat.), *N. cyclopion* (Saiff, 1975; 3 KUHS
uncat.; VW 3029), *N. erythrogaster* (Baeyens et al., 1979a–1980; SDSU uncat.), *N.
fasciata* (Meckel, 1819; Cope, 1894a, 1900; Saiff, 1975; Baeyens et al., 1979a–1980;
Cundall and Shardo, 1995; 6 KUHS uncat.; SDSU uncat.), *N. harteri* (SDSU uncat.),
N. rhombifer (Cope, 1894a, 1900; Oldham et al., 1970[1,9]; Saiff, 1975; Baeyens et al.,
1978–1980; Ramsay, 1979; Stinner, 1980[6,7]; J. D. Wallach and Boever, 1983[1,9];
Cundall and Shardo, 1995; KUHS uncat.; 2 SDSU uncat.), *N. sipedon* (Brongersma,

1957a; Lüdicke, 1962[1]; Butner, 1963a; Antipchuk, 1966b[7], 1966c[9]; Antipchuk and Sobolieva, 1976[7]; Kardong, 1972b; Ramsay, 1979; D. A. Zug and Dunson, 1979[2,3]; Chiodini et al., 1982[1,3,6,9]; VW 13–14, 669), *N. taxispilota* (Cope, 1894a, 1900; Karlstrom, 1952[4,6,7,9]; Kardong, 1972b; SDSU uncat.), *N. valida* (SDSU uncat.), *Ninia atrata* (Underwood, 1967; MCZ 87333), *N. diademata* (FMNH 70757), *N. hudsoni* (MCZ 157152), *N. maculata* (FMNH 188812), *N. oxynota* (FMNH 101007), *N. psephota* (CAS 78857–58), *N. sebae* (4 UCA uncat.), *Ninia* sp. (Wallach, 1988), *Nothopsis rugosus* (Underwood, 1967; FMNH 77603–04), *Oligodon affinis* (MCZ 3839), *O. albocinctus* (CAS 12408), *O. ancorus* (CAS 6154–476; FMNH 15052), *O. arnensis* (Schlegel, 1837b; Underwood, 1967; SDSU uncat.), *O. barroni* (FMNH 179277), *O. bitorquatus* (Brongersma, 1957a; MCZ 7501), *O. brevicaudus* (CAS 17229), *O. calamarius* (MCZ 4239), *O. chinensis* (MCZ 28825), *O. cinereus* (CAS 13253; FMNH 6696, 179256–57), *O. cruentatus* (MCZ 3210), *O. cyclurus* (CAS 8482, 8497), *O. dorsalis* (MCZ 44746), *O. everetti* (MCZ 43557), *O. fasciolatus* (FMNH 180196), *O. formosus* (LSUMZ 19352), *O. lacroixi* (CAS 9146), *O. maculatus* (LSUMZ 41806), *O. meyerinkii* (CAS 7248), *O. modestus* (CAS 26749, 26753), *O. ocellatus* (FMNH 143301), *O. octolineatus* (Schlegel, 1837b; Brongersma, 1957a; MCZ 11271), *O. ornatus* (Saiff, 1975; FMNH 24964), *O. perkinsi* (CAS 15277), *O. purpurascens* (MCZ 9326), *O. quadrilineatus* (MCZ 20372), *O. signatus* (FMNH 69989), *O. subcarinatus* (FMNH 138590), *O. sublineatus* (Butler, 1895; CAS 17234), *O. taeniatus* (LSUMZ 24684), *O. taeniolatus* (Kashyap, 1960a[9]; CAS 17239; SDSU uncat.), *O. theobaldi* (MCZ 3910), *O. torquatus* (FMNH 122255), *O. vertebralis* (CAS 28601), *O. waandersi* (MCZ 25278), *Oligodon* sp. (Wallach, 1988), *Opheodrys aestivus* (Cope, 1894a, 1900; Saiff, 1975; Cundall, 1986[5]; 2 SDSU uncat.), *Opisthotropis andersoni* (FMNH 71136), *O. balteata* (MVZ 23748), *O. jacobi* (CAS 9147), *O. kuatunensis* (MCZ 173028), *O. lateralis* (MCZ 32413, 172664), *O. latouchii* (FMNH 24866), *O. maxwelli* (MVZ 23752), *O. typicus* (FMNH 63596), *Oreocalamus hainitschi* (Wallach, 1988; FMNH 130994), *Oxybelis aeneus* (5 UCA uncat.), *O. brevirostris* (FMNH 54893), *O. fulgidus* (Cope, 1894a, 1900; SDSU uncat.; 6 UCA uncat.), *Oxyrhabdium leporinum* (FMNH 106839; USNM), *O. modestum* (Thompson, 1913b; LSUMZ 11814; VW 65, 89), *Oxyrhabdium* sp. (Wallach, 1988; USNM 497051), *Oxyrhopus clathrata* (MCZ 17893), *O. doliatus* (LSUMZ 27366), *O. fitzingeri* (Cope, 1894a, 1900; FMNH 41598), *O. formosus* (Schlegel, 1837b; LSUMZ 14598, 26846), *O. guibei* (Sazima and Abe, 1991[5]), *O. leucomelas* (LSUMZ 26873), *O. marcapatae* (LSUMZ 27368), *O. melanogenys* (LSUMZ 19710), *O. petolarius* (Meckel, 1819; Schlegel, 1837b; Brongersma, 1957a; Underwood, 1967; LSUMZ 37942; MCZ 24942; MNN 130; SDSU uncat.), *O. rhombifer* (LSUMZ 11821; SDSU uncat.), *O. trigeminus* (Butler, 1895; Thompson, 1913b; SDSU uncat.; UTA 7022), *Pareas carinatus* (Werner, 1911[6]; Brongersma, 1957c[7,9], 1958b; Antipchuk, 1966c[9]; MCZ 7528a–b), *P. chinensis* (MCZ 46902), *P. formosensis* (UMMZ 182646), *P. hamptoni* (Brongersma, 1957c[7]), *P. komaii* (FMNH 169315), *P. laevis* (Schlegel, 1837b; Stannius, 1856; Cope, 1894a, 1894b, 1895b, 1900; Brongersma, 1957c, 1958b; Antipchuk, 1966b[7], 1966c[9]; Antipchuk and Sobolieva, 1976[7]; Underwood, 1967; MCZ 43591), *P. macularius* (MCZ 8983), *P. malaccanus* (Brongersma, 1957c[7]; FMNH 71590), *P. margaritophorus* (Brongersma, 1957c[7]; FMNH 180220), *P. monticola* (MCZ 58254), *P. nuchalis* (Brongersma, 1957c[7]), *P. stanleyi* (Butner, 1963a; MCZ 45966), *P. vertebralis*

(Brongersma, 1957c[7], 1958b; Antipchuk, 1966c[9]; MCZ 43592), *Phalotris bilineatus* (CAS 85683; FMNH 80122), *P. lemniscatus* (Cope, 1894a, 1900), *P. mertensi* (SDSU uncat.), *P. tricolor* (Cope, 1894a, 1900; FMNH 195893), *Philodryas aestivus* (2 SDSU uncat.), *P. burmeisteri* (SDSU uncat.), *P. chamissonis* (Schlegel, 1837b; FMNH 31610), *P. mattogrossensis* (MCZ 20780), *P. nattereri* (MCZ 20783), *P. olfersii* (Cope, 1894a, 1900; Butler, 1895; 2 SDSU uncat.), *P. patagoniensis* (Underwood, 1967; MCZ 3013; 3 SDSU uncat.), *P. psammophideus* (SDSU uncat.), *P. simonsi* (MCZ 132712), *P. varius* (MCZ 101279), *P. viridissimus* (Meckel, 1818; Cope, 1894a, 1900; MCZ 119406), *Philothamnus angolensis* (Broadley, 1983[5]; 23 IRSL uncat.; MZUSP 8174–75, 8177; SDSNH 63865–66; UF 52485, 52900, 75991, 80395, 80396–99, 80446–47, 80671; 4 UNAZA uncat.; VW 1086, 1197, 1211, 1254, 1354–55, 1427, 1429, 1451, 1745, 1818, 1986–87, 1990, 2226; ZRC 2.3427), *P. battersbyi* (2 SDSU uncat.), *P. bequaerti* (MCZ 47846), *P. carinatus* (CAS 156699; IRSL uncat.; 4 UNAZA uncat.; LSUMZ 48421; VW 970, 1017, 1198, 1298, 1984), *P. dorsalis* (V. Wallach, pers. obs.[5]; BMNH 1979.180–1979.187; FMNH 214827; LSUMZ 40782; NMV 55549; SDSNH 63852; UF 52483, 75992, 80390–94, 80672; VW 993, 1024, 1057, 1073, 1173, 1295, 1301, 1333, 1347, 1372–73, 1646, 1651, 1705, 1752–54, 1756, 2191, 2271, 2855), *P. heterodermus* (VW 1040, 1195, 1231, 1644, 2474), *P. heterolepidotus* (FMNH 214772; LSUMZ 40781; NMV 55554; UF 80368–70; VW 1246, 1351, 1547, 1549, 1580, 1683, 1743–44, 1749, 1906, 1956, 2272; ZRC 2.3426), *P. hoplogaster* (Isemonger, 1962[5]; BYU 30895; VW 1428, 1431, 1647, 1989), *P. irregularis* (Broadley, 1957a, 1959[5]; Sweeney, 1961[5]; V. F. M. FitzSimons, 1962[5]; Isemonger, 1962[5]; Dunger, 1973[5]; MCZ 55418), *P. loveridgei* (UMMZ 172982; VW 1616, 1643, 1746, 1994, 2794–95), *P. macrops* (MCZ 23244), *P. natalensis* (Isemonger, 1962[5]), *P. occidentalis* (VW 1991), *P. ornatus* (Lambiris, 1980[5]); *P. punctatus* (MCZ 52666), *P. semivariegatus* (Thompson, 1914b; Angel, 1950[5]; Broadley, 1959[5]; Sweeney, 1961[5]; Isemonger, 1962[5]; V. J. Wilson, 1965[5]; Pienaar, 1978[5]; Visser, 1972[5]; BMNH 1979.188; BYU 31074; VW 1087), *Phimophis guerini* (MCZ 3675), *P. guianensis* (SDSU uncat.), *P. vittatus* (UMMZ 166846), *Phyllorhynchus browni* (Saiff, 1975; SDSU uncat.), *P. decurtatus* (Underwood, 1967; Saiff, 1975; Keogh, 1993[7]; 5 SDSNH; VW 2880; ZIL), *Pituophis catenifer* (Butler, 1895; Stinner, 1980[6,7,8], 1982a[8], 1982b[7], 1987c; Robbins, 1991[1]; Schnieper, 1995; 3 SDSNH; SDSU uncat.; VW 2870, 3716, 3804), *P. deppei* (Dugès, 1888[3]; Cope, 1894a, 1900; Saiff, 1975; FMNH 106078), *P. lineaticollis* (Saiff, 1975; CAS 101414), *P. melanoleucus* (Lockwood, 1875; Hopley, 1882; Cope, 1894a, 1894b, 1900; Beddard, 1906b; Gadow, 1911; Ditmars, 1936; Kelly et al., 1936; Pope, 1946[4]; W. F. Martin and Huey, 1971[3]; Kardong, 1972b; Saiff, 1975[3]; Ramsay, 1979; Keogh, 1993[7]; Young et al., 1995[3,4,7]; SDSU uncat.), *P. sayi* (C. A. White, 1884[3,4]; Shufeldt, 1885[3,4]; Packard, 1886b[3]; Cope, 1891[3,4], 1894a, 1900; Larson and van de Velde, 1969[7,8]; Weidensaul, 1991[3]; LSUMZ 46638; 4 SDSU uncat.), *Pituophis* sp. (Boulenger, 1913; Underwood, 1976a; Stoops and Wright, 1992[3]), *Plagiopholis nuchalis* (FMNH 24874, 172307), *P. styani* (Thompson, 1913b; Saiff, 1975), *Plagiopholis* sp. (Wallach, 1988), *Pliocercus elapoides* (Saiff, 1975; H. M. Smith et al., 1995; SDSU uncat.), *P. euryzonus* (Saiff, 1975; H. M. Smith et al., 1995; UMMZ 124195), *Prosymna ambigua* (BMNH 1979.189; CAS 156703; MCZ 170362; MZUSP 8138; SDSU uncat.; TAU 12634; VW 2241), *P. angolensis* (CAS 84181), *P. bivittata* (FMNH 224429), *P. meleagris* (CAS 125489), *P. pitmani* (MCZ 54521–22), *P. ruspolii* (CAS 131010), *P. somalica* (MCZ 51300), *P. sundevallii* (FMNH 205917, 224428),

Psammodynastes pictus (FMNH 148937), *P. pulverulentus* (Schlegel, 1837b; Brongersma, 1957a; VW 15), *Psammophis aegypticus* (Y. L. Werner, 1985[5]; UMMZ 177831), *P. angolensis* (FMNH 78252), *P. biseriatus* (CAS 122988), *P. condanarus* (LSUMZ 22977; SDSU uncat.), *P. crucifer* (Butler, 1895; CAS 111676), *P. elegans* (Schlegel, 1837b; Brongersma, 1957a; Y. L. Werner, 1985; UG C29E56), *P. jallae* (FMNH 142800), *P. leightoni* (MCZ 159174), *P. leithi* (SDSNH 63289), *P. lineolatus* (SDSU uncat.), *P. monilifer* (Bütschli, 1933[4]), *P. notostictus* (CAS 115892; LSUMZ 9191), *P. phillipsii* (BMNH 1979.206; CAS 156709; FMNH 214930; LSUMZ uncat., 40779, 48422–23; NMV 55564; 2 PEM; SDSU uncat.; TAU 12635; UF 52484, 80367, 80675, 101241; UG; UMMZ; VW 1874, 2193, 2227; ZRC 2.3430), *P. pulcher* (CAS 135245), *P. punctulatus* (CAS 131310), *P. rukwae* (MCZ 53441), *P. schokari* (Meckel, 1819; SDSNH 63301–02), *P. sibilans* (Hopley, 1882; Hoffmann, 1890; Thompson, 1914b; Bütschli, 1933; SDSU uncat.; UG C29S109), *P. subtaeniatus* (VW 2405, 2426, 2742), *P. tanganicus* (CAS 130253), *P. trigrammus* (LSUMZ 44665), *Psammophis* spp. (Schlegel, 1837b; Stannius, 1856; Pagenstecher, 1881; Perrier, 1928), *Psammophylax rhombeatus* (Meckel, 1819; Schlegel, 1837b; Cuvier, 1840; VW 1608), *P. tritaeniatus* (FMNH 78247), *P. variabilis* (FMNH 58339), *Pseudablabes agassizii* (FMNH 12346), *Pseudaspis cana* (Cope, 1894a, 1900; FMNH 224417; 2 SDSU uncat.), *Pseudoboa coronata* (SDSU uncat.), *P. haasi* (MCZ 20802), *P. neuwiedii* (Underwood, 1967; FMNH 165168), *P. nigra* (LSUMZ 36967; UMMZ 152959), *Pseudoboodon gascae* (MCZ 22204), *P. lemniscatus* (FMNH 12526; MCZ 8057), *Pseudoeryx plicatilis* (Wallach, 1988; FMNH 83101), *Pseudoficimia frontalis* (CAS 142447; SDSU uncat.), *Pseudoleptodeira latifasciata* (Underwood, 1967; FMNH 99670), *Pseudorabdion albonuchalis* (FMNH 151710), *P. collaris* (FMNH 138671), *P. eiselti* (FMNH 134724), *P. longiceps* (FMNH 151713), *P. mcnamarae* (CAS 137100), *P. montanum* (MCZ 142946), *P. oxycephalum* (CAS 13192; FMNH 61429, 61624), *Pseudorabdion* sp. (Wallach, 1988), *Pseudotomodon trigonatus* (CM 61548), *Pseudoxenodon bambusicola* (Young, 1992; FMNH 24824), *P. inornatus* (Brongersma, 1950, 1957a[5,6]; FMNH 128152), *P. karlschmidti* (Brongersma, 1957a; FMNH 122514), *P. macrops* (Thompson, 1914b; Young, 1992; FMNH 7757, 170636), *P. nothus* (MCZ 51409), *P. stejnegeri* (Young, 1992; FMNH 140166), *Pseudoxenodon* sp. (Brongersma, 1958b), *Pseudoxyrhopus quinquelineatus* (Underwood, 1967; BMNH 1893.9.6.2; MCZ 11651), *Pseustes poecilonotus* (do Amaral, 1930b[5]; Saiff, 1975; Greene, 1975[5]; Amaral, 1978[5]; Lancini, 1979[5]; Alvarez del Toro, 1982[5]; Freiberg, 1982[5]; Dixon and Soini, 1986[5]; Mehrtens, 1987[5]; Coborn, 1991[5]; J. C. Murphy, 1997[5]; SDSU uncat.; 3 UCA uncat.), *P. shropshirei* (Netting, 1936[5]; Rand and Ortleb, 1969[5]; MCZ 43937), *P. sulphureus* (Mole, 1924[5]; Dunn, 1944[5]; Beebe, 1946[5]; Angel, 1950[5]; Brongersma, 1957a; Rossman and Williams, 1966[5]; Saiff, 1975; C. C. Carpenter and Ferguson, 1977[5]; Amaral, 1978[5]; Emsley, 1977[5]; Moonen et al., 1979[5]; Mehrtens, 1987[5]; Pérez-Santos and Moreno, 1991[5]; Saint Girons, 1994[5]; Mattison, 1995[5]; J. C. Murphy, 1997[5]; FMNH 53649; MCZ 100500), *Pseustes* sp. (Mehrtens, 1987[5]; Cei, 1993[5]), *Psomophis joberti* (MCZ 3000), *Ptyas carinatus* (Brongersma, 1957a; FMNH 53450), *P. dhumnades* (Cantor, 1847[5]; FMNH 169098), *P. dipsas* (MCZ 171461), *P. fuscus* (FMNH 143942), *P. korros* (Lamare-Picquot, 1858; Hoffmann, 1890; Cope, 1894a, 1900; Bergman, 1952; Twerenbold, 1987; Young, 1992; CAS 55132; FMNH 6638), *P. luzonensis* (FMNH 77653), *P. mucosus* (Meckel, 1819; Cantor, 1847[5]; Flower, 1899[5]; Wall, 1905[5], 1906[5], 1921[5]; Herklots, 1934[5]; Ray, 1934[5,6,9], 1936[6,9]; H. Marcus,

1937[6]; J. C. George and Varde, 1941[6,7]; M. A. Smith, 1943; Varde, 1951[6]; Bergman, 1952; Brongersma, 1952a[9]; P. H. D. H. de Silva, 1955; J. C. George and Shah, 1956[6,7], 1965[6]; Deoras, 1965, 1970, 1978; Antipchuk, 1966b[7], 1966c[9], 1969a, 1969b, 1976[7]; Minton, 1966[5]; Antipchuk and Sobolieva, 1971[8]; D. Singh, 1971; Deoras and Vad, 1973; Saiff, 1975; Tanara, 1975[5], 1978[5]; Reitinger and Lee, 1978[5]; Whitaker, 1978[5]; R. Singh and Kar, 1982; Daniel, 1983; A. de Silva, 1990; CAS-SU 12413; FMNH 167751), *P. nigromarginatus* (FMNH 7057), *Ptyas* sp. (Angel, 1950[5]), *Pythonodipsas carinata* (FMNH 210073, 224427), *Rabdion forsteni* (Wallach, 1988; CAS 24115; MCZ 38964), *Regina alleni* (Saiff, 1975; SDSU uncat.), *R. grahami* (SDSU uncat.), *R. rigida* (SDSU uncat.), *R. septemvittata* (Brongersma, 1957a; SDSU uncat.), *Rhabdophis auriculatus* (Brongersma, 1957a[5]; Underwood, 1976a; CAS 133457), *R. barbouri* (FMNH 15039), *R. callichromus* (Underwood, 1967), *R. celebicus* (MCZ 25268), *R. chrysargoides* (Brongersma, 1957a; CAS 24116), *R. chrysargus* (Brongersma, 1957a; CAS-SU 8522), *R. conspicillatus* (FMNH 138601), *R. himalayanus* (Underwood, 1967; MCZ 58229), *R. lineatus* (CAS 133498), *R. murudensis* (Underwood, 1967; MCZ 43549), *R. nigrocinctus* (Underwood, 1967; FMNH 180160), *R. nuchalis* (Brongersma, 1957a; FMNH 18771), *R. sarasinora* (MCZ 25270), *R. spilogaster* (Brongersma, 1957a; Underwood, 1976a; CAS 15223), *R. subminiatus* (Bergman, 1956; Brongersma, 1957a[6,7]; Young, 1992; CAS 80924), *R. swinhonis* (Underwood, 1967; CAS 18978–80), *R. tigrinus* (Oidumi, 1940[6,7]; Brongersma, 1957a[5,6]; Antipchuk, 1966b[7], 1966c[9]; Antipchuk and Sobolieva, 1976[7]; Young, 1992; SDSU uncat.), *Rhachidelus brazilii* (MCZ 27671), *Rhabdops bicolor* (MCZ 24740), *R. olivaceus* (CAS 17194), *Rhabdops* sp. (Wallach, 1988), *Rhadinaea calligaster* (LSUMZ 9630), *R. decorata* (Underwood, 1967; FMNH 208134), *R. flavilata* (LSUMZ 7433), *R. gaigeae* (SDSU uncat.), *R. godmani* (LSUMZ 24398), *R. kinkelini* (LSUMZ 23828), *R. laureata* (Saiff, 1975), *R. montechristi* (LSUMZ 36594), *R. taeniata* (Saiff, 1975), *Rhadinophanes monticola* (UTA 4176), *Rhamnophis aethiopissa* (Stucki-Stirn, 1979[5]; 6 IRSL uncat; SDSNH 63873; VW 976), *R. batesi* (MCZ 13604), *Rhamphiophis acutus* (FMNH 133045), *R. oxyrhynchus* (UG C31P29), *R. rubropunctatus* (FMNH 62298), *Rhinobothryum bovallii* (FMNH 55882), *R. lentiginosum* (Cope, 1894a, 1900; MCZ 12437), *Rhinocheilus lecontei* (Cope, 1894a, 1900; Kardong, 1972b; Saiff, 1975; Ramsay, 1979; Keogh, 1993[7]; VW 2879, 2885), *Rhynchocalamus melanocephalus* (FMNH 74390), *R. satunini* (MCZ 56877), *Salvadora bairdii* (Cope, 1894a, 1900; Saiff, 1975; CAS-SU 4413), *S. deserticola* (Saiff, 1975), *S. grahamiae* (Saiff, 1975; SDSU uncat.), *S. hexalepis* (Saiff, 1975; SDSU uncat.), *S. intermedia* (Saiff, 1975; SDSU uncat.), *S. lemniscata* (MCZ 46491), *S. mexicana* (Saiff, 1975; SDSNH 36288), *Saphenophis boursieri* (FMNH 36622), *Scaphiodontophis annulatus* (Underwood, 1967; CAS 66967–68; FMNH 1961; MCZ 78849), *Scaphiophis albopunctatus* (NMV 55563; TAU 12636; UF 52480; VW 1167, 1240, 1370, 1411, 1632), *Scolecophis atrocinctus* (KU 174277; LSUMZ 33923), *Seminatrix pygaea* (SDSU uncat.), *Senticolis triaspis* (Underwood, 1967; Keogh, 1993[7]; VW 2867), *Sibon annulata* (Schlegel, 1837b; Cope, 1894a, 1894b, 1895b, 1900), *S. anthracops* (Wallach, 1995; LSUMZ 23829; MNN 118), *S. carri* (Wallach, 1995; LSUMZ 23831), *S. dimidiata* (Wallach, 1995; MCZ 38592), *S. dunni* (Wallach, 1995; UMMZ 92072), *S. nebulata* (Meckel, 1818; Cope, 1894a, 1900; Butler, 1895; Underwood, 1967, 1976a; Wallach, 1995; LSUMZ 14233; UCA uncat.), *S. sanniola* (Wallach, 1995; FMNH 153582), *Sibon* sp. (Ramsay, 1979), *Sibynomorphus mikanii* (Cope, 1894a, 1900; F. Werner, 1911[6,7];

Brongersma, 1957c[7]; Wallach, 1995; FMNH 69940), *S. turgidus* (Wallach, 1995; FMNH 195892), *S. vagus* (Wallach, 1995; MCZ 17422), *S. ventrimaculatus* (Wallach, 1995; FMNH 9258), *Sibynophis bivittatus* (MCZ 25609), *S. chinensis* (CAS 18996; MCZ), *S. collaris* (Thompson, 1914b; Underwood, 1967; FMNH 71708; MCZ 44733), *S. geminatus* (Thompson, 1914b; FMNH 131629), *S. melanocephalus* (FMNH 138630), *S. sagittarius* (FMNH 131411, 142413, 171768), *Simophis rhinostoma* (2 SDSU uncat.), *Sinonatrix aequifasciata* (Saiff, 1975; FMNH 24763), *S. annularis* (Brongersma, 1957a; FMNH 109139), *S. percarinata* (Brongersma, 1957a; FMNH 24776), *Siphlophis cervinus* (Meckel, 1833; Schlegel, 1837b; FMNH 40443), *S. pulcher* (UMMZ 65655), *Sonora aemula* (CAS 135187; SDSU uncat.), *S. michoacanensis* (Saiff, 1975; FMNH 39129), *S. semiannulata* (Saiff, 1975; 2 SDSU uncat.), *Sordellina punctata* (UMMZ 115650), *Spalerosophis arenarius* (Saiff, 1975; FMNH 109923), *S. diadema* (Fritsch, 1869[9]; Hoffmann, 1890[9]; Saiff, 1975; Twerenbold, 1987; SDSU uncat.), *S. microlepis* (FMNH 20923), *Spilotes pullatus* (Meckel, 1818, 1831; Schlegel, 1837b; Henle, 1839[4]; Hoffmann, 1890; Cope, 1894a, 1894b, 1895b, 1900; Noble, 1921[5]; Mole, 1924[5]; do Amaral, 1930a[5]; Ditmars, 1931[5]; Dunn, 1944[5]; Angel, 1950[5]; Brongersma, 1957a; Rossman and Williams, 1966[5]; Roze, 1966[5]; Kundert, 1974[5], 1984[5]; Saiff, 1975; C. C. Carpenter and Ferguson, 1977[5]; Emsley, 1977[5]; Amaral, 1978[5]; Lancini, 1979[5], 1986[5]; Gasc and Rodrigues, 1980[5]; Vanzolini et al., 1980[5]; Alvarez del Toro, 1982[5]; Mehrtens, 1987[5]; Lancini and Kornacker, 1989[5]; Coborn, 1994[5]; Lee, 1996[5]; J. C. Murphy, 1997[5]; LSUMZ 37933; MCZ 171857; MNN 149; 3 UCA uncat.; VW 2864), *Stegonotus batjanensis* (Brongersma, 1957a, 1957b[6]; MCZ 33510), *S. borneensis* (FMNH 188500), *S. cucullatus* (Saiff, 1975; Young, 1992; FMNH 97833), *S. diehli* (FMNH 43010), *S. magnus* (Brongersma, 1957a[5], 1957b), *S. modestus* (Schlegel, 1837b; Brongersma, 1957a, 1957b; Young, 1992; CAS 118881; FMNH 166902), *S. muelleri* (VW 124, 148), *S. parvus* (MCZ 137639), *Stegonotus* sp. (Brongersma, 1958b; McDowell, 1972a), *Stenophis granuliceps* (FMNH 18297, 60891; MCZ 21891), *Stenorrhina degenhardtii* (Cope, 1894a, 1900; FMNH 165894), *S. freminvillei* (BYU 18263; 9 UCA uncat.), *Stenorrhina* sp. (Wallach, 1988), *Stilosoma extenuatum* (Saiff, 1975; Keogh, 1993[7]; FMNH 38018), *Stoliczkia borneensis* (Underwood, 1967; FMNH 250000), *Storeria dekayi* (Butner, 1963a; Saiff, 1975; MZUSP 8189), *S. occipitomaculata* (Saiff, 1975; SDSU uncat.), *S. storerioides* (FMNH 65346), *Storeria* sp. (Wallach, 1985), *Symphimus leucostomus* (LSUMZ 28796), *S. mayae* (FMNH 153519), *Sympholis lippiens* (SDSU uncat.), *Synophis bicolor* (CAS 23612; MCZ 164530; UMMZ 91551), *S. lasallei* (FMNH 81313; MCZ 156873), *Tachymenis chilensis* (FMNH 212501), *T. peruviana* (Schlegel, 1837b; MCZ 45903), *Taeniophallus brevirostris* (FMNH 206031), *Tantalophis discolor* (Underwood, 1967; AMNH 103130), *Tantilla gracilis* (FMNH 30083), *T. melanocephala* (2 UCA uncat.), *T. nigriceps* (Kardong, 1972b; Ramsay, 1979), *T. schistosa* (Saiff, 1975), *T. semicincta* (FMNH 165866), *T. taeniata* (Saiff, 1975), *T. vermiformis* (LSUMZ 36972, 36974), *T. wilcoxi* (Saiff, 1975), *Tantilla* sp. (Wallach, 1988), *Tantillita lintoni* (Wallach, 1988; MCZ 32196), *Telescopus beetzii* (MCZ 159156), *T. dhara* (Beddard, 1906b; MCZ 18210), *T. fallax* (Fleischmann, 1831; 4 SDSU uncat.), *T. nigriceps* (MCZ 52263), *T. rhinopoma* (FMNH 20928), *T. semiannulatus* (Saiff, 1975; 2 SDSU uncat.), *T. tessellatus* (CAS 86460), *T. variegatus* (CAS 136096), *Teratolepis fruhstorferi* (Brongersma, 1957a; RMNH 515a), *Thamnodynastes nattereri* (Underwood, 1967), *T. pallidus* (Saiff, 1975; 2 SDSU uncat.), *T. strigatus* (Cope, 1894a, 1900; SDSU uncat.), *T. strigilis* (SDSU uncat.), *Thamnophis brachystoma* (LSUMZ 13600), *T. butleri* (SDSU uncat.), *T. chrysocephalus* (LSUMZ 24545), *T. collaris* (LSUMZ 7560), *T. couchii* (Saiff, 1975; LSUMZ 47030), *T. cyrtopsis* (SDSU uncat.), *T. elegans* (Burggren, 1977; Lillywhite, 1987a; SDSNH; SDSU uncat.; VW 8, 10, 13, 30, 41– 42, 51, 53, 61, 63–64, 69, 71–72, 75–76, 92, 94, 202), *T. eques* (Saiff, 1975; 2 SDSU uncat.), *T. fulvus* (LSUMZ 23833), *T. godmani* (LSUMZ 24575), *T. hammondi* (SDSNH 29745; ZIL), *T. melanogaster* (LSUMZ 38782), *T. mendax* (LSUMZ 35340), *T. ordinoides* (Thompson, 1914b; Daniels et al., 1995a, 1995b; SDSNH 32167), *T. proximus* (Cope, 1894a, 1900; SDSU uncat.), *T. pulchrilatus* (LSUMZ 35064), *T. radix* (Harrison and Denning, 1930[7]; Burggren, 1977; Lillywhite, 1987a; Mutschmann, 1995[3]; SDSU uncat.), *T. sauritus* (McDowell, 1972c[2]; Saiff, 1975; SDSU uncat.), *T. scalaris* (LSUMZ 38543), *T. sirtalis* (Packard, 1879[1], 1880[1], 1881[1], 1885[1], 1886a[1], 1888[1], 1889[1]; Cope, 1894a, 1900; Kellogg, 1901[1]; Atwood, 1918[6,9]; Karlstrom, 1952[6,9]; Kurtz, 1953[6,9]; Brongersma, 1957a, 1957b; Tenney and Tenney, 1970; Kardong, 1972b; Saiff, 1975; Burggren, 1977; Ramsay, 1979; Benton, 1980; Parsons and Djatschenko, 1983[6]; Pohunková and Hughes, 1985[8]; Lillywhite, 1987a; Keogh, 1993[7]; 3 SDSU uncat.; VW 19–21, 23, 26, 44–45, 86, 111, 119–21, 131), *T. sumichrasti* (LSUMZ 292), *Thamnophis* sp. (Packard, 1886; A. C. Jones, 1926[8]; Froom, 1972[1]), *Thelotornis capensis* (Pringle, 1954[5]; Broadley, 1957a[5], 1957b[5], 1959[5], 1983[5], 1990[5]; V. F. M. FitzSimons, 1962[5], 1966, 1970[5]; Isemonger, 1962[5]; Rose, 1962[5]; Lambiris, 1965[5]; Pienaar, 1966[5]; Visser, 1972[5]; Skinner, 1973[5]; Leen, 1978[5]; Visser and Chapman, 1978[5]; Branch, 1981[5], 1993[5]; Marais, 1985[5], 1992[5]; Patterson, 1986[5], 1987[5]; Coborn, 1991[5], 1994[5]; Jaroniewski, 1992[5]; Mattison, 1995[5]; Greene, 1997; FMNH 191163), *T. kirtlandii* (Cope, 1894a, 1900; E. G. Boulenger, 1914[5]; Noble, 1921[5]; Barbour, 1926[5]; Loveridge, 1928[5]; Pitman, 1938[5], 1974[5]; Cansdale, 1949b[5], 1955[5]; Rose, 1955[5]; R. Mertens, 1959[5], 1960[5]; Sweeney, 1961[5]; Isemonger, 1962[5]; Morris and Morris, 1965[5]; Minton et al., 1968[5]; Stidworthy, 1971[5]; Villiers, 1975[5]; C. C. Carpenter and Ferguson, 1977[5]; Stucki-Stirn, 1979[5]; Henderson and Binder, 1980[5]; Engelmann and Obst, 1981[5]; Marais, 1985[5]; Mehrtens, 1987[5]; Brazaitis and Watanabe, 1992[5]; Schnieper, 1995[5]; Ernst and Zug, 1996[5]; Riquier and Böhme, 1996[5]; FMNH 214828; IRSL uncat.; VW 977), *Thelotornis* sp. (Angel, 1950[5]; Bellairs, 1969[5], 1970[5]), *Thermophis baileyi* (BNHS 1600), *Thrasops flavigularis* (Cope, 1894a, 1900; Cansdale, 1949a[5], 1961[5]; Stucki-Stirn, 1979[5]; FMNH 179036), *T. jacksoni* (Tanara, 1975[5], 1978[5]; Kundert, 1984[5]; BMNH 1979.190–1979.191; MZUSP 8178–79; 5 UNAZA uncat.; UF 52476, 80359–60; VW 1077, 1083, 1230, 1232, 1965, 2350), *T. occidentalis* (Cansdale, 1961[5]; UG C34P12), *Toluca conica* (MCZ 42653), *T. lineata* (SDSU uncat.), *Tomodon dorsatus* (Wallach, 1988; FMNH 9254–55; 2 SDSU uncat.), *T. ocellatus* (SDSU uncat.), *Toxicodryas blandingii* (Cope, 1894, 1900; Isemonger, 1962[5]; H. W. Parker, 1965[2]; Spawls, 1979[5]; FMNH 191401; 9 IRSL uncat.; SDSNH; TAU 12613; UF 80667; 2 UNAZA uncat.; VW 912, 1228, 1629), *T. pulverulentus* (Saint Girons, 1994[2]; BMNH 1979.195; 5 IRSL uncat.; VW 1004, 2172), *Trachischium fuscum* (FMNH 11793), *T. guentheri* (CAS 152646), *T. monticola* (MCZ 22382), *T. tenuiceps* (FMNH 109763), *Trachischium* sp. (Wallach, 1988), *Tretanorhinus mocquardi* (FMNH 16752), *T. nigroluteus* (Underwood, 1967; MNN 137), *T. taeniatus* (FMNH 214844), *T. variabilis* (CAS 14441), *Trimetopon barbouri* (CAS 7438), *T. gracile* (LSUMZ 24731), *T. pliolepis* (MCZ 28050), *T. polylepis* (FMNH 178683), *T. slevini* (ANSP 23875), *Trimorphodon biscutatus* (Cope, 1894a, 1900;

Butner, 1963a; Underwood, 1967; SDSNH; 14 UCA uncat., VW 2891–92), *T. tau* (FMNH 71532), *Tropidoclonion lineatum* (SDSU uncat.), *Tropidodipsas annulifera* (Wallach, 1995; CAS 95774), *T. fasciata* (Wallach, 1995; FMNH 36194), *T. fischeri* (Wallach, 1995; FMNH 20274, 40877), *T. philippii* (Wallach, 1995; CAS 24068), *T. sartorii* (Underwood, 1967; Wallach, 1995; 2 SDSU uncat.), *Tropidodryas serra* (FMNH 9018), *T. striaticeps* (MCZ 39410), *Tropidonophis aenigmaticus* (Malnate and Underwood, 1988), *T. dahli* (Malnate and Underwood, 1988), *T. dendrophiops* (Malnate and Underwood, 1988; FMNH 53353), *T. doriae* (Malnate and Underwood, 1988; CAS 114109), *T. elongatus* (Brongersma, 1957a; Malnate and Underwood, 1988), *T. halmahericus* (Brongersma, 1957a; Malnate and Underwood, 1988; CAS 66199), *T. hypomelas* (Underwood, 1967; Malnate and Underwood, 1988), *T. mairii* (Brongersma, 1957a; Malnate and Underwood, 1988; LSUMZ 27765), *T. mcdowelli* (Malnate and Underwood, 1988), *T. montanus* (Malnate and Underwood, 1988), *T. multiscutellatus* (Brongersma, 1957a; Malnate and Underwood, 1988; MCZ 123633), *T. negrosensis* (Malnate and Underwood, 1988; FMNH 161638), *T. novaeguineae* (Malnate and Underwood, 1988; CAS 136578), *T. parkeri* (Malnate and Underwood, 1988; CAS 118917), *T. picturatus* (Malnate and Underwood, 1988; CAS 136589), *T. punctiventris* (Brongersma, 1957a; Malnate and Underwood, 1988), *T. statisticus* (Malnate and Underwood, 1988; MCZ 141233), *T. truncatus* (Brongersma, 1957a[5,6]; Underwood, 1967; Malnate and Underwood, 1988; MCZ 33508), *Tripanurgos compressus* (Meckel, 1833; FMNH 109815), *Umbrivaga mertensi* (FMNH 204475), *U. pygmaeus* (FMNH 28022), *Uromacer catesbyi* (Cope, 1894a, 1900; Martínez et al., 1985[7]; FMNH 18367, 42602), *U. frenatus* (Martínez et al., 1985[7]; MCZ 93150–51), *U. oxyrhynchus* (Cope, 1894a, 1900; Martínez et al., 1985[7]; CAS 111432), *U. wetmorei* (Martínez et al., 1985[7]; MCZ 135968), *Uromacerina ricardinii* (MCZ 3674), *Urotheca guentheri* (H. M. Smith et al., 1995; UCA uncat.), *Virginia striatula* (Meckel, 1819; 2 SDSU uncat.), *V. valeriae* (LSUMZ 24483), *Waglerophis merremii* (H. W. Parker and Grandison, 1977[1,2]; Cole, 1981[1]; Freiberg, 1982[3]; Singh and Kar, 1982; McCarthy, 1991[1]; Mattison, 1995[1]; 3 SDSU uncat.), *Xenelaphis hexagonotus* (Brongersma, 1957a, 1957b, 1958b; Young, 1992; CAS 8551; FMNH 128268), *Xenochrophis cerasogaster* (FMNH 121569), *X. flavipunctatus* (CAS 119941), *X. maculatus* (Brongersma, 1957a; FMNH 148860), *X. piscator* (Henle, 1839[4]; Hoffmann, 1890[4]; Mathur, 1946[9]; P. H. D. H. de Silva, 1955[5,6,9]; Brongersma, 1957a; Bergman, 1958b; Sondhi, 1958[5]; Kashyap and Velankar, 1959[9]; Gharpurey, 1962; Deoras and Vad, 1973; Singh and Kar, 1982[9]; SDSNH; SDSU uncat.), *X. punctulatus* (Underwood, 1967), *X. trianguligerus* (Brongersma, 1957a, 1957b; Bergman, 1959; FMNH 145696), *X. vittatus* (Bergman, 1950[7]; Brongersma, 1957a; FMNH 131167), *Xenodermus javanicus* (Brongersma, 1938; FMNH 67427, 138678), *Xenodon bertholdi* (FMNH 178714), *X. guentheri* (MCZ 54628), *X. neuwiedi* (2 SDSU uncat.), *X. rhabdocephalus* (Schlegel, 1837b; Stannius, 1856; Cope, 1894a, 1894b, 1895b, 1900; Underwood, 1967; Saiff, 1975; Halliday and Adler, 1986[2,3]; Shine, 1992[2]; FMNH 11186; SDSNH 25264, 25276; 2 UCA uncat.), *X. severus* (Schlegel, 1837b; Lereboullet, 1838; Cuvier, 1840; Stannius, 1856; Milne-Edwards, 1857b; Cope, 1894a, 1894b, 1895b, 1900; SDSU uncat.), *Xenopholis scalaris* (FMNH 45614; MCZ 157153), *X. undulatus* (UMMZ 108820), *Xenoxybelis argenteus* (FMNH 56140), *Xylophis perroteti* (FMNH 171805), *X. stenorhynchus* (CAS 17200), *Xylophis* sp. (Wallach, 1988).

APPENDIX C: PULMONARY CONDITIONS IN THE GENERA OF SNAKES

See Table 2.1 for definitions of character abbreviations and pages 101-104 fior taxonomic conventions.

1. SMALL LEFT LUNG AND/OR UNICAMERAL TRACHEAL LUNG

Genus	S/N	T	TE	TTR	NTR	TL	TLL	CL	HT	RAL	RL	SL	RB	RBL	RB/RL	RPT	L	LL	LLL	LL/RL	LB	LBL	LBR	LO	LOM
3. Leptotyphlopidae																									
Leptotyphlops	69/226	14-26	T	112-272	49-156	0	—	1-4	14-30	0	16-42	0(7-25)	+	4-24	16-100	34-77	20-40	0	—	—	0	—	—	0	—
Rhinoleptus	1/1	18	T	231	126	0	—	1	18	0	38	20	+	21	54	56	39	0	—	—	0	—	—	0	—
4. Anomochilidae																									
Anomochilus	1/1	23	T	173	75	0	—	1	24	—	27	12	+	1.6	5.9	51	28	0	—	—	0	—	—	0	—
5. Aniliidae																									
Anilius	1/14	23-26	S(P)	209-303	80-127	0	—	0	24-27	0.5-1.3	23-41	0/8-26	+/0	0.2-1.4	0.7-5.3	48-64	23-41	+	0.8-1.7	2.4-6.9	0+	0	1	+0	25-30
6. Cylindrophiidae																									
Cylindrophis	2/10	24-30	P:S:T	206-255	75-102	0	—	0-2	25-30	0.3-2.5	23-34	0/6-11	+	0.6-7.8	3.3-32	51-61	23-34	+	2.0-4.2	6.3-14	+(0)	0.2-0.5	1-10	+	25-31
7. Uropeltidae																									
Brachyophidium	1/2	30-31	T	165	53	0	—	0-1	30-31	—	19-28	0	+	2.1-3.4	11	51-61	21-29	+	3.4-3.7	11-18	+	0	1	+	31-33
Melanophidium	1/1	29	T	211	72	0	—	2	30	—	21	0	+	0.9	4.3	51	23	+	1.2	5.7	+	0.3	2	+	31
Platyplectrurus	1/1	26	T	227	87	0	—	5	26	—	20	5	+	0.9	4.6	46	25	0	—	—	0	—	—	0	—
Plectrurus	2/3	28-31	T	180-222	58-80	0	—	1-2	28-32	—	18-27	0	+	1.0-1.5	5.3-6.2	47-59	20-29	+	0.5-1.2	2.6-4.6	0/+	0	1	+	29-33
Pseudoplectrurus	1/1	31	T	216	69	0	—	1	32	—	24	11	+	1.8	7.1	56	26	+	1.6	6.5	+	0	1	+	32
Pseudotyphlops	1/4	26-28	S/P:T	142-168	51-66	0	—	1-2	28-33	1.1-1.5	22-30	0	+	0.7-1.3	2.5-5.7	51-60	23-30	+	3.2-6.0	15-21	+	0.5-1.3	5-9	+	28-31
Rhinophis	3/3	29-38	T/P	173-203	46-69	0	—	0	30-39	1.6	18-23	0	+	0.8-1.2	3.4-6.0	50-62	18-23	+	1.0-1.5	4.2-6.8	0/+	0.4	2	+	28-39
Teretrurus	1/2	30-31	T	177-181	58-59	0	—	2-3	31	—	16-17	0	+	1.5-2.2	8.8-13	48-49	20-21	+	1.6-2.0	11-12	+0	0	1	+	31-32
Uropeltis	16/17	23-37	T/P/S	155-353	47-114	0	—	0-4	25-37	0.7-1.7	15-32	0/3-13	+	0.1-3.7	1.1-14	52-64	16-32	+	0.9-5.8	4.0-27	+/0	0.2-0.7	1-8	+	24-38
12. Bolyeriidae																									
Bolyeria	1/1	25	T	328	124	0	—	1	27	—	23	8	+	1.6	6.8	50	24	+	3.2	13.6	+	0	1	+	28
Casarea	1/2	31	T	277-367	78-110	0	—	0-2	33	—	31-41	33	+	1.0-3.2	3.5-7.8	69-73	33-41	+	1.8-1.9	4.4-6.4	+	0.2	1-3	+	35-38
13. Xenophidiidae																									
Xenophidion	1/1	35	T	260	72	+	20	3	37	—	26	0	+	5.3	20	63	49	0	—	—	0	—	—	0	—

14-1. Tropidophiidae: Ungaliophiinae																								
Exiliboa	1/11	27-33	T	130-207	40-66	+	17-22	2-3	28-34	—	20-31	17-28	+(0)	1.6-4.3	7.7-14	50-65	42-56	0	—	—	0	—	—	0
Ungaliophis	2/4	32-38	T	187-312	56-82	+	23-25	2-3	32-40	—	24-32	15-27	+	0.7-14	2.3-46	62-68	54-580/+	0.4	1.4	0/+	0.6	5	0/+	39
14-2. Tropidophiidae: Tropidophiinae																								
Tropidophis	12/15	22-37	T	176-339	56-108	+	11-25	3-4	25-38	—	14-17	07-25	+	14-22	49-100	46-62	36-54	0	—	—	0	—	—	0
Trachyboa	1/2	30-32	T	170-176	55-56	+	18-21	3-4	32-34	—	18-22	19-27	+	12-19	67-84	52-54	42-44	0	—	—	0	—	—	0
16-1. Viperidae Azemiopinae																								
Azemiops	1/4	20-21	S	147-189	71-84	0	—	1	21-23	0.8-1.2	40-66	32-57	+	0.3-1.0	0.5-2.4	64-87	41-67	+	0.5-0.6	0.4-1.2	+	0.2-0.3	1-5	+
16-2. Viperidae: Causinae																								
Causus	5/166	26-34	T(S)	134-237	42-80	+	15-25	2-5	27-38	0.8	49-86	35-69	+	1.5-22	2.2-43	65-97	58-89	0	—	—	0	—	—	0
16-3a. Viperidae: Viperinae: Viperini																								
Bitis	3/95	27-43	T	175-249	44-71	+	6-19	3-6	31-45	—	23-41	18-37	0(+)	0.2-2.9	0.5-11	60-82	36-60	0	—	—	0	—	—	0
B. worthingtoni	1/1	36	S	210	59	+	26	4	38	0.6	40	32	+	3.8	10	76	68	0	—	—	0	—	—	0
Calechidna	7/8	27-32	T	122-202	44-68	0	—	1-6	29-33	—	30-48	12-37	+(0)	1.4-4.6	4.2-9.6	63-77	32-50	0	—	—	0	—	—	0
Cerastes	2/2	25-29	S	172-237	69-81	+	3-4	3-4	27-30	1.6-1.8	69-72	54-55	+	1.0-1.1	1.3-1.7	97-98	74-79	0	—	—	0	—	—	0
Echis	3/5	31-35	S	226-429	66-118	+	18-23	2-3	32-37	0.7-2.9	57-63	50-61	+	2.4-6.0	3.8-10	91-97	81-860/+	0.2	0.3	0	—	—	0/+	37
Eristicophis	1/1	42	T	369	89	+	21	4	44	—	39	38	+	8.5	22	82	64	0	—	—	0	—	—	0
Pseudocerastes	1/1	42	T	415	99	+	23	4	43	—	46	36	+	8.3	18	89	72	0	—	—	0	—	—	0
Vipera	7/10	31-38	T/S	169-312	50-87	+	16-24	2-5	33-40	0.3-0.6	29-45	26-43	+	1.9-10	4.4-27	68-82	57-69	0	—	—	0	—	—	0
16-3b. Viperidae: Viperinae: Atherini																								
Adenorhinos	1/2	25-30	T	126-154	42-61	+	16-17	2-4	27-31	—	33-40	27-37	+	3.4-3.6	8.5-11	60-72	52-61	0	—	—	0	—	—	0
Atheris	6/109	31-39	T(S)	160-286	49-81	+	19-28	2-4	30-41	1.0-1.6	25-58	21-59	+(0)	0.3-4.1	0.7-13	64-89	54-78	0	—	—	0	—	—	0
Montatheris	1/1	33	T	160	48	+	20	4	35	—	41	41	+	4.8	12	76	65	0	—	—	0	—	—	0
Proatheris	1/1	35	T	192	55	+	23	4	37	—	31	32	+	10	33	68	58	0	—	—	0	—	—	0
16-4a. Viperidae: Crotalinae: Agkistrodontini																								
Agkistrodon	3/9	31-38	T	190-295	56-93	+	19-26	3-5	32-41	—	20-40	16-36	+/0	0.9-4.0	7.8-13	54-79	44-69	+	0.6-3.1	1.3-4.9	+	0.1-0.9	1-3	+	33-42
Calloselasma	1/1	33	T	207	63	+	21	3	35	—	32	32	+	1.1	3.5	67	56	0	—	—	0	—	—	0
Deinagkistrodon	1/1	29	S	232	78	+	15	3	32	1.5	43	37	+	1.4	3.2	74	60	+	1.3	2.8	+	0.7	11	+	31
Gloydius	2/3	31-33	S	199-281	61-86	+	20-22	3-4	32-35	0.4-2.3	32-37	28-30	+	1.6-4.0	4.5-12	66-69	57-60	0	—	—	0	—	—	0
Hypnale	2/3	32-36	T	145-235	46-71	+	18-22	3-4	33-38	—	38-57	41-57	+	1.9-4.3	3.3-11	74-96	60-81	0	—	—	0	—	—	0

Genus	S/N	T	TE	TTR	NTR	TL	TLL	CL	HT	RAL	RL	SL	RB	RBL	RB/RL	RPT	L	LL	LLL	LL/RL	LB	LBL	LBR	LO	LOM
16-4b. Viperidae: Crotalinae: Crotalini																									
Atropoides	1/1	26	T	166	65	+	10	4	27	—	38	28	+	0.9	2.2	66	52	+	1.5	4.0	+	0.8	4	+	27
Bothriechis	3/5	31-36	T/S	240-290	79-92	+	18-27	2-4	33-38	1.4	43-57	42-56	+	1.2-2.6	2.1-5.1	81-96	65-87	+0	1.4-2.1	2.6-2.9	0/+	0.1	2	+	34-39
Bothriopsis	2/2	31-34	S:T	215-216	64-70	+	23-26	2	32-35	2.6	46-54	44-54	+	0.6-1.3	1.0-2.8	78-89	71-82	0	—	—	0	—	—	0	—
Bothrops	10/14	30-39	T(S)	191-360	62-106	+	19-26	2-4	32-40	1.4	23-46	23-43	+(0)	0.2-1.8	0.5-5.3	59-80	48-69	0/+	0.2-1.7	0.3-2.6	0+	0.1-0.4	1-7	0+	32-40
Cerrophidion	2/3	27-35	S/T	148-221	55-63	+	13-25	3	28-38	0.8-1.9	30-47	30-48	+	0.5-2.2	1.1-7.3	67-76	58-63	0/+	0.3	0.5	0+	0.3	1-2	+/0	28-29
Crotalus	24/215	31-47	T/S	128-470	60-122	+	22-36	2-4	32-49	0.4-2.5	18-50	21-50	+	0.7-9.5	1.5-2.3	66-88	56-79	0(+)	0.5-1.5	1.4-4.7	0(+)	0.2-0.4	2-5	0(+)	32-46
Ophryacus	1/1	35	T	287	82	+	26	3	37	—	35	35	+	5.8	1.7	72	64	0	—	—	0	—	—	0	—
Ovophis	3/3	31-35	S	160-220	47-67	+	17-22	3-5	33-36	1.0-2.4	24-35	21-31	+	1.0-2.4	1.8-8.4	60-68	50-56	+/0	1.4-1.6	4.3-5.3	+/0	0.3-0.6	2-5	+/0	33-35
Porthidium	3/5	30-33	T/S	168-198	51-64	+	16-23	3-4	32-35	0.8	35-42	33-41	+/0	0.7-3.1	1.7-8.1	69-77	56-67	0+	0.5-2.6	0.7-6.3	0/+	0.5	2	0/+	32-35
Protobothrops	3/6	34-39	T	292-379	74-99	+	22-24	2-3	35-41	—	31-45	28-41	+	1.1-3.3	2.7-9.6	70-86	56-69	0/+	2.0-2.3	5.0-6.3	+/0	0.2-0.4	1-5	+/0	38-40
Sistrurus	3/5	34-40	T/S	213-310	59-82	+	20-28	3-4	35-42	1.3	29-32	28-36	+	2.7-4.5	8.4-15	65-73	55-62	0	—	—	0/+	0.5	5	0/+	40
Trimeresurus	6/6	33-42	T/S	187-277	48-74	+	19-31	0-3	34-43	0.3	32-46	28-48	+	0.3-2.1	0.9-3.9	71-86	57-76	+/0	1.1-2.5	2.7-5.5	+/0	0.3-0.9	4-6	+/0	34-43
Tropidolaemus	1/2	36-37	S:T	172-183	48-49	+	24-26	2	38-40	0.6	44-53	46-54	+	0.5-2.3	1.0-4.4	84-91	73-81	+0	1.2	2.2	+	0.5-0.6	3-4	+	38
16-4c. Viperidae: Crotalinae: Lachesini																									
Lachesis	1/2	23-24	S	206-224	89-94	0	—	0-1	25	0.4-0.9	30-44	20-34	+	0.9-1.4	2.1-4.4	55-69	30-45	+	0.3	0.8-0.9	0	—	—	—	25
17-1. Atractaspididae: Atractaspidinae																									
Atractaspis	15/153	21-28	T/S(P)	173-330	72-124	0	—	0-18	20-29	0.4-1.4	31-58	18-47	+	0.3-3.6	0.7-8.5	53-77	32-69	+/0	0.2-1.9	0.4-4.7	+0	0.1-0.4	1-5	+/0	23-29
17-2. Atractaspididae: Aparallactinae																									
Amblyodipsas	8/66	19-28	S	134-264	58-110	0	—	0-19	21-30	0.6-1.8	38-54	23-42	+	0.4-2.3	0.9-5.7	63-80	39-67	+	0.2-2.7	0.8-5.8	+(0)	0.1-0.9	1-4	+	22-30
Aparallactus	8/108	16-29	S(T/P)	127-247	50-109	0	—	0-19	19-33	0.1-2.2	33-63	19-50	+(0)	0.7-3.6	1.1-8.4	54-81	35-74	+	0.4-2.3	1.1-5.3	0/+	0.2-0.7	1-3	+/0	20-34
Brachyophis	2/6	20-22	T	96-141	42-58	+	4-6	3-4	21-23	—	39-54	24-38	+	1.2-2.7	1.4-5.0	61-74	49-62	+/0	1.2-1.9	2.4-3.7	+/0	0	1	+/0	22-23
Chilorhinophis	2/26	18-31	S/T(P)	219-337	85-142	+	5-16	2-3	19-32	0.5-2.1	37-60	19-48	+(0)	0.3-2.1	0.8-3.7	59-82	50-74	0/+	0.4-1.0	0.8-2.0	0/+	0.1	1-2	+/0	20-26
Elapops	1/20	15-19	S(T)	129-204	66-91	0	—	0-9	20-25	1.1-2.3	34-50	23-38	+	0.8-2.6	1.6-6.7	54-71	41-54	+	0.9-2.2	2.0-4.9	+	0	1	+	20-27
Elapotinus	1/1	33	S	238	63	+	21	4	38	1.3	38	33	+	0.3	0.9	74	62	+	1.2	3.2	+	0.2	2	+	38
Heteroliodon	1/1	24	T	143	59	+	16	2	26	—	46	37	+	0.9	1.9	71	64	+	0.6	1.4	0	0	0	+	26
Hypoptophis	1/1	24	T	176	70	0	—	4	26	—	40	30	+	2.1	5.5	67	45	+	0.9	2.3	+	0.2	1	+	28
Macrelaps	1/13	20-25	S	138-182	65-92	0	—	2-15	21-27	0.5-2.0	35-54	21-42	+	0.6-3.1	1.4-8.1	60-77	38-58	+	0.4-1.4	1.1-4.0	+	0.1-0.5	1-4	+	22-26
Micrelaps	2/17	21-28	S/T(P)	177-283	64-107	+	11-18	2-3	22-29	0.3-1.3	39-56	31-49	+	0.5-1.7	1.2-3.7	62-79	53-69	+/0	0.4-1.0	0.7-2.1	+/0	0.1-0.3	1-4	+/0	22-29

Pararhadinaea	1/1	33	T	247	74	+	18	3	35	—	33	26	+	1.8	5	68	54	+	0.8	2.4	+	0	1	+	35
Poecilopholis	1/2	24	S	158-173	65-73	0	—	8-14	25	1.5-1.7	33-40	13-15	+	1.0-2.2	2.5-5.7	58-64	46-52	+	0.7-1.0	1.9-2.7	0	—	—	+	26-27
Polemon	12/98	22-32	S(T/P)	182-351	57-114	0	—	0-24	23-33	0.2-1.7	35-59	24-53	+(0)	0.3-3.2	0.6-6.2	63-85	39-68+/0	0.2-1.9	0.3-3.5	+/0	0.1-0.4	1-5	+/0	23-33
Xenocalamus	5/41	21-29	S(T)	224-379	85-147	0	—	0-18	22-30	0.4-2.0	32-53	25-41	+	0.5-2.1	1.2-5.6	58-81	36-67+/0	0.5-1.2	0.9-3.7	+/0	0.1-0.2	1-3	+/0	22-30

18-1a. Elapidae: Bungarinae: Bungarini

Bungarus	6/8	23-28	S	219-388	91-150	0	—	1-2	25-30	0.4-1.5	42-57	31-46	+	0.5-1.2	0.6-2.4	68-84	44-57+/0	0.4-1.0	0.9-1.8	+/0	0.1-0.4	1-6	+/0	25-28

18-1b. Elapidae: Bungarinae: Najini

Aspidelaps	2/21	20-29	T	274-294	102-105	0	—	0-2	22-30	—	39-49	26-36	+	1.5-2.0	3.9-4.5	67-70	40-49	0	—	—	0/+	0.4	4	0/i+	23-28
Boulengerina	2/21	22-30	P/S/S	308-374	124-156	0	—	0-1	23-31	0.6-1.2	31-40	13-23	+	1.7-12	4.0-3.4	56-68	32-400/+	0.3-0.6	0.8-1.6	+(0)	0.3-0.8	5-13	+	23-31
Elapsoidea	5/13	22-26	S	168-207	69-91	0	—	0-5	23-29	0.7-1.5	40-68	29-57	+	0.5-2.5	1.0-5.3	64-94	41-68+/0	0.1-1.2	0.2-2.7	+/0	0.1-0.4	1-4	+(0)	23-28
Hemachatus	1/1	20	S	135	68	0	—	0	22	0.6	49	37	+	0.5	2.2	70	49	+	0.6	1.4	+	0.5	1	+	21
Homoroselaps	2/20	20-23	S	138-207	62-110	0	—	1-14	20-25	0.5-2.2	36-58	19-48	+	0.4-2.4	0.9-5.6	57-80	43-65+(0)	0.3-1.3	0.9-2.4	+	0.1-0.3	1-3	+	21-26
Naja	8/75	22-34	S/T(P)	120-288	53-114	0	—	0-3	24-34	0.3-2.3	36-70	20-57	+(0)	0.3-2.7	0.2-5.5	61-93	37-71+(0)	0.2-2.9	0.5-6.9	+(0)	0.1-1.0	2-12	+	24-31
Paranaja	1/4	22-25	S	149-202	63-88	0	—	0	23-26	1.0-2.2	40-44	29-32	+	0.5-1.6	1.2-3.6	63-70	40-44+/0	1.4-2.7	3.4-6.0	+	0.2-0.3	1-5	+	24-27
Pseudohaje	2/3	24-27	S	282-340	118-131	0	—	0	25-28	0.8-1.8	48-68	33-54	+	0.8-1.4	1.2-2.8	73-95	48-68	+	0.3-1.6	0.7-2.4	+/0	0.1-0.2	3	+	26-29
Walterinnesia	1/2	22	T	308	138	0	—	1	23-24	—	37-43	25-31	+	0.5-1.2	1.1-3.2	62-66	38-44	0	—	—	+	0	1	+	23-24

18-1c. Elapidae: Bungarinae: Dendroaspidini

Dendroaspis	4/16	28-33	S	306-380	99-137	0	—	0-1	29-35	0.3-1.4	48-66	38-55	+/0	0.2-0.7	0.3-1.2	81-98	48-67	+	0.5-1.5	0.8-2.8	+	0.1-0.3	1-8	+	29-34

18-2a. Elapidae: Elapinae: Maticorini

Calliophis	5/14	21-27	S/T	195-326	79-140	0	—	0-17	22-28	0.5-1.7	38-69	23-49	+	0.4-1.8	0.6-4.1	62-97	48-87	0	—	—	+	0(+)	2	0(i/+)	23-25
Maticora	2/3	32-44	T	358-380	86-112	0	—	0-1	33-45	—	24-46	27-36	+	0.6-3.0	1.4-11	68-80	24-47	0	—	—	+	0	—	0	—

18-2b. Elapidae: Elapinae: Elapini

Hemibungarus	1/4	26	S	220-282	85-109	0	—	0-3	26-27	1.4-1.8	45-64	34-52	+	0.8-3.6	1.3-1.6	71-91	45-660/+	0.4	0.5	+/0	0.4	1-4	+	28
Leptomicrurus	2/4	23-26	T	230-386	89-170	0	—	0-11	23-27	—	42-47	29-39	+	0.3-1.6	0.7-3.3	67-76	44-52	0	—	—	+	0	—	0	—
Micruroides	1/2	23	S	222-226	98-106	0	—	1-2	22-24	1.0	50	35	+	1.5-2.1	2.7-3.0	73	52	0	—	—	0+	0.3	2	0+	25
Micrurus	6/8	22-26	S/T	234-259	99-105	0	—	0	23-28	0.5-2.8	30-41	15-31	+	0.3-2.2	0.9-7.0	53-67	31-410/+	0.2	0.5	0/+	0	1	0/+	27-28
Parapistocalamus	1/1	21	S	132	61	0	—	0	22	0.3	50	36	+	0.6	1.1	72	50	+	0.5	0.9	+	0.1	2	+	23

18-3. Laticaudidae

Laticauda colubrina	4	36-40	T	349	90	+	28-33	3-4	37-42	—	44-53	8-22	+	1.0-2.5	2.1-6.0	83-89	75-810/+	0.6	1.4	0+	0.2	6	0+	39-40
L. laticaudata	2	24-25	T	246	103	0	—	3-4	25-26	—	61-66	17-29	+	17-27	27-40	86-92	64-70	0.5-0.8	0.9-1.2	+	0.6-0.8	10-14	+	25-26
L. semifasciata	3	22-24	T	256	111	+	7-8	3-4	23-25	—	38-41	3-7	+	30-32	78-95	62-66	49-530/+	0.6	1.5	0	—	—	+/0	25

Genus	S/N	T	TE	TTR	NTR	TL	TLL	CL	HT	RAL	RL	SL	RB	RBL	RB/RL	RPT	L	LL	LLL	LL/RL	LB	LBL	LBR	LO	LOM
19-1a. Hydrophiidae: Acanthophiinae: Pseudechini																									
Pseudechis	4/6	20-26	S	179-257	69-104	0	—	1	21-27	1.0-1.5	43-49	29-35	+	0.8-2.5	1.3-5.4	66-74	44-50	+	0.5-2.2	1.0-5.5	+	0.1-0.3	1-3	+	22-27
19-1b. Hydrophiidae: Acanthophiinae: Demansiini																									
Demansia	4/8	21-26	S	168-234	75-99	0	—	1-5	22-27	0.6-1.3	41-49	29-38	+	0.4-1.3	0.7-3.1	63-74	42-53	+/0	0.1-0.6	0.2-1.3	+/0	0.1-0.3	1-3	+/0	22-27
19-1c. Hydrophiidae: Acanthophiinae: Pseudonajini																									
Pseudonaja	5/11	21-27	S(T)	150-330	63-132	0	—	0-7	22-28	0.9-1.5	43-67	31-55	+	0.6-1.9	0.9-4.0	66-90	43-70	+/0	0.1-0.4	0.2-0.7	+/0	0.1-0.2	1-3	+/0	23-28
19-1d. Hydrophiidae: Acanthophiinae: Oxyuranini																									
Oxyuranus	2/9	21-26	S	385	110-159	0	—	0-1	22-28	0.5-1.3	56-73	42-60	+/0	0.1-1.5	0.2-2.2	81-98	57-74	+/0	0.2-0.3	0.3-0.5	+/0	0.1-0.4	2-7	+/0	23-27
19-1e. Hydrophiidae: Acanthophiinae: Notechini																									
Austrelaps	1/11	19-23	S	140-182	60-86	0	—	0-1	20-24	0.6-2.2	40-50	26-36	+	0.7-2.9	1.9-6.1	62-70	41-51	+	0.7-2.2	1.5-4.8	+	0.2-0.3	1-3	+	22-25
Denisonia	2/4	21-26	S	141-163	61-68	0	—	5-9	23-26	0.7-1.7	33-41	14-32	+	1.4-2.7	4.3-6.6	56-67	41-50	+	0.5-1.3	1.2-3.5	+	0	1	+	24-28
Drysdalia	4/10	20-29	S	131-163	51-75	0	—	0-1	21-30	0.3-1.5	31-50	18-34	+	0.9-2.1	2.0-5.2	52-75	31-51	+	0.4-1.3	1.0-2.8	0+	0.3	1-5	+	22-30
Echiopsis	1/2	22-23	S:T	142-147	64	0	—	9-10	24-25	0.5	53-55	40-45	+	0.6-1.7	1.2-3.1	76-80	61-65	+	1.7-2.3	3.4-4.1	0	—	—	+	24-25
Hemiaspis	2/3	20-22	S	151-158	78-81	0	—	7-12	20-24	0.9-1.3	40-48	26-35	+	0.6-1.5	1.3-3.9	63-68	51-55	+	0.4-1.1	1.0-2.6	0/+	0.2	2	+	21-24
Hoplocephalus	3/6	20-23	S	138-261	68-115	0	—	1-3	21-24	0.7-1.3	44-64	28-41	+	1.1-2.5	2.3-5.0	65-89	45-67	+	0.4-1.3	0.8-2.3	+	0.2-0.5	1-5	+	21-24
Notechis	2/8	20-23	S/P:T	141-164	62-78	0	—	1-14	21-24	1.0-1.5	40-54	27-41	+/0	0.6-1.6	0.9-3.1	62-75	50-67	+/0	0.6-1.2	1.2-3.0	+/0	0.2-0.4	1-4	+	21-24
Tropidechis	1/1	21	S	140	65	0	—	1	23	1.4	51	40	+	2.1	4.0	74	52	+	1.2	2.4	+	0.3	3	+	24
19-1f. Hydrophiidae: Acanthophiinae: Acanthophiini																									
Acanthophis	2/3	26-30	S/T	173-202	59-71	0	—	9-13	27-32	0.8-2.2	36-44	21-31	+	1.6-3.8	4.5-8.7	67-71	44-53	+/0	0.7-1.0	1.8-2.7	+/0	0.2-0.4	2-3	+/0	32-33
19-1g. Hydrophiidae: Acanthophiinae: Rhinoplocephalini																									
Elapognathus	1/1	21	S	104	49	0	—	13	22	2.0	42	30	+	1.6	3.9	64	55	+	1.4	3.4	+	0	1	+	23
Rhinoplocephalus	5/11	19-23	S(T)	120-207	55-94	0	—	1-15	20-24	0.7-1.7	38-55	27-44	+	0.5-2.6	1.2-5.9	61-78	41-60	+	0.4-1.5	0.8-3.1	+/0	0.2-0.4	1-3	+	20-25
Suta	1/3	23-27	S	155-170	63-72	0	—	10-15	24-28	0.5-0.7	43-48	32-38	+	1.5-3.4	2.2-7.7	68-71	54-60	+/0	0.4-0.7	0.9-1.5	+/0	0	1	+	25-28
"Unechis"	6/7	24-27	T/S	165-216	63-91	0	—	6-18	24-28	0.8	43-53	30-43	+	0.6-4.8	1.1-11	67-80	49-65	0	—	—	0+	0.1-0.2	1-2	+	25-28
19-1h. Hydrophiidae: Acanthophiinae: Glyphodontini																									
Cacophis	3/4	23-26	T/S	154-205	58-89	0	—	3-5	25-27	1.0	37-41	26-32	+	1.0-2.0	2.6-5.0	64-69	40-46	0	—	—	0	—	—	0	—
Furina	2/4	24-27	S:T	209-242	76-102	0	—	1-18	25-29	0.8-0.9	41-47	27-34	+	0.5-1.7	1.0-3.8	69-74	51-59	+/0	0.9-1.4	1.9-3.5	+0	0	1	+/0	26-29
Glyphodon	3/4	26-27	S:T	163-257	60-97	0	—	3-13	27-28	0.9	38-47	28-33	+	0.9-2.0	2.0-5.3	65-73	39-58	+	0.3-0.9	0.6-2.3	+	0	1	+	28-30

19-1i. Hydrophiidae: Acanthophiinae: Vermicellini

Simoselaps	6/6	19-24	T	101-176	53-92	0	—	0-8	20-26	—	38-53	23-46	+	0.4-2.9	1.1-6.6	59-79	38-62+/0	0.3-1.5	0.7-2.9	+/0	0.2	1-2	+/0	21-27
Neelaps	2/3	20-21	S	101-168	51-83	0	—	1-4	21-23	—	40-64	23-51	+	0.9-2.3	2.0-5.0	62-86	41-65	0.3-05	0.5-1.2	0/+	0	1	+	22-23
Vermicella	1/4	20-26	S	191-256	82-110	+	4-9	3	21-27	1.3-1.6	44-62	35-51	+	1.1-1.6	1.3-4.2	72-83	56-69	0.5-0.8	1.1-1.3	+	0.1	1-2	+	21-27

19-1j. Hydrophiidae: Acanthophiinae: Toxicocalamini

Aspidomorphus	2/2	27-29	S:T	188-206	69-70	0	0.8	1	28-31	—	40-45	30	+	0.8-1.1	1.9-2.8	71-72	41-46	—	—	+	0.3	1-3	0	29-31
Loveridgelaps	1/1	24	T	216	89	0	—	1	25	—	40	29	+	1.0	2.4	65	41	—	—	0	—	—	0	—
Micropechis	1/1	29	S	276	96	0	—	0	30	—	41	31	+	2.0	4.8	72	42	0.6	1.5	+	0.4	4	+	31
Ogmodon	1/2	25-31	T	147-156	48-62	0	—	1-2	26-32	—	40-46	30-34	+	1.5-1.9	3.8-4.2	73	43-47	—	—	0	—	—	0	—
Salomonelaps	1/2	25-26	S	179-231	61-88	0	—	0-1	27-28	0.8	39	29-30	+	0.1-0.2	0.3-0.4	66-67	40	—	—	0	—	—	0	—
Toxicocalamus	4/5	20-28	T	210-385	104-143	0	—	0-2	21-29	—	34-44	22-34	+	0.8-1.5	2.0-4.1	56-73	35-45+/0	0.3-0.8	0.7-1.8	0+	0.2	2-3	+	22-29

19-2a. Hydrophiidae: Ephalophiinae: Hydrelapini

Hydrelaps	1/1	30	T	202	67	+	—	10	32	—	39	0	+	17	44	71	51	—	—	0	—	—	0	—

19-2b. Hydrophiidae: Ephalophiinae: Ephalophiini

Acalyptophis	1/1	43	T	486	113	+	—	29	44	—	53	7	+	1.2	2.4	97	84	—	—	0	—	—	0	—
Ephalophis	1/1	32	T	267	84	+	—	19	33	—	50	22	+	1.9	3.9	84	72	1.5	2.1	+	0	1	+	33
Parahydrophis	1/1	29	S	198	67	+	1.4	9	31	—	53	7	+	1.9	3.7	82	64	0.4	0.7	+	0.5	3	+	31

19-2c. Hydrophiidae: Ephalophiinae: Aipysurini

Aipysurus	4/4	28-34	T	257-285	78-101	+	—	14-21	29-35	—	63-68	18-35	+	1.0-32	1.6-51	94-99	81-92	—	—	+0	1.1	2-5	+0	29-30
Emydocephalus	2/2	29	T	220-290	75-100	+	—	12-15	3-5	—	60-65	12-21	+	43-47	66-79	91-96	77-83	—	—	0	—	—	0	—

19-3. Hydrophiidae: Hydrophiinae

Astrotia	1/2	32-33	T	283-398	90-119	+	—	20-22	33-35	—	64-65	4-8	0	—	—	98-99	88-89	—	—	0	—	—	0	—
Disteira	2/2	45-49	T	575-698	118-158	+	—	25-39	45-52	—	46-47	7-42	+	3.5-13	7.6-28	92-99	75-88	—	—	0	—	—	0	—
Enhydrina	1/1	44	T	431	98	+	—	17	45	—	49	16	+	1.3	2.6	94	70	s	0.4	+	0.1	1	+	46
Hydrophis	4/4	44-53	T	482-763	102-144	+	—	26-39	45-53	—	46-55	0-11	+	5.9-7.9	13-16	98-100	74-88	0.3	—	+	—	—	0	—
Kerilia	1/1	46	T	332	73	+	—	32	46	—	53	10	+	1.7	3.1	100	88	—	—	0	—	—	0	—
Kolpophis	1/1	32	T	261	81	+	—	20	34	—	65	0	+	2.9	4.5	98	87	—	—	0	—	—	0	—
Lapemis	1/2	32-34	T	256-281	75-89	+	—	19-21	33-36	—	63-67	0-6	+	1.5-2.5	2.4-3.7	98-100	87-89	—	—	0	—	—	0	—
Microcephalophis	2/2	51-57	T	770-1120	136-219	+	—	24-29	52-57	—	42-48	0-3	+	0.7-0.9	1.8	99	73-74	—	—	0	—	—	0	—
Pelamis	1/1	31	T	256	80	+	—	17	32	—	67	14	+	0.6	0.9	99	88	—	—	0	—	—	0	—
Praescutata	1/1	40	T	499	124	+	—	23	41	—	57	8	0	—	—	99	84	—	—	0	—	—	0	—

Genus	S/N	T	TE	TTR	NTR	TL	TLL	CL	HT	RAL	RL	SL	RB	RBL	RB/RL	RPT	L	LL	LLL	LL/RL	LB	LBL	LBR	LO	LOM
Thalassophis	1/1	36	T	283	80	+	20	4	37	—	63	14	+	1.8	2.8	100	87	0	—	—	—	0	—	—	0	—
20-1a. Colubridae: Xenodermatinae: Xenodermatini																									
Achalinus	5/7	23-34	T/S	176-228	57-84	+	8-21	2-4	24-35	0.6	26-37	22-34	+	0.4-2.9	1.1-1.5	56-66	46-56	0	—	—	—	0	—	—	0	—
Fimbrios	1/1	19	T	168	94	+	3	3	19	—	76	67	+	1.0	0.7	96	82	+	1.5	2.0	+	0.3	1	+	19
Stoliczkia	1/1	29	S	260	89	+	9	2	30	0.4	45	33	+	0.1	0.3	75	54	+	0.8	1.8	0	—	—	+	31
Xenodermus	1/2	29-37	T	282	77	+	17	2-4	30-38	—	27-30	0	+0	1.2	4.5	60-65	46	0	—	—	0	—	—	0	—
Xylophis	2/2	26-36	T	154-189	53-58	+	15-25	3-4	27-37	—	30-43	23-39	+	4.8-6.8	11-22	66-71	58-62	0	—	—	0	—	—	0	—
20-1b. Colubridae: Xenodermatinae: Nothopsini																									
Amastridium	1/1	34	T	228	66	+	18	4	36	—	36	30	+	1.5	4.3	72	58	0	—	—	0	—	—	0	—
Chersodromus	1/2	31	T	146-164	47-55	+	16-18	3-4	31-33	—	33-47	32-34	+	1.5-3.1	4.4-6.6	64-79	54-67	0	—	—	0	—	—	0	—
Diaphorolepis	2/2	23-38	T	200-317	84-88	+	8-22	3	24-39	—	38-67	30-61	+	1.2-1.8	2.7-3.0	78-91	62-77	0	—	—	0	—	—	0	—
Ninia	7/11	26-36	T	147-264	52-79	+	5-24	3-4	28-37	—	25-41	24-40	+	1.3-3.4	4.8-11	55-75	45-63	0	—	—	0	—	—	0	—
Nothopsis	1/2	33-34	T	?	?	+	22	3	38	—	24-26	29-30	+	1.4-1.5	5.6	62-64	48-51	0	—	—	0	—	—	0	—
Synophis	2/5	27-33	T	178-260	59-79	+	10-23	2-4	30-34	—	32-35	25-30	0	—	—	63-68	47-570/+	0.8	2.5	0/+	0.4	1	0/+	28
Xenopholis	2/3	27-37	T/S	165-247	55-67	0/+	20-22	2-3	29-38	0.3	27-40	28-36	+/0	0.6-0.7	1.5-1.9	66-72	43-600/+	0.6	1.5	0/+	0	1	0/+	29
20-2. Colubridae: Pareatinae																									
Aplopeltura	1/2	29-31	T	198-247	68-79	0	—	1	30-33	—	50-57	40-50	+	0.7-0.9	1.4-1.5	83-87	51-58	0	—	—	0	—	—	0	—
Pareas	11/12	16-26	T	112-235	60-105	0	—	1-10	18-28	—	38-63	29-55	+/0	0.7-2.4	0.5-5.3	56-85	40-64+0	0.6-1.4	1.4-3.3	0/+	0	1	+/0	25-29
20-3. Colubridae: Sibynophiinae																									
Scaphiodontophis	1/4	20-25	S	105-176	46-79	0	—	0	22-26	0.6-1.1	45-49	31-38	+	0.6-1.7	1.2-3.9	69-73	46-51	0	—	—	0	—	—	0	—
Sibynophis	6/10	20-25	S	110-207	53-85	0	—	4-11	21-27	0.7-2.2	40-51	30-40	+/0	0.3-2.1	0.6-4.6	61-75	41-58	0	—	—	0	—	—	0	—
20-4a. Colubridae: Lamprophiinae: Lamprophiini																									
Bothrophthalmus	1/18	23-29	S	192-221	82-89	0	—	0-2	23-30	0.3-1.3	34-56	26-40	+(0)	0.2-2.8	0.7-7.1	66-73	34-56+/0	0.2-0.8	0.4-1.9	+/0	0.1-0.3	2-4	+/0	24-30
Goniontophis	3/3	24-31	S	171-214	61-78	0	—	0-2	26-33	0.3-0.9	44-53	38-45	+(0)	0.3-1.0	1.3-1.9	72-79	45-540(+)	0.4	0.7	0(+)	0	1	0(+)	27
Hormonotus	1/2	28-32	T	319	99	0	—	3-9	28-33	—	65-70	57-63	+	0.2-0.7	1.1-2.9	98-99	73-75	+	0.8-1.2	1.2-1.7	0	—	—	+	29-34
Lamprophis	10/168	19-28	T(S)	171-299	80-127	0	—	0-17	20-29	0.7-1.5	32-54	27-46	+	0.6-2.3	1.0-5.1	57-80	33-700(+)	0.1-0.6	0.1-1.5	+/0	0.1-1.2	1-10	+/0	21-30
Lycodonomorphus	4/5	19-25	T	118-194	58-100	0	—	7-17	20-26	—	33-67	22-60	+	0.6-1.9	1.9-5.2	53-90	42-77+/0	0.2-0.8	0.5-2.4	+/0	0.3-1.4	1-4	+/0	21-27
Mehelya	6/58	20-28	S(T)	155-282	70-113	0	—	0-3	22-30	0.4-1.9	46-75	35-64	+/0	0.2-1.5	0.4-2.8	69-98	46-75+(0)	0.2-10	0.5-13	+/0	0.1-0.6	1-6	+(0)	22-30

20-4b. Colubridae: Lamprophiinae: Pseudaspidini

Taxon																									
Duberria	2/2	16-18	T	88	49	0	—	—	3-7	18-20	—	47-48	37-39	+	1.5-5.3	3.3-11	66-69	51-55	0	—	0	—	0	—	—
Grayia	4/181	20-33	S	122-189	60-76	0	—	—	0	20-34	0.4-1.9	32-47	18-33	+/0	0.1-1.2	0.7-3.4	55-70	32-47+(0)	0.3-1.6	0.7-4.0	+;0	0.1-0.5	1-6	+(0)	21-34
Pseudaspis	1/3	23	T	216-222	77-99	0	—	—	1-16	24-25	—	38-47	0	+	13-14	28-36	62-71	41-55	0	—	0	—	0	—	—

20-4c. Colubridae: Lamprophiinae: Pseudoxyrhophiini

Taxon																									
Amplorhinus	1/2	17-18	T	106-145	60-85	0	—	—	10	19	—	36-44	26-34	+	0.8-1.2	2.2-2.8	54-63	46-53	+	0.5-1.0	+;0	0.1-0.5	1-6	+	19-20
Ditypophis	1/2	21	T	140-143	67-68	0	—	—	3-4	23	—	46-47	36-37	+	5.5-9.0	12-19	69	48-49	0	—	+;0	—	—	0	—
Dromicodryas	2/3	20-22	S	168-216	84-106	0	—	—	0-12	21-23	0.7-1.3	54-76	40-67	+	0.4-1.7	0.7-2.2	75-98	64-77	+	0.3-0.4	+/0	0	1	+	22-24
Ithycyphus	3/4	19-25	T	160-211	80-97	0	—	—	2-2	20-26	—	64-65	55-58	+	3.9-6.9	6.0-11	84-92	66-67	+	0.5-1.1	+	0.2-0.3	2-5	+	20-27
Langaha	1/2	28-30	T	213-277	70-99	0	—	—	3	29-32	—	59-62	51-54	+	4.8-6.7	8.1-11	91-92	62-64	0	—	0	—	—	0	—
Leioheterodon	2/2	20-23	S	172-173	77-84	0	—	—	1-3	22-24	1.2-1.4	52-64	43-51	+	0.7-1.8	1.4-2.9	76-86	55-64+0	0.2	0.4	+	0.2-0.4	3-5	+	23-24
Liophidium	2/2	23	T	187-234	82-104	0	—	—	12-19	23-24	—	41-48	25-38	+	1.3-1.9	2.7-4.7	64-71	58-59	+	0.3-0.9	+	0	1	+	24
Liopholidophis	4/7	20-22	S;T	145-189	69-96	+;0	—	7-13	2-6	21-24	0.9-23	39-59	30-47	+	0.2-2.1	0.3-5.3	61-80	44-72	+	0.6-0.9	+/0	0.2	1-2	+	21-24
Madagascarophis	2/2	21-24	T	234-268	109-114	0	—	—	2-3	23-25	—	51-52	43-44	+	2.2-2.5	4.2-4.8	74-77	53	+	0.2-1.0	+	0.2-0.3	5-6	+	23-26
Pseudoxyrhopus	1/2	21-22	T	133-152	63-72	0	—	—	9-10	22	—	34-39	26-28	+	1.1-1.8	3.2-4.6	57-61	44-48	+	0.4-0.7	+;0	0.2	1	+	22-23
Pythonodipsas	1/2	24-26	T	275-344	118-134	0	—	—	2-3	25-27	—	39-40	27	+	13	31-33	64-67	42	+;0	0.3	+	0.6-0.7	1	+	25-28
Stenophis	1/3	28-29	T	264-293	91-101	0	—	—	1-13	29-30	—	53-60	46-52	+	1.2-1.6	2.0-3.0	83-90	61-74	+	0.3-0.6	+	0.2	1	+	30-31

20-4d. Colubridae: Lamprophiinae: Lycophidini

Taxon																									
Alluaudina	1/1	31	T	227	74	+	—	17	2	31	—	35	35	+	7.6	22	66	54	0	—	0	—	—	0	—
Bothrolycus	1/1	30	T	193	64	+	—	20	4	32	—	35	31	+	0.8	2.4	68	58	0	—	0	—	—	0	—
Chamaelycus	3/4	26-28	T	142-216	55-81	+	—	16-18	3	28-30	—	40-64	35-58	+	0.6-1.8	1.5-3.8	68-91	60-84	0	—	0	—	—	0	—
Cryptolycus	1/1	29	T	233	81	+	—	17	3	30	—	41	38	+	4.6	11.2	71	60	0	—	0	—	—	0	—
Dendrolycus	1/1	36	S	364	101	+	—	18	2	37	0.3	50	44	+	0.3	0.5	86	69	0	—	0	—	—	0	—
Buhoma	3/3	29	T	124-167	42-57	+	—	14-18	3	30-31	—	36-42	35-45	+	1.9-5.6	5.0-14	66-73	57-59	0	—	0	—	—	+	30
Helophis	1/1	28	T	?	?	+	—	10	4	29	—	39	22	+	2.1	5.3	68	53	+	0.5	0	—	—	0	—
Lycophidion	9/46	28-33	T	160-323	52-98	+	—	15-22	2-4	29-35	—	32-67	26-58	+/0	0.2-5.1	0.7-16	63-94	51-88	0	1.2	0	—	—	+	30
Montaspis	1/1	24	T	135	57	+	—	10	4	26	—	40	35	+	1.0	1.6	66	55	+	0.5	0	—	—	0	—
Prosymna	8/16	21-28	T	106-184	51-75	+	—	12-17	3-4	22-31	—	27-57	18-48	+	1.1-17.5	2.7-67	57-82	39-75	0	1.2	0	0.2	2	+	26
Pseudoboodon	2/3	25-31	T	236-294	82-112	+	—	15-19	3	27-32	—	33-34	30-34	+	3.0-4.4	8.8-13	61-65	53-56	0	—	0	—	—	0	—

20-5. Colubridae: Psammophiinae

Taxon																									
Dipsina	1/1	19	T	176	93	0	—	—	4	21	—	48	27	+	4.1	8.5	69	52	0	—	0	—	—	+	—

Genus	S/N	T	TE	TTR	NTR	TL	TLL	CL	HT	RAL	RL	SL	RB	RBL	RB/RL	RPT	L	LL	LLL	LL/RL	LB	LBL	LBR	LO	LOM
Dromophis	2/8	22-26	T	183-230	77-93	0	—	0-1	23-28	—	59-76	21-68	+/0	0.2-1.1	0.3-1.7	84-98	59-76	0/+	0.2	0.3	0/+	0.4-0.6	1-2	0/+	23-28
Hemirhagerrhis	2/2	20-21	S:T	170	83	0	—	0-2	21-22	1.0	46-58	39-49	+	1.4-1.7	3.0	67-79	46-60	+0	0.3	0.7	0	0	—	+/0	22
Malpolon	2/3	17-23	T	226-365	101-136	0	—	2-3	24-29	—	48-63	36-49	+	0.6-1.4	1.3-2.2	76-86	50-65	0	—	—	0/+	0	1	0/+	24
Mimophis	1/1	22	T	175	80	0	—	1	23	—	60	52	+	1.4	2.2	84	61	0	—	—	0	—	—	+	24
Psammophis	20/44	20-29	T	130-403	62-164	0	—	0-2	21-31	—	52-73	43-65	+(0)	0.2-1.7	0.3-2.5	78-99	53-74	0	—	—	+/0	0.1-0.8	1-12	+/0	21-3
Psammophylax	3/3	18-22	T	140-142	76-77	0	—	2-3	20-24	—	66-76	57-69	+	0.9-2.4	1.1-3.6	86-96	68-79	0	—	—	0	—	—	0	—
Rhamphiophis	3/3	20	T	150-304	76-152	0	—	1-2	21-22	—	56-73	47-63	+	0.5-1.1	0.9-1.5	77-93	57-74	0	—	—	0	—	—	0	—
20-6a. Colubridae: Xenodontinae: Pseudoboini																									
Clelia	6/7	20-25	T	202-325	91-132	0	—	1-15	22-26	—	36-44	25-31	+	1.0-20.0	2.8-5.5	59-66	37-52	0/+	0.5-1.0	1.4-2.5	0/+	0.2	2	0/+	22-23
Drepanoides	1/1	24	T	192	79	0	—	3	26	—	56	45	+	0.3	0.7	81	59	+	0.2	0.4	+	0.3	4	+	26
Oxyrhopus	9/15	21-27	T	159-242	61-105	0	—	1-10	22-28	—	32-64	24-56	+(0)	0.4-1.4	1.2-3.7	57-90	39-66	+	0.2-0.8	0.4-2.0	+	0.1-0.4	1-8	+	23-28
O. marcapatae	1/1	27	T	187	69	0	—	3	29	—	39	29	+	0.5	1.3	68	42	0	—	—	0	—	—	0	—
Phimophis	3/3	23-24	T	214-285	89-121	0	—	11-14	25-26	—	42-45	30-34	+	1.8-3.5	4.1-7.9	68-70	55-58	0/+	0.4	0.8	+/0	0.2-0.3	2	+/0	26
Pseudoboa	4/5	21-23	T	190-213	82-96	0	—	1-14	23-25	—	34-42	25-35	+	0.3-2.0	0.8-5.0	59-65	38-56	+/0	0.2-0.8	1.6-2.2	+	0.2-0.3	1-5	+	22-25
Rhachidelus	1/1	20	T	226	111	0	—	14	22	—	51	39	+	2.1	4.1	73	65	+	0.7	1.4	+	0.4	7	+	22
Siphlophis	2/2	23-28	T	227-253	90-98	0	—	1-10	24-29	—	50-53	43-44	+	0.7-1.3	1.5-2.4	75-82	54-60	+	0.6	1.1-1.2	+/0	0.2	2	+/0	24-30
Tripanurgos	1/1	31	T	268	88	0	—	1	32	—	49	42	+	0.9	1.8	81	50	+	0.9	1.9	+	0	1	+	32
20-6b. Colubridae: Xenodontinae: Alsophiini																									
Alsophis	2/3	22-25	T	154-243	69-96	+/0	13	1-3	23-27	—	29-44	18-35	+	1.5-2.1	2.2-7.5	67-70	29-59	0/+	0.2	0.4	0/+	0.1	2	0/+	28
Antillophis	2/3	19-21	T	136-164	67-88	0	—	1-11	20-23	—	42-50	33-39	+	1.2-2.9	1.2-6.8	62-74	43-61	+/0	0.4-0.6	0.7-1.2	+/0	0	1	+/0	23
Arrhyton	3/4	20-23	T	138-147	64-67	0	—	3-12	21-24	—	35-49	27-38	+/0	0.5-1.4	1.1-3.7	56-73	38-61	0/+	1.3	2.7	0/+	0.3	2	0/+	24
Darlingtonia	1/1	23	T	137	60	+	11	3	25	—	42	36	+	0.4	1.0	67	57	0	—	—	0	—	—	0	—
Hypsirhynchus	1/1	24	T	192	79	0	—	13	26	—	42	0	+	1.3	3.0	68	56	+	0.5	1.2	+	0.4	3	+	26
Ialtris	2/3	19-21	T	134-174	64-92	0	—	7	20-22	—	39-45	29-37	+	0.4-0.9	1.0-2.3	59-68	45-53	0/+	0.3-0.5	0.7-1.0	+/0	0.3	3-4	+/0	20-22
Manolepis	1/1	23	T	175	76	0	—	3	24	—	47	37	+	1.4	3.0	72	50	+	0.6	1.3	+	0.1	3	+	25
Uromacer	4/6	22-27	T	203-277	88-104	0	—	1-12	23-28	—	51-71	42-64	+	0.4-1.2	0.6-2.1	74-99	52-81	+	0.4-1.6	0.6-3.1	+	0.1-0.3	1-5	+	23-29
Galapagos Is. n. gen.	3/3	17-22	T	116-206	93-116	0	—	1-6	19-23	—	43-49	33-40	+/0	0.6-2.5	1.2-3.5	66-71	49-50	+	0.4-0.6	0.8-1.2	+	0.2-0.4	3-4	+	20-23
20-6c. Colubridae: Xenodontinae: Philodryadini																									
Echinanthera	2/2	23-24	T	165-170	71-73	0	—	11	24-25	—	46-58	36-48	+	0.9	1.5-2.0	71-82	57-69	0	—	—	0	—	—	0	—

Taxon																								
Hydrodynastes	2/2	20-26	T	234-270	105-118	0	—	2	21-28	—	23-25	0-5	+	22	86-96	44-53	24-27	0	—	+/0	0.1	3	+/0	28
Philodryas	11/16	18-24	T	150-246	67-122	0	—	0-13	20-25	—	35-74	22-62	+	1.0-12	17-31	56-95	36-820/+	0.4-0.5	0.7	+/0	0.2-0.6	1-9	+/0	21-24
Pseudablabes	1/1	22	T	157	71	0	—	3	24	—	42	32	+	2.7	6.4	66	45	0	—	0	—	—	0	—
Psomophis	1/1	19	T	165	87	0	—	13	20	—	42	34	+	2.8	6.6	62	55	0	—	0	—	—	0	—
Saphenophis	1/1	17	T	120	72	0	—	1	18	—	44	33	+	1.3	3.1	62	44	0	+	+	0.5	6	+	19
Sordellina	1/1	25	T	150	61	0	—	13	26	—	34	19	+	1.4	4.0	60	47	0	—	0	—	—	0	—
Tropidodryas	2/2	20-22	T	182-188	87-89	0	—	2-3	22-23	—	42-57	30-31	+	0.8-1.0	1.9	65-79	45-60	0	—	0	—	—	0/i	22
Uromacerina	1/1	31	T	190	61	+	23	3	32	—	59	52	+	0.7	1.1	92	86	+	0.7	+	0.3	4	+	33
Xenoxybelis	1/1	25	T	279	101	0	—	2	29	—	62	55	+	0.6	0.9	91	64	+	0.2	+	—	—	+	29
Peru n. gen.	1/1	20	T	156	80	0	—	0	21	—	57	45	+	0.8	1.3	78	57	0	—	0	—	—	0	—

20-6d. Colubridae: Xenodontinae: Tachymenini

Taxon																								
Pseudotomodon	1/1	18	T	126	69	+	4	3	19	0.4-2.0	41	34	+	2.5	5.8	62	50	0	—	+	0.1	2	+	21
Tachymenis	2/2	15-19	T	122-128	69-79	+	—	9	17-20	—	31-43	22-32	+	1.0	2.2-3.4	48-64	40-52+	0.6-0.8	1.5-2.5	+/0	0.3	3	+	18-21
Thamnodynastes	3/4	19-25	T	118-155	61-63	0	—	0-3	21-26	—	36-55	28-43	+	0.3-1.8	0.5-3.8	58-77	39-55	0	—	0	—	—	0/i	21
Tomodon	2/5	16-17	T	110-161	67-93	0	—	2-3	17-19	—	45-62	39-54	+	0.6-1.5	1.2-2.4	63-80	49-65+/0	0.5-1.0	0.8-2.3	+/0	0.1-0.4	2-3	+/0	18-19

20-6e. Colubridae: Xenodontinae: Xenodontini

Taxon																								
Conophis	2/21	19-24	S/T	119	62	0	—	3-16	19-25	—	40-52	26-43	+/0	0.2-2.3	0.4-4.6	62-75	42-680/+	0.4-0.8	0.8-1.6	+/0	0.2-0.6	?	+(0)	20-25
Erythrolamprus	3/3	18-19	T	173-192	91-107	0	—	0-5	19-20	—	41-43	33-35	+	1.1-1.4	2.6-3.2	61-64	42-45	0.4-0.5	0.5-1.2	+/0	0.1-0.2	2-3	+	20-21
Liophis	11/15	17-22	T	116-154	58-81	0	—	1-12	19-23	—	29-46	18-36	+	0.5-5.9	1.5-6.3	51-66	31-56+/0	0.2-1.8	0.5-5.2	+/0	0.1-0.5	1-9	+	19-24
Lystrophis	3/3	18-21	T	98-134	48-76	0	—	2-10	20-23	—	36-49	24-40	+	1.9-6.7	4.2-14	56-69	45-59+/s	0.02-1.1	0.4-3.0	+/0	0.2	1-2	+/0	20-23
Umbrivaga	2/2	20-21	T	120-126	59-61	0	—	5-8	22-23	—	33-38	23-28	+	1.5	4.1-4.5	56-61	38-47s/0	0.2	0.3	+/0	0	1	+/0	23
Waglerophis	1/3	20-23	T	112-118	51-56	0	—	7-11	22-26	—	43-63	30-52	+	0.8-1.5	1.9-2.3	68-86	53-70	0.8-1.8	1.9-3.0	+	0.2-0.3	1-2	+	22-25
Xenodon	5/10	17-32	T	82-120	45-70	0	—	2-4	18-34	—	39-67	28-58	+	0.6-2.2	1.1-4.9	57-88	44-73+(0)	0.5-2.3	0.8-3.3	+/0	0.2-0.3	1-4	+/0i	i19-34

20-6f. Colubridae: Xenodontinae: Hydropsini

Taxon																								
Helicops	12/13	22-38	T	107-231	43-85	+(0)	2-17	4-5	23-39	—	25-41	0-31	+	0.2-6.1	0.6-2.0	52-81	35-62+/0	0.2-1.4	0.6-3.4	+/0	0.1-0.5	1-5	+/0	23-31
Hydrops	2/4	32-36	T	274-337	86-104	+	20-23	3	33-37	—	35-41	19-29	+	2.3-17	6.5-48	69-74	58-63	0	—	0	—	—	—	—
Pseudoeryx	1/1	23	T	137	60	0	—	3	24	—	48	26	+	29	59	72	51	0	—	0	—	—	—	—

20-6g. Colubridae: Xenodontinae: Elapomorphini

Taxon																								
Apostolepis	7/8	20-30	T	185-310	80-155	+/0	12-15	2-4	21-32	—	18-71	8-53	+	0.3-2.1	0.9-5.4	40-93	32-850/s	0.3	0.8	0/+	0	1	0/+	32
Elapomorphus	2/4	23-28	T	180-240	65-100	0/+	6-10	2-4	25-29	—	25-45	15-36	+	0.7-1.9	17-7.1	58-71	25-54	0	—	0	—	—	0/+	29
Phalotris	3/4	23-26	T	218-253	90-108	+	11-13	2-3	24-27	—	38-65	27-53	+	1.0-2.2	1.5-5.8	64-89	48-81	0	—	0	—	—	0	—

Genus	S/N	T	TE	TTR	NTR	TL	TLL	CL	HT	RAL	RL	SL	RB	RBL	RB/RL	RPT	L	LL	LLL	LL/RL	LB	LBL	LBR	LO	LOM
20-7. Colubridae: Calamariinae																									
Calamaria	26/32	22-31	T(SP)	125-288	54-112	0	—	1-15	23-32	1.4-1.6	28-54	18-47	+	0.4-2.3	0.9-8.0	56-82	31-65	+	0.6-2.7	1.4-6.7	0+	0	1	+	22-34
Calamorhabdium	1/1	33	T	330	101	+	?	2	34	—	23	15	+	8.9	38	57	?	0	—	—	0	—	—	0	—
Collorhabdium	1/1	26	T	156	60	0	—	4	27	—	35	25	+	2.0	5.8	62	39	+	1.0	2.9	0	—	—	+	29
Elapoidis	1/1	22	S	130	58	0	—	2	24	1.4	46	35	+	1.6	3.6	69	48	+	0.8	1.8	+	—	1	+	25
Macrocalamus	1/1	27	T	237	88	+	13	3	28	—	31	27	+	0.9	2.9	58	47	0	—	—	—	—	—	0	—
Oreocalamus	1/1	20	T	?	?	0	—	2	21	—	49	38	+	1.3	2.6	70	51	+	1.3	2.6	+	0.3	1	+	21
Pseudorabdion	7/9	26-34	T	146-273	43-93	+	9-28	2-4	27-36	—	28-46	19-36	+	0.6-8.2	1.7-27	58-76	42-65+/0	+	1.0-1.9	1.9-5.0	:/0	0	1	+/0	27-32
Rabdion	1/2	25-27	T	183-190	71-74	0	—	4-9	26-28	—	32-36	22-29	+	0.9-1.4	0.8-4.4	60-62	40-41	+	1.4-2.4	4.4-6.7	+/0	0	1	+	26-29
20-8. Colubridae: Homalopsinae																									
Bitia	1/2	32-34	S	275	87	0	—	8-17	33-35	0.6-1.0	37-41	3-13	+	1.9-2.4	4.8-5.5	70-75	43-57+/0	0	0.5	1.2	+/0	0.2	2	+/0	35
Brachyorrhos	1/1	27	T	196	72	0	—	6	28	—	36	24	+	0.8	2.1	64	42	0	—	—	0	—	—	0	—
Cantoria	2/2	22-26	S/T	188-249	71-113	+	12-16	2	23-27	0.7	20-32	0	+	0.5-1.3	2.7-6.3	47-55	38-46+/0	0	0.5	1.6	+/0	0.1	2	+/0	23
Cerberus	3/5	34-36	T	199-328	56-93	+	19-23	3-4	35-37	—	23-31	0	+	0.4-1.4	1.6-5.7	60-65	49-54	0	—	—	0	—	—	0	—
Enhydris	13/14	23-46	T/S	183-349	54-94	+	8-25	3-5	24-48	0.6-0.9	26-38	0/21-29	+(0)	0.9-4.8	2.8-15	58-79	45-61+/0	+	0.3-2.0	0.8-4.2	+/0	0.2-0.3	1-4	+/0	25-47
Erpeton	1/1	42	T	290	70	+	13	5	43	—	41	29	+	0.4	1.0	85	60	0	—	3.0	0	—	4	0	—
Fordonia	1/1	26	S	179	68	+	11	3	28	0.5	27	0	+	2.4	9.1	54	41	+	0.8	3.0	+	0.3	4	+	29
Gerarda	1/2	23-26	S/T	103-158	60-67	+	11-12	3-4	25-27	1.5	28-43	0-38	+	1.1-1.8	2.5-6.5	54-67	42-58	+	0.4-0.5	1.3-1.6	+	0.3-0.5	3-4	+	25-28
Homalopsis	1/2	33-34	S/T	258-287	77-88	+	18-19	2-4	34-35	0.8	20-24	0	+	1.3-4.8	5.7-10	55-58	42-44+/0	+	1.8	8.5	0	—	—	+/0	38
Myron	1/1	24	T	211	87	+	14	3	29	—	22	7	+	1.9	8.9	51	38	0	—	—	—	—	—	0	—
20-9a. Colubridae: Dipsadinae: Heterodontini																									
Carphophis	1/2	20-24	P/T	132-137	55-69	0	—	0-1	21-25	1.0	34-37	19-24	+	1.0-1.5	2.8-4.1	55-62	35-38	0	—	—	0	—	—	0	—
Contia	1/1	17	S	195	112	0	—	2	19	0.4	58	50	+	1.3	2.3	76	60	+	1.1	1.9	+	0.5	1	+	20
Diadophis	1/4	20-22	S	126-187	59-84	0	—	12-13	21-23	0.4-1.1	41-50	17-35	+	0.4-2.3	0.8-4.6	64-72	54-62+/0	+	0.3-0.9	0.7-2.1	+	0.3	1-2	+/i	21-25
Farancia	2/3	22-24	T	168-199	71-92	0	—	3-12	23-25	—	30-43	0	0	2.3-2.6	5.2-8.7	56-69	32-52	+	0.8-1.5	2.1-4.9	+	0.1	1-2	+	24-27
Heterodon	3/5	21-22	S	130-147	61-69	0	—	0	23-25	12-17	41-48	0	+/0	1.4-3.3	2.9-7.9	64-72	54-64	+	0.7-2.1	1.7-4.4	+	0.3-0.5	1-6	+	24-26
20-9b. Colubridae: Dipsadinae: Geophiini (n.t.)																									
Adelphicos	2/6	20-25	T	130-172	57-81	0	—	7-15	21-27	—	38-44	28-35	+	1.0-1.9	2.3-4.4	61-68	50-57	+	1.0-1.5	1.8-3.6	+	0.2	1-2	+	22-28
Atractus	36/41	18-28	T(P)	117-230	45-88	0(+)	11-17	1-15	19-29	—	23-46	21-38	+	0.5-2.2	1.3-6.2	54-71	36-57+/0	+	0.3-2.5	0.7-5.1	+/0	0.2-0.3	1-3	+/0	20-30

Abractus latifrons group	2/2	21-23	T	169-180	77-81	0	—	1	22-24	—	36-38	27-30	+	1.8-1.9	4.4-4.8	62-63	40-41	+	0.9-1.1	2.5-2.8	+/0	0.2	1	+	23-26
Coniophanes	6/9	15-24	T	117-162	50-107	0	—	2-13	16-26	—	33-62	20-52	+/0	0.8-1.6	12-4.9	48-87	34-650/+	0.5-0.8	1.1-2.1	0/+	0.2-0.5	1-4	+/0	17-26
Enuliophis	1/1	23	T	160	70	0	—	7	24	—	40	33	+	0.7	1.7	65	48	+	0.5	1.2	0	—	—	+	25
Enulius	1/3	17-18	S/T	150	90	0	—	1-11	18-19	1.7	38-44	26-35	+/0	6.3-8.6	14-23	56-63	38-500/+	0.3	0.7	0	—	—	0/+	18
Geophis	10/13	22-28	T	112-237	46-89	0	—	3-16	23-29	—	29-48	22-42	+	0.3-1.9	0.7-5.7	56-74	30-520+	0.5-1.7	1.2-3.6	0/+	0.1-0.3	1-3	0/+	25-29
Hydromorphus	1/2	23-24	T	189-244	84-101	0	—	14-16	24-25	—	33-37	0	+	2.0-2.2	5.3-6.6	57-62	49-51	0	—	—	0	—	0	0	—
Ptiocercus	2/2	21-24	T	108-141	50-61	0	—	7-8	23-25	—	37-45	29-35	+	0.7-1.8	1.9-4.0	61-68	44-53+0	0.7	1.6	+	0.2	2-4	+	24-25
Rhadinaea	7/7	24-33	T/S	144-255	56-78	+	13-21	2-4	26-34	0.4	35-44	27-36	+	0.3-2.8	0.8-7.2	65-75	56-620/+	0.7-0.9	1.5-2.5	0/+	0.2	1-2	0/+/i	26-30
Rhinobothryum	2/2	24-26	T	227-295	88-121	+	—	1-2	25-27	—	63-71	54-63	+0	0.5	0.7	90-97	65-73	+	1.5-1.6	2.2-2.4	+	0.2-0.4	2-3	+	25-27
Taeniophallus	1/1	22	T	154	70	0	—	11	23	—	40	33	+	0.7	1.7	63	51	0	—	—	0	—	—	+	23
Tretanorhinus	4/4	23-29	T	152-226	60-90	0	—	7-14	24-30	—	27-37	0[-23]	+	0.7-2.0	1.6-6.6	53-60	36-48	0	—	—	—	—	—	+	23
Trimetopon	4/5	29-32	T	171-243	53-80	+	17-23	3-4	31-34	—	27-40	15-31	+	1.0-1.6	2.9-49	61-73	54-61	0	—	—	0	—	—	0	—
Tropidodipsas	5/7	21-25	T	134-210	56-84	0	—	1-3	22-27	—	43-51	35-42	+	0.4-2.0	0.9-4.2	66-77	46-53+/0	0.6-1.1	1.2-2.4	0+	0.2-0.3	1-4	+/0	22-26
Urotheca	1/1	25	S	?	?	0	—	0	26	1.4	46	36	+	0.9	2.0	72	47	?	?	?	0	—	—	+	27
20-9c. Colubridae: Dipsadinae: Dipsadini																								
Dipsas	17/20	22-42	T(S)	139-342	62-97	+	9-25	2-3	23-44	0.7	42-65	35-57	+/0	0.2-3.1	0.3-7.6	70-91	57-780+	0.2-21	0.5-21	0+	0.1-0.5	1-5	0+/i	23-39
Sibon	6/8	21-38	T	91-297	30-98	+	10-20	2-3	22-39	—	31-48	24-47	+/0	0.6-1.6	1.2-4.1	56-87	44-71+/0	s0.2-2.30	0.5-5.1	+/0	0.1-0.6	1-3	+0	25-39
Sibynomorphus	4/4	28-32	T	174-249	64-88	+	15-16	3	28-32	—	40-53	41-47	+	1.0-2.0	1.9-4.5	71-83	59-72	0	—	—	+/0	—	1-3	0	—
20-9d. Colubridae: Dipsadinae: Leptodeirini																								
Crisantophis	1/1	17	T	?	?	0	—	7	19	—	77	68	0	—	—	96	84	0	—	—	0	—	—	0	—
Cryophis	1/2	25-26	T	192-228	76-89	0	—	5-10	27	—	57-58	49-50	+	1.0-1.6	1.7-2.6	84-87	63-71	+	0.3-0.5	0.5-0.8	+/0	0	1	+	27-28
Eridiphas	1/2	24	T	233-237	97-98	+	14	2-3	26	—	40-41	34-35	+	2.1-2.4	5.2-5.9	66-67	56-57	0	—	—	0	—	0	+	27-28
Hypsiglena	2/3	25-27	T	200-252	75-98	+	14-16	3	27-28	—	37-42	31-36	+	1.1-2.6	2.8-6.0	64-69	54-61	0	—	—	0	—	0	+	—
Imantodes	5/6	28-42	T	208-437	75-112	0	—	1-10	29-43	—	48-62	40-55	+	0.5-1.3	0.9-2.1	80-95	53-64	+	0.4-0.6	0.7-1.3	+/0	0.2-0.3	1-4	+	29-43
Leptodeira	6/13	21-29	T/P	155-216	70-85	0	—	4-17	23-30	—	28-49	18-41	+/0	0.5-2.0	0.8-6.4	56-74	34-60+/0	0.3-12	0.7-2.5	+/0	0.2-0.5	1-2	+(0)	24-31
Pseudoleptodeira	1/1	23	T	199	88	0	—	4	24	—	46	40	+	1.9	4.1	70	50	0	—	—	0	—	3	+	—
Rhadinophanes	1/1	19	T	151	78	0	—	13	21	—	48	40	+	1.5	3.2	69	61	+	0.6	1.3	+	0.2	2	+	21
Tantalophis	1/1	20	T	165	84	0	—	8	21	—	50	43	+	0.7	1.3	71	58	+	0.9	1.8	+	0.1	2	+	21
20-9e. Colubridae: Dipsadinae: Boigini																								
Boiga	20/21	21-36	T	196-462	71-153	0	—	1-6	22-36	—	58-75	53-66	+(0)	0.2-0.9	0.1-1.5	92-99	59-81	+	0.3-5.5	0.4-7.6	+/0	0.1-0.5	1-10	+	22-36
Crotaphopeltis	5/85	20-24	T	120-164	59-78	0	—	2-16	20-26	—	44-74	42-61	+	0.2-2.3	0.3-22	74-95	53-80	+	0.3-1.3	0.5-1.9	+/0	0.1-0.3	2-6	+	21-24

Genus	S/N	T	TE	TTR	NTR	TL	TLL	CL	HT	RAL	RL	SL	RB	RBL	RB/RL	RPT	L	LL	LLL	LL/RL	LB	LBL	LBR	LO	LOM
Dipsadoboa	6/11	23-33	T	143-251	66-86	0	—	0-2	23-34	—	60-70	51-63	+	0.5-2.0	0.8-3.2	84-95	61-70+(0)	0.4-1.1	—	0.9-1.7	+/0	0.1-0.3	1-5	+(0)	24-34
Macroprotodon	1/1	24	T	193	80	0	—	4	26	—	48	42	+	1.4	2.9	73	52	0	—	—	0	—	—	0	—
Telescopus	7/11	19-22	T	157-286	71-135	0	—	2-8	20-24	—	51-69	42-62	+	0.3-1.9	0.5-3.0	72-91	52-74+/0	0.1-0.7	—	0.2-1.3	+/0	0.1-0.5	1-2	+/0	21-24
Toxicodryas	2/25	22-30	T	201-332	89-128	0	—	1-2	23-30	—	66-75	57-68	+(0)	0.1-0.9	0.5-1.2	92-99	68-76	1.4-8.3	—	2.0-12	+/0	0.1-0.4	1-6	+	23-31
20-10a. Colubridae: Colubrinae: Lycodontini																								
Ceraspis	1/3	30-31	S	184-245	61-85	0	—	1-3	30-32	1.0-1.4	52-54	43	+	0.7-1.7	1.4-3.1	84	54-56	0.9-1.2	—	1.7-2.2	+	0.2-0.3	1-3	+	31-32
Dinodon	4/5	20-24	T/S	179-227	77-114	0	—	0-2	21-25	0.7-1.2	46-65	36-57	+	0.8-1.2	1.2-2.5	66-88	47-65	0.5-0.9	—	0.8-1.9	+	0.1-0.4	2-5	+	21-25
Dryocalamus	4/4	25-26	S/T	236-300	89-120	0	—	1-19	25-28	0.5-1.3	64-72	56-65	+	0.5-1.8	0.7-2.8	90-98	69-84	0.7-1.3	—	1.0-1.9	+	0.1	1-2	+	26-28
Lepturophis	1/1	30	T	328	107	0	—	0	31	—	65	56	0	—	—	96	65	0.8	—	1.3	0	—	—	+	31
Lycodon	10/15	23-31	S:T(P)	165-302	70-106	0	—	1-7	23-32	0.6-0.9	49-68	40-61	+	0.2-1.5	0.4-2.8	74-98	55-71+/0	0.2-1.8	—	0.4-2.6	+/0	0.1-0.4	2-4	+/0	23-32
20-10b. Colubridae: Colubrinae: Oligodontini																								
Oligodon	36/41	18-24	S/T(P)	103-202	50-97	0	—	2-15	21-30	0.3-3.3	29-78	21-70	+(0)	0.3-2.1	0.5-5.2	51-95	31-83+/0	0.3-1.7	—	0.4-2.7	+/0	0.1-0.5	1-5	+/0	20-30
Rhynchocalamus	2/2	21-23	T	182-192	82-89	0	—	1-11	22-25	—	37-44	28-35	+	0.4-0.7	1.0-2.0	61-66	38-55	0	—	—	+/0	0.2	1	+/0	22
20-10c. Colubridae: Colubrinae: Colubrini																								
Aeluroglena	1/1	27	T	220	82	0	—	11	28	—	59	44	+	1.1	1.9	87	70	0	—	—	0	—	—	0	—
Argyrogena	1/1	21	T	235	111	0	—	8	22	—	53	43	0	—	—	75	61	0	—	—	0	—	—	0	—
Chironius	8/9	22-27	T/S	173-272	73-107	0	—	0-2	22-28	1.3	61-77	52-66	+	0.2-1.4	0.4-2.0	90-99	63-77+/0	0.2-4.1	—	0.3-6.1	+/0	0.1-0.3	1-10	+/0	23-29
Chrysopelea	6/13	19-30	T(P)	202-339	75-146	0	—	1-3	20-30	—	68-73	59-63	+	0.2-1.0	0.3-1.5	91-99	70-74+(0)	0.3-1.4	—	0.4-2.1	0/+	0.3	1-3	+	21-31
Coluber	21/28	20-28	S/T/P	157-457	74-164	0	—	0-7	21-29	0.2-1.8	41-72	31-64	+(0)	0.2-2.2	0.2-4.0	67-98	41-70(+)	0.2-1.0	—	0.2-1.7	0/+	0.1-0.4	1-6	0/+/1	22-26
Coronella	2/3	22-26	T	138-191	62-80	0	—	1-16	24-28	—	38-49	28-39	+	1.7-3.3	4.2-6.6	68-76	40-67	0.4-0.6	—	0.8-1.4	+	0.5	1-6	+	18-21
Cyclophiops	3/3	16-20	S	152-195	91-99	0	—	0-8	18-21	0.8-1.0	46-74	36-65	+	0.5-1.1	0.7-2.1	67-92	47-80	0.5-0.8	—	0.7-1.4	0	—	1-6	0/+	22
Dendrophidion	7/7	20-27	T	134-198	53-83	0	—	0-1	21-28	—	56-71	45-61	+/0	0.5-1.5	0.6-2.3	84-99	57-720/+	1.0	—	1.4	0	—	1-6	0/+	22
Dryadophis	6/7	21-26	T/S	185-243	80-102	0	—	0-7	22-28	0.3-1.4	60-70	50-61	+	0.5-1.0	0.7-1.2	87-96	62-72	0.4-0.9	—	0.6-1.4	+	0.2-0.4	1-6	+	22-28
Drymarchon	1/8	19-24	S	161-182	68-94	0	—	1-2	20-25	0.3-1.0	45-66	34-54	+	0.6-1.6	1.1-3.6	68-87	45-67	1.0-1.6	—	1.6-2.6	+	0.2-0.3	2-4	+	21-25
Drymobius	1/8	19-23	S:T	115-142	52-76	0	—	1-6	20-25	0.1-0.8	48-73	35-64	+/0	0.3-2.2	0.5-4.4	72-93	48-74+/0	0.8-1.1	—	1.1-2.1	+/0	0.1-0.2	1-3	+	21-25
Drymoluber	2/2	23-24	S	234-324	75-101	0	—	0-1	24-25	0.8-1.2	60-68	52-58	+	0.1-0.6	0.2-1.0	87-92	62-69	0.6-1.3	—	0.9-2.2	+	0.1-0.2	3-4	+	24-25
Drymophiops	2/2	29-32	S	223-256	78-79	0	—	0	30-33	—	61-62	55-57	+	0.2-0.7	0.3-1.1	92-94	61-62+/0	1.0	—	1.7	+	0.5	1-6	0/+	22
Eirenis	9/9	21-25	T/S/P	120-238	53-97	0	—	1-18	22-26	0.3-1.4	42-68	32-60	+	0.7-2.6	1.5-4.0	66-91	45-69	0	—	—	0	—	—	+/0	33
Elaphe (Old World)	29/50	17-32	S(T/P)	144-327	67-125	0	—	0-7	19-33	0.3-1.4	38-73	29-63	+/0	0.3-5.9	0.5-11	60-96	38-77+(0)	0.1-1.4	—	0.3-2.9	+(0)	0.1-0.5	1-9	+(0)	19-33
Gongylosoma	3/3	22-26	T/S	87-142	35-57	0	—	10-16	24-28	1.1	48-55	37-46	+	0.6-1.3	1.2-2.3	72-83	56-71	0.4-0.9	—	0.6-1.6	+/0	0.6	1-5	+/i	24-29

Gomyophis	1/1	21	S	203	97	—	0	0	22	0.3	75	67	+	1.4	1.9	98	76	1.7	2.3	+	0.3	3	+	22
Leptodrymus	1/2	24-26	S:T	250	106	—	0	3-10	25-27	1.2	65-70	52-59	+0	0.8	1.2	90-96	73-75	0.5	0.7	+0	0.3	5	+	25-27
Liochlorophis	1/1	18	S	88	49	—	0	6	19	1.1	67	56	+	1.2	1.8	87	73	1.1	1.6	+	0.1	1	+	20
Liopeltis	5/5	20-27	S:T/P	117-177	56-85	—	0	2-11	21-28	0.6-1.7	56-68	47-61	+	0.9-1.3	1.2-2.1	82-90	62-73+/0	0.9-1.0	1.2-1.6	+/0	0.1-0.3	1-3	+/0	22-28
Lytorhynchus	4/4	19-25	T	186-328	95-143	—	0	7-12	20-27	—	47-63	38-48	+	0.6-17	1.3-27	73-83	50-69	—	—	0	—	—	0	—
Masticophis	7/18	20-25	S(T)	211-320	105-144	—	0	0-2	21-27	0.4-1.2	61-75	52-64	+(0)	0.1-1.8	0.2-17	87-97	62-88	0.4-1.1	0.6-1.4	+(0)	0.1-0.3	1-6	+	21-27
Mastigodryas	1/1	23	T	188	81	—	0	0	25	—	61	50	+	1.0	1.7	85	61	1.2	2.0	+	0.4	4	+	29
Meizodon	4/5	20-23	S:P/T	147-266	71-113	—	0	0-8	22-25	0.3-1.3	44-56	35-45	+/0	0.3-12	0.6-22	68-80	47-65	0	0	0	—	—	0/+	24
Opheodrys	1/2	23-24	S:T	150-168	64-71	—	0	1-2	24-25	0.4	62-63	52-54	+	0.2-13	1.2-21	87	63-65	0.7-1.1	1.2-1.7	+	0.1-0.2	1	+	25
Oxybelis	3/1	26-32	T/S	275-279	91-98	—	0	0-2	28-33	0.8-1.2	64-69	54-62	+/0	0.2-0.7	1.2-2.1	94-98	65-70+/0	0.6-1.6	0.9-2.2	0/+	0.1-0.2	3-4	+	28-34
Phyllorhynchus	2/8	20-23	S	185-211	81-97	—	0	2-12	21-25	0.8-2.1	49-56	39-45	+	0.3-21	0.6-3.8	75-79	53-65	—	—	0	—	—	0/i	23
Pseustes	3/7	21-25	S/T	230-333	102-119	—	0	0-4	22-30	0.5-2.6	61-74	51-66	+	0.6-4.8	0.7-5.0	90-99	61-78	4.4-7.5	6.1-10	+	0.1-0.7	1-9	+	22-30
Ptyas	7/8	22-26	S/P	213-278	93-112	—	0	0-6	21-28	0.4-0.9	59-75	52-67	+	0.2-12	0.2-17	89-98	62-81	0.8-2.1	11-33	+	0.1-0.4	2-6	+	22-28
Rhynchophis	1/1	21	S/P	190	91	—	0	2	23	—	66	58	+	1.2	1.8	89	68	0.8	1.2	+	0.1	2	+	23
Salvadora	6/6	20-25	S/P	201-250	85-108	—	0	0-9	22-27	0.7-1.7	56-75	47-64	+	0.3-12	0.3-17	80-97	58-83+/0	0.4-0.6	0.6-1.0	+/0	0.2-0.3	2-6	+/0	22-28
Scaphiophis	1/8	17-28	S/T	420	88	—	0	0-2	18-30	0.7-1.8	56-75	45-66	+/0	0.1-0.3	0.4-2.0	85-99	59-770/+	0.3-1.0	0.5-1.8	+/0	0.1-0.3	?	+/0	19-29
Senticolis	1/1	24	S	384	157	—	0	5	26	0.4	58	50	+	1.3	23	84	61	0.3	0.8	+	0.1	3	+	26
Spalerosophis	3/3	25-31	T	264-433	105-140	—	0	1-8	26-32	—	52-69	42-61	+	0.9-1.8	1.3-3.35	84-94	54-77	—	—	0	—	—	0	—
Spilotes	1/7	22-27	S/T	207-294	78-126	—	0	1-2	23-28	0.6-1.7	63-74	51-63	+0	0.4-1.1	0.7-1.6	91-98	65-75+0	2.9-6.1	4.2-8.3	+/0	0.2-0.6	1-11	+	23-28
Symphimus	2/2	22-23	T	147-155	66-69	—	0	7-8	24	—	64-66	53-56	+	1.4-1.6	2.1-2.6	88-89	71-73	0.7-1.0	1.0-1.6	+	0.2	1-2	+	24-25
Sympholis	1/1	21	S	169	82	—	0	3	22	1.1	48	38	+	1.1	2.8	70	50	0.4	0.8	+	0.3	3	+	23
Thermophis	1/1	19	S	142	74	—	0	2	20	2.5	57	45	+	0.7	1.3	77	59	0.5	0.9	+	0.3	6	+	20
Trimorphodon	2/18	20-23	T:S	184-198	84-92	—	0	1-12	20-25	0.6-1.6	54-76	50-69	+(0)	0.3-17	0.4-22	80-99	58-80+	0.2-1.1	0.3-1.3	+/0	0.1-0.2	1-3	+	21-26
20-10d. Colubridae: Colubrinae: Dasypeltini																								
Dasypeltis	6/38	15-20	T/S	114-146	59-89	—	0	1-5	16-22	0.4-1.3	69-82	58-74	+(0)	0.2-1.0	0.2-33	90-99	70-850/+	0.2-1.1	0.3-1.5	0/+	0.1-0.7	1-4	0/+	16-21
Elachistodon	1/1	24	T	159	65	—	0	3	26	—	71	65	+	1.4	1.9	98	74	0.9	1.3	+	0.2	1	+	27
20-10e. Colubridae: Colubrinae: Philothamnini																								
Dendrelaphis	5/10	22-27	T:S	190-244	78-114	—	0	0-2	23-28	0.7-2.5	70-74	58-67	+(0)	0.2-1.0	0.3-1.4	97-100	72-74+(0)	0.4-2.5	0.5-3.5	0/+	0.2-0.3	?	+	23-28
Gastropyxis	1/29	26-30	T	237-275	86-105	—	0	0-2	27-31	—	64-71	55-62	+(0)	0.2-1.1	0.4-16	94-99	64-71	0.4-1.4	0.6-2.0	+/0	0.1-0.6	2-5	+	28-31
Hapsidophrys	1/24	25-31	T	186-238	66-88	—	0	0-4	26-33	—	65-72	55-64	+(0)	0.2-12	0.2-17	94-99	66-75+(0)	0.8-2.8	12-4.0	+/0	0.1-0.4	1-4	+	26-33
Leptophis	8/10	23-28	S:T(P)	179-248	68-100	—	0	0-2	23-29	0.4-1.0	65-72	58-64	+	0.3-12	0.4-1.8	93-98	66-73	0.5-1.5	0.7-2.3	+	0.1-0.2	1-3	+	25-30
Philothamnus	14/140	21-33	S/T	134-232	59-122	—	0	0-4	22-34	0.3-1.5	61-74	51-71	+(0)	0.1-2.1	0.1-3.1	90-100	61-75+/0	0.4-2.6	0.6-3.9	+/0	0.1-0.7	1-7	+(0)	23-34

Genus	S/N	T	TE	TTR	NTR	TL	TLL	CL	HT	RAL	RL	SL	RB	RBL	RB/RL	RPT	L	LL	LLL	LL/RL	LB	LBL	LBR	LO	LOM
20-10f. Colubridae: Colubrinae: Dispholidini																									
Dispholidus	1/4	24-27	S	166-231	69-88	0	—	0-2	25-29	0.7-1.8	68-70	57-60	+/0	0.1-1.2	0.2-0.5	94-99	69-72 +	0.8-2.4	1.2-3.4	+0	0.1	—	1	+	25-30
Rhamnophis	2/9	26-28	S/T	203-238	78-85	0	—	0	27-29	0.5-1.1	64-71	53-62	+0	0.1-1.6	0.2-2.4	90-99	65-72+/0	0.5-1.6	0.7-2.3	0+	0.1-0.2	—	1-2	+/0	27-29
Thelotornis	2/4	25-28	S:T	184	75	0	—	0	26-29	0.7-0.8	65-72	56-63	+	0.5-1.6	0.7-2.5	94-99	66-72 +	0.4-1.6	0.6-2.5	0/+	0.1	—	2	+	26-30
Thrasops	3/18	22-30	S/T	195-266	83-101	0	—	0-1	23-31	0.2-1.7	63-73	50-60	+/0	0.2-1.7	0.2-2.3	93-99	63-73+/0	1.6-4.5	2.3-8.7	0/+	0.1	—	1-2	+	24-31
20-10g. Colubridae: Colubrinae: Ahaetullini (n. t)																									
Ahaetulla	6/14	32-36	T	261-489	77-136	0	—	1	34-38	—	55-63	48-54	+/0	0.1-1.6	0.2-2.5	90-99	56-63 +	0.8-2.3	1.3-4.1	+/0	0.1-0.2	—	1-3	+	34-39
Psammodynastes	2/2	31-44	T	348	79	+	23-29	2-3	34-46	—	30-48	32-42	+	1.2-4.0	2.6-13	76-82	62-74 0	—	—	0	—	—	—	0	—
20-10h. Colubridae: Colubrinae: Lampropeltini																									
Arizona	1/3	23-26	S/P	257-272	105-121	0	—	0-1	24-27	0.2-0.7	56-59	47-49	+	27-51	46-91	82-85	57-61 0	—	0/+	0/+	0.3	—	2	0/+	26
Bogertophis	2/5	23-28	S/T	246-303	105-130	0	—	0-3	24-29	0.3-1.0	45-64	35-51	+	82-14	14-19	78-93	45-65 0	—	+/0	+/0	0.1-0.4	—	2-8	+/0	24-26
Cemophora	1/2	20-21	T	167	82	0	—	0-6	22	—	43-59	34-52	+	32-43	73-75	65-81	53-59 0	—	0	0	—	—	—	0	—
Elaphe (New World)	5/10	19-24	S/T	167-245	81-111	0	—	0-2	20-26	0.3-0.9	58-73	49-61	+	6.8-14	11-21	83-95	59-75 +	0.3-1.2	0.4-1.7	+	0.1-0.4	—	1-6	+	21-25
Lampropeltis	8/22	18-23	T/S	162-217	79-105	0	—	0-6	19-25	1.6-3.1	38-65	27-58	+	26-47	58-98	63-90	44-650/+	0.2-0.7	0.4-1.4	0(+)	0.3-0.5	—	4-5	+/0	21-24
Pituophis	5/14	22-28	S(T)	224-365	103-152	0	—	0-2	23-30	0.5-1.7	52-71	41-59	+	12-34	17-61	77-96	52-910/+	0.1-0.3	0.2-0.3	+/0	0.2-0.4	—	2-6	+/0	24-30
Rhinocheilus	1/2	20-24	S:T	207	105	0	—	0-1	21-25	0.4	61-63	49-51	+	53-54	85-86	85-86	61-65 0	—	0	0	—	—	—	0	—
Stilosoma	1/1	20	T	200	102	0	—	1	20	—	75	66	+	40	54	96	76 0	—	0	0	—	—	—	0	—
20-10i. Colubridae: Colubrinae: Sonorini																									
Chilomeniscus	3/3	22-25	T	118-125	53-54	0	—	1-2	24-26	—	46-51	32-39	+	0.5-1.2	1.1-2.4	69-77	47-53 0	—	0	—	—	—	—	0	—
Chionactis	2/8	20-26	S/P	157-202	72-101	0	—	1-8	21-28	—	48-56	37-45	+/0	0.4-1.5	0.7-2.5	73-81	50-630/+	0.1	0.3	0/+	0.2-0.3	—	1-3	+/0/i	24-27
Conopsis	2/2	21-22	S:T	121-152	57-68	0	—	11-12	23-24	1.5	44-46	33-35	+	1.5-2.3	3.5-5.1	67-70	56-57 0	—	+0	+0	0.4	—	4	+0	24
Ficimia	3/4	19-23	S	136-160	63-81	0	—	3-6	21-27	0.7-1.7	29-47	25-35	+/0	1.3-2.4	3.1-5.0	62-70	32-52 +	0.3-0.9	0.8-2.3	+/0	0.2	—	1-8	+	22-26
Geagras	1/1	23	T	121	52	0	—	2	24	—	41	32	+	1.4	3.4	66	43 0	—	0	0	—	—	—	0	—
Gyalopion	2/2	20-23	S	116-138	58-60	0	—	7-15	22-25	1.0-1.4	41-48	31-38	+	1.5-2.6	3.6-5.4	66-70	55-56+0	0.7	1.4	+0	0	—	1	+i	24-26
Pseudoficimia	1/2	20-22	S	158-172	73-86	0	—	5-8	21-23	1.4-1.9	61	51	+	1.1-1.4	1.8-2.3	83-84	66-69 +	1.2-3.0	1.9-5.0	+	0.2-1.0	—	5-9	+	22-23
Scolecophis	1/2	23-24	T	179-195	77-79	+	9-15	2-3	24-26	—	41-43	33	+	0.8-1.0	1.9-2.4	67-68	55-60 +	0.4-0.6	0.8-1.4	+	0.2	—	1-2	+	25
Simophis	1/2	21-26	S	202	95	0	—	0	23-27	0.7-0.8	56-59	48-56	+	0.2-0.3	0.4-0.7	83-90	57-60 +	0.3-0.4	0.6-0.7	0	—	—	—	+	23-27
Sonora	3/5	22-25	S/T	126-159	56-68	0	—	5-10	23-27	0.7-1.4	43-55	35-42	+	0.9-1.9	1.9-3.5	72-79	52-630/s	0.2	0.4	0/+	0.5	—	3	0+	25
Stenorrhina	2/11	19-26	S/T	133-146	62-68	0	—	0-11	20-29	0.8-1.9	43-57	31-47	+/	0.3-1.5	0.5-3.3	67-80	44-60+(0)	0.6-1.2	1.3-2.1	+(0)	0	—	1	+(0)	20-25

Tantilla	4/6	22–24	T/S	117–213	48–92	0	—	2–8	24–27	0.8	34–64	26–56	+/0	0.8–2.6	2.1–5.8	60–91	0	—	—	0	—	—	25
Tantillita	1/1	30	T	127	42	+	12	5	32	—	48	33	+	0.8	1.7	79	0	—	—	0	—	—	25
Toluca	2/2	22–23	S:P	129–144	59–63	0	—	1–3	24–25	1.0–1.4	39–44	30–33	+	1.0	2.2–2.6	63–69	+:0	0.4	0.8	+:0	1	+:0	25

20–11a. Colubridae: Natricinae: Hydraethiopsini

Afronatrix	1/2	22	P:T	149–153	69–71	+	4–5	2–3	23	1.0	31–35	0	+	1.7–1.8	4.9–6.0	54–58	+	0.6–0.9	1.9–2.4	+	0.4	1–2	24
Hydraethiops	2/2	25	S:T	162–195	66–79	0	—	1–15	26	1.0	29–32	7–19	+	1.7	5.1–5.6	55–59	+	0.3–0.4	1.1–1.3	+	0.1	1	27
Limnophis	1/1	26	T	167	65	0	—	4	27	—	30	18	+	0.8	2.7	58	0	—	—	0	—	1	27
Lycognathophis	1/1	23	S	186	80	0	—	10	25	0.9	54	44	+	0.9	1.6	78	+	0.2	0.3	+	0	1	25
Natriciteres	3/243	20–26	S(T)	83–144	39–67	0	—	0	20–27	0.3–2.1	40–70	28–60	+(0)	0.3–1.2	0.5–5.2	60–77	40–54+/0	0.2–1.5	0.7–2.9	+/0	0.1–0.4	1–3	22–30

20–11b. Colubridae: Natricinae: Natricini

Amphiesma	22/23	19–24	S(P)	98–180	50–82	0	—	0–11	19–26	0.4–1.5	34–61	26–53	+/0	0.2–1.6	0.4–2.7	56–86	35–68+/0	0.1–1.4	0.2–2.8	+/0	0.1–0.5	1–6	+/0 20–27
Amphiesmoides	1/1	22	S	150	67	0	—	1	23	0.8	68	56	+	1.5	2.2	92	69	0.5	0.7	0	—	—	25
Atretium	2/2	20–23	S:T	119–167	53–85	0	—	3–10	21–24	2.6	32–38	21–28	+	1.2–2.1	3.6–5.5	58–59	40–43	0.4–1.0	1.0–3.1	+	0.2–0.5	1–5	+ 22–25
Hydrablabes	1/1	23	S	191	82	0	—	14	24	0.3	34	20	+	0.4	1.2	59	48	0.5	1.6	+	0	1	24
Macropisthodon	1/1	22	S	127	58	0	—	1	24	1.5	57	47	+	0.5	0.9	81	59	0.6	1.1	+	0	1	24
Natrix	3/6	17–24	T/S	119–181	60–81	0	—	4–8	19–26	1.2	35–53	25–42	+	0.2–1.7	0.4–3.5	59–70	39–57	0.4–0.8	1.1–1.6	+	0.2–0.5	2–3	20–26
Opisthotropis	8/9	20–23	S/P	104–210	44–103	0	—	1–10	21–24	0.4–1.6	31–52	0–37	+	0.5–2.0	1.4–5.4	52–74	34–61	0.5–1.2	1.4–3.6	+:0	0.3	1–2	21–25
Rhabdophis	9/9	20–22	S/T	96–167	47–77	0	—	1–13	22–24	0.5–1.8	46–66	37–57	+/0	0.3–1.5	0.6–3.0	66–89	46–68+:0	0.6–1.3	1.2–2.2	+:0	0.2–0.3	1–2	21–24
Sinonatrix	3/3	19–22	S	142–169	74–78	0	—	1–10	22–23	1.1–1.8	42–45	27–32	+	0.6–1.1	1.5–2.4	64–68	43–54+/0	0.7–0.9	1.5–2.0	+/0	0.3	1–2	+/0 22–24
Tropidonophis	10/10	18–23	S:T(P)	99–176	50–83	0	—	1–2	19–25	0.8–1.2	37–56	27–46	+	0.2–10.4	0.4–23	59–78	38–57+:0	0.1–0.7	0.2–1.5	+/0	0.1–0.5	1–4	+/0 19–25
Xenochrophis	6/7	20–24	S	129–168	60–75	0	—	0–17	21–25	0.5–1.6	31–70	22–58	+	0.2–1.5	0.4–3.2	52–94	32–86	0.3–1.5	0.9–3.8	+	0.2–0.3	1–4	21–26

20–11c. Colubridae: Natricinae: Aspidurini

Aspidura	3/3	24–32	S	137–159	43–60	0/+	20	2–10	20–28	0.8–1.5	33–49	0–35	+	0.5–1.6	1.0–4.8	66–75	53–55+/0	0.6–1.2	1.2–2.6	+/0	0.3	1–2	+/0 25–28
Blythia	1/1	20	S	158	77	0	—	3	22	0.6	37	26	+	2.8	7.8	58	39	0.7	1.9	+	0	1	24
Cyclocorus	2/2	24	T	133–170	55–71	+	7	3–4	25–26	—	40–47	29–38	+	0.6–0.7	12–1.7	65–72	50–57	0	—	0	—	—	—
Etheridgeum	1/1	26	T	120	48	0	—	3	27	—	36	24	+	1.4	3.9	64	40	0	—	0	—	1	28
Haplocercus	1/1	23	S	258	110	0	—	17	24	0.5	24	12	+	1.8	7.4	48	41	+	0.5	2.1	0	i	24
Hologerrhum	1/1	27	S	174	64	+	10	3	29	—	33	20	+	1.3	3.8	62	46	0	—	0	—	1	+
Myersophis	1/1	27	S	244	90	0	—	2	29	—	37	23	+	1.0	2.5	67	40	+	1.0	2.5	+	0	1	29
Oxyrhabdium	2/4	20–24	T	155–189	73–94	0	—	1–5	21–26	—	36–56	25–46	+	0.2–1.8	0.4–4.9	63–78	40–62+/0	0.6–0.9	1.2–1.3	+	0.3–0.5	1–4	+ 21–27
Rhabdops	2/2	21–27	S:T	150–174	81–93	0	—	3–17	22–29	0.4	32–34	12–18	+	0.8–1.1	2.4–3.4	56–61	35–51	+	0.8	2.4–2.6	+:0	0.4	4	+ 22–29

Genus	S/N	T	TE	TTR	NTR	TL	TLL	CL	HT	RAL	RL	SL	RB	RBL	RB/RL	RPT	L	LL	LLL	LL/RL	LB	LBL	LBR	LO	LOM
Teratolepis	1/1	19	S	156	82	0	—	7+	20	0.5	36	26	+	0.4	1.0	56	42+	+	0.6	1.7	+	0.2	2	+	20
Trachischium	4/4	21-25	T/PS	128-179	52-74	0	—	1-8	22-27	1.0-1.1	30-37	20-27	+	0.7-1.1	2.1-3.3	56-59	34-40+	/s0	0.3-0.9	0.7-2.6	+/0	0	1	+/0	22-26
20-11c. Colubridae: Natricinae: Thamnophiini																									
Adelophis	2/3	16-17	S	92-145	57-84	0	—	0-10	17-18	1.3-1.8	34-41	23-30	+	0.9-1.6	2.8-3.9	51-59	35-51	+	0.6-1.1	1.6-3.2	+/0	0	1	+	18-19
Chilpoma	2/3	19-20	S	140-160	71-83	0	—	7-13	21	0.7-1.0	30-45	21-37	+/0	1.2-1.7	2.3-4.5	51-66	37-58	+	0.2-1.0	0.6-2.1	+	0.3-0.4	1-2	+	21-22
Clonophis	1/1	25	S	131	51	0	—	0	26	1.7	32	19	+	0.7	1.6	58	333	+	0.8	2.6	+	0.2	2	+	27
Nerodia	9/22	19-27	S	113-216	55-90	0	—	0-11	20-29	0.5-2.1	26-51	15-43	+(0)	0.5-1.5	1.1-4.4	47-73	29-61	+(0)	0.4-1.5	0.8-4.2	+(0)	0.1-0.7	1-5	+	20-29
Regina	4/4	19-24	S	117-211	53-111	0	—	0-10	20-25	0.2-0.8	23-34	13-24	+	0.5-2.4	1.5-7.5	46-57	30-39	+	0.6-1.8	2.0-5.8	+0	0.2	1-2	+	21-27
Semnatrix	1/1	26	T	126	44	0	—	10	28	—	33	18	+	1.0	3.1	61	43	+	0.8	2.4	+	0.3	1	+	28
Storeria	3/3	16-17	S	99-108	61-68	0	—	2-6	17-18	0.8-1.9	37-63	28-53	+	0.4-1.9	2.3-4.6	62-81	42-65	+/0	0.4-0.6	0.9-1.2	+/0	0.2	2	+	18-19
Thamnophis	21/63	16-21	S	70-216	34-112	0(+)	8-11	0-11	16-23	0.6-2.3	32-60	21-50	+(0)	0.2-1.6	0.6-4.8	52-81	35-64	+	0.2-1.3	1.0-3.0	+/0	0.2-0.5	1-2	+	18-23
Tropidoclonion	1/1	18	S	126	71	0	—	0	19	1.3	39	28	+	1.7	4.4	57	39	+	1.3	3.3	0	—	—	+	20
Virginia	2/3	18-20	S	116-176	65-90	0	—	0-5	19-22	0.9-1.6	36-46	26-35	+	0.6-1.4	1.3-3.9	58-65	41-47	+	0.6-1.0	1.3-2.4	+/0	0.4	1-2	+	19-22

2. LARGE LEFT LUNG

Genus	S/N	T	TE	TTR	NTR	TL	CL	HT	RAL	RL	RSL	RB	RBL	RB/RL	RPT	LAL	LLL	LSL	LPT	LL/RL	LB	LBL	LBR	LO	LOM	L
8. Xenopeltidae																										
Xenopeltis	1/3	26-31	S	330-337	110-125	0	0	28-32	1.1-1.7	29-38	0	+	0.8-1.7	2.5-4.7	59-65	1.2-1.7	14-16	0	41-46	38-51	+/0	0.3	1-2	+	28-32	47-53
9. Loxocemidae																										
Loxocemus	1/4	27-32	S	230-311	85-104	0	0	27-33	1.2-1.9	28-34	0	+	0.2-1.9	0.9-6.5	58-64	0.9-2.2	16-22	0	44-54	53-78	+	0.5	5-6	+	28-33	45-55
10. Pythonidae																										
Antaresia	1/1	28	S	338	123	0	0	28	1.3	32	0	+	2.0	6.0	60	1.0	14	0	42	43	+	0.5	5	+	29	47
Aspidites	1/1	27	S	387	145	0	0	28	1.1	47	0	+	0.5	1.0	75	0.5	30	0	58	63	+	0.2	0	+	28	78
Bothrochilus	1/1	31	S	529	171	0	0	31	1.0	31	0	+	?	?	63	0.7	21	0	53	67	+	0.3	5	+	32	54
Liasis	2/2	27-28	S	370-417	134-156	0	0	28	1.1-2.0	33-40	0	+	1.3-1.9	0.6-3.2	61-67	1.1-1.8	14	0	45-46	48-53	+	0.1-0.4	3-4	+	28-29	53-59
Morelia	3/4	26-31	S	338-426	129-140	0	0	28-31	0.9-1.3	26-37	+0	+	1.0-1.6	2.3-2.7	56-68	0.3-1.1	15-21	0	43-47	40-64	+/0	0.1-0.3	1-5	+	27-32	45-59
Python	5/45	23-35	S	281-579	90-234	0	0	24-37	0.4-1.9	27-43	0	+	0.2-1.8	0.5-5.6	51-73	0.5-3.8	19-27	0	43-59	51-82	+	0.1-0.9	1-12	+	24-36	50-70

11-1. Boidae: Boinae

Acrantophis	2/2	30	S	338-370	112-124	0	31-33	0.5-1.2	33-41	0	+	0.8-1.7	2.5-4.2	65-72	0.8-1.2	22	0	52-53	53-64	+	0.8-0.9	5-8	+	31-32	56-64
Boa	1/3	27-32	S	282-318	99-118	0	28-34	0.7-2.4	26-42	0	+	7.5-12	22-42	56-69	0.4-1.2	11-20	0	42-49	33-58	+	0.3-0.7	1-7	+	28-33	43-60
Candoia	3/3	27-28	S	249-339	89-120	0	28-30	0.3-1.8	27-67	0	+	1.6-22	3.3-5.9	56-96	0.5-1.8	17-23	0	46-52	34-64	+	0.4-1.1	2-12	+	29-30	46-90
Corallus	3/3	27-31	S	333-429	118-141	0	28-32	0.6-1.4	36-39	0	+	1.1-2.9	3.3-7.4	55-69	0.9-1.4	23-27	0	41-55	50-64	+	0.3-0.4	4-6	+	29-32	40-64
Epicrates	9/12	26-35	S	303-434	87-150	0	27-31	0.6-1.6	28-35	0/10-24	+	0.4-5.0	1.3-18	56-66	0.2-2.7	9-27	0/6-10	41-55	27-67	+	0.3-1.2	4-11	+	27-32	44-63
E. gracilis	1/1	30	S	365	120	0	31	1.2	68	59	+	1.2	1.8	99	0.9	10	5	40	14	+	0.1	2	+	31	78
Eunectes	2/2	27-29	S	334-360	117-132	0	28-30	0.8	23	0	+	2.1-4.9	8.6-20	51-54	0.8-1.4	17	0	45-47	70-75	+	0.8-1.4	5-19	+	28-30	41
Sanzinia	1/1	32	S	338	105	0	34	0.5	28	0	+	6.9	26	61	0.5	18	0	51	64	+	1.4	6	+	34	45

11-2. Boidae: Erycinae

Calabaria	1/7	22-27	S	190	80	0	23-25	0.9-1.4	28-38	0	+	12-22	41-64	53-61	0.7-1.3	13-21	0	38-45	30-57	+	0.5-1.6	12-21	+	22-25	41-59
Charina	1/2	19-20	S	155-163	75-82	0	20-21	1.4-2.0	39-44	0	+	4.6-4.9	10-12	61-62	1.6-2.5	12-16	0	31-36	29-36	+	1.4	13	+	21-22	53-60
Eryx	6/8	23-31	S	189-312	74-106	0	24-32	0.6-1.5	24-45	0	+	9.9-27	34-80	56-69	0.4-1.6	3-24	0	31-47	9-53	+	0.7-4.5	5-57	+	24-33	34-69
Gongylophis	1/2	27-29	S	200	74	0	29-31	1.2-1.5	25-36	0	+	15-17	41-65	51-64	1.5-1.8	15-18	0	45-46	48-58	+	2.1-3.0	18-21	+	29-32	39-55
Lichanura	1/2	21-29	S	252	86	0	24-31	1.1-2.2	30-61	0	+	1.6-5.2	16-25	62-83	0.7-1.9	13-16	0	35-46	21-50	+	0.3	?	+	24-31	47-74

3. MULTICAMERAL VASCULAR TRACHEAL LUNG

Genus	S/N	T	TE	TTR	NTR	TLT	TF	FT	FL	TL	CLT	CF	CL	HT	RLT	RF	RL	RB	RBL	RB/RL	RPT	TLF	L	LL	LB	LO
1. Anomalepididae																										
Anomalepis	1/3	35-42	T	282-288	66-82	U	—	—		21-30	U	—	3-4	32-40	U	—	10-18	+	3.3-7.3	18-59	48-53	—	38-46	0	0	0
Helminthophis	4/9	29-42	T	272-369	59-118	M/P	20-43	C		19-26	U	—	3-4	29-43	U	—	13-15	+	10-17	55-86	44-47	20-43	37-40	0	0	0
Liotyphlops	5/16	30-33	T	244-318	81-101	M	29-55	C		23-26	U	—	3-4	31-33	U	—	10-18	+	5-13	39-86	43-51	29-55	38-48	0	0	0
Typhlops	1/3	30-33	T	205-227	77-80	M	31-33	C		22-23	U	—	4	31-33	U	—	13-15	+	8-11	61-73	42-46	31-33	36-41	0	0	0
2 Typhlopidae																										
Acutotyphlops	4/14	34-45	T	280-396	75-96	M	18-80	A-C		19-28	M	2-12	4-7	35-42	M	5-14	11-23	+	6-15	53-79	49-64	34-91	38-59	0	0	0
Ramphotyphlops	39/134	27-39	T	177-552	46-140	M	11-55	A,D		16-27	M/U	1-10	3-6	29-40	M/U/P	2-9	8-34	+	2-10	82-90	42-67	18-58	35-58	0	0	0
Rhinotyphlops	28/65	26-36	T	216-453	70-152	M(P)	24-45	A-D		14-26	M/U/P	4-10	3-5	27-37	M/P/U	2-18	9-44	+	1-14	2.4-83	39-78	22-58	28-68	0(+)	0(+)	0(+)
Typhlops	103/291	27-40	T	128-413	48-118	M/U/P	14-47	A-D		15-31	M/P/U	2-9	3-6	30-42	M/P/U	1-14	10-32	+	1-18	4.2-100	39-64	31-53	31-55	0(+)	0(+)	0(+)
Xenotyphlops	1/1	25	T	247	108	—	—	—		0	U	—	?	24	U	—	21	+	6	29	44	—	22	0	0	0

Genus	S/N	T	TE	TTR	NTR	TLT	TF	FT	TL	CLT	CF	CL	HT	RLT	RF	RL	RB	RBL	RB/RL	RPT	TLF	L	LL	LB	LO
15. Acrochordidae																									
Acrochordus arafurae	4	43-46	T	475-509	109-129	2M	90-106	G.A	34-38	U	—	3-5	44-47	U	—	46-52	+	0.6-1.5	1.2-3.2	92-99	90-106	84-93	0	0	0
A. javanicus	3	49-50	T	595-603	118-122	2M	135-151	G	36-39	U	—	3-4	50-52	U	—	45-47	+	29-46	85-99	97-98	135-151	86-87	0	0	0
A. granulatus	14	46-51	T	490-642	95-140	4M	209	G.H	40-44	U	—	3-4	46-53	U	—	44-49	+	0.3-2.5	0.7-5.1	95-100	95-140	90-94	0	0	0

4. MULTICAMERAL AVASCULAR TRACHEAL LUNG

Genus	S/N	T	TE	TTR	NTR	TLT	TF	TLL	CL	HT	RAL	RL	SL	RB	RBL	RB/RL	RPT	L	LL	LLL	LL/RL	LB	LBL	LBR	LO	LOM
11a. Elapidae Bungarinae Bungarini																										
Ophiophagus	1/2	28	S	343	123	M	23-33	24	0	29	0.6-1.5	44-45	32-37	+	0.1-0.2	0.2-0.4	73-75	44-45	+	2.1-2.5	4.5-5.5	+	0.2-0.3	1	+	29-30
14-4c. Colubridae Lamprophiinae: Pseudoxyrhophiini																										
Leioheterodon modestus	1/1	18	S	153	84	M	1	8	0	20	1.5	69	57	+	1.2	1.7	89	79	+	0.9	1.3	+	0.3	3	+	21
14-10a. Colubrinae Colubrinae: Lycodontini																										
Lialaphis	5/6	23-28	S	171-284	61-106	P-M	11-15	7-15	2-3	24-29	0.6-1.4	42-61	32-52	+	0.5-1.7	0.9-3.8	70-88	56-71	+	0.4-1.2	0.7-2.8	+	0.2-0.6	3-6	+	24-29
L. dumerilii	1/2	29-30	S	149-240	52-81	P-M	12-21	5-8	1	30	0.3-1.0	62-64	53-56	+	0.7-1.4	1.1-2.2	92-94	71	+	0.5-1.0	0.8-1.6	+/0	0.2	0	+	30-31
Stegonotus	2/3	24-25	S	235	97	M	18-29	11-14	2-3	25-26	0.4-0.9	60-70	51-63	+/0	0.8-1.1	1.3-1.8	86-95	75-85	+	0.7-0.9	1.1-1.4	+	0.3-0.5	3	+	25-26
14-10c. Colubrinae Colubrini																										
Elaphe hodgsonii	1/1	20	S	225	115	M	1	4	1	21	1.4	69	60	+	2.1	3.0	90	77	+	0.4	0.6	+	0.1	3	+	22
Gonyosoma	1/3	23-25	S	221-295	88-129	M	16-20	18-19	2-3	24-26	0.8-1.6	65-72	56-64	+	0.6-0.9	0.9-1.4	92-98	73-90	+	5.6-7.5	8.5-11	+	0.1-0.7	3-9	+	24-27
Ptyas korros	1/2	20-25	SP	156-166	62-82	M	7-23	10-12	3	22-27	0.8	58-66	47-56	+/0	0.4	0.7	85-88	70-81	+	0.6-0.8	1.0-1.2	+	0.2-0.6	3-5	+	21-26
Xenelaphis	1/2	24-27	S	194-257	71-107	M	8-19	13-20	3-4	25-29	0.6-1.0	35-38	24-27	+	0.2	0.5	64	55-57	+	0.4-0.8	1.1-2.4	+	0.5-0.7	6	+	25-28
14-11b. Colubridae Natricinae Natricini																										
Amphiesma	2/2	20-21	S	136-183	66-87	M	9-16	11-12	3-5	22-23	0.3-0.4	45-48	35-36	+	0.3-1.2	0.7-2.4	66-70	59-62	0	—	—	0	—	—	0	—
Balanophis	1/1	20	S	122	60	M	21	14	2	22	1.3	53	47	+	0.3	0.5	75	70	+	0.5	1.0	0	—	—	+	22
Macropisthodon	3/3	17-20	S	105-151	61-62	M	6-9	9-13	0-3	19-26	0.9-2.1	58-65	48-55	+	0.2-0.9	0.3-1.9	77-91	69-77	+/0	1.3-3.0	1.9-4.9	+/0	0.2-0.3	2	+/0	22-26
Plagiopholis	2/2	18	S	96-103	53-56	M	8-9	11-12	0-2	19-20	1.5-1.9	39	23-27	+	0.9-1.3	2.3-3.3	58-59	51-53	+	0.8-1.6	1.9-4.1	+	0	1	+	20
Pseudoxenodon	7/7	19-24	S	106-195	47-88	M	4-7	14-17	1-5	20-26	1.2-2.4	62-74	49-65	+	0.2-1.2	0.3-1.9	84-94	79-90	+	0.7-1.8	0.9-2.8	+	0.2-0.4	1-3	+	21-26
Rhabdops	6/8	15-22	S/P/T	97-160	57-82	M-P	3-15	6-17	0-3	16-23	0.2-1.2	38-70	27-61	+	0.2-1.4	0.4-3.3	59-94	50-90	+/0	0.3-1.0	0.7-2.0	+	0.1-0.4	1-4	+/0	17-23

REFERENCES

Abbatius, B. A. (1589). *De Admirabili Viperae Natura*. Bartholomaeum Ragusium, Urbino, 151 pp.

Abbatius, B. A. (1603). *De Admirabili Viperae Natura*, 2nd ed. Seb. Heusler, Nüremberg, 133 pp.

Abbatius, B. A. (1660). *De Admirabili Viperae Natura*, 3rd ed. Sam. Broun, The Hague. 186 pp.

Acolat, L. (1943). *Contribution à l'anatomie comparée du coeur, et en particulier du ventricle, chez les batraciens et chez les reptiles*. Imprimerie de l'Est, Besançon, 126 pp.

Acolat, L. (1955). Note preliminaire sur le pneumogastrique chez les ophidiens. *Ann. Sci. Univ. Besançon, Zool. Physiol.*, ser. 2, 4, 17–24.

Agarwal, P. N., and Sharma, S. (1979). On the brain and the cranial nerves of the Indian cobra, *Naja naja naja* (Linn.). Fam. Elapidae. *Indian J. Zool.* 7, 23–34.

Ahrenfeldt, R. T. (1955). Two British anatomical studies on American reptiles (1650–1750)—II. Edward Tyson: Comparative anatomy of the timber rattlesnake. *Herpetologica* 11, 49–69.

Aldrovandi, U. (1640). *Serpentum, et Draconu Historiae*, vol 2. M. Antony Bernie Bibliopole Bononiensis, Bononiae, 427 pp.

Alvarez del Toro, M. (1960). *Reptiles de Chiapas*. Instituto Zoologico del Estado, Tuxtla Gutiérrez, 204 pp.

Alvarez del Toro, M. (1973). *Los Reptiles de Chiapas*, 2nd ed. (updated and augmented). El Gobierno del Estado de Chiapas, Tuxtla Gutiérrez (1972), 178 pp.

Alvarez del Toro, M. (1982). *Los Reptiles de Chiapas*, 3rd. ed. (corrected and augmented). Instituto de Historia Natural del Estado, Tuxtla Gutiérrez, 248 pp.

Albright, R. G., and Nelson, E. M. (1959). Cranial kinetics of the generalized colubrid snake *Elaphe obsoleta quadrivittata*. I. Descriptive morphology. *J. Morph.* 105, 193–239.

Amaral, A. do. (1978). *Serpentes do Brasil: Iconografia Colorida (Brazilian Snakes: a Color Iconography)*. Editoriá da Universidade de São Paulo, São Paulo (1977), 248 pp.

Angel, F. (1950). *Vie et Moeurs des Serpents*. Payot, Paris.

Antipchuk, Y. P. (1966a). Structure and function of the reptilian heart. *Akad. Nauk SSSR* 169, 1465–1466 [In Ukrainian].

Antipchuk, Y. P. (1966b). Types of lungs in representatives of the suborder Serpentes. *Akad. Nauk URSR* 1966, 1081–1084 [in Ukrainian].

Antipchuk, Y. P. (1966c). Comparative anatomy of pulmonary vessels in species of the suborder Serpentes. *Akad. Nauk URSR* 1966, 1352–1354 [in Ukrainian].

Antipchuk, Y. P. (1967a). Comparative morphology of the aortic arch of reptiles. *Akad. Nauk URSR* 1967, 79–81 [in Ukrainian].

Antipchuk, Y. P. (1967b). The trends of lung evolution in the reptiles. *Akad. Nauk URSR* 1967, 657–659 [in Ukrainian].

Antipchuk, Y. P. (1969a). Comparative physiology of pulmonary blood circulation in reptiles and mammals. *J. Evol. Biokhim. Fiziol.* 5, 391–397 [in Russian].

Antipchuk, Y. P. (1969b). Comparative physiology of pulmonary blood circulation in reptiles and mammals. *J. Evol. Biochem. Physiol.* 5, 318–323.

Antipchuk, Y. P., and Sobolieva, A. (1971). *Comparative Histology of the Lungs of Vertebrates*. State Publisher of Soviet Science, Novosibirsk, 176 pp. [in Russian].

Antipchuk, Y. P., and Sobolieva, A. (1976). *The Evolution of the Respiratory Systems* (A. F. Nikiforov, ed.). State Publisher of Soviet Science, Novosibirsk, 207 pp. [in Russian].

Appleby, L. G. (1971). *British Snakes*. John Baker, London, 150 pp.

Aristotle, A. (1513). *De Natura Animalium, de Partibus Animalium, de Generatione Animalium. — Theophrastus, de Historia Plantarum . . . de Causis Plantarum. — Aristotoles, Problemata. — Alexander Aphrodisius, Problemata.* Aldus, Venice, 273 pp.

Aristotle, A. (1862). *Aristotle's History of Animals*, book 2 (R. Cresswell, trans.). Henry G. Bohn, London, 326 pp.

Atwood, W. H. (1916). The visceral anatomy of the black snake (*Zamenis constrictor*). *Washington Univ. Stud.*, Sci. ser. 4, 4, 1–38.

Atwood, W. H. (1918). The visceral anatomy of the garter snake. *Trans. Wisconsin Acad. Sci. Arts Lett.* 19, 531–552.

Atwood, W. H. (1923). *Comparative Vertebrate Dissection*. P. Blakiston's Son, Philadelphia, 248 pp.

Auerbach, R. D. (1985). *The Reptiles of Gaborone; a Guide to the Reptiles of the South-Eastern Hardveld of Botswana*. Botswana Book Centre, Gaborone, 48 pp.

Auerbach, R. D. (1987). *The Amphibians and Reptiles of Botswana*. Mokwepa Consultants, Gaborone, 295 pp.

Baer, J. G. (1964). *Comparative Anatomy of Vertebrates* (J. Mahon, trans.). Butterworths, Washington.

Baeyens, D. A., McAllister, C. T., and Morgans, L. F. (1978). Some physiological and morphological adaptations for underwater survival in *Natrix rhombifera* and *Elaphe obsoleta*. *Proc. Arkansas Acad. Sci.* 32, 18–21.

Baeyens, D. A., Patterson, M. W., and McAllister, C. T. (1979a). A comparative physiological study of diving in three species of *Nerodia* and *Elaphe obsoleta*. SSAR-Herpetologists' League Annual Meeting Abstracts, Univ. Tennessee, Knoxville, p. 18.

Baeyens, D. A., Patterson, M. W., and McAllister, C. T. (1979b). Hematology as related to diving characteristics of *Elaphe obsoleta, Nerodia erythrogaster, Nerodia fasciata,* and *Nerodia rhombifera*. *Proc. Arkansas Acad. Sci.* 33, 17–18.

Baeyens, D. A., Patterson, M. W., and McAllister, C. T. (1980). A comparative physiological study of diving in three species of *Nerodia* and *Elaphe obsoleta*. *J. Herpetol.* 14, 65–70.

Baker, L. (1990). *Snakes*. Puffin Books, New York, 32 pp.

Bal, D. V., and Navathe, K. V. (1949). The circulatory system of *Hydrophis caerulescens* (Shaw). *J. Univ. Bombay*, ser. 2, 17B, 1–14.

Ballard, W. W. (1964). *Comparative Anatomy and Embryology*. Ronald Press, New York, 618 pp.

Barbour, T. (1926). *Reptiles and Amphibians: Their Habits and Adaptations*. George G. Harrap, London, 125 pp.

Bargar, S., and Johnson, L. (1986a). *Cobras*. Watermill Press, Mahwah, New Jersey, 24 pp.

Bargar, S., and Johnson, L. (1986b). *Cottonmouths*. Watermill Press, Mahwah, New Jersey, 24 pp.

Bargar, S., and Johnson, L. (1986c). *Mambas*. Watermill Press, Mahwah, New Jersey, 24 pp.

Bargar, S., and Johnson, L. (1987a). *Coral snakes*. Watermill Press, Mahwah, New Jersey, 24 pp.

Bargar, S., and Johnson, L. (1987b). *Pythons*. Watermill Press, Mahwah, New Jersey, 24 pp.

Barker, D. G., and Barker, T. M. (1994). *Pythons of the World*, vol. 1. Advanced Vivarium Systems, Lakeside, California, 171 pp.

Barker, D. G., and Barker, T. M. (1995). The mechanics of *Python* reproduction. *Vivarium* 6(5), 30–33.

Barme, M. (1968). Venomous sea snakes (Hydrophiidae). In *Venomous Animals and Their Venoms* (W. Bücherl, E. E. Buckley, and V. Deulofeu, eds.). Academic Press, New York, vol. 1, pp. 285–308.

Barnard, S. M. (1996). *Reptile Keeper's Handbook*. Krieger Publ. Co., Malabar, Florida.

Bartlett, D., Jr., Mortola, J. P., and Doll, E. J. (1986). Respiratory mechanics and control of the ventilatory cycle in the garter snake. *Resp. Physiol.* 64, 13–27.

Bartram, W. (1791). *Travels through North & South Carolina, Georgia, East & West Florida, the Cherokee Country, the Extensive Territories of the Muscogulges, or Creek Confederacy, and the Country of the Chactaws; Containing an Account of the Soil and Natural Productions of those Regions, together with Observations on the Manners of the Indians*. James & Johnson, Philadelphia, 522 pp.

Baskett, J. N., and Ditmars, R. L. (1902). *The Story of the Amphibians and the Reptiles*. D. Appleton, New York, 217 pp.

Batsch, A. J. G. C. (1788). *Versuch einer Anleitung zur Kenntniss und Geschichte der Thiere und Mineralien, für akademische Vorlesungen entworfen, und mit den nöthigsten Abbildungen versehen*. Erster Theil. Akademische Buchhandlung, Jena, 452 pp.

Bauchot, R. (1994). A portrait of snakes. In *Snakes: A Natural History* (R. Bauchot, ed.). Sterling, New York, pp. 14–25.

Baudrimont, A. (1929). Dispositifs musculaire et élastique du poumon des vertébrés: étude histologique et histophysiologique. *Bull. Station Biol. d'Arcachon* 26, 1–232.

Baudrimont, A. (1952). Considérations sur la répartition des capillaires respiratoires dans la paroi alvéolaire du poumon des vertébrés dans ses rapports avec les facteurs, mécaniques extrinsèques de la respiration. *Arch. Anat. Hist. Embryol.* 34, 49–54.

Baudrimont, A. (1956). Organisation générale du poumon et structure des alvéoles pulmonaires des vertébrés (amphibiens, reptiles, mammifères) considérées dans leurs rapports avec la mécanique respiratoire, la circulation pulmonaire fonctionnelle et l'activité métabolique de ces animaux. *Archs. Anat. Hist. Embryol.* 39, 97–136.

Baumann, M. (1902). Note sur les premiers développements de l'appareil pulmonaire chez la couleuvre (*Tropidonotus natrix*). *Bibl. Anat.* 10, 304–311.

Baumeister, L. (1908). Beiträge zur Anatomie und Physiologie der Rhinophidien. *Zool. Jb., Abt. Anat. Ontog. Tiere* 26, 423–526.

Bazantová, I. (1986). The relationship of lymphatics to the blood-air barrier in the lungs of reptiles. *Verh. Anat. Ges.* 80, 383–385.

Beddard, F. E. (1903). On the trachea, lungs, and other points in the anatomy of the hammadryad snake (*Ophiophagus bungarus*). *Proc. Zool. Soc. Lond.* 1903, 319–328.

Beddard, F. E. (1904a). Notes upon the anatomy of certain snakes of the family Boidae. *Proc. Zool. Soc. Lond.* 1904, 107–121.

Beddard, F. E. (1904b). Contribution to the knowledge of the visceral anatomy of the pelagic serpents *Hydrus platyurus* and *Platyurus colubrinus*. *Proc. Zool. Soc. Lond.* 1904, 147–154.

Beddard, F. E. (1904c). Contributions to our knowledge of the circulatory system in the Ophidia. *Proc. Zool. Soc. Lond.* 1904, 331–370.

Beddard, F. E. (1904d). Preliminary note on certain points in the anatomy of *Eryx* and other Boidae, partly indicative of their basal position among the Ophidia. *Ann. Mag. Nat. Hist.*, ser. 7, 13, 233–236.

Beddard, F. E. (1906a). Contributions to the anatomy of the Ophidia. *Proc. Zool. Soc. Lond.* 1906, 12–44.

Beddard, F. E. (1906b). Contributions to the knowledge of the vascular and respiratory systems in the Ophidia, and to the anatomy of the genera *Boa* and *Corallus*. *Proc. Zool. Soc. Lond.* 1906, 499–532.

Beddard, F. E. (1907). Contributions to the knowledge of the systematic arrangement and anatomy of certain genera and species of Squamata. *Proc. Zool. Soc. Lond.* 1907, 35–68.

Beddard, F. E. (1908). A comparison of the Neotropical species of *Corallus, C. cookii*, with *C. madagascariensis*: and on some points in the anatomy of *Corallus caninus*. *Proc. Zool. Soc. Lond.* 1908, 135–158.

Beddard, F. E. (1909). Some notes upon *Boa occidentalis* and *Boa* (*Pelophilus*) *madagascariensis*. *Proc. Zool. Soc. Lond.* 1909, 918–927.

Bedriaga, J. von (1884). *Amphisbaena cinerea* Vand. und *A. Strauchi* v. Bedr. Erster Beitrag zur Kenntniss der Doppelschleichen. *Arch. Naturw.* 1, 23–77.

Beebe, W. (1946). Field notes on the snakes of Kartabo, British Guiana, and Caripito, Venezuela. *Zoologica* 31, 11–52.

Bellairs, A. d'A. (1957). *Reptiles.* Hutchinson's University Library, London, 195 pp.

Bellairs, A. d'A. (1969). *The Life of Reptiles*, vol. 1–2. Weidenfeld and Nicholson, London, 590 pp.

Bellairs, A. d'A. (1970). *Reptiles*, 3rd ed. Hutchinson University Library, London, 200 pp.

Bellairs, A. d'A. (1972). Comments on the evolution and affinities of snakes. In *Studies in Vertebrate Evolution* (K. A. Joysey and T. S. Kemp, eds.). Winchester Press, New York, pp. 157–172.

Bellairs, A. d'A., and Boyd, J. D. (1950). The lachrymal apparatus in lizards and snakes.—II. The anterior part of the lachrymal duct and its relationship with the palate and with the nasal and vomeronasal organs. *Proc. Zool. Soc. Lond.* 120, 269–310.

Bellairs, A. d'A., and Boyd, J. D. (1957). Anomalous cleft palate in snake embryos. *Proc. Zool. Soc. Lond.* 129, 525–539.

Bellairs, A. d'A., and Carrington, R. (1966). *The World of Reptiles*. American Elsevier, New York, 154 pp.

Bellairs, A. d'A., and Underwood, G. (1951). The origins of snakes. *Biol. Rev.* 26, 193–237.

Bemmelen, J. F. van (1886). Die Visceraltaschen und Aortenbogen bei Reptilien und Vögeln. *Zool. Anz.* 9, 528–532.

Bemmelen, J. F. van (1888). Beiträge zur Kenntniss der Halsgegend bei Reptilien. I. Anatomischer Theil. *Bijdragen tot de Dierkunde* 16, 101–146.

Benninghoff, A. (1922). Über die Beziehungen des Reizleitungssystems und der Papillarmuskeln zu den Konturfasern des Herzschlauches. *Verh. Anat. Ges.* 55, 185–208.

Benninghoff, A. (1931). Die Architektur des Herzmuskels. Eine vergleichend-anatomische und vergleichend-funktionelle Betrachtung. *Gegenbaurs Morph. Jb.* 67, 262–317.

Benninghoff, A. (1933). Herz. In *Handbuch der vergleichenden Anatomie der Wirbeltiere*, vol. 6. (L. Bolk, E. Göppert, E. Kallius, and W. Lubosch, eds.). Urban & Schwarzenberg, Berlin and Vienna, pp. 467–556.

Benton, M. (1980). Geographic variation in the garter snake (*Thamnophis sirtalis*) of the north-central United States, a multivariate study. *Zool. J. Linn. Soc.* 68, 307–323.

Bergman, R. A. M. (1949). The anatomy of *Lapemis hardwickei* Gray. I and II. *Proc. K. Ned. Akad. Wet.* 52C, 882–898.

Bergman, R. A. M. (1950). The anatomy of *Natrix vittata* (L.). *Zoöl. Meded.* 31, 13–24.

Bergman, R. A. M. (1951). The anatomy of *Homalopsis buccata*. *Proc. K. Ned. Akad. Wet.* 54C, 511–524.

Bergman, R. A. M. (1952). L'anatomie du genre *Ptyas* a Java. *Revta. Biol. Colon.* 12, 5–42.

Bergman, R. A. M. (1953). The anatomy of *Cylindrophis rufus* (Laur.). I and II. *Proc. K. Ned. Akad. Wet.* 56C, 650–660.

Bergman, R. A. M. (1954). *Thalassophis anomalus* Schmidt. Universidad Nacional de Cordoba, Cordoba, 16 pp.

Bergman, R. A. M. (1955a). *Dendrophis pictus*. *Proc. K. Ned. Akad. Wet.* 58C 206–218.

Bergman, R. A. M. (1955b). L'anatomie de *Cerberus rhynchops*. *Archs. Néerl. Zool.* 11, 113–126.

Bergman, R. A. M. (1955c). The anatomy of *Xenopeltis unicolor*. *Zoöl. Meded., Leiden* 33, 209–225.

Bergman, R. A. M. (1955d). L'anatomie de *Enhydris enhydris*. *Revta. Biol. Colon.* 15, 5–28.

Bergman, R. A. M. (1956). The anatomy of *Natrix subminiata*. *Biol. Jaarb.* 23, 306–326.

Bergman, R. A. M. (1958a). The anatomy of the Acrochordinae. I, II, III, and IV. *Proc. K. Ned. Akad. Wet.* 61C, 145–184.

Bergman, R. A. M. (1958b). The anatomy of *Natrix piscator*. *Biol. Jaarb.* 26, 77–99.

Bergman, R. A. M. (1959). *Natrix chrysarga, Natrix trianguligera*. *Biol. Jaarb.* 27, 73–98.

Bergman, R. A. M. (1960). The anatomy of some Homalopsinae. *Biol. Jaarb.* 28, 119–138.

Bergman, R. A. M. (1961a). The anatomy of *Coluber radiatus* and *Coluber melanurus*. *Pacific Sci.* 15, 144–154.

Bergman, R. A. M. (1961b). The anatomy of some Viperidae (I and II). *Acta Morph. Neerl.-Scand.* 4, 195–211.

Bergman, R. A. M. (1961c). The anatomy of some Viperidae (III). *Acta Morph. Neerl.-Scand.* 4, 212–230.

Bergman, R. A. M. (1962). Die Anatomie der Elapinae. *Z. Wiss. Zool.* 167, 291–337.

Bergman, R. A. M. (1963). The anatomy of *Ablabes baliodeira*, a colubrid snake from Java. *J. Ohio Herpetol. Soc.* 4, 1–14.

Bergman, R. A. M. (1965). The anatomy of *Calamaria multipunctata* (Boie). *Bull. Natl. Mus. Singapore* 33, 35–56.

Berkhoudt, H., Kardong, K. V., and Zweers, G. A. (1995). Mechanics of drinking in the brown tree snake, *Boiga irregularis*. *Zoology, Analysis of Complex Systems* 98, 92–103.

Berridge, W. S. (1935). *All About Reptiles and Batrachians*. George G. Harrap, London, 271 pp.

Bert, P. (1869). Des mouvements respiratoires chez les batraciens et les reptiles. *J. Anat. Physiol.* 6, 113–169.

Berthold, A. A. (1827). Ueber die Bedeutung und den Nutzen der Luftröhrenringe. *Isis von Oken* 22, 761–766.

Bingley, W. (1829). *Animal Biography, or, Popular Zoology; illustrated by Authentic Anecdotes of the Economy, Habits of Life, Instincts, and Sagacity, of the Animal Creation*, vol. 3. Longman, Rees, Orme, Brown, and Green, London.

Black, D., and Woodward, J., eds. (1989). *The Illustrated Encyclopedia of Wildlife.*, vol. 28. Orbis Publishing, London, pp. 1621–1680.

Blasius, G. (1674). *Observata Anatomica in Homine, . . . Serpente, Ardea, Variisque Animalibus aliis*. Lugd. Batav., Amsterdam, 141 pp. (not seen)

Blasius, G. (1681). *Anatome Animalium, Terrestrium Variorum, Volatilium, Aquatilium, Serpentum, Insectorum, Ovorumque, Structuram Naturalem ex Veterum, Recentiorium, Propriisque Observationibus Proponens, Figuris Variis Illustrata.* Joannis à Someren, Henrici & Viduae Theodori Boom, Amsterdam, 496 pp.

Blumenbach, J. F. (1803). *Manuel d'Histoire Naturelle*, vol. 1 (S. Artaud, trans.). Collignon, Metz, 526 pp.

Blumenbach, J. F. (1805). *Handbuch der vergleichenden Anatomie*. Heinrich Dieterich, Göttingen, 549 pp.

Blumenbach, J. F. (1815). *Handbuch der vergleichenden Anatomie*, 2nd ed. (improved and augmented). Heinrich Dieterich, Göttingen, 555 pp.

Blumenbach, J. F. (1824). *Handbuch der vergleichenden Anatomie*, 3rd ed. (improved and augmented). Dieterichschen Buchhandlung, Göttingen, 559 pp.

Blumenbach, J. F., Lawrence, W., and Coulson, W. (1827). *A Manual of Comparative Anatomy, Translated from the German of J. F. Blumenbach, with Additional Notes, by William Lawrence, Esq. F.R.S.*, 2nd ed. (revised and augmented by William Coulson). W. Simpkin and R. Marshall, London, 379 pp.

Boas, J. E. V. (1888). *Laerebog i Zoologien. Naermest til brug for Studerende og Laerere*. P. G. Philipsens Forlag, Kjøbenhavn, 563 pp.

Boas, J. E. V. (1890). Lehrbuch der Zoologie. Für Studierende und Lehrer (J. W. Spengel, trans.). Gustav Fischer, Jena, 578 pp.

Bogert, C. M. (1940). Herpetological results of the Vernay Angola expedition. Part I—Snakes, including an arrangement of African Colubridae. Bull. Amer. Mus. Nat. Hist. 77, 1–107.

Bogert, C. M., and Cowles, R. B. (1947). Results of the Archbold expeditions. No. 58. Moisture loss in relation to habitat selection in some Floridian reptiles. Amer. Mus. Novit. 1358, 1–34.

Bohr, C. (1904). Ueber den respiratorischen Stoffwechsel beim Embryo kalfblütiger Thiere. Skand. Arch. Physiol. 15, 23–24. (not seen)

Boilstone, M. (1994). The colubrids of Laos. Reptilian Mag. 2(6), 32–37.

Böker, H. (1937). Einführung in die vergleichende biologische Anatomie der Wirbeltiere, vol. 2. Gustav Fischer, Jena, 258 pp.

Boltt, R. E., and Ewer, R. F. (1964). The functional anatomy of the head of the puff adder, Bitis arietans (Merr.). J. Morph. 114, 83–106.

Bonnaterre, J. P. (1790). Tableau Encyclopédique et Méthodique des Trois Regnes de la Nature. Ophiologie. Panckoucke, Paris, 76 pp.

Bonnaterre, J. P. (1795). Tableau Encyclopédique et Méthodique des Trois Regnes de la Nature, dédié à la Sérénissime Republique de Venise: Cétologie, Ophiologie, Erpétologie. Padoue, pp. 165–272. (Italian trans. of Bonaterre, 1790)

Borgert, A. (1897). Über eine zweiköpfige Kreuzotter. Verh. Naturwiss. Ver. Hamburg (1896), ser. 3, 4, 50–57.

Bothner, R. C. (1959). Gross anatomy of the heart and neighboring vessels in the northern subspecies of the copperhead, Agkistrodon contortrix mokeson (Daudin). Sci. Stud. St. Bonaventure Univ. 20, 27–44.

Boué, H., and Chanton, R. (1959). Biologie Animale: Zoologie, vol. 2. G. Doin, Paris, 583 pp.

Boulenger, E. G. (1914). Reptiles and Batrachians. J. M. Dent & Sons, London, 278 pp.

Boulenger, G. A. (1893). Catalogue of the Snakes in the British Museum (Natural History), vol. 1. British Museum (Natural History), London, 448 pp.

Boulenger, G. A. (1894). Catalogue of the Snakes in the British Museum (Natural History), vol. 2. British Museum (Natural History), London, 382 pp.

Boulenger, G. A. (1896). Catalogue of the Snakes in the British Museum (Natural History), vol. 3. British Museum (Natural History), London, 727 pp.

Boulenger, G. A. (1913). The Snakes of Europe. Methuen, London, 269 pp.

Bourgeois, M. (1968). Contribution à la morphologie comparée du crane des ophidiens de l'Afrique centrale. Publ. Univ. Off. Congo, Lubumbashi 18, 1–293.

Bourgondien, T. van, and Bothner, R. C. (1969). A comparative study of the arterial systems of some New World Crotalinae (Reptilia: Ophidia). Amer. Midl. Nat. 81, 107–147.

Boyd, J. D. (1942). The nerve supply of the branchial arch arteries in Vipera berus. J. Anat. 76, 248–257.

Bragdon, D. E. (1953). A contribution to the surgical anatomy of the water snake, Natrix sipedon sipedon. Anat. Rec. 117, 145–160.

Branch, W. R. 1981. Venomous snakes of southern Africa. 3. Concluding part: Colubridae. Bull. Maryland Herpetol. Soc. 17, 125–150.

Branch, W. R. (1988). *Field Guide to the Snakes and other Reptiles of Southern Africa.* Ralph Curtis, Sanibel Island, Florida, 326 pp.

Branch, W. R. (1993). *Southern African Snakes and other Reptiles: A Photographic Guide.* New Holland, London, 144 pp.

Brandt, E. (1865). Ueber einen eigenthuemlichen, spaeter meist obliterirenden Ductus Caroticus der gemeinen Kreuzotter (*Pelias berus*). *Melanges Biol.* 5, 353–362.

Brattstrom, B. H. (1959). The functions of the air sac in snakes. *Herpetologica* 15, 103–104.

Brazaitis, P., and Watanabe, M. E. (1992). *Snakes of the World.* Crescent Books, New York, 176 pp.

Brehm, A. E., ed. (1878). Vierte Ordnung. Die Schlangen (Ophidia). In *Die Kriechthiere und Lurche.* Erster Band. Brehms Thierleben. Allgemeine Kunde des Thierreichs. Dritte Abtheilung — Kriechthiere, Lurche und Fische. Bibliographischen Instituts, Leipzig, pp. 265–532.

Brehm, A. E. (1885). *Les Reptiles et les Batraciens* (E. Sauvage, trans.). J.-B. Baillère et Fils, Paris, 726 pp.

Brehm, A. E., and Werner, F. (1913). *Brehms Tierleben. Allgemeine Kunde des Tierreichs. Lurche und Kriechthiere*, vol. 2. Bibliographisches Institut, Leipzig and Vienna, 598 pp.

Brehm, A. E., and Werner, F. (1920). *Brehms Tierleben. Allgemeine Kunde des Tierreichs. Erster Band. Die Lurche und Kriechthiere (Brückenechsen, Schildkröten, Panzerechsen).* Bibliographisches Institut, Leipzig and Vienna, 572 pp.

Brenner, A. (1883). Ueber das Verhältniss der Nervus laryngeus inferior vagi zu einigen Aortenvarietäten des Menschen und zu dem Aortensystem der durch Lungen athmenden Wirbelthiere überhaupt. *Arch. Anat. Physiol., Anat. Abt.* 1883, 373–396.

Broadley, D. G. (1957a). Snakes of Southern Rhodesia — 2. The northern green snake, *Philothamnus irregularis irregularis* (Leach). *African Wildlife* 2, 53–55.

Broadley, D. G. (1957b). Snakes of Southern Rhodesia — 4. The south-eastern vine or twig snake. *African Wildlife* 2, 297–300.

Broadley, D. G. (1959). The herpetology of Southern Rhodesia. Part 1. Snakes. *Bull. Mus. Comp. Zool. Harvard Univ.* 120, 1–100.

Broadley, D. G. (1966). A review of the Natal green snake, *Philothamnus natalensis* (A. Smith), with a description of a new subspecies. *Ann. Natal Mus.* 18, 417–423.

Broadley, D. G. (1983). *FitzSimons' Snakes of Southern Africa*, 2nd ed. Delta Books, Johannesburg, 376 pp.

Broadley, D. G. (1990). *FitzSimons' Snakes of Southern Africa*, 3rd ed. Jonathan Ball and Ad. Donker, Parklands, 387 pp.

Broadley, D. G., and Cock, E. V. (1975). *Snakes of Rhodesia.* Longman Rhodesia, Southerton, 152 pp.

Broadley, D. G., and Wallach, V. (1996). Remarkable new worm snake (Serpentes: Leptotyphlopidae) from the East African coast. *Copeia* 1966, 162–166.

Broadley, D. G., and Wallach, V. (1997a). A review of the worm snakes of Mozambique (Serpentes: Leptotyphlopidae) with the description of a new species. *Arnoldia Zimbabwe* 10, 111–119.

Broadley, D. G., and Wallach, V. (1997b). A review of the genus *Leptotyphlops* (Serpentes: Leptotyphlopidae) in Kwazulu-Natal, South Africa, with the description of a new forest dwelling species. *Durban Mus. Novit.* 22, 37–42.

Broderip, W. J. (1825a). Some account of the mode in which the *Boa constrictor* takes its prey, and of the adaptation of its organization to its habits. *Zool. J., Lond.* 1, 215–221.

Broderip, W. J. (1825b). Quelques faits relatifs à la manière dont le *Boa constrictor* saisit sa proie, et de la disposition de son organisme par rapport à ses habitudes. *Ferussac Bull. Sci. Nat. Géol., Paris* 5, 429–430. (abstract of Broderip, 1825a)

Broderip, W. J. (1828). Ueber die Art, wie *Boa constrictor* ihren Raub ergreift. *Isis von Oken, Jena* 21, 941–943. (abstract of Broderip, 1825a)

Bröer, W. (1978). Rotschwanznatter *Goniosoma oxycephala*, ihre Pflege und Zucht. *Das Aquarium* 104, 79–81.

Bröer, W., and Engelhardt, M. (1981). Haltung und Zucht einer selten importierten Schlange: *Elaphe helena* (Daudin, 1803), (Reptilia: Serpentes: Colubridae). *Salamandra* 17, 63–70.

Broman, I. (1904). *Die Entwickelungsgeschichte der Bursa omentalis und ähnlicher Rezessbildungen bei den Wirbeltieren*. J. F. Bergmann, Wiesbaden, 611 pp.

Broman, I. (1937). Coelom. In *Handbuch der vergleichenden Anatomie der Wirbeltiere*. (L. Bolk, E. Goeppert, E. Kallius, and W. Lubosch, eds.). Urban und Schwarzenberg, Berlin and Vienna, vol. 3, pp. 989–1018.

Brongersma, L. D. (1938). *Het Belang van Anatomisch Onderzoek voor de Systematiek*. E. J. Brill, Leiden, 11 pp.

Brongersma, L. D. (1949). On the main branches of the pulmonary artery in some Viperinae. *Bijdr. Dierk.* 28, 57–64.

Brongersma, L. D. (1950). Notes on *Pseudoxenodon inornatus* (Boie) and *Pseudoxenodon jacobsonii* Lidth. *Proc. K. Ned. Akad. Wet.* 53C, 1498–1505.

Brongersma, L. D. (1951a). Some remarks on the pulmonary artery in snakes with two lungs. *Zool. Verh., Leiden* 14, 1–36.

Brongersma, L. D. (1951b). Some notes upon the anatomy of *Tropidophis* and *Trachyboa* (Serpentes). *Zool. Med., Leiden* 31, 107–124.

Brongersma, L. D. (1951c). De arteria pulmonalis bij Boidae en bij *Xenopeltis* (Serpentes). *Ned. Tijdschr. v. Geneesk.* 95, 2490–2491.

Brongersma, L. D. (1952a). On two cases of duplicitas anterior in snakes. *Proc. K. Ned. Akad. Wet.* 55C, 49–61.

Brongersma, L. D. (1952b). Notes upon the arteries of the lungs in *Python reticulatus* (Schn.). *Proc. K. Ned. Akad. Wet.* 55C, 62–73.

Brongersma, L. D. (1952c). On the tracheal lung and lung in *Acrochordus* and some other snakes. *Arch. Néerl. Zool.* 9, 561–562.

Brongersma, L. D. (1954). On the arteria pulmonalis in the Boidae and in some other snakes. *Arch. Néerl. Zool.* 10, 514.

Brongersma, L. D. (1956a). Notes on New Guinean reptiles and amphibians. IV. *Proc. K. Ned. Akad. Wet.* 59C, 447–453.

Brongersma, L. D. (1956b). Notes on New Guinean reptiles and amphibians. V. *Proc. K. Ned. Akad. Wet.* 59C, 599–610.

Brongersma, L. D. (1957a). Notes upon the trachea, the lungs, and the pulmonary artery in snakes. I. *Proc. K. Ned. Akad. Wet.* 60C, 299–308.

Brongersma, L. D. (1957b). Notes upon the trachea, the lungs, and the pulmonary artery in snakes. II. *Proc. K. Ned. Akad. Wet.* 60C, 309–313.

Brongersma, L. D. (1957c). Notes upon the trachea, the lungs, and the pulmonary artery in snakes. III. *Proc. K. Ned. Akad. Wet.* 60C, 451–457.

Brongersma, L. D. (1958a). Upon some features of the respiratory and circulatory systems in the Typhlopidae and some other snakes. *Arch. Néerl. Zool.*, Suppl. 1, 13, 120–127.

Brongersma, L. D. (1958b). Les organes de respiration et l'artère pulmonaire chez les serpents. *Comp. Rend. Assoc. Anat., Leiden* 97, 205–210.

Brongersma, L. D. (1959). Some snakes from the Lesser Antilles. *Stud. Fauna Curaçao Other Carib. Is.* 37, 50–60.

Brongersma, L. D. (1960). Tracheale long of linker long? *Proc. K. Ned. Akad. Wet.* 69, 125–128.

Brongersma, L. D. (1969). Note on *Liasis boeleni* Brongersma. *Proc. K. Ned. Akad. Wet.* 72C, 124–128.

Brongersma, L. D., and Helle, W. (1951). Notes on Indo-Australian snakes. I. *Proc. K. Ned. Akad. Wet.* 54C, 5–10.

Brooks, R. E. (1970). Lung alveolar cell cytosomes: A consideration of their significance. *Z. Zellforsch. Mikrosk. Anat.* 106, 484–497.

Browne, P. (1756). *The Civil and Natural History of Jamaica*. T. Osborne and J. Shipton, London, 503 pp.

Bruno, S. (1984). *Guida ai Serpenti d'Italia*. Giunti Martello, Firenze, 191 pp.

Bruno, S. (1985). *Le Vipere d'Italia e d'Europa*. Edagricole, Bologne, 269 pp.

Bruno, S., and Maugeri, S. (1990). *Serpenti d'Italia e d'Europa*. Editoriale Giorgio Mondadori, Milan, 223 pp.

Bullock, R., and Tanner, W. (1966). A comparative osteological study of two species of Colubridae (*Pituophis* and *Thamnophis*). *Brigham Young Univ. Sci. Bull., Biol.* 8, 1–30.

Bumpus, H. C. (1888). Class VIII.—Reptilia. In *The Riverside Natural History*. (J. S. Kingsley, ed.). Houghton and Mifflin, Boston, vol. 3, pp. 345–468.

Burger, W. L., and Natsuno, T. (1974). A new genus for the Arafura smooth seasnake and redefinition of other seasnake genera. *The Snake* 6, 61–75.

Burggren, W. W. (1977). Circulation during intermittent lung ventilation in the garter snake *Thamnophis*. *Can. J. Zool.* 55, 1720–1725.

Burt, D. R. R. (1944). Snakes. *Loris* 3, 115–118.

Burton, M. (1973a). *The World of Reptiles & Amphibians*. Bounty Books, New York, 128 pp.

Burton, M. (1973b). Boomslang. In *Encyclopedia of Animal Life* (M. Burton, ed.). Marshall Cavendish, New York., part 9, pp. 269–271.

Burton, M. (1978). *Venomous Animals*. Crescent Books, New York, 64 pp.

Burton, J. A. (1991). *The Book of Snakes*. Crescent Books, New York, 144 pp.

Bushman [pseudonym] (1944). Tiger snake call. *Victorian Nat.* 60, 175.

Butler, G. W. (1892). On the subdivisions of the body cavity in snakes. *Proc. Zool. Soc. Lond.* 1892, 477–498.

Butler, G. W. (1895). On the complete or partial suppression of the right lung in the Amphisbaenidae and of the left lung in snakes and snake-like lizards and amphibians. *Proc. Zool. Soc. Lond.* 1895, 691–712.

Butner, A. N. (1963a). "A taxonomic evaluation of the aortic arch and lung variation in snakes." M. S. thesis, Adelphi College, New York, 105 pp.

Butner, A. N. (1963b). An addition to the boid snake subfamily Tropidophinae. *Copeia* 1963, 160–163.

Bütschli, O. (1933). Luftatemorgane. In *Vorlesungen über vergleichende Anatomie 6. Lieferung Atemorgane* (C. Hamburger, F. Blochmann, and W. von Buddenbrock, eds.). Julius Springer, Berlin (1934), pp. 589–700.

Buys, P. J., and Buys, P. J. C. (1981). *Snakes of South West Africa.* Gamsberg, Windhoek, 64 pp.

Cadle, J. E. (1984a). Molecular systematics of Neotropical xenodontine snakes: I. South American xenodontines. *Herpetologica* 40, 8–20.

Cadle, J. E. (1984b). Molecular systematics of Neotropical xenodontine snakes: II. Central American xenodontines. *Herpetologica* 40, 21–30.

Calori, A. (1842). De vasis pulmonum ophidiorum secundariis observationes novae. *Novi Comm. Acad. Sci. Ist. Bononiensis* 5, 395–412.

Calori, L. (1841). Sua memoria intorno ai vasi polmonali secondari degli ofidi. *Rendiconto Nuovi Annali Sci. Nat. Bologna* 5, 57–60.

Campden-Main, S. M. (1970). *A Field Guide to the Snakes of South Vietnam.* Smithsonian Institution, Washington, 114 pp.

Cansdale, G. S. (1948). Field notes on some Gold Coast snakes (illustrated). *Nigerian Field* 13, 43–50.

Cansdale, G. S. (1949a). Further notes on Gold Coast snakes. *Nigerian Field* 14, 52–54.

Cansdale, G. S. (1949b). Further notes on Gold Coast snakes [II]. *Nigerian Field* 14, 106–113.

Cansdale, G. S. (1955). *Reptiles of West Africa.* Penguin Books, London, 104 pp.

Cansdale, G. S. (1961). *West African Snakes.* Longman and Green, London, 74 pp.

Canton, E. (1895). *Conferencias sobre Zoologia Medica.* Imprenta Helvetia, Buenos Aires, 306 pp.

Cantoni, A. F. (1921). Casi di dicefalia in *Tropidonotus natrix. Atti Soc. Ligustica Sci. Natur. Geogr.* 32, 131–142.

Cantor, T. (1841). Observations upon pelagic serpents. *Trans. Zool. Soc. Lond.* 2, 303–312.

Cantor, T. (1847). Catalogue of reptiles inhabiting the Malayan Peninsula and islands, collected or observed. *J. Asiatic Soc. Bengal* 16, 897–952.

Capula, M., and Behler, J. L. (1989). *Simon & Schuster's Guide to Reptiles and Amphibians of the World.* Simon & Schuster, New York, 256 pp.

Carlson, A. J., and Luckhardt, A. B. (1920). Studies on the visceral sensory nervous system. III. Lung automatism and lung reflexes in Reptilia (Turtles: *Chrysemys elegans* and *Malaclemmys lesueurii.* Snake: *Eutaenia elegans*). *Am. J. Physiol.* (1920–1921) 54, 261–306.

Carmichael, P., and Williams, W. (1991). *Florida's Fabulous Reptiles and Amphibians.* World Publications, Tampa, 120 pp.

Carpenter, C. C., and Ferguson, G. W. (1977). Variation and evolution of stereotyped behavior in reptiles. In *Biology of the Reptilia.* (C. Gans and D. W. Tinkle, eds.). Academic Press, London, vol. 7, pp. 335–403.

Carpenter, W. B. (1839). *Principles of General and Comparative Physiology, Intended as an Introduction to the Study of Human Physiology, and as a Guide to the Philosophical Pursuit of Natural History.* John Churchill, London, 478 pp.

Carpenter, W. B. (1844). *Popular Cyclopaedia of Natural Science. Zoology, being a Sketch of the Classification, Structure, Distribution, and Habits of Animals,* vol. 1. Wm. S. Orr, London, 576 pp.

Carpenter, W. B. (1848). *Animal Physiology,* 2nd. ed. Wm. S. Orr, London, 579 pp.

Carpenter, W. B. (1851). *Animal Physiology,* vol. 1, rev. ed. William S. Orr, London, Bell & Daldy, London.

Carpenter, W. B. (1854). *Principles of Comparative Physiology,* 5th ed. Blanchard and Lea, Philadelphia, 752 pp.

Carpenter, W. B. (1859). *Animal Physiology,* 3rd ed. H. G. Bohn, London, 604 pp.

Carpenter, W. B. (1867). *Animal Physiology,* rev. ed. Bell & Daldy, London, 604 pp.

Carpenter, W. B., and Dallas, W. S. (1857). *Zoology; being a Systematic Account of the General Structure, Habits, Instincts, and Uses of the Principal Families of the Animal Kingdom; as well as of the Chief Forms of Fossils Remains,* vol. 1, 2nd ed. Henry G. Bohn, London, 586 pp.

Carpenter, W. B., and Dallas, W. S. (1866). *Zoology; being a Systematic Account of the General Structure, Habits, Instincts, and Uses of the Principal Families of the Animal Kingdom; as well as of the Chief Forms of Fossil Remains.* Bell and Daldy, London.

Carr, A. (1963). *The Reptiles.* Time Incorporated, New York, 192 pp.

Carr, A. (1979). *The Reptiles.* Time-Life Books, Alexandria, Virginia, 128 pp.

Carus, C.-G. (1827). *Introduction to the Comparative Anatomy of Animals; compiled with Constant Reference to Physiology,* vol. 2 (R. T. Gore, trans.). Longman, Rees, Orme, Brown, and Green, London, 400 pp.

Carus, C.-G. (1828). *Grundzüge der vergleichenden Anatomie und Physiologie.* Drittes Bändchen. P. G. Hilschersche, Dresden, 89 pp.

Carus, C.-G. (1835). *Traité Elémentaire d'Anatomie Comparée, suivi de Recherches d'Anatomie Philosophique ou Transcendante sur les Parties Primaires Système Nerveux et du Squelette Intérieur et Extérieur,* vol. 2 (A.-J.-L. Jourdan, trans.). J.-B. Baillière, Paris, 508 pp.

Carus, C.-G. (1838). *Traité Elémentaire d'Anatomie Comparée, suivi de Recherches d'Anatomie Philosophique ou Transcendante sur les Parties Primaires Système Nerveux et du Squelette Intérieur et Extérieur,* vol. 2, 2nd ed. (J.-L. Jourdan, trans.). Meline et Cans, Bruxelles, 808 pp.

Carus, C.-G., and Otto, A. W. (1835). *Erläuterungstafeln zur vergleichenden Anatomie,* part 4. Joh. Ambr. Barth, Leipzig, 24 pp.

Castells, M. T., Ballesta, J., Madrid, J. F., Hernandez, F., Martinez-Menarguez, J. A., and Marin, J. A. (1990). Histochemistry of glycoconjugates in the lung of several vertebrates. *Zool. Jb., Abt. Anat.* 120, 331–346.

Cei, J. M. (1993). Reptiles del noroeste, nordeste y este de la Argentina. *Mus. Reg. Sci. Nat. Monogr.* 14, 1–949.

Charas, M. (1669). *Nouvelles Experiences sur la Vipere ou l'on verra une Description Exacte de Toutes ses Parties, la Source de son Venin, ses Divers Effets, et les remedes Exquis que les Artistes peuvent tirer de la Vipere, tant pour la Guerison de ses Morsures, que pour celle de plusiers autres Maladies.* M. Charas, Paris, 218 pp.

Charas, M. (1670). *New Experiments upon Vipers. Containing also an Exact Description of all the Parts of a Viper, the Seat of its Poyson, and the Several Effects thereof, together with the Exquisite Remedies, that by the Skillful may be Drawn from the Vipers, as well for the Cure of their Bitings, as for that of other Maladies.* F. Martyn, London, 223 pp. (trans. of Charas, 1669)

Charas, M. (1672). *Nouvelles Experiences sur la Vipere, ou l'on verra une Description Exacte de Toutes ses Parties, la Source de son Venin, ses Divers Effets, & les Remedes Exquis que les Artistes peuvent tirer de la Vipere, et une Dissertation sur son Venin, pour servir de Replique à une Lettre que Monsieur Francois Redi Gentil-homme d'Arezzo a écrite à Messieurs Bourdelot & Morus, imprimée à Florence en l'année 1670.* M. Charas, Paris, 245 pp.

Charas, M. (1673). *New Experiments upon Vipers with Exquisite Remedies, that may be Drawn from Them, as well for the Cure of their Bitings, as for that of other Maladies. Also a Letter of Francisco Redi, concerning some Objections made upon his Observations about Vipers. Written to Monsieur Bourdelot and M. Alex. Morus. Together with the Sequel of New Experiments upon Vipers, in a Reply to a Letter Written by Sign. F. Redi.* F. Martyn, London, 223 pp. (trans. of Charas, 1672)

Charas, M. (1693). *Nouvelles Experiences sur la Vipere.* M. Charas, Paris, 367 pp.

Charas, M. (1694). *Nouvelles Experiences sur la Vipere, ou l'on verra une Description Exacte de Toutes ses Parties, la Source de son Venin, ses Divers Effets, & les Remedes Exquis que les Artistes peuvent tirer du Corps de cet Animal,* 2nd ed. Laurent d'Houry, Paris, 367 pp.

Chaves-Mora, F., Alvarado-Alvarado, J., Aymerich-Blen, R., and Solórzano-López, A. (1990). *Aspectos Basicos sobre las Serpientes de Costa Rica.* Universidad de Costa Rica, San José, 58 pp.

Chenu, J. C., and Desmarest, E. (1857). *Encyclopedie d'Histoire Naturelle ou Traite Complet de cette Science d'apres les Travaux des Naturalistes les plus Eminents de Tous les Pays et de Toutes les Epoques: Buffon, Daubenton, Lacépède, G. Cuvier, F. Cuvier, Geoffroy Saint-Hilaire, Latreille, de Jussieu, Brongniart, etc., etc. Reptiles et Poissons.* Marescq, Paris, 360 pp.

Chiodini, R. J., Sundberg, J. P., and Czikowsky, J. A. (1982). Gross anatomy of snakes. *Vet. Med. Sm. Anim. Clin.* 77, 413–419.

Cihar, J. (1979). *A Colour Guide to Familiar Amphibians and Reptiles.* Octopus Books, London, 192 pp.

Cihar, J. (1990). *A Magna Field Guide: Amphibians and Reptiles.* Magna Books, Pragua, 192 pp.

Claus, C. (1868). *Grundzüge der Zoologie, zum Gebrauche an Universitäten und höhern Lehranstalten. Leitfaden zur Einführung in das wissenschaftliche Studium der Zoologie.* N. G. Elwert'sche, Marburg, 839 pp.

Claus, C. (1885). *Elementary Text-Book of Zoology. Special Part: Mollusca to Man,* (A. Sedgwick and F. G. Heathcote, eds. and trans.). Macmillan, New York, 352 pp.

Claus, C. (1897). *Lehrbuch der Zoologie.* Sechste umgearbeitete Auflage. N. G. Elwert'sche, Marburg, 966 pp.

Clausen, H. J. (1934). The effect of aggregation on oxygen consumption in snakes. *Anat. Rec.* 60, Suppl., 49.

Clausen, H. J. (1936). The effect of aggregation on the respiratory metabolism of the brown snake, *Storeria dekayi. J. Cell. Comp. Physiol.* 8, 367–386.

Cleave, A. (1994). *Snakes & Reptiles: A Portrait of the Animal World.* Magna Books, Leicester, 80 pp.

Cloquet, J. (1821). *Mémoire sur l'Existence et la Disposition des Voies Lacrymales dans les Serpens.* Béchet Jeune, Paris, 28 pp.

Coborn, J. (1987). *Snakes & Lizards. Their Care and Breeding in Captivity.* Ralph Curtis, Sanibel Island, Florida, 208 pp.

Coborn, J. (1991). *The Atlas of Snakes of the World.* T.F.H. Publications, Neptune City, New Jersey, 591 pp.

Coborn, J. (1994). *The Mini-Atlas of Snakes of the World.* T.F.H. Publications, Neptune City, New Jersey, 736 pp.

Cöiter, V. (1573). *Externarum et Internarum Principalium Humani Corporis partium Tabulae, atque Anatomicae Exercitationes Observationesque variae, Nouis, Diversis, Acartificiossimis Figuris, Illustratae,* .... T. Gerlatzeni, Noribergae, 133 pp. (not seen)

Cole, F. J. (1944). *A History of Comparative Anatomy from Aristotle to the Eighteenth Century.* Macmillan, London, 524 pp.

Cole, J. (1981). *A Snake's Body.* William Morrow, New York, 48 pp.

Collins, R. F., and Carpenter, C. C. (1970). Organ position-ventral scute relationship in the water moccasin (*Agkistrodon piscivorus leucostoma*), with notes on food habits and distribution. *Proc. Oklahoma Acad. Sci.* 49, 115–118.

Colton, B. P. (1894). *An Elementary Course in Practical Zoölogy.* D. C. Heath, Boston, 185 pp.

Colton, B. P. (1903a). *Zoölogy; Descriptive and Practical,* part 1. D. C. Heath, Boston, 375 pp.

Colton, B. P. (1903b). *Zoölogy; Descriptive and Practical,* part 2. D. C. Heath, Boston. 204 pp.

Cope, E. D. (1891). Remarks on the epiglottis in colubrine snakes. *Am. Nat.* 25, 156–157.

Cope, E. D. (1894a). On the lungs of the Ophidia. *Proc. Am. Phil. Soc.* 33, 217–224.

Cope, E. D. (1894b). The classification of snakes. *Am. Nat.* 28, 831–844.

Cope, E. D. (1895a). The pulmonary structures of the Ophidia. *Proc. Am. Assoc. Adv. Sci., 43rd meetings, Brooklyn* 43, 254.

Cope, E. D. (1895b). The classification of the Ophidia. *Trans. Am. Phil. Soc.,* ser. 2, 18, 186–219.

Cope, E. D. (1900). The crocodilians, lizards, and snakes of North America. *Ann. Rep. Smithsonian Inst.* 1898, 153–1294.

Cox, M. J. (1991). *The snakes of Thailand and their Husbandry.* Robert E. Krieger, Malabar, Florida, 526 pp.

Couvreur, E. (1901). Sur le pneumogastrique des ophidiens et en particulier du *Boa constrictor. Comp. Rend. Assoc. Anat. Lyon* 1901, 212–216.

Cundall, D. (1986). Variations of the cephalic muscles in the colubrid snake genera *Entechinus, Opheodrys,* and *Symphimus. J. Morph.* 187, 1–21.

Cundall, D., and Shardo, J. (1995). Rhinokinetic snout of thamnophiine snakes. *J. Morph.* 225, 31–50.

Cundall, D., Wallach, V., and Rossman, D. A. (1994). The systematic relationships of the snake genus *Anomochilus*. *Zool. J. Linn. Soc.* 109, 275–299.

Curran, C. H., and Kauffeld, C. (1937). *Snakes and their Ways*. Harper and Brothers, New York, 285 pp.

Cuvier, G. L. C. F. D. (1798). *Tableau Elementaire de l'Histoire Naturelle des Animaux*. Baudouin, Paris, 710 pp.

Cuvier, G. L. C. F. D. (1805). *Leçons d'Anatomie Comparée, Recueillies et Publiées sous ses Yeux par G. L. Duvernoy*, vol. 4. Baudouin, Paris, 539 pp.

Cuvier, G. L. C. F. D. (1817 [1816]). *Le Règne Animal Distribue d'apres son Organisation, pour Servir de Base à l'Histoire Naturelle des Animaux et d'Introduction à l'Anatomie Comparée*, vol 2. Deterville, Paris, 532 pp.

Cuvier, G. L. C. F. D. (1829). *Le Règne Animal Distribue d'apres son Organisation, pour Servir de Base à l'Histoire Naturelle des Animaux et d'Introduction à l'Anatomie Comparée*, vol. 2, 2th ed. Deterville, Paris. 406 pp.

Cuvier, G. L. C. F. D. (1831). *The Animal Kingdom Arranged in Conformity with its Organization by the Baron Cuvier*, vol. 2 (H. M'Murtrie, trans.). G. & C. & H. Carvill, New York, 475 pp.

Cuvier, G. L. C. F. D. (1835). *Leçons d'Anatomie Comparée de Georges Cuvier, Recueillies et Publiées par G. L. Duvernoy*, vol. 4, 2nd ed. Crochard et Cie., Paris. 628 pp.

Cuvier, G. L. C. F. D. (1836). *Le Règne Animal Distribue d'apres son Organisation, pour Servir de Base à l'Histoire Naturelle des Animaux et d'Introduction à l'Anatomie Comparée*, vol. 1, 3rd ed. Louis Hauman, Bruxelles, 626 pp.

Cuvier, G. L. C. F. D. (1839). *Leçons d'Anatomie Comparée de Georges Cuvier, Rédigées et Publiées par G.-L. Duvernoy*, vol. 6, 2nd ed. Crochard, Paris, 559 pp.

Cuvier, G. L. C. F. D. (1840). *Leçons d'Anatomie Comparée de Georges Cuvier, Rédigées et Publiées par G.-L. Duvernoy*, vol. 7, 2nd ed. Fortin et Masson, Paris, 656 pp.

d'Alton, E. (1834). Beschreibung des Muskelsystems eines *Python bivittatus*. *Archiv. Anat. Physiol. Wiss. Med.* 1, 346–364.

Dallas, W. S. (1855). *A System of Natural History: Being a Structural and Classified Arrangement of Plants and Animals, forming a Basis for the Study of Botany and Zoology*, vol. 2. Houlston and Stoneman, London, 538 pp.

Daniel, J. C. (1983). *The Book of Indian Reptiles*. Bombay Natural History Society, Bombay, 141 pp.

Daniels, C. B., Orgeig, S., and Smits, A. W. (1995a). The evolution of the vertebrate pulmonary surfactant system. *Physiol. Zoöl.* 68, 539–566.

Daniels, C. B., Smits, A. W., and Orgeig, S. (1995b). Pulmonary surfactant lipids in the faveolar and saccular lung regions of snakes. *Physiol. Zoöl.* 68, 812–830.

Daubenton, L. J. M. (1784). Cinquième ordre. Serpens, des écailles, sans pieds et sans nageoires. In *Encyclopédie Méthodique. L'Histoire Naturelle*. P. G. Simon et N. H. Nyon, Paris, vol. 2, pp. 545–712.

Davies, P. M. C. (1981). Anatomy and physiology. In *Diseases of the Reptilia*. (J. E. Cooper and O. F. Jackson, eds.). Academic Press, London, vol. 1, pp. 9–73.

de Cunha, O. R. (1968). Um teratódimo deródimo em jibóia (*Constrictor constrictor constrictor* (Linn., 1766)). (Ophidia; Boidae). *Bol. Mus. Para. Emílio Goeldi*, ser. 2, 67, 1–17.

Deoras, P. J. (1965). *Snakes of India*. National Book Trust, India, New Delhi, 144 pp.

Deoras, P. J. (1970). *Snakes of India*, 2nd ed. National Book Trust, India, New Delhi, 144 pp.

Deoras, P. J. (1978). *Snakes of India*, 3rd ed. National Book Trust, India, New Delhi, 156 pp.

Deoras, P. J., and Vad, N. E. (1966). Studies on snakes of Maharashtra State. II. Observation on the morphology of *Echis carinatus*. *J. Univ. Bombay*, ser. 2, 34, 57–94.

Deoras, P. J., and Vad, N. E. (1973). Lung reduction in snakes and toxicity of salivary secretions. *J. Univ. Bombay*, ser. 2, 42, 81–86.

Deraniyagala, P. E. P. (1955). *A Colored Atlas of some Vertebrates from Ceylon*, vol. 3. Colombo National Museum, Colombo, 121 pp.

de Saint-Aubain, M. L. (1984). A comparative study of the functional anatomy of pulmonary vaso-constriction in lung-breathing vertebrates. *Z. Zool. Syst. Evolut.-Forsch.* 22, 118–136.

de Silva, A. (1976). Venomous snakes of Sri Lanka. *The Snake* 8, 31–42.

de Silva, A. (1990). *Colour Guide to the Snakes of Sri Lanka*. R & A Publications, Avon, U.K. 130 pp.

de Silva, P. H. D. H. (1953). The arterial system in Ceylon snakes — *Naja naja naja* Linné. (The Ceylon cobra). *Spolia Zeylanica* 27, 47–58.

de Silva, P. H. D. H. (1955). The arterial system in Ceylon snakes — (2) *Natrix piscator asperrimus* (Boulenger). *Spolia Zeylanica* 27, 257–275.

de Witte, G.-F. (1948). *Faune de Belgique. Amphibiens et Reptiles*. 2nd ed. Musée Royal d'Histoire Naturelle de Belgique, Bruxelles, 321 pp.

de Witte, G.-F. (1962). Genres des serpents du Congo et du Ruanda-Urundi. *Ann. Mus. R. Afrique Cen., Sci. Zool., Tervuren*, ser. 8, 104, 1–203.

Dillon, B. (1831). Notice of the breathing-tube of the *Boa*. *Mag. Nat. Hist.* 4, 20–21.

Ditmars, R. L. (1907). *The Reptile Book. A Comprehensive Popularized Work on the Structure and Habits of the Turtles, Tortoises, Crocodilians, Lizards and Snakes which Inhabit the United States and Northern Mexico*. Doubleday, Page, & Co., New York, 472 pp.

Ditmars, R. L. (1931). *Snakes of the World*. Macmillan, New York, 207 pp.

Ditmars, R. L. (1936). *The Reptiles of North America. A Review of the Crocodilians, Lizards, Snakes, Turtles and Tortoises Inhabiting the United States and Northern Mexico*, 2nd ed. Doubleday, Garden City, New Jersey, 476 pp.

Divers, S. (1995). Veterinary corner: respiratory disease in snakes. *Reptilian Mag.* 3(5), 41–46.

Dixon, J. R., and Soini, P. (1977). The reptiles of the upper Amazon Basin, Iquitos region, Peru. II. Crocodilians, turtles and snakes. *Milwaukee Pub. Mus., Contr. Biol. Geol.* 12, 1–91.

Dixon, J. R., and Soini, P. (1986). *The Reptiles of the Upper Amazon Basin, Iquitos Region, Peru*, parts 1–2. Milwaukee Pub. Mus., Milwaukee, 154 pp.

Dixon, J. R., Wiest, J. A., and Cei, J. M. (1993 [1995]). Revision of the Neotropical snake genus *Chironius* Fitzinger (Serpentes, Colubridae). *Mus. Reg. Sci. Nat. Torino, Monogr.* (? 1993) 13, 1–279.

do Amaral, A. (1930a). Estudos sobre ophidios neotropicos. XIX. Revisão do genero *Spilotes* Wagler, 1830. *Mem. Inst. Butantan* (1929) 4, 275–298.

do Amaral, A. (1930b). Estudos sobre ophidios neotropicos. XX. Revisão do genero *Phrynonax* Fitzinger. *Mem. Inst. Butantan* (1929) 4, 301–320.

Donald, J. A., and Lillywhite, H. B. (1989a). Vasoactive intestinal polypeptide-immunoreactive nerves in the pulmonary vasculature of the aquatic file snake *Acrochordus granulatus*. *Cell Tissue Res.* 255, 585–588.

Donald, J. A., and Lillywhite, H. B. (1989b). Adrenergic nerves and 5-hydroxytryptamine-containing cells in the pulmonary vasculature of the aquatic file snake *Acrochordus granulatus*. *Cell Tissue Res.* 256, 113–118.

Donald, J. A., O'Shea, J. E., and Lillywhite, H. B. (1990). Neural regulation of the pulmonary vasculature in a semi-arboreal snake, *Elaphe obsoleta*. *J. Comp. Physiol.* 159B, 677–685.

Donnelly, P. M., and Woolcock, A. J. (1972). Ventilation and gas exchange in snake lungs. *Proc. Aust. Physiol. Pharm. Soc.* 2, 77–78.

Donnelly, P. M., and Woolcock, A. J. (1977). Ventilation and gas exchange in the carpet python, *Morelia spilotes variegata*. *J. Comp. Physiol.* 122B, 403–418.

Donnelly, P. M., and Woolcock, A. J. (1978). Stratification of inspired air in the elongated lungs of the carpet python, *Morelia spilotes variegata*. *Respir. Physiol.* 35, 301–315.

Donoso-Barros, R. (1965). *Las Serpientes*. Museo Nacional de Historia Natural, Santiago, Chile, 24 pp.

Dorner, H. (1873). Eine Kreuzotter mit zwei Köpfen. *Zool. Garten* 14, 407–410.

Dottrens, E., and Aellen, V. (1963). *Batraciens et reptiles d'Europe*. Éditions Delachaux & Niestlé, Neuchatel, 261 pp.

Dowling, H. G. (1959). Classification of the Serpentes: a critical review. *Copeia* 1959, 38–52.

Dowling, H. G., and Duellman, W. E. (1978). Systematic herpetology: a synopsis of families and higher categories. *Herpetological Information Search Service Publ.* 7, 1–240.

Dowling, H. G., Hass, C. A., Hedges, S. B., and Highton, R. (1996). Snake relationships revealed by slow-evolving proteins: a preliminary survey. *J. Zool.* 240, 1–28.

Dowsett, J. M. (1928). *Snake Life Simply Told*, 2nd ed. John Bale, Sons, and Danielsson, London, 63 pp.

Dugès, A. (1827). Recherches anatomiques et physiologiques sur la déglutition dans les reptiles. *Ann. Sci. Nat.* 12, 337–395.

Dugès, A. (1888). Erpetología del Valle de México. *La Naturaleza*, ser. 2, 1, 97–146.

Dulzetto, F. (1968). *Anatomia Comparata dei Vertebrati*, vol. 2. Edizioni Calderini, Bologna, pp. 1186–2221.

Duméril, A. M. C., and Bibron, G. (1844). *Erpétologie Générale ou Histoire Naturelle Complète des Reptiles*, vol. 6. Librairie Encyclopédique de Roret, Paris, 609 pp.

Duncker, H.-R. (1978a). General morphological principles of amniotic lungs. In *Respiratory Function in Birds, Adult and Embryonic* (J. Piiper, ed.). Springer-Verlag, Berlin, pp. 2–15.

Duncker, H.-R. (1978b). Coelom-Gliederung der Wirbeltiere-Funktionelle Aspekte. *Verh. Anat. Ges.* 72, 91–112.

Duncker, H.-R. (1978c). Funktionsmorphologie des Atemapparates und Coelomgliederung bei Reptilien, Vögeln und Säugern. *Verh. Deutsch. Zool. Ges.* 1978, 99–132.

Duncker, H.-R. (1981). Stammesgeschichte der Struktur- und Funktionsprinzipien der Wirbeltierlungen. *Verh. Anat. Ges.* 75, 279–303.

Dunger, G. T. (1973). The snakes of Nigeria. Part 4: The harmless green snakes of Nigeria. *Nigerian Field* 38, 158–180.

Dunn, E. R. (1944). Los generos de anfibios y reptiles de Colombia, III. Tercera parte: Reptiles; orden de las serpientes. *Caldasia* 3, 155–224.

Dunson, W. A. (1971). The sea snakes are coming. *Nat. Hist.* 80(4), 52–61.

Dunson, W. A. (1975a). Adaptations of sea snakes. In *The Biology of Sea Snakes* (W. A. Dunson, ed.). University Park Press, Baltimore, pp. 3–19.

Dunson, W. A. (1975b). Salt and water balance in sea snakes. In *The Biology of Sea Snakes* (W. A. Dunson, ed.). University Park Press, Baltimore, pp. 329–353.

Dutrochet, H. (1830a). Observations sur une vipère à deux têtes. *Analyse* [*Suite de l'extrait du Compte-Rendu des Travaux de l'Académie Royale des Sciences*], 9, pagination unknown. (not seen)

Dutrochet, H. (1830b). Monstruosités. Observations sur une phénomène analogue; une vipère à deux têtes. *Trans. Méd., Paris* 1, 416–417. (reprint of Dutrochet, 1830a)

Duvernoy, G. L. (1832). Mémoire sur les caractères tirés de l'anatomie pour distinguer les serpens venimeux des serpens non venimeux. *Ann. Sci. Nat., Paris* 26, 113–160.

Duvernoy, G. L. (1833). Ueber die anatomischen Kennzeichen zur Unterscheidung der Giftschlangen von den Ungiftigen. *Isis von Oken* 1833, 626–642. (German trans. of Duvernoy, 1832)

Eaton, T. H., Jr. (1960). *Comparative Anatomy of the Vertebrates*, 2nd ed. Harper and Row, New York, 383 pp.

Eberth, C. J. (1863). Ueber den feineren Bau der Lunge. *Z. Wiss. Zool.* 12, 427–454.

Edgeworth, F. H. (1935). *The Cranial Muscles of Vertebrates*. Cambridge University Press, Cambridge, 493 pp.

Ehmann, H. (1993a). Family Boidae. In *Fauna of Australia* (C. J. Glasby, G. J. B. Ross, and P. L. Beesley, eds.). Australian Government Publishing Service, Canberra, vol. 2A, pp. 284–289.

Ehmann, H. (1993b). Family Colubridae. In *Fauna of Australia* (C. J. Glasby, G. J. B. Ross, and P. L. Beesley, eds.). Australian Government Publishing Service, Canberra, vol. 2A, pp. 290–294.

Elenz, E. (1864). Ueber das Lungenepithel. *Würzburger Naturwiss. Z.* 5, 66–83.

Emsley, M. (1977). Snakes, and Trinidad and Tobago. *Bull. Maryland Herpetol. Soc.* 13, 201–304.

Engelmann, W.-E., and Obst, F. J. (1981). *Snakes: Biology, Behavior, and Relationship to Man*. Exeter Books, New York, 222 pp.

Ernst, C. H., and Zug, G. R. (1996). *Snakes in Question. The Smithsonian Answer Book*. Smithsonian Inst. Press, Washington, 203 pp.

Evans, H. E. (1955). The osteology of a worm snake, *Typhlops jamaicensis* (Shaw). *Anat. Rec.* 122, 381–396.

Ferrarezzi, H. (1994). Nota sobre o gênero *Phalotris* com revisão do grupo *nasutus* e descrição de três novas espécies (Serpentes, Colubridae, Xenodontinae). *Mem. Inst. Butantan* 55, suppl. 1, 21–38.

Fischer, G. (1813). *Zoognosia Tabulis Synopticus Illustrata*, vol. 2. Nicolai Sergeidis Vsevolozsky, Moscow.

Fischer, P.-H. (1942). *Guides Techniques du Naturaliste*, vol. 2. Paul Lechevalier, Paris, 202 pp.

FitzSimons, F. W. (1912). *The Snakes of South Africa, their Venom and the Treatment of Snake Bite*, 2nd ed. T. Maskew Miller, Cape Town, 547 pp.

FitzSimons, F. W. (1921). *The Snakes of South Africa, their Venom and the Treatment of Snake Bite*, 3rd ed. T. Maskew Miller, Cape Town, 550 pp.

FitzSimons, V. F. M. (1962). *Snakes of Southern Africa*. Macdonald, London, 423 pp.

FitzSimons, V. F. M. (1966). Some South African snakes. *African Wild Life* 20(1), 41–48.

FitzSimons, V. F. M. (1970). *A Field Guide to the Snakes of Southern Africa*. Collins, London, 221 pp.

Fleischmann, F. L. (1831). *Dalmatiae nova Serpentum Genera*. C. Heyderi, Erlangae, 30 pp.

Fleming, J. (1822). *The Philosophy of Zoology*, vols. 1–2. Archibald Constable, Edinburgh, 618 pp.

Flower, S. S. (1899). Notes on a second collection of reptiles made in the Malay Peninsula and Siam from November 1896 to September 1898, with a list of the species recorded from those countries. *Proc. Zool. Soc. Lond.* 1899, 600–696.

Folk, D. M. (1971). "Some aspects of the anatomy of *Eryx conicus*, a primitive semifossorial snake." M.S. thesis, Boston University, Boston, 108 pp.

Fowler, A. (1992). *It's Best to Leave a Snake Alone*. Children's Press, Chicago, 32 pp.

Fowler, M. E. (1980). Differential diagnosis of pneumonia in reptiles. In *Reproductive Biology and Diseases of Captive Reptiles* (J. B. Murphy and J. T. Collins, eds.). Society for the Study of Amphibians and Reptiles, Athens, Ohio, Contr. Herpetol. 1, pp. 227–233.

Frank, W. (1978). *Schlangen im Terrarium: Haltung und Pflege ungiftiger Schlangen.* — 1. Aufl. Franckh, Stuttgart. (not seen)

Frank, W. (1979). *Boas and Other Non-Venomous Snakes* (U. E. Friese, trans.). T.F.H. Publications, Neptune City, New Jersey, 95 pp. (trans. of Frank, 1978)

Fraser, A. G. L. (1937). The snakes of Deolali. With notes on their comparative osteology and peculiarities of dentition. *J. Bombay Nat. Hist. Soc.* 39, 264–290.

Frazzetta, T. H. (1966). Studies on the morphology and function of the skull in the Boidae (Serpentes). II. Morphology and function of the jaw apparatus in *Python sebae* and *Python molurus*. *J. Morph.* 118, 217–295.

Freiberg, M. (1982). *Snakes of South America*. T.F.H. Publications, Neptune City, New Jersey, 189 pp.

Freiberg, M., and Walls, J. G. (1984). *The World of Venomous Animals*. T.F.H. Publications, Neptune City, New Jersey, 191 pp.

Frenkel, G., and Kochva, E. (1970). Visceral anatomy of *Vipera palaestinae*: an illustrated presentation. *Israel J. Zool.* 19, 145–163.

Frenzelius, S. F. (1665). *Sapientissimo autore Naturae Fortunante! Serpentem, athenis leucoreis ad diem XXIIX Junii sub praesidio viri Praeclarissimi M. Simonis Friderici Frenzelii, Amplissimae Facultatis Philosophicae adjuncti Meritissimi, Dn. Favitoris ac Praeceptoris sui aeternum colendi, Publicae Eruditorum Contemplationi sistit Arnoldus Berninck, Hamburgensis, author, in Acroaterio Majori.* Johannis Haken, Wittebergae, 34 pp.

Fritsch, G. (1869). Zur vergleichenden Anatomie der Amphibienherzen. *Arch. Anat. Physiol. Wiss. Medecin* 1869, 654–758.

Frivaldszky, E. (1823). *Monographia Serpentum Hungariae.* Nobilis Joannis Thomae Trattner de Petróza, Pestini, 62 pp.

Frommhold, E. (1959). *Wir Bestimmen Lurche und Kriechtiere Mitteleuropas.* Neumann Verlag, Radebeul, 219 pp.

Froom, B. (1972). *The Snakes of Canada.* McClelland and Stewart, Toronto, 128 pp.

Frye, F. L. (1984). Euthanasia, a necropsy technique and comparative histology of reptiles. In *Diseases of Amphibians and Reptiles* (G. L. Hoff, F. L. Frye, and E. R. Jacobson, eds.). Plenum Press, New York, pp. 703–755.

Frye, F. L. (1991). *Reptile Care: An Atlas of Diseases and Treatments,* vol. 2. T.F.H. Publications, Neptune City, New Jersey, 637 pp.

Fuhn, I. E., and Vancea, S. (1961). *Fauna Republicii Romine. Reptilia (Testoase, Sopirle, Serpi),* vol. 14, fasc. 2. Academiei Republicii Populare Romine, Bucuresti, 349 pp.

Fürbringer, M. (1922). *Das Zungenbein der Wirbeltiere insbesondere der Reptilien und Vögel.* Walter de Gruyter, Berlin, 164 pp.

Gadow, H. (1901). *Amphibia and Reptiles. Cambridge natural history,* vol. 8 (S. F. Harmer and A. E. Shipley, eds.). Macmillan, London, 668 pp.

Gadow, H. (1911). Reptiles. In *Encyclopaedia Britannica: a Dictionary of Arts, Sciences, and General Literature.* University Press, Cambridge, vol. 23, 11th ed., pp. 136–176.

Gadow, H. (1923). *Amphibia and Reptiles. Cambridge natural history,* vol. 8 (S. F. Harmer and A. E. Shipley, eds.). Macmillan, London. 668 pp.

Gans, C. (1959). A taxonomic revision of the African snake genus *Dasypeltis* (Reptilia: Serpentes). *Ann. Mus. Roy. Congo Belge Tervuren,* ser. 8, Sci. Zool. 74, 1–237.

Gans, C. (1974). *Biomechanics: an Approach to Vertebrate Biology.* J. P. Lippincott, Philadelphia, 261 pp.

Gans, C. (1975a). Tetrapod limblessness: evolution and functional corollaries. *Am. Zool.* 15, 455–467.

Gans, C. (1975b). *Reptiles of the World.* Ridge Press, Toronto, 159 pp.

Gans, C. (1978). Ventilation mechanisms: problems in evaluating the transition to birds. In *Respiratory Function in Birds, Adult and Embryonic* (J. Piiper, ed.). Springer-Verlag, Berlin, pp. 16–22.

Gans, C., and Clark, B. D. (1978). Air flow in reptilian ventilation. *Comp. Biochem. Physiol.* 60A, 453–457.

Gans, C., and Maderson, P. F. A. (1973). Sound production in Recent reptiles: review and comment. *Am. Zool.* 13, 1195–1203.

Gans, C., and Richmond, N. D. (1957). Warning behavior in snakes of the genus *Dasypeltis. Copeia* 1957, 269–274.

Garman, S. (1883). The reptiles and batrachians of North America. *Mem. Mus. Comp. Zool., Harvard Coll.* 8, 1–185.

Garrigues, N. W. (1962). Placement of internal organs in snakes in relation to ventral scalation. *Trans. Kansas Acad. Sci.* 65, 297–300.

Gasc, J.-P., and Rodrigues, M. T. (1980). Liste préliminaire des serpents de la Guyane française. *Bull. Mus. Natn. Hist. Nat., Paris*, ser. 4, 2A, 559–598.

Gavrilov, K. (1979). *Curso de anatomia y fisiologia comparadas. VI. Organos respiratorios (tercera parte).* Universidad Nacional de Tucumán, San Miguel de Tucumán, 197 pp.

Gee, J. H. (1987). Subsurface buoyancy control by the sea snake *Pelamis platurus. Australian Soc. Herpetol. Newsletter* 29, 46. (abstract)

Gegenbaur, C. (1870). *Grundzüge der vergleichenden Anatomie*, 2nd ed. (revised). Wilhelm Engelmann, Leipzig, 892 pp.

Gegenbaur, C. (1874). *Grundriss der vergleichenden Anatomie.* Wilhelm Engelmann, Leipzig, 660 pp.

Gegenbaur, C. (1878a). *Grundriss der vergleichenden Anatomie*, 2nd ed. (improved). Wilhelm Engelmann, Leipzig, 655 pp.

Gegenbaur, C. (1878b). *Elements of Comparative Anatomy* (F. J. Bell and E. R. Lankester, trans.). Macmillan, London, 645 pp.

Gelderen, C. van (1933). Venensystem, mit einem Anhang über den Dotter- und Plazentarktreislauf. In *Handbuch der vergleichenden Anatomie der Wirbeltiere*, (L. Bolk, E. Göppert, E. Kallius, and W. Lubosch, eds.). Urban & Schwarzenberg, Berlin and Vienna, vol. 6, pp. 685–744.

George, J. C., and Shah, R. V. (1956). Comparative morphology of the lung in snakes with remarks on the evolution of the lung in reptiles. *J. Anim. Morph. Physiol.* 3, 1–7.

George, J. C., and Shah, R. V. (1965). Evolution of air sacs in Sauropsida. *J. Anim. Morph. Physiol.* 12, 255–263.

George, J. C., and Varde, M. R. (1941). A note on the modification of the lung and the trachea in some Indian snakes. *J. Univ. Bombay*, ser. 2, 10B, 70–73.

George, W. C. (1923). A note on the pulmonary circulation in vertebrates. *Anat. Rec.* 25, 31–39.

Gervais, P. (1847). Ophidiens. In *Dictionnaire Universel d'Histoire Naturelle, Résumant et Complétant.* (C. d'Orbigny, ed.). Renard et Martinet, Paris, vol. 9, pp. 123–130.

Gervais, P. (1848). Reptiles. In *Dictionnaire Universel d'Histoire Naturelle, Résumant et Complétant.* (C. d'Orbigny, ed.). Renard et Martinet, Paris, vol. 11, pp. 1–816.

Gervais, P. (1866). *Éléments des Sciences Naturelles. Zoologie, comprenant l'Anatomie, la Physiologie, la Classification et l'Histoire Naturelle des Animaux.* L. Hachette, Paris, 448 pp.

Gervais, P. (1869). *Bibliothèque des Sciences Naturelles. Zoologie, Reptiles Vivants et Fossiles.* Germer Baillière, Paris, 80 pp.

Geus, A. (1992). *The Proper Care of Snakes.* T.F.H. Publications, Neptune City, New Jersey, 256 pp.

Gharpurey, K. G. (1962). *Snakes of India and Pakistan*, 5th ed. Popular Prakashan, Bombay, 156 pp.

Gibbons, W. (1983). *Their Blood Runs Cold: Adventures with Reptiles and Amphibians.* University of Alabama Press, University, Alabama, 164 pp.

Gibson, F. W. (1966). Head muscles of *Boa constrictor*. *Zoologica* 51(3), 29–48.

Gillian, L. A., and Conklin, R. E. (1938). Removal of foreign substances by the lymphatics of the snake lung. *Am. J. Physiol.* 123, 598–607.

Glass, M. L., and Johansen, K. (1976). Control of breathing in *Acrochordus javanicus*, an aquatic snake. *Physiol. Zoöl.* 49, 328–340.

Gloyd, H. K., and Conant, R. (1990). *Snakes of the* Agkistrodon *Complex: a Monographic Review*. Society for the Study of Amphibians and Reptiles, Oxford, Ohio, Contr. Herpetol. 6, vi+614 pp.

Gnanamuthu, C. P. (1937). Comparative study of the hyoid and tongue of some typical genera of reptiles. *Proc. Zool. Soc. Lond.* 107B, 1–63.

Goin, C. J., and Goin, O. B. (1971). *Introduction to Herpetology*, 2nd ed. W. H. Freeman, San Francisco, 353 pp.

Goin, C. J., Goin, O. B., and Zug, G. R. (1978). *Introduction to Herpetology*, 3rd ed. W. H. Freeman, San Francisco, 378 pp.

Gomes, N., and Puorto, G. (1994). Atlas anatômico de *Bothrops jararaca* Wied, 1824 (Serpentes: Viperidae). *Mem. Inst. Butantan* (1993) 55, Suppl. 1, 69–100.

Gomes, N., Puorto, G., Buononato, M. A., and de Fátima M. Ribeiro, M. (1989). Atlas anatomico de *Boa constrictor* Linnaeus, 1758 (Serpentes; Boidae). *Monogr. Inst. Butantan* 2, 1–59.

Gomi, T. (1982). Electron microscopic studies on the alveolar brush cell of the striped snake (*Elaphe quadrivirgata*). *J. Med. Soc. Toho Univ.* 29, 481–489.

Goodman, J. D., and Goodman, J. M. (1976). Possible mimetic behavior of the twig snake, *Thelotornis kirtlandi kirtlandi* (Hallowell). *Herpetologica* 32, 148–150.

Goodrich, E. S. (1919). Note on the reptilian heart. *J. Anat.* 53, 298–304.

Goodrich, E. S. (1930). *Studies on the Structure and Development of Vertebrates*. Constable, London. 837 pp. (reprinted as 2 vols. in 1958 by Dover Publications, New York)

Göppert, E. (1899). Der Kehlkopf der Amphibien und Reptilien. II. Theil. Reptilien. *Gegenbaurs Morph. Jb.* 28, 1–27.

Göppert, E. (1937). Atmungssystem (Organe der Luftatmung). I. Kehlkopf und Trachea. In *Handbuch der vergleichenden Anatomie der Wirbeltiere. 3 (III,B)*. (L. Bolk, E. Göppert, E. Kallius, and W. Lubosch, eds.). Urban und Schwarzenberg, Berlin, Wien, pp. 797–866.

Gosse, P. H. (1850). *Natural History. Reptiles*. Society for Promoting Christian Knowledge, London, 296 pp.

Gow, G. (1989). *Graeme Gow's Complete Guide to Australian Snakes*. Angus and Robertson, North Ryde, Australia, 171 pp.

Graham, J. B. (1973). Aquatic respiration and the physiological responses to submersion of the sea snake *Pelamis platurus*. *Am. Zool.* 13, 1296 (abstract).

Graham, J. B., Gee, J. H., and Robison, F. S. (1975). Hydrostatic and gas exchange functions of the lung of the sea snake *Pelamis platurus*. *Comp. Biochem. Physiol.* 50A, 477–482.

Graham, J. B., Gee, J. H., Motta, J., and Rubinoff, I. (1987a). Subsurface bouyancy regulation by the sea snake *Pelamis platurus*. *Physiol. Zoöl.* 60, 251–261.

Graham, J. B., Lowell, W. R., Rubinoff, I., and Motta, J. (1987b). Surface and subsurface swimming of the sea snake *Pelamis platurus*. *J. Exp. Biol.* 127, 27–44.

Grant, C. (1933). Notes on *Epicrates inornatus* (Reinhardt). *Copeia* 1933, 224–225.

Grant, M. M., Brain, J. D., and Vinegar, A. (1981). Pulmonary defense mechanisms in *Boa constrictor*. *J. Appl. Physiol., Respir. Environ. Exercise Physiol.* 50, 979–983.

Grant, M. M., Vinegar, A., and Brain, J. D. (1979). Respiratory defense mechanisms in the *Boa constrictor*. *Fed. Proc.* 38, 1246.

Gratz, R. K. (1978). Ventilation and gas exchange in the diamondback water snake, *Natrix rhombifera*. *J. Comp. Physiol.* 127B, 299–305.

Gratz, R. K., Ar, A., and Geiser, J. (1981). Gas tension profile of the lung of the viper, *Vipera xanthina palaestinae*. *Respir. Physiol.* 44, 165–176.

Gravier, L. (1994). Snake diseases. In *Snakes: a Natural History* (R. Bauchot, ed.). Sterling, New York, p. 180.

Gray, J. E. (1842). Monographic synopsis of the water snakes, or the family Hydridae. *Zool. Misc.* 2, 59–68.

Green, C. R., and Sanford, W. R. (1984). *The Rattlesnake.* Crestwood House, Mankato, Minnesota, 47 pp.

Greene, H. W. (1977). "Phylogeny, convergence, and snake behavior." Ph.D. dissertation, Univ. Tennessee, Knoxville, 112 pp.

Greene, H. W. (1979). Behavioral convergence in the defensive displays of snakes. *Experientia* 35, 747–748.

Greene, H. W. (1988). Antipredator mechanisms in reptiles. In *Biology of the Reptilia.* (C. Gans and R. B. Huey, eds.). Alan R. Liss, New York, vol. 16, pp. 3–152.

Greene, H. W. (1997). *Snakes: The Evolution of Mystery in Nature.* Univ. California Press, Berkeley, 351 pp.

Greene, H. W., and Burghardt, G. M. (1978). Behavior and phylogeny: constriction in ancient and modern snakes. *Science* 200, 74–77.

Greene, H. W., and McDiarmid, R. W. (1981). Coral snake mimicry: does it occur? *Science* 213, 1207–1212.

Greil, A. (1903). Beiträge zur vergleichenden Anatomie und Entwicklungsgeschichte des Herzens und des Truncus arteriosus der Wirbelthiere. *Gegenbaurs Morph. Jb.* 31, 123–310.

Griner, L. A. (1983). *Pathology of Zoo Animals.* Zoological Society of San Diego, San Diego, 608 pp.

Groombridge, B. C. (1979). Variations in morphology of the superficial palate of henophidian snakes and some possible systematic implications. *J. Nat. Hist.* 13, 447–475.

Groombridge, B. C. (1980). "A phyletic analysis of viperine snakes." Ph.D. dissertation, City of London Polytechnic and British Museum (Natural History), London, 268 pp.

Guibé, J. (1962). *Les Reptiles.* Presses Universitaires de France, Paris, 125 pp.

Guibé, J. (1970a). L'appareil circulatoire. In *Traité de Zoologie: Anatomie, Systématique, Biologie.* (P.-P. Grassé, ed.). Masson, Paris, vol. 14, pp. 429–473.

Guibé, J. (1970b). L'appareil respiratoire. In *Traité de Zoologie: Anatomie, Systématique, Biologie.* (P.-P. Grassé, ed.). Masson, Paris, vol. 14, pp. 499–520.

Günther, A. C. L. G. (1886). Reptiles. In *Encyclopaedia Britannica: a Dictionary of Arts, Sciences, and General Literature.* (T. S. Baynes and W. R. Smith, eds.). A. & C. Black, Edinburgh, vol. 20, 9th ed., pp. 432–473.

Haast, W. E., and Anderson, R. (1981). *Complete Guide to Snakes of Florida*. Phoenix, Miami, Florida, 139 pp.

Hackbarth, R. (1985). *Krankheiten der Reptilien*. Kosmos, Stuttgart, 88 pp.

Hafferl, A. (1933). Das Arteriensystem. In *Handbuch der vergleichenden Anatomie* (L. Bolk, E. Göppert, E. Kallius, and W. Lubosch, eds.). Urban und Schwarzenberg, Berlin and Vienna, vol. 6, pp. 563–684.

Haller, R. (1971). The diamondback rattlesnakes. *Herpetology* (Pasadena, California) 5, 1–34.

Halliday, T., and Adler, K. (1986). *Reptiles & Amphibians*. Torstar Books, New York, 160 pp.

Hance, H. E. (1972). Water snake respiration. *Bull. Philadelphia Herpetol. Soc.* 20, 3–13.

Hanna, M. Y. (1963). Carbohydrates, fat, and water content of the tissues of the snake *Psammophis sibilans*. *Proc. Zool. Soc. United Arab Rep.* 1, 25–31.

Harrison, B. M., and Denning, N. E. (1930). Embryonic development of the pharyngeal region in *Thamnophis radix*. *Anat. Rec.* 44, 101–116.

Harrisson, T. (1950). Chick versus king cobra. *Sarawak Mus. J.* 5, 326–327.

Hartline, P. H. (1971). Physiological basis for detection of sound and vibration in snakes. *J. Exp. Biol.* 54, 349–371.

Hartline, P. H., and Campbell, H. W. (1969). Auditory and vibratory responses in the midbrain of snakes. *Science* 163, 1221–1223.

Hatch, J. L. (1890). Some original investigations upon the *Python molurus*. *J. Comp. Med. Vet. Arch.* 11, 415–435.

Heasman, W. J. (1933). The anatomy of a double-headed snake. *J. Anat.* 67, 331–345.

Heatwole, H. (1975). Voluntary submergence times of marine snakes. *Marine Biol.* 32, 205–213.

Heatwole, H. (1977). Voluntary submergence time and breathing rhythm in the homalopsine snake, *Cerberus rhynchops*. *Aust. Zool.* 19, 155–167.

Heatwole, H. (1981). Role of the saccular lung in the diving of the sea krait, *Laticauda colubrina* (Serpentes: Laticaudidae). *Aust. J. Zool.* 1, 11–16.

Heatwole, H. (1987). *Sea Snakes*. New South Wales University Press, Kensington, New South Wales, 85 pp.

Heatwole, H., and Cogger, H. G. (1993). Family Hydrophiidae. In *Fauna of Australia*. (C. J. Glasby, G. J. B. Ross, and P. L. Beesley, eds.). Australian Government Publishing Service, Canberra, vol. 2A, pp. 310–318.

Heatwole, H., and Guinea, M. L. (1993). Family Laticaudidae. In *Fauna of Australia*. (C. J. Glasby, G. J. B. Ross, and P. L. Beesley, eds.). Australian Government Publishing Service, Canberra, vol. 2A, pp. 319–321.

Heatwole, H., and Seymour, R. S. (1975a). Pulmonary and cutaneous oxygen uptake in sea snakes and a file snake. *Comp. Biochem. Physiol.* 51A, 399–405.

Heatwole, H., and Seymour, R. S. (1975b). Diving physiology. In *The Biology of Sea Snakes*. (W. A. Dunson, ed.). University Park Press, Baltimore, pp. 289–327.

Heatwole, H., Minton, S. A., Jr., and Taylor, R. (1978). Underwater observations on sea snake behavior. *Rec. Aust. Mus.* 31, 737–761.

Hedges, N. G. (1983). *Reptiles and Amphibians of East Africa*. Kenya Literature Bureau, Nairobi, 139 pp.

Hediger, H. (1975). Introduction to snakes. In *Grzimek's Animal Life Encyclopedia*.

(B. H. Grzimek, H. Hediger, K. Klemmer, O. Kuhn, and H. Wermuth, eds.). Van Nostrand Reinhold, New York, vol. 6, pp. 345–358.

Heilmann, P. (1914). Die Entwicklung der Reptillunge. *Morph. Jb.* 48, 483–512.

Heine, H. (1976). Stammes- und Entwicklungs-geschichte des Herzens Lungenatmender. *Abh. Senckenberg. Naturforsch. Ges.* 535, 1–152.

Heinrich, M. L., and Klaassen, H. E. (1985). Side dominance in constricting snakes. *J. Herpetol.* 19, 531–533.

Helfenberger, N. (1989). "Morphologie und Organtopographie bei Vertretern der Schlangengattung *Elaphe* Fitzinger, 1833 (Reptilia, Serpentes)." M.S. thesis, Univ. Zürich, Zürich, 71 pp.

Henderson, R. W., and Binder, M. H. (1980). The ecology and behavior of vine snakes (*Ahaetulla, Oxybelis, Thelotornis, Uromacer*): a review. *Contr. Biol. Geol. Milwaukee Pub. Mus.* 37, 1–38.

Henle, B. (1839). *Vergleichend-anatomische Beschreibung des Kehlkopfs, mit besonderer Berücksichtigung des Kehlkopfs der Reptilien.* Leopold Voss, Leipzig, 83 pp.

Hering, E. (1860). Notizen zur Anatomie der *Boa constrictor* L. *Jahres. Ver. Väterl. Naturkunde Württemberg, Stuttgart* 16, 103–105.

Herklots, G. A. C. (1934). Land snakes of Hong Kong. Part II. *Hong Kong Nat.* 5, 23–30.

Heurn, W. C. van (1929). *Coluber radiatus*, de "tjaoe asak." *Trop. Nat.* 18, 128–130.

Heyder, G. (1966). "Ein Beitrag zur Anatomie der inneren Organe von *Typhlops vermicularis* Merrem (1820)." Ph.D. dissertation, Martin-Luther-Universität, Halle-Wittenberg, 104 pp.

Heyder, G. (1968). Das Respirationssystem von *Typhlops vermicularis* Merrem (1820), unter besonderer Berücksichtigung der Tracheallunge. *Z. Wiss. Zool.* 177, 393–402.

Heyder, G. (1973). Das Blutgefässsystem von *Typhlops vermicularis* Merrem (1820). *Gegenbaurs Morph. Jb.* 119, 492–513.

Heyder, G. (1974). Das Verdauungssystem von *Typhlops vermicularis* Merrem (1820). *Gegenbaurs Morph. Jb.* 120, 185–197.

Hilber, H. (1933). Der formative Einfluss der Luft auf die Atemorgane. (Vergleichende Untersuchung über Bau und Entwicklung von Reptilien- und Säugerlungen.). *Gegenbaur Morph. Jb.* 71, 184–265.

Hildebrand, M. (1995). *Analysis of Vertebrate Structure*, 4th ed. John Wiley and Sons, New York, 657 pp.

Hilf, M., Wagner, R. A., and Yu, V. L. (1990). A prospective study of upper airway flora in healthy boid snakes and snakes with pneumonia. *J. Zoo. Wildlife Med.* 21, 318–325.

Hilzheimer, M. (1912). Reptilien. In *Handbuch der Biologie der Wirbeltiere.* (M. Hilzheimer and O. Haempel, eds.). Ferdinand Enke, Stuttgart, 1st half, pp. 231–374.

Hochstetter, F. (1892). Beiträge zur Entwicklungsgeschichte des Venensystems der Amnioten. II. Reptilien (*Lacerta, Tropidonotus*). *Morph. Jb.* 19, 428–502.

Hochstetter, F. (1901). Über Varietäten der Aortenbogen, Aortenwurzeln und der von ihnen entspringenden Arterien bei Reptilien. *Morph. Jb.* 29, 415–438.

Hoesch, W. (1960). Von der Baumschlange *Dispholidus typus* und ihren Beutetieren. *Natur und Volk* 90, 177–185.

Hoffman, M. (1988). *Animals in the Wild: Snake*. Scholastic, New York, 24 pp.

Hoffmann, C. K. (1890). Schlangen und Entwicklungsgeschichte der Reptilien. In *Dr. H. G. Bronn's Klassen und Ordungen des Thier-Reichs, wissenschaftliche dargestellt in Wort und Bild*. C. F. Winter'sche, Leipzig, vol. 6, Part 3, pp. 1401–2089.

Hofmeister, F. (1889). Beiträge zur Lehre vom Kreislauf der Kaltblüter. *Pflüger's Arch. Ges. Physiol.* (1888–1889) 44, 360–427.

Hoge, A. R., and Romano-Hoge, S. A. R. W. L. (1981). Poisonous snakes of the world. Part I. Check list of the pit vipers, Viperoidea, Viperidae, Crotalinae. *Mem. Inst. Butantan* (1978–79) 42–43, 179–310.

Holbrook, J. E. (1840). *North American Herpetology; or, a Description of the Reptiles Inhabiting the United States*, vol. 4. J. Dobson, Philadelphia, 126 pp.

Holbrook, J. E. (1842). *North American Herpetology; or, a Description of the Reptiles Inhabiting the United States*, vol. 4, 2nd ed. J. Dobson, Philadelphia, 138 pp.

Honders, J., ed. (1975). *The World of Reptiles and Amphibians*. Peebles Press, New York, 160 pp.

Hopkinson, J. P., and Pancoast, J. (1837). On the visceral anatomy of the *Python* (Cuvier), described by Daudin as the *Boa reticulata*. *Trans. Am. Phil. Soc.*, ser. 2, 5, 121–134.

Hopley, C. C. (1882). *Snakes: Curiosities and Wonders of Serpent Life*. Griffith and Farran, London, 614 pp.

Huang, M.-H., and Tsu, Y.-H. (1983). *Five step snake*. Scientific Publishing House, Beijing, 196 pp. [in Chinese].

Hughes, B. (1983). African snake faunas. *Bonn. Zool. Beitr.* 34, 311–356.

Hughes, G. M. (1973). *The Vertebrate Lung*. Oxford University Press, London, 16 pp. (reprinted in 1978 by Carolina Biological Supply Co., Burlington)

Huntington, H. E. (1973). *Let's Look at Reptiles*. Doubleday, Garden City, New Jersey, 107 pp.

Hutchinson, M. N. (1990). The generic classification of the Australian terrestrial elapid snakes. *Mem. Queensland Mus.* 29, 397–405.

Hyrtl, J. (1837). *Strena Anatomica de Novis Pulmonum Vasis, in Ophidiis Nuperrime Observatis*. Typis Filiorum Theophili Haase, Prague, 19 pp.

Ihle, J. E. W., ed. (1947). *Leerboek der Vergelijkende Ontleedkunde van de Vertebraten. Deel II. Zintuigen — lichaamsholte — spijsverteringsorganen — pharynx en zijn derivaten — bloeden lymphvaatstelsel — urogenitaalorganen*. Derde druk. A. Oosthoek, Utrecht, 415 pp.

Ihle, J. E. W., van Kampen, P. N., Nierstrasz, H. F., and Versluys, J. (1924). *Leerboek der Vergelijkende Ontleedkunde van de Vertebraten. Deel I. Inleiding — systeem — huid — zenuwstelsel — zintuigen — lichaamsholte — spijsverteringsorganen — ademhalingsorganen — bloedsomloop*. A. Oosthoek, Utrecht, 428 pp.

Ihle, J. E. W., van Kampen, P. N., Nierstrasz, H. F., and Versluys, J. (1927). *Vergleichende Anatomie der Wirbeltiere* (G. C. Hirsch, trans.). Julius Springer, Berlin, 906 pp.

Inger, R. F. (1966). Reptile. In *Encyclopaedia Britannica*. William Benton, Chicago, pp. 173–191.

Isemonger, R. M. (1955). *Snakes and Snake Catching in Southern Africa*. Bailey Brothers and Swinfen, London, 105 pp.

Isemonger, R. M. (1962). *Snakes of Africa: Southern, Central and East*. Thomas Nelson and Sons, Johannesburg, 236 pp.

Isemonger, R. M. (1968). *Snakes of Africa*. Books of Africa, Cape Town, 284 pp.

Iwahori, N., Kiyota, E., and Nakamura, K. (1987). Olfactory and respiratory epithelia in the snake, *Elaphe quadrivirgata*. *Okajimas Folia Anat. Japonica* 64, 183–192.

Jacobs, J. S., and Coons, L. B. (1981). Ultrastructure of lung parenchyma in the copperhead (*Agkistrodon contortrix*). SSAR-Herpetologists' League Meeting Abstracts, Memphis State University, Memphis, p. 50.

Jacobaeus, O. (1680). Serpentum et viperarum anatome. In *Acta Medica et Philosophica Hafniensia* (T. Bartholinus, ed.). Hafniae, vol. 5, 266–272. (not seen)

Jacquart, H. (1855). Mémoire sur les organes de la circulation chez le serpent *Python. Ann. Sci. Nat., Zool.*, ser. 4, 4, 321–364.

Jacquart, H. (1856). De l'appareil circulatoire sanguin chez le serpent *Python. Comp. Rend. Acad. Sci., Paris* 42, 1125–1128.

Jacquart, H. (1864). De la distribution des nerfs pneumogastriques dans les poumons des ophidiens. *J. Anat. Physiol* 1, 371–377.

Jammes, L. (1904). *Zoologie Pratique basée sur la Dissection des Animaux les plus Répandus Ouvrage à l'Usage des Candidats au Certificat d'Etudes Physiques, Chemiques et Naturelles (P. C. N.) et aux Certificats d'Etudes Supérieures de Zoologie et d'Anatomie Comparée*. Masson, Paris, 565 pp.

Jaroniewski, W. (1992). *Jadowite Weze Swiata*. Wydawnictwa Szkolne i Pedagogiczne, Warszawa, 144 pp.

Jessop, N. M. (1988). *Theory and Problems of Zoology*. McGraw-Hill, New York, 484 pp.

Johansen, K., and Hol, R. (1960). A cineradiographic study of the snake heart. *Circ. Res.* 8, 253–259.

Johnson, C. R. (1975). Defensive display behaviour in some Australian and Papuan-New Guinean pygopodid lizards, boid, colubrid and elapid snakes. *Zool. J. Linn. Soc.* 56, 265–282.

Johnson, S. A. (1986). *The World of Snakes*. Lerner, Minneapolis, 48 pp.

Jollie, M. (1962). *Chordate Morphology*. Reinhold, New York, 478 pp.

Jones, A. C. (1926). Innervation and nerve terminations of the reptilian lung. *J. Comp. Neurol.* 40, 371–388.

Jones, J. (1856). *Investigations, Chemical and Physiological, Relative to Certain American Vertebrata*. Smithsonian Contributions to Knowledge, Washington, 137 pp.

Jonstonus, J. (1653). *Historiae Naturalis de Serpentibus et Draconibus, Libri Duo*. Haeredum Merianaeorum, Francofurti, 40 pp.

Jonstonus, J. (1657). *Historiae Naturalis de Serpentibus*, book 2, 2nd ed. Joannem Jacobi Fil. Schipper, Amstelodami, 37 pp.

Jullien, A., Acolat, L., and Provost, L. (1960). Étude anatomique du pneumogastrique chez quelques ophidiens colubridés. *Ann. Sci. Univ. Besançon, Zool. Physiol.*, ser. 2, 14, 111–122.

Kaban, L. W. (1978). "A comparative study of organ placement in *Charina bottae* and *Lichanura roseofusca* (Serpentes: Boidae)." M.S. thesis, California State University, Long Beach, 68 pp.

Kabish, K. (1974). *Die Ringelnatter: Natrix natrix (L.)*. A. Ziemsen, Wittenberg Lutherstadt, 88 pp.

Kabisch, K. (1990). *Wörterbuch der Herpetologie*. Gustav Fischer, Jena, 477 pp.

Kalmus, H. (1984). Zu Haltung und Nachzucht von *Dasypeltis scabra* (Linnaeus, 1758) (Serpentes: Colubridae). *Salamandra* 20, 11–20.

Kang, J., Wu, Q., Zhang, Y., and Wang, Z. (1986). The lungs of boas and pythons. *Acta Herpetol. Sinica* 5, 231–232. [in Chinese].

Kardong, K. V. (1972a). Morphology of the respiratory system and its musculature in different snake genera (part 1): *Crotalus* and *Elaphe*. *Gegenbaurs Morph. Jb.* 117, 285–302.

Kardong, K. V. (1972b). Morphology of the respiratory system and its musculature in different snake genera (part 2): *Charina bottae*. *Gegenbaurs Morph. Jb.* 117, 364–376.

Kardong, K. V. (1977). Kinesis of the jaw apparatus during swallowing in the cottonmouth snake, *Agkistrodon piscivorus*. *Copeia* 1977, 338–3348.

Kardong, K. V., and Haverly, J. E. (1993). Drinking by the common boa, *Boa constrictor*. *Copeia* 1993, 808–818.

Karlstrom, E. L. (1952). "Functional anatomy of the respiratory systems of *Natrix taxispilota* and *Thamnophis o. ordinatus*." M. S. thesis, Washington State University, Pullman, Washington, 86 pp.

Karsen, S. J., Lau, M. W.-N., and Bogadek, A. (1986). *Hong Kong Amphibians and Reptiles*. Urban Council, Hong Kong, 136 pp.

Kashyap, H. V. (1950). The structure of the heart of *Typhlops* (Reptilia: Ophidia). *J. Zool. Soc. India* 2, 42–48.

Kashyap, H. V. (1960a). Morphology of the reptilian heart. *Bull. Zool. Soc., Coll. Sci., Nagpur* 3, 23–34.

Kashyap, H. V. (1960b). The reptilian heart. *Proc. Natl. Inst. Sci. India* 26B, 234–254.

Kashyap, H. V., and Sohoni, P. R. (1973). The heart and arterial system of *Acrochordus granulatus* (Schneider). *J. Univ. Bombay* 42, 34–52.

Kashyap, H. V., and Velankar, S. R. (1959). The circulatory system of *Natrix piscator piscator* (Schneider) (Reptilia: Ophidia). *J. Zool. Soc. India, Calcutta* (1958) 10, 176–194.

Kathariner, L. (1898). Ueber den Verdauungscanal und die "Wirbelzähne" von *Dasypeltis scabra* Wagler. *Zool. Jb., Abt. Anat.* 11, 501–518.

Kellicott, D. S. (1898). *The Dissection of the Ophidian*. Hann and Aldair, Columbus, Ohio, 72 pp. (reprinted in 1938 by General Biological Supply House, Chicago)

Kellogg, V. L. (1901). *Elementary Zoology*. Henry Holt, New York, 492 pp.

Kelly, H. A., Davis, A. W., and Robertson, H. C. (1936). *Snakes of Maryland*. Natural History Society of Maryland, Baltimore, 103 pp.

Kent, G. C. (1969). *Comparative Anatomy of the Vertebrates*, 2nd ed. C. V. Mosby, St. Louis, 437 pp.

Kent, G. C. (1978). *Comparative Anatomy of the Vertebrates*, 4th ed. C. V. Mosby, St. Louis, 465 pp.

Kent, G. C. (1983). *Comparative Anatomy of the Vertebrates*, 5th ed. C. V. Mosby, St. Louis, 604 pp.

Keogh, J. S. (1993). "Comparative visceral topography and phylogenetic systematics of the tribe Lampropeltini (Reptilia: Serpentes)." M.S. Thesis, Illinois State University, Normal, Illinois, 417 pp.

Keogh, J. S. (1996). Evolution of the colubrid snake tribe Lampropeltini: a morphological perspective. *Herpetologica* 52, 406–416.

Keogh, J. S., and Wallach, V. (In press). Allometry of lung morphology in the prairie rattlesnake, *Crotalus viridis viridis*. *Copeia*, accepted for publication.

Khaire, A., and Khaire, N. (1984). Birth of a bicephalus snake. *Hammadryad* 9, 7.

Kinghorn, J. R. (1964). *The Snakes of Australia*. Angus and Robertson, Sydney, 197 pp.

Kingsley, J. S., ed. (1888). Lower Vertebrates. In *The Riverside Natural History*. Houghton, Mifflin and Co., Boston, vol. 3, 488 pp.

Kingsley, J. S. (1897). *Elements of Comparative Zoology*. Henry Holt, New York, 357 pp.

Kingsley, J. S. (1917). *Outlines of Comparative Anatomy of Vertebrates*, 2nd ed. P. Blackiston's Son, Philadelphia, 449 pp.

Kingsley, J. S. (1926). *Outlines of Comparative Anatomy of Vertebrates*, 3rd ed. P. Blackiston's Son, Philadelphia, 470 pp.

Klauber, L. M. (1947). Classification and ranges of the gopher snakes of the genus *Pituophis* in the western United States. *Bull. Zool. Soc. San Diego* 22, 1–81.

Klauber, L. M. (1956). *Rattlesnakes: Their Habits, Life Histories, and Influence on Mankind*, vols. 1–2. University of California Press, Berkeley, 1476 pp.

Kluge, A. G. (1991). Boine snake phylogeny and research cycles. *Misc. Publ. Mus. Zool. Univ. Michigan* 178, 1–58.

Kluge, A. G. (1993a). *Calabaria* and the phylogeny of erycine snakes. *Zool. J. Linn. Soc.* 107, 293–351.

Kluge, A. G. (1993b). *Aspidites* and the phylogeny of pythonine snakes. *Rec. Aust. Mus.* Suppl. 19, 1–77.

Kluge, A. G., Frye, B. E., Johansen, K., Liem, K. F., Noback, C. R., Olsen, I. D., and Waterman, A. J. (1977). *Chordate Structure and Function*, 2nd ed. Macmillan, New York, 628 pp.

Klynstra, F. B. (1959). *Gonyosoma oxycephalum* (Boie). *Lacerta* 18, 17–18.

Knight, C. (1858). *The Pictorial Museum of Animated Nature*, vol. 2. Charles Knight, London.

Kropach, C. (1972). "A field study of the sea snake *Pelamis platurus* (Linnaeus) in the Gulf of Panama." Ph.D. dissertation, City College of New York, Queens College, New York.

Kundert, F. (1974). *Fascination: Schlangen und Echsen, Serpents et Lezards, Snakes and Lizards*. Fred Kundert, Spreitenbach. 201 pp.

Kundert, F. (1984). *Das Neue Schlangenbuch in Farbe*, 2nd ed. Albert Müller, Rüschlikon-Zürich, 39 pp.

Kurtz, W. V. (1953). "The visceral anatomy of the garter snake." M.S. thesis, University of Colorado, Boulder, 90 pp.

Lacepède, B. G. E. de (1790). *Histoire Naturelle des Serpens*, vol. 3. Hotel de Thou, Paris. 432 pp.

Lacepède, B. G. E. de (1802). *Natural History of Oviparous Quadrupeds and Serpents, Arranged and Published from the Papers and Collections of the Count de Buffon, by the Count de la Cepède*, vol. 3 (R. Kerr, trans.). W. Creech, Edinburgh, 383 pp.

Lacoste, A., and Baudrimont, A. (1942). Considérations sur l'anatomie générale du poumon des vertébrés pulmonés (oiseaux exceptés) dans ses rapports avec les dispoitifs de la mécanique respiratoire. *Bull. Histol. Appl. Physiol. Pathol. Tech. Micros.* 19, 153–174.

Ladeiro, J. M. (1935). Um caso de atlodimia no *Tropidonotus natrix* Linn. *Mem. Est. Mus. Zool. Univ. Coimbra*, ser. 4, 2, 1–4.

Ladeiro, J. M. (1944). Monstro duplo, autositário, monosomiano, atlódimo. *Mem. Est. Mus. Zool. Univ. Coimbra*, ser. 2, 153, 24.

Lamare-Picquot, M. (1858). Sur l'appareil pulmonaire de la couleuvre demnha. *Comp. Rend. Acad. Sci.* 47, 794.

Lambiris, A. J. L. (1965). Some observations on certain reptiles and amphibians in captivity. *J. Herpetol. Assoc. Rhodesia* 23–24, 53–55.

Lambiris, A. J. L. (1980). *Philothamnus ornatus* Bocage near Salisbury, Zimbabwe. *J. Herpetol. Assoc. Africa* 23, 11–12.

Lancini, A. R. (1979). *Serpientes de Venezuela*. Ernesto Armitano, Caracas, 262 pp.

Lancini, A. R. (1986). *Serpientes de Venezuela*, 2nd ed. Ernesto Armitano, Caracas, 264 pp.

Lancini, A. R., and Kornacker, P. M. (1989). *Die Schlangen von Venezuela*. Armitano Editores, Caracas, 381 pp.

Lanka, V., and Vit, Z. (1985a). *Amphibians and Reptiles*. Hamlyn, Feltham, England, 224 pp.

Lanka, V., and Vit, Z. (1985b). *Reptiles et Amphibiens*. Gründ, Paris, 224 pp. (trans. of Lanka and Vit, 1985a)

Larousse. (1980). *The New Larousse Encyclopedia of Animal Life*. Bonanza Books, New York, 640 pp.

Larson, E. J., and van de Velde, R. L. (1969). Studies on the pulmonary microcirculation of the common bull snake (*Pituophis sayi sayi*). *Bibl. Anat.* 10, 278–280.

Lataste, F. (1876). *Essai d'une Faune Herpetologique de la Gironde avec une Note Inédite de M. A. de l'Isle du Dréneuf sur l'Accouplement de l'Alyte Accoucheur.* Imprimerie Ve. Cadoret, Bordeaux, 352 pp.

Lataste, F., and Blanchard, R. (1879). Le péritoine du python de Séba accompagne et ne dépasse pas les organes génitaux. *Bull. Soc. Zool. France* 4, 95–112.

Latter, O. H. (1923). *Elementary Zoology*. E. P. Dutton, New York, 333 pp.

Lavies, B. (1990). *The Secretive Timber Rattlesnake*. Dutton Children's Books, New York, 32 pp.

Lawrence, K. (1985). Snakes. In *Manual of Exotic Pets* (J. E. Cooper, M. F. Hutchison, O. F. Jackson, and R. J. Maurice, eds.) British Small Animal Veterinary Association, Cheltenham, 2nd ed., pp. 179–185.

Lécuru-Renous, S., and Platel, R. (1970a). Contribution à l'étude du système veineux de la vipère *Vipera aspis* (L.) — Reptilia — Ophidia — Viperidae. *Morph. Jb.* 115, 238–256.

Lécuru-Renous, S., and Platel, R. (1970b). *Atlas Photographiques de Morphologie et de Dissections. La Vipère Aspic, Vipera aspis (L.).* Doin-Deren, Paris, 153 pp.

Lee, J. C. (1996). *The Amphibians and Reptiles of the Yucatan Peninsula*. Comstock, Cornell Univ. Press, Ithaca, 500 pp.

Leen, N. (1963). Strange world of snakes. *Life Magazine* 54(9), 37–49, 52, 54A.

Leen, N. (1978). *Snakes*. Holt, Rinehart and Winston, New York, 80 pp.

Leene, J. E., and Vorstman, A. G. (1930). Note on the structure of the heart of

Varanus as compared with other reptilian hearts. *Tijdschr. Neder. Dierk. Ver.,* Leiden, ser. 3, 2, 62–66.

Leetz, T. (1991). *Snakes . . . as a Hobby.* T.F.H. Publications, Neptune City, New Jersey, 99 pp.

Leighton, G. R. (1901). *The Life-History of British Serpents and their Local Distribution in the British Isles.* William Blackwood and Sons, Edinburgh, 383 pp.

Lereboullet, A. (1838). "Anatomie comparée de l'appareil respiratoire, dans les animaux vertébrés." Ph.D. dissertation, University of Strasbourg, 155 pp.

Leunis, J., and Ludwig, H. (1883). *Synopsis der Thierkunde. Ein Handbuch für höhere Lehranstalten und für Alle, welche sich wissenschaftlich mit der Naturgeschichte der Thiere beschäftigen wollen. Erster Band. Zoologie.* Hahn'sche Buchhandlung, Hannover, 1083 pp.

Leviton, A. E. (1959). "Systematics and zoogeography of Philippine snakes." Ph.D. dissertation, Stanford University, Palo Alto, California, 865 pp.

Leviton, A. E. (1970). *Reptiles and Amphibians of North America.* Doubleday, New York, 250 pp.

Leviton, A. E., Gibbs, R. H., Jr., Heal, E., and Dawson, C. E. (1985). Standards in herpetology and ichthyology: part I. Standard symbolic codes for institutional resource collections in herpetology and ichthyology. *Copeia* 1985, 802–832.

Levy, C. K. (1983). *A Field Guide to Dangerous Animals of North America, including Central America.* Stephen Greene Press, Brattleboro, Vermont, 164 pp.

Leydig, F. (1857). *Lehrbuch der Histologie des Menschen und der Thiere.* Meidinger Sohn & Comp., Frankfurt am Main, 551 pp.

Leydig, F. (1866). *Traité d'Histologie de l'Homme et des Animaux.* (R. Lahillonne, trans.). Germer Baillière, Paris, 629 pp.

Liem, K. F., Marx, H., and Rabb, G. B. (1971). The viperid snake *Azemiops:* its comparative cephalic anatomy and phylogenetic position in relation to Viperinae and Crotalinae. *Fieldiana: Zool.* 59, 65–126.

Lillywhite, H. B. (1987a). Circulatory adaptations of snakes to gravity. *Am. Zool.* 27, 81–95.

Lillywhite, H. B. (1987b). Snakes under pressure. *Nat. Hist.* 1987(11), 58–66.

Lillywhite, H. B. (1993). The airbag mystery. *League Florida Herpetol. Societies,* January, 13–18.

Lillywhite, H. B., and Donald, J. A. (1987). Neurovascular structure and function in the elongate lung of an aquatic snake. *Physiologist* 30, 190.

Lillywhite, H. B., and Gallagher, K. P. (1985). Hemodynamic adjustments to head-up posture in the partly arboreal snake, *Elaphe obsoleta. J. Exp. Zool.* 235, 325–334.

Lillywhite, H. B., and Smits, A. W. (1992). The cardiovascular adaptations of viperid snakes. In *Biology of the Pitvipers* (J. A. Campbell and E. D. Brodie, Jr., eds.). Selva Publ., Tyler, Texas, pp. 143–153.

Lim, L. B. (1958). The harlequin monitor lizard. *Malayan Nat. J.* 13, 70–72.

Lim, L. K., and Lee, T.-M. (1989). *Fascinating Snakes of Southeast Asia — an Introduction.* Tropical Press Sdn. Bhd, Kuala Lumpur, 124 pp.

Lin, J., Xu, K.-M., and Liu, D.-G. (1995). Studies on the distribution of trace elements in *Agkistrodon blomhoffii brevicaudus* Stejneger. *Asiatic Herpetol. Res.* 6, 62–68.

Linzey, D. W. (1979). *Snakes of Alabama.* Strode, Huntsville, Alabama, 136 pp.

List, J. C. (1954). A rare snake anomaly. *Am. Midl. Nat.* 51, 312–313.

Little, M. E. (1932). *Structure of the Vertebrates.* Farrar and Rinehart, New York, 392 pp.

Liu, Y.-L., and Chen, C.-C. (1983). Morphological structure of the respiratory system of *Hydrophis cyanocinctus* (Daudin) (Reptilia: Hydrophiidae). *Wuyi Sci. J.* 3, 84–89.

Livini, F. (1896). Intorno alla struttura della trachea. Ricerche d'isolgia comparata. Nota riassuntiva. *Monit. Zool. Ital.* 7, 69–74, 91–103, 185–191.

Lockwood, S. (1875). The pine snake of New Jersey. *Am. Nat.* 9, 1–14.

Lönnberg, E. (1894). Notes on reptiles and batrachians collected in Florida in 1892 and 1893. *Proc. U. S. Natl. Mus.* 17, 317–339.

Loveridge, A. (1928). Notes on snakes and snake-bites in East Africa. *Bull. Antivenin Inst. Amer.* 1, 106–117; 2, 1–5, 32–41.

Luce, C. (1963). "Contribution à l'étude comparée de l'appareil circulatoire chez les ophidiens: anatomie du système artériel en avant du coeur chez *Natrix natrix* (Linné) et *Vipera aspis* (Linné)." M.S. thesis, Université de Paris, Paris, 66 pp.

Luchtel, D. L., and Kardong, K. V. (1981). Ultrastructure of the lung of the rattlesnake, *Crotalus viridis oreganus.* *J. Morph.* 169, 29–47.

Lüdicke, M. (1939). Die Blutmenge in der Lunge und in der Niere der Schlangen. *Zool. Jb., Abt. Zool. Physiol.* 59, 463–552.

Lüdicke, M. (1940). Über die Kapillargebiete des Blutgefäss-systems im Kopf der Schlangen (*Tropidonotus natrix* L. und *Zamenis dahli* Fitz.). *Z. Morph. Ökol. Tiere* 36, 401–445.

Lüdicke, M. (1962–1964). Ordnung der Klasse Reptilia, Serpentes. In *Handbuch der Zoologie, eine Naturgeschichte der Stämme des Tierreiches* (W. Kükenthal, ed.). Walter de Gruyter, Berlin, vol. 7, 1st Half, Part 6, pp. 1–298.

Lütken, C. F. (1882). *Dyreriget. En Haand- og Laerebog til brug ved Højere Laereanstalter. (Laerebog I Zoologien nr. 1).* Gyldendalske Boghandels Forlag, Kjøbenhavn, 699 pp.

Lydekker, R., Cunningham, J. T., Boulenger, G. A., and Thomson, J. A. (1912). *Reptiles, Amphibia, Fishes and Lower Chordata.* Methuen, London, 510 pp.

Lyon, B. (1973). Observations on the common keelback snake, *Natrix mairii* in Brisbane, south-eastern Queensland. *Herpetofauna* 6, 2–5. (not seen).

Ma, J.-F. (1982a). Respiratory system of the pointed-mouth pit viper. In *Deinagkistrodon acutus: Its Morphology, Ecology, Toxicology and Applications* (E.-M. Zhao, ed.). *Acta Herpetol. Sinica* 6, 38–39 [in Chinese].

Ma, J.-F. (1982b). Circulatory system of the pointed-mouth pit viper. In *Deinagkistrodon acutus: Its Morphology, Ecology, Toxicology and Applications* (E.-M. Zhao, ed.). *Acta Herpetol. Sinica* 6, 40–46 [in Chinese].

MacAlister, A. (1878). *An Introduction to the Systematic Zoology and Morphology of Vertebrate Animals.* Hodges, Foster and Figgis, Dublin, 365 pp.

MacLeish, K. (1972). Diving with sea snakes. *Natl. Geog.* 141, 564–578.

Mahendra, B. C. (1984). Handbook of the snakes of India, Ceylon, Burma, Bangladesh, and Pakistan. *Ann. Zool., Agra* 22B, 1–412.

Maina, J. N. (1989). The morphology of the lung of the black mamba *Dendroaspis polylepis* (Reptilia: Ophidia: Elapidae). A scanning and transmission electron microscopic study. *J. Anat., Lond.* 167, 31–46.

Malnate, E. V., and Underwood, G. (1988). Australasian natricine snakes of the genus *Tropidonophis*. *Proc. Acad. Nat. Sci. Philad.* 140, 59–201.

Manthey, U., and Grossmann, W. (1997). *Amphibien & Reptilien Südostasiens*. Natur und Tier, Münster, 512 pp.

Mao, S.-H. (1993). Common terrestrial venomous snakes of Taiwan. *Natl. Mus. Nat. Sci. Spec. Publ.* 5, 1–108.

Mao, S.-H., and Chen, B.-Y. (1980). *Sea Snakes of Taiwan: A Natural History of Sea Snakes*. National Science Council, Taipei, 62 pp.

Mara, W. P. (1993). *Venomous Snakes of the World*. T.F.H. Publications, Neptune City, New Jersey, 224 pp.

Marais, J. (1985). *Snake versus Man: A Guide to Dangerous and Common Harmless Snakes of Southern Africa*. Macmillan South Africa, Johannesburg, 102 pp.

Marais, J. (1992). *A Complete Guide to the Snakes of Southern Africa*. Blanford, London, 208 pp.

Marcus, H. (1927). Der vergleichenden Anatomie der Lungen. *Anat. Anz.* 63, 141–144.

Marcus, H. (1928a). Lungenstudien III und IV. *Gegenbaurs Morph. Jb.* 59, 297–342.

Marcus, H. (1928b). Lungenstudien V. Vergleichende Untersuchungen über die respiratorische Oberfläche und ihr Verhältnis zum Körpergewicht. *Gegenbaurs Morph. Jb.* 59, 561–566.

Marcus, H. (1937). Atmungssystem (Organe der Luftatmung.). III. Schwimmblase und Lungen. B. Lungen, 3 (III, B). In *Handbuch der vergleichenden Anatomie der Wirbeltiere* (L. Bolk, E. Göppert, E. Kallius, and W. Lubosch, eds.). Urban und Schwarzenberg, Berlin and Vienna, vol. 3, pp. 909–988.

Marcus, L. C. (1981). *Veterinary Biology and Medicine of Captive Amphibians and Reptiles*. Lea and Febiger, Philadelphia, 239 pp.

Martin, P. (1902). *Lehrbuch der Anatomie der Haustiere*. Schickhardt und Ebner, Stuttgart, vol. 1, 888 pp.

Martin, W. F., and Huey, R. B. (1971). The function of the epiglottis in sound production (hissing) of *Pituophis melanoleucus*. *Copeia* 1971, 752–754.

Martínez, D. R., Lucio, J. A., and Schwartz, A. (1985). Topografía interna de las culebras del genero *Uromacer* (Colubridae). *Caribaea* 1, 48–59.

Masci, P., and Kendall, P. (1995). *The Taipan: The World's most Dangerous Snake*. Kangaroo Press, Kenthurst, 90 pp.

Mathur, P. N. (1946). The anatomy of the reptilian heart. Part II. Serpentes, Testudinata and Loricata. *Proc. Indian Acad. Sci.* 23B, 129–152.

Mattison, C. (1986). *Snakes of the World*. Facts on File, New York, 190 pp.

Mattison, C. (1991). *The World of Snakes*. Derrydale Books, New York, 46 pp.

Mattison, C. (1995). *The Encyclopedia of Snakes*. Facts On File, New York, 256 pp.

Mavridis, S. C., Hipolito, M., Baldassi, L., Calil, E. M. B., Moulin, A. A. P., and Barbosa, M. L. (1994). Inquérito bacteriológico de Serpentes doentes e mortas mantidas em cativeiro. *Mem. Inst. Butantan* (1993) 55, Suppl. 1, 55–62.

McCarthy, C. J. (1986). Relationships of the laticaudine sea snakes (Serpentes: Elapidae: Laticaudinae). *Bull. Brit. Mus. Nat. Hist., Zool.* 50, 127–161.

McCarthy, C. J. (1987). *Poisonous Snakes*. Gloucester Press, London, 32 pp.

McCarthy, C. J. (1991). *Eyewitness Books: Reptile*. Alfred A. Knopf, New York, 64 pp.

McDonald, H. S. (1959). Respiratory functions of the ophidian air sac. *Herpetologica* 15, 193–198.

McDowell, S. B. (1967). *Aspidomorphus*, a genus of New Guinea snakes of the family Elapidae, with notes on related genera. *J. Zool., Lond.* 151, 497–543.

McDowell, S. B. (1969a). Notes on the Australian sea-snake *Ephalophis greyi* M. Smith (Serpentes: Elapidae, Hydrophiinae) and the origin and classification of sea-snakes. *J. Linn. Soc., Zool.* 48, 333–349.

McDowell, S. B. (1969b). *Toxicocalamus*, a New Guinea genus of snakes of the family Elapidae. *J. Zool., Lond.* 159, 443–511.

McDowell, S. B. (1970). On the status and relationships of the Solomon Island elapid snakes. *J. Zool., Lond.* 161, 145–190.

McDowell, S. B. (1972a). The species of *Stegonotus* (Serpentes, Colubridae) in Papua New Guinea. *Zool. Meded.* 47, 6–26.

McDowell, S. B. (1972b). The genera of sea-snakes of the *Hydrophis* group (Serpentes: Elapidae). *Trans. Zool. Soc. Lond.* 32, 189–247.

McDowell, S. B. (1972c). The evolution of the tongue of snakes, and its bearing on snake origins. In *Evolutionary Biology* (T. Dobzhansky, M. K. Hecht, and W. Steere, eds.). Appleton-Century-Crofts, New York, vol. 6, pp. 191–273.

McDowell, S. B. (1974a). A catalogue of the snakes of New Guinea and the Solomons, with special reference to those in the Bernice P. Bishop Museum. Part I. Scolecophidia. *J. Herpetol.* 8, 1–57.

McDowell, S. B. (1974b). Additional notes on the rare and primitive sea-snake, *Ephalophis greyi*. *J. Herpetol.* 8, 123–128.

McDowell, S. B. (1975). A catalogue of the snakes of New Guinea and the Solomons, with special reference to those in the Bernice P. Bishop Museum. Part II. Anilioidea and Pythoninae. *J. Herpetol.* 9, 1–79.

McDowell, S. B. (1979). A catalogue of the snakes of New Guinea and the Solomons, with special reference to those in the Bernice P. Bishop Museum. Part III. Boinae and Acrochordoidea. *J. Herpetol.* 13, 1–92.

McDowell, S. B. (1986). The architechture of the corner of the mouth of colubroid snakes. *J. Herpetol.* 20, 353–407.

McDowell, S. B. (1987). Systematics. In *Snakes: Ecology and Evolutionary History* (R. A. Seigel, J. T. Collins, and S. S. Novak, eds.). Macmillan, New York, pp. 3–50.

Mead, R. (1702). *A Mechanical Account of Poisons in Several Essays*. Ralph South, London, 175 pp.

Mead, R. (1708). *A Mechanical Account of Poisons in Several Essays*, 2nd ed. Ralph South, London, 189 pp.

Mead, R. (1747). *A Mechanical Account of Poisons in Several Essays*, 4th ed. J. Brindley, London, 320 pp.

Meban, C. (1980). Thickness of the air-blood barriers in vertebrate lungs. *J. Anat.* 131, 299–307.

Meckel, J. F. (1818). Ueber das Respirationssystem der Reptilien. *Meckel's Deutsches Arch. Physiol.* 4, 60–89, 162–164.

Meckel, J. F. (1819). Beiträge zur Geschichte der Respirationssystems der Amphibien. *Meckel's Deutsches Arch. Physiol.* 5, 213–230.

Meckel, J. F. (1829a). *System der vergleichenden Anatomie. Vierter Theil. Zweiter Theil. Besondere Anatomie. Zweites Buch. Organe des Bildens. Erstes Hauptstück. Bildungsorgane zur Erhaltung des Individuums. Erster Abtheilung. Vom Verdauungssystem.* Rengerschen, Halle, 741 pp.

Meckel, J. F. (1829b). Beitrag zur Entwickelungsgeschichte der Lungen. *Arch. Anat. Physiol., Leipzig* 4, 230–232.

Meckel, J. F. (1831). *System der vergleichenden Anatomie. Fünfter Theil. Zweiter Theil. Besondere Anatomie. Zweites Buch. Organe des Bildens. Erstes Hauptstück. Bildungsorgane zur Erhaltung des Individuums. Zweite Abtheilung. Gefäfssystem.* Rengerschen, Halle, 356 pp.

Meckel, J. F. (1833). *System der vergleichenden Anatomie. Sechster Theil. Zweiter Theil. Besondere Anatomie. Zweites Buch. Organe des Bildens. Erstes Hauptstück. Bildungsorgane zur Erhaltung des Individuums. Dritte Abtheilung. Respirationssystem.* Waisenhauses, Halle, 552 pp.

Méhes, S. (1810). *De Respiratione Animalium Commentatio.* Libraria Pfaehleriana, Heidelberg, 60 pp.

Mehrtens, J. R. (1987). *Living Snakes of the World in Color.* Sterling, New York, 480 pp.

Mell, R. (1928). Beobachtungen über das Sinnesleben chinesischer Reptilien, insbesondere Schlangen. *Z. Wiss. Biol., Abt. Morph.* 11, 539–569.

Mell, R. (1929). *Beiträge zur Fauna sinica. IV. Grundzüge einer Ökologie der chinesischen Reptilien und einer herpetologischen Tiergeographie Chinas.* Walter de Gruyter, Berlin, 282 pp.

Meneghel, M. (1991). Procedimiento sencillo para facilitar el diseño de anatomia de ofidios. *Bol. Soc. Zool. Uruguay* 6, 60.

Mertens, C. (1978). Functional anatomy of the lungs of the green lizard, *Lacerta viridis. J. Anat.* 125, 421–431.

Mertens, R. (1930). Die Amphibien und Reptilien der Inseln Bali, Lombok, Sumbawa und Flores (Beiträge zur Fauna der Kleinen Sunda-Inseln, I). *Abh. Senckenb. Naturf. Ges.* 42, 115–344.

Mertens, R. (1946). Die Warn- und Droh-Reaktionen der Reptilien. *Abh. Senckenberg. Naturf. Ges.* 471, 1–108.

Mertens, R. (1955). Die Amphibien und Reptilien Südwestafrikas. Aus den Ergebnissen einer im Jahre 1952 ausgeführten Reise. *Abh. Senckenb. Naturf. Ges.* 490, 1–172.

Mertens, R. (1960). *The World of Amphibians and Reptiles* (H. W. Parker, trans.). George G. Harrap, London, 207 pp.

Miller, J. R. (1963). How to dissect the rattlesnake. *Bull. Ross Allen's Reptile Institute, Silver Springs* 11, 1–3.

Miller, W. S. (1893). The structure of the lung. *J. Morph.* 8, 165–188.

Milne-Edwards, H. (1845). Zoologie. In *Cours Élémentaire d'Histoire Naturelle.* (H. Milne-Edwards, F.-S. Beudant, and A. de Jussieu, eds.). Langlois et Leclercq, Paris, 572 pp. (not seen).

Milne-Edwards, H. (1855). Zoologie. In *Cours Élémentaire d'Histoire Naturelle.* (H. Milne-Edwards, A. de Jussieu, and F.-S. Beudant, eds.). Victor Masson, Paris, 7th ed, 583 pp.

Milne-Edwards, H. (1857a). Zoologie. In *Cours Élémentaire d'Histoire Naturelle*. (H. Milne-Edwards, A. de Jussieu, and F.-S. Beudant, eds.). Victor Masson et Fils, Paris, 10th ed., 618 pp.

Milne-Edwards, H. (1857b). *Leçons sur la Physiologie et l'Anatomie Comparée de l'Homme et des Animaux faites a la Faculté des Sciences de Paris*, vol. 2. Victor Masson, Paris. 655 pp.

Milne-Edwards, H. (1871). Zoologie. In *Cours Élémentaire d'Histoire Naturelle*. (H. Milne-Edwards, A. de Jussieu, and F.-S. Beudant, eds.). Victor Masson et Fils, Paris, 11th ed., 628 pp.

Milne-Edwards, H., and Compte, A. (1855). *Cahiers d'Histoire Naturelle*, new ed. 1st part. — Zoologie. Victor Masson, Paris, 230 pp.

Milsom, W. K. (1989). Mechanisms of ventilation in lower vertebrates: adaptations to respiratory and nonrespiratory constraints. *Can. J. Zool.* 67, 2943–2955.

Minton, S. A., Jr. (1966). A contribution to the herpetology of West Pakistan. *Bull. Amer. Mus. Nat. Hist.* 134, 27–184.

Minton, S. A., Jr., Dowling, H. G., and Russell, F. E., eds. (1968). *Poisonous Snakes of the World*. Department of the Navy, Washington, 212 pp.

Mocquard, F. (1888). Observations sur des embryons de *Pelophilus madagascariensis*. *Bull. Soc. Philom. Paris* (1887–1888), ser. 7, 12, 34–41.

Mojsvár, A. M. E. von (1885). *Leitfaden bei zoologisch-zootomischen Präparirübungen*, 2nd ed. (augmented). Wilhelm Engelmann, Leipzig, 259 pp.

Mole, R. R. (1924). The Trinidad snakes. *Proc. Zool. Soc. Lond.* 1924, 235–278.

Moonen, J., Eriks, W., and van Deursen, K. (1979). *Surinaamse Slangeninkleur*. C. Kersten, Paramaribo, 119 pp.

Morgans, L. F., Baeyens, D. A., and Bowen, W. R. (1978). A comparative histological study of the lung in the diamondback water snake (*Natrix rhombifera*) and the black rat snake (*Elaphe obsoleta*). *Anat. Rec.* 190, 485.

Morris, R., and Morris, D. (1965). *Men and Snakes*. McGraw-Hill, New York, 224 pp.

Moser, F. (1902). Beiträge zur vergleichenden Entwicklungsgeschichte der Wirbeltierlunge (Amphibien, Reptilien, Vögel, Säuger.). *Archiv. Mikrosk. Anat.* 60, 587–668.

Müller, J. (1832). Beiträge zur Anatomie und Naturgeschichte der Amphibien. *Tiedemann und Treviranus Z. Physiol.* 4, 190–275.

Müller, L. (1910). Beiträge zur Herpetologie Kameruns. *Abh. K. Bayer. Akad. Wiss., II. Klasse, München* 24, 545–626.

Murphy, J. B., and Shadduck, J. A. (1977). Reproduction in the Eastern diamondback rattlesnake, *Crotalus adamanteus* in captivity, with comments regarding a teratoid birth anomaly. *Brit. J. Herpetol.* 5, 727–733.

Murphy, J. C. (1997). *Amphibians and Reptiles of Trinidad and Tobago*. Krieger, Malabar, Florida, 245 pp.

Mutschmann, F. (1995). *Die Strumpfbandnattern: Biology, Verbreitung, Haltung*. Westarp Wissenschaften, Magdeburg, 172 pp.

Nagaishi, C., Okada, Y., Ishiko, S., and Daido, S. (1964). Electron microscopic observations of the pulmonary alveoli. *Exp. Med. Surg.* 22, 81–117.

Nakamura, K. (1938). Studies on some specimens of double monsters of snakes and tortoises. *Mem. College Sci., Kyoto Imp. Univ.* 14B, 171–191.

Nakamura, K. (1941). Studies on the blind snake (1). *Trans. Nat. Hist. Soc. Formosa* 31, 299–305 [in Japanese].

Netting, M. G. (1936). Notes on a collection of reptiles from Barro Colorado Island, Panama Canal Zone. *Ann. Carnegie Mus.* 25, 113–120.

Nicholson, E. (1874). *Indian Snakes. An Elementary Treatise on Ophiology with a Descriptive Catalogue of the Snakes found in India and the Adjoining Countries*, 2nd ed. Higginbotham, Madras, 188 pp.

Nicholson, H. A. (1872). *Text-Book of Zoology for Schools and Colleges.* D. Appleton, New York, 353 pp.

Nicholson, H. A. (1873). *A Manual of Zoology, for the Use of Students with a General Introduction on the Principles of Zoology*, 3rd ed. William Blackwood and Sons, Edinburgh, 706 pp.

Nicholson, H. A. (1887). *A Manual of Zoology, for the Use of Students with a General Introduction on the Principles of Zoology*, 7th ed. William Blackwood and Sons, Edinburgh, 939 pp.

Niimi, T. (1965). On a dichotomous snake, *Elaphe climacophora* (Boie). *Acta Herpetol. Japonica* 1, 31–32.

Niimi, T. (1971). Additional report on the dichotomous snakes. *Acta Herpetol. Japonica* 4, 5–11.

Nilsson, S. (1842). *Skandinavisk Fauna. Tredje delen. Amphibierna.* C. W. K. Gleerups, Lund, 119 pp.

Nitzsch, C. L. (1808). *Commentatio de Respiratione Animalium.* Bibliopolio Zimmermanniano, Vitebergae, 56 pp.

Noble, G. K. (1921). Snakes that inflate. *Nat. Hist.* 21, 166–171.

Nutaphand, W. (1988). The green tweezer-mouthed snake, the green tokay gecko-headed snake, the sleepy in the jungle snake, and the lullaby snake. *Bull. Thai Zool. Ctr., Bangkok* 3, 67–76 [in Thai].

Nutaphand, W., and Tumwipart, B. (1982). *Poisonous Snakes of Thailand and the Cure from Snakebites.* Pickanet, Bangkok, 162 pp. [in Thai].

Obst, F. J., Richter, K., Jacob, U., Engelmann, W.-E., Eulenberger, K., and Köhler, H. (1988). *The Completely Illustrated Atlas of Reptiles and Amphibians for the Terrarium* (U. E. Friese, trans.). T.F.H. Publications, Neptune City, New Jersey, 830 pp.

O'Donoghue, C. H. (1912). The circulatory system of the common grass-snake (*Tropidonotus natrix*). *Proc. Zool. Soc. Lond.* 1912, 612–647.

O'Donoghue, C. H. (1917). A note on the ductus caroticus and ductus arteriosus and their distribution in the Reptilia. *J. Anat. Physiol.* 51, 137–149.

Ogawa, C. (1920). Contributions to the histology of the respiratory spaces of the vertebrate lungs. *Am. J. Anat.* 27, 333–393.

Ogo, S. H., Abe, A. S., and Focesi, A., Jr. (1979). Oxygen dissociation constants in hemoglobins of *Helicops modestus* and *Liophis miliaris*, two water-snakes with different morphological adaptations to their aquatic environment. *Comp. Biochem. Physiol.* 63A, 285.

Oidumi, S. (1940). Über das Vorhandensein der linken Lunge und des linken Hauptbronchus bei den einheimischen ungiftigen Schlangen. *Okajimas Folia Anat. Japonica* 19, 121–125.

Okada, Y., Ishiko, S., Daido, S., Kim, J., and Ikeda, S. (1962). Comparative morphology of the lung with special reference to the alveolar lining cells. II. Lung of the Reptilia. *Acta Tuberculosa Japonica* 12, 1–10.

Oldham, J. C. (1968). "Laboratory manual of snake anatomy." M.S. Thesis, Black Hills State College, Spearfish, South Dakota, 51 pp.

Oldham, J. C., and Smith, H. M. (1992). The generic status of the smooth green snake, *Opheodrys vernalis*. *Bull. Maryland Herpetol. Soc.* 27, 201–215.

Oldham, J. C., Smith, H. M., and Miller, S. A. (1970). *A Laboratory Perspectus of Snake Anatomy*. Stipes, Champaign, 98 pp.

Oliver, J. A. (1948). The relationships and zoogeography of the genus *Thalerophis* Oliver. *Bull. Amer. Mus. Nat. Hist.* 92, 157–280.

Oliver, J. A. (1958). *Snakes in Fact and Fiction*. Macmillan, New York, 199 pp.

Oppel, A. (1905). *Lehrbuch der vergleichenden mikroskopische Anatomie der Wirbeltiere*. Sechster Teil. Atmungsapparat. Gustav Fischer, Jena, 824 pp.

Orr, R. T. (1982). *Vertebrate Biology*, 5th ed. Saunders College, Philadelphia, 568 pp.

Orton, J. (1876). *Comparative Zoology, Structural and Systematic. For Use in Schools and Colleges*. Harper and Brothers, New York, 396 pp.

Orton, J. (1883). *Comparative Zoology, Structural and Systematic, for Use in Schools and Colleges*, 2nd ed. Harper and Brothers, New York, 413 pp.

Orton, J. (1888). *Comparative Zoology, Structural and Systematic, for Use in Schools and Colleges*, Rev. ed. Harper and Brothers, New York, 413 pp.

Orton, J. (1894). *Comparative Zoology, Structural and Systematic, for Use in Schools and Colleges*, 3rd ed. Harper and Brothers, New York. (not seen)

Orton, J., and Dodge, C. W. (1903). *General Zoology: Practical, Systematic and Comparative, being a Revision and Rearrangement of Professor Orton's Comparative Zoölogy*. American Book, New York, 512 pp.

Oulahan, R. (1977). *Wild, Wild World of Animals: Reptiles & Amphibians*. Time-Life Films, New York, 128 pp.

Owen, C. (1742). *An Essay towards a Natural History of Serpents: In Two Parts. I. The first exhibits a general view of serpents, in their various aspects; such as their kinds, bulk, food, motion, propagation, coverture, colours. In which is inserted a short account of vegetable, mineral, and animal poison, particularly that of the serpent; and its cure in various nations; where also the serpent is used as food and physick. II. The second gives a view of most serpents that are known in the several parts of the world; described by their various names, different countries, and qualities*. Charles Owen, London, 240 pp.

Owen, R. (1866). *On the Anatomy of Vertebrates*, vol. 1. Longmans and Green, London, 650 pp.

Packard, A. S. (1879). *Zoology for Students and General Readers*. Henry Holt, New York, 719 pp. (not seen)

Packard, A. S. (1880). *Zoology for High Schools and Colleges*, 2nd ed. Henry Holt, New York. (not seen)

Packard, A. S. (1881). *Zoology for High Schools and Colleges*, 3rd ed. Henry Holt, New York, 719 pp. (not seen)

Packard, A. S. (1885). *Zoology for High Schools and Colleges*, 4th ed. Henry Holt, New York, 334 pp. (not seen)

Packard, A. S. (1886a). *Zoology for High Schools and Colleges*, 5th ed. Henry Holt, New York, 722 pp.

Packard, A. S. (1886b). *First Lessons in Zoology, Adapted for Use in Schools*. Henry Holt, New York, 290 pp.

Packard, A. S. (1888). *Zoology for High Schools and Colleges*, 6th ed. Henry Holt, New York, 722 pp.

Packard, A. S. (1889). *Zoology for High Schools and Colleges*, 7th ed. Henry Holt, New York, 722 pp.

Padgaonkar, A. S., and Warbhuwan, A. P. (1991). Parathyroid and ultimobranchial glands of the snake *Argyrogena fasciolatus* (Shaw). *Biol. Structures Morphogen.* (1990–1991) 3, 97–100.

Padoa, E. (1963). *Manuale di Anatomia Comparata dei Vertebrati*. Feltrinelli Editore, Milan, 827 pp.

Pagenstecher, H. A. (1878). *Allgemeine Zoologie oder Grundgesetze des thierischen Baus und Lebens*, part 3. Wiegandt, Hempel, & Parey, Berlin, 419 pp.

Pagenstecher, H. A. (1881). *Allgemeine Zoologie oder Grundgesetze des thierischen Baus und Lebens*, part 4. Parey, Berlin, 959 pp.

Panizza, B. (1833). *Sopra il Sistema Linfatico dei Rettili Ricerche Zootomiche di Bartolomeo Panizza. P. O. di Notomia Umana nell'I. R. Università di Pavia*. Pietro Bizzoni, Pavia, 43 pp.

Parker, H. W. (1963). *Snakes*. Robert Hale, London, 191 pp.

Parker, H. W. (1965). *Natural History of Snakes*. British Museum (Natural History), London, 95 pp.

Parker, H. W. (1977). *Snakes of the World: Their Ways and Means of Living*. Dover Publications, New York, 191 pp. (reprint of Parker, 1963)

Parker, H. W., and Grandison, A. G. C. (1977). *Snakes: A Natural History*, 2nd ed. British Museum (Natural History), London, 108 pp.

Parker, S. (1993). *Focus on Reptiles*. Shooting Star Press, New York, 32 pp.

Parker, T. J., and Haswell, W. A. (1897). *A Text-Book of Zoology*, vol. 2. Macmillan, London, 635 pp. (not seen)

Parker, T. J., Haswell, W. A, and Cooper, C. F. (1928). *A Text-Book of Zoology*, vol. 2, 4th ed. Macmillan, London, 720 pp.

Parker, T. J., Haswell, W. A, and Cooper, C. F. (1930). *A Text-Book of Zoology*, vol. 2, 5th ed. Macmillan, London, 722 pp.

Parker, T. J., Haswell, W. A, and Cooper, C. F. (1940). *A Text-Book of Zoology*, vol. 2, 6th ed. Macmillan, London, 758 pp.

Parker, T. J., Haswell, W. A, and Cooper, C. F. (1962). *A Text-Book of Zoology*, vol. 2, 7th ed. Macmillan, London, 950 pp.

Parsons, T. S. (1959). Studies on the comparative embryology of the reptilian nose. *Bull. Mus. Comp. Zool., Harvard Univ.* 120, 103–277.

Parsons, T. S. (1970). The nose and Jacobson's Organ. In *Biology of the Reptilia* (C. Gans and T. S. Parsons, eds.). Academic Press, London, vol. 2, pp. 99–191.

Parsons, T. S., and Djatschenko, L. (1983). Variation in the left lung and bronchus of *Thamnophis sirtalis parietalis*. In *Advances in herpetology and evolutionary biology* (A. Rhodin and K. Miyata, eds.). Museum of Comparative Zoology, Harvard Univ., Cambridge, pp. 298–304.

Pastor, L. M. (1990). A morphological study of the tracheal epithelium of the snake *Natrix maura*. *J. Anat.* 172, 47–57.

Pastor, L. M. (1995). The histology of the reptilian lung. In *Histology, Ultrastructure and Immunohistochemistry of the Respiratory Organs in Non Mammalian Vertebrates* (L. M. Pastor, ed.). University of Murcia, Murcia, Spain, pp. 129–153.

Pastor, L. M., and Pallares, J. (1995). The extrapulmonary airways in reptiles. In *Histology, Ultrastructure and Immunohistochemistry of the Respiratory Organs in Non Mammalian Vertebrates* (L. M. Pastor, ed.). University of Murcia, Murcia, Spain, pp. 115–126.

Patt, D. I., and Patt, G. R. (1969). *Comparative Vertebrate Histology*. Harper & Row, New York, 438 pp.

Patterson, R. (1986). *Snakes*. C. Struik, Cape Town, 64 pp.

Patterson, R. (1987). *Reptiles of Southern Africa*. C. Struik, Cape Town, 128 pp.

Pattle, R. E. (1976). The lung surfactant in the evolutionary tree. In *Respiration of Amphibious Vertebrates* (G. M. Hughes, ed.). Academic Press, London, pp. 233–255.

Pattle, R. E. (1978). Lung surfactant and lung lining in birds. In *Respiratory Function in Birds, Adult and Embryonic* (J. Piiper, ed.). Springer-Verlag, Berlin, pp. 23–32.

Pérez-Santos, C., and Moreno, A. G. (1991). Serpientes de Ecuador. *Mus. Reg. Sci. Nat. Monogr.* 11, 1–538.

Perkins, C. B. (1938). The snakes of San Diego County with descriptions and keys. *Bull. Zool. Soc. San Diego* 13, 1–66.

Perkins, L. (1974). *All Color Book of Reptiles*. Crescent Books, New York, 72 pp.

Perrier, E. (1928). Développement embryogénique des vertébrés allantoïdiens les reptiles. In *Traité de Zoologie* (R. Perrier, ed.). Masson, Paris, Fasc. 8, pp. 2885–3118.

Perry, S. F. (1981). Morphometric analysis of pulmonary structure: methods for evaluation and comparison of unicameral lungs. *Mikroskopie, Wien* 38, 278–293.

Perry, S. F. (1983). Reptilian lungs: functional anatomy and evolution. In *Advances in Anatomy, Embryology and Cell Biology* (F. Beck, W. Hild, J. van Limborgh, R. Ortmann, J. E. Pauly, and T. H. Schiebler, eds.). Springer-Verlag, Berlin, vol. 79, pp. 1–81.

Perry, S. F. (1989a). Mainstreams in the evolution of vertebrate respiratory structures. *In Form and Function in Birds* (A. S. King and J. McLelland, eds.). Academic Press, London, vol. 4, pp. 1–67.

Perry, S. F. (1989b). Morphometry of crocodilian lungs. In *Trends in Vertebrate Morphology*. (H. Splechtna and H. Hilgers, eds.). Fortschritte der Zoologie. Gustav Fischer, Stuttgart, vol. 35, pp. 546–549.

Perry, S. F. (1989c). Structure and function of the reptilian respiratory system. In *Comparative Physiology. Current Concepts* (S. C. Wood, ed.). Marcel Dekker, New York, pp. 193–236.

Perry, S. F. (1990). Recent advances and trends in the comparative morphometry of vertebrate gas exchange organs. In *Advances in Comparative and Environmental Physiology* (R. G. Boutilier, ed.). Springer-Verlag, Berlin, vol. 6, pp. 45–71.

Perry, S. F., and Duncker, H.-R. (1978). Lung architechture, volume and static mechanics in five species of lizards. *Respir. Physiol.* 34, 61–81.

Perry, S. F., and Duncker, H.-R. (1980). Interrelationship of static mechanical factors and anatomical structure in lung evolution. *J. Comp. Physiol.* 138B, 321–334.

Peters, W. C. H. (1861). *De Serpentum Familia Uropeltaceorum.* G. Reimer, Berolini. 22 pp.

Peters, W. C. H. (1882). *Naturwissenschaftliche Reise nach Mossambique auf Befehl seiner Majestät des Königs Friedrich Wilhelm IV. In den Jahren 1842 bis 1848 ausgeführt. Zoologie. III. Amphibien.* G. Reimer, Berlin, 191 pp.

Petzold, H.-G. (1984). *Die Anakondas.* A. Ziemsen, Wittenberg Lutherstadt, 142 pp.

Phelps, T. (1981). *Poisonous Snakes.* Blandford, Poole, 237 pp.

Phelps, T. (1989). *Poisonous Snakes,* 2nd ed. Blandford, Poole, 237 pp.

Phisalix, M. (1922). *Animaux Venimeux et Venins; la Fonction Venimeuse chez les Animaux; les Appareils Venimeux, les Venins et leurs Propriétés; les Fonctions et Usages des Venins; l'Envenimation et son Traitement,* vol. 2. Masson, Paris, 864 pp.

Phleger, C. F., Smith, D. G., Macintyre, D. H., and Saunders, B. (1978). Alveolar and saccular lung phospholipids of the anaconda, *Eunectes murinus. Can. J. Zool.* 56, 1009–1013.

Pickersgill, S., and Meek, R. (1988). Husbandry notes on the Asian rat snake *Gonyosoma oxycephala. Brit. Herpetol. Soc. Bull.* 23, 23–24.

Pickwell, G. V. (1972). The venomous sea snakes. *Fauna* 4, 16–32.

Pienaar, U. de V. (1966). The reptiles of the Kruger National Park. *Koedoe* 1, 1–223.

Pienaar, U. de V. (1978). *The Reptile Fauna of the Kruger National Park,* 2nd ed. National Parks Board of South Africa, Pretoria, 222 pp.

Pinney, R. (1981). *The Snake Book.* Doubleday, Garden City, New York, 248 pp.

Pirlot, P. (1969). *Morphologie Évolutive des Chordés.* Les Presses de l'Université de Montréal, Montreal, 1068 pp.

Pisano, A., and Barbieri, F. D. (1967). *Anatomía Comparada de los Vertebrados.* Universitaria de Buenos Aires, Buenos Aires, 365 pp.

Pischinger, A. (1937). Kiemenanlagen und ihre Schicksale bei Amnioten — Schilddrüse und epitheliale Organe der Pharynxwand bei Tetrapoden. In *Handbuch der vergleichenden Anatomie der Wirbeltiere* (L. Bolk, E. Göppert, E. Kallius, and W. Lubosch, eds.). Urban und Schwarzenberg, Berlin and Vienna, vol. 3, pp. 279–348.

Pitman, C. R. S. (1938). *A Guide to the Snakes of Uganda.* Uganda Society, Kampala. 362 pp.

Pitman, C. R. S. (1974). *A Guide to the Snakes of Uganda,* 2nd ed. Wheldon and Wesley, Codicote, U.K., 290 pp.

Platt, D. R. (1969). Natural history of the hognose snakes *Heterodon platyrhinos* and *Heterodon nasicus. Univ. Kansas Publ. Mus. Nat. Hist.* 18, 253–420.

Pohunková, H. (1986). The structure of the interstitial space of pulmonary alveolar septa in vertebrates. *Verh. Anat. Ges.* 80, 373–375.

Pohunková, H., and Hughes, G. M. (1982). A comparative SEM study of the lungs of some lower vertebrates with particular reference to the condition of their surface lining following different treatments. *Folia Morph., Prague* 30, 291–294.

Pohunková, H., and Hughes, G. M. (1985). Ultrastructure of the lungs of the garter snake. *Folia Morph.* 33, 254–258.

Pooley, H. (1946). Tiger snake's calls. *Victorian Nat.* 63, 103.

Pope, C. H. (1946). *Snakes Alive and How They Live.* Viking, New York, 238 pp.

Pope, C. H. (1955). *The Reptile World: A Natural History of the Snakes, Lizards, Turtles, and Crocodilians.* Alfred A. Knopf, New York, 325 pp.

Porter, K. R. (1972). *Herpetology.* W. B. Saunders, Philadelphia, 524 pp.

Portmann, A. (1948). *Einführung in die vergleichende Morphologie der Wirbeltiere.* Benno Schwabe, Basel, 335 pp.

Pough, F. H. (1973). Heart rate, breathing and voluntary diving of the elephant trunk snake, *Acrochordus javanicus. Comp. Biochem. Physiol.* 44A, 183–189.

Pough, F. H. (1977). Ontogenetic change in molecular and functional properties of blood of garter snakes, *Thamnophis sirtalis. J. Exp. Zool.* 201, 47–55.

Prange, H. D., and Schmidt-Nielsen, K. (1969). Evaporative water loss in snakes. *Comp. Biochem. Physiol.* 28, 973–975.

Pringle, J. A. (1954). *Common Snakes.* Longmans and Green, London, 29 pp.

Quirling, D. P. (1950). *Functional Anatomy of the Vertebrates.* McGraw-Hill, New York, 624 pp.

Rage, J.-C. (1972). *Eryx* Daudin et *Gongylophis* Wagler (Serpentes, Boidae). Étude ostéologique. *Bull. Mus. Natl. Hist. Nat., Paris,* ser. 3, 78, 893–898.

Rage, J.-C. (1984). Serpentes. In *Handbuch der Paläoherpetologie* (P. Wellnhofer, ed.). Gustav Fischer, Stuttgart, Part 11, pp. 1–80.

Rage, J.-C. (1987). Fossil history. In *Snakes: Ecology and Evolutionary Biology* (R. A. Seigel, J. T. Collins, and S. S. Novak, eds.). Macmillan, New York, pp. 51–76.

Rage, J.-C. (1994). Snake diversity. In *Snakes: A Natural History* (R. Bauchot, ed.). Sterling, New York, pp. 34–47.

Railliet, A. (1895). *Traité de Zoologie Médicale et Agricole,* 2nd ed. Asselin et Houzeau, Paris, 1303 pp.

Rajendran, M. V. 1986. *Snakes of Our Land.* Jaya Publications, Palayamkottai, 279 pp. [in Tamil].

Ramsay, E. G. (1979). "An investigation of the lungs and skin of snakes from a number of different aquatic habitats." Honours thesis, University of New England, Armidale, 108 pp.

Rand, A. S., and Ortleb, E. P. (1969). Defensive display in the colubrid snake *Pseustes poecilonotus shropshirei. Herpetologica* 25, 46–48.

Rasmussen, J. B. (1979). An intergeneric analysis of some boigine snakes — Bogert's (1940) Group XIII and XIV (Boiginae, Serpentes). *Vidensk. Meddr. dansk naturh. Foren.* 141, 97–155.

Rasmussen, J. B. (1985). A re-evaluation of the systematics of the African rear-fanged snakes of Bogert's Groups XIII–XVI, including a discussion of some evolutionary trends within Caenophidia. In *Proceedings of the International Symposium on African Vertebrates: Systematics, Phylogeny and Evolutionary Ecology* (K.-L. Schuchmann, ed.). Zoologisches Forschungsinstitut und Museum Alexander Koenig, Bonn, pp. 531–548.

Rasmussen, J. B. (1986). On the taxonomic status of *Dipsadoboa werneri* (Boulenger), *D. shrevei* (Loveridge), and *Crotaphopeltis hotamboeia kageleri* Uthmoller (Boiginae, Serpentes). *Amphibia-Reptilia* 7, 51–73.

Rasmussen, J. B. (1989a). On the taxonomic status of *Dipsadoboa aulica aulica* Günther and *D. aulica flavida* Broadley and Stevens, with the description of a new subspecies of *D. flavida* Broadley and Stevens (Boiginae, Serpentes). *Amphibia-Reptilia* 10, 35–62.

Rasmussen, J. B. (1989b). A taxonomic review of the *Dipsadoboa duchesnei* complex. *Bonn. Zool. Beitr.* 40, 249–264.

Rasmussen, J. B. (1993a). The current taxonomic status of Tornier's cat-snake (*Crotaphopeltis tornieri*). *Amphibia-Reptilia* 14, 395–409.

Rasmussen, J. B. (1993b). A taxonomic review of the *Dipsadoboa unicolor* complex, including a phylogenetic analysis of the genus (Serpentes, Dipsadidae, Boiginae). *Steenstrupia* 19, 129–196.

Rathke, H. (1839). *Entwickelungsgeschichte der Natter* (Coluber natrix). Gebrüder Bornträger, Koenigsberg, 232 pp.

Rau, A. S. (1924). Observations on the anatomy of the heart of *Tiliqua scincoides* and *Eunectes murinus. J. Anat.* 59, 60–71.

Ray, H. C. (1934). On the arterial system of the common Indian rat-snake, *Ptyas mucosus* (Linn.). *J. Morph.* 56, 533–569.

Ray, H. C. (1936). On the venous system of the common Indian rat-snake, *Ptyas mucosus* (Linn.). *J. Morph.* 59, 517–544.

Rayer, M. (1850). Sur un nouveau cas de monstruosité (atlodyme, Isid. Geoffroy-Saint-Hilaire) observé sur une espèce de reptile ophidien (*Homalopsis schneiderii*). *Comp. Rend. Séances Mém. Soc. Biol.* (1849) 1, 185.

Read, J., and Donnelly, P. M. (1972). Stratification of blood flow in the elongated lungs of the carpet python. *J. Appl. Physiol.* 32, 842–846.

Redi, F. (1664). *Osservazioni Intorno alle Vipere fatte da Francesco Redi Gentiluomo Aretino, Accademico della Crusca. E da lui Scritte in una Lettera all'Illustrissimo Signor Lorenzo Magalotti Gentiluomo della Camera del Ser.^{mo} G. Duca di Tosc.^{na}* Insegna della Stella, Firenze, 91 pp.

Redi, F. (1670). *Lettera di Francesco Redi Gentilvomo Aretino. Sopra alcune Opposizioni fatte alle sue Osservazioni Intorno alle Vipere.* Nella Stamperia della Stella, Firenze, 47 pp.

Redi, F. (1684). *Osservazione Intorno agli Animali Viventi che si Trovano negli Animali Viventi.* Opera di F. Redi, Milano (1810) 3, 203–435. (not seen)

Rees, A. (1820). Reptiles. In *The Cyclopaedia; or Universal Dictionary of Arts, Sciences, and Literature* (A. Rees, ed.). Longman, Hurst, Rees and Orme, London, vol. 29, pp. 1–7.

Reese, A. M. (1926). The occlusion of the oesophagus and trachea in Crocodilia and snakes. *Am. J. Anat.* 37, 195–212.

Reitinger, F. F., and Lee, J. K. S. (1978). *Common Snakes of South East Asia and Hong Kong.* Heinemann Educational Books, Hong Kong, 114 pp.

Remane, A. (1924). Reptilia. Kriechtiere. In *Biologie der Tiere Deutschlands* (P. Schulze, ed.). Gebrüder Borntraeger, Berlin, Part 9, pp. 50.1–50.29.

Renous, S. (1985). Interprétation de l'organisation des arcs aortiques de *Dibamus* (Reptiles, squamates) à l'aide d'informations fournies par les autres groupes de squamates serpentiformes. *Gegenbaurs Morph. Jb.* 131, 309–328.

Rensch, B. (1946). Morphologie und Entwicklungsgeschichte der Wirbeltiere. *Naturforschung Medizin Deutschland* (1939–1946) 55, 97–116.

Resetar, A. (Unpublished manuscript). The status of the African snakes *Chilorhinophis carpenteri* (Parker) and *Chilorhinophis butleri* Werner (Serpentes: Atractaspididae). Field Museum of Natural History, Chicago.

Retzius, A. (1830). *Anatomisk Undersökning öfver Nagra delar af* Python bivittatus *jemte Comparativa Anmärkningar*. P. A. Norstedt & Söner, Stockholm, 36 pp.

Retzius, A. (1832). Anatomische Untersuchungen über verschiedene Theile des *Python bivittatus*, nebst vergleichenden Bemerkungen. *Isis von Oken* 25, 511–531. (trans. of Retzius, 1830)

Reyes, L. M., Habacon, E., Tansiel, R., and Morafka, D. (1989). The stability and utility of visceral topography as phylogenetic characters in crotaline snakes. In *First World Congress of Herpetology (11–19 September 1989)* (T. Halliday, J. Baker, and L. Hosie, eds.). First World Congress Herpetol., Canterbury, U.K. (abstract).

Rieppel, O. (1977). Studies on the skull of the Henophidia (Reptilia: Serpentes). *J. Zool., Lond.* 181, 145–173.

Rieppel, O. (1979). A cladistic classification of primitive snakes based on skull structure. *Z. Zool. Syst. Evol.-Forsch.* 17, 140–150.

Rieppel, O. (1980). The trigeminal jaw adductors of primitive snakes and their homologies with the lacertilian jaw adductors. *J. Zool., Lond.* 190, 447–471.

Rieppel, O. (1983). A comparison of the skull of *Lanthanotus borneensis* (Reptilia: Varanoidea) with the skull of primitive snakes. *Z. Zool. Syst. Evol.-Forsch.* 21, 142–153.

Rieppel, O. (1988a). The classification of the Squamata. In *The Phylogeny and Classification of the Tetrapods* (M. J. Benton, ed.). Clarendon Press, Oxford, vol. 1, pp. 261–293.

Rieppel, O. (1988b). A review of the origin of snakes. In *Evolutionary Biology* (M. K. Hecht, B. Wallace, and G. T. Prance, eds.). Plenum Press, New York, vol. 22, pp. 37–130.

Rietschel, P. (1968). Ernährungsorgane, Atmungsorgane, Kreislauforgane, Leibeshöhlen, Ausscheidungsorgane, Fortpflanzungsorgane. In *Vergleichende Anatomie der Wirbeltiere* (H. Giersberg and P. Rietschel, eds.). Gustav Fischer, Jena, vol. 2, 288 pp.

Riquier, M., and Böhme, W. (1996). Bemerkungen zu Verbreitung und geographischer Variation sowie zu Freileben und Haltung der Lianennatter, *Thelotornis kirtlandii* (Hallowell, 1844). *Herpetofauna* 18, 27–34.

Risley, P. L. (1941). Origin and migration of primordial germ cells in snake embryos. *Anat. Rec.* 81, 82.

Robb, J. S. (1960). The internal anatomy of *Typhlops* Schneider (Reptilia). *Aust. J. Zool.* 8, 181–216.

Robbins, A. C. (1991). Anatomy drawing of a nonpoisonous (gopher) snake. *Bull. Chicago Herpetol. Soc.* 26, 110.

Roberton, M. (1838). Sur la respiration et la deglutition du *Boa constrictor*. *Rev. Mag. Zool., Paris* 1, 205–206.

Rogers, E. (1986). *Looking at Vertebrates: A Practical Guide to Vertebrate Adaptations*. Longman, Essex, U.K., 195 pp.

Roman, B. (1980). *Serpents de Haute-Volta*. Centre National de la Recherche Scientifique et Technologique, Ouagadougou, 129 pp.

Romer, A. S. (1956). *Osteology of the Reptiles*. University of Chicago Press, Chicago, 772 pp.

Romer, A. S., and Parsons, T. S. (1983). *Anatomia Comparada* (I. Lebedeff, trans.). Quinta ed. Nueva Editorial Interamericana, Mexico City, 428 pp.

Roots, C. (1974). *Animals of the Dark*. David & Charles, Newton Abbot, 200 pp.

Röse, C. (1890). Beiträge zur vergleichenden Anatomie des Herzens der Wirbelthiere. *Morph. Jb.* 16, 27–96.

Rose, W. (1929a). *Veld & Vlei. An Account of South African Frogs, Toads, Lizards, Snakes, & Tortoises*. Specialty Press of South Africa, Wynberg, 240 pp.

Rose, W. (1929b). *South African Snakes*. Specialty Press of South Africa, Cape Town, 264 pp.

Rose, W. (1950). *The Reptiles and Amphibians of Southern Africa*. Maskew Miller, Cape Town, 378 pp.

Rose, W. (1955). *Snakes–Mainly South African*. Maskew Miller, Cape Town, 213 pp.

Rose, W. (1956). Snakes–mainly South African. *African Wild Life* 10, 171.

Rose, W. (1962). *The Reptiles and Amphibians of Southern Africa*, 2nd ed. Maskew Miller, Cape Town, 494 pp.

Röseler, P., and Lamprecht, H. (1914). *Handbuch für biologische Übungen. Zoologischer Teil*. Julius Springer, Berlin, 574 pp.

Rosenberg, H. I. (1973). Functional anatomy of pulmonary ventilation in the garter snake, *Thamnophis elegans*. *J. Morph.* 140, 171–184.

Rosenzweig, P. A. (1981). "Functional anatomy of ventilation of the red-bellied black snake, *Pseudechis porphyriacus* (Shaw)." Honours thesis, University of Adelaide, Adelaide, 162 pp.

Ross, R. A., and Marzec, G. (1990). *The Reproductive Husbandry of Pythons and Boas*. Institute for Herpetological Research, Stanford, California, 270 pp.

Rossman, D. A., and Eberle, W. G. (1977). Partition of the genus *Natrix*, with preliminary observations on evolutionary trends in natricine snakes. *Herpetologica* 33, 34–43.

Rossman, D. A., and Williams, K. L. (1966). Defensive behavior of the South American colubrid snakes *Pseustes sulphureus* (Wagler) and *Spilotes pullatus* (Linnaeus). *Proc. Louisiana Acad. Sci.* 29, 152–156.

Rossman, N. J., Rossman, D. A., and Keith, N. K. (1982). Comparative visceral topography of the New World snake tribe Thamnophiini (Colubridae, Natricinae). *Tulane Stud. Zool. Bot.* 23, 123–164.

Rothley, H. (1930a). "Über den feineren Bau der Luftröhre und der Lunge der Reptilien." Ph.D. dissertation, Julius Springer, Berlin, 62 pp.

Rothley, H. (1930b). Über den feineren Bau der Luftröhre und der Lunge der Reptilien. *Z. Morph. Ökol. Tiere* 20, 1–62.

Rothley, H. (1931). Nachtrag zu der Arbeit: "Über den feineren Bau der Luftröhre und der Lunge der Reptilien. (Zeitschr. f. Morph. u. Ökol. 20, 1930)." *Z. Morph. Ökol. Tiere* 24, 78–81.

Roze, J. A. (1966). *La Taxonomia y Zoogeográfia de los Ofidios de Venezuela*. Universidad Central de Venezuela, Caracas, 362 pp.

Ruben, J. A. (1976a). Aerobic and anaerobic metabolism during activity in snakes. *J. Comp. Physiol.* 109, 147–157.

Ruben, J. A. (1976b). Correlation of enzymatic activity, muscle myoglobin concentration and lung morphology with activity metabolism in snakes. *J. Exp. Zool.* 197, 313–320.

Rufz, E. (1859). *Enquete sur le Serpent de la Martinique (Vipère fer de Lance, Bothrops lancéolé,etc.)*, 2nd ed. Germer Baillière, Paris, 402 pp.

Ruschenberger, W. S. W. (1852). *Elements of Herpetology, and of Ichthyology: Prepared for the Use of Schools and Colleges. From the Text of Milne Edwards, and Achille Comte, Professors of Natural History in the Colleges of Henri IV, and Charlemagne.* Lippincott and Grambo, Philadelphia, 145 pp.

Russell, F. E. (1980). *Snake Venom Poisoning.* J. B. Lippincott, Philadelphia, 562 pp.

Russell, F. E. (1983). *Snake Venom Poisoning*, 2nd ed. Scholium International, Great Neck, 562 pp.

Saiff, E. (1975). Preglottal structures in the snake family Colubridae. *Copeia* 1975, 589–592.

Saint-Aubain, M. L. de (1984). A comparative study of the functional anatomy of pulmonary vaso-constriction in lung-breathing vertebrates. *Z. Zool. Syst. Evolut.-Forsch.* 22, 118–136.

Saint Girons, H., and Saint Girons, M.-C. (1974). Les reptiles. In *Encyclopédie de la Pléiade. Zoologie. IV. Tétrapodes, domaines faunistiques, zoogéographie.* Andrée Tétry, Éditions Gallimard, Paris, pp. 109–292.

Saint Girons, M.-C. (1994). Postures & behavior: defense or intimidation. In *Snakes: A Natural History* (R. Bauchot, ed.). Sterling, New York, pp. 162–171.

Saunders, J. T., and Manton, S. M. (1931). *A Manual of Practical Vertebrate Morphology.* Clarendon Press, Oxford, 220 pp.

Saunders, J. T., and Manton, S. M. (1949). *A Manual of Practical Vertebrate Morphology*, 2nd ed. Oxford University Press, Oxford, 255 pp.

Saunders, J. T., and Manton, S. M. (1959). *A Manual of Practical Vertebrate Morphology*, 3rd ed. Oxford University Press, Oxford, 272 pp.

Saunders, J. T., Manton, S. M, and Brown, M. E. (1969). *A Manual of Practical Vertebrate Morphology*, 4th ed. Clarendon Press, Oxford, 288 pp.

Saunders, J. W., Jr. (1970). *Patterns and Principles of Animal Development.* Collier-Macmillan, London, 282 pp.

Savitzky, A. H. (1974). "The relationships of the xenodontine colubrid snakes related to *Ninia*." M.S. thesis, University of Kansas, Lawrence, 64 pp.

Sazina, I., and Abe, A. S. (1991). Habits of five Brazilian snakes with coral-snake pattern, including a summary of defensive tactics. *Stud. Neotrop. Fauna Environ.* 26, 159–164.

Scanlon, J. D. (1985). "Phylogeny and relationships of the elapid snake genus *Simoselaps* Jan, 1859: the evolution of a group of burrowing snakes." Honours thesis, University of Sydney, Sydney, 153 pp.

Schimkewitsch, W., Maier, H. N., and Sukatschoff, B. W. (1910). *Lehrbuch der vergleichenden Anatomie der Wirbeltiere.* E. Schweizerbart'sche, Stuttgart, 649 pp.

Schimkewitsch, W., Maier, H. N., and Sukatschoff, B. W. (1921). *Lehrbuch der vergleichenden Anatomie der Wirbeltiere.* E. Schweizerbart'sche, Stuttgart, 652 pp.

Schlegel, H. (1837a). *Essai sur la Physionomie des Serpens*, vol. 1. Arnz, Leiden, 251 pp.

Schlegel, H. (1837b). *Essai sur la Physionomie des Serpens*, vol. 2. Arnz, Leiden. 606 pp.

Schlegel, H. (1843). *Essay on the Physiognomy of Serpents.* Maclachlan and Stewart, Edinburgh, 254 pp. (trans. of Schlegel, 1837a–b by T. S. Traill)

Schlemm, F. (1826). Description anatomique du système vasculaire sanguin des serpents. *Bull. Sci. Nat. Géol., Paris* 9, 353–356.

Schlemm, F. (1827). Anatomische Beschreibung des Blutgefässystems der Schlangen. *Tiedemann & Treviranus Z. Physiol.* 2, 101–124.

Schmalhausen, J. J. (1905). Die Entwickelung der Lungen bei *Tropidonotus natrix*. *Anat. Anz.* 27, 511–520.

Schmidt, E. O. (1865). *Handbuch der vergleichenden Anatomie. Leitfaden bei zoologischen und zootomischen Vorlesungen*, 5th ed. Mauke, Jena, 367 pp.

Schmidt, E. O. (1872). *Handbuch der vergleichenden Anatomie. Leitfaden bei zoologischen und zootomischen Vorlesungen*, 6th ed. Mauke, Jena, 402 pp.

Schmidt, K. P. (1927). The reptiles of Hainan. *Bull. Amer. Mus. Nat. Hist.* 54, 395–465.

Schmidt, K. P. (1950). Modes of evolution discernible in the taxonomy of snakes. *Evolution* 4, 79–86.

Schmidt, K. P., and Inger, R. F. (1957). *Living Reptiles of the World*. Hanover House, Garden City, 287 pp.

Schnieper, C. (1995). *Snakes: Silent Hunters*. Carolrhoda Books, Minneapolis, Minnesota, 48 pp.

Schroeder, C. R., and Radcliffe, C. (1989). Rattlesnakes. *Zoobooks, San Diego* 6(11), 1–16.

Schulz, K.-D. (1986). Die hinterasiatischen Kletternattern der Gattung *Elaphe*. Teil VII. *Elaphe radiata* (Schlegel, 1837). *Sauria* 8(4), 3–6.

Schulz, K.-D. (1988). Asian rat snakes of the *Elaphe* genus. Part VII. *Elaphe radiata* (Schlegel, 1837). *Snake Keeper* 2(8), 12–15.

Schulz, K.-D. (1996). *A Monograph of the Colubrid Snakes of the Genus Elaphe Fitzinger*. Koeltz Scientific Books, Koenigstein, 439 pp.

Schulze, F. E. (1871). Die Lungen. In *Handbuch der Lehre von den Geweben des Menschen und der Thiere* (S. Stricker, ed.). Wilhelm Engelmann, Leipzig, vol. 1, pp. 464–488.

Scortecci, G. (1939). *Gli Ofidi Velenosi dell'Africa Italiana*. Istituto Sieroterapico Milanese, Milano, 292 pp.

Scott, G. C., and Kendall, J. I. (1935). *The Microscopic Anatomy of Vertebrates*. Lea & Febiger, Philadelphia, 306 pp.

Seba, A. (1735). *Locupletissimi rerum Naturalium Thesauri Accurata Descriptio, et Iconibus Artificiosissimis Expressio, per Universam Physices Historiam. Opus, cui, in hoc rerum Genere, Nullum par Exstitit. Ex toto Terrarum orbe Collegit, Digessit, Descripsit, et Depingendum curavit Albertus Seba, etzela Oostfrisius . . .*, vol. 2. Janssonio-Waesbergios, J. Wetstenium, & Gul. Smith, Amstelaedami, 154 pp.

Sedgwick, A. 1905. *A Student's Text-Book of Zoology*. Swan Sonnenschein and Co., London, 705 pp.

Severinus, M. A. (1645). *Zootomia Democritaea, id est Anatome Generalis totius Animantium Opificii, Libris Quinque Distincta, Quorum Setiem Sequens Facias Delineabit*. Literis Endterianis, Noribergae. (not seen)

Severinus, M. A. (1651). *Vipera Pythia. Id est, de Viperae Natura, Veneno, Medicina, Demonstrationes, & Experimenta Nova*. Pauli Frambotti, Patavii, 522 pp.

Seymour, R. S. (1978). Gas tensions and blood distribution in sea snakes at surface pressure and at simulated depth. *Physiol. Zoöl.* 51, 388–407.

Seymour, R. S. (1981). Distribution of ventilation and perfusion in the sea snake, *Pelamis platurus. J. Comp. Physiol.* 145B, 109–115.

Seymour, R. S. (1982). Physiological adaptations to aquatic life. In *Biology of the Reptilia* (C. Gans and F. H. Pough, eds.). Academic Press, London, vol. 13, pp. 1–51.

Seymour, R. S., Dobson, G. P., and Baldwin, J. (1981a). Respiratory and cardiovascular physiology of the aquatic snake, *Acrochordus arafurae*. *J. Comp. Physiol.* 144B, 215–227.

Seymour, R. S., Spragg, R. G., and Hartman, M. T. (1981b). Distribution of ventilation and perfusion in the sea snake, *Pelamis platurus*. *J. Comp. Physiol.* 145B, 109–115.

Shaw, R. D. (1956). Mamba encounter. *African Wild Life* 10, 172.

Shea, G., Shine, R., and Covacevich, J. C. (1993). Family Elapidae. In *Fauna of Australia* (C. J. Glasby, G. J. B. Ross, and P. L. Beesley, eds.). Australian Government Publishing Service, Canberra, vol. 2A, pp. 295–309.

Shine, R. (1991). *Australian Snakes: A Natural History.* Cornell University Press, Ithaca, 223 pp.

Shine, R. (1992). Snakes. In *Reptiles and Amphibians* (H. G. Cogger and R. G. Zweifel, eds.). Smithmark, New York, pp. 174–211.

Shine, R., and Houston, D. (1993). Family Acrochordidae. In *Fauna of Australia.*(C. J. Glasby, G. J. B. Ross, and P. L. Beesley, eds.). Australian Government Publishing Service, Canberra, vol. 2A, pp. 322–324.

Shipley, A. E., and MacBride, E. W. (1920). *Zoology: An Elementary Text-Book,* 4th ed. Cambridge University Press, Cambridge, 752 pp.

Shufeldt, R. W. (1885). The voice of serpents. *Science* 5, 267.

Singh, D. (1971). Trachea — a comparative study. *Indian J. Zool.* 12, 121–125.

Singh, R., and Kar, I. (1982). Morphology of lungs in some ophidian species and its phylogenetic significance. *Indian J. Zootomy* 23, 13–17.

Singh, R., and Kar, I. (1984). Parathyroid gland structure in some species of Squamata. *Zool. Jb., Abt. Anat.* 112, 491–498.

Siwe, S. A. (1937). Die großen Drüsen des Darmkanals. In *Handbuch der vergleichenden Anatomie der Wirbeltiere* (L. Bolk, E. Göppert, E. Kallius, and W. Lubosch, eds.). Urban & Schwarzenberg, Berlin, Vienna, vol. 3, pp. 725–774.

Skinner, H. A. (1973). *Snakes and Us: An Introduction to East African Herpetology.* East African Literature Bureau, Nairobi, 146 pp.

Sledz, D. M., Mawhinney, J. R., and Vernick, S. H. (1963). Some notes on the circulatory system of *Natrix natrix* (Linnaeus), the European grass snake. *Copeia* 1963, 570.

Sloane, H. (1725). *A Voyage to the Islands Madera, Barbadoes, Nieves, St. Christophers, and Jamaica; with the Natural History of the Herbs and Trees, Four-Footed Beasts, Fishes, Birds, Insects, Reptiles, &c. To which is Prefix'd, an Introduction, wherein is an Account of the Inhabitants, Air, Waters, Diseases, Trade, &c. of that Place; with some Relations concerning the Neighbouring Continent, and Islands of America. Illustrated with the Figures of the Things Described, which have not been heretofore Engraved,* vol. 2. Hans Sloane, London, 499 pp.

Smith, D. G., and Macintyre, D. H. (1979). Autonomic innervation of the visceral and vascular smooth muscle of a snake lung (Ophidia: Colubridae). *Comp. Biochem. Physiol.* 62C, 187–191.

Smith, H. M. (1954). *Lectures in Comparative Anatomy.* Hutner and Wroughton, Danville, 279 pp.

Smith, H. M., Smith, R. B., and Sawin, H. L. (1977). A summary of snake classification (Reptilia, Serpentes). *J. Herpetol.* 11, 115–121.

Smith, H. M., Wallach, V., and Chiszar, D. (1995). Observations of the snake genus *Pliocercus*, I. *Bull. Maryland Herpetol. Soc.* 31, 204–214.

Smith, M. A. (1914). The snakes of Bangkok. *J. Nat. Hist. Soc. Siam* 1, 93–104.

Smith, M. A. (1943). *The Fauna of British India, Ceylon and Burma, including the Whole of the Indo-Chinese Sub-Region. Reptilia and Amphibia*, vol. 3. Taylor and Francis, London, 583 pp.

Smith, M. A. (1951). *The British Amphibians and Reptiles*. Collins, London. 315 pp.

Smith, M. A. (1954). *The British Amphibians and Reptiles*, 2nd ed. Collins, London, 322 pp.

Soderberg, P. S. (1972). Striking behavior in the common green whip snake (*Ahaetulla nasutus*). *J. Bombay Nat. Hist. Soc.* 68, 839.

Soderberg, P. (1973). On eleven Asian elapid snakes with special reference to their occurrence in Thailand. *Nat. Hist. Bull. Siam Soc.* 24, 203–317.

Sondhi, K. C. (1958). The hyoid and associated structures in some Indian reptiles. *Ann. Zool.* 2, 155–239.

Sonnini, C. S., and Latreille, P. A. (1801). *Histoire Naturelle des Reptiles, avec Figures Dessinées d'après Nature*, vol. 3. Deterville, Paris, 335 pp.

Sparing, S. (1976). "Das Innere Flächen- und Hohlraumsystem der Viperiden-Lunge." M.S. thesis, Ruprecht-Karl-Universität, Heidelberg, 65 pp.

Spawls, S. (1979). *Sun, Sand and Snakes*. William Morrow, New York, 254 pp.

Standaert, T. A., and Johansen, K. (1974). Cutaneous gas exchange in snakes. *J. Comp. Physiol.* 89, 313–320.

Staniszewski, M. (1990). *The Manual of Lizards & Snakes*. Tetra Press, Morris Plains, New Jersey, 156 pp.

Stannius, H. (1846). Wirbelthiere. In *Lehrbuch der vergleichenden Anatomie* (C. T. de Siebold and H. Stannius, eds.). Veit, Berlin, Part 2, 482 pp.

Stannius, H. (1850). Animaux vertébrés. In *Nouveau manuel d'anatomie comparée*, vol. 2 (C. T. de Siebold and H. Stannius, eds.). Librairie Encyclopédique de Roret, Paris, 528 pp.

Stannius, H. (1856). Die Wirbelthiere. Zweites Buch. Die Amphibien. In *Handbuch der Zootomie* (C. T. de Siebold and H. Stannius, eds.). Veit, Berlin, 2nd ed., 270 pp.

Staszko, R., and Walls, J. G. (1994). *Rat Snakes: A Hobbyist's Guide to Elaphe and Kin*. T.F.H. Publications, Neptune City, New Jersey, 208 pp.

Stebbins, R. C. (1954). *Amphibians and Reptiles of Western North America*. McGraw-Hill, New York, 528 pp.

Steche, O. (1922). *Grundriss der Zoologie. Eine Einführung in die Lehre vom Bau und von den Lebenserscheinungen der Tiere für Studierende der Naturwissenschaften und der Medizin*, 2nd ed. (unchanged). Vereinigung Wissenschaftlicher Verleger, Berlin, 508 pp.

Stefanelli, A. (1943). *Biologia e Zoologia Generale*, 2nd ed. Casa Editrice Dott. Luigi Macrì, Castello, 1073 pp.

Stidworthy, J. (1971). *Snakes of the World*. Grosset and Dunlap, New York, 159 pp.

Stinner, J. N. (1980). "Pulmonary anatomy, gas exchange, and acid-base balance in the gopher snake, *Pituophis melanoleucus catenifer*." Ph.D. dissertation, University of California, Riverside, 135 pp.

286 / Van Wallach

Stinner, J. N. (1982a). Ventilation, gas exchange and blood gases in the snake, *Pituophis melanoleucus*. *Respir. Physiol.* 47, 279–298.

Stinner, J. N. (1982b). Functional anatomy of the lung of the snake *Pituophis melanoleucus*. *Am. J. Physiol.* 243, 251–257.

Stinner, J. N. (1987a). Cardiovascular and metabolic responses to temperature in *Coluber constrictor*. *Am. J. Physiol.* 253, R222–R227.

Stinner, J. N. (1987b). Thermal dependence of air convection requirement and blood gases in the snake *Coluber constrictor*. *Am. Zool.* 27, 41–47.

Stinner, J. N. (1987c). Gas exchange and air flow in the lung of the snake, *Pituophis melanoleucus*. *J. Comp. Physiol.* 157B, 307–314.

Stoops, E. D., and Wright, A. T. (1992). *Snakes*. Sterling, New York, 80 pp.

Strahl, H. (1883). Beiträge zur Entwickelung der Reptilien. *Arch. Anat. Physiol., Anat.* 1883, 1–43.

Stratton, C. J., and Wetzstein, H. (1979). The histochemistry and SSEM [sic] comparative anatomy of primate, rodent, avian, reptilian and amphibian lungs. *Anat. Rec.* 193, 696. (abstract)

Stucki-Stirn, M. C. (1979). *Snake Report 721*. Herpeto-Verlag, Teuffenthal, Switzerland, 650 pp.

Suomalainen, P. (1939). Wie lange vermag die Kreuzotter, *Vipera berus* L., mit dem Luftvorrat ihrer Lunge und des Luftsackes auszukommen? Zugleich ein Beitrag zur makroskopischen und mikroskopischen Anatomie der Kreuzotterlunge. *Ann. Soc. Zool.-Bot. Fennicae Vanamo, Helsinki* 7, 3–9.

Sweeney, R. C. H. (1961). *Snakes of Nyasaland*. Nyasaland Society, Zomba, 200 pp.

Tanara, M. U. (1975). *Il Mondo degli Anfibi e dei Rettili*. Arnoldo Mondadori Editore, Milan. (not seen)

Tanara, M. U. (1978). *The World of Amphibians and Reptiles* (S. Pleasance, trans.). Abbeville Press, New York, 256 pp.

Taub, A. M. (1967). Comparative histological studies on Duvernoy's gland of colubrid snakes. *Bull. Amer. Mus. Nat. Hist.* 138, 1–50.

Tenney, S. (1865). *Natural History. A Manual of Zoölogy for Schools, Colleges, and the General Reader*, 3rd ed. Charles Scribner, New York, 540 pp.

Tenney, S. (1866). *Natural History. A Manual of Zoölogy for Schools, Colleges, and the General Reader*, 4th ed. Charles Scribner, New York, 540 pp.

Tenney, S. (1867). *Natural History. A Manual of Zoölogy for Schools, Colleges, and the General Reader*, 5th ed. Charles Scribner, New York, 540 pp.

Tenney, S. (1875). *Elements of Zoölogy. A Text-Book*. Charles Scribner's Sons, New York, 503 pp.

Tenney, S. (1876). *Elements of Zoölogy. A Text-Book*. Charles Scribner's Sons, New York, 503 pp.

Tenney, S. M., and Tenney, J. B. (1970). Quantitative morphology of cold-blooded lungs: Amphibia and Reptilia. *Respir. Physiol.* 9, 197–215.

Terent'ev, P. V. (1956). Manual of Vertebrate Zoology. State Publisher of Soviet Science, Moscow, 519 pp. [in Russian].

Terent'ev, P. V. (1961). Herpetology: A Manual on Amphibians and Reptiles. Higher School State Publisher, Moscow, 336 pp. [in Russian].

Terent'ev, P. V. (1965). *Herpetology: A Manual on Amphibians and Reptiles* (Israel Program for Scientific Translation, trans.). Smithsonian Institution, Washington, 313 pp. (trans. of Terent'ev 1961)

Test, F. H., Sexton, O. J., and Heatwole, H. (1966). Reptiles of Rancho Grande and vicinity, Estado Aragua, Venezuela. *Misc. Publ. Mus. Zool. Univ. Michigan* 128, 1–63.

Thäter, K. (1910). Das Munddach der Schlangen und Schildkröten. In *Die Kopfregion der Amnioten* (A. Fleischmann, ed.). Wilhelm Engelmann, Leipzig, pp. 471–518.

Thompson, J. C. (1913a). *Oxyrhopus trigeminus* Duméril and Bibron the type of *Erythroxyrhopus* gen. nov. *Proc. Acad. Nat. Sci. Philad.* 65, 78–80.

Thompson, J. C. (1913b). Notes on serpents in the family Colubridae. *Proc. Acad. Nat. Sci. Philad.* 65, 213–218.

Thompson, J. C. (1913c). Contributions to the anatomy of the Ophidia. *Proc. Zool. Soc. Lond.* 1913, 414–425.

Thompson, J. C. (1914a). Contribution to the anatomy of the Ilysiidae. *Proc. Acad. Nat. Sci. Philad.* 66, 285–293.

Thompson, J. C. (1914b). Further contributions to the anatomy of the Ophidia. *Proc. Zool. Soc. Lond.* 1914, 379–402.

Thomson, D. F. (1946). The truth about snakes. *Loris* 4, 324.

Thomson , J. A. (1892). *The Study of Animal Life*, 2nd ed. John Murray, Thomson London.

Thomson, J. A. (1895). *Outlines of Zoology*, 2nd ed. D. Appleton, New York, 820 pp.

Thomson, J. A. (1917). *The Study of Animal Life*, 4th ed. Charles Scribner's Sons, New York.

Thomson, J. A. (1920). *Outlines of Zoology*, 7th ed. Henry Frowde, Edinburgh, 869 pp.

Thomson, J. A. (1929). *Outlines of Zoology*, 8th ed. (revised). Humphrey Milford, London, 972 pp.

Thorpe, R. (1975). Quantitative handling of characters useful in snake systematics with particular reference to intraspecific variation in the ringed snake *Natrix natrix* (L.). *Biol. J. Linn. Soc.* 7, 27–43.

Thorpe, R. (1984a). Multivariate patterns of geographic variation between the island and mainland populations of the eastern grass snake (*Natrix natrix natrix*). *J. Zool., Lond.* 204, 551–561.

Thorpe, R. (1984b). Coding morphometric characters for constructing Distance Wagner networks. *Evolution* 38, 244–255.

Thorpe, R. (1985). Character number and the multivariate analysis of simple patterns of geographic variation: categorical or "stepped clinal" variation. *Syst. Zool.* 34, 127–139.

Thorpe, R. (1987). Complex clines: the predictivity of complicated patterns of geographic variation portrayed by multivariate analysis. *Biol. J. Linn. Soc.* 31, 75–88.

Tiedemann, F. (1831). Beschreibung einiger seltenen Thier-Monstra. *Z. Physiol.* 4, 121–124.

Tokar, A. A. (1989). A revision of the genus *Eryx* (Serpentes, Boidae) based upon osteological data. *Vestnik Zool.* 1989, 46–55 [in Russian].

Toland, G. F., and Dehne, G. L. (1960). Laboratory observations of the anatomy of the snake. *Amer. Biol. Teacher* 22, 278–285.

Topsell, E. (1608). *The Historie of Serpents. Or, the Second Booke of Living Creatures: wherein is Contained their Divine, Naturall, and Morall Descriptions, with their lively Figures, Names, Conditions, Kindes and Natures of all Venomous Beasts: with their Severall Poysons and Antidotes; their deepe Hatred to Mankind, and the Wonderfull Worke of God in their Creation, and Destruction.* W. Jaggard, London, 306 pp.

Topsell, E. (1658). *The History of Four-Footed Beasts and Serpents: Describing at large their True and Lively Figure, their Several Names, Conditions, Kinds, Virtues (both Natural and Medicinal), Countries of their Breed, their Love and Hatred to Mankind, and the Wonderful Work of God in their Creation, Preservation, and Destruction. Interwoven with curious variety of Historical Narrations out of Scriptures, Fathers, Philosophers, Physicians, and Poets: Illustrated with Divers Hieroglyphiks and Emblems, both Pleasant and Profitable for Students in all Faculties and Protections. Collected out of the Writings of Conrad Gesner and other Authors. Whereupon is now added, the Theater of Insects; or, lesser Living Creatures: as Bees, Flies, Caterpillars, Spiders, Worms, etc. A most Elaborate Work: by T. Muffet, Dr. of Physick. The whole Revised, Corrected, and Inlarged with the Addition of Two Useful Physical Tables, by J. R. M.D.* E. Cotes, London, 818 pp. & 889–1130 pp.

Tourneux, F., and Herrmann, G. (1876). Recherches sur quelques épithéliums plats dans la série animale. (1). (Première partie). *J. Anat. Physiol. Norm. Path. Homme Anim., Paris* 12, 199–221.

Tropea, S. (1987). *Snakes: A Photo-Fact Book.* Kidsbooks, Chicago, 24 pp.

Trutnau, L. (1975). *Europäische Amphibien und Reptilien.* Belser, Stuttgart, 212 pp.

Tweedie, M. W. F. (1953). *The Snakes of Malaya.* Government Printing Office, Singapore., 143 pp.

Tweedie, M. W. F. (1983). *The Snakes of Malaya,* 3rd ed. Singapore National Printers, Singapore, 167 pp.

Twerenbold, P. (1987). "Anatomische Untersuchungen an Vertretern der Schlangenfamilie Colubridae." Master's thesis, Universität Zürich, Zürich, 35 pp.

Tyson, E. (1683). *Vipera caudi-sona Americana,* or the anatomy of a rattlesnake dissected at the repository of the Royal Society in January, 1682/3. *Philos. Trans. R. Soc. Lond.* 13, 25–58.

Tyson, E. (1693). In J. Ray, *Synopsis Methodica Animalium Quadrupedum et Serpentini Generis.* Royal Society, London, pp. 291–324. (trans. of Tyson, 1683, by J. Ray)

Tyson, E. (1751). *The Anatomy of a Pigmy . . . to which is Added the Anatomy and Description of a Rattlesnake,* 2nd ed. Royal Society, London, 25 pp. (not seen)

Underwood, G. (1967). *A Contribution to the Classification of Snakes.* British Museum (Natural History), London, 179 pp.

Underwood, G. (1976a). Simplification and degeneration in the course of evolution of squamate reptiles. *Coll. Intern. Centre Nat. Rech. Sci.* 266, 341–352.

Underwood, G. (1976b). A systematic analysis of boid snakes. In *Linnean Society Symposium Series* (A. d'A. Bellairs and C. Cox, eds.). Academic Press, London, no. 3, pp. 151–175.

Underwood, G. (1979). Classification and distribution of venomous snakes in the world. In *Handbook of Experimental Pharmacology* (G. V. R. Born, A. Farah, H. Herken, and A. D. Welch, eds.). Springer-Verlag, Berlin, vol. 52, pp. 15–40.

Underwood, G., and Kochva, E. (1993). On the affinities of the burrowing asps *Atractaspis* (Serpentes: Atractaspididae). *Zool. J. Linn. Soc.* 107, 3–64.

Valentini, M. B. (1720). *Amphitheatrum Zootomicum, Tabulis aeneis Quamplurimis exhibens Historiam Animalium Anatomicam è Miscellaneis S.R.I. Academiae Naturae Curiosorum, diariis Societatum Scientiarum Regiarum, Parisiensis, Anglicae & Prussiacae, actis Hafniensibus & Lipsiensibus, Zootomiis Anatomicorum Celeberrimorum Aliisque Scriptis Rarioribus Collectam. Accedit Methodus Secandi Cadav. Humana, cum Enchiresibus Injiciendi ceram, Hydrargyrum & Stannum in vasa Sanguifera & Lymphatica, ars Dealbandi ossa pro Sceletopoeia, cum Osteologia, Tabulis Myologicis Aliisque mss. Rauianis, hactenus Summoperè Expetitis, Accurante Variisque Notis & Figuris Illustrante.* Pars alterna. Johannis Mulleri, Gissae, 231 pp.

van Bemmelen, J. F. (1886). Die Visceraltaschen und Aortenbogen bei Reptilien und Vögeln. *Zool. Anz.* 9, 528–532.

van Bemmelen, J. F. (1888). Beiträge zur Kenntniss der Halsgegend bei Reptilien. *Bijdr. Dierk. Nat. Artis Magistra* 16, 101–146.

van Beneden, P. J. (1852–1854). *Encyclopédie Populaire. Anatomie Comparée.* Société pour l'Émancipation Intellectuelle, Bruxelles, 348 pp.

van den Eeckhoudt, J.-P. (1968). *Cours de Biologie. II. Zoologie (Classe de Cinquième).* Sciences et Lettres, Liège, 237 pp.

van der Hoeven, J. (1833). *Handboek der Dierkunde, of Grondbeginsels der natuurlijke geschiedenis van het dierenrijk,* vol. 2, part 2. C. G. Sulpke, Amsterdam, 698 pp.

van der Hoeven, J. (1853). *Handbuch der Zoologie,* vol. 2 (Wirbelthiere). Leopold Voss, Leipzig, 817 pp. (trans. of second Dutch edition by F. Schlegel and R. Leuckart)

van der Hoeven, J. (1855). *Handboek der Dierkunde,* vol. 2, 2nd ed. J. C. A. Sulpke, Amsterdam, 1068 pp.

van der Hoeven, J. (1858). *Handbook of Zoology,* vol. 2. Longman, Brown, Green, Longmans, and Roberts, Cambridge, 775 pp. (trans. of second Dutch edition by W. Clark)

van der Hoeven, J. (1859). Kruipende Dieren. In *Handboek der Dierkunde,* vol. 2, 3rd ed. J. C. A. Sulpke, Amsterdam, pp. 433–592.

van Gelderen, C. (1933). Venensystem, mit einem Anhang über den Dotter- und Plazentarktreislauf. In *Handbuch der vergleichenden Anatomie der Wirbeltiere* (L. Bolk, E. Göppert, E. Kallius, and W. Lubosch, eds.). Urban and Schwarzenberg, Berlin and Vienna, vol. 6, 685–744.

van Heurn, W. C. (1929). *Coluber radiatus,* de "tjaoe asak." *De Tropische Natuur* 18, 128–130.

van Hoesel, J. K. P. (1959). *Ophidia Javanica.* Pertjetakan Archipel, Bogor, 188 pp.

Vanzolini, P. E., Ramos-Costa, A. M. A., and Vitt, L. J. (1980). *Repteis das Caatingas.* Academia Brasileira de Ciências, Rio de Janeiro, 161 pp.

Varde, M. R. (1951). The morphology and histology of the lung in snakes. *J. Univ. Bombay* 19B, 79–89.

Vesey-FitzGerald, D. F. (1958). The snakes of Northern Rhodesia and the Tanganyika borderlands. *Proc. Trans. Rhodesia Sci. Assoc., Salisbury* 46, 17–102.

Vesey-FitzGerald, D. F. (1968). *The World of Reptiles.* Pelham Books, London, 128 pp.

Vesey-FitzGerald, D. F. (1975). A guide to the snakes of the Tanzania and Kenya borderlands. *J. East African Nat. Hist. Soc. Natl. Mus.* (149), 1–26.

Veslingi, J. (1664). *Observationes Anatomicae et Epistolae Medicae ex Schedis Posthumis Selectae et Editae a T. Bartholino.* Petrum Hauboldum, Hafniae, 248 pp.

Villa, J. (1962). *Las Serpientes Venenosas de Nicaragua.* Published by the author, Managua, 90 pp.

Villa, J., Wilson, L. D., and Johnson, J. D. (1988). *Middle American Herpetology: a Bibliographic Checklist.* University of Missouri Press, Columbia, 131 pp.

Villiers, A. (1950). *Les Serpents de l'Ouest Africain.* Institut Fondamental d'Afrique Noire, Dakar, 148 pp.

Villiers, A. (1975). *Les Serpents de l'Ouest Africain,* 3rd ed. Les Nouvelles Éditions Africaines, Dakar, 195 pp.

Visser, J. (1972). *What Snake is That?* Purnell, Cape Town, 84 pp.

Visser, J., and Chapman, D. S. (1978). *Snakes and Snakebite: Venomous Snakes and Management of Snakebite in Southern Africa.* Purnell, Cape Town, 152 pp.

Vogt, C. (1839). Das Herz von *Python tigris.* In *Zur Anatomie der Amphibien.* G. A. Jenni, Bern, pp. 1–8.

Vogt, C. (1851). *Zoologische Briefe. Naturgeschichte der lebenden und untergegangenen Thiere, für Lehrer, höhere Schulen und Gebildete aller Stände,* vol. 2. Literarische Anstalt, J. Rütten, Frankfurt am Main, 640 pp.

Vogt, R. C. (1981). *Natural History of Amphibians and Reptiles in Wisconsin.* Milwaukee Public Museum, Milwaukee, 205 pp.

Volsøe, H. (1939). The sea snakes of the Iranian Gulf and the Gulf of Oman. With a summary of the biology of the sea snakes. In *Danish Scientific Investigations in Iran* (K. Jessen and R. Spark, eds.). Ejnar Munksgaard, Copenhagen, Part 1, pp. 9–45.

Voris, H. K. (1977). A phylogeny of the sea snakes (Hydrophiidae). *Fieldiana: Zool.* 70, 79–166.

Vsevolojsky, N. de. (1812). Sur un serpent à deux têtes vivant, lue à la rentrée de la Societé Impériale des Naturalistes de Moscou. *Mem. Soc. Imp. Nat. Moscou* 3, 284–288.

Wahlström, J. E. (1868). *Elementarkurs Zoologien.* Zacharias Haeggströms Förlag, Stockholm, 232 pp.

Waite, E. R. (1918). Review of the Australian blind snakes (Family Typhlopidae). *Rec. South Aust. Mus.* 1, 1–38.

Walker, R., ed. (1990). *Animal Anatomy on File.* Facts on File, New York, 200 pp.

Walker, W. F., Jr. (1987). *Functional Anatomy of the Vertebrates: an Evolutionary Perspective.* Saunders College, Philadelphia, 781 pp.

Wall, F. (1905a). Notes on snakes collected in Cannanore from 5th November 1903 to 5th August 1904. *J. Bombay Nat. Hist. Soc.* 16, 292–317.

Wall, F. (1905b). A popular treatise on the common Indian snakes. Illustrated by coloured plates and diagrams. Part I. *J. Bombay Nat. Hist. Soc.* 16, 533–554.

Wall, F. (1906). A popular treatise on the common Indian snakes. Part III—The dhaman or common ratsnake (*Zamenis mucosus*). *J. Bombay Nat. Hist. Soc.* 17, 259–273.

Wall, F. (1909). Notes on snakes collected in Upper Assam. *J. Bombay Nat. Hist. Soc.* 19, 609–623.

Wall, F. (1910). A popular treatise on the common Indian snakes. Illustrated by coloured plates and diagrams. Part XII. *J. Bombay Nat. Hist. Soc.* , 775–792.

Wall, F. (1913). A popular treatise on the common Indian snakes. Illustrated by coloured plates and diagrams. Part XIX. *J. Bombay Nat. Hist. Soc.* 22, 22–28.

Wall, F. (1914). A popular treatise on the common Indian snakes. Illustrated by coloured plates and diagrams. Part XXIII. *J. Bombay Nat. Hist. Soc.* 23, 206–215.

Wall, F. (1921). *Ophidia Taprobanica, or the Snakes of Ceylon.* H. R. Cottle, Colombo, 581 pp.

Wallace, A. R. (1853). *A Narrative of Travels on the Amazon and Rio Negro, with an Account of the Native Tribes, and Observations on the Climate, Geology, and Natural History of the Amazon Valley.* Reeve, London, 541 pp.

Wallach, J. D., and Boever, W. J. (1983). *Diseases of Exotic Animals: Medical and Surgical Management.* W. B. Saunders, Philadelphia, 1159 pp.

Wallach, V. (1985). A cladistic analysis of the terrestrial Australian Elapidae. In *Biology of Australasian Frogs and Reptiles* (G. Grigg, R. Shine, and H. Ehmann, eds.). Royal Zoological Society of New South Wales, Chipping North, pp. 223–253.

Wallach, V. (1988). Status and redescription of the genus *Padangia* Werner, with comparative visceral data on *Collorhabdium* Smedley and other genera (Serpentes: Colubridae). *Amphibia-Reptilia* 9, 61–76.

Wallach, V. (1991). "Comparative visceral topography of African colubrid snakes of the subfamilies Aparallactinae and Atractaspidinae." M.S. thesis, Louisiana State University, Baton Rouge, 490 pp.

Wallach, V. (1993a). Presence of a left lung in the Typhlopidae (Reptilia: Serpentes). *J. Herpetol. Assoc. Africa* 42, 32–33.

Wallach, V. (1993b). A new species of blind snake, *Typhlops marxi*, from the Philippines (Serpentes: Typhlopidae). *Bull. Raffles Mus.* 41, 263–278.

Wallach, V. (1994a). *Aparallactus lineatus* (Peters) and *A. niger* Boulenger: two valid species from West Africa. *J. Herpetol.* 28, 95–99.

Wallach, V. (1994b). The status of the Indian endemic *Typhlops acutus* (Duméril & Bibron) and the identity of *Typhlops psittacus* Werner (Reptilia, Serpentes, Typhlopidae). *Bull. Inst. Roy. Sci. Nat. Belgique* 64, 209–229.

Wallach, V. (1995a). Revalidation of the genus *Tropidodipsas* Günther, with notes on the Dipsadini and Nothopsini (Serpentes: Colubridae). *J. Herpetol.* 29, 476–481.

Wallach, V. (1995b). New records of dicephalic snakes in museum collections. *Herpetol. Rev.* 26, 127–128.

Wallach, V. (1995c). A new genus for the *Ramphotyphlops subocularis* species group (Serpentes: Typhlopidae), with description of a new species. *Asiatic Herpetol. Res.* 6, 132–150.

Wallach, V. (1996a). Notes and corrections on two scolecophidians: *Ramphotyphlops albiceps* and *Leptotyphlops brasiliensis. Herpetol. Rev.* 27, 10.

Wallach, V. (1996b). The systematic status of the *Ramphotyphlops flaviventer* (Peters) complex (Serpentes: Typhlopidae). *Amphibia-Reptilia* 17, 341–359.

Wallach, V. (1996c). *Leptotyphlops drewesi* n. sp., a worm snake from central Kenya (Serpentes: Leptotyphlopidae). *J. African Zool.* 110, 1–7.

Wallach, V. (1997a). Two new blind snakes of the *Typhlops ater* species group from Papua New Guinea (Serpentes: Typhlopidae). *Russian J. Herpetol.* (1996) 3, 107–118.

Wallach, V. (1997b). *Leptotyphlops broadleyi*, a new species of worm snake from Côte d'Ivoire (Serpentes: Leptotyphlopidae). *Afr. J. Herpetol.* 46, accepted for publication.

Wallach, V. (1997c). *Typhlops meszoelyi*, a new species of blind snake from northeastern India (Serpentes: Typhlopidae). *Herpetologica*, accepted for publication.

Wallach, V., and Ineich, I. (1996). Redescription of a rare Malagasy blind snake, *Typhlops grandidieri* Mocquard, with placement in a new genus (Serpentes: Typhlopidae). *J. Herpetol.* 30, 367–376.

Wallach, V., and Günther, R. (1997a). Typhlopidae vs. Anomalepididae: the identity of *Typhlops mutilatus* Werner (Reptilia: Serpentes). *Mitt. Zool. Mus. Berlin* 73, 333–342.

Wallach, V., and Günther, R. (1997b). Visceral anatomy of the Malaysian snake genus *Xenophidion*, with allocation to a new family (Serpentes: Xenophidiidae). *Amphibia-Reptilia*, submitted for publication.

Wallach, V., and Smith, H. M. (1992). *Boella tenella* is *Epicrates inornatus* (Reptilia: Serpentes). *Bull. Maryland Herpetol. Soc.* 28, 162–170.

Walter, H. E. (1929). *Biology of the Vertebrates. A Comparative Study of Man and his Animal Allies*. Macmillan, New York, 789 pp.

Waterman, A. J., Frye, B. E., Johansen, K., Kluge, A. G., Moss, M. L., Noback, C. R., Olsen, I. D., and Zug, G. R. (1971). *Chordate Structure and Function*. Macmillan, New York, 587 pp.

Weale, J. P. (1871). Protective resemblances. *Nature* 3, 507–508.

Webb, G. J. W. (1972). A new hypothesis on the pattern of blood-flow through the squamate heart. *Search* 3, 138–140.

Webb, G. J. W., Heatwole, H., and de Bavay, J. (1974). Comparative cardiac anatomy of the Reptilia. II. A critique of the literature on the Squamata and Rhynchocephalia. *J. Morph.* 142, 1–20.

Weber, A., and Buvignier, A. (1903). L'Origine des ébauches pulmonaires chez quelques vertébrés supérieurs. *Bibl. Anat.* 12, 249–289.

Webster, D., and Webster, M. (1974). *Comparative Vertebrate Morphology*. Academic Press, New York, 517 pp.

Weichert, C. K. (1951). *Anatomy of the Chordates*. McGraw-Hill, New York, 921 pp.

Weichert, C. K. (1965). *Anatomy of the Chordates*, 3rd ed. McGraw-Hill, New York, 758 pp.

Weidensaul, S. (1990). *Venomous Animals*. Gallery Books, New York, 64 pp.

Weidensaul, S. (1991). *Snakes of the World*. Chartwell Books, Secaucus, New Jersey, 128 pp.

Welch, K. R. G. (1982). *Herpetology of Africa: a Checklist and Bibliography of the Orders Amphisbaenia, Sauria and Serpentes*. Robert E. Krieger, Malabar, Florida, 293 pp.

Wenslaw, A. (1926). Étude cytologique comparée de l'epithelium pulmonaire. Reptiles. *Comp. Rend. Soc. Biol.* 95, 702–703.

Werner, F. (1910). *Amphibien und Reptilien II*. (Anpassung der Organe an die Lebensweise). *Naturwiss. Wegweiser* 16A, 1–84. (reprinted in 1911 by Strecker und Schröder, Stuttgart)

Werner, F. (1911). Beiträge zur Anatomie einiger seltenerer Reptilien, mit besonderer Berücksichtigung der Atmungsorgane. *Arb. Zool. Inst. Univ. Wien Zool. Sta. Triest.* 19, 373–424. (reprinted in 1912 by Alfred Hölder, Vienna)

Werner, F. (1917). Versuch einer Synopsis der Schlangenfamilie der Glauconiiden. *Mitt. Zool. Mus. Hamburg* 34, 191–208.

Werner, F. (1921a). Synopsis der Schlangenfamilie der Typhlopiden auf Grund des Boulenger'schen Schlangenkatalogs (1893–1896). *Arch. Natur.* 87A, 266–338.

Werner, F. (1921b). Synopsis der Schlangenfamilie der Boiden auf Grund des Boulenger'schen Schlangenkatalogs (1893/96). *Arch. Natur.* 87A, 230–265.

Werner, F. (1922a). Synopsis der Schlangenfamilie der Amblycephaliden und Viperiden nebst Übersicht über die kleineren Familie und die Colubriden der Acrochordinengruppe. Auf Grund des Boulenger'schen Schlangenkatalogs (1893–1896). *Arch. Natur.* 88A, 185–244.

Werner, F. (1922b). *Das Tierreich. III, Reptilien und Amphibien,* vol. 1, 2nd ed. Walter de Gruyter, Berlin, 140 pp.

Werner, F. (1923). Übersicht der Gattungen und Arten der Schlangen der Familie Colubridae. I. Teil. Mit einem Nachtrag zu den übrigen Familien. *Arch. Natur., Berlin* 89A, 138–199.

Werner, F. (1924). Übersicht der Gattungen und Arten der Schlangen der Familie Colubridae. II. Teil (Dipsadomorphinae und Hydrophiinae). *Arch. Natur., Berlin* 90A, 108–166.

Werner, F. (1929). Übersicht der Gattungen und Arten der Schlangen aus der Familie Colubridae. III. Teil (Colubrinae). Mit einem Nachtrag zu den übrigen Familien. *Zool. Jb., Abt. Syst.* 57, 1–196.

Werner, Y. L. (1985). Defensive behavior in a boigine snake: first record of throat inflation in *Psammophis. Israel J. Zool.* 33, 69–71.

Westphal, C. G. H. (1806). *De Organis Circulationis et Respirationis Reptilium.* Officina Batheana, Halae, 59 pp.

Whitaker, R. (1978). *Common Indian Snakes: A Field Guide.* Macmillan India, Delhi, 154 pp.

White, C. A. (1878). Note on the garter snake. *Am. Nat.* 12, 53.

White, C. A. (1884). On the character and function of the epiglottis in the bull snake (*Pityophis*). *Am. Nat.* 18, 19–21.

White, F. N. (1959). Circulation in the reptilian heart. *Anat. Rec.* 135, 129–134.

Wiedersheim, R. E. E. (1883). *Lehrbuch der vergleichenden Anatomie der Wirbelthiere auf Grundlage der Entwicklungsgeschichte.* Gustav Fischer, Jena, 905 pp.

Wiedersheim, R. E. E. (1884). *Grundriss der vergleichenden Anatomie der Wirbelthiere für Studierende bearbeitet.* Gustav Fischer, Jena, 272 pp.

Wiedersheim, R. E. E. (1886). *Lehrbuch der vergleichenden Anatomie der Wirbelthiere auf Grundlage der Entwicklungsgeschichte,* 2nd ed. Gustav Fischer, Jena, 890 pp.

Wiedersheim, R. E. E. (1898). *Grundriss der vergleichenden Anatomie der Wirbelthiere für Studierende bearbeitet,* 4th ed. (completely revised). Gustav Fischer, Jena, 559 pp.

Wiedersheim, R. E. E. (1909). *Grundriss der vergleichenden Anatomie der Wirbelthiere für Studierende bearbeitet,* 7th ed. (greatly revised and augmented). Gustav Fischer, Jena, 935 pp.

Wiedersheim, R. E. E., and Parker, W. N. (1886). *Elements of the Comparative Anatomy of vertebrates* (W. N. Parker, trans.). Macmillan, London, 345 pp.

Wiedersheim, R. E. E., and Parker, W. N. (1907). *Comparative Anatomy of Vertebrates*, 3rd ed. Macmillan, London, 576 pp. (trans. of 6th German ed. by W. N. Parker)

Wilder, H. H. (1902). *A Synopsis of Animal Classification*. Henry Holt, New York, 57 pp.

Willard, D. E. (1977). Constricting methods of snakes. *Copeia* 1977, 379–382.

Williams, K. L., and Wallach, V. (1989). *Snakes of the World*, vol. 1. Robert E. Krieger, Malabar, Florida, 234 pp.

Williams, T. (1859). Organs of respiration. In *Cyclopaedia of Anatomy and Physiology* (R. B. Todd, ed.). Longman, Brown, Green, Longmans, and Roberts, London, vol. 5, Suppl., 258–293.

Willnow, R. (1961). Vitalmikroskopie der Tetrapodenlunge. *Eur. Konf. Mikrozirkulation, Hamburg* 1, 120–127.

Wilson, S. K., and Knowles, D. G. (1988). *Australia's Reptiles: A Photographic Reference to the Terrestrial Reptiles of Australia*. William Collins, Sydney, 447 pp.

Wilson, V. J. (1965). The snakes of the eastern province of Zambia. *The Puku* 3, 149–170.

Withers, P. C., and O'Shea, J. E. (1993). Morphology and physiology of the Squamata. In *Fauna of Australia* (C. J. Glasby, G. J. B. Ross, and P. L. Beesley, eds.). Australian Government Publishing Service, Canberra, vol. 2A, pp. 172–196.

Witte, G. F. de (1948). *Faune de Belgique. Amphibiens et reptiles*. Musée Royal d'Histoire Naturelle, Bruxelles, 321 pp.

Wolf, S. (1933). Zur Kenntnis von Bau und Funktion der Reptilienlunge. *Zool. Jb., Abt. Anat.* 57, 139–190.

Wong, K. (1994). "Visceral topography of the three genera of blind snakes of the family Typhlopidae (Reptilia: Serpentes)." M.S. thesis, Northeastern University, Boston, 145 pp.

Worm, O. (1655). *Museum Wormianum. Seu Historia Rerum Rariorum, tam Naturalium, quam Artificialium, tam Domesticarum, quam Exoticarum, quae Hafniae Danorum in Aedibus Authoris Servantur*. Iohannem Elsevirium, Lugduni Batavorum, 388 pp.

Wurmbach, H., ed. (1985). *Lehrbuch der Zoologie*, vol. 2. Gustav Fischer, Stuttgart, 1107 pp.

Wyman, J. (1849a). Lectures on comparative physiology, by Prof. Wyman, before the Lowell Institute. Lecture VIII. Delivered on Friday evening and Saturday afternoon, Feb. 16 and 17, 1849. Daily Evening Traveller, Boston, 20 Feb. 1849, pp. 1, 4.

Wyman, J. (1849b). *Twelve Lectures on Comparative Physiology, Delivered before the Lowell Institute in Boston, January and February, 1849*. Henry Flanders, Boston, 72 pp.

Yahya, S. A. (1978). Hearing ability of brown tree snake (*Dendrelaphis tristis*). *J. Bombay Nat. Hist. Soc.* 75, 930.

Yao, C. (1985). Anatomical studies on the circulatory and urogenital systems in *Eryx miliaris*. *Acta Herpetol. Sinica* 4, 331–336.

Yoshihara, M., Uchiyama, M., and Murakami, T. (1979). Notes on the ultimobranchial glands of some Japanese snakes. *Zool. Mag., Tokyo* 88, 180–184.

Young, B. A. (1991). Morphological basis of "growling" in the king cobra, *Ophiophagus hannah. J. Exp. Zool.* 260, 275–287.

Young, B. A. (1992). Tracheal diverticula in snakes: possible functions and evolution. *J. Zool., Lond.* 227, 567–583.

Young, B. A., Lillywhite, H. B., and Wassersug, R. J. (1993). On the structure of the aortic valves in snakes (Reptilia: Serpentes). *J. Morph.* 216, 141–159.

Young, B. A., Street, S. L., and Wassersug, R. J. (1994). Anatomical and gravitational influences on cardiac displacement in snakes (Lepidosauria, Serpentes). *Zoomorphology* 114, 169–175.

Young, B. A., Sheft, S., and Yost, W. (1995). Sound production in *Pituophis melanoleucus* (Serpentes: Colubridae) with the first description of a vocal cord in snakes. *J. Exp. Zool.* 273, 472–481.

Zingg, A. (1968). Zur Fortpflanzung von *Dispholidus typus* (Reptilia, Colubridae). *Salamandra* 4, 37–43.

Zinyakova, M. P., and Rudenko, P. P. (1979). Comparison of topography of the inner organs of two species of snake. In *Herpetologiy* (I. S. Darevsky, V. Garanin, L. I. Khozatsky, T. I. Zhukova, and M. P. Zinyakova, eds.). Kuban State University, Krasnodar, pp. 93–100 [in Russian].

Ziswiler, V. (1976). *Spezielle Zoologie. Wirbeltiere*, vol. 2. Georg Thieme, Stuttgart, 658 pp.

Zug, D. A., and Dunson, W. A. (1979). Salinity preference in fresh water and estuarine snakes (*Nerodia sipedon* and *N. fasciata*). *Florida Sci.* 42, 1–8.

Zug, G. R. (1993). *Herpetology: an Introductory Biology of Amphibians and Reptiles.* Academic Press, San Diego, 527 pp.

Wallach, V. (1998). The lungs of snakes. In *Biology of the Reptilia*, vol. 19 (Morphology G) (C. Gans and A. S. Gaunt, eds.). Society for the Study of Amphibians and Reptiles, Ithaca, New York, Contrib. Herpetol., vol. 14, pp. 93–295.

3

Pulmonary Function in Reptiles

TOBIAS WANG, ALLAN W. SMITS, AND WARREN W. BURGGREN

CONTENTS

I. INTRODUCTION

Reptiles represent a broad and diverse class of vertebrates. In part, this taxonomic diversity is artificial, for the class Reptilia is generally recognized as paraphyletic, including the Crocodylia, which are much more closely related to birds than to other reptiles. Yet, even within recognized and sanctioned taxonomic groups such as the testudines (turtles, tortoises, and terrapins) or the lepidosaurians (lizards, snakes, and amphisbaenians), there is still a broad range in pulmonary structure and function. In this chapter on pulmonary function in reptiles, we will attempt to achieve two somewhat contradictory goals: (1) to review general features of structure and function, and (2) to emphasize the diversity of pulmonary function and how it serves the various taxa that constitute the Reptilia. Although we will review much material new to the

Biology of the Reptilia series, space does not allow a comprehensive review at a detailed level of all material that has emerged since the last treatment by S. C. Wood and Lenfant (1976) in the *Biology of the Reptilia*. Consequently, the reader is directed to recent reviews on reptilian lung anatomy (Perry, 1989; Perry, this volume) and physiology (Seymour, 1989; Milsom, 1990a; Powell, 1994).

We begin with gas exchange as the primary purpose of the lungs of most reptiles and include the role of the lungs in acid-base balance. In addition, we give a detailed review of two new areas of pulmonary function: lung fluid balance and the role of surfactants. Some of these lung functions are also discussed by Perry in a companion chapter in this volume, which focuses on functional morphology and complements the material in this chapter.

II. GAS EXCHANGE

The primary purpose of the lungs of all vertebrates is to exchange oxygen and carbon dioxide between the inspired gas and the blood perfusing the lungs. Other functional roles of the lungs either stem directly from pulmonary-affected changes in blood gas chemistry (e.g., acid-base balance) or have evolved secondarily from the consequences of having an internalized gas-filled compartment (e.g., buoyancy, vocalization, defense).

A. Pulmonary versus Cutaneous Gas Exchange in Reptiles

The general body surface can serve as the sole site of gas exchange whenever animals are small, or whenever metabolic rate is low due to, for example, low body temperatures or inactivity. With the shift to air breathing, vertebrates have evolved specialized gas exchange structures (external and internal gills, gas bladders, and lungs) independently and numerous times. In each case, the development of specialized respiratory structures was thought to be critical for the evolution of larger, more active animals with higher metabolic rates. A very few amphibious vertebrates cope exclusively with cutaneous gas exchange (e.g., salamanders of the family Plethodontidae). However, almost all air-breathing, amphibious or terrestrial vertebrates—and certainly all reptiles—utilize lungs for uptake of oxygen and excretion of carbon dioxide at least during the part of their life cycle in which the major activities of feeding, growth, and reproduction occur. Under special situations, most notably during hibernation (see Ultsch, 1989), some aquatic reptiles can go for days, weeks, or even months without breathing air. However, pulmonary gas exchange is the norm for most reptiles.

Our emphasis on the universal importance of pulmonary gas exchange to reptiles does not mean that cutaneous gas exchange is insignificant. Indeed, many reptiles supplement the former with the latter (Fig. 3.1). Surveys of the relative importance of pulmonary versus cutaneous gas exchange routinely show that numerous species of snakes, lizards, and even turtles and tortoises exchange significant quantities of gas across their integument at ambient temperatures ranging from about 5 to 30°C (reviewed by Feder and Burggren, 1985a, 1985b). Those reptiles with the greatest dependence on cutaneous gas exchange occur in lineages occupying freshwater or marine environments—e.g., turtles and aquatic snakes (Seymour, 1982). An extreme example is the sea snake *Pelamis platurus*, which when swimming in water obtains about 40% of its O_2 and eliminates nearly 74% of its CO_2 across its skin by this route (Graham, 1974). Perhaps more typical is the 7% of total $\dot{M}_{O_2}$ and 33% of total $\dot{M}_{CO_2}$ achieved across the skin of the aquatic snake *Acrochordus javanicus* (Standaert and Johansen, 1974). Resting soft-shelled turtles, *Apalone asper* (*Trionyx spinifer asper*), can exist almost entirely on cutaneous respiration in water (Dunson, 1960). Yet, as for other reptilian taxa, turtles show wide discrepancies in the relative balance between pulmonary and

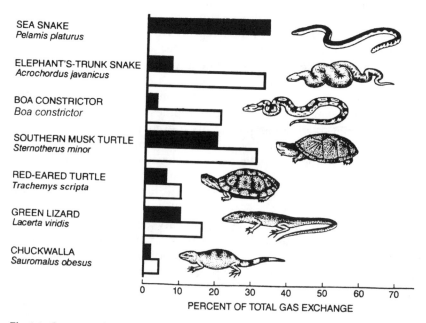

Fig. 3.1. Cutaneous (non-pulmonary) gas exchange in a variety of reptiles. Note the large variation in both the absolute degree of dependence on cutaneous exchange as well as the differing levels of use of non-pulmonary sites for oxygen uptake (solid bars) versus carbon dioxide elimination (open bars).

cutaneous respiration. Sea turtles such as *Chelonia mydas*, which are quite active and highly aerobic, have minimal capability to support metabolism via cutaneous gas exchange (Butler et al., 1984). The clearest pattern that emerges in the consideration of pulmonary versus cutaneous respiration in reptiles is that in most species examined—regardless of body mass, habitat, or systematics—the skin plays a greater role in eliminating CO_2 than in taking up O_2.

Special circumstances can alter the importance of pulmonary versus cutaneous gas exchange. Seymour (1989) discusses in detail the implications of the balance between pulmonary and cutaneous gas exchange of diving in reptiles such as sea snakes, which may descend to depths exceeding 100 m (Heatwole and Seymour, 1975). As the depth increases, compression of the gas in the lung raises alveolar P_{O_2} above that of the surrounding water. Oxygen would not only be transferred into pulmonary venous blood, but also from blood to surrounding water across the skin unless lung gas can be "physiologically isolated" during diving. This could be achieved either by extreme intracardiac right-to-left shunting or by an intrapulmonary shunt. Either can prevent the loss of pulmonary oxygen to the surrounding water, the P_{O_2} of which does not increase as a function of depth. Unfortunately, we lack direct data on cutaneous gas exchange during simulated or actual diving in snakes or other reptiles. At least in the deep-diving snake *Hydrophis*, P_{O_2} of the blood stays well below that of seawater to a depth of over 40 m, suggesting that at least the P_{O_2} gradient for cutaneous oxygen uptake remains favorable.

Hibernation, which involves a combination of low body temperature and special metabolic state, may cause reptiles to eschew lung ventilation altogether, relying completely upon exchange across the skin to support the small amount of ongoing metabolism (Ultsch, 1989). At the opposite end of the metabolic extreme, elevated rates of metabolism during activity or exposure to high ambient temperatures (or a combination of the two) will most likely be supported almost exclusively by increases in pulmonary gas exchange. Although limited data exist for reptiles, studies of cutaneous and pulmonary gas exchange in amphibians indicate that, as metabolic rate increases, pulmonary gas exchange assumes almost all of the increased respiratory demand (for review, see Burggren and Pinder, 1991). This probably occurs because pulmonary gas exchange can be enhanced by a variety of mechanisms including increases in ventilation on one side of the diffusion barrier and in blood flow and capillary recruitment on the other side. In contrast, cutaneous gas exchange is largely diffusion-limited, poorly regulated relative to pulmonary gas exchange, and is most effective in periods of low gas exchange demand.

B. Control of Ventilation

1. GENERAL INTRODUCTION

In this section we will outline the general trends that characterize the control of lung ventilation in reptiles, but because many aspects are yet unsolved, we also discuss experimental studies and concepts from other vertebrate classes. Before reviewing the role of lung ventilation in blood gas regulation, it is imperative to stress the implications arising from the presence of cardiac shunts in reptiles. In the presence of cardiac shunts, the arterial blood gases do not directly reflect lung gas composition as is the case in mammals. Rather, arterial P_{O_2} and P_{CO_2} are dependent variables, determined by the gas contents of arterial blood and the respective blood gas affinities and capacities (for reviews, see S. C. Wood, 1982, 1984; Wang and Hicks, 1996; Hicks, this volume). Because the cardiac shunts effectively alter the arterial blood gas contents, there exists the possibility that cardiac shunting can regulate arterial blood gas composition *independently* of lung ventilation (e.g., Burggren et al., 1989). On the basis of simple models for gas exchange, Wang and Hicks (1996) argued that, during normoxia, realistic changes in shunts may be more powerful determinants of arterial P_{O_2} than changes in ventilation. Unfortunately, very few experimental studies on reptiles have investigated the sensory mechanisms that may regulate cardiac shunts (for a review, see Wang et al., 1997). Thus, although an integration of cardiovascular and ventilatory control mechanisms is pivotal for understanding arterial blood gas control in amphibians and reptiles, this task must await the collection of additional experimental data.

Ventilatory control is typically investigated by measuring breathing frequency and tidal volume while blood gas composition is disturbed through inhalation of hypoxic or hypercapnic gases. Conversely, the immediate surroundings of a given receptor can be experimentally altered or maintained. For example, the cerebrospinal fluid (CSF), which provides the stimulus for central chemoreceptors, has been manipulated experimentally by perfusion with artificial mock solutions. An essential problem in all these experiments is that it is virtually impossible to alter any parameter without changing other parameters; if ventilation is stimulated by exposure to hypoxia, a respiratory alkalosis normally follows, which, in turn, inhibits ventilation. More severe hypoxia, however, may be accompanied by a metabolic acidosis that acts as an additional drive to ventilation. In both cases, the ventilatory response is a combined result of both the direct stimulation of reduced oxygen levels in the blood and the altered acid-base status. Potentially, these problems can be avoided in studies on anaesthetized or decerebrated animals. Under these circumstances, it is easier to regulate experimentally lung and blood blood gases, but it is difficult to assess the effects of anesthesia on central integration and receptor function. Recently, even more isolated preparations, such as isolated brain stems, have been employed, and it is clear that an array of these approaches is required to understand ventilatory control. The immediate challenge for future research is to combine the data from isolated preparations with those obtained on free-moving, unanesthetized animals.

Presumably, control of blood gas composition has evolved to safe-guard O_2 supply and CO_2 removal (and thus acid-base balance) to and from the metabolizing tissue. Reptiles (and mammals) seldom face external hypoxia or hypercapnia—with the exception of the relatively few species that occupy burrows (e.g., Abe and Johansen, 1987) or live at high altitude. A given ventilatory response to hypoxic and hypercapnic exposures does, therefore, not necessarily represent an adaption to a given environment. Rather, it is plausible that the control mechanisms have evolved as adaptive responses to disease (for example, increased diffusion limitation in the lung) and to conditions during which metabolism is increased, such as exercise. Thus, although studies of physiological responses to hypoxia and hypercapnia provide extremely valuable insight to the underlying control mechanisms, it is important to emphasize that these responses need not reflect an adaptation to a given environment.

2. Ventilation Patterns at Rest and Ventilatory Responses

In all reptiles, ventilation is achieved through aspiration, but the exact mechanism creating the air flows is very diverse (Gans, 1970; S. C. Wood and Lenfant, 1976; Gans and Clark, 1976; Clark et al., 1978; Liem, 1985). Early studies reported ventilatory airflow to be triphasic, but most contemporary studies agree that, in all reptiles, the airflow during the ventilatory cycle is biphasic, commencing with exhalation followed by inhalation (for references and discussion, see Gans and Clark, 1978). In all species studied, both inspiration and expiration are active.

The ventilatory patterns exhibited by reptiles are very diverse, and it is probably inappropriate to classify a "reptilian pattern." However, with this caveat in mind, the ventilatory pattern can be characterized as arrhythmic with significant non-ventilatory periods or apnea (for reviews, see Milsom, 1988, 1990a, 1991). In general, two basic patterns exist: (a) single breaths separated by periods of breath holding and (b) episodes of consecutive lung ventilations followed by long non-ventilatory periods lasting from a few minutes to more than an hour (see Fig. 3.2). As a general trend, aquatic animals seem to exhibit the episodic breathing pattern (top panel), whereas terrestrial reptiles tend to breathe in single breaths (Glass et al., 1978). Also, aquatic reptiles often have longer non-ventilatory periods than terrestrial animals. Nevertheless, there are numerous exceptions to this generalization; for example, *Chelonia mydas* normally takes only a single breath (Jackson and Prange, 1976; Butler et al., 1984).

Whenever breathing is stimulated by reductions in inspired O_2 levels (hypoxia) or elevation of inspired CO_2 (hypercapnia), ventilation increases predominantly through a reduction of the non-ventilatory periods (e.g., Glass and Johansen, 1976; Glass et al., 1985). In testudines, which certainly are the best studied reptiles, the number of breaths per breathing cycle increases during hypercapnia but decreases during hypoxia (e.g., Frankel et al., 1969; Glass et al., 1978, 1983; Milsom and Jones, 1980). The underlying mechanisms explaining why hypoxia and hypercapnia change the length of ventilatory cycles in opposite direction are not understood. Nevertheless, from a gas exchange point of view, it seems favorable to prolong the ventilatory periods during hypercapnia to facilitate excretion of CO_2, which builds up in tissue and blood during breath hold (e.g., Ackerman and White, 1979; Hicks and White, 1992). The stimulus to commence and terminate the ventilatory periods is not yet well understood. N. H. West et al. (1989) found a close correlation between arterial P_{CO_2} and the termination of ventilatory periods in *Chelydra serpentina* during normoxia and hyperoxia. As in other species, hypoxia shortened the non-ventilatory periods. Collectively, these data suggest that both P_{CO_2} (and the related pH) and P_{O_2} act to terminate the non-ventilatory period, but that the importance of these two stimuli varies. In addition, pulmonary stretch receptors sensitive to lung volume seem also to be involved in determination of the non-ventilatory period. Increased resting lung volume prolongs the non-ventilatory pe-

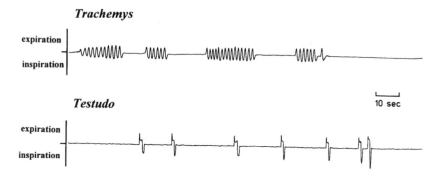

Fig. 3.2. The ventilatory patterns of reptiles are traditionally divided into two basic types: episodes of consecutive lung ventilations followed by long, non-ventilatory periods (top trace) and single breaths separated by periods of breath holding (bottom trace). These particular examples show the ventilation patterns in an aquatic turtle, *Trachemys scripta*, and a terrestrial tortoise, *Testudo graeca*. (From Milsom, 1995.)

riods in sea turtles (Milsom and Johansen, 1975) and elevates the number of breaths per breathing cycle, but not overall ventilation, in freshwater testudines (Milsom and Chan, 1986). During normal breath hold, lung volume decreases during the non-ventilatory period because of extrapulmonary excretion of CO_2 and the higher blood and tissue capacitance for CO_2 compared to O_2 (Lenfant et al., 1970; Ackerman and White, 1979; Burggren and Shelton, 1979). The fall in lung volume would, in some manner, be directly proportional to pulmonary oxygen uptake and could, therefore, provide a relation between metabolic rate and breathing frequency (Johansen, 1970). The correlation between lung volume and the length of the non-ventilatory period is, however, quite variable and does not provide a complete explanation for the initiation of ventilation (Lenfant et al., 1970; Milsom and Johansen, 1975; Ackerman and White, 1979; Burggren and Shelton, 1979).

In most reptiles and other air-breathers, the increase in ventilation elicited by hypoxia and hypercapnia is accomplished through different changes in tidal volume and breathing frequency. In general, hypercapnia causes considerable increases in tidal volume, whereas hypoxia acts predominantly to increase breathing frequency (Glass et al., 1979; Benchetrit and Dejours, 1980; Nolan and Frankel, 1982; Glass et al., 1983; Milsom, 1990a, 1995; Wang and Warburton, 1995), but several exceptions exist (e.g., Glass and Johansen, 1976; Abe and Johansen, 1987). Hypoxia and hypercapnia increase ventilation through different sets of receptors (see following sections), and these different responses are probably explained by the inhibitory role of CO_2 on pulmonary stretch receptor sensitivity (Jones and Milsom, 1982; Powell et al., 1988; Douse et al., 1989) and a resulting reduction of the Hering-Breuer reflex (see Section II.B.3.f).

Generally, ventilation increases more linearly during acute hypercapnic exposure than during hypoxia (for reviews, see Milsom, 1990a, 1995). The maximum increase of ventilation is often higher during hypercapnia than during hypoxia, but there is large variability in the responses between species. In fact, a decrease in ventilation during acute hypercapnia has been reported for many species of squamates (e.g., Templeton and Dawson, 1963, Nielsen, 1961; Glass and Johansen, 1976; Gratz, 1979). Again, several exceptions exist. For example, in amphisbaenians, both hypoxia and hypercapnia elicit large increases in ventilation (Abe and Johansen, 1987). The apparent inconsistency of this response may arise partly from differences in techniques or adapted responses. Furthermore, two additional factors may add to the variability; intrapulmonary chemoreceptors can account for ventilatory depression during hypercapnia (see Section II.B.3.f), and, because hypercapnia decreases blood oxygen affinity, increases in arterial P_{O_2} may reduce the oxygen drive to breathing. On similar grounds, Milsom (1990a) warned that, although ventilatory responses to changes of inhaled F_{CO_2} may be suitable for studies of environmental hypercapnia, these studies may be inappropriate for studies of ventilatory responses to increased metabolic CO_2 production. This warning is supported by differences in the relation between ventilation and arterial P_{CO_2} (and pH) whenever the hypercapnia is produced by inhalation of CO_2 rather than to elevations of P_{CO_2} by other means (Milsom et al., 1981; Jones et al., 1985; Furilla et al., 1991; Section II.B.3.f).

The interaction of O_2 and CO_2 in the control of breathing and their relative importance has not received much attention in reptiles. Two studies on the toad *Bufo marinus*, however, promise valuable avenues for future research. Lung ventilation ceases completely in hyperoxic toads in spite of the resulting acidosis (Toews and Kirby, 1985), suggesting that oxygen provides the main drive to breathing. However, in unidirectionally ventilated and anesthetized toads, ventilation ceases during normoxic hypocapnia, indicating a mainly acid-base oriented drive to breathing (N. H. West et al., 1987). Clearly, a deeper understanding of the interaction of O_2 and CO_2 in reptiles, as well as in amphibians, must await new and more detailed experiments.

a. TEMPERATURE SENSITIVITY OF VENTILATORY RESPONSES

Ventilatory responses to both hypoxia and hypercapnia in reptiles and other ectothermic vertebrates are highly temperature dependent. Invariably, the hypoxic threshold for elevated ventilation increases as body temperature rises (Jackson, 1971, 1973; Glass et al., 1983,1986; Kruhoffer et al., 1987; Dupre et al., 1989). A more vigorous response to hypercapnia with elevated temperature is also well documented for many species of both amphibians and reptiles (Jackson et al., 1974; Davies et al., 1982; Funk and Milsom, 1987; Glass et al., 1985; Branco et al., 1993; Branco and Wood, 1993).

Over a broad range of body temperatures, hypoxic threshold seems to correlate well with arterial O_2 content or hemoglobin-O_2 (HbO_2) saturation in many species (for a review, see Boggs, 1995). This observation has led to the speculation that the ventilatory response to hypoxia is determined by arterial O_2 content or HbO_2 saturation. Nevertheless, as discussed later in this chapter, this possibility remains to be rigorously tested.

The effects of temperature on the ventilatory responses to hypercapnia are often evaluated in relation to the alphastat hypothesis, which, as discussed in more detail below, proposes ionization of an alpha imidazole moiety as the regulated variable for ventilation. According to the alphastat hypothesis, ventilatory responses are temperature insensitive if expressed as a function of alpha imidazole ionization. However, no studies have convincingly discussed how to perform this evaluation. Although some studies present relationships between air convection requirements ($\dot{V}_E / \dot{V}_{O_2}$) and arterial P_{CO_2} or pH (e.g., Jackson et al., 1974), other studies present correlations between relative changes in ventilation or air convection requirements and inspired CO_2 (e.g., Funk and Milsom, 1987). Finally, a third group of studies correlate air convection requirements and alpha imidazole ionization (Hitzig, 1982; Davies et al., 1982; Branco and Wood, 1993). In support of the alphastat hypothesis, some studies on testudines and alligators suggest a temperature independent relationship between imidazole ionization and air convection requirements (Davies et al., 1982; Hitzig, 1982; Branco and Wood, 1993). However, as there is no agreement regarding the presentation of the ventilatory responses, the same data set may be used as confirmation or rejection for the alphastat hypothesis. Thus, a serious evaluation of whether the alphastat hypothesis adequately explains the effect of temperature on the hypercapnic ventilatory response must await the development of a consensus as how to perform the data presentation and analysis.

At very high body temperatures, panting has been reported in several species of lizards (Templeton, 1967; Dupre and Crawford, 1986; Abe, 1991). An example of this response for *Tupinambis merianae* (formerly *T. teguixin*) in shown in Figure 3.3. As the temperature is increased from 35° to 40°C, this lizard exhibits high frequency flushings of the pharyngeal cavity, also referred to as buccal movements. These air flows are not involved in gas exchange as evidenced from the end-expired gas composition. In this example, the elevation in body temperature is, nevertheless, associated with an increase in ventilation relative to metabolic rate, which accounts for the elevation of lung P_{O_2} and the decrease in lung P_{CO_2} (Abe, 1991).

b. COST OF VENTILATION AND THE "OPTIMAL VENTILATORY RESPONSE"
As discussed earlier, the level of ventilation is normally adjusted through changing the duration of the non-ventilatory periods, rather than tidal volume. On basis of experiments on *Gekko gecko*, and subsequent experiments on *Trachemys scripta*, Milsom (1984) and Vitalis and Milsom (1986a, 1986b) suggested that these changes in ventilatory pattern reflect an optimization of the work required for breathing.

Pulmonary ventilation requires energy because the respiratory muscles must overcome the elastic and non-elastic forces associated with expansion of the lungs and chest. The energetic cost of this work, sometimes expressed relative to resting metabolic rate, is termed the "cost of breathing." In reptiles, which possess relatively simple and compliant

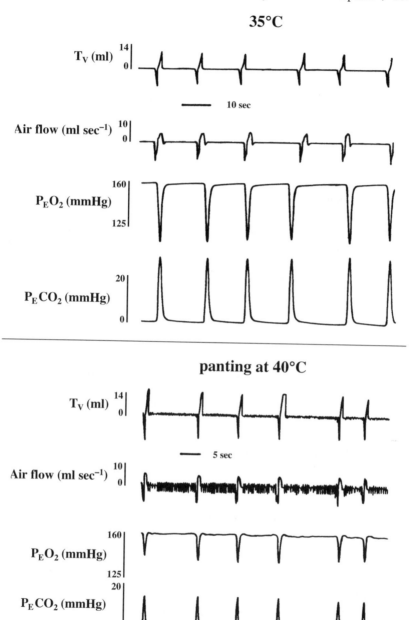

Fig. 3.3. Recording of ventilatory air flows and expired gas composition in the lizard *Tupinambis merianae* at 35°C and during panting at 40°C. At each temperature, the tidal volume (T_V), the air flow across the nostrils, and expired P_{O_2} and P_{CO_2} (P_EO_2 and P_ECO_2, respectively) are depicted. (From Abe, 1991.)

lungs relative to mammals, most of the work required for breathing is used to overcome elastic forces in the chest wall (Perry and Duncker, 1978; Milsom and Vitalis, 1984, Vitalis and Milsom, 1986a). Compliance of lungs and body wall depend upon the rate of inflation and, therefore, on breathing frequency. In general, the respiratory system stiffens as breathing frequency increases, and the dynamic compliance is, accordingly, less than the corresponding static compliance. In mammals, this reduction is usually relatively small, but in testudines and geckos, the dynamic compliance decreases 50–70% over a 5- to 10-fold increase in breathing frequency (Milsom and Vitalis, 1984; Vitalis and Milsom, 1986a). The morphological basis for these changes is not well understood but seems to involve changes in the viscoelastic properties of the body wall.

On theoretical grounds, it has long been hypothesized that the mechanical cost of breathing changes with tidal volume and breathing frequency (Rohrer, 1925; Otis et al., 1950). Subsequent direct measurements of pulmonary mechanics have confirmed these theoretical predictions. For any given level of alveolar ventilation, there exists an optimal combination of tidal volume and breathing frequency that minimizes the mechanical cost of breathing (Crosfill and Widdicombe, 1961; Milsom and Vitalis, 1984; Vitalis and Milsom, 1986a; Milsom, 1989). In short, although the work required to overcome non-elastic forces is independent of breathing frequency, the work required to overcome elastic forces decreases with increased frequency. Thus, a given level of ventilation is energetically cheaper to obtain with a combination of high frequency and low tidal volume. This simple relationship, however, does not hold true for alveolar ventilation. Because dead space constitutes a fixed volume, the level of alveolar ventilation diminishes as tidal volume decreases, and a higher level of total ventilation is required. Accordingly, the optimal combination of tidal volume and breathing frequency represents a compromise of these opposing effects. Although these predictions are based on a continuous breathing pattern with passive expiration (Otis, 1954), this analysis, as discussed below, has been applied successfully to lizards and testudines.

The existence of an ideal combination of tidal volume and breathing frequency allows prediction of energetically efficient breathing patterns and optimal ventilatory responses to altered demands. This model predicts that the most energetically efficient intermittent breathing pattern intersperses periods of optimal-frequency ventilation with non-ventilatory periods (Milsom 1988, 1989). Furthermore, increased ventilation through increased tidal volume is extremely energetically expensive (Milsom, 1984, 1989; Vitalis and Milsom, 1986b). Therefore, the most energetically efficient way to increase ventilation would be to shorten non-ventilatory periods while maintaining constant tidal volume and breathing frequency within the ventilatory period. Interestingly, resting breathing patterns of mammals, lizards, and testudines correspond closely with this prediction (Crosfill and Widdicombe, 1961; Milsom, 1984; Vitalis and Milsom, 1986b; Milsom, 1989). For example, Figure 3.4 depicts the mechanical work required to maintain three levels of alveolar ($\dot{V}_A$, closed circles) and total ventilation ($\dot{V}_I$, open circles) at different levels of tidal volume and breathing frequency in *Trachemys scripta*. The

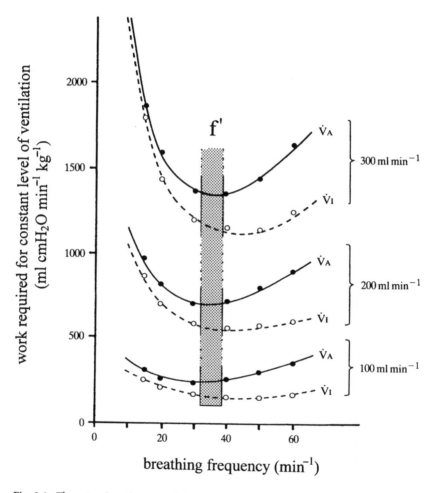

Fig. 3.4. The rate of work required to produce various levels of alveolar ($\dot{V}_A$) and total ventilation ($\dot{V}_I$) as a function of breathing frequency. The shaded area represents the range of instantaneous breathing frequencies (f') measured in spontaneously breathing testudines. (From Vitalis and Milsom, 1986a, 1986b.)

instantaneous breathing frequency observed in this species is represented by the shaded area and seems to correspond very well to the breathing pattern that requires the least amount of mechanical work. Whereas these data strongly suggest that the ventilatory patterns typically exhibited by reptiles save energy, the magnitude of the energetic saving is debatable. In aquatic reptiles that breathe while immersed, the water displaced during inhalation complicates this issue (Gaunt and Gans, 1969).

The actual oxidative cost of ventilation in reptiles is disputed: some studies indicate a high oxidative cost of breathing (Kinney and White, 1977), but others indicate low cost (Jackson et al., 1991; Wang and Warburton, 1995). A large part of this controversy undoubtedly stems from the fact that the oxidative cost of breathing cannot be measured directly, but rather must be assessed indirectly. A commonly applied approach is to alter ventilation by different means and ascribe any changes in oxygen uptake to the observed changes in ventilation, thus assuming that the non-ventilatory metabolism remains constant. Two different, but conceptually similar, approaches have been applied to testudines. Kinney and White (1977) compared oxygen uptake during ventilation in air to oxygen uptake during artificial lung ventilation, which abolished intrinsic ventilation and estimated cost of ventilation from the fall in metabolic rate to be 10–30% of resting metabolism. In contrast, Jackson et al. (1991) estimated the cost of ventilation to be 1 to 2% of resting metabolic rate on the basis of the small increases in oxygen uptake whenever ventilation was stimulated by hypercapnia. The very different estimates of the oxidative cost of ventilation between these two studies are not easily explained. Nevertheless, as a parsimonious explanation, it may be suggested that initiation of ventilatory period is expensive, whereas a prolongation of the ventilatory period is less costly. Also, in other vertebrates, the costs of breathing are disputed. In teleost fish, early studies pointed to high cost of ventilation, but more recent experiments challenged this perception and indicate that the cost of ventilation is less than 10% (e.g., Steffensen and Lomholt, 1983; Steffensen, 1985). In frogs, N. H. West and Jones (1975) calculated the cost of breathing on basis of the power output from the buccal pump and estimated it to constitute approximately 5% of resting metabolic rate. Finally, in resting humans, the cost of breathing has been estimated to be 1–3% (Otis, 1954), but may increase to approximately 10% of metabolic rate during heavy exercise (Aaron et al., 1992a, 1992b).

A study on the relationship between oxygen uptake and ventilation in alligators illustrates some of the problems associated with interpreting the oxidative cost of ventilation (Wang and Warburton, 1995). Figure 3.5 shows the changes in oxygen uptake at different levels of ventilation during hypercapnic and hypoxic exposures. If oxygen uptake increases linearly with increased ventilation, the slope of the regression lines (solid lines in Fig. 3.5) indicates the cost of ventilation. It is immediately apparent that the estimated oxidative cost of ventilation is high if based on the data from hypoxic exposures, but low if based on data from the hypercapnic exposures. In fact, whereas hypoxic exposures estimate the cost of breathing to be 13% of resting metabolic rate, the hypercapnic exposures estimate a negative cost of breathing and thus, paradoxically, project the cost of ventilation to constitute −1.5% of resting metabolic rate. Because there is no reason to expect that hypoxia and hypercapnia differentially affect the actual cost of respiratory muscle contraction, these results strongly suggest that the assumption that non-ventilatory oxygen uptake remains constant has been violated. If non-ventilatory metabolism increases during hypoxia or hypercapnia, the oxidative cost of breathing will be over-estimated; if non-ventilatory metabolism decreases, the cost of breathing is under-estimated. It is dif-

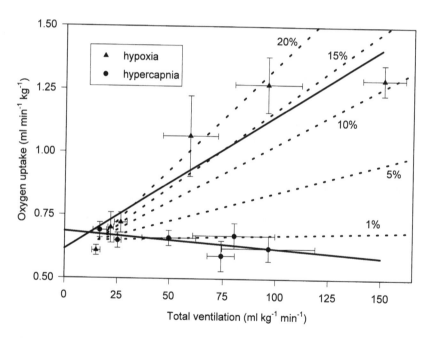

Fig. 3.5. Oxygen uptake at varying levels of total ventilation in juvenile *Alligator mississippiensis*. Individual points represent mean values and corresponding standard errors at each hypoxic (triangles) and hypercapnic (circles) exposure. The two solid lines are linear regressions for the hypercapnic and hypoxic exposures. Also shown are dotted lines depicting calculated oxygen uptake ventilation relationships for five different costs of breathing, relative to resting metabolic rate (see text for further explanation). (From Wang and Warburton, 1995.)

ficult to speculate on the changes in non-ventilatory metabolism under conditions such as hypercapnia and hypoxia; severe hypoxia may compromise oxygen uptake, but milder hypoxia could cause agitation, leading to increases in non-ventilatory metabolism. Severe hypercapnia and the associated acidosis may depress metabolism (e.g., Busa and Nuccitelli, 1984) and even act as an anesthetic (e.g., Wang et al., 1993). In light of these considerations, it is interesting that the low estimate of cost of breathing obtained in the study on testudines by Jackson et al. (1991) was based on experiments involving hypercapnia, whereas Kinney and White (1977) obtained a high estimate after abolishing ventilation by artificial ventilation. The differences between these two studies are, therefore, qualitatively similar to the differences observed between the hypoxic and hypercapnic experiments on alligators. Nevertheless, in spite of these difficulties, Wang and Warburton (1995) concluded that the oxidative cost of ventilation at rest constitutes less than 10% of the resting metabolic rate.

3. CHEMORECEPTORS INVOLVED IN VENTILATORY CONTROL

Overall ventilation is the result of central integration of information arising from both receptors and central pattern and rhythm generators. In mammals, this integration is believed to take place within the brain stem, where nuclei receiving afferent inputs have been isolated (Feldman et al., 1990; Milsom, 1990b; Smatresk, 1990). Similar neural organization and pattern of activation have been reported in testudines (Takeda et al., 1986), but the central integration of receptor input and the genesis of ventilatory patterns in both mammals and reptiles are, nevertheless, far from clear. In alligators, where the ventilatory pattern is normally divided into ventilatory and long-lasting, non-ventilatory periods, anesthesia or brain stem section converts this pattern into a single breath pattern (Naifeh et al., 1971a, 1971b). On this basis, it has been suggested that burst breathing pattern is generated by an input on the medullary respiratory neurons from higher (supramedullary) brain stem structures (Milsom, 1988, 1990a, 1990b).

If lung gases are kept constant (in a combination of high O_2 and low CO_2) by unidirectionally ventilating the lungs, both amphibians and reptiles cease to breathe (e.g., Kinney and White, 1977; N. H. West et al., 1987). Traditionally, therefore, it has been assumed that the afferent input from peripheral and central chemoreceptors sensing the fluctuations in blood gas compostion provide a sufficient stimulus to commence and terminate breathing episodes (e.g., N. H. West et al., 1989). However, a recent and rapidly emerging understanding of central rhythm generators points to an additional and important role of intrinsic patterns within the central nervous system for the expression of breathing patterns. Even

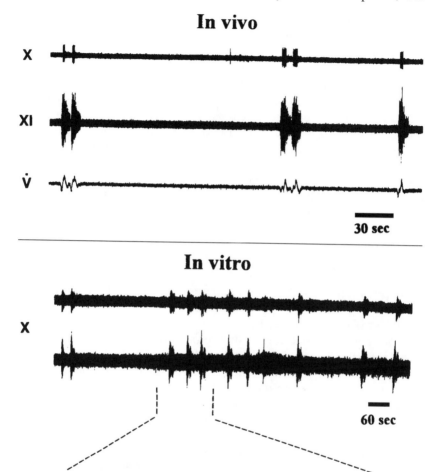

Fig. 3.6. Episodic burst activity of efferent cranial roots in an anaesthetized *Trachemys scripta* in an in vivo (top panel) and in an in vitro (bottom panel) isolated brain stem—spinal cord preparation. In vivo: Measurements of efferent neural activity recorded from the vagus nerve (X), activity from spinal accessory nerves (XI) and ventilatory air flows (V̇). In vitro: Efferent neural activity from the vagal outlet (top trace) and the contralateral vagal outlet (bottom trace) in vitro. (From Douse and Mitchell, 1990.)

in the absence of any chemoreceptor input, such central pattern and rhythm generators are capable of producing a respiratory related motor output that resembles that observed in the intact animal. An example is shown in Figure 3.6. In this *in vitro* turtle brain stem preparation, Douse and Mitchell (1990) found that complete removal of all peripheral input resulted in the persistence of an episodic respiratory related cranial motor neuron output. Similar intrinsic properties of the central nervous system have recently been demonstrated in bullfrogs (Kogo et al., 1994; Kogo and Remmers, 1994; Kinkead et al., 1994). The breathing patterns of reptiles, therefore, seem to reflect an interplay between afferent chemoreceptor input and intrinsic pattern generators within the central nervous system (e.g., Milsom, 1990b; Smatresk, 1990). However, the interaction, at rest and under other conditions, between afferent chemoreceptor input and the intrinsic rhythms remains to be resolved. At present, it may be hypothesized that, although the final breathing pattern to some extent reflects a centrally generated rhythm, afferent input is essential for the expression of this rhythm. It also seems safe to assume that afferent input strongly modifies the expression of the breathing pattern.

a. CENTRAL CHEMORECEPTORS
The presence of a central chemoreceptor in mammals has been recognized since the start of the century (e.g., Winterstein, 1911; see Konig and Seller, 1991). Many years later, experiments perfusing the ventricular system with mock cerebrospinal fluid (CSF) have provided the conclusive evidence of central chemoreception sensitive to pH and/or P_{CO_2} (e.g., Leusen, 1954; R. A. Mitchell et al., 1963; Pappenheimer et al., 1965). Similarly, in amphibians and reptiles, the presence of a central chemoreceptor had long been deduced from the persistence of ventilatory response to hypercapnia after peripheral denervation, but final proof was not obtained until Hitzig and Jackson (1978) recorded a vigorous ventilatory response during acidic perfusion of the fourth ventricle of the brain in testudines. This finding was verified by several subsequent studies and extended to a broad temperature range (Hitzig, 1982; Hitzig et al., 1985; Davies and Sexton, 1987), and the existence of central chemoreceptors is now well established in bufonids and in *Alligator mississippiensis* (Smatresk and Smits, 1991; Branco et al., 1992, 1993; Branco and Wood, 1993).

Figure 3.7 shows the effects of cerebrospinal pH on the ventilatory response to hypercapnia in *Alligator mississippiensis* at three temperatures (15, 25, and 35°C). The normal ventilatory response to hypercapnia is shown in the open circles, whereas the closed circles depict the ventilatory response whenever cerebrospinal pH is maintained constant by perfusion using a catheter placed immediately above fourth ventricle (Branco and Wood, 1993). Regardless of temperature, perfusion of the fourth ventricle greatly reduces the ventilatory response to hypercapnia, pointing to a dominant role of central chemoreception in this response. Although such studies show that a receptor close to the fourth ventricle is sensitive to pH_{CSF}, they cannot exclude the possibility of additional chemosensitive areas in the central nervous system.

It has been debated repeatedly whether CO_2 or H^+ (pH) exerts the specific stimulus for the central chemoreceptor, but an evaluation of this question is complicated, as both parameters normally change simultaneously. On the basis of experiments on cats, Shams (1985) concluded that P_{CO_2} and pH do indeed exert independent effects on ventilation via the central chemoreceptor. Investigating the same question in Pekin ducks, Dodd and Milsom (1987) reported that ventilation is a single function of arterial pH, and P_{CO_2} does not seem to provide an independent stimulus. These experiments monitored the ventilatory response of intact birds, and the response is, therefore, not solely attributable to the central chemoreceptor. No similar experiments have been conducted in reptiles.

Although it is generally believed that the central chemoreceptor responds to changes in pH_{CSF}, the intracellular pH of cells at the cen-

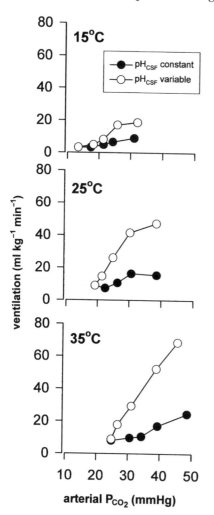

Fig. 3.7. The role of central chemoreception on the ventilatory response of *Alligator mississippiensis* to hypercapnia. In these experiments, the fourth ventricle could be artificially perfused with a mock cerebrospinal fluid (CSF) solution. At each of the three temperatures, ventilation is shown as a function of arterial P_{CO_2} when the fourth ventricle was not perfused (open circles) and when the fourth ventricle was perfused with a mock CSF solution to keep the pH surrounding the central chemoreceptor constant (filled circles). (From Branco and Wood, 1994.)

tral chemoreceptor may also play an important role. Indeed, it has been suggested that, in mammals, intracellular pH provides a stronger receptor stimulus than does extracellular pH (Lassen, 1990). Studies on dilution acidosis strongly suggest that intracellular pH is important in the regulation of breathing in Pekin ducks (Kasserra et al., 1991; Kasserra and Jones, 1996). During acute increases in plasma osmolality, extracellular pH decreased, but brain pH remained constant, and ventilation either remained constant or even decreases in spite of the extracellular acidosis. To date, no studies on reptiles have differentiated the roles of intracellular *versus* extracellular pH in the control of breathing.

b. SPECULATION ON THE EVOLUTION OF CENTRAL CHEMORECEPTION

The presence of a central chemoreceptor in fish has often been suggested, but direct evidence is lacking, and, in fact, no direct attempts have been able to localize a central receptor. For example, in the air-breathing fish *Amia calva*, perfusion of the medullary region with acidic solution does change ventilation (Hedrick et al., 1991). Nevertheless, hypercapnia seems to increase ventilation in teleost fish (Janssen and Randall, 1975) and elasmobranchs (Randall et al., 1976). It is possible that hypercapnic hyperventilation in teleost fish results from the reduction of the arterial O_2 content caused by the decrease in pH (Root and Bohr effects), which may explain why hyperoxia abolishes the ventilatory response to hypercapnia in trout (F. M. Smith and Jones, 1982). However, elasmobranchs lack a Root effect and show no simple correlation between ventilation and blood O_2 content (reviewed by Perry and Wood, 1989). The existence of a central chemoreceptor could explain this response, but ventilation is not well correlated with pH_{CSF} in skates (Graham et al., 1990; C. M. Wood et al., 1990). Additionally, catecholamines may explain part of the observed changes in ventilation during hypercapnia in fish (Aota et al., 1990; Kinkead et al., 1993). In *Bufo*, the presence of a central chemoreceptor involved in control of ventilation is now well documented and seems responsible for approximately 80% of the ventilatory response to hypercapnia (Smatresk and Smits, 1991; Branco et al., 1992, 1993). Nevertheless, not all amphibians respond to hypercapnia with elevated ventilation. In the aquatic urodele, *Amphiuma tridactylum*, ventilation is essentially unaffected by high CO_2 levels (Toews, 1971), but apodan amphibians increase ventilation, or at least ventilatory frequency, during hypercapnia (Toews and MacIntyre, 1978). Therefore, it seems that central chemoreception is related to the evolution of air breathing, and a similar transition takes place when anuran amphibians metamorphose from strictly water-breathing tadpoles to predominantly air-breathing adults. In *Rana catesbeiana*, the young, water-breathing tadpoles are virtually insensitive to hypercapnia and exhibit an oxygen-dominated control of breathing. As the tadpoles develop and commence air breathing, ventilation becomes sensitive to hypercapnia (Burggren and Infantino, 1994). Tautologically, an O_2-oriented control of breathing seems advantageous in aquatic environments because of the low oxygen capacitance in water. By the same token, a CO_2/acid-base-oriented control of breathing seems advantageous for air breathers, in which oxygen delivery is more easily secured.

c. ARTERIAL CHEMORECEPTORS

All air-breathing vertebrates possess arterial chemoreceptors (e.g., Jones and Milsom, 1982). These chemoreceptors are primarily involved in regulation of O_2 and consist of glomus cells (type I cells) enclosed by sustentacular cells (type II cells). The glomus cells are believed to act as receptor cells and are, in contrast to the sustentacular cells, excitable. During excitation, neurotransmitters are released from glomus cells in proportion to the intensity of stimulation (reviewed by Gonzalez et al., 1995). The cellular basis underlying O_2 reception and accompanying transmitter release from glomus cells is far from understood, but glomus cell P_{O_2} is believed to exert the specific stimulus. Glomus cell P_{O_2} is determined by oxygen delivery (the product of blood flow and blood O_2 content) and O_2 consumption of the chemoreceptor structure. A chemoreceptor can, therefore, sense blood O_2 content if hemoglobin bound O_2 participates in O_2 delivery to the receptor. This seems to be the case for mammalian aortic bodies (Lahiri et al., 1980, 1981). In reptiles and amphibians, the ventilatory responses to hypoxia at different temperatures are well correlated with arterial O_2 content (Glass et al., 1983; Wood and Glass, 1992). This correlation has fostered the hypothesis that the arterial chemoreceptors in these animals are sensitive to arterial O_2 content or, alternatively, hemoglobin oxygen saturation (reviewed by Boggs, 1995). However, in testudines, reducing blood oxygen-carrying capacity by bleeding does not affect the hypoxic ventilatory response (Wang et al., 1997), and similar findings have been reported for *Bufo* (Wang et al., 1994; Branco and Glass, 1995). These studies strongly suggest that the oxygen-sensitive receptors driving ventilation in toads are sensitive to arterial P_{O_2} rather than to O_2 content.

In addition to their sensitivity to O_2, the carotid and aortic bodies in mammals are sensitive to CO_2. At present, no coherent theory explains the underlying mechanism for CO_2 reception, although it is generally assumed that the mechanism is different from that for O_2 perception (e.g., Mulligan and Lahiri, 1982). Increases in discharge frequencies of arterial chemoreceptors during hypercapnia at constant P_{O_2} have been reported for *Bufo marinus;* as in mammals, the combined effects of CO_2 and O_2 on these receptors are more than just additive (Van Vliet and West, 1992; Ishii et al., 1986; Fitzgerald and Lahiri, 1986).

d. Location of Arterial Chemoreceptors

The structure of the oxygen-sensitive chemoreceptors is very similar among different groups of vertebrates, but this similarity does not hold true for location (Jones and Milsom, 1982). In mammals, the carotid bodies lie at the bifurcations of the common carotid artery, and aortic bodies lie at the aortic arch. Carotid bodies are innervated by the sinus nerve (a branch of the glossopharyngeal), whereas aortic bodies are innervated by the aortic nerve (a branch of the vagus). Information on arterial chemoreceptors is not available for all reptilian orders. In lizards, morphological observations suggest the presence of chemoreceptive tissue at the common and internal carotid arteries with vagal and maybe glossopharyngeal innervation (Adams, 1958; Rogers, 1967; Kobayashi, 1971). Recordings have not been made from these receptors, but injection of blood with low P_{O_2} into the junction of the carotid arch stimulates ventilation; this response is abolished by denervation (Courtice, 1980). In tortoises, a chemo- and baroreceptive area at the dorsal carotid artery is innervated by the glossopharyngeal nerve (Ishii et al., 1986). Discharge frequency increases during perfusion with anoxic, hypercapnic, or NaCN containing Ringer (Ishii et al., 1986). Also, a chemo- and baroreceptive site innervated by branches from the vagus nerve lies at the aortic arches of tortoises (Ishii et al., 1985). Again, discharge frequency increases during perfusion with NaCN containing Ringer.

Apart from the traditional arterial chemoreceptors, additional receptors on the pulmocutaneous arch have been identified in testudines (Ishii et al., 1985), and Benchetrit et al. (1977) concluded that ventilatory responses of testudines to NaCN injections are predominantly due to chemoreceptors at this site. Nevertheless, the relative importance of these receptors remains to be investigated. A significant contribution from chemoreceptors located at the pulmocutaneous arch would have very important implications for our understanding of ventilatory control in reptiles. In contrast to the arterial receptors, a chemoreceptor at the pulmocutaneous arch would be sensitive (depending on the magnitude of L-R cardiac shunt) to venous blood composition. Because venous blood gas compostion depends on the oxygen extraction, these receptors would be sensitive to changes in metabolic rate even in the absence of changes in arterial blood gases. Clearly, it is important to establish the physiological role of these receptors, and they may prove to be pivotal for understanding ventilatory responses to hypoxia and particularly elevated metabolic rate.

e. Contribution of Arterial Chemoreceptors to Ventilation

Most studies in mammals demonstrate that the ventilatory response to hypoxia derives mainly from the carotid bodies with only minimal contribution from the aortic bodies, although these may assume an important role under certain circumstances (e.g., Fitzgerald and Lahiri, 1986). In contrast to carotid bodies, the aortic bodies appear to be responsible for control of the cardiovascular system (Hatcher et al., 1978). No studies on reptiles have determined the contribution of arterial chemoreceptors to ventilation at rest or their contribution to ventilatory responses. Several studies on testudines, snakes, and lizards have shown that inhalation of hyperoxic gases reduces ventilation (Glass and Johansen, 1976; Benchetrit et al., 1977; Glass et al., 1978). This reduction in ventilation indicates an O_2 drive to breathing at normoxia, and this drive seems to increase with elevated temperature (Benchetrit et al., 1977; Glass et al., 1983). Depending on the magnitude of cardiac R-L shunt, inhalation of hyperoxic gases may, however, not result in significant increases of arterial P_{O_2}. Determination of the role of arterial chemoreceptors is further complicated by the limited knowledge regarding the exact anatomical location of these receptors in most reptiles. In absence of this information, it is difficult to establish whether all receptors have been artificially stimulated or denervated. This problem is apparent from studies on amphibians. In voluntarily diving *Xenopus laevis* (Evans and Shelton, 1984; Jones and Chu, 1988) and unidirectionally ventilated *Bufo marinus* (N. H. West et al., 1987), denervation of the carotid labyrinth reduces ventilation but does not abolish ventilatory response to hypoxia.

In mammals, arterial chemoreceptors are less involved in the ventilatory response to hypercapnia than to hypoxia (Berkenbosch et al., 1979; Heeringa et al., 1979), and this general trend seems to hold true for at least some reptiles. However, the contribution of the arterial chemoreceptors proper has not been throroughly determined in any reptile. As discussed earlier for alligators, whenever pH_{CSF} is maintained constant by artificial perfusion, the ventilatory response to hypercapnia is greatly reduced (Branco and Wood, 1993). These authors assumed that the remaining ventilatory response is attributable to peripheral chemoreceptors and concluded that arterial chemoreceptors are responsible for only 10–30 % of the ventilatory response to hypercapnia; a similar estimate has been obtained for *Bufo paracnemis* in an identical protocol (Branco et al., 1993). However, in these studies, the contribution from intrapulmonary and upper airway chemoreceptors were ignored, which may influence the estimated role of arterial chemoreceptors. In contrast to the study on alligators, the ventilatory response to hypercapnia of *Nerodia sipedon* is virtually abolished whenever the arterial and pulmonary chemoreceptors are denervated by vagotomy (Gratz, 1984). At present, it is difficult to establish whether this conflicting conclusion reflects differences among taxa or differences in experimental approaches. More detailed studies involving selective denervation of pulmonary, upper airway, and arterial chemoreceptors are needed.

f. CHEMO- AND MECHANORECEPTORS IN THE LUNGS AND UPPER AIRWAYS
In common with other air-breathing vertebrates, the lungs and upper airways of reptiles possess chemo- and mechanoreceptors that are involved in control of ventilation. In the lungs, vagally innervated receptors convey information regarding the rate and depth of lung inflation. These receptors have different modalities and can be classified as either pulmonary stretch receptors or intrapulmonary chemoreceptors.

i. Pulmonary Stretch Receptors
Pulmonary stretch receptors are present in testudines, lizards, snakes, and alligators (Fedde et al., 1977; Scheid et al., 1977; Milsom and Jones, 1976, 1979; Jones and Milsom, 1979; Ishii et al., 1986; Powell et al., 1988; Furilla and Bartlett, 1988). These receptors are sensitive to lung volume and thus provide feedback regarding lung filling and emptying, and with that, of tidal volume. In general, activation of stretch receptors suppresses inspiration and enhances expiration (Breuer-Hering reflex). Although the exact stimulus is still debated, it seems, in contrast to mammals, to be lung volume per se (Jones and Milsom, 1979, 1982; Milsom, 1990b). Snakes and alligators have both rapidly and slowly adapting stretch receptors (Furilla and Bartlett, 1988; Powell et al., 1988). Consistent with mammals, the sensitivity of the pulmonary stretch receptors in reptiles is depressed and, in some instances, even silenced by CO_2 (Milsom and Jones, 1976; Fedde et al., 1977; Jones and Milsom, 1979; Ishii et al., 1986; Powell et al., 1988; Furilla and Bartlett, 1988).

ii. Intrapulmonary Chemoreceptors
In addition to the stretch receptors, most reptiles possess intrapulmonary chemoreceptors sensitive to CO_2 (Gatz et al., 1975; Fedde et al., 1977; Ishii et al., 1986; Douse and Mitchell, 1988; Furilla and Bartlett, 1988; Scheid et al., 1977). Similar receptors are well documented in birds (Fedde and Peterson, 1970; Osborne et al., 1977) but have not been demonstrated in amphibians or mammals (Fedde and Kuhlmann, 1978; Milsom and Jones, 1977; Furilla and Bartlett, 1988). Also, although the stretch receptors of turtles are CO_2-sensitive, they lack true intrapulmonary chemoreceptors (Milsom and Jones, 1976). The discharge frequency of the intrapulmonary chemoreceptors (often referred to as IPC's) is inversely proportional to P_{CO_2}, and the receptors seem to be insensitive to both hypoxia and hyperoxia as well as physiologically realistic lung volumes or pressures (Fedde et al., 1977; Scheid et al., 1977; Furilla and Bartlett, 1988, Douse and Mitchell, 1988, Powell et al., 1988). Figure 3.8 shows the difference in discharge patterns and receptor modality of pulmonary stretch receptors (f_{PSR}) and intrapulmonary chemoreceptors (f_{IPC}) in an alligator (Powell et al., 1988). The discharge frequency of the PSR

increases with lung inflation and is not affected by the change in inspired CO_2. In contrast, the discharge frequency of the IPC is virtually unaffected by lung inflation whereas inspired CO_2 (F_{CO_2}) was high, but increased rapidly as the first wave of low CO_2 reached the lung. As CO_2 washes out, IPC discharge remains high and shows only little phasic discharge with lung inflation (Powell et al., 1988). Note that the highest level of IPC activity appears when the tidal changes in CO_2 are highest. The exact receptor modality of IPC's is not completely understood, but H^+ and CO_2 apparently exert independent effects (Burger et al., 1974; Powell et al., 1978; Scheid et al., 1978). In lizards, snakes, and alligators, the sensitivity of these receptors increases with temperature (Furilla and Bartlett, 1988; Douse and Mitchell, 1988; Douse et al., 1989), but in a fashion that cannot be accounted for by calculated changes in receptor imidazole ionization (Douse and Mitchell, 1988; Douse et al., 1989).

The aforementioned depressing effect of hypercapnia on minute ventilation in both amphibians and reptiles (e.g., Nielsen, 1962; Glass and Johansen, 1976; Sakakibara, 1978; reviewed by Milsom, 1990a, 1995) is

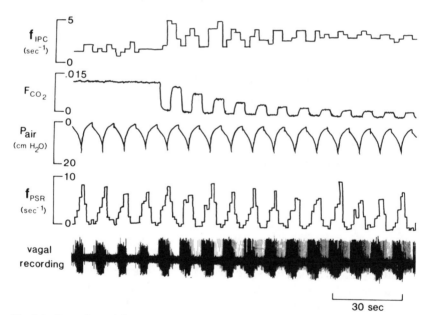

Fig. 3.8. Recording of the nervous activity in the vagus nerve in an anesthetized and artificially ventilated *Alligator mississippiensis* (the tidal ventilation can been as changes in the air pressure, P_{air}). These traces show a simultaneous recording of the nervous activity of an intrapulmonary chemoreceptor (f_{IPC}) and the nervous activity of a pulmonary stretch receptor (f_{PSR}) within the same vagal strand. In this experiment, the inspired CO_2 concentration (F_{CO_2}) was reduced in a stepwise fashion. See text for further explanation. (From Powell et al., 1988.)

often attributed to an inhibitory role of CO_2 on IPC's (and nasal chemoreceptors—see below). It is, for example, well documented that many reptiles hyperventilate promptly after removal of high CO_2 levels in the inhaled air, which could be explained by the sudden removal of a inhibitory input from these receptors (e.g., Nolan and Frankel, 1982; Glass and Johansen, 1976).

The physiological role of IPC may very well be different from that observed during hypercapnic exposures. Recent studies on unidirectionally ventilated garter snakes show that the contribution of these receptors varies throughout the ventilatory cycle (Furilla and Bartlett, 1989; Furilla, 1991). Thus, although apnea is induced whenever CO_2 is removed from the lung gas during breath hold, removal of CO_2 at the beginning of inspiration elicites a prolongation as well as an increase of the inspiration volume (Furilla and Bartlett, 1989). In addition, breathing frequency correlates well with the rate of rise in lung P_{CO_2}, whereas tidal volume seems to be determined by peak lung P_{CO_2} (Furilla, 1991). Thus, when lung CO_2 changes in a physiologically realistic fashion, IPC's may in fact stimulate, rather than depress, ventilation as observed during hypercapnic exposures. It is, therefore, entirely possible that IPC's play an important role in regulating ventilation whenever metabolic rate is increased (Milsom et al., 1981; Furilla, 1991). This possibility is especially intriguing for the conditions during digestion when metabolic rate increases severalfold, but the attendant "alkaline tide" could act to depress ventilation (e.g., Wang et al., 1995a).

iii. Chemoreceptors in the Upper Airways

Apart from intrapulmonary chemoreceptors, reptiles have additional CO_2 sensitive receptors in the upper airways. These are thought to be localized at the olfactory epithelium and innervated by the olfactory nerves (Ballam, 1985; Coates and Ballam, 1987, 1989; Ballam and Coates, 1989). Similar receptors are well documented in anuran amphibians (Sakakibara, 1978; Coates and Ballam, 1990). The role of upper airway receptors in ventilatory control has been studied in *Tupinambis teguixin* (formerly *T. nigropunctatus*) equipped with an endotracheal catheter that allowed CO_2 to be administered separately through the nares, to the mouth, and to the lungs (Ballam, 1985; Coates and Ballam, 1987; Coates and Ballam, 1989). Nasal administration of CO_2 markedly decreases breathing frequency, but tidal volume remains unaffected. This response is abolished after transection of the olfactory peduncle. Administration of CO_2 to the mouth has no effect. Subsequent studies show that phasic changes in nasal CO_2 level do not affect ventilation (Ballam and Coates, 1989; Coates et al., 1991). A similar depressing effect of CO_2 delivered to the upper airways on breathing frequency with no changes in tidal volume has been obtained in garter snakes (Coates and Ballam, 1989).

The physiological role of these receptors is virtually unknown, but several ideas are noted in the literature. Ballam (1985) suggested that nasal receptors enable prey detection, i.e., detection of CO_2 buildup in occupied burrows. Nasal CO_2 has also been suggested to inhibit breathing whenever ambient CO_2 is higher than that of systemic blood (Coates and Ballam, 1987). Finally, as discussed above, upper airways may play a role in breath-to-breath control of ventilation by monitoring expired P_{CO_2}.

C. Lung Performance in Gas Exchange

1. GENERAL CONSIDERATIONS Although highly variable, the lungs of reptiles may be characterized, on average, by a slightly thicker blood-gas barrier and much lower respiratory surface area than those of mammals. The anatomical diffusion factor (surface area relative to thickness) is, therefore, an order of magnitude lower in reptiles than in mammals. The morphology and anatomy of the reptilian lung is reviewed extensively by S. F. Perry in the present volume and a selection of additional papers within the last several years (Maina, 1989; Perry, 1983, 1989, 1992, Perry et al., 1989).

2. PULMONARY DIFFUSING CAPACITY

Direct measurement of pulmonary diffusing capacity for oxygen (D_{LO_2}) is technically difficult as it requires detailed measurements of P_{O_2} in pulmonary capillary blood. Therefore, most studies on reptiles (e.g., Glass and Johansen, 1981; Glass et al., 1981a, 1981b) have determined the pulmonary diffusing capacity for CO (D_{CO}) as initially described by Krogh and Krogh (1910). Hemoglobin has a very high affinity for CO, and the resulting high blood capacitance ensures that capillary P_{CO} ("back pressure") remains insignificant during measurements. On the basis of the difference in solubility and molecular weight, the values obtained for D_{CO} can be converted to D_{LO_2} ($D_{LO_2} = 1.23\ D_{CO}$). This technique measures the overall diffusing capacity of the lung, which is the integrated result of lung area, thickness of the blood-gas barrier, pulmonary blood flow and other parameters. In addition, the CO rebreathing technique determines the summed resistances of the blood-gas barrier and that of the blood cells. The red blood cells in reptiles are relatively large and may, therefore, impose a substantial diffusion limitation. Nevertheless, use of a stopped flow technique to determine O_2-transfer kinetics in red blood cells of Trachemys scripta allowed Yamaguchi et al. (1989) to conclude that the blood-gas barrier contributes a larger resistance to O_2 uptake than does blood.

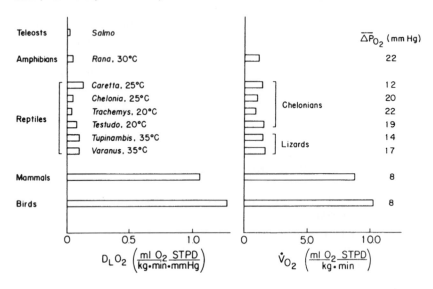

Fig. 3.9. A comparison of the pulmonary diffusing capacity (D_{LO_2}) and O_2 uptake ($\dot{V}_{O_2}$) in various vertebrates. The calculated P_{O_2} difference between lung gas and pulmonary venous blood ($\overline{\Delta P}_{O_2} = P_{AO_2} - P_{PVO_2}$) is shown in the column on the right. (Modified from Glass, 1991.)

Glass (1991) recently reviewed the available data on D_{O_2} in several different vertebrates (Fig. 3.9). Reptiles and other ectothermic vertebrates have a much lower D_{LO_2} than do birds and mammals. As described by Bohr (1909), the diffusion relative to oxygen uptake can be used indirectly to predict P_{O_2} differences between the lung (P_{AO_2}) and the pulmonary venous return (P_{PVO_2}):

$$\dot{V}_{O_2}/D_{LO_2} = P_{AO_2} - P_{cap O_2} \qquad \text{(Eq. 3.1)}$$

Although the metabolic rate of reptiles is considerably lower than that of mammals, the much lower D_{O_2} in reptiles predicts the $P_{AO_2} - P_{PVO_2}$ difference to be 2 to 3 times higher than for mammals and birds (Fig. 3.9). Only two studies on reptiles have determined P_{PVO_2} over a wide range of P_{AO_2} values (Burggren and Shelton, 1979; Hicks and White, 1992); the data from the alligator study are presented in Figure 3.10. In both *Trachemys scripta* and *Alligator mississippiensis*, P_{PVO_2} is 10–20 mmHg lower than P_{AO_2}. This difference is considerably higher than the equivalent alveolar-arterial gradient in resting mammals of approximately 3 to 8 mmHg (Piiper, 1989), suggesting that it is not as good an O_2 exchanger as the alveolar mammalian lung.

In the following section, the possible physiological mechanisms explaining these high $P_{A_{O_2}} - P_{pv_{O_2}}$ differences are discussed. Before doing so, it must be emphasized that, in animals with the potential for intracardiac shunts, arterial blood gas composition rarely reflects that of the pulmonary venous return. Therefore, in reptiles, studies on pulmonary gas transfer must be based on blood gases sampled from the pulmonary veins or the left atrium.

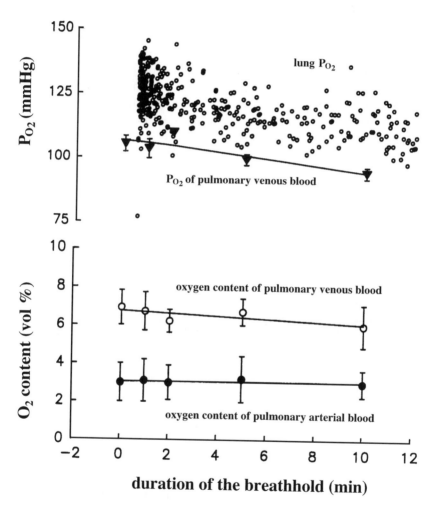

Fig. 3.10. Relationship between lung P_{O_2} (open circles) and pulmonary venous blood during ventilation and apnea of varying duration in *Alligator mississippiensis*. The lower panel depicts pulmonary venous oxygen content and pulmonary arterial O_2 content. (From Hicks and White, 1992.)

3. Physiological Mechanisms Explaining P_{O_2} Differences Between Lung and Blood Gases

In a perfect lung (in terms of gas exchange), the gas composition of the blood leaving the lung (pulmonary venous return, P_{pv}) is identical to that within the lung (P_A). Therefore, the P_{O_2} of pulmonary venous return (P_{pvO_2}) would equal that of the lungs (P_{AO_2}). This is rarely the case as three principal causes exist for P_{pvO_2} being lower than P_{AO_2}: (1) diffusion limitation, (2) pulmonary shunts or venous admixture, and (3) unequal distribution of ventilation and perfusion ($\dot{V}/\dot{Q}$ mismatching). These three conceptually different contributors to $P_{AO_2} - P_{pvO_2}$ differences are presented in Figure 3.11. A quantification of each of these factors (as discussed below) is a major future challenge in comparative physiology, and it is reasonable to expect that the contribution of each of these parameters differs among species and varies according to the physiological state. Only a few studies have attempted to quantify the limitations to gas exchange in the reptilian lung, and the available data strongly suggest that all three factors contribute significantly to $P_{AO_2} - P_{pvO_2}$ difference. Below, diffusion limitation, pulmonary shunts, and $\dot{V}/\dot{Q}$ mismatching are discussed separately.

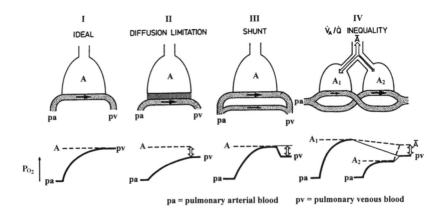

pa = pulmonary arterial blood   pv = pulmonary venous blood

Fig. 3.11. Physiological mechanisms that can cause difference in the partial pressure of lung gas compared to that of pulmonary venous blood ($P_{AO_2} - P_{pvO_2}$). The ideal lung (I) lacks a $P_{AO_2} - P_{pvO_2}$ difference. In the case of diffusion limitation (II), the $P_{AO_2} - P_{pvO_2}$ difference is due to incomplete diffusive equilibration. In the presence of intrapulmonary shunts (III), admixture of pulmonary arterial blood causes a drop in end-capillary O_2 content. In the case of ventilation-perfusion inequality (IV), the $P_{AO_2} - P_{pvO_2}$ difference is caused by mixing of blood from the two compartments with different $\dot{V}/\dot{Q}$ ratios. Abbreviations: A, alveolar; A_1, alveolar value in left lung; A_2, alveolar value in right lung. (Figure is based on Piiper, 1993.)

a. DIFFUSION LIMITATION AND STRATIFICATION

If there is no diffusion limitation, blood traversing a lung capillary quickly attains gas partial pressures equivalent to the lung gases (e.g., $P_{cap}O_2 = P_{A}O_2$) as depicted in Figure 3.11I. In contrast, if diffusion limits gas transfer, the respiratory gases do not attain full equilibrium between lung and blood gas while traversing the capillary (see Fig. 3.11II). Using the traditional, simplest one-compartment model and basic assumptions, it can be shown that the degree of alveolar-capillary equilibration [$(P_A - P_{PV}) \div (P_A - P_V)$] is determined by lung diffusion capacity (D) relative to the product of blood flow ($\dot{Q}$) and capacitance coefficient of the blood (β; change in blood gas content for a given change in partial pressure). The ratio—$D/\dot{Q}\beta$—has been termed the "equilibrium coefficient," and the reader is referred to the numerous publications of Johannes Piiper and Peter Scheid for an in-depth treatment and derivation of this important concept (Piiper, 1961, 1989; Piiper and Scheid, 1975, 1989). The equilibrium coefficient is of fundamental importance because it allows predictions for limitations of lung gas exchange; if D is high, relative to $\dot{Q}\beta$, equilibration is attained faster than if D is low, relative to $\dot{Q}\beta$. Also, a high equilibrium coefficient indicates that gas exchange is primarily perfusion-limited, whereas a low equilibrium coefficient points to a predominantly diffusion-limited system. It has been documented from several species of reptiles that the mean thickness of the air-blood barrier varies within the lung (Perry, 1978, 1983, 1989; Stinner, 1982a; Perry et al., 1994), suggesting that the diffusing capacity is inhomogeneously distributed. Based on a simple model consisting of a single gas phase and two perfusion units, Piiper (1961, 1992) showed that, for a given β, inhomogeneous distribution of diffusion capacity relative to blood flow ($D/\dot{Q}$) impairs gas exchange efficiency; increased inhomogeneity augments the equilibration deficit [$(P_A - P_{PV}) \div (P_A - P_V)$] and, therefore, increases the $P_{A}O_2 - P_{PV}O_2$ difference. The importance of diffusion-perfusion inhomogeneity for lung gas exchange efficiency is virtually unknown and is difficult to assess experimentally (Piiper, 1992; Yamaguchi et al., 1991). Because CO has a much higher capacitance in blood (and, thus, a very low $D/\dot{Q}\beta$), the effect of this inhomogeneity would be much lower than for O_2. Thus, in the presence of large diffusion-perfusion inhomogeneities, it may be erroneous to convert the experimentally determined diffusion capacity for CO to an O_2-diffusion capacity by simply multiplying by 1.23.

Ventilation-perfusion inhomogeneity can also affect measurements of diffusion limitations. As discussed in more detail below, P. D. Wagner and his colleagues have developed a method to estimate $D_{L}O_2$ in the presence of $\dot{V}/\dot{Q}$ inhomogeneity. With this method, diffusion limitation is assessed as the part of the $P_{A}O_2 - P_{PV}O_2$ difference that cannot be accounted for by intrapulmonary shunts and $\dot{V}/\dot{Q}$ mismatching. Using this approach, Hopkins et al. (1996) estimated that diffusion limitation may account for a $P_{AO_2} - P_{PvO_2}$ difference of as much as 15–20 mmHg in anaesthetized and mechanically ventilated *Trachemys scripta*. However, in non-anesthetized *Varanus exanthematicus*, diffusion limitation does not contribute significantly to the $P_{AO_2} - P_{PvO_2}$ difference at rest, but appears to be responsible for 14 mmHg of the $P_{AO_2} - P_{PvO_2}$ during exercise (Hopkins et al., 1995). This finding agrees well with studies on mammals in which diffusion limitation is insignificant at rest but may account for up to 70% of the $P_{AO_2} - P_{aO_2}$ difference (equivalent to the $P_{AO_2} - P_{PvO_2}$ in reptiles) at maximal exercise (Wagner et al., 1986, 1989; Powell, 1993 and 1994 contain excellent discussions of diffusion limitation in a comparative context).

The faveolar compartments in reptiles are considerably larger than the equivalent mammalian alveoli and a substantial gas diffusion limitation, usually referred to as "stratification," may be expected (reviewed by Powell, 1993; Piiper, 1993). Powell and Gray (1989) estimated that stratification could account for approximately 10 mmHg of the observed $P_{AO_2} - P_{PvO_2}$ gradient in anesthetized and artificially ventilated alligators. The tubular, elongate lungs of snakes represent an extreme example of stratification because they may extend almost the entire length of the body. Morphologically, snake lungs can be divided into an anterior, highly vascularized section and a posterior, virtually non-vascularized region, which has also been termed the "air sac" (Brattstrom, 1959; McDonald, 1959; Stinner, 1982b). Using intravenously injected, radioactively labeled macroaggregates, Read and Donnelly (1972) demonstrated that the anterior region receives 75% of lung blood flow in *Morelia spilota*. Later studies on this and two other species (*Vipera xanthina* and *Pelamis platurus*) showed that ventilation is distributed primarily to the anterior region, and that P_{O_2} is low and P_{CO_2} high in the anterior region (Donnelly and Woolcock, 1972, 1977, 1978; Gratz et al., 1981; Seymour et al., 1981; Fig. 3.12). In accordance with the expectation of a high degree of stratification, Donnelly and Woolcock (1978) also showed that the large differences in gas composition persist for many minutes (more than 10 min) during breath holding.

b. Intrapulmonary Shunts

Intrapulmonary shunts represent a portion of the pulmonary blood flow that completely bypasses exposure to the lung gas and, therefore, does not partake in the exchange of respiratory gases (Fig. 3.11III). Intrapulmonary shunts can be expressed either as a fraction of blood flow (relative measure) or as the absolute flow and reduce P_{PvO_2} in a conceptually identical manner to that of right-to-left intracardiac shunts.

Importantly, the effect of intrapulmonary shunts on P_{PVO_2} depends on both the shunt fraction and the O_2 content of pulmonary arterial blood. For example, at a given shunt fraction and faveolar P_{O_2}, a reduction of pulmonary arterial oxygen content results in a lower pulmonary venous oxygen content and P_{O_2}.

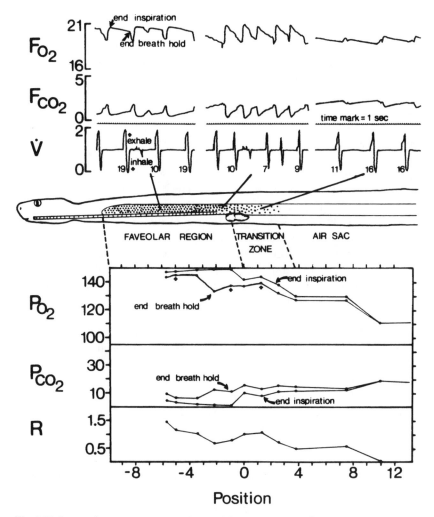

Fig. 3.12. Intrapulmonary gas composition in *Vipera xanthina*. In this experiment, the fractional concentration of O_2 and CO_2 (F_{O_2} and F_{CO_2}, respectively) were determined from three locations in the lung during spontaneous ventilation ($\dot{V}$ is the ventilatory flow and the numbers are the inspired tidal volume in liters BTPS min^{-1}). The lower panels show the regional gas tensions (P_{O_2}, P_{O_2}) and the local respiratory gas exchange ratio (R) at various positions relative to the heart (position 0). (Modified from Gratz et al., 1981.)

Large intrapulmonary blood shunts have been reported for reptiles. This is in contrast to mammals and birds, in which intrapulmonary shunts are virtually absent (e.g., Piiper, 1993 and Powell, 1993). *Trachemys scripta* and *Laticauda colubrina* have intrapulmonary shunts of 10–20% and 16%, respectively (Seymour, 1978, 1980). These intrapulmonary shunts were assessed from the effects of hyperoxia on pulmonary venous oxygen content. Assuming that hyperoxia eliminates the diffusion limitation and greatly reduces the effect of $\dot{V}/\dot{Q}$ mismatching (see below), the persistence of low pulmonary venous oxygen content can be ascribed to intrapulmonary shunts. A more sensitive method for determination of intrapulmonary shunts is based on venous infusion of a highly insoluble gas such as SF_6. Because of its low solubility, SF_6 will diffuse into the lung if there is any contact between the capillary and the alveolar space and detection of such a gas in the pulmonary venous blood allows calculation of the intrapulmonary shunt. In *Trachemys scripta*, this method estimated the pulmonary shunt to be 16% of pulmonary blood flow (Hopkins et al., 1996). Infusion of SF_6 has also been employed in *Tupinambis teguixin* (formerly *T. nigropunctatus*) (Hlastala et al., 1985) and *Alligator mississippiensis* (Powell and Gray, 1989). Unfortunately, in both of these studies, arterial systemic rather than pulmonary venous blood was analyzed for SF_6 content. Consequently, it is difficult to distinguish between intracardiac right-to-left shunt and intrapulmonary shunts, although both studies point to sizeable intrapulmonary shunts. Using the same method as above, but sampling blood from the left atrium, Hopkins et al. (1995) reported a pulmonary shunt of 5% in resting, non-anaesthetized *Varanus exanthematicus*. During moderate exercise, this shunt fraction decreases to only 2%.

The very large intrapulmonary shunts in reptiles certainly reduce the gas exchange efficiency of the lungs. In both testudines and sea snakes, the magnitude of pulmonary shunting increases with reduced lung volume. Seymour (1978) suggested this trait to be of functional significance whenever the lung is compressed during breath hold diving. Under these circumstances, an increased intrapulmonary shunt leads to a reduction in arterial P_{O_2}, which may reduce O_2 loss to the water due to a reduction in the O_2 diffusion gradient. Although this explanation is intuitively appealing for diving reptiles, it cannot explain the presence of large intrapulmonary shunts in terrestrial species. The anatomical basis of the intrapulmonary shunts in reptiles is not known.

c. Ventilation-Perfusion Mismatching

Even in a lung without diffusion impairment and shunts, P_{pvO_2} may be lower than P_{AO_2} if ventilation and perfusion are not *spatially* matched. Such a situation is presented in a highly schematized form in Figure

3.11IV, in which one of the two lung compartments receives a high ventilation ($\dot{V}$) and a low perfusion ($\dot{Q}$) relative to the other compartment. The respective differences in $\dot{V}/\dot{Q}$ between the two compartments result in the high $\dot{V}/\dot{Q}$ compartment having a high P_{O_2}, whereas the low $\dot{V}/\dot{Q}$ compartment has a low P_{O_2}. Because pulmonary venous blood constitutes the weighed mean of blood from all compartments, a relatively high blood flow to a compartment with low $\dot{V}/\dot{Q}$ leads to a lower P_{PvO_2} than the average P_{AO_2}. Intuitively, the spatial matching of ventilation and blood flows may not seem to be a problem in the reptilian lung because of its structural simplicity. Contrary to this expectation, several studies on reptiles point to a potentially important role of $\dot{V}/\dot{Q}$ mismatching in determining $P_{AO_2} - P_{PvO_2}$ difference. Before reviewing this literature, it is important to distinguish the difference between *spatial* and *temporal* ventilation-perfusion matching. In reptiles, pulmonary blood flow commonly increases during ventilation (e.g., Shelton and Burggren, 1976), and this *temporal* matching of ventilation and perfusion has often been interpreted as evidence for improved $\dot{V}/\dot{Q}$ matching. However, an increase in bulk blood flow during ventilation does not imply that highly ventilated portions of the lung receive proportional blood flow.

If ventilation and perfusion are poorly matched spatially, gas composition in the different lung compartments is heterogenous and $\dot{V}/\dot{Q}$ heterogeneity may, accordingly, be assessed from analyzing lung gases sampled from different portions of the lung. Using this strategy, Burggren et al. (1978) found only minute (although statistically significant) differences in P_{O_2} and P_{CO_2} of gases sampled from several chambers in *Trachemys* and *Testudo* lungs. In the same study and a prior study by Crawford et al. (1976), nitrogen washout following inspiration of 100% O_2 was shown to be monoexponential, which also suggests that regional variations in $\dot{V}/\dot{Q}$ are small. In contrast, Spragg et al. (1980) followed the distribution of ^{133}Xe added to the inhaled gas and noted that ventilation is markedly inhomogeneous. These authors also argued that because overall washout of ^{133}Xe could be monoexponential, in spite of the inhomogeneous ventilation, the aforementioned monoexponential N_2 washout curves (Crawford et al., 1976; Burggren et al., 1978) cannot be used to argue that ventilation is homogeneous (Spragg et al., 1980). It is noteworthy that ventilatory inhomogeneity and limited intrapulmonary gas mixing are probably responsible for the gas phase diffusion limitations, that were discussed as "stratification" above.

Although the above-mentioned techniques can be used to assess $\dot{V}/\dot{Q}$ heterogeneity, they do not allow for a quantification of the contribution of $\dot{V}/\dot{Q}$ heterogeneity to the P_{O_2} difference between lung and blood gases ($P_{AO_2} - P_{PvO_2}$). It is, nevertheless, possible to quantify this contribution by use of the multiple inert gas elimination technique (MIGET), developed by Wagner et al. (1974). Although this technique is technically demanding and requires substantial data analysis, the underlying principle of the MIGET is relatively simple (Farhi, 1967). Namely, the amount of gas that is excreted from the blood perfusing a "lung gas—blood unit" depends on (1) the partial pressure of the gas of the blood perfusing the unit, (2) the solubility of this gas in blood, and (3) the ventilation-perfusion ratio of this particular unit. Thus, in a compartment with a given $\dot{V}/\dot{Q}$, a relatively insoluble gas diffuses more readily from the blood to the gas phase than does a soluble one and a larger fraction of the insoluble gas will, therefore, be eliminated through the exhaled gas. In practice, six inert gases covering a very wide range of solubilities are infused intravenously, and pulmonary excretion and blood retention of these gases are measured. The obtained data are, subsequently, fitted to a model consisting of 50 compartments arranged in parallel, but with variable $\dot{V}/\dot{Q}$. Use of this multi-compartmental $\dot{V}/\dot{Q}$ model (along with measures of pulmonary arterial blood gas composition, metabolic rate, and absolute levels of ventilation), allows prediction of arterial P_{O_2} and P_{CO_2}. The MIGET, therefore, quantifies the contribution of intrapulmonary shunt and $\dot{V}/\dot{Q}$ mismatching to the measured $P_{AO_2} - P_{pvO_2}$ differences. As mentioned above, this model ascribes any remaining $P_{AO_2} - P_{pvO_2}$ difference not accounted for by $\dot{V}/\dot{Q}$ heterogeneity or intrapulmonary shunt to diffusion limitation (although other possibilities exist, such as extrapulmonary shunts), which is assumed to be distributed in proportion to either ventilation or blood flow.

In this context, it is important to realize that the absolute magnitude of the $P_{AO_2} - P_{pvO_2}$ differences that are attributed to either $\dot{V}/\dot{Q}$ mismatch or diffusion limitation depends on the shape of the blood dissociation curve. Because the blood O_2 dissociation curve is non-linear, a given reduction in O_2 content corresponds to a variable change in blood P_{O_2} (large changes at high P_{O_2} when the ODC is "flat" and small changes around P_{50} where the curve is "steep"). To overcome this problem, it may be more informative to express the effects of diffusion limitation or $\dot{V}/\dot{Q}$ heterogeneity as the reduction in O_2 content rather than P_{O_2} (Hempleman and Hughes, 1991).

The MIGET has proven extremely powerful for understanding of the limitations for gas exchange in mammals and, recently, this technique has used successfully in reptiles. For *Tupinambis teguixin* (formerly *T. nigropunctatus*), Hlastala et al. (1985) reported a very poor spatial matching of ventilation-perfusion matching compared to mammals. On the basis of Hlastala's data for tegu lizards, Powell (1993) calculated that the observed $\dot{V}/\dot{Q}$ heterogeneity would cause $P_{AO_2} - P_{pvO_2}$ of approximately 20 mmHg. This finding is contrary to the expectation that lizards with a structurally very simple lung would possess a very uniform $\dot{V}/\dot{Q}$ distribution. However, Powell and Gray (1989) found that alligators have a $\dot{V}/\dot{Q}$ heterogeneity similar to that of mammals and that this only explains a small part of the $P_{AO_2} - P_{PvO_2}$ difference. In *Trachemys scripta*, the $\dot{V}/\dot{Q}$ heterogeneity is similar to mammals whenever pulmonary blood flow is high, but the degree of heterogeneity increases whenever pulmonary blood flow is reduced (Hopkins et al., 1996). In all these studies, the animals were anesthetized and artificially ventilated, which may have resulted in a different gas-mixing pattern within the lungs compared to that in fully recovered and resting animals.

Recently, Hopkins et al. (1995) provided the first MIGET measurements on non-anesthetized lizards during both rest and treadmill exercise. In resting *Varanus exanthematicus*, the $\dot{V}/\dot{Q}$ heterogeneity is very similar to that of mammals and could, in concert with the small intrapulmonary shunt (5%), account for all of the observed $P_{AO_2} - P_{PvO_2}$ difference (28 mmHg). Although the $P_{AO_2} - P_{PvO_2}$ difference remains virtually unaffected (31 mmHg), the mechanisms underlying this difference changed during exercise. Intrapulmonary shunt decreased to 2% and $\dot{V}/\dot{Q}$ heterogeneity increased markedly. Because these parameters could not explain the observed $P_{AO_2} - P_{PvO_2}$ gradient, diffusion limitation was assumed to account for 14 mmHg of this gradient. The savannah monitors, therefore, resemble humans, for which increased $\dot{V}/\dot{Q}$ heterogeneity and increased diffusion limitation during exercise are well documented, although the mechanism remains unclear (Wagner et al., 1986).

3. PULMONARY OXYGEN STORAGE

Numerous studies now show unequivocally that most dives in most species of reptiles are carried out largely or entirely aerobically (Ackerman and White, 1979; Seymour, 1979; Gleeson, 1980; Gatten, 1981; Seymour et al., 1985; Eckert et al., 1986; Rubinoff et al., 1986; Seymour, 1989). This requires that the animals either dive for extremely brief periods of time *or* store sufficient oxygen to allow more lengthy diving. In fact, many aquatic reptiles can dive for periods of many minutes without showing an appreciable fall in plasma pH or the appearance of lactate in the plasma—two indicators that accessible oxygen stores have been depleted. Clearly, such animals carry with them adequate oxygen to support aerobic metabolism during most dives. This oxygen can be carried in one of two forms:

- *oxygen in body fluids*: oxygen bound to hemoglobin in the blood, myoglobin in the muscle, and (to a much lesser extent) dissolved as molecular oxygen in body fluids could all contribute to the oxygen store available during diving.

- *oxygen stored in lung gas*: most reptiles inhale as the last ventilatory act before submerging for a dive, thus ensuring that their lungs are filled with gas that potentially could be drawn upon for oxygen during the dive.

It might be anticipated that mechanisms for oxygen storage in diving would have been increased through natural selection, as compared with non-diving reptiles. As Seymour (1989) emphasizes, however, the potential sites of oxygen storage of diving reptiles appear unremarkable when contrasted with non-diving, more continuously breathing reptiles. Divers do not have higher blood volume and blood oxygen capacity (Burggren et al., 1977; Seymour, 1982; Burggren, 1988), and similarly, maximal lung volumes are similar in both diving and non-diving forms. Interestingly, this same poor correlation between blood and lung oxygen stores with diving lifestyle is also evident in amphibians (Burggren, 1989). These observations in reptiles and amphibians do not suggest that oxygen stores are unimportant to diving animals, but rather that

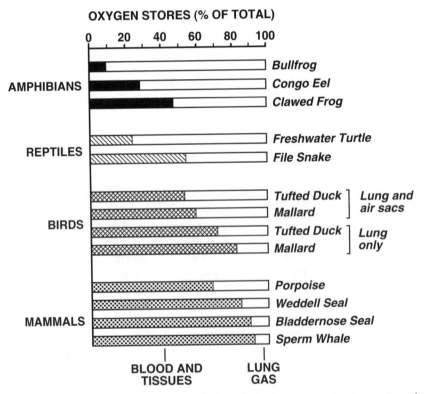

Fig. 3.13. Location of oxygen stores available at the beginning of diving in a variety of vertebrates. (From Burggren, 1988.)

the stores associated with normal gas exchange and transport can be exploited to support aerobic metabolism during diving. To what extent do reptiles depend on blood versus lung oxygen stores during apnea? The calculations of such dependency involve knowledge of numerous factors including blood volume, blood oxygen capacitance, blood gas levels, oxygen-hemoglobin binding kinetics, lung volume, and lung gas partial pressures. Such values must be known both before and after a period of diving. It is not surprising that relatively few studies produce all of these data, and so there are few quantitative estimates of the role of blood versus lung gas in diving reptiles. Expressed as a proportion of total O_2 stored, lung gas variously occupies between 20% (freshwater testudine) and 50% (file snake) of the total O_2 available at the beginning of the dive (Fig. 3.13). Of course, such data do not reveal whether there is a disproportionate use of lung versus body fluids during a dive. A reptile might have large lungs (and thus a large potential oxygen store) primarily because the lungs are used in buoyancy.

Several studies indicate that oxygen removal from the lungs during diving is controlled and variable. Figure 3.14 shows two different patterns of oxygen removal during voluntary diving in *Trachemys scripta*. During most short aerobic dives, lung and arterial oxygen partial pressure fall in parallel before rising with the onset of the next breathing bout. In many longer dives, however, a different pattern emerges in which arterial P_{O_2} plunges rapidly while lung P_{O_2} initially remains unchanged. Well into the dive, however, arterial P_{O_2} begins to rise sharply, coincident with a decrease in alveolar P_{O_2}. These data suggest that pulmonary perfusion is sharply curtailed early in the dive, reducing or eliminating pulmonary gas exchange, but that lung blood flow increases later in the dive, effectively transferring oxygen stored in the lungs into the blood. Direct evidence of changes in pulmonary blood flow during diving has been presented for *Chelodina longicollis* (Burggren et al., 1989). As had been predicted from blood and lung gas studies in *Trachemys*, blood is intermittently pulsed through the lungs in *Chelodina*, transferring oxygen from lung gas to arterial blood (Fig. 3.15). The control mechanisms responsible for triggering blood flow during apnea are unknown and warrant exploration.

D. Ventilatory Patterns and Gas Exchange Whenever Metabolic Rate is Elevated

1. GENERAL When metabolic rate changes, lung ventilation must change appropriately to safeguard oxygen delivery and arterial blood gas composition. In reptiles, large increases in metabolic rate occur with elevated body temperature, during exercise, and following feeding (Specific Dynamic Action; SDA). The effects of temperature ventilation are compli-

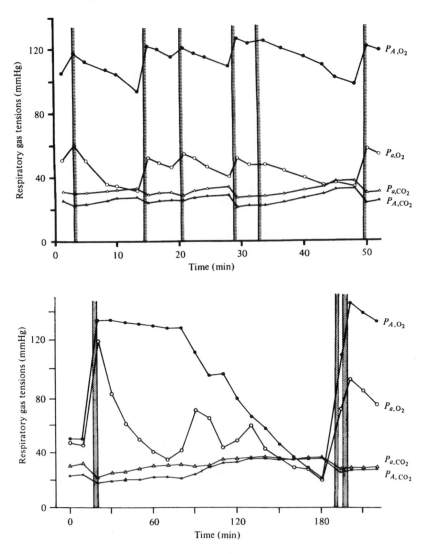

Fig. 3.14. Changes in arterial (P_a) and alveolar (P_A) O_2 and CO_2 at 20° C during voluntary dives in *Trachemys scripta*. Vertical bars represent breathing bouts. The top panel shows a sequence of short dives and the bottom panel shows an unusual three-hour dive characterized by a transfer of oxygen from lungs to blood after 1.5 hours. (From Burggren, 1988, after Burggren and Shelton, 1979.)

cated by attending changes in acid-base balance and are, therefore, discussed separately in the section on acid-base balance. Lung function during the post prandial period has not been studied in any reptile, but promises an interesting avenue for future research, because metabolic rate during digestion may approach or even exceed that attained during muscular exercise (Benedict, 1932; Coulson et al., 1950; Preest, 1991; Secor and Diamond, 1995; Abe et al., 1995).

2. VENTILATION AND GAS EXCHANGE DURING EXERCISE

It is well established that ventilation increases proportionally more than oxygen uptake during muscular exercise in mammals (for a review see Dempsey et al., 1995). Some early studies on lizards and snakes have reported considerable increases in ventilation during activity (Wilson, 1971; Dmi'el, 1972; Bennett, 1973; Cragg, 1978). Presumably, the increase in ventilation is accomplished through large increases in tidal volume and only small changes in breathing frequency. However, these studies were conducted on physically restrained animals, and activity was induced by pinching the legs or through electrical shocks. Further, several reported variables for activity were, in fact, obtained during the after recovery period (e.g., Bennett, 1973); accordingly, the value of these studies is very limited. In subsequent studies on *Varanus exanthematicus* and *Iguana iguana* moving freely on a treadmill, G. S. Mitchell et al. (1981a, 1981b) measured arterial blood gases and calculated pulmonary ventilation on the basis of arterial P_{CO_2}. Both species increased ventilation at

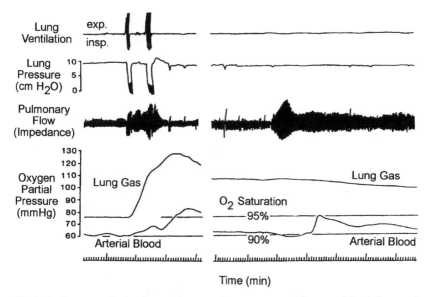

Fig. 3.15. Lung ventilation, intrapulmonary lung pressure, pulmonary blood flow, and the P_{O_2} of lung gas and systemic arterial blood in an unrestrained, undisturbed turtle, *Chelodina longicollis*. The left-hand section of the tracing indicates events at the end of a dive and during two brief bouts of lung ventilation. The right-hand section shows records between 6 and 19 minutes of diving. (After Burggren et al., 1989.)

speeds that are several times above maximal aerobic capacity. Subsequently, Carrier (1987a) challenged this finding in a study in which inspired air flows across the nostrils were measured using hot wire manometry in four species of lizards during rest and activity. In this study, all four species (*Iguana iguana, Ctenosaura similis, Varanus exanthematicus,* and *V. salvator*) displayed a progressive decrease in tidal volume with increasing speed, leading to a decrease in total ventilation in spite of an increase in breathing frequency. On this basis, Carrier (1987a) suggested that lizards are mechanically constrained from breathing while locomoting because the hypaxial muscles contribute to both ventilatory and locomotory movements. This interpretation is also supported by electromyographic recordings of the hypaxial muscles during walking and ventilation in *Iguana iguana* (Carrier 1989, 1990).

The disparity between the studies by Mitchell et al. (1981a, 1981b) and Carrier (1987a) is not easily explained because ineffective pulmonary ventilation during locomotion must result in predictable changes in arterial blood gases. However, because lizards often employ intermittent locomotion, even on treadmills, it is possible that blood gases are maintained by ventilating the lungs during the brief pauses between locomotory activity. Therefore, Wang et al. (1995b) recently reinvestigated the question of ventilation during locomotion in lizards. Lung ventilation was measured directly by means of pneumotachography in *Varanus exanthematicus* and *Iguana iguana* moving freely at different speeds on a treadmill. This study unequivocally shows that both varanids and iguanas are capable of ventilating their lungs during locomotor strides (even at speeds above maximum aerobic speed), but it also shows that the breathing pattern changes consistently during locomotion compared to rest. As shown in Figure 3.16, the breathing pattern during exercise is characterized by higher airflow velocities of short duration. Also, both inspiratory and expiratory airflows change frequently and abruptly. In *V. exanthematicus*, ventilation (Fig. 3.16A and B) and gas exchange were consistently increased above both pre- and post-exercise levels (Wang et al., 1995b). *Iguana iguana* exhibit a different ventilatory pattern. In this species, both ventilation and gas exchange are highest immediately following exercise (Fig. 3.16C). This study, therefore, suggests that Carrier (1987a) underestimated ventilation during activity in *Varanus*. However, in *Iguana*, the large reductions in tidal volume and the reduction in gas exchange are consistent with Carrier's original suggestion of the existence of a mechanical interference (or even conflict) between ventilation and locomotion. Given the substantial differences between the two species thus far studied, it seems worthwhile to measure the ventilatory patten during locomotion of other species of reptiles.

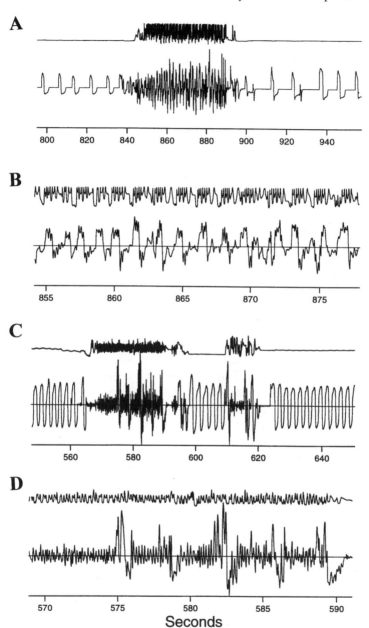

Fig. 3.16. Ventilatory patterns before, during, and after treadmill locomotion in *Varanus exanthematicus* (A & B) and *Iguana iguana* (C & D). In each figure, the trace in the top panel is a measure of lateral bending of the trunk, whereas the lower panel depicts inspiratory and expiratory airflows across the nostrils. Figures B and D are expansions of the traces in A and C. (From T. Wang, D. R. Carrier, and J. W. Hicks, unpublished.)

Chelonia mydas increases ventilation relative to metabolic rate (increase in $\dot{V}_E/\dot{V}_{O_2}$) during swimming (Jackson and Prange, 1979; Butler et al., 1984). These animals increase ventilation entirely by increasing breathing frequency, but maintain constant tidal volume. Nevertheless, *Chelonia* does not breathe when moving its flippers (D. C. Jackson, personal communication) nor during locomotory strides on land (Jackson and Prange, 1979). A small increase in arterial P_{O_2} during exercise is consistent with the relative hyperventilation (Jackson and Prange, 1979). However, because arterial and not left atrial blood gases were measured, it is quite possible that the increase in P_{O_2} stems from large reductions in cardiac R-L shunt, and this study does not allow interpretation of lung gas exchange efficiency.

Carrier (1987a, 1987b) suggested that mechanical constraints imposed on the hypaxial musculature limit ventilation, especially at high running speeds and, thus, render lizards incapable of sustained locomotion. This possibility, obviously, has important implications for the evolution of sustained activity in birds and mammals (Carrier, 1987b; Ruben, 1995) but remains to be tested experimentally. If ventilation, indeed, is the limiting step in the oxygen transport cascade during exercise, an increased ventilation during exercise should sustain a higher oxygen uptake. For a given systemic blood flow, lung ventilation limits systemic O_2 delivery (blood flow × systemic arterial O_2 content), whenever lung P_{O_2} falls to a level at which pulmonary venous blood is no longer saturated. The lung P_{O_2} at which HbO_2 saturation of pulmonary venous blood is compromised depends on both blood oxygen affinity and the P_{O_2} difference between lung and blood leaving the lungs. In *Varanus exanthematicus*, Hopkins et al. (1995) have documented an increase in left atrial P_{O_2} during exercise, in spite of an increased $\dot{V}/\dot{Q}$ heterogeneity. This does not support the suggestion that lung P_{O_2} limits O_2 delivery to the muscles. This study was, however, conducted at relatively low running speeds (1.0 km h^{-1}).

In reptiles, no studies have determined all of the O_2 transfer components (i.e., transfer rates between inhaled gas, the lungs, pulmonary capillary blood, systemic blood oxygen transport, and O_2 diffusion between systemic capillary blood and mitochondria) and it is, at present, very difficult to establish whether a single limiting step in the O_2 transport cascade exists. The long time constants before attaining steady state in reptiles complicate matters further, because a transient reduction in transfer rate at one step in the O_2 transport cascade does not necessarily indicate an oxygen transport limitation. Nevertheless, based on the relative hyperventilation (G. S. Mitchell et al., 1981a, 1981b) and the attainment of maximal cardiac output and arterial-venous O_2 differences at maximal aerobic speeds in *Iguana* and *Varanus*, it has been concluded that the circulatory system, and not ventilation, sets the limit for aerobic activity in reptiles (Gleeson et al., 1980; reviewed by Bennett, 1994).

III. ACID-BASE BALANCE
A. General Introduction

Whole animal acid-base balance is controlled through alteration of tissue fluid P_{CO_2} and by transepithelial ion exchanges. During steady state, production of acidic or alkaline metabolites is balanced by respiratory CO_2 loss and transepithelial ion exchange. Arterial (and tissue) P_{CO_2} is predominantly determined by pulmonary ventilation, whereas transepithelial ion exchanges occur primarily in the kidneys. The role of the reptilian kidney in acid-base balance is not well investigated (for a review see Jackson, 1986), but existing studies point to an only minor importance whenever acid-base balance is disturbed through long-term hypercapnia or bicarbonate infusion (Silver and Jackson, 1985, 1986; Glass and Heisler, 1986). Therefore, at least on a short term basis, the lungs are the major organs for acid-base regulation.

Plasma pH shows only small differences among reptiles and other vertebrates, provided comparisons are made at identical temperatures. Similar pH values, however, may stem from very different combinations of P_{CO_2} values and plasma $[HCO_3^-]$, as illustrated by the Henderson-Hasselbalch equation,

$$pH = pK' + \log\{[HCO_3^-]_{pl} \div (\alpha CO_2 \times P_{CO2})\}. \quad \text{(Eq. 3.2)}$$

The Henderson-Hasselbalch equation is often applied to evaluate the acid-base balance, and the following discussion will, in this spirit, focus on changes in P_{CO_2}, $[HCO_3^-]$ and pK values. It is, however, important from a conceptual point of view to emphasize that plasma $[HCO_3^-]$ represents only a part of the ionic picture with respect to acid-base balance. Bicarbonate concentration is, as pointed out by Stewart (1981, 1983), dependent on strong ion difference (SID), defined as the difference between net electric charge of strong cations and strong anions, and the concentration of weak acids. Though still controversial (for a recent and provocative discusion see Fencl and Leith, 1993), Stewart's view of acid-base balance has contributed enormously in clarifying that the three independent variables in acid-base regulation are SID, $[A_{TOT}]$ and P_{CO_2}, whereas $[HCO_3^-]$ is a dependent variable that can be altered only through changes in independent variables.

B. Temperature and Acid-Base Regulation

1. GENERAL Arterial pH decreases consistently and systematically with increasing temperature in virtually all ectothermic vertebrates (for a very thorough review of the literature, see Heisler, 1986). In fishes, changes in arterial acid-base status caused by temperature are primarily due to alternations in plasma HCO_3^- (e.g., Cameron, 1984). In contrast, in amphibians and reptiles the decrease of arterial pH with temperature results predominantly from an increase in arterial P_{CO_2}, which is created by a decrease in pulmonary ventilation relative to CO_2 production (e.g., Jackson, 1971, 1989; Giordano and Jackson, 1973; Glass et al., 1983; Dupre et al., 1989; cf. S. C. Wood et al., 1977). Early studies on reptiles and amphibians showed constant plasma HCO_3^-, regardless of body temperature (Howell et al., 1970; Reeves, 1972; Jackson and Kagen, 1976). More recent studies, however, have documented changes in plasma HCO_3^- after temperature changes (Stinner and Wardle, 1988; Stinner, 1982b; Heisler, 1986). A brief evaluation of the physicochemical effects of temperature may be appropriate before continuing the discussion of whole animal acid-base regulation.

2. Physicochemical Effects of Temperature on Acid-Base Parameters

Temperature affects a number of acid-base parameters. Neutral pH decreases with temperature, solubility of CO_2 decreases, and, importantly, pK values for proteins and the "bicarbonate system" change. A specific pH at different temperatures, therefore, does not represent identical acid-base status.

Given that neutral pH changes with temperature, it may, for a biological system, be more appropriate to evaluate the effect of temperature on proteins rather than on pH per se. Protein structure and function are dependent on ionization of titratable groups. The fraction of total titratable groups that are ionized (α) can be related to pK and pH by

$$\alpha = 10^{(pH - pK)} \div (1 + 10^{(pH - pK)}). \qquad \text{(Eq. 3.3)}$$

It is immediately evident from this equation that protein ionization remains constant when the changes in blood pH and protein pK are identical, and that changes in protein ionization depend on the difference between pH and pK. Alternations of protein ionization for a given pH change will be small if the difference, pH − pK, is large and vice versa. The changes in pK (ΔpK) with temperature can, given a value for heat of enthalpy (ΔH), be calculated from the van't Hoff equation:

$$\Delta pK = \Delta H(T_2 - T_1) \div 2.303 \times RT_1 T_2, \qquad \text{(Eq. 3.4)}$$

where R is the gas constant and T_1 and T_2 are the absolute temperatures in question (°K). The heat of enthalpy (and with that $\Delta pK / \Delta T$) for a given protein depends on the amino acid sequence and the surrounding microenvironment.

3. TEMPERATURE EFFECTS ON ARTERIAL ACID-BASE STATUS AND THE ALPHASTAT HYPOTHESIS

Although the changes in arterial acid-base status with temperature have been well described and agreed upon by different researchers, we lack a generally accepted model that describes them. The only coherent model, the alphastat hypothesis, has been subjected to extensive and often aggressive criticism. When the alphastat hypothesis was proposed by Reeves in 1972, the available experimental data was an average in vivo $\Delta pH/\Delta T$ of approximately −0.020 and a temperature-independent plasma bicarbonate concentration (Robin, 1962; Rahn, 1966; Howell et al., 1970). Furthermore, the plasma bicarbonate levels seemed to be temperature insensitive, indicating that no non-bicarbonate buffering had taken place following temperature changes. Therefore, at the time that the alphastat hypothesis was formulated, the available data suggested that protein ionization remained constant, regardless of temperature, whereas pH per se changed. By a process of elimination, Reeves focused on the alpha imidazole moiety of histidine as the principal protein buffer group. The pK of this moiety is close to physiological pH values, and the ΔH of approximately 7 kcal mole^{-1} results in a $\Delta pK/\Delta T$ in the range of −0.017 to −0.023. As this value resembled in vivo changes in arterial pH (Howell et al., 1970; Reeves, 1972), Reeves suggested that plasma pH in vivo changed with temperature in a fashion that would keep ionization of alpha imidazole constant. This hypothesis was shortly thereafter extended also to include intracellular compartments (Malan et al., 1976; Reeves and Malan, 1976). Accordingly, the alphastat hypothesis changed the focus from pH per se, proposing imidazole ionization as the regulated variable. The actual regulation was proposed to take place through changes in P_{CO_2} (i.e., adjustments of ventilation relative to CO_2 production). Reeves was not specific as to how this regulation should take place, but involvement of a central receptor was implied (Reeves, 1972, 1977).

The alphastat hypothesis is, indeed, attractive. By addressing protein ionization, the hypothesis focuses on maintaining protein function. From a tautological point of view, it is, furthermore, a simple way to regulate pH; only alternations of P_{CO_2} are required, and no ion exchanges are necessary.

The alphastat hypothesis is basically founded on a semi-closed system, that is, a system closed for ionic species but open for CO_2 (Reeves, 1976a, 1976b). Therefore, in its strictest sense, the alphastat hypothesis requires fulfillment of the following prerequisites (Reeves 1972, 1976a, 1977; Reeves and Malan, 1976; Heisler, 1986):

- The $\Delta pH/\Delta T$ in vivo has to match $\Delta pK/\Delta T$ for the histidine imidazole.
- No changes in bicarbonate concentrations in any body compartment.
- No transepithelial or transmembrane exchange of acid-base relevant ions.

In spite of its attractive nature, the alphastat hypothesis has been subjected to extensive criticism. The pK values for histidine and other free imidazole compounds varies from around 6 to 9, and the corresponding $\Delta pK/\Delta T$ range from -0.018 to -0.024 (Edsall and Wyman, 1958). Effects of temperature on plasma pH that have been reported for many reptilian and amphibian species have been summarized in an extensive and enlighting review by Heisler (1986). In both amphibians and reptiles, the average $\Delta pH/\Delta T$ is considerably lower than predicted on the basis of the $\Delta pK/\Delta T$ of free imidazole (-0.015 and -0.011 for amphibians and reptiles, respectively). In addition, the average $\Delta pH/\Delta T$ value for intracellular compartments is -0.010 (Heisler, 1986), which also is considerably lower than predicted by the alphastat hypothesis. In conclusion, arterial pH does not seem to change by the magnitude proposed (and required) by the hypothesis.

Changes in plasma bicarbonate following temperature changes have also received a lot of attention in amphibians and reptiles. Indeed, plasma bicarbonate concentration changes with temperature in the majority of the species investigated (for a review see Heisler, 1986). For example, Stinner and Wardle (1988) reported substantial changes in the respiratory exchange ratio for testudines and snakes following temperature changes, indicating changes of whole body bicarbonate. However, in most instances, the changes are not large and normally do not contribute significantly to pH changes. The time courses of ion changes after acute changes of temperature are surprisingly little investigated. Heisler and Neumann (1976) altered the body temperature of *Tupinambis teguixin* (formerly *T. nigropunctatus*) between 25 and 35°C and found that, although pH stabilizes almost instantaneously at a new level, five days are required for the plasma bicarbonate to stabilize. In contrast, Douse and Mitchell (1991) reported constant bicarbonate and strong ions levels after temperature changes in *Alligator mississippiensis*. In conclusion, changes in plasma bicarbonate with temperature are well documented, and this is often interpreted as a strong argument against alphastat regulation.

4. Has the Alphastat Hypothesis Been Refuted?

The critique of the alphastat hypothesis outlined above seems at first glance sufficient to disprove the hypothesis. However, it is important to emphasize that the alphastat hypothesis predicts that P_{CO_2} is controlled through ventilation in a manner that causes pH to change similarly to changes in the pK of imidazole. The hypothesis, therefore, addresses ventilation relative to CO_2 production ($\dot{V}_E/\dot{V}_{CO_2}$) as possibly controlled through a central receptor (Reeves, 1977). Hence, the regulated variable may be imidazole ionization at the central receptor. In this case, it should be expected that pH regulation would follow the $\Delta pK/\Delta T$ value of the receptor molecules. This value cannot be expected to be identical to "whole body $\Delta pK/\Delta T$." The $\Delta pK/\Delta T$ values for a given imidazole moiety depend on the surrounding microenvironment and, therefore, may not be identical to that of free imidazole in solution.

Human hemoglobin provides an informative example. The pK values of the 11 titratable histidine residues range from 4.0 to 8.48, depending on oxygenation state (Matthew et al., 1979). As a result, the relation between pH and degree of ionization for hemoglobin is virtually linear in contrast to the sigmoidal shape that describes a single free imidazole (for an instructive discussion, see Cameron, 1989). It is, therefore, entirely possible that the central chemoreceptor alters ventilation in response to changes in protein (possibly imidazole) ionization at the receptor. Some experiments support the hypothesis that the central chemoreceptor is monitoring imidazole ionization. Nattie (1986a, 1986b, 1988, 1990) used the acetylating agent, diethyl pyrocarbonate, which binds to histidine imidazole and forms a relatively stable product, and showed that ventilatory responses of conscious rabbits to CO_2 and pH are attenuated after this agent is introduced into their cerebrospinal fluid.

Thus, in defense of the alphastat hypothesis, it can be argued that the observation that $\Delta pH/\Delta T$ in vivo does not exactly match $\Delta pK/\Delta T$ for imidazole in free solution is insufficient to reject the Reeves's hypothesis. By the same token, given the diversity in pK values, it would be too simplistic to assume that no non-bicarbonate buffering would take place after temperature changes; absolutely constant levels of plasma bicarbonate are, therefore, not to be expected.

Finally, it is important to emphasize that the alphastat hypothesis focuses on ventilatory control exclusively as a mean of regulating acid-base balance. Ventilation is, at the same time and without any doubt, also influenced by oxygen. Accordingly, an evaluation of the alphastat needs to involve an assessment of the concomitant O_2 drive to breathing. Unfortunately, the interaction, and possible conflict, between acid-base regulation and oxygen transport at different temperatures has not been investigated in any published studies on reptiles. As previously discussed, the O_2 drive to breathing seems augmented at elevated body temperatures, and O_2 transport may, accordingly, assume increased priority as body temperature rises (Stinner, 1987; Wood and Glass, 1992). This increased priority may safeguard O_2 loading at the lungs; increased temperature decreases blood O_2 affinity and necessitates a higher lung P_{O_2} for full saturation of pulmonary venous blood. Therefore, it is possible that the increased O_2 drive to breathing at high body temperatures curtails further decreases in air convection requirement. If so, the increase in P_{CO_2} is diminished, which, in turn, results in a lower $\Delta pH/\Delta T$

than predicted by the alphastat hypothesis. This possibility could be experimentally addressed by studying acid-base regulation during hyperoxia at different temperatures. This approach will eliminate, or at least abate, the influence of oxygen on ventilation and allow pH regulation to exert its full effect.

In summary, it seems difficult to disprove the alphastat hypothesis given the data at hand. At the same time, this hypothesis is equally difficult to prove. As long as the relevant $\Delta pK / \Delta T$ values are unknown, the expected $\Delta pHa / \Delta T$ values cannot be predicted.

IV. LUNG FLUID BALANCE
A. Transcapillary Fluid Flux

Like all other vertebrates, reptiles must deal with the physical forces (hydrostatic and osmotic) exerted on their "closed" circulatory systems that tend either to drive fluid out of blood vessels (filtration) or to draw it back in (absorption). The lung is a perfused organ at particular risk with respect to transcapillary fluid flux because of its low interstitial volume capacity and the deleterious effects of edema on diffusional gas transport.

In contrast to mammalian lungs, in which the degree of pulmonary fluid filtration is minute (except in pathologic states), the several species of reptiles that have been examined demonstrate large filtration fluxes of plasma into the lung (Burggren, 1982; Smits, 1989). Large increases in pulmonary blood flow during intermittent breathing in conscious *Trachemys scripta* result in as much as 20–30% of the pulmonary blood flow being filtered into the lung interstitium (Burggren, 1982). High rates of pulmonary filtration are not unique to turtles, as similar rates of net transcapillary filtration have been observed in resting *Sauromalus hispidus* and *Varanus exanthematicus*.

B. Basis for Pulmonary Capillary Filtration

The basis for the high net filtration of plasma in reptilian lungs has yet to be experimentally determined. However, several investigations either directly or indirectly point to both an imbalance of the transcapillary fluid forces (Starling pressures) and an inherent leakiness of the endothelial capillary wall. As most reptiles have an undivided cardiac ventricle, intracardiac shunting can lead to highly variable systemic and pulmonary arterial pressures (Johansen and Burggren, 1980). Whenever this variability is applied to the microcirculation, fluctuations in capillary pressure result in surprisingly high rates of transcapillary fluid fluxes (Burggren, 1982; Lillywhite and Smith, 1981; Lillywhite and Smits, 1984; Smits and Lillywhite, 1985; Smits and Kozubowski, 1985). Simultaneously, the primary Starling pressure that opposes filtration, namely, the capillary oncotic pressure, is comparatively low (Fig. 3.17). Therefore, unlike the situation seen in mammals, the capillary oncotic pressure of reptiles conferred by the presence of plasma proteins is not sufficiently large to favor capillary absorption, which may lead to a prevailing filtration bias.

Given the enormous capacity for fluid mobilization across reptilian microcirculations, it has also been argued that reptilian capillaries are inherently more permeable to bulk fluid flow than are those of mammals (for review, see Smits, 1989). Thus, when even small imbalances in Starling pressures are initiated, the comparatively lower resistance of the capillary wall to fluid flux might lead to comparatively large rates of filtration or absorption. Hemorrhage studies on snakes (Lillywhite and Smith, 1981) and testudines (Smits and Kozubowski, 1985) appear indirectly to implicate the leakiness of the capillary wall. Conclusions concerning the role of capillary structure on reptilian lung fluid balance await confirmation by direct measurement using whole lung perfusion (capillary filtration coefficient) or single capillary perfusion (hydraulic conductivity). An important but unaddressed consideration for reptilian lung fluid balance is the effect of body temperature. Large changes is body temperature, especially common in reptiles, drastically influence the viscosity of the blood. Such viscosity changes not only change the peripheral resistance of all perfused organs (affecting blood pressure), but may also have direct effects on the geometry of the capillary endothelium (affecting permeability; Wolf and Watson, 1985).

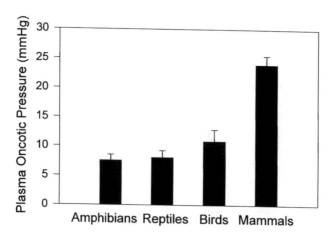

Fig. 3.17. Mean plasma oncotic pressures measured in four vertebrate classes. Number of species and samples included in the analysis are: amphibians 5, 12; reptiles 8, 8; birds 3, 3; mammals 56, 58.

C. Dealing with High Pulmonary Filtration

The consequences of such high rates of pulmonary filtration in reptiles are that (1) reptiles tolerate a comparatively high accumulation of pulmonary filtrate ("wet-lung" syndrome) in the pulmonary interstitium or (2) there is adequate capacity of the pulmonary lymphatic system to deal with this filtration bias. To our knowledge, there are no studies to suggest which consequence pertains to reptilian lungs. A detailed anatomical review (Ottaviani and Tazzi, 1977) indicates that lymphatic drainage from reptilian lungs is similar but less complex than that seen in mammals. In particular, the major lymphatic collecting vessels ensheathe the pulmonary arteries, veins, and bronchi. Because reptiles possess comparatively long pulmonary blood vessels, lymphatic return may be augmented in these animals by vessel pulsation and appropriate one-way valving. Although reptiles possess a single pair of true lymph hearts, the position of these hearts in the caudal region of the body is probably too distant for a significant effect on the lymphatics of the lung.

The only known documentation of pulmonary edema in reptiles is for the sea snake, *Aipysurus laevis* (Lillywhite *in* Smits, 1989). Head-up tilting (out of water) of *Aipysurus* causes substantial accumulation of lung fluid and erythrocytes in the lung, suggesting not only filtration but also a rupture of lung capillaries. Although experimentally induced, this observation (and the lack of pulmonary dysfunction noted in more terrestrial and arboreal species subjected to similar head-up tilting) illustrates the effect of gravity as a selection pressure on the evolution of pulmonary design, particularly in reptiles such as snakes, which have characteristically elongate lungs. Whenever snakes climb, the elongate pulmonary arteries and veins are oriented vertically and generate increased hydrostatic pressure in the dependent microcirculation. The hydrostatic effects due to gravity on the pulmonary circulation are directly related to the absolute length of the vascular portion of the lung and its relationship (anterior or posterior) to the heart. Aquatic snakes are relatively exempt from gravitational forces on their circulations due to the counteracting external water pressures. In these animals, the vascular lungs extend nearly the length of the body cavity, and the heart is placed at mid-body (Lillywhite and Pough, 1983). Various arboreal and other climbing snakes possess vascular lungs that extend for only 15 to 20% of their body length and lie largely anterior to the heart (Lillywhite, 1987). Effects of hydrostatic pressure on non-ophidian reptiles, whether gravitationally induced or affected by water pressures, have not been investigated; these effects deserve attention with respect to cardiovascular pulmonary function. Under this presumed state of high pulmonary filtration, reptilian lungs might be further protected from edema by virtue of their pulmonary surfactant system.

V. PULMONARY SURFACTANT IN REPTILIAN LUNGS

A. General

Pulmonary surfactant is a complex mixture of lipids and specific proteins that forms a monolayer at the alveolar air-water interface, where it modifies the interfacial surface tension (Goerke and Clements, 1985). Reduction in alveolar circumference during lung deflation causes a dynamic compression of this interface. Some lipid molecules are preferentially eliminated, so that the monolayer becomes enriched in disaturated phospholipids (DSP), which are the primary components of mammalian surfactant. The dynamic interplay within the monolayer between the amounts of saturated and unsaturated phospholipids, as well as cholesterol, controls the surface tension of the fluid that lines the inner surface of the alveoli. In mammals, the control of surface tension has the recognized benefit of enhancing compliance, maintaining alveolar stability (which prevents atelectasis), and preventing alveolar edema (J. B. West, 1974).

Work by Clements, Pattle, and associates in the 1960's and 1970's established that reptiles (and probably all lunged vertebrates) deal with the problems associated with high surface tensions at an air-water interface by producing pulmonary surfactant (Clements et al., 1970; Pattle, 1976; Pattle and Hopkinson, 1963). However, the "quality" and function of surfactants from the "lower" vertebrate groups have frequently been questioned. It now appears that much of the confusion associated with the efficacy of surfactant from different vertebrates relates to (1) the influence of temperature on the physicochemical nature of the lipids and (2) the structural differences between the respiratory units of non-mammals and mammals (Daniels et al., 1995a, 1995b). Temperature has a profound influence on the structural form of the lipids and, thereby, affects lipid fluidity and other properties. For example, pure dipalmitoyl phosphatidylcholine (DPPC), the saturated phospholipid of greatest importance in mammalian lungs, has a phase transition temperature of 41°C and enters a rigid, crystalline state at lower temperatures (Goerke and Clements, 1985). This may explain why reptiles, which demonstrate oscillating daily body temperatures (averaging less than 37°C) or constantly low body temperatures (during hibernation), may sacrifice a DPPC-rich surfactant (with a very low surface tension monolayer) for a surfactant incorporating more unsaturated phospholipids and cholesterol that keeps the surfactant fluid and spreadable (Daniels et al., 1989, 1990, 1995b; Lau and Keough, 1981). Variations in the phospholipid head groups, the ratio of unsaturated to saturated fatty acids that form the "tails" of the primary phospholipids, as well as the chain lengths of the fatty acid tails, will all have profound effects on fluidity (Daniels et al., 1995a).

Reptilian lungs characteristically have much larger respiratory units than do those of mammals and are at least an order of magnitude more compliant (Perry and Duncker, 1978, 1980; Perry, 1983, 1989; Milsom, 1989). Hence, reptiles might not require pulmonary surfactant to fulfill two of the three established functions of surfactant observed in mammalian lungs. Evaluation of reptilian pulmonary surfactant by Daniels and collaborators have greatly clarified the influence of body temperature and lung structure on the composition and function of surfactants (for reviews, see Daniels et al., 1995a, 1995b; Orgeig, 1994). This work is briefly summarized below.

B. Amount and Composition

Pulmonary surfactant has been found in the lungs of all reptiles examined so far (Table 3.1). In comparative terms, absolute amount of surfactant per gram of wet lung mass is similar to that of mammalian lungs, but greatly exceeds that of mammals by up to 70-fold when expressed per unit surface area (Daniels et al., 1995a, 1995b). Whenever compared on the basis of respiratory surface area, amphibians and reptiles possess 6 to 30 times the amount of pulmonary surfactant measured in mammalian lungs (Daniels et al., 1995a, 1995b). Virtually all species lavaged at 23°C (the exception was *Crotalus atrox*), demonstrated very similar proportions of DSP to total phospholipid (PL) of 23 to 33%. Both the heliothermic *Crotalus atrox* and the thermophilic *Ctenophorus nuchalis*, tested at 37°C, possessed mammalian-like DSP/PL ratios of around 45% (Table 3.1). *Graptemys geographica* maintained at 5°C for 3 months had a significantly lower DSP/PL ratio than individuals maintained at 32°C (Table 3.1; Lau and Keough, 1981). Only *Thamnophis* possessed a cholesterol/PL ratio that differed significantly from the 7–10% range at 23°C (Table 3.1). The saccular region of *Crotalus atrox* possesses an elevated Chol/DSP ratio, whereas animals with multicameral lungs also exhibit a significantly elevated Chol/DSP ratio compared to species with unicameral lungs at 23°C. Cold (18°C) lizards (*Ctenophorus nuchalis*) exhibit a significantly greater Chol/PL ratio than warm (37°C) ones, after a 4-hr step change in body temperature (Table 3.1; Daniels et al., 1990).

The phospholipid classes present are remarkably constant across the groups of reptiles (see Daniels, et al., 1995a). As seen in mammals, phosphatidylcholine is the dominant phospholipid (60–80% of the lipid). Phosphatidylinositol/serine, lysophosphatidylcholine, phosphatidylethanolamine and sphingomyelin occur in much smaller amounts. Phosphatidylglycerol has been located only in the lungs of *Thamnophis ordinoides*.

As with the headgroups, there is a remarkable consistency in the dominant fatty acid chains found in three reptilian species examined (*Ctenophorus nuchalis, Pogona vitticeps, Graptemys geographica*). Saturated

Table 3.1. Lipid composition of reptilian pulmonary surfactant.

	n	μgPL/gWL (% of PL)	DSPC	DSP/PL	Chol/PL	Chol/DSP
Testudines						
Graptemys geographica[a]						
5°C	4	267.5	10.2±4.4	—	—	—
14°C	4	185.0	13.4±3.9	—	—	—
22°C	4	347.5	18.6±3.4	—	—	—
32°C	4	465.0	25.6±0.8	—	—	—
Caretta caretta[b]	5	2756.0±78.8	—	26.7±2.1	9.9±1.9	36.0±4.7
Natator depressa[b]	5	1472.0±138.8	—	27.9±4.3	6.1±1.6	22.3±5.7
Emydura krefftii[b]	4	170.7±55.9	—	30.0±3.4	—	—
Crocodylia						
Crocodylus porosus[b]	3	962.2±108.6	—	27.7±0.8	6.7±0.1	24.2±0.2
Squamata						
Ctenophorus nuchalis[c]						
10°C	6	1992±360	—	—	18.3±2.7	—
18°C	15	2640±310	—	—	14.9±1.0	31.8±2.2
27°C	6	2200±400	—	—	9.9±1.2	—
37°C	6	2070±425.7	—	46.4±1.5	8.0±0.8	15.8±0.9
43°C	6	2260±430	—	—	10.7±1.8	—
Pogona vitticeps[d]						
18°C	7	20233±2648*	—	—	8.3±0.9	—
37°C	7	27853±3334*	—	—	8.6±1.1	—
Tiliqua nigrolutea[b]	2	1608.0	—	28.3	3.0	10.8
Thamnophis ordinoides R[e]	4	687.3±134.5	—	33.9±2.0	3.5±0.3	10.5±1.2
Thamnophis ordinoides S[e]	3	2277.9±563.6	—	33.82±1.7	4.1±0.5	12.2±1.6
Crotalus atrox R[e]	3	2419.9±260.0	—	43.6±1.8	7.6±0.9	14.9±1.2
Crotalus atrox S[e]	3	111.4±43	—	23.5±12.1	11.3±2.0	91.6±45.5
Hydrophis elegans[b]	3	99.8±39.8	—	23.8±5.3	—	—

[a]Lau and Keough (1981); [b]Daniels et al. (1995a); [c]Daniels et al. (1990); [d]P. G. Wood et al. (1995); [e]Daniels et al. (1995b). *Data presented as gPL/g Dry Lung Mass. 'R' and 'S' after snake species identify "Respiratory" and "Saccular" portions of lungs. Abbreviations: PL, total phospholipid; DSP, disaturated phospholipid; Chol, cholesterol; DSPC, disaturated phosphatidylcholine.

fatty acids, particularly palmitic acid (16C, fully saturated), dominate the PC profile and that of the total lipids generally. Oleic acid (18C, unsaturated with one double bond) is the dominant mono-unsaturated fatty acid, while polyunsaturates make up about a fifth of the total fatty acid profile. For *C. nuchalis* and *P. vitticeps*, short-term changes in temperature (2–4 h) did not affect the relative proportions of the fatty acids (Table 3.1). However, protracted periods of cold significantly decrease the presence of 16C, fully saturated fatty acids in testudine lavage phospholipid and on PC alone (Lau and Keough, 1981).

C. Surfactant Function

In contrast to the condition in mammals, there is no evidence that pulmonary surfactant increases lung compliance in reptiles. Measurements of lung inflation pressures of reptilian lungs (at 60% of total lung capacity, during continuous filling, and at a variety of temperatures) show no differences in response to removal of lung surfactant (see table 2 in Daniels et al., 1995a). However, most reptiles (and, in fact, most non-mammals) demonstrate an elevation in opening pressure after lung lavage (opening pressure is the initial pressure required to open a completely collapsed lung during continuous infusion of air at around 1 ml min^{-1}) (Daniels et al., 1995a). This suggests that the lungs are inherently more "sticky" and, hence, more difficult to inflate once the surfactant has been removed. This observation has led Daniels and colleagues to conclude that reptilian pulmonary surfactant acts primarily as an "anti-glue" to prevent adjacent epithelial surfaces from adhering.

Smits et al. (1995) have suggested that pulmonary surfactant plays a major anti-edema function in reptilian lungs as well. Although this function has long been recognized in mammals (Guyton et al., 1984; Pattle, 1955; Staub, 1983), there are two reasons why it is more likely to play a major role in the lungs of lower vertebrates. First, the movement of fluid from capillaries into lung tissue (filtration) appears to be one to several orders of magnitude higher in amphibians and reptiles than in mammals (Burggren, 1982; Smits, 1989; Smits et al., 1986). Coupled with the apparent efficacy of the lung lymphatic system of removing this excess fluid (Smits, 1994; Smits et al., 1986) and the notably high resistance of the alveolar epithelium to fluid flux (Crandall and Kim, 1981), the pulmonary surfactant may represent an integral defense against alveolar flooding. Second, the lungs of many of the lower vertebrates are characterized by bulging of capillaries into the air spaces (McGregor et al., 1993; Okada et al., 1962, 1963; Perry and Duncker, 1978; Perry et al., 1989), unlike the mammalian condition in which the capillaries are apparently embedded in interstitial tissue (Weibel, 1973). The pulmonary capillary hydrostatic pressure would, therefore, be expected to lead to fluid extravazation into the air spaces. A low surface tension fluid film lining the epithelial surfaces reduces the negative pressure in the hypophase to levels equal to or below that of the interstitium, thereby aiding fluid return into the interstitium and lymph and preventing alveolar flooding. In a recent test of this anti-edema function in lungs of *Pogona vitticeps*, Smits et al. (1995) showed that the degree of influx of fluorescently labeled inulin from the blood space into the alveolar air space is greatly enhanced following the removal of surfactant. These data provide the first indication of the importance of pulmonary surfactant as an anti-edema agent in non-mammalian vertebrates.

The surfactant in amphibians and reptiles may have the additional function of aiding the muco-ciliary escalator by bathing the cilia in a fluid of low surface tension and low viscosity, thereby facilitating their beating (reviewed in Daniels et al., 1995a). As non-mammalian vertebrates lack a true diaphragm, they may be unable to generate the pressures required to cough up inhaled particles. Therefore, they probably rely solely on the action of the muco-ciliary escalator to transport inhaled particles from the lungs to the throat. In mammals, surfactant has been located in the distal airways in association with cilial tracts (Morgenroth and Bolz, 1985). Kilburn (1969) observed that frog surfactant facilitates the action of the muco-ciliary escalator by bathing the cilia in a fluid of low surface tension and viscosity. In addition, surfactant may prevent the adhesion of mucus onto the ciliated epithelia (Allegra et al., 1985) and assist in the unidirectional movement of particles within the respiratory units during the expansion-contraction cycle of breathing (Rensch et al., 1983).

The revelation that the structure and function of reptilian pulmonary surfactant has poor phylogenetic correlates but strong temperature and life-history correlates is, perhaps, no surprise, but it establishes a baseline for future research. How body temperature (and other related physiological parameters such as lung ventilation and catecholamine release) modulates surfactant composition and turnover is an obvious mechanistic question that begs attention. On a larger scale, the relationships between surfactant composition, surface forces, faveolar interdependence, and ventilatory movements must be mathematically modeled and empirically tested.

VI. FUTURE DIRECTIONS IN REPTILIAN PULMONARY RESEARCH

Despite many decades of research and hundreds of published papers, our knowledge of pulmonary function in reptiles remains incomplete, even fragmentary. Part of the problem—and part of the fascination—of investigating pulmonary function in reptiles springs from the huge anatomical and physiological variation evident in the paraphyletic group we call reptiles. From the simple sac-like lungs of lacertid lizards through the combined saccular/alveolar lungs of some snakes to the alveolar lungs of sea turtles, the lungs present a variety of adaptations to the varied lifestyles and metabolic demands of reptiles. Consequently, few sweeping generalizations on pulmonary function in reptiles stand up to scrutiny.

We estimate that 90% of research in reptilian pulmonary physiology has been carried out on less than 1% of reptilian species. It is difficult not to generalize to all reptiles from the relatively substantial studies that have focused on *Trachemys scripta*, for example. Perhaps best illustrating the focus on a single species as typical are the numerous studies on the genus *Varanus*, which is widely recognized as a spectacular but highly derived and diverse group of lizards.

It would be true, but not very helpful, to indicate that all areas of reptilian pulmonary biology require much additional research! However, some areas deserve special mention as well worth additional investigation:

- the role of intrinsic vascular regulation in modulating the gas exchange performance of reptilian lungs.
- metabolic functions of the lungs (e.g., lactate clearance, and hormone production), which have been largely ignored.
- pulmonary function in "real" states—that is, non-steady states—such as during activity.
- changes in lung function and morphology during embryonic development, hatching, and growth.
- fluid balance in reptilian lungs, including the roles of both lymphatics and surfactants.

These and numerous other unresolved issues in reptilian pulmonary biology will prove to be fruitful areas of research in the coming decade.

ACKNOWLEDGMENTS

We are extremely grateful to Frank Powell for insightful suggestions and for carefully reading the section on pulmonary gas exchange. William K. Milsom provided an illuminating critique on several aspects of ventilatory control, and we thank David R. Carrier for general criticism and, in particular, for enjoyable discussions regarding ventilation during locomotion in lizards. Finally, we wish to thank Stephen J. Warburton for his many good suggestions on an earlier version of this manuscript.

APPENDIX: REPTILIAN SPECIES DISCUSSED

TESTUDINES

Apalone [as *Trionyx*] *spinifer asper*
  Dunson, 1960.
Caretta caretta
  Daniels et al., 1995a
Chelodina longicollis
  Burggren et al., 1989
Chelonia mydas
  Butler et al., 1984
  Jackson and Prange, 1976
Chelus [as *Chelys*] *fimbriata*
  Lenfant et al., 1970

Chelydra serpentina
  West et al., 1989
Chinemys [as *Geoclemmys*] *reevesii*
  Ishii et al., 1985
Chrysemys picta
  Jones and Milsom, 1979
  Glass et al., 1983
  Glass et al., 1985
  Silver and Jackson, 1985
  Milsom and Chan, 1986
  Silver and Jackson, 1986

Jackson et al., 1991
Dermochelys coriacea
  Eckert et al., 1986
Emydura krefftii
  Daniels et al., 1995a
Graptemys [as *Malaclemys*] *geographica*
  Lau and Keough, 1981
Natator depressa
  Daniels et al., 1995a
Pseudemys floridana
  Kinney and White, 1977
Testudo sp.
  Crawford et al., 1976
  Burggren et al., 1978
Testudo graeca
  Milsom, 1995
Testudo hermanni
  Ishii et al., 1986
Testudo horsfieldii
  Benchetrit et al., 1977
  Benchetrit and Dejours, 1980

Trachemys sp.
  Crawford et al., 1976
  Burggren et al., 1978
Trachemys [as *Pseudemys* or *Chrys-emys*] *scripta*
  Milsom, 1955
  Perry, 1978
  Seymour, 1978
  Ackerman and White, 1979
  Burggren and Shelton, 1979
  Seymour, 1980
  Spragg et al., 1980
  Gatten, 1981
  Milsom, 1984
  Smits and Kozubowski, 1985
  Vitalis and Milsom, 1986a
  Vitalis and Milsom, 1986b
  Burggren, 1988
  Stinner and Wardle, 1988
  Yamaguchi et al., 1989
  Hopkins et al., 1996

SAURIA

Amblyrhynchus cristatus
  Gleeson, 1980
Crotaphytus collaris
  Templeton and Dawson, 1963
Ctenophorus nuchalis
  Daniels et al., 1990
  McGregor et al., 1993
Ctenosaura similis
  Carrier, 1987a
Dipsosaurus dorsalis
  Dupre and Crawford, 1986
Gekko gecko
  Milsom, 1984
  Milsom and Vitalis, 1984
Iguana iguana
  Giordano and Jackson, 1973
  G. S. Mitchell et al., 1981a
  G. S. Mitchell et al., 1981b
  Carrier, 1987a
  Wang et al., 1995b
Pogona vitticeps
  Smits et al., 1995
  P. G. Wood et al., 1995

Rhacodactylus leachianus
  Perry et al., 1989
Sauromalus hispidus
  Smits, 1989
Sauromalus obesus
  Templeton, 1967
Tiliqua nigrolutea
  Daniels et al., 1995a
Tiliqua occipitalis
  Rogers, 1967
Tiliqua [as *Trachysaurus*] *rugosa*
  Rogers, 1967
Tupinambis merianae [as *T. teguixin*]
  Glass and Johansen, 1981
Tupinambis teguixin [as *T. nigro-punctatus*]
  Gatz et al., 1975
  Heisler and Neumann, 1976
  Ballam, 1985
  Hlastala et al., 1985
  Glass and Heisler, 1986
  Coates and Ballam, 1987
  Douse and Mitchell, 1988

Coates and Ballam, 1989
Douse et al., 1989
Abe, 1991
Coates et al., 1991
Varanus exanthematicus
  Glass et al., 1979
  G. S. Mitchell et al., 1981a

G. S. Mitchell et al., 1981b
Carrier, 1987a
Hopkins et al., 1995
Wang et al., 1995b
Varanus salvator
  Carrier, 1987a

AMPHISBAENIA

Amphisbaena alba
  Abe and Johansen, 1987

SERPENTES

Acrochordus javanicus
  Standaert and Johansen, 1974
  Glass and Johansen, 1976
Aipysurus laevis
  Lillywhite *in* Smits, 1989
Coluber constrictor
  Nolan and Frankel, 1982
  Stinner, 1987
Crotalus atrox
  Daniels et al., 1995a
  Daniels et al., 1995b
Crotalus durissus
  Wang et al., 1993
  Abe et al., 1995
Dendroaspis polylepis
  Maina, 1989
Elaphe obsoleta
  Lillywhite and Smith, 1981
Hydrophis elegans
  Daniels et al., 1995a
Laticauda colubrina
  Seymour, 1978
  Seymour, 1980
Morelia spilota
  Donnelly and Woolcock, 1972
  Read and Donnelly, 1972
  Donnelly and Woolcock, 1977
  Donnelly and Woolcock, 1978

Gratz et al., 1981
Seymour et al., 1981
Nerodia [as *Natrix*] *rhombifer*
  Gratz, 1979
Nerodia sipedon
  Gratz, 1984
Pelamis platurus
  Donnelly and Woolcock, 1972
  Graham, 1974
  Donnelly and Woolcock, 1977
  Donnelly and Woolcock, 1978
  Gratz et al., 1981
  Seymour et al., 1981
  Rubinoff et al., 1986
Pituophis melanoleucus
  Stinner, 1982a
  Stinner, 1982b
Thamnophis ordinoides
  Daniels et al., 1995a
  Daniels et al., 1995b
Thamnophis sirtalis
  Furilla and Bartlett, 1988
Vipera xanthina
  Donnelly and Woolcock, 1972
  Donnelly and Woolcock, 1977
  Donnelly and Woolcock, 1978
  Gratz et al., 1981
  Seymour et al., 1981

CROCODYLIA

Alligator mississippiensis
  Powell et al., 1988
  Powell and Gray, 1989

Douse and Mitchell, 1991
Smatresk and Smits, 1991
Branco et al., 1992

Hicks and White, 1992
Branco and Wood, 1993
Branco et al., 1993
Wang and Warburton, 1995

Crocodylus porosus
Seymour et al., 1985
Daniels et al., 1995a

REFERENCES

Aaron, E. A., Johnson, B. D., Seow, K. C., and Dempsey, J. A. (1992a). Oxygen cost of exercise hyperpnea: measurement. *J. Appl. Physiol.* 72, 1810–1817.

Aaron, E. A., Seow, K. C., Johnson, B. D., and Dempsey, J. A. (1992b). Oxygen cost of exercise hyperpnea: implications for performance. *J. Appl. Physiol.* 72, 1818–1825.

Abe, A. S. (1991). Effect of the environment on ventilation in reptiles. In *The Vertebrate Gas Transport Cascade* (J. E. P. W. Bicudo, ed.). CRC Press, Boca Raton, pp. 87–93.

Abe, A. S., and Johansen, K. (1987). Gas exchange and ventilatory responses to hypoxia and hypercapnia in *Amphisbaena alba* (Reptilia: Amphisbaenia). *J. Exp. Biol.* 127, 159–172.

Abe, A. S., Andrade, D. V., and Cruz-Neto, A. P. (1995). Energetics of feeding in the rattlesnake, *Crotalus durissus. Physiol. Zool.* 68, 108.

Ackerman, R. A., and White, F. N. (1979). Cyclic carbon dioxide exchange in the turtle *Pseudemys scripta. Physiol. Zool.* 52, 378–389.

Adams, W. E. (1958). *The Comparative Morphology of the Carotid Body and Carotid Sinus.* Thomas, Springfield, Illinois.

Allegra, L., Bossi, R., and Braga, P. (1985). Influence of surfactant on mucociliary transport. *Eur. J. Resp. Dis. Suppl.* 142, 71–76.

Aota, S., Holmgren, K. D., Fletcher, P., and Randall, D. J. (1990). A possible role for catecholamines in the ventilatory responses associated with internal acidosis or external hypoxia in rainbow trout, *Oncorhyncus mykiss. J. Exp. Biol.* 151, 57–70.

Ballam, G. O. (1985). Breathing response of the tegu lizard to 1–4% CO_2 in the mouth and nose or inspired into the lungs. *Respir. Physiol.* 62, 375–386.

Ballam, G. O., and Coates, E. L. (1989). Effect of upper airway CO_2 pattern on ventilatory frequency in the tegu lizard. *Am. J. Physiol.* 257, R156–R161.

Benchetrit, G., and Dejours, P. (1980). Ventilatory CO_2 drive in the tortoise, *Testudo hermanii. J. Exp. Biol.* 87, 229–236.

Benchetrit, G., Armand, J., and Dejours, P. (1977). Ventilatory chemoreflex drive in the tortoise *Testudo horsfieldi. Respir. Physiol.* 31, 183–191.

Benedict, F. G. (1932). *The Physiology of Large Reptiles with Special Reference to The Heat Production of Snakes, Tortoises, Lizards and Alligators.* Carnegie Inst., Washington (Publ. 425).

Bennett, A. F. (1973). Ventilation in two species of lizards during rest and activity. *Comp. Biochem. Physiol.* 46A, 653–672.

Bennett, A. F. (1994). Exercise performance in reptiles. In *Comparative Vertebrate Exercise Physiology. Phyletic Adaptations* (J. H. Jones, ed.). Academic Press, New York, pp. 113–138.

Berkenbosch, A., Heringe, J. Olievier, C. N., and Kruyt, E. W. (1979). Artificial perfusion of the pontomedullary region of cats, a method for separation of central and peripheral effects of chemical stimulation of ventilation. *Respir. Physiol.* 37, 381–390.

Boggs, D. F. (1995). Hypoxic ventilatory control and hemoglobin oxygen affinity. In *Hypoxia and the Brain* (J. R. Sutton, C. S. Houston, and G. Coates, eds.). Queen City Printers, Burlington, Vermont, pp. 69–86.

Bohr, C. (1909). Über die spezifische Tätigkeit der Lungen bei der respiratorischen Gasaufnahme und ihr Verhalten zu der durch die Alveolenwand stattfindende Gasdiffusion. *Scand. Arch. Physiol.* 22, 221–280.

Branco, L. G. S., and Glass, M. L. (1995). Ventilatory responses to carboxy-haemoglobinaemia and hypoxic hypoxia in *Bufo paracnemis*. *J. Exp. Biol.* 198, 1417–1421.

Branco, L. G. S., and Wood, S. C. (1993). Effect of temperature on central chemical control of breathing in the alligator, *Alligator mississippiensis*. *J. Exp. Biol.* 179, 261–272.

Branco, L. G. S., Glass, M. L., and Hoffmann, A. (1992). Central chemoreceptor drive to breathing in unanesthetized toads, *Bufo paracnemis*. *Respir. Physiol.* 87, 195–204.

Branco, L. G. S., Glass, M. L., Wang, T., and Hoffmann, A. (1993). Central chemoreceptor drive to breathing toad (*Bufo paracnemis*): Effects of temperature. *Respir. Physiol.* 93, 337–346.

Brattstrom, B. H. (1959). The functions of the air sac in snakes. *Herpetologica* 15, 103–104.

Burger, R. E., Osborne, J. L., and Banzett, R. B. (1974). Intrapulmonary chemoreceptors in *Gallus domesticus*: adequate stimulus and functional localization. *Respir. Physiol.* 22, 87–97.

Burggren, W. W. (1982). Pulmonary blood filtration in reptiles: a "wet" vertebrate lung. *Science* 215, 77–78.

Burggren, W. W. (1988). Cardiovascular responses to diving and their relation to lung and blood oxygen stores in vertebrates. *Can. J. Zool.* 66, 20–28.

Burggren, W. W. (1989). Lung structure and function. In *Comparative Pulmonary Physiology: Current Concepts* (S. C. Wood, ed.). Marcel Dekker Inc., New York, pp. 153–192.

Burggren, W. W., and Infantino, R. L. (1994). The respiratory transition from water to air breathing during amphibian metamorphosis. *Am. Zool.* 34, 238–246.

Burggren, W. W., and Pinder, A. (1991). Ontogeny of cardiovascular and respiratory physiology of lower vertebrates. *Ann. Rev. Physiol.* 53, 107–135.

Burggren, W. W., and Shelton, G. (1979) Gas exchange and transport during intermittent breathing in chelonian reptiles. *J. Exp. Biol.* 82, 75–92.

Burggren, W. W., Hahn, C. E. W., and Foëx, P. (1977). Properties of blood oxygen transport in the turtle *Pseudemys scripta* and the tortoise *Testudo graeca*: effects of temperature, CO_2 and pH. *Respir. Physiol.* 31, 39–50.

Burggren, W. W., Glass, M. L., and Johansen, K. (1978). Intrapulmonary variation of gas partial pressures and ventilation inequalities in chelonian reptiles. *J. Comp. Physiol.* 126, 203–209.

Burggren, W. W., Smits, A. W., and Evans, B. (1989). Arterial oxygen homeostasis during diving in the turtle *Chelodina longicollis*. *Physiol. Zool.* 62, 668–686.

Busa, W. B., and Nuccitelli, R. (1984). Metabolic regulation via intracellular pH. *Am. J. Physiol.* 246, R409–R438.

Butler, P. J., Milsom, W. K., and Woakes, A. J. (1984). Respiratory, cardiovascular and metabolic adjustments during steady state swimming in the green turtle, *Chelonia mydas*. *J. Comp. Physiol.* 154, 167–174.

Cameron, J. N. (1984). The acid-base of fish at different temperatures. *Am. J. Physiol.* 246, R452–R459.

Cameron, J. N. (1989). Acid-base homeostasis: past and present perspectives. *Physiol. Zool.* 62, 845–865.

Carrier, D. R. (1987a). Lung ventilation during walking and running in four species of lizards. *Exp. Biol.* 47, 33–42.

Carrier, D. R. (1987b). The evolution of locomotor stamina in tetrapods: circumventing a mechanical constraint. *Paleobiology* 13, 326–341.

Carrier, D. R. (1989). Ventilatory action of the hypaxial muscles of the lizard *Iguana iguana*: a function of a slow muscle. *J. Exp. Biol.* 143, 435–457.

Carrier, D. R. (1990). Activity of the hypaxial muscles during walking in the lizard *Iguana iguana*. *J. Exp. Biol.* 152, 453–470.

Clark, B. D., Gans, C., and Rosenberg, H. I. (1978). Air flow in snake ventilation. *Respir. Physiol.* 32, 207–212.

Clements, J. A., Nellenbogen, J., and Trahan, H. J. (1970). Pulmonary surfactant and evolution of the lungs. *Science* 169, 603–604.

Coates, E. L., and Ballam, G. O. (1987). Upper airway CO_2 receptors in tegu lizards: localization and ventilatory sensitivity. *J. Comp. Physiol.* 157, 483–487.

Coates, E. L., and Ballam, G. O. (1989). Breathing and upper airway CO_2 in reptiles: role of the nasal and vomeronasal systems. *Am. J. Physiol.* 256, R91–R97.

Coates, E. L., and Ballam, G. O. (1990). Olfactory receptor response to CO_2 in bullfrogs. *Am. J. Physiol.* 258, R1207–R1212.

Coates, E. L., Furilla, R. A., Ballam, G. O., and Bartlett, D., Jr. (1991). A decrease in nasal CO_2 stimulates breathing in the tegu lizard. *Respir. Physiol.* 86, 65–75.

Coulson, R. A., Hernandez, T., and Dessauer, H. C. (1950). Alkaline tide of the alligator. *Proc. Soc. Exp. Biol. Med.* 74, 866–869.

Courtice, G. P. (1980). Stimulation of carotid arterial chemoreceptors by hypoxia and hypercapnia in a lizard. *Adv. Physiol. Sci.* 14, 368.

Cragg, P. A. (1978). Ventilatory patterns and variables in rest and activity in the lizard, *Lacerta*. *Comp. Biochem. Physiol.* 60A, 399–410.

Crandall, E. D., and Kim, K. J. (1981). Transport of water and solutes across bullfrog alveolar epithelium. *J. Appl. Physiol.* 50, 1263–1271.

Crawford, E. C., Gatz, R. N., Magnussen, H., Perry, S. F., and Piiper, J. (1976). Lung volumes, pulmonary blood flow and carbon monoxide diffusing capacity in turtles. *J. Comp. Physiol.* 107, 167–178.

Crossfill, M. L., and Widdicombe, J. G. (1961). Physical characteristics of the chest and lungs and the work of breathing in different mammalian species. *J. Physiol* 158, 1–14.

Daniels, C. B., Barr, H. A., and Nicholas, T. E. (1989). A comparison of the surfactant associated lipids derived from reptilian and mammalian lungs. *Respir. Physiol.* 75, 335–348.

Daniels, C. B., Barr, H. A., Power, J. H. T., and Nicholas, T. E. (1990). Body temperature alters the lipid composition of pulmonary surfactant in the lizard. *Exp. Lung Res.* 16, 435–449.

Daniels, C. B., Orgeig, S., and Smits, A. W. (1995a). The evolution of the vertebrate pulmonary surfactant system. *Physiol. Zool.* 68, 539–566.

Daniels, C. B, Orgeig, S., and Smits, A. W. (1995b). The composition and function of reptilian pulmonary surfactant. *Respir. Physiol.* 102, 121–135.

Davies, D. G., and Sexton, J. A. (1987). Brain ECF pH and central chemical control of ventilation during anoxia in turtles. *Am. J. Physiol.* 252, R848–R852.

Davies, D. G., Thomas, J. L., and Smith, E. N. (1982). Effect of body temperature on ventilatory control in the alligator. *J. Appl. Physiol.* 52, 114–118.

Dempsey, J. A., Ainsworth, D. M., and Forster, H. V. (1995). Regulation of hyperpnea, hyperventilation, and respiratory muscle recruitment during exercise. In *Regulation of Breathing* (J. A. Dempsey and A. I. Pack, eds.). Marcel Dekker, New York, pp. 1065–1134.

Dmi'el, R. (1972). Effect of activity and temperature on metabolism and water loss in snakes. *Am. J. Physiol.* 223, 510–516.

Dodd, G. A. A., and Milsom, W. K. (1987). Effects of H$^+$ *versus* pH on ventilation in the Pekin duck. *Respir. Physiol.* 68, 189–201.

Donnelly, P. M., and Woolcock, A. J. (1972). Ventilation and gas exchange in snake lungs. *Proc. Aust. Physiol. Pharm. Soc.* 3, 77–78.

Donnelly, P. M., and Woolcock, A. J. (1977). Ventilation and gas exchange in the carpet python, *Morelia spilotes variegata. J. Comp. Physiol.* 122, 403–418.

Donnelly, P. M., and Woolcock, A. J. (1978). Stratification of inspired air in the elongated lungs of the carpet python, *Morelia spilotes variegata. Respir. Physiol.* 35, 301–315

Douse, M. A., and Mitchell, G. S. (1988). Temperature effects on CO$_2$ sensitive intrapulmonary chemoreceptors in the lizard *Tupinambis nigropunctatus. Respir. Physiol.* 72, 327–342.

Douse, M. A., and Mitchell, G. S. (1990). Episodic respiratory related discharge in turtle cranial motorneurons: *in vivo* and *in vitro* studies. *Brain Res.* 536, 297–300.

Douse, M. A., and Mitchell, G. S. (1991). Time courses of temperature effects on arterial acid-base status in *Alligator mississippiensis. Respir. Physiol.* 83, 87–102

Douse, M. A., Powell, F. L., Milsom, W. K., and Mitchell, G. S. (1989). Temperature effects on pulmonary receptor responses to airway pressure and CO$_2$ in *Alligator mississippiensis. Respir. Physiol.* 78, 331–344.

Dunson, W. A. (1960). Aquatic respiration in *Trionyx spinifer asper. Herpetologica* 16, 277–283.

Dupré, R. K., and Crawford, E. C. (1986). Elevation of the panting threshold of the desert iguana, *Dipsosaurus dorsalis*, during dehydration: potential roles of changes in plasma osmolarity and body fluid volume. *J. Comp. Physiol.*, ser. B, 156, 377–381.

Dupré, R. K., Hicks, J. W., and Wood, S. C. (1989). Effect of temperature on chemical control of breathing in Mexican black iguanas. *Am. J. Physiol.* 257, R1258–R1263.

Eckert, S. A., Nellis, D. W., Eckert, K. L., and Kooyman, G. L. (1986). Diving patterns of two leatherback sea turtles (*Dermochelys coriacea*) during nesting intervals at Sandy Point, St. Croix, U. S. Virgin Islands. *Herpetologica* 42, 381–388.

Edsall, J. T., and Wyman, J. (1958). *Biophysical Chemistry*, vol. 1. Academic Press, New York.

Evans, B. K., and Shelton, G. (1984). Ventilation in *Xenopus laevis* after lung or carotid body labyrinth denervation. In *First Congress of Comparative Physiology and Biochemistry* (R. Giles, ed.). Liege, Belgium, p. A75.

Farhi, L. E. (1967). Elimination of inert gas by the lung. *Respir. Physiol.* 3, 1–11.

Fedde, M. R., and Kuhlmann, W. D. (1978). Intrapulmonary carbon dioxide sensitive receptors: amphibians to mammals. In *Respiratory Function in Birds, Adult and Embryonic* (J. Piiper, ed.). Springer Verlag, Berlin, pp. 33–50.

Fedde, M. R., and Peterson, D. F. (1970). Intrapulmonary receptor response to changes in airway-gas composition in *Gallus domesticus. J. Physiol.* 209, 609–625.

Fedde, M. R., Kuhlmann, W. D., and Scheid, P. (1977). Intrapulmonary receptors in tegu lizard: I. Sensitivity to CO_2. *Respir. Physiol.* 29, 35–48.

Feder, M. E., and Burggren, W. W. (1985a). Skin breathing in vertebrates. *Scient. Am.* 253,126–130

Feder, M. E., and Burggren, W. W. (1985b). Cutaneous gas exchange in vertebrates: design, patterns, control and implications. *Biol. Rev.* 60,1–45.

Feldman, J. L., Smith, J. C., Ellenberger, H. H., Connelly, A., Liu, G., Greer, J. J., Lindsay, A. D., and Otto, M. R. (1990). Neurogenesis of respiratory rhythm and pattern: emerging concepts. *Am. J. Physiol.* 259, R879–R886.

Fencl, V., and Leith, D. E. (1993). Stewart's quantitative acid-base chemistry: applications in biology and medicine. *Respir. Physiol.* 91, 1–16.

Fitzgerald, R. S., and Lahiri, S. (1986). Reflex responses to chemoreceptor stimulation. In *Handbook of Physiology* (A. P. Fishman, N. S. Cherniak, J. G. Widdicombe, and S. R. Geiger, eds.). American Physiological Society, Bethesda, Maryland, vol. 2, pp. 313–362

Frankel, H. M., Spitzer, A., Blaine, K., and Schoener, E. P. (1969). Respiratory response of turtles *Pseudemys scripta* to changes in arterial blood gas composition. *Comp. Biochem. Physiol.* 31, 535–546.

Funk, G. D., and Milsom, W. K. (1987). Changes in ventilation and breathing pattern produced by changing temperature and inspired CO_2 in turtles. *Respir. Physiol.* 67, 37–51.

Furilla, R. A. (1991). Rate of rise of intrapulmonary CO_2 drives breathing frequency in garter snakes. *J. Appl. Physiol.* 71, 2304–2308.

Furilla, R. A., and Bartlett, D., Jr. (1988). Intrapulmonary receptors in the garter snake (*Thamnophis sirtalis*). *Respir. Physiol.* 74, 311–322.

Furilla, R. A., and Bartlett, D., Jr. (1989). Intrapulmonary CO_2 inhibits inspiration in garter snakes. *Respir. Physiol.* 78, 207–218.

Furilla, R. A., Coates, E. L., and Bartlett, D., Jr. (1991). The influence of venous CO_2 on ventilation in garter snakes. *Respir. Physiol.* 83, 47–60.

Gans, C. (1970). Strategy and sequence in the evolution of the external gas exchangers of ectothermal vertebrates. *Forma Functio* 3, 61–104.

Gans, C., and Clark, B. D. (1976). Studies on ventilation of *Caiman crocodilus* (Crocodilia: Reptilia). *Respir. Physiol.* 26, 285–301.

Gans, C., and Clark, B. D. (1978). Air flow in reptilian ventilation. *Comp. Biochem. Physiol.* 60A, 453–457.

Gatten, R. E., Jr. (1981). Anaerobic metabolism in freely diving painted turtle (*Chrysemys scripta*). *J. Exp. Zool.* 216, 377–385.

Gatz, R. N., Fedde, M. R., and Crawford, E. C. (1975). Lizard lungs: CO_2 sensitive receptors in *Tupinambis nigropunctatus*. *Experientia* 31, 455–456.

Gaunt, A. S., and Gans, C. (1969). Mechanics of respiration in the snapping turtle, *Chelydra serpentina* (Linne). *J. Morph.* 128, 195–228.

Giordano, R. V. and Jackson, D. C. (1973). The effect of temperature on ventilation in the green iguana (*Iguana iguana*). *Comp. Biochem. Physiol.* 45A, 235–238.

Glass, M. L. (1991) Pulmonary diffusion capacity of ectothermic vertebrates. In *The Vertebrate Gas Transport Cascade* (J. E. P. W. Bicudo, ed.). CRC Press, Boca Raton, Florida, pp. 154–161.

Glass, M. L., and Heisler, N. (1986). The effects of hypercapnia on the arterial acid-base status in the tegu lizard, *Tupinambis nigropunctatus* (Spix). *J. Exp. Biol.* 122, 13–24.

Glass, M. L., and Johansen, K. (1976). Control of breathing in *Acrochordus javanicus*, an aquatic snake. *Physiol. Zool.* 49, 328–340.

Glass, M. L., and Johansen, K. (1981) Pulmonary oxygen diffusion capacity of the lizard *Tupinambis tequixin*. *J. Exp. Zool.* 219, 385–388.

Glass, M. L., Burggren, W. W., and Johansen, K. (1978). Ventilation in an aquatic and a terrestrial chelonian reptile. *J. Exp. Biol.* 72, 165–179.

Glass, M. L., Wood, S. C., Hoyt, R. W., and Johansen, K. (1979). Chemical control of breathing in the lizard, *Varanus exanthematicus*. *Comp. Biochem. Physiol.* 62A, 999–1003.

Glass, M. L., Abe, A. S., and Johansen, K. (1981a). Pulmonary diffusing capacity in reptiles: relations to temperature and O_2 uptake. *J. Comp. Physiol.* 142, 509–514.

Glass, M. L., Burggren, W. W., and Johansen, K. (1981b). Pulmonary diffusing capacity of the bullfrog (*Rana catesbeiana*). *Acta Physiol. Scand.* 113, 485–490.

Glass, M. L., Boutilier, R. G., and Heisler, N. (1983). Ventilatory control of arterial pO_2 in the turtle, *Chrysemys picta belli*: effects of temperature and hypoxia. *J. Comp. Physiol.* 151, 145–153.

Glass, M. L., Boutilier, R. G., and Heisler, N. (1985). Effect of body temperature on respiration, blood gases and acid-base status in the turtle, *Chrysemys picta belli*. *J. Exp. Biol.* 114, 37–51.

Glass, M. L., Ishimatsu, A., and Johansen, K. (1986). Responses of aerial ventilation to hypoxia and hypercapnia in *Channa argus*, an air-breathing fish. *J. Comp. Physiol.* 156, 425–430.

Gleeson, T. T. (1980). Lactic acid production during field activity in the Galapagos marine iguana, *Amblyrhynchus cristatus*. *Physiol. Zool.* 53, 157–162.

Gleeson, T. T., Mitchell, G. S., and Bennett, A. F. (1980). Cardiovascular responses to graded activity in the lizards *Varanus* and *Iguana*. *Am. J. Physiol.* 239, R174–R179.

Goerke, J., and Clements, J. A. (1985). Alveolar surface tension and lung surfactant. In *Handbook of Physiology* (P. T. Macklem and J. Mead, eds.). American Physiological Society, Bethesda, Maryland, vol. 3(1), pp. 247–260.

Gonzalez, C., Dinger, B. C., and Fidone, S. J. (1995). Mechanisms of carotid body chemoreception. In *Regulation of Breathing* (J. A. Dempsey and A. I. Pack, eds.). Marcel Dekker, New York, pp. 391–471.

Graham, J. B. (1974). Aquatic respiration in the sea snake, *Pelamis platurus*. *Respir. Physiol.* 21, 1–7.

Graham, M. S., Turner, J. D., and Wood, C. M. (1990). The control of ventilation during during hypercapnia in the skate, *Raja ocellata*. I. Blood and extradural fluid chemistry. *Respir. Physiol.* 80, 259–277.

Gratz, R. K. (1979). Ventilatory responses of the diamondback water snake, *Natrix rhombifera* to hypoxia, hypercapnia and increased oxygen demand. *J. Comp. Physiol.* 129, 105–110.

Gratz, R. K. (1984). Effect of bilateral vagotomy on the ventilatory responses to of the water snake, *Nerodia sipedon*. *Am. J. Physiol.* 246, R221–R227.

Gratz, R. K., Ar, A., and Geiser, J. (1981). Gas tension profile of the lung of the viper, *Vipera xanthina palaestinae*. *Respir. Physiol.* 44, 165–176.

Guyton, A. C., Moffat, D. S., and Adair, T. H. (1984). Role of alveolar surface tension in transepithelial movement of fluid. In *Pulmonary Surfactant* (B. Robertson, L. M. G. van Golde, and J. J. Batenburg, eds.). Elsevier Science Publishers, Amsterdam, pp. 171–185.

Hatcher, J. D., Chiu, L. K., and Jennings, D. B. (1978). Anemia is a stimulus to aortic and carotid chemoreceptors in the cat. *J. Appl. Physiol.* 44, 696–702.

Heatwole, H., and Seymour, R. S. (1975). Diving Physiology. In *The Biology of Sea Snakes* (W. A. Dunson, ed.). University Park Press, Baltimore, London, pp. 289–327.

Hedrick, M. S., Burleson, M. L., Jones, D. R., and Milsom, W. K. (1991). An examination of central chemosensitivity in an air-breathing fish (*Amia calva*). *J. Exp. Biol.* 155, 165–174.

Heeringa, M. S., Berkenbosch, A., De Goede, J., and Olievier, C. N. (1979). Relative contribution of central and peripheral chemoreceptors to the ventilatory response to CO_2 during hyperoxia. *Respir. Physiol.* 37, 365–379.

Heisler, N. (1986). Comparative aspects of acid-base regulation. In *Acid-base Regulation in Animals* (N. Heisler, ed.). Elsevier Science Publishers, Amsterdam, pp. 297–450.

Heisler, N., and Neumann, P. (1976). Kinetics of arterial pH, P_{CO_2} and bicarbonate adjustment after changes of temperature in a lizard (*Tupinambis nigropunctatus*). *Pflügers Arch.* 362 (Suppl.), R18.

Hempleman, S. C., and Hughes, J. M. B. (1991). Estimating exercise DLO_2 and diffusion limitation in patients with interstitial fibrosis. *Respir. Physiol.* 83, 167–178.

Hicks, J. W. (1997). Cardiac shunting in reptiles: mechanisms, regulation, and physiological functions. In *Biology of the Reptilia* (C. Gans and A. S. Gaunt, eds.). Society for the Study of Amphibians and Reptiles, Ithaca, NY, vol. 19, pp. 425–483.

Hicks, J. W., and White, F. N. (1992). Pulmonary gas exchange during intermittent ventilation in the American alligator. *Respir. Physiol.* 88, 23–36.

Hitzig, B. M. (1982). Temperature induced changes in turtle CSF pH and control of ventilation. *Respir. Physiol.* 49, 205–222.

Hitzig, B. M., and Jackson, D. C. (1978). Central chemical control of ventilation in the unanesthetized turtle. *Am. J. Physiol.* 253, R257–R264.

Hitzig, B. M., Allen, J. C., and Jackson, D. C. (1985). Central chemical control of turtles to inspired CO_2. *Am. J. Physiol.* 249, R323–R328.

Hlastala, M. P., Standaert, T. A., Pierson, D. J., and Luchtel, D. L. (1985). The matching of ventilation and perfusion in the lung of the tegu lizard, *Tupinambis nigropunctatus*. *Respir. Physiol.* 60, 277–294.

Hopkins, S. R., Hicks, J. W., Cooper, T. K., and Powell, F. L. (1995). Ventilation and pulmonary gas exchange during exercise in the savannah monitor lizard (*Varanus exanthematicus*). *J. Exp. Biol.* 198, 1783–1789.

Hopkins, S. R., Wang, T., and Hicks, J. W. (1996). The effect of altering pulmonary blood flow on pulmonary gas exchange in the turtle *Trachemys (Pseudemys) scripta*. *J. Exp. Biol.* 199, 2207–2214.

Howell, B. J., Baumgardner, F. W., Bondi, K., and Rahn, H. (1970). Acid-base balance in cold-blooded vertebrates as a function of body temperature. *Am. J. Physiol.* 218, 600–606.

Ishii, K., Ishii, K., and Kusakabe, T. (1985). Electrophysical aspects of reflexogenic area in the chelonian, *Geoclemmys reevesii*. *Respir. Physiol.* 59, 45–54.

Ishii, K., Ishii, K., and Dejours, P. (1986). Activity of vagal afferent fibers innervating CO_2-sensitive receptors in the tortoise, *Testudo hermanii*. *Japan. J. Physiol.* 36, 1015–1026.

Jackson, D. C. (1971). The effect of temperature on ventilation in the turtle *Pseudemys scripta elegans*. *Respir. Physiol.* 12, 131–140.

Jackson, D. C. (1973). Ventilatory responses to hypoxia in turtles at various temperatures. *Respir. Physiol.* 18, 178–187.

Jackson, D. C. (1986). Acid base regulation in reptiles. In *Acid-base Regulation in Animals* (N. Heisler, ed.). Elsevier Science Publishers, Amsterdam, pp. 235–263.

Jackson, D. C. (1989). Control of breathing: effects of temperature. In *Lung Biology in Health and Disease* (S. C. Wood, ed.). Marcel Dekker, New York, vol. 39, pp. 621–641.

Jackson, D. C., and Kagen, R. D. (1976). Effects of temperature transients on gas exchange and acid-base status of turtles. *Am. J. Physiol.* 230, 1389–1393.

Jackson, D. C., and Prange, H. D. (1976). Ventilation, gas exchange and metabolic scaling of sea turtle. *Respir. Physiol.* 27, 369–377.

Jackson, D. C., and Prange, H. D. (1979). Ventilation and gas exchange during rest and exercise in adult green sea turtles. *J. Comp. Physiol.*, ser. B, 134, 315–319.

Jackson, D. C., Palmer, S. E., and Meadow, W. L. (1974). The effects of temperature and carbon dioxide breathing on ventilation and acid-base status of turtles. *Respir. Physiol.* 20, 131–146.

Jackson, D. C., Singer, J. H., and Downey, P. T. (1991). Oxidative cost of breathing in the turtle *Chrysemys picta bellii*. *Am. J. Physiol.* 261, R1325–R1328.

Janssen, R. G., and Randall, D. J. (1975). The effects of changes in pH and P_{CO_2} in blood and water on breathing in rainbow trout, *Salmo gairdneri*. *Respir. Physiol.* 25, 235–245.

Johansen, K. (1970). Air breathing in fishes. In *Fish Physiology* (W. S. Hoar and D. J. Randall, eds.). Academic Press, London, vol. 4, pp. 361–411.

Johansen, K., and Burggren, W. W. (1980). Cardiovascular function in lower vertebrates. In *Hearts and Heart-Like Organs* (G. H. Bourne, ed.). Academic Press, New York, vol. 1, pp. 61–117.

Jones, D. R., and Chu, C. (1988). Effect of denervation of carotid labyrinths on breathing in unrestrained *Xenopus laevis*. *Respir. Physiol.* 73, 243–256.

Jones, D. R., and Milsom, W. K. (1979). Functional characteristics of slowly adapting pulmonary stretch receptors in the turtle (*Chrysemys picta*). *J. Physiol.* 291, 37–49.

Jones, D. R., and Milsom, W. K. (1982). Peripheral receptors affecting breathing and cardiovascular function in non-mammalian vertebrates. *J. Exp. Biol.* 100, 59–91.

Jones, D. R., Milsom, W. K., and Butler, P. J. (1985). Ventilatory response to venous CO_2 loading by gut ventilation in ducks. *Can. J. Zool.* 63, 1232–1236.

Kasserra, C. E., and Jones, D. R. (1996). Diluton acidosis: evidence for a role of intracellular pH in the control of ventilation. *J. Appl. Physiol.* 80, 1804–1810.

Kasserra, C. E., Jones, D. R., and Hughes, M. R. (1991). Acid-base disturbances and ventilatory response to changes in plasma osmolality in Pekin ducks. *Respir. Physiol.* 85, 383–393.

Kilburn, K. H. (1969). Alveolar clearance of particles. A bullfrog lung model. *Arch. Environ. Health* 18, 556–563.

Kinkead, R., Aota, S., Perry, S. F., and Randall, D. J. (1993). Propanolol impairs the hyperventilatory response to acute hypercapnia in rainbow trout. *J. Exp. Biol.* 175, 115–126.

Kinkead, R., Filmyer, W. G., Mitchell, G. S., and Milsom, W. K. (1994). Vagal input enhances responsiveness of respiratory discharge to central changes in pH/CO_2 in bullfrogs. *J. Appl. Physiol.* 77, 2048–2051.

Kinney, J. L., and White, F. N. (1977). Oxidative cost of ventilation in a turtle, *Pseudemys floridana*. *Respir. Physiol.* 31, 327–332.

Kobayashi, S. (1971). Comparative cytological studies of the carotid body. 1. Demonstration of monoamine-storing cells by correlated chromaffin reaction and fluorescence histochemistry. *Arch. Histol. Japon.* 31, 9–19.

Kogo, N., and Remmers, J. E. (1994). Neural organization of the ventilatory activity in the frog, *Rana catesbeiana* II. *J. Neurobiol.* 25, 1080–1094.

Kogo, N., Perry, S. F., and Remmers, J. E. (1994). Neural organization of the ventilatory activity in the frog, *Rana catesbeiana* I. *J. Neurobiol.* 25, 1067–1079.

Konig, S. A., and Seller, H. (1991). Historical development of current concepts on central chemosensitivity. *Arch. Ital. Biol.* 129, 223–237.

Krogh, A., and Krogh, M. (1910). The rate of diffusion of CO into the lungs of man. *Scand. Arch. Physiol.* 23, 236–247.

Kruhoffer, M., Glass, M. L., Abe, A. S., and Johansen, K. (1987). Control of breathing in an amphibian *Bufo paracnemis*: effects of temperature and hypoxia. *Respir. Physiol.* 69, 267–275.

Lahiri, S., Nishino, T., Mokashi, A., and Mulligan, E. (1980). Relative responses of aortic body and carotid body chemoreceptors to hypotension. *J. Appl. Physiol.* 48, 781–788.

Lahiri, S., Mulligan, E., Nishino, T., Mokashi, A., and Davies, R. O. (1981). Relative responses of aortic body and carotid body chemoreceptors to carboxyhemoglobinemia. *J. Appl. Physiol.* 50, 580–596.

Lassen, N. A. (1990). Is central chemoreceptor sensitive to intracellular rather than extracellular pH? *Clin. Physiol.* 10, 311–319.

Lau, M. J., and Keough, K. M. W. (1981). Lipid composition of lung and lung lavage fluid from map turtles (*Malaclemys geographica*) maintained at different environmental temperatures. *Can. J. Biochem.* 59, 208–219.

Lenfant, C. J. M., Johansen, K., Petersen, J. A., and Schmidt-Nielsen, K. (1970). Respiration in the fresh water turtle *Chelys fimbriata*. *Respir. Physiol.* 8, 261–275.

Leusen, I. (1954). Chemosensitivity of the respiratory center. Influence of CO_2 in the cerebral ventricles on respiration. *Am. J. Physiol.* 176, 39–44.

Liem, K. F. (1985). Ventilation. In *Functional Vertebrate Morphology* (M. Hildebrand, D. M. Bramble, K. F. Liem, and D. B. Wake, eds.). Harvard University Press, Cambridge, pp. 185–209.

Lillywhite, H. B. (1987). Circulatory adaptations of snakes to gravity. *Am. Zool.* 27, 81–95.

Lillywhite, H. B., and Pough, F. H. (1983). Control of arterial pressure in aquatic sea snakes. *Am. J. Physiol.* 244, R66–R73.

Lillywhite, H. B., and Smith, L. H. (1981). Hemodynamic responses to hemorrhage in the snake, *Elaphe obsoleta obsoleta*. *J. Exp. Biol.* 94, 275–283.

Lillywhite, H. B., and Smits, A. W. (1984). Lability of blood volume in snakes and its relation to activity and hypertension. *J. Exp. Biol.* 110, 267–274.

Maina, J. N. (1989). The morphology of the lung of the black mamba *Dendroaspis polylepis* (Reptilia: Ophidia: Elapidae). A scanning and transmission electron microscopic study. *J. Anat.* 167, 31–46.

Malan, A., Wilson, T. L., and Reeves, R. B. (1976). Intracellular pH in coldblooded vertebrates as a function of body temperature. *Respir. Physiol.* 28, 29–47.

Matthew, J. B., Hanania, G. I. H., and Gurd, F. R. N. (1979). Electrostatic effects in hemoglobin: hydrogen ion equilibria in human deoxy- and oxyhemoglobin A. *Biochemistry* 18, 1919–1928.

McDonald, H. S. (1959). Respiratory functions of the ophidian air sac. *Herpetologica* 15, 193–198.

McGregor, L. K., Daniels, C. B., and Nicholas, T. E. (1993). Lung ultrastructure and the surfactant-like system of the central netted dragon, *Ctenophorus nuchalis*. *Copeia* 1993, 326–333.

Milsom, W. K. (1984). The interrelationship between pulmonary mechanics and the spontaneous breathing pattern in the tokay lizard, *Gekko gecko*. *J. Exp. Biol.* 113, 203–214.

Milsom, W. K. (1988). Control of arrhythmic breathing in aerial breathers. *Can. J. Zool.* 66, 99–108.

Milsom, W. K. (1989). Comparative aspects of vertebrate pulmonary mechanics. In *Comparative Pulmonary Physiology: Current Concepts* (S. C. Wood, ed.). Marcel Dekker Inc., New York, pp. 597–619.

Milsom, W. K. (1990a). Control and coordination of gas exchange in air breathers. In *Advances in Comparative and Environmental Physiology* (R. G. Boutilier, ed.). Springer-Verlag, Berlin, vol. 6, pp. 347–400.

Milsom, W. K. (1990b). Mechanoreceptor modulation of endogenous respiratory rhythms in vertebrates. *Am. J. Physiol.* 259, R898–R910.

Milsom, W. K. (1991). Intermittent breathing in vertebrates. *Ann. Rev. Physiol.* 53, 87–105.

Milsom, W. K. (1995). Regulation of respiration in lower vertebrates: role of CO_2 / pH chemoreceptors. In *Advances in Comparative and Environmental Physiology* (N. Heisler, ed.). Springer-Verlag, Berlin, vol. 21, pp. 61–104.

Milsom, W. K., and Chan, P. (1986). The relationship between lung volume, respiratory drive and breathing pattern in the turtle, *Chrysemys picta*. *J. Exp. Biol.* 120, 233–247.

Milsom, W. K., and Johansen, K. (1975). The effect of buoyancy induced lung volume changes on respiratory frequency in a chelonian (*Caretta caretta*). *J. Comp. Physiol.* 98, 157–160.

Milsom, W. K., and Jones, D. R. (1976). Are reptilian pulmonary receptors mechano- or chemosensitive? *Nature* 261, 327–328.

Milsom, W. K., and Jones, D. R. (1977). Carbon dioxide sensitivity of pulmonary receptors in the frog. *Experientia* 33, 1167–1168.

Milsom, W. K., and Jones, D. R. (1979). Pulmonary receptor chemosensitivity and the ventilatory response to inhaled CO_2 in the turtle. *Respir. Physiol.* 37, 101–107.

Milsom, W. K., and Jones, D. R. (1980). The role of vagal afferent information and hypercapnia in control of the breathing pattern in Chelonia. *J. Exp. Biol.* 87, 53–63.

Milsom, W. K., and Vitalis, T. Z. (1984). Pulmonary mechanics and the work of breathing in the lizard, *Gekko gecko*. *J. Exp. Biol.* 113, 187–202.

Milsom, W. K., Jones, D. R., and Gabbot, G. R. J. (1981). On chemoreceptor control of ventilatory responses to CO_2 in unanesthetized ducks. *J. Appl. Physiol.* 50, 1121–1128.

Mitchell, G. S., Gleeson, T. T., and Bennett, A. F. (1981a). Ventilation and acid-base balance during graded activity in lizards. *Am. J. Physiol.* 240, R29–R37.

Mitchell, G. S., Gleeson, T. T., and Bennett, A. F. (1981b). Pulmonary oxygen transport during activity in lizards. *Respir. Physiol.* 43, 365–375.

Mitchell, R. A., Loeschcke, H. H., Massion, W. H., and Severinghaus, J. W. (1963). Respiratory responses mediated through superficial chemosensitive areas on the medulla. *J. Appl. Physiol.* 18, 523–533.

Morgenroth, K., and Bolz, J. (1985). Morphological features of the interaction between mucus and surfactant on the bronchial mucosa. *Respiration* 47, 225–231.

Mulligan, E., and Lahiri, S. (1982). Separation of carotid body chemoreceptor responses to O_2 and CO_2 by oligomycin and by antimycin A. *Am. J. Physiol.* 242, C200–C206.

Naifeh, K. H., Huggins, S. E., and Hoff, H. E. (1971a). Studies of the control of crocodilian respiration by anesthestic dissection. *Respir. Physiol.* 12, 251–260.

Naifeh, K. H., Huggins, S. E., and Hoff, H. E. (1971b). Effects of brain stem section on respiratory patterns of crocodilian reptiles. *Respir. Physiol.* 13, 186–197.

Nattie, E. E. (1986a). Intracisternal diethylpyrocarbonate inhibits central chemosensitivity in conscious rabbits. *Respir. Physiol.* 64, 161–176.

Nattie, E. E. (1986b). Diethyl pyrocarbonate (an imidazole binding substance) inhibits rostral VLM CO_2 sensitivity. *J. Appl. Physiol.* 61, 843–850.

Nattie, E. E. (1988). Diethyl pyrocarbonate inhibits rostral ventrolateral medullary H^+ sensitivity. *J. Appl. Physiol.* 64, 397–403.

Nattie, E. E. (1990). The alphastat hypothesis in respiratory control and acid-base balance. *J. Appl. Physiol.* 69, 1201–1207.

Nielsen, B. (1961). On the regulation of respiration in reptiles. I. The effect of temperature and CO_2 on the respiration of lizards (*Lacerta*). *J. Exp. Biol.* 38, 301–314.

Nielsen, B. (1962). On the regulation of respiration in reptiles. II. The effect of hypoxia with and without moderate hypercapnia on the respiration and metabolism of lizards. *J. Exp. Biol.* 39, 107–117.

Nolan, W. F., and Frankel, H. M. (1982). Effects of temperature on ventilation and acid-base status in the black racer snake, *Coluber constrictor*. *Comp. Biochem. Physiol.* 73A, 57–61.

Okada, Y., Ishiko, S., Diado, S., Kim, J., and Ikeda, S. (1962). Comparative morphology of the lung with special reference to the alveolar epithelial cells. I. Lung of the Amphibia. *Acta Tuberc. Japon.* 11, 63–73.

Okada, Y., Ishiko, S., Daido, S., Kim, J., and Ikeda, S. (1963). Comparative morphology of the lung with special reference to the alveolar lining cells. 2. Lung of Reptilia. *Acta Tuberc. Japon.* 12, 1–10.

Orgeig, S. (1994). "The Relationship Between Cholesterol and Phospholipids in Vertebrate Pulmonary Surfactant." Ph.D. Thesis, Flinders University, Adelaide, South Australia.

Osborne, J. L., Burger, R. E., and Stoll, P. J. (1977). Dynamic responses of CO_2 sensitive avian intrapulmonary chemoreceptors. *Am. J. Physiol.* 233, R15–R22.

Otis, A. B. (1954). The work of breathing. *Physiol. Rev.* 34, 449–458.

Otis, A. B., Fenn, W. O., and Rahn, H. (1950). Mechanics of breathing in man. *J. Appl. Physiol.* 8, 427–443.

Ottaviani, G., and Tazzi, A. (1977). The lymphatic system. In *Biology of the Reptilia* (C. Gans and T. S. Parsons, eds.). Academic Press, New York, vol. 6, pp. 315–462.

Pappenheimer, J. R., Fencl, V., Heeysey, S. R., and Held, D. (1965). Role of the cerebral fluids in control of respiration as studied in unanaesthetized goats. *Am. J. Physiol.* 208, 436–450.

Pattle, R. E. (1955). Properties, function and origin of the alveolar lining layer. *Nature* 173, 1125–1126.

Pattle, R. E. (1976). The lung surfactant in the evolutionary tree. In *Respiration of Amphibious Vertebrates* (G. M. Hughes, ed.). Academic Press, London, pp. 233–253.

Pattle, R. E., and Hopkinson, D. A. (1963). Lung lining in bird, reptile and amphibian. *Nature* 200, 894–894.

Perry, S. F. (1978). Quantitative anatomy of the lungs of the red eared turtle, *Pseudemys scripta elegans*. *Respir. Physiol.* 35, 245–262.

Perry, S. F. (1983). Reptilian lungs. Functional anatomy and evolution. *Adv. Anat. Embryol. Cell Biol.* 79, 1–81.

Perry, S. F. (1989). Structure and function of the reptilian respiratory system. In *Comparative Pulmonary Physiology: Current Concepts* (S. C. Wood, ed.). Marcel Dekker Inc., New York, pp. 193–236.

Perry, S. F. (1992). Gas exchange strategies in reptiles and the origin of the avian lung. *Lung Biol. Health Dis.* 56, 149–167.

Perry, S. F. (1996). Lungs: comparative anatomy, functional morphology, and evolution. In *Biology of the Reptilia* (C. Gans and A. S. Gaunt, eds.). Society for the Study of Amphibians and Reptiles, Ithaca, NY, vol. 19, pp. 1–92.

Perry, S. F., and Duncker, H. R. (1978). Lung architecture, volume and static mechanics in five species of lizards. *Respir. Physiol.* 34, 61–81.

Perry, S. F., and Duncker, H. R. (1980). Interrelationships of static and mechanical factors and anatomical structure in lung evolution. *J. Comp. Physiol.*, ser. B, 138, 321–334.

Perry, S. F., and Wood, C. M. (1989). Control and coordination of gas transfer in fishes. *Can. J. Zool.* 67, 2961–2970.

Perry, S. F., Bauer, A. M., Russell, A. P., Alston, J. T., and Maloney, J. E. (1989). Lungs of the gecko *Rhacodactylus leachianus* (Reptilia: Gekkonidae): a correlative gross anatomical and light and electron microscopic study. *J. Morph.* 199, 23–40.

Perry, S. F., Hein, J., and van Deiken, E. (1994). Gas exchange morphometry of the lungs of the tokay, *Gekko gecko* L. (Reptilia: Squamata: Gekkonidae). *J. Comp. Physiol.* 164, 206–214.

Piiper, J. (1961). Unequal distribution of pulmonary diffusing capacity and the alveolar-arterial P_{O_2} differences: theory. *J. Appl. Physiol* 16, 493–498.

Piiper, J. (1989). Modelling of gas exchange in lung gills and skin. In *Vertebrate gas exchange: From Environment to Cell* (R. G. Boutilier, ed.). Springer-Verlag, Berlin, pp. 5–44.

Piiper, J. (1992). Diffusion-perfusion inhomogeneity and alveolar-arterial O_2 diffusion limitation: theory. *Respir. Physiol.* 87, 349–356.

Piiper, J. (1993). Medium-blood gas exchange: diffusion, distribution and shunt. In *The Vertebrate Gas Transport Cascade* (J. E. P. W. Bicudo, ed.). CRC Press, Boca Raton, Florida, pp. 106–120.

Piiper, J., and Scheid, P. (1975). Gas transport efficacy of gills, lungs and skin: theory and experimental data. *Respir. Physiol.* 23, 209–221.

Piiper, J., and Scheid, P. (1989). Gas exchange: theory, models, and experimental data. In *Comparative Pulmonary Physiology: Current Concepts* (S. C. Wood, ed.). Marcel Dekker Inc., New York, pp. 369–416.

Powell, F. L. (1993). Comparing the effects of diffusion and heterogeneity on vertebrate gas exchange. In *The Vertebrate Gas Transport Cascade* (J. E. P. W. Bicudo, ed.). CRC Press, Boca Raton, Florida, pp. 121–131.

Powell, F. L. (1994). Respiratory gas exchange during exercise. *Adv. Vet. Sci. Comp. Med.* 38A, 253–285.

Powell, F. L., and Gray, A. T. (1989). Ventilation-perfusion relationships in the alligator. Respir. Physiol. 78, 83–94.

Powell, F. L., Gratz, R. K., and Scheid, P. (1978). Responses of intrapulmonary chemoreceptors in the duck to changes in P_{CO_2} and pH. Respir. Physiol. 35, 65–77.

Powell, F. L., Milsom, W. K., and Mitchell, G. S. (1988). Effect of intrapulmonary CO_2 on pulmonary vagal afferent activity in the alligator. Respir. Physiol. 35, 349–359.

Preest, M. R. (1991). Energetic costs of prey ingestion in a scincid lizard, Scincella lateralis. J. Comp. Physiol. 161, 327–332.

Rahn, H. (1966). Gas transport from external environment to the cell. In Development of the Lung (A. V. S. de Reuck and R. Porter, eds.). J. & A. Churchill Ltd., London, pp. 3–23.

Randall, D. J., Heisler, N., and Dress, F. (1976). Ventilatory response to hypercapnia in the larger spotted dogfish, Scyliorhinus stellaris. Am. J. Physiol. 230, 590–594.

Read, J., and Donnelly, P. M. (1972). Stratification of blood flow in the elongated lungs of the carpet python. J. Appl. Physiol. 32, 842–846.

Reeves, R. B. (1972). An imidazole alphastat hypothesis for vertebrate acid-base regulation: tissue carbon dioxide content and body temperature in bullfrogs. Respir. Physiol. 14, 219–236.

Reeves, R. B. (1976a). Temperature induced changes in blood acid-base status: pH and P_{CO_2} in a binary buffer. J. Appl. Physiol. 40, 752–761.

Reeves, R. B. (1976b). Temperature induced changes in blood acid-base status: Donnan r^{Cl-} and red cell volume. J. Appl. Physiol. 40, 762–767.

Reeves, R. B. (1977). The interaction of body temperature and acid base balance in ectothermic vertebrates. Ann. Rev. Physiol. 39, 559–586.

Reeves, R. B., and Malan, A. (1976). Model studies of intracellular acid-base temperature responses in ectotherms. Respir. Physiol. 28, 49–63.

Rensch, H., von Seefeld, H., Gebhardt, K. F., Renzow, D., and Sell, P.-J. (1983). Stop and go particle transport in the peripheral airways? A model study. Respiration 44, 346–350.

Robin, E. D. (1962). Relationship between temperature and plasma pH and carbon dioxide tension in the turtle. Nature 195, 249–251.

Rogers, D. C. (1967). The structure of the carotid bifurcation in the lizards Tiliqua occipitalis and Trachysaurus rugosus. J. Morphol. 122, 115–130.

Rohrer, F. (1925). Physiologie der Atembewegung. In Handbuch der normalen und pathologischen Physiologie (A. T. J. Bethe, ed.). Springer-Verlag, Berlin, vol. 2, pp. 70–127.

Ruben, J. A. (1995). The evolution of endothermy in mammals and birds: from physiology to fossils. Annu. Rev. Physiol. 57, 69–95.

Rubinoff, I., Graham, J. B., and Motta, J. (1986). Diving of the sea snake Pelamis platurus in the Gulf of Panama. I. Dive depth and duration. Mar. Biol. 91, 181–191.

Sakakibara, Y. (1978). Localization of CO_2 sensor related to the inhibition of bullfrog respiration. Japan. J. Physiol. 28, 721–735.

Scheid, P., Kuhlmann, W. D., and Fedde, M. R. (1977). Intrapulmonary receptors in the tegu lizard: II. Functional characteristics and localization. *Respir. Physiol.* 29, 49–62.

Scheid, P., Gratz, R. K., Powell, F. L., and Fedde, M. R. (1978). Ventilatory response to CO_2 in birds. II. Contribution by intrapulmonary chemoreceptors. *Respir. Physiol.* 35, 361–372.

Secor, S. M., and Diamond, J. (1995). Adaptive responses to feeding in Burmese pythons: pay before pumping. *J. Exp. Biol.* 198, 1313–1325.

Seymour, R. S. (1979). Blood lactate in free-diving sea snakes. *Copeia* 1979, 494–497.

Seymour, R. S. (1978). Gas tensions and blood distribution in sea snakes at surface pressure and at simulated depth. *Physiol. Zool.* 51, 388–407.

Seymour, R. S. (1980). Functional venous admixture in the lungs of the turtle, *Chrysemys scripta. Respir. Physiol.* 53, 99–107.

Seymour, R. S. (1982). Physiological adaptation to aquatic life. In *Biology of the Reptilia* (C. Gans and F. H. Pough, eds.). Academic Press, London, vol. 12, pp. 1–51.

Seymour, R. S. (1989). Diving physiology: reptiles. In *Comparative Pulmonary Physiology: Current Concepts* (S. C. Wood, ed.). Marcel Dekker Inc., New York, pp. 697–720.

Seymour, R. S., Spragg, R. G., and Hartman, M. T. (1981). Distribution of ventilation and perfusion in the sea snake, *Pelamis platurus. J. Comp. Physiol.* 145, 109–115.

Seymour, R. S., Bennett, A. F., and Bradford, D. F. (1985). Blood gas tensions and acid-base regulation in the salt-water crocodile, *Crocodylus porosus*, at rest and after exhaustive exercise. *J. Exp. Biol.* 118, 143–159.

Shams, H. (1985). Differential effects of CO_2 and H^+ as central stimuli of respiration in the cat. *J. Appl. Physiol.* 58, 357–364.

Shelton, G., and Burggren, W. W. (1976). Cardiovascular dynamics of the Chelonia during apnoea and lung ventilation. *J. Exp. Biol.* 64, 323–343.

Silver, R. B., and Jackson, D. C. (1985). Ventilatory and acid-base responses to long-term hypercapnia in the freshwater turtle, *Chrysemys picta bellii. J. Exp. Biol.* 114, 661–672.

Silver, R. B., and Jackson, D. C. (1986). Ionic responses with no renal responses to chronic hypercapnia in the freshwater turtle, *Chrysemys picta bellii. Am. J. Physiol.* 20, R1228–R1234.

Smatresk, N. J. (1990). Chemoreceptor modulation of endogenous respiratory rhythms in vertebrates. *Am. J. Physiol.* 28, R887–R897.

Smatresk, N. J., and Smits, A. W. (1991). Effects of central and peripheral chemoreceptor stimulation on ventilation in the marine toad, *Bufo marinus. Respir. Physiol.* 83, 223–238.

Smith, F. M., and Jones, D. R. (1982). The effect of changes in blood oxygen carrying capacity on ventilation volume in the rainbow trout, *Salmo gairdneri. J. Exp. Biol.* 97, 325–334.

Smits, A. W. (1989). Fluid balance in vertebrate lungs. In *Comparative Pulmonary Physiology: Current Concepts* (S. C. Wood, ed.). Marcel Dekker, Inc., New York, vol. 39, pp. 503–537.

Smits, A. W. (1994). Lack of edema in toad lungs after pulmonary hypertension. *Am. J. Physiol.* 35, R1338–R1344.

Smits, A. W., and Kozubowski, M. M. (1985). Partitioning of body fluids and cardiovascular responses to circulatory hypovolaemia in the turtle, *Pseudemys scripta elegans*. *J. Exp. Biol.* 116, 237–250.

Smits, A. W., and Lillywhite, H. B. (1985). Maintenance of blood volume in snakes: transcapillary shifts of extravascular fluids during acute hemorrhage. *J. Comp. Physiol.* 155, 305–310.

Smits, A. W., West, N. H., and Burggren, W. W. (1986). Pulmonary fluid balance following pulmocutaneous baroreceptor denervation in the toad. *J. Appl. Physiol.* 61, 331–337.

Smits, A. W., Orgeig, S., and Daniels, C. B. (1995). Surfactant functions as an anti-edema agent in lungs of the lizard (*Pogona vitticeps*). *Fed. Amer. Soc. Exp. Biol. J.* 9, A861.

Spragg, R. G., Ackerman, R. A., and White, F. N. (1980). Distribution of ventilation in the turtle *Pseudemys scripta*. *Respir. Physiol.* 42, 73–86.

Standaert, T. A., and Johansen, K. (1974). Cutaneous gas exchange in snakes. *J. Comp. Physiol.* 89, 313–320.

Staub, N. C. (1983). Alveolar flooding and clearance. *Am. Rev. Resp. Dis.* 127, 545–551.

Steffensen, J. F. (1985). The transition between branchial pumping and ram ventilation in fishes: energetic consequences and dependence on water oxygen tension. *J. Exp. Biol.* 114, 141–150.

Steffensen, J. F., and Lomholt, J. P. (1983). Energetic cost of active branchial ventilation in the sharksucker, *Echeneis naucrats*. *J. Exp. Biol.* 103, 185–192.

Stewart, P. A. (1981). *How to Understand Acid-Base Balance: A Quantitative Acid-Base Primer to Biology and Medicine.* Elsevier Biomedical Press, Amsterdam.

Stewart, P. A. (1983). Modern quantitative acid-base chemistry. *Can. J. Physiol. Pharm.* 61, 1442–1461.

Stinner, J. N. (1982a). Functional anatomy of the lung of the snake, *Pituophis melanoleucus*. *Am. J. Physiol.* 243, R251–R257.

Stinner, J. N. (1982b). Ventilation, gas exchange and blood gases in the snake, *Pituophis melanoleucus*. *Respir. Physiol.* 47, 279–298.

Stinner, J. N. (1987). Thermal dependence of air convection requirement and blood gases in the snake *Coluber constrictor*. *Am. Zool.* 27, 41–47.

Stinner, J. N., and Wardle, R. L. (1988). Effect of temperature upon carboon dioxide stores in the snake *Coluber constrictor* and the turtle *Chrysemys scripta*. *J. Exp. Biol.* 137, 529–548.

Takeda, R., Remmers, J. E., Baker, J. P., Madden, K. P., and Farber, J. P. (1986). Postsynaptic potentials of bulbar respiratory neurons of the turtle. *Respir. Physiol.* 64, 149–160.

Templeton, J. R. (1967). Panting and pulmonary inflation, two mutually exclusive responses in the chuckwalla, *Sauromalus obesus*. *Copeia* 1967, 224–225.

Templeton, J. R., and Dawson, W. R. (1963). Respiration in the lizard *Crotaphytus collaris*. *Physiol. Zool.* 36, 104–121.

Toews, D. P. (1971). Factors affecting the onset and termination of ventilation in the salamander, *Amphiuma tridactylum*. *Can. J. Zool.* 49, 1231–1237.

Toews, D. P., and Kirby, S. (1985). The ventilatory and acid-base physiology of the toad, *Bufo marinus*, during exposure to environmental hyperoxia. *Respir. Physiol.* 59, 225–230.

Toews, D. P., and Macintyre, D. H. (1978). Respiration and circulation in an apodan amphibian. *Can. J. Zool.* 46, 998–1004.

Ultsch, G. R. (1989). Ecology and physiology of hibernation and overwintering among freshwater fishes, turtles and snakes. *Biol. Rev.* 64, 435–516.

Van Vliet, B. N., and West, N. H. (1992). Functional characteristics of arterial chemoreceptors in an amphibian (*Bufo marinus*). *Respir. Physiol.* 88, 113–127.

Vitalis, T. Z., and Milsom, W. K. (1986a). Pulmonary mechanics and the work of breathing in the semi-aquatic turtle, *Pseudemys scripta*. *J. Exp. Biol.* 125, 137–155.

Vitalis, T. Z., and Milsom, W. K. (1986b). Mechanical analysis of spontaneous breathing in the semi-aquatic turtle, *Pseudemys scripta*. *J. Exp. Biol.* 125, 157–171.

Wagner, P. D., Saltzman, H. A., and West, J. B. (1974). Measurement of continous distributions of ventilation-perfusion ratios: theory. *J. Appl. Physiol.* 36, 588–599.

Wagner, P. D., Gale, G. E., Moon, R. E., Torre-Bueno, J. R., Stolp, B. W., and Saltzman, H. A. (1986). Pulmonary gas exchange in humans exercising at sea level and simulated altitude. *J. Appl. Physiol.* 61, 260–270.

Wagner, P. D., Gillespie, J. R., Landgren, G. L., Fedde, M. R., Jones, B. W., Debowes, R. M., Pieschl, R. L., and Erickson, H. H. (1989). Mechanism of exercise-induced hypoxemia in horses. *J. Appl. Physiol.* 66, 1227–1233.

Wang, T., and Hicks, J. W. (1996). The interaction of pulmonary ventilation and the right-left shunt on arterial oxygen levels. *J. Exp. Biol.* 199, 2121–2129.

Wang, T., and Warburton, S. J. (1995). Breathing pattern and cost of breathing in alligators. *Respir. Physiol.* 102, 29–37.

Wang, T., Fernandes, W., and Abe, A. S. (1993). Blood pH and O_2 homeostasis upon CO_2 anesthesia in the rattlesnake, *Crotalus durissus*. *The Snake* 25, 21–26.

Wang, T., Branco, L. G. S., and Glass, M. L. (1994). Ventilatory responses to hypoxia in the toad *Bufo paracnemis* before and after decrease in HbO_2-capacity. *J. Exp. Biol.* 186, 1–8.

Wang, T., Burggren, W. W., and Nobrega, E. (1995a). Metabolic, ventilatory, and acid-base responses associated with specific dynamic action in the toad *Bufo marinus*. *Physiol. Zool.* 68, 192–205.

Wang, T., Carrier, D. R., and Hicks, J. W. (1995b). Ventilation and gas exchange in exercising lizards. *Physiol. Zool.* 68, 91.

Wang, T., Krosniunas, E., and Hicks, J. W. (1997). The role of cardiac shunts in the regulation of arterial blood gases. *Am. Zool.* 37, 12–22.

Weibel, E. R. (1973). Morphological basis of alveolar-capillary gas exchange. *Physiol. Rev.* 53, 419–495.

West, J. B. (1974). *Respiratory Physiology—the Essentials*. Williams and Wilkins Company, Baltimore, Maryland.

West, N. H., and Jones, D. R. (1975). Breathing movements in the frog *Rana pipiens* II. The power output and efficiency of breathing. *Can. J. Zool.* 53, 345–353.

West, N. H., Topor, Z. L., and Van Vliet, B. N. (1987). Hypoxemic treshold for lung ventilation in the toad. *Respir. Physiol.* 70, 377–390.

West N. H., Smits, A. W., and Burggren, W. W. (1989). Factors terminating non-ventilatory periods in the turtle, *Chelydra serpentina. Respir. Physiol.* 77, 337–350.

Wilson, K. J. (1971). "The Relationships of Activity, Energy, Metabolism, and Body Temperature in Four Species of Lizards." Ph.D. Thesis, Monash University, Clayton, Australia.

Winterstein, H. (1911). Die Regulierung der Atmung durch das Blut. *Pflügers Arch.* 138, 167.

Wolf, M. B., and Watson, P. D. (1985). Effect of temperature on fluid movement in isolated cat hindlimb. *Am. J. Physiol.* 249, H792–H798.

Wood, C. M., Turner, J. D., Munger, R. S., and Graham, M. S. (1990). The control of ventilation during hypercapnia in the skate, *Raja ocellata.* II. Cerospinal fluid chemistry and intracellular pH in the brain and other tissues. *Respir. Physiol.* 80, 279–297.

Wood, P. G., Daniels, C. B., and Orgeig, S. (1995). Functional significance and control of release of pulmonary surfactant in the lizard lung. *Amer. J. Physiol.* 269, R838–R847.

Wood, S. C. (1982). The effect of oxygen affinity on arterial P_{O_2} in animals with vascular shunts. *J. Appl. Physiol.* 53, 1360–1364.

Wood, S. C. (1984). Cardiovascular shunts and oxygen transport in lower vertebrates. *Am. J. Physiol.* 247, R3–R14.

Wood, S. C., and Glass, M. L. (1992). Respiration and thermoregulation of amphibians and reptiles. In *Physiological Strategies for Gas Exchange and Metabolism* (A. Woakes, M. Grieshaber, and C. Bridges, eds.). Cambridge University Press, Cambridge, pp. 107–124.

Wood, S. C., and Lenfant, C. J. M. (1976). Respiration, mechanics, control and gas exchange. In *Biology of the Reptilia* (C. Gans and W. R. Dawson, eds.). Academic Press, London, vol. 5, pp. 225–274.

Wood, S. C., Glass, M. L., and Johansen, K. (1977). Effects of temperature on respiration and acid-base balance in a monitor lizard. *J. Comp. Physiol.* 116, 287-296.

Yamaguchi, K., Glass, M. L., Scheid, P., and Piiper, J. (1989). Oxygen transfer kinetics of red blood cells of the turtle *Pseudemys scripta elegans. Respir. Physiol.* 75, 371-384.

Yamaguchi, K, Kawai, A., Mori, M., Asanao, K., Takasugi, T., Umeda, A., Kawashiro, T., and Yokoyama, T. (1991). Distribution of ventilation and of diffusing capacity to perfusion in the lung. *Respir. Physiol.* 86, 171-187.

Wang, T., Smits, A. W., and Burggren, W. W. (1998). Pulmonary function in reptiles. In *Biology of the Reptilia*, vol. 19 (Morphology G) (C. Gans and A. S. Gaunt, eds.). Society for the Study of Amphibians and Reptiles, Ithaca, New York, Contrib. Herpetol., vol. 14, pp. 297–374.

4

Comparative Aspects of
Heart Morphology

A. P. FARRELL, A. K. GAMPERL, AND E. T. B. FRANCIS

CONTENTS

I. INTRODUCTION

This chapter describes the characteristic anatomical features of reptilian hearts. Like most other aspects of their biology, the cardiac anatomy of reptiles shows considerable diversity. This diversity undoubtedly reflects the fact that extant species comprise a phylogenetically complex group occupying very diverse environments. Although reptiles were the first tetrapods to colonize successfully the terrestrial environment, their modern day habitats include trees, deserts, lakes, and oceans. Perhaps their most striking circulatory design features are those allowing them preferentially to perfuse their systemic circulation by partial or complete bypass of the respiratory circulation. The design features that allow for this circulatory feat are shared by the amphibians but not by either water-breathing fishes or air-breathing birds and mammals. Pulmonary bypass is associated with intermittent (arrhythmic) air breathing and with extreme behavioral patterns, including prolonged underwater diving, slow swallowing of very large meals, hibernation in anoxic water, and passive defense strategies against predators. Other factors that have helped to shape the design of the circulatory system include gravitational stress (arboreal and aquatic species) and body shape.

Despite the diversity, this chapter attempts to provide a synthetic account of reptilian cardiac anatomy. We have avoided reporting exhaustive detail, but instead identify major anatomical differences wherever possible. In addition, we provide extensive referencing for the reader to find more detail on the subject. Cardiac anatomy is discussed in two major phyletic groupings: the crocodylians and the non-crocodylians (e.g., testudines, lizards, and snakes). This organization is based simply on the fact that crocodylian hearts have an anatomically divided ventricle. In contrast, the non-crocodylian ventricle is not anatomically divided, although pulmonary and systemic blood flow can be functionally separated and regulated.

This leads into our final introductory point, that of the function of a particular anatomical design. Although our primary focus is on describing the anatomy of the heart, we emphasize functional relevance whenever possible. In these discussions, we limit speculation and refer readers to the literature characterizing any controversy. Our task in this regard is complicated by the fact that the anatomical terminology for reptiles is anything but uniform.

II. GENERAL ANATOMY

A few generalizations can be made about the reptilian heart. The heart, as in all vertebrates, lies within a coelomic space—the pericardial cavity—and is covered by a reflexion of the epicardium, the serous membrane lining this cavity. The cavities of the heart are lined by the endocardium, another membrane, which itself is continuous with the endothelial lining of the blood vessels. Between these two membranes lie muscle and connective tissue, together known as the myocardium. Externally, the reptilian heart consists of four chambers, namely the sinus venosus, the two atria, and the ventricle. The ventricle in all reptiles, except the Crocodylia, must be regarded morphologically as a single chamber; only in crocodylians is the ventricular septum complete. Nonetheless, the ventricular division of the Crocodylia is hardly visible externally.

According to Hess (1921), heart mass relative to body mass in reptiles ranges between 0.20% and 0.32%, values that are comparable to those reported for amphibians (0.16 to 0.32%) but greater than those reported for non-scombrid fish (0.04 to 0.15%). In contrast, Poupa (1972) reported that the mean relative heart mass for reptiles (0.19%) is intermediate between those for fishes (0.08%) and amphibians (0.30%). Among the fishes, relative heart mass is greater in active species (e.g., skipjack tuna) as compared with sluggish fish such as the sea raven or flounder (Farrell, 1991; Farrell and Jones, 1992). Reptiles may show a similar relationship between activity "athleticism" and heart mass. Poupa and Lindström (1983) reported a large variation in relative heart mass among snakes; thus that of the tree snake *Dispholidus typus* is very high (0.45%). In addition, the heart mass of inactive species such as the tortoise (*Emydura signata* [0.16%]; C. E. Franklin, unpublished observations) and the slowworm (*Anguis fragilis* [0.16%]; Hess, 1921) is well below those generally reported for the lizards *Lacerta* (approx. 0.21%) and *Pogona vitticeps* (0.29%; Else and Hulbert, 1983), and many snakes (approx. 0.31%; Poupa and Lindström, 1983). It seems likely that this variation in relative heart mass may be primarily related to pressure development with regard to gravitational effects and athleticism.

There is among reptiles considerable variability in the volume of cardiac chambers and in the muscularity of their walls. Large volume hearts do not always have well developed walls and vice versa (compare pythons and testudines, for example). The reason for this is that the heart generates both blood flow and blood pressure, and animals with high cardiac outputs do not necessarily have high blood pressures and thick-walled ventricles. The best examples of this sort of trade off in cardiac anatomy are exemplified in fish. Skipjack tuna (*Katsuwonus pelamis*) and the hemoglobin-free Antarctic icefish (Channichthyidae) have similar cardiac outputs and ventricular masses. However, the stroke volume of the tuna ventricle is about 1/10th that of the icefish, and the pressures developed are about five-times higher (Farrell and Jones, 1992). As a result, tuna ventricles have a much thicker wall and a lower internal volume. Thus, proper assessment of these aspects of functional anatomy require some knowledge of physiological variables for the species in question.

In reptiles, the position of the heart within the body varies considerably. In some reptiles, for example *Hemidactylus flaviviridis* (Mahendra, 1942), the heart lies far anteriorly in the gular position (as in Amphibia), whereas in others it may be situated as far posteriorly as the body midline (e.g., Crocodylia, Grigg, 1989). To gain some understanding of the determinants of heart position in reptiles, one can look at the close association between heart position and lifestyle in snakes (Seymour, 1987; Lillywhite, 1987). The heart is located 15 to 25% of the total body length from the head in terrestrial and aboreal species, but 25 to 45% in totally aquatic species. In addition, according to Seymour (1987), an anterior heart is favored in snakes that climb or raise their head; the positional shift reduces the hydrostatic pressure above the heart and tends to stabilize cephalic blood pressure. Thus, an anteriorly positioned heart may be favored in terrestrial reptiles with long necks or in those in which the body is often vertically oriented.

The sinus venosus is always distinct in reptiles. It is either triangular or tubular and lies on the dorsal aspect of the heart at the confluence of the three caval veins (Fig. 4.1). Its size can also vary, but it is generally smaller than the remainder of the heart. The walls of the sinus venosus are the thinnest of all the heart chambers. Its ventral wall is usually joined to the dorsal wall of the ventricle by a fibrous strand called the dorsal ligament.

The atria are best viewed from the ventral aspect, where they lie squarely on top of the ventricle with the bases of the arterial trunks lying between them (Fig. 4.1). The right atrium is either larger (e.g., snakes) or the same size (e.g., varanid lizards) as the left atrium (see Section IX). The size difference is nearly double in some cases, reflecting lateral dilation and sometimes posterior extension. Externally, a distinct groove, the coronary sulcus, often marks the junction between

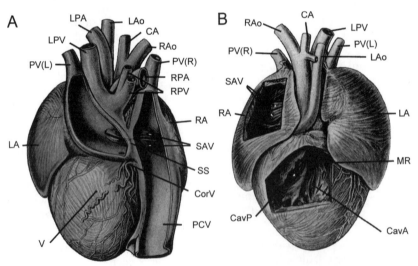

Fig. 4.1. *Varanus bengalensis* heart showing the general features of non-crocodylian reptiles. A. Dorsal view with the sinus venosus opened to show the interior. B. Ventral view with windows cut in the right atrium and the ventricle to show the interior. Abbreviations: CA, carotid artery; CavA, cavum arteriosum; CavP, cavum pulmonale; CorV, coronary veins in dorsal ligament; LA, left atrium; LAo, left aortic arch; LPA, left pulmonary artery; LPV, left pulmonary vein; MR, muscular ridge; PCV, postcaval vein; PV(L), precaval vein (left); PV(R), precaval vein (right); RA, right atrium; RAo, right aortic arch; RPA, right pulmonary artery; RPV, right pulmonary vein; SAV, sinoatrial valves; SS, sinus septum; V, ventricle. (Adapted from Meinertz, 1952.)

the atria and the ventricle. This groove is transverse if the atria are of equal size, but oblique in many snakes in which the right atrium is much larger than the left.

The ventricle has the form of an inverted cone with rounded angles (Fig. 4.1). The ventricle may be broad (that is, the base may be greater than the height of the cone) as in many Testudines, or elongated as in most Serpentes, but typically the base and height are approximately equal. In Testudines, the ventricle tends to be flattened dorsoventrally, whereas in Serpentes and many other orders, it is approximately circular. The apex of the ventricle may lie freely in the pericardium, or it may be anchored to the pericardium by the ligamentous gubernaculum cordis. The gubernaculum cordis generally occurs in Testudines, Sauria, and Crocodylia. In *Lacerta*, the gubernaculum cordis is not a vestige of the mesocardium but arises secondarily from villous outgrowths of the epicardium covering the apex of the ventricle (Greil, 1903). This has also been shown for *Emys* and crocodylians (Hochstetter, 1906).

In most groups, the conus arteriosus (bulbus cordis) is almost completely absorbed into the right portion of the ventricle. However, vestiges are evident in many taxa, especially in Testudines and in Rhynchocephalia (Simons, 1965).

The three arterial trunks are the pulmonary and the right and left aortic arches (Fig. 4.1). They leave the ventricle usually towards the right side, and often twist dextrally around one another through an angle of approximately 180°. This twisting of the aortic trunks is a characteristic of reptiles.

III. CARDIAC DESIGN IN NON-CROCODYLIANS
A. Cardiac Anatomy

In Rhynchocephalia and the Testudines, the sinus venosus is a relatively large, simple, and undivided chamber that opens into the right atrium through the sinoatrial valve. The sinus septum of Sauria and Serpentes usually is indicated externally by a constriction between the enlarged terminal portion of the left precaval vein and the confluent right precaval and postcaval ones (e.g., Fig. 4.2). The extent to which the sinus septum develops is variable; it may be only a rudimentary fold in the wall of the left precaval vein, or it may become sufficiently developed to join the bases of the sinoatrial valves, as is the case in Serpentes (Fig. 4.2). The function of the sinus septum is poorly understood, but it may prevent reflux of blood from the left precaval vein into the postcaval vein.

The walls of the sinus venosus contain cardiac muscle (Buchanan, 1956) that act as the pacemaker of the heart. The relative size of the sinus venosus varies among species. In Gekkonidae, for example, the volume

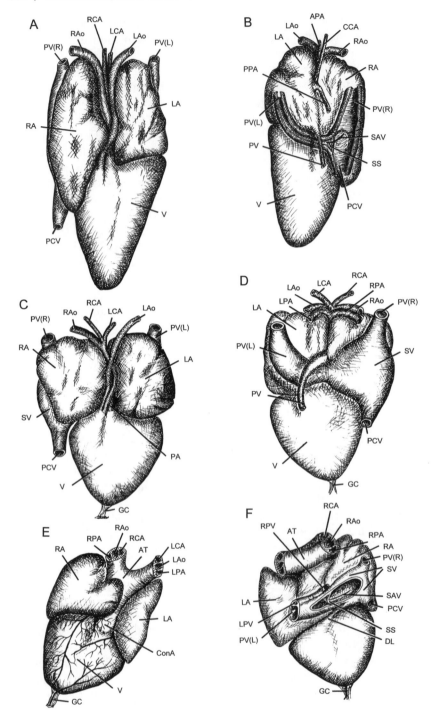

of the sinus is large, but the right atrial volume is relatively small (right and left atria having nearly equal volumes). However, in *Naja naja*, the sinus venosus is reduced and the right atrium enlarged (Fig. 4.2). Connective tissue is plentiful in the sinus venosus.

The oblique sinoatrial opening into the right atrium is guarded by a pair of membranous, flap-like valves developed from the endocardium. By far the most usual arrangement of these valves is one in which the anterior (or left) valve overlaps the posterior (or right) valve at the posterior end, whereas at the anterior extremity, the two valves run parallel to each other and fuse to form a so-called suspensory ligament. This suspensory ligament, in turn, becomes continuous with a prominent muscular bundle in the wall of the right atrium (Fig. 4.3).

The atrial musculature forms a network strengthened by the development of muscular pillars and trabeculae so that the walls are best described as sponge-like. The atria generally contain no compact myocardium. However, the atria of varanids and some Serpentes possess a cortical layer of compact muscle (MacKinnon and Heatwole, 1981). The right atrium is highly distensible and larger than the left atrium, especially in Serpentes (Fig. 4.2) and to a lesser extent in Testudines. The left atrium is not only smaller than the right but its wall is less muscular. The left atrium receives the pulmonary vein through an opening in the dorsal wall near the interatrial septum and not far from the sinoatrial opening. The pulmonary vein opening is frequently, but not always, guarded by a lip-like outpocketing of the endocardium that overlaps its anterior margin.

The portion of the atria adjacent to the ventricle takes the form of an inverted, truncated cone of muscle that extends for a short distance downwards into the base of the ventricle. This atrioventricular funnel, as it is called, is much thinner than the adjoining atrial walls and has muscle fibers that assume a circular arrangement around the atrioventricular opening (Fig. 4.4). The atrial and ventricular muscles contact each other only at the posterior extremity of the funnel.

Fig. 4.2. Ventral (A) and dorsal (B) views of the heart of *Naja naja*. Ventral (C) and dorsal (D) views of the heart of *Teratolepis fasciata*. Ventral (E) and dorsal (F) views of the heart of *Sphenodon punctatus*. Abbreviations: APA, anterior pulmonary artery; AT, arterial trunk; ConA, conus arteriosus; CCA, common carotid artery; DL, dorsal ligament; GC, gubernaculum cordis; LA, left atrium; LAo, left aortic arch; LCA, left carotid artery; LPA, left pulmonary artery; LPV, left pulmonary vein; PA, pulmonary arch; PCV, postcaval vein; PPA, posterior pulmonary artery; PV, pulmonary vein; PV(L), precaval vein (left); PV(R), precaval vein (right); RA, right atrium; RAo, right aortic arch; RCA, right carotid artery; RPA, right pulmonary artery; RPV, right pulmonary vein; SAV, sinoatrial valves; SS, sinus septum; SV, sinus venosus; V, ventricle. (A–D: redrawn from Kashyap, 1960; E–F: redrawn from Simons, 1965.)

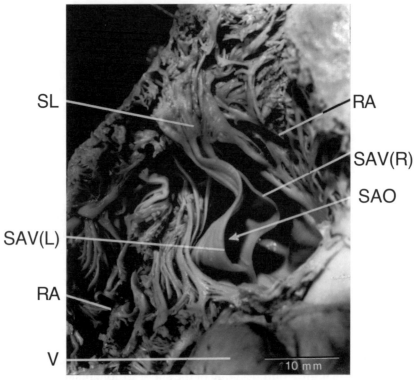

SL

RA

SAV(R)

SAO

SAV(L)

RA

V

10 mm

Fig. 4.3. *Python reticulatus.* Photograph of heart with the right atrium opened to show the sinoatrial valve. Abbreviations: RA, right atrium; SAO, sinoatrial opening; SAV (L), sinoatrial valve (left); SAV(R), sinoatrial valve (right); SL, suspensory ligament; V, ventricle.

The septal cusps are the main functional components of the atrioventricular valves in all reptiles. In addition, a pair of marginal atrioventricular valves that pair with the septal cusps to form a bicuspid valve for each atrioventricular orifice may be present. These marginal cusps are never very large and may easily be overlooked in preserved hearts.

The ventricle usually has a distinct compact (cortical) myocardium surrounding a more spongy, medullary myocardium (Fig. 4.5). Connective tissue is sparse in the ventricle, and muscle fibers are arranged in layers with differing directionality (Shaner, 1924; Benninghoff, 1933; Fig. 4.6). The fibers run lengthwise in the outermost layer (primitive longitudinal layer) and form a very thin muscular sheet extending from the gubernaculum cordis (apical ligament) towards the base of the ventricle. A second spirally arranged sheet of muscle fibers (spinospiral muscle) arises from the dorsal aspect of the atrioventricular ring and sweeps around the wall of the cavum venosum and the apical part of the cavum arteriosum and merges with the ventral vestige of the conus arteriosus. The third layer (bulbospiral muscle) arises ventrally from the atrioventricular ring, adjoining the conal vestige, sweeps around the cavum arteriosum towards the dorsal aspect; here the fibers tuck beneath those of the spirospinal component and form the vertical septum. Together, these two spiral layers represent the "circular" muscular layer. They contribute to both the compact and spongy layers, the spongy layer composed mainly of the inner terminations of the fibers forming the compact sheets (MacKinnon and Heatwole, 1981).

The spongy layer of the ventricular muscle is organized into a series of ridges running anteriorly from the apex in a dorsoventral plane. Thus, the apical portion of the ventricular cavity is divided into chambers of which there are usually seven. However, there is some variation; narrow hearts may have fewer (six in *Ophisaurus* and five in *Anguis*), but that of *Tupinambis* has at least ten. The terminology used to describe the most prominent of these ridges, and that describing the chambers separated by these muscular ridges, is variable and highly confusing. The following outlines the terminology adopted here. To assist the reader with the primary literature, we list the homologous terms.

The terminology of the three major ventricular chambers is based on that introduced by Goodrich (1919, 1930): namely, cavum pulmonale, cavum venosum, and cavum arteriosum. The cavum pulmonale has also been termed: cavum ventriculi ventrali (Greil, 1903); left chamber (O'Donoghue, 1918); ventral ventricle (de Marees van Swinderen, 1929; Leene and Vorstman, 1930; Vorstman, 1933; Benninghoff, 1933); and

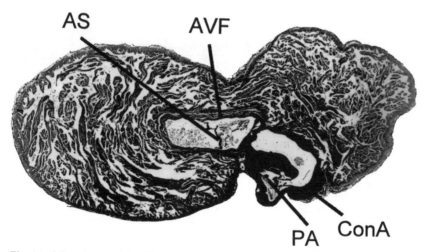

Fig. 4.4. *Sphenodon punctatus.* Transverse section through the heart of a juvenile specimen stained with haematoxylin and eosin (×47). Abbreviations: AS, atrial septum; AVF, atrioventricular funnel; ConA, conus arteriosus; PA, pulmonary artery.

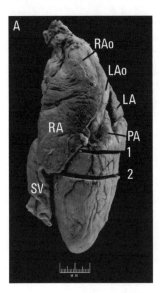

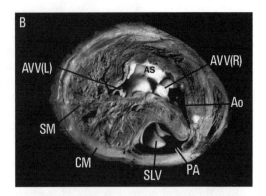

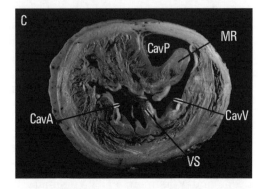

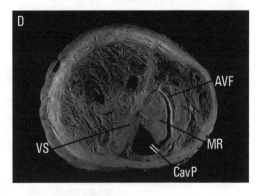

Fig. 4.5. *Python reticulatus.* Photographs of the heart, illustrating some of the external and internal features of a squamate heart. A. Ventral view from the right side of the heart showing the position of slices used to provide panels B, C, and D. B. Anterior (cranial) surface of cut 1. The cut passes through the interventricular canal. Note that the pulmonary arch is well caudal to those of the right and left aortae which are out of sight in the photograph, and that the longitudinal muscle is much thicker on the left than on the right side of the heart. C. The posterior (caudal) surface of cut 1. Note how the planes of the vertical septum and the interatrial septum coincide. This is better appreciated if one imagines panel B to be hinged downwards over C. D. Anterior surface of cut 2 showing junction of the muscular ridge and the vertical septum. Abbreviations: Ao, aortic arch opening; AS, interatrial septum; AVF, atrioventricular funnel; AVV(L), left atrioventricular valve; AVV(R), right atrioventricular valve; CavA, cavum arteriosum; CavP, cavum pulmonale; CavV, cavum venosum; CM, compact myocardium; LA, left atrium; LAo, left aortic arch; MR, muscular ridge; PA, pulmonary arch; RA, right atrium; RAo, right aortic arch; SLV, semilunar valves of the pulmonary arch opening; SM, spongy myocardium; SV, sinus venosus; VS, ventricular septum. Scale bar in panel A applies to all panels.

pulmonary compartment (Acolat, 1935). The cavum venosum has also been termed: cavum ventriculi dorsale dextrum (Greil, 1903); the right part of the dorsal ventricle (Leene and Vorstman, 1930; Vorstman, 1933; Benninghoff, 1933); the right part of the ventricle (Acolat, 1932); interventricular space (Acolat, 1935); cavum dextrum (Mathur, 1944); and right part of cavum dorsale (Mathur, 1946). The cavum arteriosum has also been termed: cavum ventriculi dorsali (Greil, 1903); cavum aorticum (Rau, 1924; Mahendra, 1942); left part of dorsal ventricle (Leene and Vorstman, 1930; Vorstman, 1933; Benninghoff, 1933; Acolat, 1932) left ventricle (Acolat, 1935); and left part of cavum dorsale (Mathur, 1946).

The ridge between the cavum arteriosum and the cavum venosum is termed the vertical septum (Leene and Vorstman, 1930) (also called incomplete septum; septum ventriculorum; and interventricular septum). This muscular septum does not completely partition these two cava, but its more prominent size serves as a landmark to demarcate the cavum arteriosum and cavum venosum (Fig. 4.5C). Although the functional role of the vertical septum in separating blood ejected from the two atria has not been experimentally established, numerous authors suggest that its position (immediately posterior to the interarterial septum) is crucial for separating pulmonary and systemic venous blood during ventricular diastole (atrial systole; see below). Because the vertical septum lies approximately opposite to the caudal edge of the interatrial septum, it

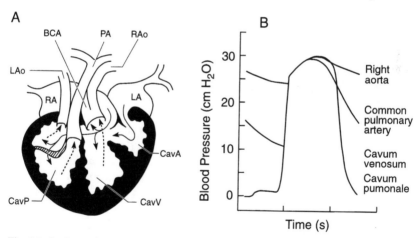

Fig. 4.6. A. Generalized anatomy and blood flow patterns in the turtle heart (solid arrows indicate flow during ventricular diastole; broken arrows indicate flow during ventricular systole). B. The intraventricular and aortic pressures during a cardiac cycle indicating that the ventricular cava function as a single pump. Abbreviations: BCA, base of carotid arch; CavA, cavum arteriosum; CavP, cavum pulmonale; CavV, cavum venosum; LA, left atrium; LAo, left aortic arch; PA, pulmonary arch; RA, right atrium; RAo, right aortic arch. (Adapted from Burggren, 1985; Heisler and Glass, 1985; Johansen and Burggren, 1980.)

is analogous to the muscular part of the ventricular septum in Crocodylia. The cavum arteriosum and cavum venosum communicate by way of the common space (interventricular canal) lying between the free margin of the vertical septum and the atrioventricular valves.

Perhaps the most characteristic, prominent, and functionally controversial ventricular ridge is the Muskelleiste (Greil, 1903) or muscular septum (Goodrich, 1919) (also termed septum ventriculorum; ridge-like partition; horizontal septum; muscular ridge; and helicoid septum). The muscular ridge demarcates, and in some species may even functionally separate, the cavum venosum and cavum pulmonale (Fig. 4.5). It consists of a strong band of muscle that arises from the fibrous (or cartilaginous, see below) base of the aortic arches between the pulmonary arch and the right aorta. From the base of the aortic arches, the muscular ridge spirals towards the apical part of the dorsal aspect of the ventricle; here it joins the dorsal portion of the vertical septum (see above). The muscular ridge is continuous with the ventral wall of the ventricle, but is incomplete dorsolaterally. Dorsolaterally, it is attached only anteriorly and posteriorly, leaving the middle as a free edge in close association with the ventricular wall (Webb et al., 1971). The size and disposition of the muscular ridge varies with the development of the vertical septum. When the vertical septum is well developed, the muscular ridge will be short and nearly horizontal in disposition, but whenever the vertical septum is short, the muscular ridge will be longer and more vertical in direction.

The more than 30 species of reptiles belonging to the genus *Varanus* display an important variation in the design of the ventricle as compared with that of other squamates (Fig. 4.1). The cavum arteriosum is enlarged and the cavum venosum reduced (cf. Fig. 4.7 to Fig. 4.5). This arrangement gives the varanid heart a greater appearance of bilateral symmetry. Furthermore, the muscular ridge is in close opposition with the aortic valves, the importance of which is explained below.

There are two major arterial outflow routes from the ventricle. The

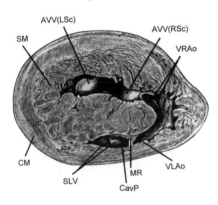

Fig. 4.7. *Varanus bengalensis.* Transverse section across the base of the ventricle. AV(LSc), septal cusp of left atrioventricular valve; AVV(RSc), septal cusp of right atrioventricular valve; CM, compact myocardium; CavP, cavum pulmonale; MR, muscular ridge; SLV, semilunar valves of the of the pulmonary arch opening; SM, spongy myocardium; VLAo, valves of left aortic arch; VRAo, valves of the right aortic arch. (Adapted from Meinertz, 1952.)

pulmonary artery is derived from the cavum pulmonale. The pulmonary trunk is relatively short in Testudines and Sauria, dividing into separate left and right pulmonary arteries that supply each lung. In those snakes that have only a single functional lung, the pulmonary trunk is unbranched. The aortic arches arise from the cavum venosum through two valved orifices.

Evolutionary parallels are often drawn between the arterial outflow vessels of the amphibian and reptilian ventricles. Blood leaves the amphibian ventricle by way of the conus arteriosus with its characteristic "spiral valve." This "spiral valve" leads to the truncus arteriosus, which consists of the confluent bases of the aortic arches, and the pulmonary arteries. In amphibians, the conus arteriosus is a true heart chamber with walls of cardiac muscle; the truncus anteriosus is arterial in origin; and the spiral valve is usually stiffened by cartilage. In reptiles, the conus has been absorbed into the ventricle so that the aortic trunks appear to rise directly from the right side of the ventricle. Only in Testudines, Rhynchocephalia (Simons, 1965), Chameleontidae, and a few other lizards are traces of a vestigial conus arteriosus visible externally (cf. Fig. 4.4). In some snakes (Young, 1994), and many reptiles (e.g., Gekkonidae; Webb, 1969) a cartilago cordis (cardiac cartilage) is found within the aorticopulmonary septum. However, Young (1994) was unable to ascribe a function to this structure. The presence of a cartilago cordis did not correlate with body size, taxonomic relationship, or habitat preference. Another internal vestige of the amphibian heart is the valve, derived from the endothelium of the conus, at the pulmonary outflow. This proposed origin for the pulmonary aortic valves suggests that the cavum pulmonale has "absorbed" the conus arteriosus. Thus, the muscular ridge, which arises from the cardiac cartilage when present, has been described as a vestige of the dorsal wall of the conus arteriosus (Acolat, 1943).

B. Functional Aspects and Blood Flow Patterns

Though the functional aspects of the reptilian heart are not the primary focus of this chapter, several anatomical features need to be placed into a functional context. We start with perhaps the most controversial, the blood flow patterns through the ventricle. The reader is directed to Johansen and Burggren (1980), Farrell (1991), Burggren et al. (1997), and Hicks (this volume) for a more complete review of the primary literature on the physiology of the reptilian heart.

The central anatomical features of the non-crocodylian ventricle are that: (1) the cavum arteriosum has direct left atrial input of pulmonary venous return, and arterial output must be directed through the cavum venosum before reaching the aortic valves; (2) the cavum pulmonale has a direct pulmonary arterial output, but no direct atrial input. Instead, right atrial blood must pass through the cavum venosum before reaching the cavum pulmonale (Fig. 4.6); and (3) the cavum venosum has direct systemic arterial outputs as well as a direct right atrial input of systemic venous blood. However, it would be erroneous to conclude that none of the blood entering the cavum venosum from the right atrium enters the systemic circuit via the aortic openings. This seemingly complicated ventricular anatomy appears to facilitate intracardiac shunting, such that the pattern of blood flow varies as a function of breathing.

The non-crocodylian ventricle is an anatomically continuous single chamber. In addition, there is no doubt that the non-crocodylian heart, with the exception of that of varanids (Fig. 4.8), operates as a single pump. The evidence for this statement is that blood pressures measured in each of the three ventricular cava are superimposable during the entire cardiac cycle in *Trachemys scripta*, *Testudo graeca* (Shelton and Burggren, 1976), and *Thamnophis* (Burggren, 1977) (e.g., Fig. 4.6). Thus, there is always potential for some mixing of right and left atrial blood within the ventricle. However, the ventricular anatomy is such that there is typically a high degree of separation between the systemic and pulmonary venous inputs. Consequently, the typical situation in non-crocodylian reptiles during ventilation is that most of the systemic

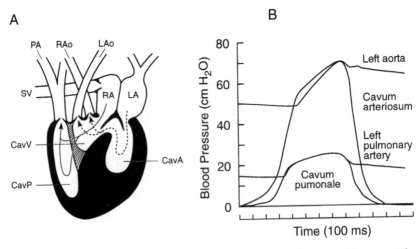

Fig. 4.8. A. Generalized anatomy and blood flow patterns in the varanid heart. B. The intraventricular and aortic pressures during a cardiac cycle indicating that the cavum pulmonale functions as a separate pump and develops lower systolic blood pressures. Abbreviations: CavA, cavum arteriosum; CavP, cavum pulmonale; CavV, cavum venosum; LA, left atrium; LAo, left aortic arch; PA, pulmonary arch; RA, right atrium; RAo, right aortic arch; SV, sinus venosus. (Adapted from Burggren, 1985; Heisler and Glass, 1985; Johansen and Burggren, 1980.)

venous input into the cavum venosum passes into the cavum pulmonale and leaves the ventricle via the pulmonary trunk. Similarly, most of the pulmonary venous input into the cavum arteriosum passes into the cavum venosum and leaves via the systemic arches. Because the diastolic blood pressure is lower in the pulmonary compared with systemic arches, flow starts in the pulmonary arteries before the systemic arteries. Furthermore, during ventilation, ventricular systemic output and pulmonary ventricular output tend to be matched, and intracardiac mixing is low; i.e., the percentages of right-to-left and left-to-right intracardiac shunting are low.

The beauty and adaptability of reptilian intracardiac shunting is realized during apneic states. During breath holding, pulmonary blood flow decreases substantially (Burggren, 1977, 1987) through vasoconstriction of the pulmonary arterial vessels. This greatly reduces the amount of pulmonary venous return (to be directed to the systemic arches via the cavum venosum). In addition, most of the systemic venous return is directed from the cavum venosum into the systemic arches (instead of entering the cavum pulmonale and leaving via the pulmonary trunk). In this case, right-to-left intracardiac shunting is very great. Clearly, their capacity for intracardiac shunting permits reptiles (like amphibians) to perfuse their systemic circulation independent of the pulmonary circulation. This cardiovascular feat is coincident with their arrhythmic breathing pattern.

What determines the degree of intracardiac shunting is controversial (see Heisler and Glass, 1985; Burggren, 1985; Hicks, this volume) and awaits careful study. Ventricular end-systolic volume, relative venous return, the extent of turbulent flow, changes in the speed of depolarization across the ventricle (Burggren, 1987), differences in the contractility of the atria and ventricle, and washout from the cavum venosum all play a role in intracardiac shunting. However, the relative vascular resistance of the pulmonary and systemic circuits and washout (referred to as the "washout hypothesis") have the greatest influence on the degree of intracardiac shunting. Outflow resistances influence the pattern of intracardiac shunting through their effects on cardiac emptying and venous return. In Testudines, the primary physiological determinant of intracardiac shunting appears to be the vascular resistance of the outflow vessels, particularly the pulmonary aorta (Hicks, this volume). In addition, "washout" from the cavum venosum contributes to the variable levels of intracardiac shunting observed in different species and under different physiological states. At its basic level, the "washout hypothesis" suggests that the degree of intracardiac shunting is in part determined by the amount of blood remaining in the cavum venosum (see Hicks and Malvin, 1992; Heisler et al., 1983). Although during contraction of the right atrium most of the systemic venous return passes through the cavum venosum en route to the cavum pulmonale, a residual amount of the systemic venous blood may still be in the cavum venosum when the cavum arteriosum contracts, ejecting blood via the cavum venosum into the systemic arches. This action results in the mixing of the two atrial supplies and a right-to-left intracardiac shunt. In contrast, left-to-right intracardiac shunting involves two cardiac cycles. There can be a residual amount of pulmonary venous blood in the cavum venosum at the end of ventricular systole (i.e., end-systolic volume of the cavum venosum is not zero). On the next heart beat, systemic venous blood pumped from the right atrium through the cavum venosum and into the cavum pulmonale will mix with this residual pulmonary venous blood resulting in a left-to-right intracardiac shunt.

The primary anatomical determinants of this intracardiac shunting would appear to be the volume of the cavum venosum, the prominence of the muscular ridge and the height of the vertical septum. (Note, however, that Grigg and Simons (1972) report that, although the vertical septum in Rhynchocephalia is low, systemic venous blood is effectively distributed into the pulmonary trunk). In this regard, the septal cusps of the atrioventricular valves may prove to be of great importance. Usually, the atrioventricular valves consist (entirely or mainly) of a single cusp carried on the edge of the interatrial septum. If one or both of these septal cusps are of sufficient length to contact each other and/or the vertical septum when forced downwards during atrial contraction (i.e., for varanids, see Heisler et al., 1983), blood flow through the atrioventricular canal would be stopped or severely reduced. The possible contributions of the general shape of the heart, the orientation of the muscle fibers in the ventricle, and the presence or absence of a gubernaculum cordis (which anchors the apex of the ventricle) to intracardiac shunting are unknown at this time.

Fig. 4.9. *Crocodylus porosus*. Schematic diagram of the crocodylian heart and major arteries. The right-hand panels show the heart opened dorsally and ventrally, along the lines A—A and B—B, respectively, shown in the adjacent left-hand panels. The location of the foramen of Panizza is indicated in the drawings on the right side by a black dot. Top right figure, solid arrows indicate the direction of blood flow during normal air breathing from left atrium to left ventricle to systemic arch. Bottom right figure, the solid arrows show the direction of flow during normal air breathing from right atrium to right ventricle to pulmonary arch. The dashed arrow, from right ventricle to left systemic arch, indicates the direction of flow when the pulmonary bypass shunt operates (e.g., during diving). Abbreviations: CCA, common carotid artery; FP, foramen of Panizza; LA, left atrium; LAo, left aortic arch; LAVC; left anterior vena cava; LPA, left pulmonary artery; LPV, left pulmonary vein; LV, left ventricle; PCV, postcaval vein; RA, right atrium; RAo, right aortic arch; RAVC, right anterior vena cava; RPA, right pulmonary artery; RPV, right pulmonary vein; RV, right ventricle; SCA, subclavian artery; SV, sinus venosus. (From Grigg, 1989.)

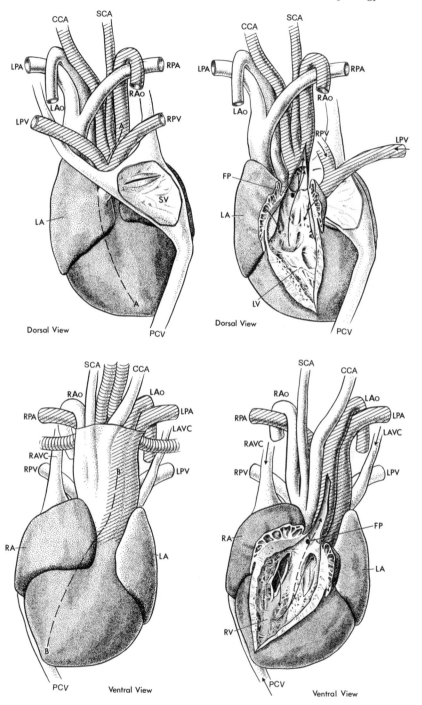

Dorsal View

Dorsal View

Ventral View

Ventral View

With regard to intracardiac shunting, the cardiac function of varanid lizards is unique among the non-crocodylians. In addition to increased bilateral symmetry and presence of a reduced cavum venosum, the entire varanid heart is more muscular, and the muscular ridge is more prominent. Nonetheless, the cavum pulmonale, as in other reptiles, is much thinner walled than the cavum arteriosum. More importantly, the ventricle functions as a double pump, generating considerably higher pressures in the cavum venosum and systemic arches than in the cavum pumonale and pulmonary arteries (Heisler et al., 1983) (Fig. 4.8). This is possible because, during systole, the cavum pulmonale becomes functionally separated from the cavum venosum and cavum arteriosum. At this moment, the muscular septum presses tightly against the bulbuslamelle on the opposing interior surface of the ventricle. This functional separation between the cavum pulmonale and the other two cava in the varanid heart likely precludes outflow resistances from influencing intracardiac shunting during ventricular systole. Consequently, the "washout hypothesis" probably explains the majority of intracardiac shunting in varanids.

IV. CARDIAC DESIGN IN CROCODYLIANS
A. Cardiac Anatomy

Shaner (1924), White (1956), and Mathur (1971) have examined the functional cardiac anatomy of *Alligator mississippiensis, Caiman crocodilus,* and *Crocodylus porosus,* respectively. Webb (1979) provides an extremely detailed description of the heart of *C. porosus,* and directly compares its anatomy with those of *Alligator mississippiensis, Caiman crocodilus, Crocodylus johnsoni,* and *C. novaeguineae.* Anatomical differences between species are minimal (Webb, 1979). In addition, Davies et al. (1952) studied the histological aspects of the crocodylian heart and concluded that, in *A. mississippiensis* and *Crocodylus niloticus,* the musculature of the chambers has uniform histological structure. Figures 4.9 and 4.10 illustrate the external anatomy of the crocodylian heart and associated vessels.

The sinus venosus has the form of an elongated pyramid, the short base of which lies cranially and the apex caudally. In *Crocodylus porosus* (Webb, 1979), the sinus venosus is formed by the confluence of the right precaval vein, the hepatic vein, and the postcaval vein. The left precaval vein is separated from this main chamber by a dorsal sinus septum. A dorsal ligament, containing the coronary vein, some small arteries, and a small ribbon-like strand of hollow tissue attaches the sinus venosus to the dorsal surface of the heart. The sinoatrial valve extends beneath the sinus septum, and its left margin lies within the left precaval vein. The walls of the sinus venosus contain cardiac muscle and are smooth and non-trabeculate internally.

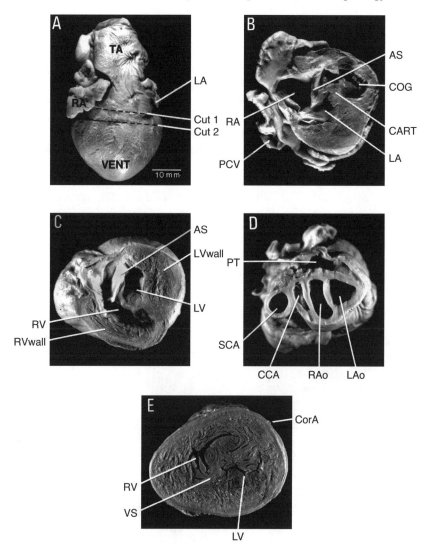

Fig. 4.10. *Alligator mississippiensis.* Photographs of the heart, illustrating some of the external and internal features of a crocodylian heart. A. Ventral view from the right side of the heart showing the position of cuts used in the transverse sections. B. Anterior (cranial) view of the tranverse section at cut 1. C. Posterior (caudal) view of the tranverse section at cut 1. D. Section through the truncus arteriosus. E. Anterior view of the tranverse section at cut 2. Abbreviations: AS, interatrial septum; CorA, coronary arteries; CART, cartilage; CCA, common carotid artery; COG, lobes of "cog-valve" guarding left aortic arch; LA, left atrium; LAo, left aortic arch; LV, left ventricle; LVwall, left ventricular wall; PCV, postcaval vein; PT, pulmonary trunk; RA, right atrium; RAo, right aortic arch; RV, right ventricle; RVwall; right ventricular wall; SCA, subclavian artery; TA, truncus arteriosus; VENT, ventricle; VS, ventricular septum. Scale bar in A applies to all panels.

The two atria are nearly equal in size. The right atrium, which over-hangs the anterior ventrolateral surface of the ventricle, is more compartmentalized than the left. The lateral portion of the right atrium is trabecularized and extends around the truncus to the ventral side of the heart, where it can be broadly subdivided into anterior and posterior chambers. In addition, two distinct compartments on the dorsal surface of the right atrium contain trabeculae. The posterior of these compartments is a thin-walled outpushing of the atrium located just anterior to the atrioventricular valves. This posterior outpushing of the right atrium is prominent in all species studied and is unique among reptiles. The interatrial septum possesses a continuous muscular sheet between the two endocardial layers rather than the open meshwork found in Sauria. There are no valves between the pulmonary veins and the left atrium. However, a small vertically oriented trabecular bundle lies under the entrance of the left and right pulmonary veins. This bundle is associated with a distinct outpushing of the left atrial wall. The atrial funnel extends well into the dorsal side of the ventricle, and its posterior extremity contains the atrioventricular (AV) valves. Both atrioventricular valves

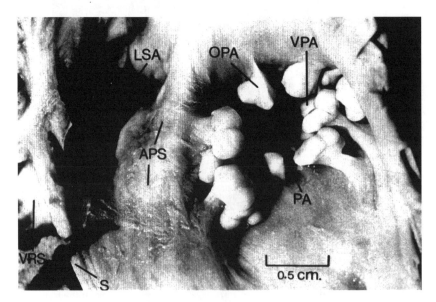

Fig. 4.11. *Crocodylus porosus.* The "cog-valve" in the anterior extremity of the right ventricle of a 4.2 m specimen as seen from the ventricle. Abbreviations: APS, aorticopulmonary septum; LSA, left systemic artery posterior to aortic arch valves; OPA, outpushings of the pulmonary artery wall posterior to aortic arch valves; PA, pulmonary arch; VPA, valve of the pulmonary artery, anterior to the outpushings; VRS, medial valve of left ventricle; S, membranous septum which, has been cut to allow access to the left ventricle. (From Webb, 1979.)

are composed of a septal and a marginal cusp. Although both cusps of the left AV valves are membranous, the marginal cusp of the right AV valve is a thick, lip-like structure.

The heart of crocodylians is distinct from that of all other reptiles; it has two ventricles that are morphologically separated by a distinct muscular septum. In addition, the posterior third of the ventricle is heavily trabecularized. The tightly packed trabeculae that compose the intraventricular septum create small (1.5 mm) spaces that extend from one ventricle to another. The function of these passages is unknown. About mid-ventricle, a ventral branch of the muscular septum functionally divides the right ventricle into lateral and ventral chambers. Further anteriorly, this branch is called the aorticopulmonary septum and separates the pulmonary artery from the left systemic one. Near the base of the ventricle, the dorsal portion of the muscular septum is thin and membranous. This "membranous septum" terminates in the interatrial septum on the dorsal side of the ventricle, whereas it merges into the muscular septum on the ventral side to form the interaortic septum. The walls of the right ventricle, which lead to the pulmonary aortic valve, contain connective tissue blocks (lobes) that appear to fit together like the teeth of opposing cogs (Fig. 4.11). The external interventricular sulcus, or groove, marks the junction between the right and left ventricles.

There are three major outflow vessels from the crocodylian ventricles. The right aorta leaves the left ventricle, dividing anteriorly to form the carotid and subclavian arteries and posteriorly to form the dorsal aorta. The pulmonary artery leaves the right ventricle and supplies the right and left lungs. An additional outflow from the right ventricle is the left aorta. The right and left aortae are interconnected at two locations. An opening between the right and left aortae, known as the foramen of Panizza (Panizza, 1833), lies just above (distal to) the bicuspid valves that guard the openings of the aortae (Fig. 4.12A). Distally, the left and right aortae may be connected by a small vessel (the dorsal connecting vessel), with the left aorta continuing on to supply the viscera. Alternatively, the left and right aortae join to form a single vessel.

Each of the outflow arteries has a bicuspid valve at its base. In both aortae, the cusp associated with the interaortic septum (medial cusp) is longer than the lateral cusp. The medial cusps on the right aorta extend anteriorly during ventricular systole and cover the foramen of Panizza. At the level of the aortic valves, the left aorta, right aorta, and pulmonary artery have a similar diameter. However, further anteriorly, the pulmonary and right systemic arteries expand into large aortic "sinuses" that extend to a level approximated by the anterior extremity of the atria. The two aortae and the pulmonary artery are bound by a thick connective tissue sheath. Because of the expansion of the pulmonary and right

Fig. 4.12. A. Schematic diagram to show the position of the foramen of Panizza in the common wall of the left and right aortae and obscured by a semilunar valve. B. Schematic diagram of blood flow patterns from the right (solid arrows) and left (broken arrows) ventricles during (1) normal air breathing and (2) apneic states. Abbreviations: CCA, common carotid artery; LAo, left aortic arch; LV, left ventricle; PA pulmonary artery; RAo, right aortic arch; RV, right ventricle; SCA, subclavian artery. (Adapted from Grigg, 1989.)

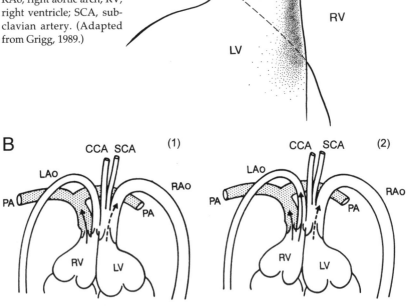

systemic artery into "sinuses," this connective tissue forms a truncus that is significantly broader than that of other reptiles. This common sheath has been erroneously labelled the "bulbus" by some authors (e.g., Swett, 1923; Greil, 1903); however, it consists solely of fibrous tissue, smooth muscle, and "cardiac cartilage." This cartilaginous strut sweeps around the distal margin of the foramen of Panizza (see White, 1956). A small conus arteriosus is detectable (although not externally visible) as a spiral bend of muscle around the pulmonary arch.

All species thus far examined have a gubernaculum cordis. In large specimens of *Crocodylus porosus* and *C. johnstoni*, the gubernaculum cordis consists of a single primary trunk (strand), whereas smaller specimens have up to ten secondary strands in addition to the primary one. The primary gubernacular strand of *C. porosus* contains a blood vessel that can be traced anteriorly into the lumen of the right ventricle. In contrast to other reptiles, the gubernaculum cordis of crocodylians extends from the right ventricle (not from the heart apex as in Testudines and Sauria).

B. Functional Aspects and Blood Flow Patterns

The functional significance of the dual outflow (pulmonary and systemic) from the right ventricle and the interconnections of the left and right aortae have been the subject of much investigation and speculation (White, 1956, 1969; Greenfield and Morrow, 1961; Webb, 1979; Grigg and Johansen, 1987; Axelsson et al. 1989; Grigg, 1989, 1991; Shelton and Jones, 1991; Pettersson et al., 1992; M. Axelsson et al., pers. comm.; Jones and Shelton, 1993). Nonetheless, it is clear that the crocodylian heart can function in two ways: whenever the animal has free access to air, the heart functions in a manner analogous to the mammalian heart with matched outputs to the pulmonary and systemic circulations; during apnea, it functions in a manner analogous to other reptilian hearts with a right-to-left shunt. The key to this dual mode of pumping is the left aortic opening in the right ventricle, coupled with active control of outflow resistance to the pulmonary circuit.

During free access to air, pressures developed by the right ventricle are much lower than those developed by the left ventricle as a result of a much lower pulmonary vascular resistance as compared with the systemic vascular resistance. In addition, the blood pressures in the left and right aortae are equal because the interconnections between the two vessels (i.e., the foramen of Panizza and the dorsal connecting vessel) are patent. Consequently, the bicuspid valve that guards the orifice of the left aorta remains closed (right ventricular systolic pressure does not exceed left aortic blood pressure). In this situation, all of the right ventricular output goes to the lungs. In addition, the output of the left ventricle goes primarily into the right aorta because one of the tricuspid valves guarding the right aorta folds back to cover the entire foramen of Panizza during systole. However, elastic recoil may drive a small amount of blood from the right aorta to left aorta during diastole.

During apnea, there may develop a pulmonary bypass of as much as 25%. This right-to-left shunt is mediated by several key events. Foremost, the resistance to pulmonary outflow must increase; this increase is most likely achieved via active regulation of the diameter of the cog-like valve at the base of the pulmonary artery rather than vasoactivity in the pulmonary artery per se (D. R. Jones, pers. comm.). The active regulation causes right ventricular pressures to rise. Provided that right ventricular systolic pressure exceeds the diastolic pressure in the left systemic aorta, there can be simultaneous output from the right ventricle into the left aorta and the pulmonary arteries. The distribution of blood flow will be set by the relative resistances of the two circuits (systemic resistance can decrease and pulmonary outflow resistance can increase). Because a portion of the systemic venous return by-passes the pulmonary circuit (a right-to-left shunt), left ventricular output decreases proportionately. The fate of blood entering the left aorta is unclear at this time. Most of the blood probably follows the course of the left aorta. However, some blood could pass into the right aorta via the foramen of Panizza.

V. RELATIVE ATRIAL VOLUMES

The greater volume (size) of the right atrium relative to the left atrium is a curiosity of certain reptiles that has yet to be studied physiologically. From a functional standpoint, the different volumes of the right and left atria have two possible implications. End-systolic volume of an enlarged right atrium would have to be greater than that of the left atrium under conditions where total pulmonary and total systemic flows are reasonably well-matched (i.e., in ventilating reptiles). However, under apneic conditions, an enlarged right atrium could accommodate the increased systemic venous return associated with a right-to-left intracardiac shunt. Interestingly, unequal atrial volumes are characteristic of Testudines and Serpentes, both of which engage in long apneic periods. Thus, a large right atrial volume could have evolved in association with relatively high levels of right-to-left shunting.

Alternately, the functional significance of the large right atrial volume in association with a low sinus venosus volume in Serpentes (and other Reptilia) may be related to venous blood reservoirs and the mode of locomotion. Skeletal muscle contractions associated with locomotion in snakes will tend to move venous blood caudally. Because blood is stored primarily in the venous side of the circulatory system, it would seem advantageous for snakes to store venous blood in the atrium rather than in the sinus venosus. Blood stored in the atrium would be prevented from refluxing into the venous system because of the well developed sinoatrial valve. In contrast, a large sinus venosus with no valve to prevent reflux may be susceptible to venous return problems during locomotion. A greater knowledge of the relative degrees of right-to-left and left-to-right intracardiac shunting, and atrial end-systolic volume, is needed before the functional significance of the disparity in atrial size can be fully resolved.

VI. THE CORONARY CIRCULATION

The reptilian heart, like that of many other lower vertebrates (Burggren et al., 1997), receives a dual O_2 supply: from the coronary circulation as well as from the venous blood contained in the cardiac chambers. This situation contrasts with avian and mammalian hearts (in which almost the entire myocardium is dependent on the coronary circulation) because only the compact layer of myocardium apparently has a coronary circulation (Juhász-Nagy et al., 1963). The O_2 delivery to spongy myocardium, which makes up approximately 60 to 80% of ventricular mass (Burggren et al., 1996), is entirely dependent upon the venous blood that percolates through its trabeculate structure. The distribution pattern of the coronary circulation in reptiles, like that in other lower vertebrates, has not been extensively studied. However, Grant and Regnier (1926) provide a general overview of the reptilian coronary vasculature, and MacKinnon and Heatwole (1981) provide a detailed description of the coronary arterial supply of numerous reptilian families.

Coronary vessels are generally restricted to the reptilian ventricle, and the extent of coronary development appears to be related to the level of cardiac work. "Fine" coronary vessels are found on the ventricle of squamate lizards, whereas the ventricle of varanid lizards has larger vessels (MacKinnon and Heatwole, 1981). The varanid heart generates higher systemic blood pressure compared with that of other squamates. Similarly, the coronary circulation is more extensive on the left then on the right side of the crocodylian heart.

The reptilian atrium and sinus venosus often lack a compact layer and a coronary circulation. This condition may be directly related to the relatively lower work output of the atrium and sinus venosus as compared with that of the ventricle. However, both the atria and the sinus venosus of varanid lizards and elapid snakes have coronary vessels (MacKinnon and Heatwole, 1981). In addition, numerous reptilian families possess coronary arteries that supply the atria and sinus venosus to varying degrees (e.g., Helodermatidae, Agamidae, Acrochordidae, Boidae, Colubridae). Burggren et al. (in press) have suggested that a coronary supply to the atria may become more important in those reptiles that grow quite large and in which the atrial wall necessarily thickens. Control of coronary blood flow and coronary vasoactivity has received virtually no attention beyond the studies of Juhász-Nagy et al. (1964) on *Emys orbicularis* and Drury and Smith (1924) on *Testudo*.

In reptiles, the coronary circulation has two possible sites of origin. All reptiles possess either one or two anterior (cranial, cephalad) coronary arteries derived from the right (and sometimes the left) systemicocarotid trunk (Fig. 4.13). The origin of the artery varies somewhat in the exact distance from the heart, but usually it is located prior to the division of the right aorta. An exception to this general pattern is seen in *Chelodina longicollis* (MacKinnon and Heatwole, 1981) in which the coronary artery arises from the right esophageal artery. In some families, there is an additional posterior (caudal) origin from the coeliacomesenteric or epigastric (internal mammary) artery that passes through the gubernaculum cordis and usually goes to the apex of the ventricle. However, the presence of a gubernaculum cordis does not necessarily mean that it contains a coronary artery.

When one anterior coronary artery is present, it passes ventrally along the aortic arches and bifurcates into ventral and dorsal branches (Fig. 4.13). The ventral branch is usually smaller and chiefly supplies the ventral right side of the ventricle (Grant and Regnier, 1926). The dorsal branch travels along the right auriculoventricular sulcus and bifurcates into a main stem and a smaller posttruncal (intertruncal) artery. The dorsal branch supplies blood to the dorsal ventricular surface, the atria, and the sinus venosus (Grant and Regnier, 1926). The posttruncal artery supplies the atria, aor-

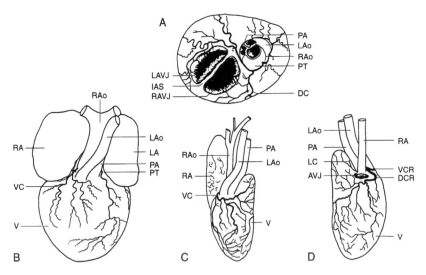

Fig. 4.13. Composite drawings to illustrate the coronary circulation on the surface of reptilian hearts. A. *Varanus varius* showing origin and major branches near the arterial trunks. B. *Varanus varius* in ventral view showing areas of distribution. C. Ventral view (with left atrium not shown) and D. dorsal view (with atria removed) in *Dendrelaphis punctulatus* showing coronary artery distribution pattern. Abbreviations: AVJ, atrioventricular junction; DC, dorsal division of coronary artery; DCR, dorsal division of right coronary artery; IAS, interaortic septum; LA, left atrium; LAo, left aortic arch; LAVJ, left atrioventricular junction; LC, left coronary artery; PA, pulmonary arch; PT, posttruncal branch of the coronary artery; RA, right atrium; RAo, right aortic arch; RAVJ, right atrioventricular junction; V, ventricle; VC, ventral division of coronary artery; VCR, ventral division of right coronary artery. (From MacKinnon and Heatwole, 1981.)

tic arches, and the ventral surface of the ventricle to varying degrees. When two coronary arteries are present, the right coronary artery corresponds to the ventral coronary artery plus the main stem of the dorsal coronary artery. The left coronary artery, which also arises from the right aorta, appears on the dorsal surface of the truncus arteriosus between the right aorta and the pulmonary artery. It then travels behind the pulmonary artery and generally supplies the same areas as the posttruncal artery (the ventral surface of the atria and ventricle).

Descriptions of the coronary veins in Reptilia are also limited. In *Testudo graeca* and *Lacerta viridis* (Grant and Regnier, 1926), the coronary veins are arranged into three groups that usually unite on the base of the ventricle before passing to the sinus venosus via the dorsal ligament (see Fig. 4.1). In addition, a vein draining the apex of the heart occurs in the gubernaculum cordis, and is connected to the abdominal veins (*Testudo*) or abdominal vein (*Lacerta*).

VII. CONDUCTING TISSUES

Histologically, the musculature of the reptilian heart consists of elongated, striated, branching muscle fibers of remarkably uniform structure. Some variation in breadth of fibers may occur, but it does not follow a uniform or regular pattern (Davies et al., 1952). Fibrous connective tissue surrounds the muscle fibers and serves to insulate them from each other except at their ends, where junctions with neighboring fibers are established. Connective tissue is extensive in the sinus venosus, moderate in the atria, and sparse in the ventricle.

In addition to the striated, parallel-sided muscle fibers common to all parts of the heart throughout reptiles, there are also other fibers that are characterized by large, conspicuous, peripheral, and sometimes multiple nuclei that lie in a clear cytoplasm devoid of striations. Such fibers do not stain as readily as the "normal" type and are not parallel-sided. Instead, these fibers are wider in the region of the nucleus than elsewhere. Robb (1953) provides a good description of these fibers in the heart of *Trachemys scripta elegans*. They occur in scattered strands in the sinus venosus, atria, and ventricle of this species, both deep within the myocardium and subendocardially. Although Robb calls them "Purkinje-like" because their clear perinuclear zone and faint peripheral striations recall the features characteristic of mammalian Purkinje fibers, she notes that there is no experimental evidence to suggest that these cells have specialized conducting properties similar to those demonstrated for the latter.

In agreement with the prevailing dogma that there are no "Purkinje fibers" in lower vertebrates, Buchanan (1956) found no "Purkinje" fibers or nodal fibers in a skink (*Oligosoma grande*). In addition, Buchanan suggests that the "Purkinje fibers" described by Robb were probably normal muscle fibers that showed localized bulgings.

The junctional fibers that separate the musculature of one cardiac chamber from that of the next show little or no specialization in reptiles, except that fibers at these sites tend to follow an annular or circular pathway, especially at the atrioventricular junction. Thus, it would appear that, in reptiles as in amphibians (Davies and Francis, 1941), it is the topographical arrangement of the muscle fibers at the junctional sites, rather than their histological specialization, that accounts for the pauses occurring between the contraction of one cardiac chamber and the next.

Robb (1953) describes an invaginated atrioventricular funnel, comparable to that of amphibians, at the atrioventricular junction of *Trachemys*. In addition, Davies et al. (1952) reported an annular, or ring-like arrangement of muscle at both the sinoatrial and atrioventricular junctions of a crocodile; the right portion of the funnel being more extensive than the left. These authors show that, at the sinoatrial junction, the bases of the sinoatrial valves are muscular and contain components from both the sinus venosus and the right atrium. Detailed description of the heart of *Oligosoma grande* shows that the sinoatrial valve is entirely muscular with a tri-laminar structure formed of sinus and atrial muscle separated by connective tissue (Buchanan, 1956); hence, in this lizard, the muscular junction between sinus and right atrium occurs at the free edge of the valve. The muscle fibers of the atrioventricular funnel follow a largely circular arrangement, particularly at the base of the funnel, at which the atrial wall is thickened and there is an abrupt change from the trabecular arrangement found elsewhere in the atria; this forms the atrioventricular ring (Fig. 4.4). At the caudal end of the funnel, muscle fibers of the atria and ventricle are freely continuous, although ventrally and to the right, near the origins of the great vessels, they remain separated by fibrous tissue (Buchanan, 1956).

VIII. CARDIAC INNERVATION

There is little information on the anatomy of the vagal and sympathetic nerves that supply the reptilian heart. Vagal parasympathetic (cholinergic) innervation is well developed and appears to be the principle mode for neural modulation of chronotropy and inotropy in reptiles. In contrast, there is little sympathetic (adrenergic) contribution to the heart from the cervical vagus nerve. In crocodylians, cardiac sympathetic fibers approach the vagus only close to the heart (Gaskell, 1884; Gaskell and Gadow, 1884). This finding was confirmed by physiological measurements on *Tiliqua rugosa* (de la Lande et al., 1962; Berger, 1971). It was reported that cardiac sympatho-mimetic responses to vagal stimulation occur only when the stimulating electrodes are placed very close (within 1–2 cm) to the heart.

In reptiles, sympathetic innervation of the heart appears to be associated with fibers from the "stellate ganglion complex," which lies near the level of the heart (Gaskell, 1884; Berger, 1971).

Based on histochemical evidence in *Tiliqua rugosa*, Furness and Moore (1970) concluded that the caval veins, sinus venosus, atria, and papillary muscle of the ventricle receive adrenergic innervation. In contrast, Burnstock (1969) indicates that there is little evidence for adrenergic innervation of reptilian ventricles.

IX. STRUCTURAL VARIATION ASSOCIATED WITH REPTILIAN ORDERS AND FAMILIES (EXCLUDING CROCODYLIA)

A. General

The cardiac morphology of numerous reptilian orders and families has been described in greater detail than presented above. However, because these studies were completed by several authors, the descriptions often lack uniformity, and specific inter-group comparisons are difficult. This section provides some additional detail to the morphological features that are generally characteristic of most reptilian families by describing the cardiac anatomy of specific examples. Where appropriate, we highlight features that distinguish each group from other reptilian taxa. These examples were selected because they have been examined in the most detail. The appendix to this chapter lists all of the species for which we found information on cardiac anatomy.

B. Order Testudines

Burne (1905), O'Donoghue (1918), Goodrich (1919), Acolat (1938), Mathur (1946), and Girgis (1961) may be cited among the more recent general studies on the testudinian heart, whereas Robb (1953), Fawcett and Selby (1958), Bergmann (1960), and March (1961) have made significant contributions on matters of detail.

Apart from the breadth of the heart, the most noteworthy external features of the testudinian heart are the widely separated atria and the absence of any auricular appendages (Fig. 4.14). The left and right atria are quadrangular and triangular in appearance, respectively, when viewed from the ventral aspect. In addition, two authors have described openings between the two aortic trunks. Although these orifices may appear to be analogous with the foramen of Panizza of the crocodylian heart, they are certainly not homologous with it. In both *Testudo graeca* (Price, 1954) and *Dermochelys* (Adams, 1962), this opening (foramen) provides for the admixture of blood between the left aorta and the brachiocephalic trunk. In contrast with the foramen of Panizza in Crocodylia, these openings are quite distal to the heart.

The testudinian family Trionychidae is peculiar in having the heart displaced towards the right side of the body. Girgis (1961) studied the hearts of the nine then-recognized genera of this family in some detail. He believed that this highly characteristic asymmetry is due to the co-incidence of two factors: a highly retractile (and protractile) neck and a very flat carapace. The flatness of the carapace gives very little space to accommodate the retracted neck and the muscles that retract it, as well as the viscera. Therefore, the heart and the liver are displaced over to the right, and the stomach is displaced to the left. These morphological adaptations presumably make room for the neck and its muscles. In the genus *Cyclanorbis*, the carapace is more convex, and, consequently, the asymmetry is much less marked than in the above genera (e.g., *Trionyx*).

The heart of members of the family Trionychidae shows fairly normal testudinian structure apart from its position in the body. The sinus venosus lies outside the pericardial cavity, is triangular in shape, and is formed by the confluence of the three caval veins and the hepatic vein; the hepatic vein merges with the left precaval vein at the base angle of the sinus venosus. Internally, the sinus venosus of Testudines differs from that of saurians or Serpentes in that it is undivided and has a robust sinoatrial valve. The sinoatrial valve comprises two large cusps that overlap when it is closed and that join dextrally to a slip of muscle. This muscle merges anteriorly, and to the right, with the pectineal muscles of the right atrium. The sinus venosus varies considerably in size from one genus to another. It is small in *Chelonia mydas*, larger in *Caretta caretta*, *Geochelone denticulata*, and the Emydidae, and very large (as large as the right atrium) in *Macroclemys temminckii*. In *Dermochelys*, the sinus venosus is connected to the ventricle by a discrete ligament that contains coronary veins, a small artery, and 14 nerves.

The right atrium of Testudines is considerably larger than the left, and the ventricle appears from the ventral aspect "as a flat body with a bluntly rounded apex" (Girgis, 1961) (Fig. 4.14). In addition, both atria, but particularly the right, are spongy and contain numerous strong pectineal muscles. Thus, in general, the atrial walls are well developed in Testudines as compared with those in other reptiles. The aortic arches are relatively large, and their roots form a vestigial conus arteriosus that occupies about two-thirds of the ventricle towards the right. Both atrioventricular openings are guarded by membranous septal valves, the right cusp usually larger than the left. The muscular ridge is well developed and commonly arises from a cardiac cartilage located in the aorticopulmonary trunk. This cartilage frequently has a bony nucleus. The muscular ridge curves in a slight arc towards the dorsal wall of the ventricle, but does not extend as far towards the apex as it does in Sauria and Serpentes. The interventricular canal, which lies between the vertical septum and the atrioventricular valves, is relatively large in broad hearts but more restricted in elongated ones. The left portion particularly varies in extent, being small in *Chelonia mydas*, the radial septa of which are relatively high, intermediate in *Dermochelys*, and larger and more significant in *Caretta*. Usually, there are eight peripheral, dorso-ventral chambers that lie between the radial septa towards the apex of the ventricles. The radial septa frequently terminate at their apices in filaments comprising both muscular and connective tissues that anastomose to form a network; this is a feature peculiar to testudinian hearts.

C. Order Rhynchocephalia

1. FAMILY SPHENODONTIDAE *Sphenodon* has been studied by O'Donoghue (1920), Simons (1965), and Webb et al. (1974). The sinus venosus is a thin-walled, muscular sac lying at the junction of the postcaval and right precaval veins and is joined on the left by the left precaval vein (Fig. 4.2F). The terminal portion of the left precaval vein passes transversely across the coronary sulcus, and its opening into the sinus is marked by a distinct ridge. The sinoatrial opening is at a 75° angle to the vertical axis, and the bases of the sinoatrial valves are thickened and muscular.

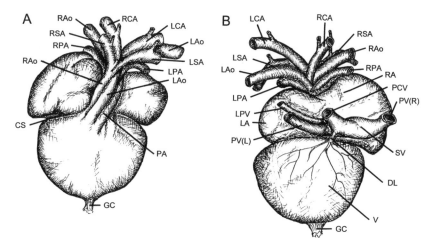

Fig. 4.14. *Dermochelys coriacea.* Ventral (A) and dorsal (B) views of the heart. Abbreviations: CS, coronary sulcus; DL, dorsal ligament; GC, gubernaculum cordis; LA, left atrium; LAo, left aortic arch; LCA, left carotid artery; LPA, left pulmonary artery; LPV, left pulmonary vein; LSA, left sciatic artery; PCV, postcaval vein; PA, pulmonary arch ; PV(L), precaval vein (left); PV(R), precaval vein (right); RA, right atrium; RAo, right aortic arch; RCA, right carotid artery; RPA, right pulmonary artery; RSA, right sciatic artery; SV, sinus venosus; V, ventricle. (Redrawn from O'Donoghue, 1918.)

The right atrium has a greater volume than the left. However, this feature is not apparent externally because there is no caudal extension of the right atria. Most of the right atrium is relatively thin-walled, but the posterior lateral section is thicker walled and has numerous interlacing pectineal muscles internally. In the right atrium, O'Donoghue (1920) described "a small, sac-like diverticulum with thin walls which, when distended with blood, showed above the diverging bases of the carotid arteries." Simons (1965) confirms this arrangement for *Sphenodon punctatus*, but says it is not a constant feature. The left atrium is similar in general structure to the right. The pulmonary veins enter the left atrium through an unvalved aperture located in the medial dorsal wall.

The ventricle is clearly demarcated from the atria by the transverse coronary sulcus. The arterial trunks leave the ventricle from a small anterior projection just to the right of the midline. This "anterior projection" is clearly a conus arteriosus, the striated muscles of which encircle the base of the pulmonary arch (see Fig. 4.4). The ventricle is very spongy, having little compact muscle. In young hearts, the ventricular lumen often extends right to the epicardium (Fig. 4.4); however, Simons (1965) describes a thin (0.8 mm), cortical muscle layer in larger, and presumably older, specimens.

The ventricle contains both a vertical septum and a muscular ridge. However, the vertical septum has a low profile and spongy texture, and the muscular ridge is not highly developed. This muscular ridge, which arises from the cartilage within the pulmoarterial septum, extends caudally and towards the right and fuses with the ventricular muscle before reaching the vertical septum. A delicate gubernaculum cordis, containing a small coronary artery, is usually present.

The heart of *Sphenodon* has been described by some authors as a "primitive" reptilian heart. The reasons given for this suggestion are: (1) the presence of a distinct conus arteriosus; (2) the poor development of the vertical septum and muscular ridge; and (3) the absence of a well developed compact muscle layer.

D. Order Squamata

1. SUBORDER SAURIA

a. FAMILY AGAMIDAE Bhatia (1929a, 1929b) gives a general account of the anatomy of the agamid heart. A good comparative account of the internal features of the ventricle and of the origin of the arterial arches is provided by Webb (1969).

The large sinus venosus is partially divided into right and left moieties by a well-marked constriction, visible externally and marked internally by a well developed sinus septum. In *Calotes* (E. T. B. Francis, unpublished observations), the sinoatrial opening lies in the anterior margin of the right atrium, and the opening of the pulmonary vein into the left atrium lies very close to the thin but muscular interatrial septum. The pulmonary opening of *Calotes* is not "valved." However, *Uromastyx hardwickii* (Bhatia, 1929b; Webb, 1969) and *Draco dussumieri* (Prakash and Raghaveuah, 1957; Webb, 1969) have a pulmonary vein orifice guarded by a lip-like outgrowth of the endocardium at its exterior aspect. Bhatia (1929a, 1929b) indicates that the sinoatrial aperture is not "valved," but is associated with "thick and muscular lips." In *Calotes*, in contrast, the sinoatrial opening is guarded by the usual pair of valvular cusps.

According to Bhatia (1929a, 1929b), the right atrium is larger than the left, and possesses a sac-like diverticulum. Although the atrial walls are generally thin, thickening of some sections of the right atrial wall is associated with "interlacing muscular ridges."

All agamids have both a vertical septum and a muscular ridge, although there are specific differences in their development relative to each other. The muscular ridge is broad and ribbon-like. Webb (1969) has described a distinct trans-sulcal membrane in *Physignathus lesueurii* that crosses the prominent interventricular sulcus leaving a space between the membrane and the myocardium. He can ascribe no function to this structure and gives no precise account of the position of the space. Presumably it is subepicardial, but may be intraepicardial. He suggests that the membrane "has some restricting influence on ventricular expansion or contraction," but, in the absence of histological details, it is difficult to see reasons for this assumption. All agamids have a gubernaculum cordis that carries coronary vessels to the apex of the pyramidal-shaped ventricle.

b. Family Chameleontidae

The heart of the chameleon has not attracted the attention of many workers, and apart from the statement of Acolat (1943) that the ventricle of *Chamaeleo chameleon* possesses the seven apical chambers typical of the reptilian heart, no other observations worthy of note seem to have been made concerning its internal features. Drawings by Kashyap (1960) clearly illustrate the external features of the chameleon heart (Fig. 4.15). The sinus venosus is well developed, and a substantial constriction is visible between the swollen terminal portion of the left precaval vein and the confluence of the postcaval and right precaval veins. The right and left atria are nearly equal in size, and a well-developed atrial diverticulum is visible between the two carotid arteries. These carotid arteries arise by means of a short common carotid stem that leaves the right aortic arch (Fig. 4.15). A vestigial conus arteriosus is present at the base of the arterial trunk, and a gubernaculum cordis attaches the apex of the ventricle to the pericardium (Fig. 4.15). The apical two-thirds of the ventricle is anchored to the pericardium by a mesocardial membrane. Whether this membrane is a vestige of an embryonic structure or a subsequent structural development is unclear.

c. FAMILY GEKKONIDAE

The most complete descriptions of gekkonid cardiac anatomy are provided by Mahendra (1942) and Webb (1969). In *Hemidactylus flaviviridis*, the sinus venosus is dorso-ventrally flattened and disposed transversely (Mahendra, 1942). It consists of a large right and a small left portion, but there is no constriction or valve separating these two regions. The sinoatrial opening of *H. flaviviridis* is bounded by thickened muscular lips unfurnished by definite membranous extensions. However, *Gehyra variegata* and *Oedura* have well-developed sinoatrial valves (Webb, 1969).

In the Gekkonidae, the atria are nearly equal in size, and apical diverticuli are generally absent (for an exception see *Hemidactylus leschenaultii*). The ventricle is attached to the pericardium by an avascular gubernaculum cordis, and some species (e.g., *Gekko verticillatus*; Das and Das, 1931) also have "thread-like tendons." In general, the vertical septum is restricted to the apical region. The mus-

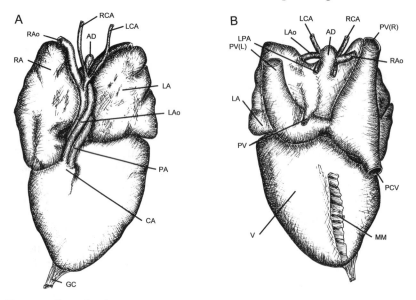

Fig. 4.15. *Chamaeleo chamaeleon*. Ventral (A) and dorsal (B) views of the heart. Abbreviations: AD, atrial diverticulum; LA, left atrium; LAo, left aortic arch; LCA, left carotid artery; LPA, left pulmonary artery; MM, mesocardial membrane; PCV, postcaval vein; PV, pulmonary vein; PV(L), precaval vein (left); PV(R), precaval vein (right); RAo, right aortic arch; RCA, right carotid artery; V, ventricle. (Redrawn from Kashyap, 1960.)

cular ridge is well developed and appears "thick and square" in transverse sections (Webb, 1969). Cartilage is present within the aorticopulmonary trunk (Webb, 1969). In addition, the bases of the aortic arches separate from the ventricle before the right and left aortic arches become distinct in section.

d. FAMILY TEIIDAE

Tupinambis teguixin has been studied and described in some detail (Acolat, 1943). The sinus venosus is partially divided by a fold between the larger right and the smaller left sections. The opening of the pulmonary vein into the left atrium is guarded by a small fold of endocardium. There are at least ten well-marked apical chambers in the ventricle, separated from one another by vertical septa. This number of apical chambers is exceptionally high (cf. Section III). The ventricle has a well developed muscular ridge.

e. FAMILY SCINCIDAE

The skinks have been more extensively studied than most groups of saurians. The genera *Acontias, Egernia, Lygosoma, Mabuya, Oligosoma, Sphenomorphus,* and *Tiliqua* are particularly well documented (Rau, 1924; van der Merwe, 1943; Kashyap, 1951; Buchanan, 1956; Rastogi, 1959; Webb, 1969).

In *Oligosoma grande* (Buchanan, 1956), the sinus venosus possesses a constriction between the larger right and smaller left portions and is connected to the ventricle by a dorsal ligament. However, there appears to be a considerable amount of variation in the shape of the sinus venosus. *Lygosoma guentheri* (Kashyap, 1951) has a triangular sinus venosus that is confined to the dorsal aspect of the right atrium, with the left precaval vein crossing transversely across the left atrium, as in *Sphenodon*. The sinus venosus of *Acontias meleagris* (van der Merwe, 1943) receives not only three caval veins and a coronary vein, but also anterior and posterior azygous veins. In *Oligosoma grande*, the coronary vein is contained within the dorsal ligament.

The sinoatrial orifice in *Oligosoma grande* is crescentic, obliquely placed (as is usual), and is guarded by a pair of thin, muscular cusps that end freely on the left, but are attached to a suspensory ligament on the right. The posterior (or right) cusp is bi-laminar, containing reflexions of both sinus and atrial musculature that become directly continuous at the free margin. As with the sinus venosus, variations in the orientation and structure of the sinoatrial valves have been recorded. In *Lygosoma guentheri* and *Tiliqua scincoides* (Rau, 1924; Webb, 1969), the sinoatrial opening is almost transverse. In *T. scincoides*, the posterior sinoatrial cusp is continuous with the interarterial septum.

In *Oligosoma grande*, the larger right atrium has a small, sac-like diverticulum lying between the bases of the carotid arteries, and the orifice of the pulmonary vein is bordered by a thickening of the left atrial wall and a caudal membranous flap of endocardium. Because the heart of *Acontias meleagris* is generally elongate and both atria are relatively large, they overhang the ventricle; the right atrium is only slightly longer than the left. *Oligosoma grande* has a well marked atrioventricular funnel and atrioventricular ring. Buchanan describes a small pair of marginal (lateral) cusps developed from the lateral walls of the atrioventricular funnel that assist the much larger septal cusps of the atrioventricular valve to close the atrioventricular openings at systole. Neither set of cusps is associated with chordae tendinae. There is a detailed account of the aortic arches and their valves for *Tiliqua scincoides* (Webb, 1969).

In some skinks, the conus region is well defined by the presence of two sulci. The large one on the left is called the "interventricular" sulcus; the right one is called the "right bulboventricular sulcus" (Buchanan, 1956). A prominent cardiac cartilage is usually present in most skinks (for an exception see Buchanan, 1956); in some species (e.g., *Tiliqua scincoides*) this cartilage is divided into a larger anterior and a smaller posterior portion. Both a vertical septum and a muscular ridge are present in the ventricle, although there is interindividual variation. In *Tiliqua scincoides*, the vertical septum is of medium height, and the muscular ridge has a caudal end that is parallel with the vertical septum. Contrary to most skinks, *Oligosoma grande* lacks a gubernaculum cordis. In *Tiliqua scincoides*, the gubernaculum cordis is avascular.

f. FAMILY LACERTIDAE
Acolat (1943) examined four species of lacertids—namely *Lacerta agilis*, *L. lepida*, *L. viridis*, and *Podarcis muralis*—but made no mention of specific differences between them. Foxon et al. (1956) give a short description of the heart of *L. viridis* preliminary to discussing its mode of action in greater detail. These authors describe a triangular sinus venosus, lying dorsal to the right atrium and receiving the three venae cavae separately, one at each corner. The sinoatrial opening is almost transverse and is guarded by the usual bicuspid valve. The opening of the pulmonary vein is not valved.

g. FAMILY ANGUIDAE
The hearts of the legless lizards, *Anguis fragilis* and *Ophisaurus apodus*, are included among the species studied by Acolat (1943). The only special points to be mentioned are the elongated shape of the heart, conforming to the elongate body form of the Anguidae. The muscular ridge is accordingly also narrow and elongate. The number of apical chambers in the ventricle is six in *Ophisaurus* and five in *Anguis*.

h. FAMILY HELODERMATIDAE

Only two authors seem to have studied the heart of *Heloderma*, namely Shufeldt (1890) and Acolat (1943), the former reporting on *H. suspectum* and the latter on *H. horridum*. Shufeldt finds that "the entrance and emergence of the principal veins and arteries as they take place from the cardiac cavities . . . agrees rather with *Lacerta* than it does with *Varanus*."

i. FAMILY VARANIDAE

Although earlier studies exist (e.g., Corti, 1847; Vorstman, 1933), the first detailed study of the varanid heart was that of Mathur (1944). This work has been supplemented by numerous subsequent descriptions (e.g., Meinertz, 1952; Khalil and Zaki, 1964; Webb et al., 1971).

Mathur (1944) describes the heart of *Varanus salvator* in particular and indicates that it is almost as broad as long, thus resembling the heart of Testudines rather than those of other Sauria. In addition, the varanid heart lies just behind the sternum, a position more posterior than found in most lizards (Webb et al., 1971).

The right precaval and the postcaval veins merge imperceptibly into the sinus venosus, and there is a slight constriction near the base of the left precaval vein that partially divides the sinus into a small left and a larger right chamber (Fig.4.3). The bicuspid sinoatrial valve guards the obliquely transverse sinoatrial opening, which lies almost midway along the dorsal wall of the right atrium. The posterior cusp is larger than the anterior one and, therefore, overhangs it. The two cusps are united at their right extremity and extend beyond the opening, at which point they join a muscular ridge in the right atrial wall generally called the suspensory ligament.

The larger right atrium has prominent pectineal muscles in its walls, but no sac-like diverticulum. Mathur (1944) notes two prominent bundles, one near the cranial and the other, larger one near the caudal extremity. Both atria are invaginated into the base of the ventricle to form the atrioventricular funnel. The atrioventricular valves in *Varanus salvator* have both marginal and septal cusps, but Webb et al. (1971) claimed that the marginal cusps are absent in *V. gouldii* and was uncertain about the condition in *V. bengalensis*. There are no chordae tendinae attached to the free ends of the atrioventricular valves.

Both a vertical septum and a muscular ridge are present, and both are well developed. The muscular ridge may be extremely large in some species, in which it extends caudally to become nearly horizontal. Webb et al. (1971) indicate that the muscular ridge is comprised of three surfaces and that the free edge of the muscular ridge closes against the bulbuslamelle of the ventricular wall during systole. Anteriorly, the muscular ridge is composed of connective tissue and forms the aorticopulmonary septum. Unlike the condition in other Sauria and some Serpentes, there is no cartilaginous rod. According to Webb et al. (1971), the combined cavum arteriosum and cavum venosum form a distinct chamber, the cavum latero-dorsale. This chamber is surrounded by a cone-shaped structure composed of tightly grouped trabeculae. Because these muscular trabeculae are particularly well developed at the ventricular apex, the cavum latero-dorsale does not extend as far posteriorly as the cavum pulmonale. There is no gubernaculum cordis, although Webb (1969) reported a vestige of this structure at the ventricular apex.

2. AMPHISBAENIA

The first account of the amphisbaenid heart was by Bedriaga (1884), who described and illustrated the heart of *Blanus cinereus* and compared it, in a general manner, with that of a snake. Beddard (1905) examined the heart of *Bronia brasiliana* and noted differences between it and that of *Blanus* as described by Bedriaga. He was the first to note that "the left systemic arch of *Bronia brasiliana* is considerably larger than the right."

Francis (1977) dissected the heart of *Amphisbaena alba* and studied the heart of *Agamodon anguliceps* by means of serial transverse sections. The morphological and histological details of his observations are described below.

The oblique sinoatrial opening is guarded by a pair of membranous valves, the anterior cusp overlapping the posterior. In addition, the sinoatrial opening is attached to muscular trabeculae that radiates from each side of the orifice. The atria are large and elongate, and the right atrium is the larger of the two. The walls of both atria are spongy and trabeculate except for the surfaces of the atrial septum and atrioventricular funnel. The atrial septum lies in a nearly vertical plane, and two large, membranous, valvular cusps arise from its free border. Chordae tendinae anchor the free borders of these cusps to the ventricle in the trogonophid, *Agamodon*.

The ventricle is triangular in outline and contains seven vertical septa, which run from the apex towards the base of the ventricle. In *Blanus*, the vertical septum extends farther anteriorly than in *Agamodon*. Thus, the interventricular canal is quite small in *Blanus* but extensive in *Agamodon*. In both species, the muscular ridge extends for only a short distance before joining the ventral wall of the ventricle. A distinct vestige of the conus arteriosus is present.

3. SUBORDER SERPENTES (OPHIDIA)

a. GENERAL   In general, snake hearts are elongate and narrow, conforming with the body form of these animals. This elongation is usually marked in Colubridae, moderate in short-tailed vipers, and minimal in

Boidae. The ventricular walls are thick and muscular, and the ventricular ridges are deep. The coronary sulcus is often oblique owing to two unusual factors: (1) a considerable auricular appendage to the right atrium; and (2) the forward, shoulder-like extension of the left ventricle (Fig. 4.2A). In general, the sinus venosus is small relative to the heart, and the confluence of the right precaval and postcaval veins is separated from the enlarged base of the left precaval vein by an external constriction and/or internal septum. However, in some species (e.g., *Naja naja*, Fig. 4.2A) the base of the left precaval vein is not enlarged, and the sinus venosus is tubular. The right atrium may be almost twice the size of the left, and the interatrial fissure is very deep. The apex of the ventricle is displaced to the left side of the mid-longitudinal axis, and, consequently, the postcaval vein occupies a sub-median position. No gubernaculum cordis is present.

b. FAMILY TYPHLOPIDAE

Kashyap (1950), Robb (1960), and Webb (1969) have all described various typhlopid hearts (Fig. 4.16). The account of Robb follows that of Kashyap very closely and adds little new information. Webb (1969), however, added several important details and corrected Kashyap's account of the ventricular architecture. The species studied by Kashyap were *Ramphotyphlops braminus* and *Typhlops acutus*, whereas Webb dissected *R. polygrammicus* and *T. proximus*.

The tubular sinus venosus is thin walled, and the left precaval vein opening is bounded by a valve and a ridge-like thickening of the dorsal wall. The sinoatrial opening is about 45°. The right atrium is only slightly larger than the left, and the septal atrioventricular valves are not associated with chordae tendinae.

The apex of the ventricle turns slightly towards the left (Fig. 4.16). The typhlopid ventricle has a particularly dense myocardium and minimal spongy myocardium, a feature that allows for large cavities that extend well down toward the ventricular apex. The thinner muscle layers of the cavum pulmonale allows this to be easily distinguished from the cavum arteriosum. The vertical septum, which has a cranial membranous portion, is high and reaches almost to the level of the interatrial septum. By contrast, the muscular ridge is slight and reduced. Kashyap (1950) described a cartilaginous rod within the aorticopulmonary septum of *R. braminus*; however, this must be regarded as unusual.

c. FAMILY BOIDAE

The heart of *Python reticulatus* was first described by Hopkinson and Pancoast (1837) and has been detailed here (Fig. 4.3). The sinus venosus is tubular, lies on the dorsal aspect of the right atrium, and appears to dilate from the base of the postcaval vein without interruption. This description varies considerably from the sinus of *Boa constrictor* (Acolat, 1943) and the anaconda (*Eunectes murinus*, Rau, 1924) but closely resembles that for *Liasis amethystinus* (Webb, 1969). In *P. reticulatus*, the two precaval veins enter the anterior end of the sinus through bicuspid valves. The left precaval vein enters close to the right precaval vein and far forward of the sinoatrial opening. This forward position is unusual in reptiles and is very different from the condition illustrated for *Eryx johnii* (Kashyap, 1959). Apart from Webb's (1969) description of *Liasis*, there appears to be no other account of a valved precaval vein opening in reptiles.

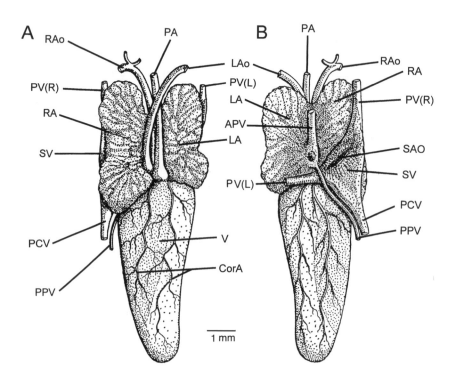

Fig. 4.16. *Typhlops acutus.* Ventral (A) and dorsal (B) views of the heart (×7.6). Abbreviations: APV, anterior pulmonary vein; CorA, coronary arteries; LA, left atrium; LAo, left aortic arch; PA, pulmonary arch; PCV, postcaval vein; PPV, posterior pulmonary vein; PV(L), precaval vein (left); PV(R), precaval vein (right); RA, right atrium; RAo, right aortic arch; SAO, sinoatrial opening; SV, sinus venosus; V, ventricle. (Redrawn from Kashyap, 1950.)

The relatively large and obliquely placed sinoatrial aperture of *Python reticulatus* is guarded by a pair of substantial muscular valves (Fig. 4.3), the cranial (left) cusp overlapping the right. The lateral ends of both cusps are attached to a muscular ridge (suspensory ligament) from the right atrium. The right atrium of *P. reticulatus* is considerably larger than the left (Fig. 4.3), and both atria have substantial, spongy walls. The right atrium of the anaconda (*Eunectes murinus*) is also larger than the left and has "fairly thick" walls with prominent pectinate muscles (Rau, 1924). However, the sinoatrial valves of *E. murinus* are membranous, and the sinoatrial opening is transversely placed. The left atrium in *Liasis amethystinus* bears a diverticulum. This is in contrast to the situation in Sauria in which the diverticulum is associated with the right atrium. In both *E. murinus* and *Boa constrictor* (Acolat, 1943), the aperture of the pulmonary vein is guarded by a flap from the left atrial wall. Webb (1969) indicates that *Liasis amethystinus* has an atrioventricular funnel and that the atrioventricular valves have chordae tendinae. *Boa constrictor* has septal cusps that are associated with a right marginal cusp and a poorly developed left marginal cusp.

Boas, pythons, and anacondas have a well developed vertical septum that severely constricts the interventricular canal. The muscular ridge is very distinct, and in *Liasis amethystinus* it separates a large cavum pulmonale from a small cavum venosum.

d. FAMILY UROPELTIDAE

No adequate description of the hearts in this family has been found; however, Kashyap (1960) does compare the heart of *Uropeltis rubrolineatus* with other ophidian hearts. The heart lies very close to the anterior end of the body. The two atria, which are of equal size, lack diverticula, and basal shoulder-like extensions of the left ventricle.

e. FAMILY ACROCHORDIDAE

Acrochordus granulatus is peculiar in that the heart is broadly oval and lies far back in the body. Although no details about the heart's internal anatomy have been published, the drawings of Kashyap (1960) show that the atria are of nearly the same size and that the base of the left precaval vein is separated from the confluence of the right precaval vein and the postcaval vein by a significant constriction.

f. FAMILY COLUBRIDAE

Although the heart of *Ptyas mucosus* is the best documented example (Ray, 1934), the hearts of *Xenochrophis piscator* (Mathur, 1946), *Natrix natrix* (Webb, 1969), and *Spalerosophis diadema* (Khalil and Zaki, 1964) have been described.

In *Ptyas mucosus* and *Xenochrophis piscator*, the sinus venosus is tubular and the small left precaval vein is completely separated from the sinus by a vertical, median valve. In *P. mucosus*, the right atrium is much larger than the left, has an oblique sinoatrial opening, and numerous pectineal muscles are on its inner surface. In *P. mucosus* and *X. piscator*, the dorsal part of the interatrial septum forms a prominent fold exactly at the place where the pulmonary vein opens. Webb (1969) described both a vertical septum and a muscular ridge in the ventricle of *Natrix tropidonotus*. This is contrary to the findings of other authors who claim that the vertical septum is absent.

g. FAMILY ELAPIDAE

Information on the Elapidae is limited to the drawings of Kashyap (1960; Fig. 4.2A) for *Naja naja* and a brief mention by Webb (1969) of *Suta dwyeri*. From Figure 4.2A it is clear that, except for the tubular sinus venosus, the heart of *N. naja* is typical of that of Serpentes. In *S. dwyeri*, Webb (1969) found that: (1) both a vertical septum and a muscular ridge are present; (2) that there "is considerable communication between the left and right systemics"; and (3) that there are "a number of peculiarities in the atrioventricular valves (and the left part of the ventricle) resulting from the asymmetry imposed on the heart."

h. FAMILY HYDROPHIIDAE

Webb (1969) provides the only description of a sea-snake (*Hydrophis*) heart. The only notable structural features are the presence of two sinoatrial valves (the left being continuous with the interatrial septum), an atrioventricular funnel, and a vestigial gubernaculum cordis.

i. FAMILY VIPERIDAE

A limited description of the copperhead (*Agkistrodon contortrix mokeson*) heart was provided by Bothner (1959). According to this author, the right atrium overlaps the cranial third of the ventricle, and the atrioventricular junction is very oblique.

ACKNOWLEDGMENTS

This chapter was initiated by the late E. T. B. Francis several years ago. His early draft provided the basic framework for the present version. However, his death precluded his input into the revisions that resulted in this chapter. We appreciate the secretarial support of Wendy Powell and Anna Day in completing the numerous layers of revisions. APF has research support from the Natural Sciences and Research Council of Canada, and AKG was a recipient of a postdoctoral fellowship from the same agency.

APPENDIX: REPTILIAN SPECIES DISCUSSED

Unattributed statements in the original draft of this chapter by E. T. B. Francis are indicated by an asterisk (*).

TESTUDINES

Caretta caretta
  E. T. B. Francis, MS*
Chelodina longicollis
  MacKinnon and Heatwole, 1981
Chelonia mydas
  E. T. B. Francis, MS*
Cyclanorbis sp.
  Girgis, 1961
Dermochelys coriacea
  Burne, 1905
  O'Donoghue, 1918
  Adams, 1962
Emydura signata
  C. E. Franklin, unpubl. obs.
Emys orbicularis
  Juhász-Nagy et al., 1964

Geochelone denticulata [as *Testudo tabulata*]
  E. T. B. Francis, MS*
Macroclemys temminckii
  E. T. B. Francis, MS*
Testudo sp.
  Drury and Smith, 1924
Testudo graeca
  Grant and Regnier, 1926
  Price, 1954
  Shelton and Burggren, 1976
Trachemys [as *Chrysemys* and *Pseudemys*] *scripta*
  Robb, 1953
  Shelton and Burggren, 1976
  Hicks and Malvin, 1992
Trionyx sp.
  Girgis, 1961

RHYNCHOCEPHALIA

Sphenodon punctatus
  O'Donoghue, 1920

Simons, 1965
Grigg and Simons, 1972

SAURIA

Acontias meleagris
  van der Merwe, 1943
Agamodon anguliceps
  Francis, 1977
Anguis fragilis
  Hess, 1921
  Acolat, 1943
Calotes sp.
  E. T. B. Francis, unpubl. obs.
Chamaeleo chamaeleon
  Acolat, 1943
  Kashyap, 1960
Draco dussumieri
  Prakash and Raghaveuah, 1957
  Webb, 1969
Egernia sp.
  Webb, 1969

Gehyra variegata
  Webb, 1969
Gekko verticellatus
  Das and Das, 1931
Heloderma horridum
  Acolat, 1943
Heloderma suspectum
  Shufeldt, 1890
Hemidactylus flaviviridis
  Mahendra, 1942
Hemidactylus leschenaulti
  E. T. B. Francis, MS*
Lacerta agilis
  Hess, 1921
  Acolat, 1943
Lacerta lepida
  Acolat, 1943

Lacerta viridis
  Grant and Regnier, 1926
  Acolat, 1943
  Foxon et al., 1956
Lygosoma [as *Riopa*] *guentheri*
  Kashyap, 1951
Mabuya carinata
  Rastogi, 1959
Oedura sp.
  Webb, 1969
Oligosoma [as *Leiolopisma*] *grande*
  Buchanan, 1956
Ophisaurus apodus
  Acolat, 1943
Physignathus lesueurii
  Webb, 1969
Podarcis [as *Lacerta*] *muralis*
  Acolat, 1943
Pogona [as *Amphibolurus*] *vitticeps*
  Else and Hulbert, 1983
Sphenomorphus sp.
  Webb, 1969
Teratolepis [as *Tetrolepis*] *fasciata*
  Mathur, 1944
  Kashyap, 1960
Tiliqua rugosa
  de la Lande et al., 1962
  Furness and Moore, 1970
  Berger, 1971

Tiliqua scincoides
  Rau, 1924
  Webb, 1969
Tupinambis teguixin [as *T. nigropunctatus*]
  Acolat, 1943
Uromastyx hardwickii
  Bhatia, 1929b
  Webb, 1969
Varanus sp.
  Johansen and Burggren, 1980
  Burggren, 1985
  Heisler and Glass, 1985
Varanus bengalensis [including *V. monitor*]
  Meinertz, 1952
  Webb et al., 1971
Varanus exanthematicus
  Heisler et al., 1983
Varanus gouldii
  Webb et al., 1971
Varanus komodoensis
  Meinertz, 1952
  Vorstman, 1933
Varanus salvator
  Mathur, 1944
Varanus varius
  MacKinnon and Heatwole, 1981

AMPHISBAENIA

Amphisbaena alba
  Francis, 1977
Blanus cinereus
  Bedriaga, 1884

  Beddard, 1905
Bronia brasiliana
  Beddard, 1905

SERPENTES

Acrochordus granulatus
  Kashyap, 1960
Agkistrodon contortrix
  Bothner, 1959
Boa constrictor
  Acolat, 1943
  Webb, 1969
Dendrelaphis punctulatus
  MacKinnon and Heatwole, 1981

Dispholidus typus
  Poupa and Lindström, 1983
Eryx johnii
  Kashyap, 1959
Eunectes murinus
  Rau, 1924
Hydrophis sp.
  Webb, 1969

Morelia amethistina [as *Liasis amethystinus*]
Webb, 1969
Naja naja
Kashyap, 1960
Natrix natrix [as *N. tropidonotus*]
Webb, 1969
Ptyas mucosus
Ray, 1934
Python reticulatus
Hopkinson and Pancoast,1837
Ramphotyphlops [as *Typhlops*] *braminus*
Kashyap, 1950
Ramphotyphlops polygrammicus [as *Typhlops nigrescens*]

Webb, 1969
Spalerosophis diadema
Khalil and Zaki, 1964
Suta dwyeri
Webb, 1969
Thamnophis sp.
Burggren, 1977
Typhlops acutus
Kashyap, 1950
Typhlops proximus
Webb, 1969
Uropeltis rubrolineatus [as *U. phillipsi*]
Kashyap, 1960
Xenochrophis [as *Natrix*] *piscator*
Mathur, 1946

CROCODYLIA

Alligator mississippiensis
Panizza, 1833
Shaner, 1924
Davies et al., 1952
Webb, 1979
Caiman crocodilus
White, 1956
Webb, 1979
Crocodylus johnsoni
Webb, 1979

Crocodylus niloticus
Davies et al., 1952
Crocodylus novaeguineae
Webb, 1979
Crocodylus porosus
Mathur 1971
Webb, 1979
Grigg and Johansen, 1987
Grigg, 1989

REFERENCES

Acolat, L. (1932). Étude de l'appareil circulatoire central et de la circulation des sangs artériel et veneux chez la couleuvre et la vipére. *Comp. Rend. Congr. Soc. Sav. Paris.* 1932, 197–204.

Acolat, L. (1935). Contribution à l'anatomie compareé du coeur en particulier du ventricule des batraciens et des reptiles. *Bull. Soc. Hist. Nat. Doubs* 46, 71–81.

Acolat, L. (1938). Contribution à l'anatomie du coeur de la tortue luth (*Sphargis coriacea*, L.). *Bull. Assoc. Anat.* 47, 1–8.

Acolat, L. (1943). "Contribution à l'anatomie comparée du coeur et en particulier du ventricule chez les batraciens et chez les reptiles." Thesis à la Faculté des Sciences de Nancy, Besançon. 126 pp.

Adams, W. E. (1962). The carotid sinus — carotid body problem in the Chelonia (with a note on a foramen of Panizza in *Dermochelys*). *Arch. Int. Pharmacol.* 139, 28–37.

Axelsson, M., Holmgren, S., and Nilsson, S. (1989). Flow dynamics of the crocodylian heart. *Am. J. Physiol.* 256, R875–R879.

Beddard, F. E. (1905). Some additions to the knowledge of the anatomy, principally of the vascular system, of *Hatteria, Crocodilus*, and certain Lacertilia. *Proc. Zool. Soc. Lond.* 2, 461–489.

Bedriaga, J. von (1884). *Amphisbaena cinerea*. Erster Beitrag zur Kenntnis der Doppelschleichen. *Arch. Naturgesch.* 50, 23–77.

Benninghoff, A. (1933). Das Herz. In *Handbuch der vergleichenden Anatomie der Wirbelthiere* (L. Bolk, E. Göppert, E. Kallius, and W. Lubosch, eds.). Urban and Schwartzenberg, Berlin, Wien, vol. 6, 467–556.

Berger, P. J. (1971). The vagal and sympathetic innervation of the heart of the lizard *Tiligua rugosa*. *Aust. J. Exp. Biol. Med. Sci.* 49, 297–304.

Bergman, R. A. (1960). A note on the fine structure of the turtle heart. *Bull. Johns Hopkins Hosp.* 106, 46–54.

Bhatia, M. L. (1929a). On the arterial system of the lizard, *Uromastix hardwickii* Gray. *J. Morph. Physiol.* 48, 292–315.

Bhatia, M. L. (1929b). On the venous system of the lizard, *Uromastix hardwickii* Gray. *Zool. Anz.* 85, 15–27.

Bothner, R. C. (1959). The gross anatomy of the heart and neighboring vessels in the northern subspecies of the copperhead, *Agkistrodon contortrix mokeson* (Daudin). *Sci. Stud. St. Bonaventure Univ.* 20, 27–44.

Buchanan, J. G. (1956). The gross and minute anatomy of the heart of the lizard, *Leiolopisma grande* Gray. *Trans. Roy. Soc. New Zealand* 84, 103–120.

Burggren, W. W. (1977). Circulation during intermittent lung ventilation in the garter snake, *Thamnophis*. *Can. J. Zool.* 55, 1720–1725.

Burggren, W. W. (1985). Hemodynamics and regulation of central cardiovascular shunts in reptiles. In *Cardiovascular Shunts: Phylogenetic, Ontogenetic, and Clinical Aspects* (K. Johansen and W.W. Burggren, eds.). Munksgaard, Copenhagen, pp. 121–142

Burggren, W. W. (1987). Form and function in reptilian circulations. *Am. Zool.* 27, 5–20.

Burggren, W. W., Farrell, A. P., and Lillywhite, H. B. (1997). Vertebrate cardiovascular systems. In *Handbook of Comparative Physiology* (W. H. Dantzler, ed.). American Physiological Society, Washington, D.C., vol. 1, pp. 215–308.

Burne, R. H. (1905). Notes on the muscular and visceral anatomy of the leathery turtle (*Dermochelys coriacea*). *Proc. Roy. Soc. Lond.* 1, 319–320.

Burnstock, G. (1969). Evolution of the autonomic innervation of visceral and cardiovascular systems in vertebrates. *Pharmacol. Rev.* 21, 247–324.

Corti, A. (1847). De systemate vasorum Psammosauri grisei. Congregat. Mechithar., Vienna, 69 pp.

Das, G. M., and Das, B. K. (1931). Observations on the structure and mechanism of a heart of the rare lizard of Bengal, *Gecko verticillatus*. *Proc. Indian Sci. Congress, Calcutta* 18, 109.

Davies, F., and Francis, E. T. B. (1941). The heart of a salamander (*Salamandra salamandra* L.) with special reference to the conducting (connecting) system and its bearing on the phylogeny of the conducting systems of mammalian and avian hearts. *Phil. Trans. Roy. Soc.*, ser. B, 231, 99–130.

Davies, F., Francis, E. T. B., and King, T. S. (1952). The conducting (connecting) system of the crocodilian heart. *J. Anat. Lond.* 86, 152–161.

de la Lande, I. S., Taylor, M. J., and Pridmore, B. R. (1962). Pharmacology of the heart of *Tiliqua rugosa* (the sleepy lizard). *Aust. J. Exp. Biol. Med. Sci.* 40, 129–138.

de Marees van Swinderen, J. W. (1929). Het reptielenhart. *Ned. Tijdsch. Geneesk.* 1, 397–398.

Drury, A. N., and Smith, F. M. (1924). Observations relating to the nerve supply of the coronary artery of the tortoise. Part I. Direct observations of the artery. *Heart* 11, 71–79.

Else, P. L., and Hulbert, A. J. (1983). A comparative study of the metabolic capacity of the hearts from reptiles and mammals. *Comp. Biochem. Physiol. A.* 76, 553–557.

Farrell, A. P. (1991). Cardiac scope in lower vertebrates. *Can. J. Zool.* 69, 1981–1984.

Farrell, A. P., and Jones, D. R. (1992). The Heart. In *Fish Physiology* (W. S. Hoar, D. J. Randall and A. P. Farrell, eds.). Academic Press, New York, London, vol. 12A, pp. 1–88.

Fawcett, D. W., and Selby, C. C. (1958). Observations on the fine structure of the turtle atrium. *J. Biophys. Biochem. Cytol.* 4, 63–72.

Foxon, G. E. H., Griffith, J., and Price, M. (1956). The mode of action of the heart of the green lizard, *Lacerta viridis*. *Proc. Zool. Soc. Lond.* 126, 145–157.

Francis, E. T. B. (1977). Amphisbaenia: heart and arterial arches. *Brit. J. Herpetol.* 5, 607–610.

Furness, J. B., and Moore, J. (1970). The adrenergic innervation of the cardiovascular system of the lizard *Trachysaurus rugosus*. *Z. Zellforsch.* 108, 150–176.

Gaskell, W. H. (1884). On the augmentor (accelerator) nerves of the heart of cold-blooded animals. *J. Physiol. Lond.* 4, 43–127.

Gaskell, W. H., and Gadow, H. (1884). On the anatomy of the cardiac nerves in certain cold blooded vertebrates. *J. Physiol. Lond.* 5, 362–372.

Girgis, S. (1961). Observations on the heart in the family Trionychidae. *Bull. Brit. Mus. Nat. Hist. Zool.* 8, 73–107.

Goodrich, E. S. (1919). Notes on the reptilian heart. *J. Anat. Lond.* 53, 298–304.

Goodrich, E. S. (1930). *Studies on the Structure and Development of Vertebrates*. Macmillan, London, pp. 553–561.

Grant, R. T., and Regnier, M. (1926). The comparative anatomy of the cardiac coronary vessels. *Heart* 13, 285–317.

Greenfield, L. J., and Morrow, A. G. (1961). The cardiovascular haemodynamics of Crocodilia. *J. Surg. Res.* 1, 97–103.

Greil, A. (1903). Beiträge zur vergleichenden Anatomie und Entwicklungsgeschichte des Herzens und des Truncus Arteriosus der Wirbelthiere. *Morphol. Jb.* 31, 123–210.

Grigg, G. C. (1989). The heart and patterns of cardiac outflow in Crocodilia. *Proc. Austal. Physiol. Pharmacol. Soc.* 20, 43–57.

Grigg, G. C. (1991). Central cardiovascular anatomy and function in Crocodilia. In *Physiological Adaptations in Vertebrates: Respiration, Circulation and Metabolism. Lung Biology in Health and Disease* (S. C. Wood, R. E. Weber, A. R. Hargens and R. W. Millard, eds.). Marcel Dekker, New York, N.Y., vol. 56, pp. 339–353.

Grigg, G. C., and Johansen, K. (1987). Cardiovascular dynamics in *Crocodylus porosus* breathing air and during voluntary aerobic dives. *J. Comp. Physiol.* 157, 381–392.

Grigg, G. C., and Simons, J. R. (1972). Preferential distribution of the left and right auricular blood into the arterial arches of the tuatara, *Sphenodon punctatus*. *J. Zool.* 167, 481–486.

Heisler, N., and Glass, M. L. (1985). Mechanisms and regulation of central vascular shunts in reptiles. In *Cardiovascular Shunts: Phylogenetic, Ontogenetic and Clinical Aspects* (K. Johansen and W. W. Burggren, eds.). Munksgaard, Copenhagen, pp. 334–353.

Heisler, N., Neumann, P., and Maloiy, G. M. O. (1983). The mechanism of intracardiac shunting in the lizard, *Varanus exanthematicus*. *J. Exp. Biol.* 105, 15–31.

Hess, R. (1921). Das Herzgewicht der Wirbeltiere. *Zool. Jb.* 38, 243–364.

Hicks, J. W., and Malvin, G. M. (1992). Mechanism of intracardiac shunting in the turtle *Pseudemys scripta*. *Am. J. Physiol.* 262, R986–R992.

Hochstetter, F. (1906). Die Entwicklung des Blutgefasssystems. In *Handbuch der Vergleichenden und Experimentellen Entwicklungslehre der Wirbeltiere* (O. Hertwig, ed.). Verlag von Gustav Fischer, Jena, pp. 83–163.

Hopkinson, J. P., and Pancoast, J. (1837). On the visceral anatomy of the python (Cuvier), described by Daudin as the *Boa reticulata*. *Trans. Am. Phil. Soc.* 5, 121–136.

Johansen, K., and Burggren, W. W. (1980). Cardiovascular function in the lower vertebrates. In *Hearts and Heart-like organs* (G. H. Bourne, ed.). Academic Press, Inc., New York, vol. 1, pp. 61–117.

Jones, D. R., and Shelton, G. (1993). The physiology of the alligator heart—left aortic flow patterns and right-to-left shunts. *J. Exp. Biol.* 176, 247–269.

Juhász-Nagy, A., Szentiványi, M., Szabó, M., and Vámosi, B. (1963). Coronary circulation of the tortoise heart. *Acta. Physiol. Hungar.* 23, 33–48.

Juhász-Nagy, A., Szentiványi, M., Imre, S., and Szodoray, P. (1964). Physiological role of coronary constriction in the tortoise, (*Emys orbicularis*). *Experientia* 20, 313–314.

Kashyap, H. V. (1950). The structure of the heart of *Typhlops* (Reptilia: Ophidia). *J. Zool. Soc. India* 2, 42–48.

Kashyap, H. V. (1951). The structure of the heart of *Riopa guentheri* (Peters) (Reptilia: Sauria). *J. Zool. Soc. India* 3, 31–40.

Kashyap, H. V. (1959). The reptilian heart. *Proc. Nat. Inst. Sci. India* 26, 234–254.

Kashyap, H. V. (1960). Morphology of the reptilian heart. *Bull. Zool. Soc. Nagpur* 3, 23–34.

Khalil, F., and Zaki, K. (1964). Distribution of blood in the ventricle and aortic arches in Reptilia. *Z. Vergl. Physiol.* 48, 663–689.

Leene, J. E., and Vorstman, A. G. (1930). A note on the structure of the heart of *Varanus* as compared with other reptilian hearts. *Tijdschr. Med. Dierk. Vereen. Leiden* 2, 62–66.

Lillywhite, H. B. (1987). Circulatory adaptations of snakes to gravity. *Am. Zool.* 27, 81–95.

MacKinnon, M. R., and Heatwole, H. (1981). Comparative cardiac anatomy of the Reptilia. IV. The coronary arterial circulation. *J. Morph.* 170, 1–27.

Mahendra, B. C. (1942). Contribution to the bionomics, anatomy, reproduction, and development of the Indian house gecko, *Hemidactylus flaviviridis* (Rüppell). Part III, The heart and venous system. *Proc. Indian Acad. Sci.* 15B, 231–252.

March, H. W. (1961). Persistence of a functioning bulbus cordis homologue in the turtle heart. *Am. J. Physiol.* 201, 1109–1112.

Mathur, P. N. (1944). The anatomy of the reptilian heart. I. *Varanus monitor* (Linné). *Proc. Indian Acad. Sci.* 20B, 1–29.

Mathur, P. N. (1946). The anatomy of the reptilian heart. II. Serpentes, Testudinata and Loricata. *Proc. Indian Acad. Sci.* 23, 129–152.

Mathur, P. N. (1971). The heart and conducting (connecting) system in *Crocodylus porosus* (Schneider). *J. Anim. Morph. Physiol.* 18, 84–90.

Meinertz, T. (1952). The heart and large blood vessels in the lizard, *Placovaranus komodoensis* Ouw. *Zeitsch. Anat. Entwickgesch.* 116, 315–324.

O'Donoghue, C. H. (1918). The heart of the leathery turtle, *Dermochelys (Sphargis) coriacea.* With a note on the septum ventriculorum in the Reptilia. *J. Anat.,* ser. 3, 13, 467–480.

O'Donoghue, C. H. (1920). The blood vascular system of the tuatara, *Sphenodon punctatus. Phil. Trans. Roy. Soc. Lond.* B, 210, 175–252.

Panizza, B. (1833). Sulla structura del cuore e sulla circolazione del sonque del *Crocodilus lucius. Biblioth. Ital.* 70, 87–91.

Pettersson, K., Axelsson, M., and Nilsson, S. (1992). Shunting of blood flow in the caiman: Blood flow patterns in the right and left aortae and pulmonary artery. In *Lung Biology in Health and Disease* (C. Lenfant, R. Millard, A. Hargens, and R. Weber, eds.). Marcel Dekker, New York, vol. 30, pp. 1–23.

Poupa, O. (1972). Heart under unusual conditions: effects of gravitation and chronic hypoxia. In *Myocardiology, Recent Advances in Studies of Cardiac Structure and Metabolism* (G. Rona and E. Bogusz, eds.). University Park Press, Baltimore, vol. 1, pp. 779–802.

Poupa, O., and Lindström, L. (1983). Comparative and scaling aspects of heart and body weights with reference to blood supply of cardiac fibers. *Comp. Biochem. Physiol.* 76A, 413–421.

Prakash, R., and Raghaveuah, S. C. (1957). The heart of the Indian flying lizard *Draco dussumieri* with special reference to the conducting system. *J. Anat. Soc. India* 6, 107–114.

Price, M. (1954). Records of abnormalities in the heart of a frog and in the arterial trunks of a tortoise. (2) An abnormal communication between the left systemic arch and the brachiocephalic artery in the tortoise (*Testudo graeca* Linn.). *Ann. Mag. Nat. Hist.* 7, 641–647.

Rastogi, S. C. (1959). The structure of the heart of the Indian skink *Mabuya carinata* (Boulenger) (Reptilia: Sauria). *Proc. Zool. Soc. Lond.* 12, 27–34.

Rau, A. S. (1924). Observations on the anatomy of the heart of *Tiliqua scincoides* and *Eunectes murinus. J. Anat. Lond.* 59, 60–71.

Ray, H. C. (1934). On the arterial system of the common Indian rat snake, *Ptyas mucosus* (Linn.). *J. Morph.* 56, 533–568.

Robb, J. S. (1953). Specialized (conducting) tissue in the turtle. *Am. J. Physiol.* 172, 7–13.

Robb, J. S. (1960). The internal anatomy of *Typhlops* Schneider (Reptilia). *Aust. J. Zool.* 8, 181–216.

Seymour, R. S. (1987). Scaling of cardiovascular physiology in snakes. *Amer. Zool.* 27, 97–107.

Shaner, R. F. (1924). On the muscular architecture of the ventricles of the alligator heart, with a note on the formation of the interventricular septum of birds and mammals. *Anat. Rec.* 29, 21–32.

Shelton, G., and Burggren, W. W. (1976). Cardiovascular dynamics of the Chelonia during apnoea and lung ventilation. *J. Exp. Biol.* 64, 323–343.

Shelton, G., and Jones, D. R. (1991). The physiology of the alligator heart: the cardiac cycle. *J. Exp. Biol.* 158, 539–564.

Shufeldt, R. W. (1890). Contributions to the study of *Heloderma suspectum*, arterial system. *Proc. Zool. Soc. Lond.* 148, 35–43.

Simons, J. R. (1965). The heart of the tuatara (*Sphenodon punctatus*). *J. Zool. Lond.* 146, 451–466.

Swett, F. H. (1923). The connecting systems of the reptile heart — alligator. *Anat. Rec.* 26, 129–140.

van der Merwe, N. J. (1943). Die algemene anatomie en die bloedvatstelsel van *Acontias meleagris*. *Tydskr. Wet Kuns. Bloemfontein N.R.* 4, 135–153.

Vorstman, A. G. (1933). The septa in the ventricle of the heart of *Varanus komodoensis*. *Proc. Roy. Acad. Amsterdam* 26, 911–913.

Webb, G. J. W. (1969). "The squamate heart: a recapitulation of the literature and an examination of the structure of the heart in a number of species," vols. 1–2. B.Sc. Hons. Thesis, Univ. New England, Australia.

Webb, G. J. W. (1979). Comparative cardiac anatomy of the Reptilia. III. The heart of crocodilians and an hypothesis on the completion of the interventricular septum of crocodilians and birds. *J. Morph.* 161, 221–240.

Webb, G. J. W., Heatwole, H., and de Bavay, J. (1971). Comparative cardiac anatomy of the Reptilia. I. The chambers and septa of the varanid ventricle. *J. Morph.* 134, 335–350.

Webb, G. J. W., Heatwole, H., and de Bavay, J. (1974). Comparative cardiac anatomy of the Reptilia. II. A critique of the literature of the Squamata and Rhynchocephalia. *J. Morph.* 142, 1–35.

White, F. N. (1956). Circulation in the reptilian heart (*Caiman sclerops*) *Anat. Rec.* 125, 417–431.

White, F. N. (1969). Redistribution of cardiac output in the diving alligator. *Copeia* 1969(3), 567–570.

Young, B. A. (1994). Cartilago cordis in serpents. *Anat. Rec.* 240, 243–247.

Farrell, A. P., Gamperl, A. K., and Francis, E. T. B. (1998). Comparative Aspects of Heart Morphology. In *Biology of the Reptilia*, vol. 19 (Morphology G) (C. Gans and A. S. Gaunt, eds.). Society for the Study of Amphibians and Reptiles, Ithaca, New York, Contrib. Herpetol., vol. 14, pp. 375–424.

5

Cardiac Shunting in Reptiles: Mechanisms, Regulation, and Physiological Functions

JAMES W. HICKS

CONTENTS

I. INTRODUCTION

Historically, the evolution of the vertebrate heart was portrayed as a continuous progression from the two-chambered heart of fish to the completely divided, four-chambered heart of birds and mammals. The three-chambered heart of non-crocodylian reptiles, with the resulting mixing of oxygen rich and oxygen poor blood (cardiac shunting), was viewed as an intermediate phylogenetic step, functionally inefficient compared to the circulation of "higher" vertebrates (Foxon, 1955). This perception changed during the 1960s, 1970s, and 1980s, when studies showed that cardiac shunting is probably regulated and the amount of central mixing of blood varies with ventilatory state (White and Ross, 1966; White, 1969, 1970; Shelton and Burggren, 1976; Burggren and Shelton, 1979; Burggren, 1985; Burggren et al.,1989; White et al., 1989; Hicks and Malvin, 1992; Comeau and Hicks, 1994; Hicks and Comeau, 1994; Hicks, 1994). The ability to control cardiac shunts is hypothesized to provide several unique physiological advantages to reptiles (White, 1976; Johansen and Burggren, 1980; Burggren, 1985), giving rise to the opinion that cardiac shunting is a highly derived condition representing a successful adaptation for animals with low metabolic rates and intermittent breathing patterns (Burggren and Warburton, 1994).

It has been two decades since the last review of cardiac shunting in reptiles was presented in this series (see White, 1976). The present chapter reviews the cardiac anatomy, defines cardiac shunts, and discusses the models now used to analyze and interpret cardiac shunt patterns. In addition, it will discuss, in detail, the mechanisms and factors that regulate the size of cardiac shunting in both crocodylian and non-crocodylian reptiles. Finally, this chapter reviews the effects of different physiological states on cardiac shunting and presents the possible physiological significance of cardiac shunts.

II. REPTILIAN CARDIOVASCULAR ANATOMY
A. Testudines and Squamata

The anatomy of the heart of turtles, snakes, and lizards has been extensively studied for over 100 years (see Griel, 1903 for review of 19th century work; Goodrich, 1916, 1919; Rau, 1924; Mathur, 1946; O'Donoghue, 1918; White, 1959, 1968; Webb et al., 1971, 1974; Van Mierop and Kutsche, 1981, 1985; Farrell et al., this volume). This section gives a brief overview of the basic cardiac anatomy so as to provide a framework for understanding cardiac shunts.

The heart consists of two atrial chambers, separated by a complete septum and a single ventricle. There are two atrioventricular ostia, with each ostium having a set of cup-shaped valves. These valves originate from the base of the interatrial septum and from the ventral and dorsal ventricular wall (Van Mierop and Kutsche, 1985). The right and left atrioventricular ostia open into the ventricle.

The internal structure of the ventricle is complex; it is divided into small chambers by many muscular trabeculae (Fig. 5.1). The muscular ridge—or Muskelleiste (Brücke, 1852)—is a distinctive feature of the ventricular anatomy. In its natural position in reptiles, the muscular ridge lies approximately in the horizontal plane; hence, it sometimes is referred to as the "horizontal septum" (Leene and Vorstman, 1930; Holmes, 1975; Van Mierop and Kutsche, 1981). The muscular ridge is the most prominent ventricular septum in testudines and squamates. It originates from the ventral ventricular wall, runs from apex to base, and divides the ventricle into two main chambers, namely a smaller right ventrolateral chamber, the cavum pulmonale (CP), and a larger left dorsolateral chamber, the cavum dorsale (Van Mierop and Kutsche, 1981, 1985). The

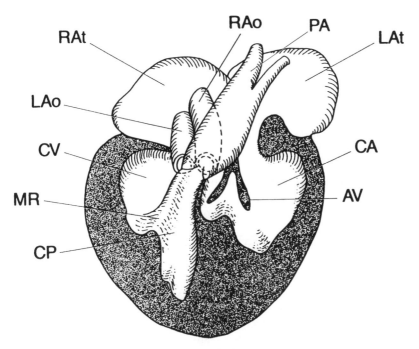

Fig. 5.1. A diagrammatic illustration of the heart of non-crocodylian reptiles. The heart is shown in the ventral aspect. Abbreviations: AV, atrioventricular valves; CA, cavum arteriosum; CP, cavum pulmonale; CV, cavum venosum; MR, muscular ridge; PA, pulmonary artery; RAo, right aortic arch; RAt, right atrium; LAo, left aortic arch; LAt, left atrium. (Redrawn from Hicks, 1994. Illustration based on an original unpublished drawing by F. N. White.)

dorsolateral border of the muscular ridge is free, resulting in potential communication between the CP and cavum dorsale. Opposite the free border of the muscular ridge is the Bulbuslamelle (Griel, 1903), another ridge-like structure that abuts perfectly with the free edge of the muscular ridge in fixed hearts and separates the CP from the cavum dorsale (Van Mierop and Kutsche, 1985). The development of the muscular ridge may vary among species, appearing least developed in turtles and most fully in varanid lizards (Van Mierop and Kutsche, 1981). However, a complete phylogenetic study of the muscular ridge is lacking. Associated with the muscular ridge is the "Bojanusscher Knorpel," a small nodule of hyaline cartilage situated between the bases of the pulmonary artery and left aortic arch (Bojanus, 1821). This anatomical structure may help to rigidify the muscular ridge during systole (White,1959).

Some reptiles have a prominent vertical septum originating from the dorsal aspects of the muscular ridge and subdividing the cavum dorsale into the cavum arteriosum (CA) and the cavum venosum (CV) (Van Mierop and Kutsche, 1985). A small passage over the anterior border of the vertical septum and just below the atrioventricular valves is termed the interventricular canal (White, 1959). The vertical septum is highly developed in *Python* and in *Varanus* (Webb et al., 1971). However, not all reptiles have a recognizable vertical septum. The hearts of *Chelonia mydas*, *Pseudemys floridana*, *Kinosternon* sp., *Iguana iguana*, *Boa constrictor*, and *Crotalus adamanteus* do not show a discrete vertical septum (Van Mierop and Kutsche, 1985). Rather, the cavum dorsale of these species contains many sagittally oriented septa similar to the ventricular septa observed in anurans (Van Mierop and Kutsche, 1985).

In all reptiles, three great vessels arise from the ventricle: the pulmonary artery (PA), the right aortic arch (RAo), and the left aortic arch (LAo). The pulmonary artery emerges to the left of the two aortic arches and originates from the CP. The RAo and LAo arise from the CV. The RAo divides into subclavian and carotid arteries, and a third branch of the RAo (the brachiocephalic) unites with the LAo mediocaudally to form the dorsal aorta. In *Trachemys scripta*, a third systemic arch has been reported emerging from the CV (Shelton and Burggren, 1976; Johansen and Burggren, 1980; Burggren, 1985). Most studies of the testudinian cardiovascular system (Griel, 1903; Mathur, 1946; Khalil and Zaki, 1964; Van Mierop and Kutsche, 1985) have not disclosed this third systemic arch, which occurs only rarely and is not representative of the general anatomical arrangement (White et al., 1989).

Based on the anatomical features described above, a general scheme of blood flow during the cardiac cycle is as follows (White, 1959): during diastole, systemic venous blood flows from the right atrium, through the AV ostia, into the CV and around the free edge of the muscular ridge into the CP. Simultaneously, pulmonary venous blood returning from the lungs enters the left atrium, flows through the AV ostia, and is directed into the CA. During ventricular systole, the AV valves close, preventing regurgitation of blood into the atria. As systole continues, the free edge of the muscular ridge adpresses against the dorsal wall of the ventricle, contacting the Bulbuslamelle, which separates the CP from the CV and CA. The blood within the CP is ejected into the pulmonary artery, whereas blood from the CA and CV is ejected into the left and right aortic arches. The hemodynamic events during systole and diastole are important determinants to cardiac shunting. These events may be altered under various physiological conditions and will be discussed in more detail in the later sections of this chapter.

B. Crocodylians

The anatomy and physiology of the crocodylian circulatory system have also been intensely studied for over 160 years (Panizza, 1833; Fritsche, 1869; White, 1956, 1969; Greenfield and Morrow, 1961; Webb, 1979; Grigg and Johansen, 1987; Grigg, 1989; Axelsson et al., 1989, 1991; Shelton and Jones, 1991; Jones and Shelton, 1993; Franklin and Axelsson, 1994). A detailed morphological analysis of the heart of *Crocodylus porosus* and comparisons with *Alligator, Caiman*, and two other species of *Crocodylus* suggest a high degree of similarity in the basic anatomy of the hearts of crocodylians (Webb, 1979). This anatomy is very different from that of the heart of turtles, snakes, and lizards, but is similar to that of birds and mammals. The crocodylian heart is four chambered, with complete separation between the atria and ventricles (Fig. 5.2). In addition, the ventricular chambers are large and contain few trabeculae. However, as in other reptiles, two aortae emerge from the ventricular cham-

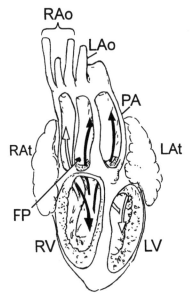

Fig. 5.2. *Alligator mississippiensis.* Diagrammatic illustration of the heart. The outflow tracts, the pulmonary artery, left aortic arch and right aortic arch are bound together within a connective tissue sheath. The two aortae communicate via the foramen of Panizza and the anastomosis in the upper abdominal region. Abbreviations: FP, foramen of Panizza; LAt, left atrium; LAo, left aortic arch; LV, left ventricle; PA, pulmonary artery; RAt, right atrium; RAo, right aortic arch; RV, right ventricle. (Illustration from Hicks and Wang, 1996.)

bers. The LAo emerges from the right ventricle (RV) alongside the pulmonary artery, whereas the RAo emerges from the left ventricle (LV). The LAo, RAo, and pulmonary arterial trunk are enclosed in a common connective tissue sheath. The anatomical arrangement of the great vessels suggests that the RV is equivalent to the CV and CP of noncrocodylian reptiles (Van Mierop and Kutsche, 1985), i.e., the LV corresponds to the CA and that portion of the CV just below the right aortic valve (Van Mierop and Kutsche, 1985).

An unique feature of the crocodylian heart is that the RAo and LAo communicate at two distinct points. As the aortae emerge from the heart, they run side by side, sharing a common wall for several centimeters. Near the base of the common wall and just distal to the bicuspid aortic valves, there is a small opening called the foramen of Panizza (Panizza, 1833). This foramen allows flow between the RAo, and LAo. In excised hearts, the diameter of the foramen is 1–2 mm in animals ranging from 26–30 kg (Greenfield and Morrow, 1961). However, in vivo, the size of the foramen may be larger due to the distension caused by intraaortic pressure and active muscle contraction in the aortic wall (Grigg and Johansen, 1987; Malvin et al., 1995; Axelsson et al., 1996). The second point of communication between the aortae is via an arterial anastomosis in the abdomen. Beyond this anastomosis, the RAo continues as the dorsal aortal, and the LAo becomes the coeliac artery. The coeliac artery gives rise to smaller arteries that supply most of the blood flowing to the gut (Fig. 5.2).

III. CARDIAC SHUNT
A. Definitions, Concepts, and Models

The word shunt means "to divert or turn away from" and is commonly used to define an alternative pathway that diverts flow from one main route to another. In cardiovascular physiology, shunts specifically represent connections between the chambers of the heart or between the systemic and pulmonary vessels resulting in alternative pathways for the flow of blood. In mammals and birds, the pulmonary and systemic circulations are normally separated, therefore, cardiac shunts do not occur unless there are congenital cardiac abnormalities. In reptiles, the normal morphological features of the heart and great vessels provide the potential for cardiovascular shunts.

Cardiac shunts are classified either as right-to-left (R-L) or left-to-right (L-R). A R-L shunt represents the recirculation of systemic venous blood (deoxygenated) back into the systemic arterial circulation. The shunted portion of blood has no chance of being oxygenated because it bypasses the lungs. In contrast, a L-R shunt represents the recirculation of pulmonary venous blood (oxygenated) back into the

Conventional Shunt Model

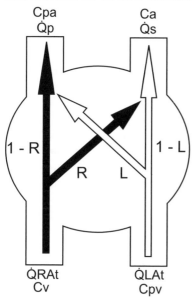

Fig. 5.3. The conventional model for analysis of intracardiac shunting. Abbreviations: C, O_2 content; $\dot{Q}$, blood flow rate; p, pulmonary; s, systemic; pa, pulmonary artery; pv, pulmonary vein; a, arterial; LAt, left atrium; RAt, right atrium; L, left-to-right shunt; R, right-to-left shunt. Filled arrows, deoxygenated blood; open arrows, oxygenated blood. (Diagram redrawn from Ishimatsu et al., 1988.)

pulmonary arterial circulation (Fig. 5.3). Such flow distributions affect the blood oxygen levels in the systemic and pulmonary circulations. A R-L shunt lowers the arterial oxygen saturation by the addition of systemic venous blood (deoxygenated) to pulmonary venous blood (oxygenated). In contrast, a L-R shunt raises the pulmonary arterial oxygen saturation by the addition of pulmonary venous blood to systemic venous blood.

The size of the cardiac shunt can be determined from measurments of blood flow ($\dot{Q}$) and can be expressed as the difference between the pulmonary (p) and systemic (s) blood flows ($\dot{Q}p - \dot{Q}s$). This difference is termed the net or "anatomic" shunt flow ($\dot{Q}$shunt) (Berman, 1985; Hicks, 1993). The shunt magnitude can also be expressed as shunt fraction, which is defined as the fractional contribution of the shunt flow to either pulmonary or systemic blood flow. The R-L shunt fraction is equal to the ($\dot{Q}s - \dot{Q}p$)/$\dot{Q}s$, and the L-R shunt fraction is equal to the ($\dot{Q}p - \dot{Q}s$)/$\dot{Q}p$. If we assume steady state conditions, the shunt fraction can be calculated from measurements of blood oxygen content using the standard shunt equation, which is derived from the Fick principle (Berggren, 1942). The conventional model used for this analysis is shown in Figure 5.4A, and the resulting equation for R-L shunt fraction is:

$$R-L = \frac{(CpvO_2 - CaO_2)}{(CpvO_2 - C\bar{v}O_2)} \qquad \text{(Eq. 5.1)}$$

in which $CpvO_2$ is the oxygen content of blood in the pulmonary vein, CaO_2 the oxygen content of blood in the systemic artery, and CvO_2 the oxygen content of blood in the right atrium.

The L-R shunt fraction is calculated in a similar way, but uses oxygen content in the pulmonary arterial blood:

$$L - R = \frac{(CpaO_2 - C\bar{v}O_2)}{(CpvO_2 - C\bar{v}O_2)} \qquad (Eq.\ 5.2)$$

in which $CpaO_2$ is the oxygen content of blood in the pulmonary artery. Cardiac shunts can, in addition, be operationally defined as "unidirectional" or "bidirectional." These definitions are based not necessarily on the flow distribution, but rather on the separation of oxygenated and deoxygenated blood. For example, in a unidirectional R-L cardiac shunt, the $\dot{Q}s$ exceeds $\dot{Q}p$, and the systemic arterial oxygen saturation is reduced from the value in the left atrium (LAt = pulmonary venous blood). In addition, the oxygen saturation of pulmonary arterial blood is equal to the oxygen saturation in the right atrium (RAt = systemic venous blood) as there is no L-R shunt. Under these conditions, the shunt fraction, determined from blood flow measurements, is equivalent to the value calculated from blood oxygen contents (Equation 5.1). In contrast, bidirectional shunting means that R-L and L-R shunts occur simultaneously during the cardiac cycle. Consequently, the analysis of shunting patterns is complicated as the resulting pulmonary and systemic blood flows may not reveal the absolute magnitude of these two

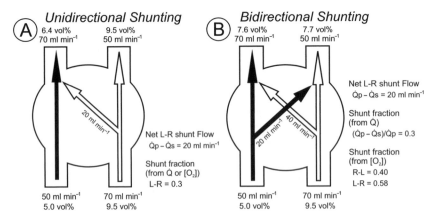

Fig. 5.4. A. Unidirectional shunting in the conventional model. Note that the shunt fractions, calculated from blood oxygen content (see equation 2 in text) or determined from the direct measurement of blood flows, are equal. B. Bidirectional shunting. Note that in the presence of bidirectional intracardiac shunting, the left-to-right (L-R) shunt fraction determined from the direct measurement of blood flow will not agree with the L-R shunt fraction calculated from blood oxygen contents (equation 2 in text). In addition, in this example, the presence of a right-to-left (R-L) shunt will not be detected by the measurement of blood flows. Abbreviations: $\dot{Q}$, blood flow rate; p, pulmonary; s, systemic. Filled arrows, deoxygenated blood; open arrows, oxygenated blood.

shunts. For example, even though $\dot{Q}p$ exceeds $\dot{Q}s$, indicating a net L-R shunt, substantial R-L shunting can still occur. A simple steady-state model illustrates this point (Fig. 5.4B). In this example, the $\dot{Q}p$ is 70 ml min^{-1} and is the sum of systemic venous return of 50 ml min^{-1} ($\dot{Q}RAt$) and L-R shunt flow ($\dot{Q}L\text{-}R$; 40 ml min^{-1}) minus R-L shunt flow ($\dot{Q}R\text{-}L$; 20 ml min^{-1}). The $\dot{Q}s$ is 50 ml min^{-1} and is the sum of pulmonary venous return ($\dot{Q}LAt$; 70 ml min^{-1}) and $\dot{Q}R\text{-}L$ (20 ml min^{-1}) minus $\dot{Q}L\text{-}R$ (40 ml min^{-1}). The net L-R shunt flow detected from direct measurements of blood flow is 20 ml min^{-1} and the $\dot{Q}L\text{-}R$ shunt fraction is 0.30. However, as shown (Fig. 5.4B), the actual L-R shunt flow is twice as large (40 ml min^{-1}, and the shunt fraction should be 0.58. More important, the direct measurements of blood flow cannot detect the R-L shunt. In bidirectional cardiac shunting, the shunt fractions must be determined by simultaneous measurements of blood oxygen content from the four central vascular sites as expressed in the standard shunt equations (5.1 and 5.2 above). Using these equations and the values for oxygen content in the central vascular sites (see Fig. 5.4B), we calculate a L-R shunt fraction of 0.58 and a R-L shunt fraction of 0.40. Combining these values with the direct measurement of $\dot{Q}p$ and $\dot{Q}s$ determines the actual shunt flows, i.e., $\dot{Q}R\text{-}L = 0.4 \times \dot{Q}s$ and $\dot{Q}L\text{-}R = 0.58 \times \dot{Q}p$. It is important to note that bidirectional cardiac shunting can occur in non-crocodylian reptiles (Heisler and Glass, 1985; Ishimatsu et al., 1988; White et al., 1989; Hicks and Comeau, 1994). Therefore, a complete description of the cardiac shunting requires the simultaneous measurement of pulmonary and systemic blood flow as well as of pulmonary and systemic oxygen concentrations in the arterial blood.

In all reptiles, the qualitative and quantitative analysis of R-L cardiac shunting is further complicated by the differential distribution of oxygen-rich and oxygen-poor blood into the two aortae. In general, the O_2 level in the RAo is higher than that in the LAo. Specifically, in *Testudo kleinmanni*, consistently higher blood O_2 levels are measured in the RAo as compared to the LAo (Khalil and Zaki, 1964) and, similarly, the PO_2 of the RAo is always greater than in the LAo in both acute and chronic studies of *Trachemys scripta* (White et al., 1989; Hicks and Comeau, 1994). In *Varanus exanthematicus*, both the PO_2 and O_2 content levels in the RAo are higher than in the LAo (Burggren and Johansen,1982). In *V. niloticus*, the difference between the RAo and LAo PO_2 increases as the body temperature is reduced from 35 to 25 C (Ishimatsu et al.,1988). Finally, in crocodylians, a similar blood oxygen distribution pattern during R-L shunts, in which the blood PO_2 and O_2 content of the RAo is higher than that in the LAo, has been measured (White, 1956; Greenfield and Morrow, 1961; Khalil and Zhaki, 1964; Grigg and Johansen, 1987; Malvin et al.,1995).

The potential for differential distributions of systemic venous blood into the arterial circulation is not trivial and can signficantly alter interpretations of cardiac shunting patterns. A study by Ishimatsu et al., (1988) that examined the effects of body temperature on cardiac shunting patterns in *Varanus niloticus* illustrates this point. At 25°C, the blood oxygen content in the RAo is slightly lower than the blood oxygen content in the left atrium (LAt), suggesting a small R-L shunt fraction (Ishimatsu et al., 1988). As body temperature increases from 25° to 35°C, the oxygen content difference between the RAo and LAt remains constant, leading to the conclusion that the R-L shunt fraction does not change as the body temperature increases. However, this conclusion is altered when simultaneous blood oxygen measurements are made in the RAo and LAo. Specificially, the LAo blood has a lower oxygen saturation than the RAo blood at 25°C (70% vs 95% respectively). As body temperature increases the oxygen saturation in the LAo increases and becomes identical to the value in the RAo (~95%). Thus, the total R-L shunt fraction is large at 25°C, with most of the shunt blood directed into the LAo, whereas the total R-L shunt fraction decreases at 35°C (Ishimatsu et al., 1988).

Three-Vessel Blood Flow Model

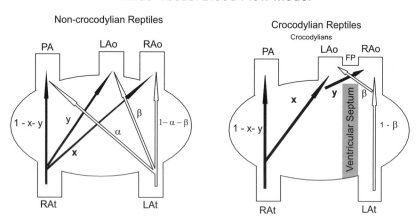

Fig. 5.5. The three-vessel blood flow model. Left panel. Description of intracardiac blood flow patterns in non-crocodylian reptiles. The left-to-right shunt (L-R) is designated by the partition fraction "α." The right-to-left (R-L) shunt is the sum of two partition fractions, x and y. Note that β represents the fraction of pulmonary venous return that is distributed into the RAo (Redrawn from Ishimatsu et al., 1988). Right panel. Application of the three-vessel model to the crocodylian circulation. Note that the shunt fractions x and y represent the fraction of blood flowing through the foramen of Panizza, respectively. Abbreviations: LAo, left aortic arch; LAt, left atrium; PA, pulmonary artery; RAt, right atrium; RAo, right aortic arch. Filled arrows, deoxygenated blood; open arrows, oxygenated blood.

A differential distribution of systemic venous blood into the aortic arches means that the two-vessel shunt model does not accurately describe R-L cardiac shunting patterns in reptiles. An alternative three-vessel model has been proposed (Ishimatsu et al., 1988; Fig. 5.5A). This model contains three outflow vessels (RAo, LAo, and PA) and six potential intracardiac flow patterns (Fig. 5.5A). The differential distribution of the systemic venous blood into the LAo and RAo are designated as x and y (Fig. 5.5A). These variables, termed partition fractions (Ishimatsu et al., 1988), represent the fraction of systemic venous blood entering the LAo and RAo respectively. The sum, x + y, is equal to the total R-L shunt fraction. The fraction of pulmonary venous blood that recirculates into the PA (L-R; α) is not different from that predicted by the standard two-vessel model. In the crocodylians, the equations of the three vessel model are modified. The presence of a complete ventricular septum precludes a L-R shunt. Therefore, the L-R shunt term (α) is unnecessary (Fig. 5.5B). In crocodylians, the partition fractions y and β represent the fraction of blood flowing through the foramen of Panizza.

All of the analyses described in the preceding paragraphs are based in large part on steady-state assumptions, which are often difficult to apply to reptiles. As will be discussed in some detail in this chapter, the heart rate, vascular resistances, cardiac output, and blood flow distributions are very labile, varying with time and physiological state. However, this should not imply that cardiac shunts cannot be studied accurately; rather, the reader is forewarned that the cardiac shunting patterns in the reptilian heart are complicated, and that interpreting blood gas and blood flow measurements can be quite complex.

B. Summary

Cardiac shunts are defined by their direction and magnitude. A R-L shunt represents blood flow bypassing the pulmonary circulation. A L-R shunt represents blood flow recirculating through the pulmonary circulation. The magnitude of the shunt is expressed as the net shunt flow, i.e., the difference between the systemic and pulmonary blood flow. In addition, the magnitude of the shunt can be expressed as the fractional contribution of the shunt flow to the systemic or pulmonary blood flow (shunt fraction). If there is unidirectional shunting, the shunt fraction, determined from direct flow measurement, is equivalent to the shunt fraction calculated from blood oxygen contents. If bidirectional shunting occurs, then the information from direct measurement of flow is insufficient for accurate deciphering of the intraventricular blood flow patterns. Additional measurements of blood oxygen content are needed. Finally, the measurement of blood oxygen levels from only one systemic arterial site may not provide sufficient information on the shunt distribution into the systemic circulation. Instead, analysis of shunting patterns in reptiles requires a three-vessel model.

IV. MECHANISMS OF CARDIAC SHUNTING
A. General Mechanisms

Cardiac shunts result from anatomical communication between the pulmonary and systemic circuits and may be determined by four conditions. These are: (1) differences in hydraulic pressures between the two circuits, (2) differences in the kinetic energy of the blood between two vascular circuits, (3) mixing within an open interface, and (4) arterial and venous blood occupying a common compartment of the ventricle during different phases of the cardiac cycle. In reptiles, these four conditions are not mutually exclusive; all may be contributing to the development of cardiac shunts.

Differences in the hydraulic pressure across two vascular circuits may transfer blood from one circuit to the next through a direct communication, called a "pressure difference shunt" (Heisler and Glass, 1985). The shunt flow between the two circuits is determined by the magnitude of the pressure difference, the size of the communication between the two circuits, and the outflow resistances from each site (Berman, 1985). In mammalian circuits, these factors result in shunt flows across atrial and septal defects (Rudolf, 1974).

In some conditions, pulmonary and systemic venous bloods mix within a common chamber. This is termed an "open interface shunt" (Heisler and Glass, 1985), and the degree of mixing depends on the extent of turbulent flow that occurs (Faber et al., 1985). For example, in the embryonic circulation, Reynolds numbers (values that reflect the extent of turbulent flow) are so low that the blood does not mix within the single ventricle (Yoshida et al., 1983).

Shunting—either in an open interface or across a direct communication—can also be influenced by kinetic energy. This condition is termed a "kinetic shunt" because the velocity and direction of blood flow determine the shunt flow. Kinetic shunts are not usually emphasized, but the contribution of the kinetic energy to the shunt flow may be very important, particularly in low pressure circuits. For example, in fetal lambs, the kinetic energy of the venous blood is as important in determining the flow through the foramen ovale (a connection between the two atria) as is the pressure difference between the left and right atria (Faber et al., 1985).

Finally, shunts result whenever arterial and venous blood occupies a common cardiac chamber during different phases of the cardiac cycle. This type of shunt is called a "washout shunt" and results from the specific cardiac anatomy of non-crocodylian reptiles (Heisler and Glass, 1985). This shunt mechanism is discussed in greater detail in Section IV.C.2.

B. Crocodylians

The complex circulatory arrangement in crocodylians results in six possible flow patterns, of which only four have been observed (Malvin et al., 1995; Fig. 5.6). In Pattern 1, all of the RV blood is ejected into the pulmonary artery, and the LV blood is ejected into the RAo. During diastole, a portion of blood within the RAo flows through the foramen of Panizza into the LAo. In Pattern 2, a fraction of the RV blood is ejected into the pulmonary artery and into the LAo. The total LAo flow is augmented by additional blood flowing through the foramen of Panizza from the RAo. Blood does not flow from the LAo into the RAo. Pattern 3 is almost identical to Pattern 2, except that blood from the LAo enters

Blood Flow Patterns in the Crocodylians

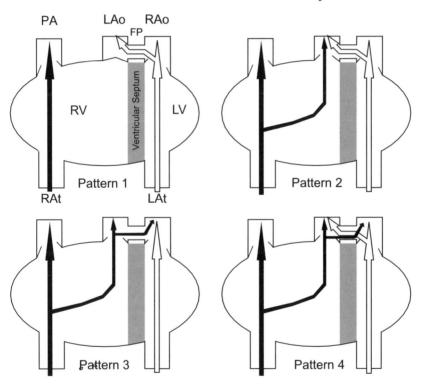

Fig. 5.6. Schematic representation of the potential blood flow patterns in the crocodylian heart. Abbreviations: PA, pulmonary artery; RAt, right atrium; LAt, left atrium; RV, right ventricle; LV, left ventricle; RAo, right aortic arch; LAo, left aortic arch and FP, foramen of Panizza. Filled arrows, deoxygenated blood; open arrows, oxygenated blood. (Diagram redrawn from Malvin et al., 1995.)

Table 5.1. Blood flow patterns in the crocodylians.

Species	Measurement	Flow Pattern and Experimental Condition	Reference
Caiman crocodilus	aortic and intracardiac [O$_2$]	1*- anesthetized, ventilated	White, 1956
Alligator mississippiensis	central vascular pressure	2 - anesthetized, ventilated	White, 1956
	indicator injected into atria	2 - anesthetized, ventilated	Greenfield and Morrow, 1961
	aortic and intracardiac [O$_2$]	4 - anesthetized, ventilated	Greenfield and Morrow, 1961
Crocodylus niloticus	aortic and intracardiac [O$_2$]	4 - anesthetized, ventilated	Khalil and Zaki, 1964
Alligator mississippiensis	central vascular pressures	1 - conscious, restrained	White, 1969
		3 - forced diving	White, 1969
Crocodylus porosus	central vascular pressures, PO$_2$ in Rao, LAo, and PA	1 & 2 - conscious, unrestrained airbreathing	Grigg and Johansen, 1987
		3 - conscious, unrestrained, diving	Grigg and Johansen, 1987
Caiman crocodilus	central vascular pressures, aortic blood flows	1 - conscious, unrestrained airbreathing	Axelsson et al., 1989
		1 - diving, unrestrained	Axelsson et al., 1989
		1 - anesthetized, ventilated	Axelsson et al., 1989
Alligator mississippiensis	central vascular PO$_2$'s, He tracer	1, 2, 3 & 4 - anesthetized, ventilated	Malvin et al., 1995
		3 & 4 - anesthetized, ventilated, vagal stimulation	Malvin et al., 1995
Alligator mississippiensis	central vascular pressues, aortic blood flows	1 & 2 - anesthetized, ventilated	Shelton and Jones, 1991

* The four potential blood flow patterns in the crocodylian heart are shown in figure 5.6.

the RAo via the foramen of Panizza. In this case, no blood from the RAo enters the LAo. In Pattern 4, blood from the RV is ejected into both the PA and LAo. Blood from the LAo enters the RAo, and a fraction of the blood from the RAo enters the LAo. This pattern is unique because of the bidirectional shunting between the two aortae that occurs through the foramen of Panizza. Previous studies, in both acute and chronic preparations, have reported flow patterns consistent with Patterns 1–4 (Table 5.1). For completeness, the circulatory arrangement results in two additional flow patterns. In Pattern 5, RV blood is ejected into the PA only, whereas blood from the LV is ejected into the RAo, and no blood enters the LAo. Finally, Pattern 6 represents a complete pulmonary bypass, in which all RV blood is ejected into the LAo, and a fraction flows into the RAo via the foramen of Panizza. In this condition, no blood flows into the left side of the heart. These final two blood flow patterns have been observed neither in acute nor in chronic preparations.

The mechanism responsible for a R-L shunt in crocodylians is best appreciated after briefly reviewing the basic hemodynamic events that occur during the cardiac cycle. These events have been well described (Greenfield and Morrow, 1961; White, 1956; Grigg and Johansen, 1987; Shelton and Jones, 1991; Jones and Shelton, 1993; Axelsson et al., 1996). The following brief description of the cardiac cycle and the specific terminology is based on Shelton and Jones (1991). In the LV, systole is initiated by an isovolumic ventricular contraction phase (L1), followed by ejection of LV blood into the RAo and a subsequent rise and peak in RAo pressure (L2 and L3; Fig. 5.7). Diastole begins with a relaxation of the ventricle, a fall in aortic pressure, and closure of the aortic valve (L3), terminating in an isovolumic relaxation phase (L4) and reduction of LV pressure to near zero (L5). In contrast to the left ventricle, pulmonary circulation is at a lower pressure, and the right ventricle exhibits two distinct stages of pressure generation during systole (Fig. 5.7). Sys-

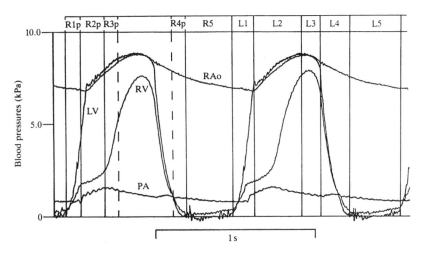

Fig. 5.7. Basic cardiac cycle in *Alligator mississippiensis*. Tracings are simultaneous recordings from the left ventricle (LV), right ventricle (RV), pulmonary artery (PA), and right aorta (RAo) from a 3.6 kg alligator. The letters above the tracings (R1p, R2p, R3p, R4p, R5, L1, L2, L3, L4, and L5) indicate the phases of the cardiac cycle (see text for detailed description). Note that blood pressures are in kPa. (Tracings are from Shelton and Jones, 1991.)

tole in the RV is initiated by an isovolumic contraction phase (R1p), which is synchronous with the LV contraction. Subsequently, the rate of rise in RV pressure is diminished (R2p), coincident with a rising pulmonary arterial pressure, approximately 80–100 ms preceding systemic ejection. The ejection of blood into the pulmonary artery, before systemic arterial ejection, results from a lower diastolic pressure in the pulmonary artery.

As phase R2p ends, there is a second rapid rise in RV pressure, without a concomitant rise in pulmonary arterial pressure. This two-stage pressure event in the RV is not an artifact and represents a distinguishing hemodynamic characteristic of the crocodylian heart during ventricular systole (Shelton and Jones, 1991). The second stage rise in RV pressure results from the unique anatomy of the pulmonary outflow tract, which is made up of a subcompartment that is demarcated by fibrous nodules extending from the walls of the ventricle, just proximal to pulmonary valves. During the latter stage of systole, these nodules fit together like opposing "cogs" (Webb, 1979; Axelsson et al., 1996), increasing the resistance of the pulmonary outflow tract and preventing further ejection of the blood into the pulmonary artery (R3p).

The two-stage pressure development by the RV is important. It indicates that the RV can generate pressures that are equal to systemic arterial pressures. Such high pressures are important in the maintenance of systemic cardiac output during periods of pulmonary bypass (Shelton and Jones, 1991). The closure of the pulmonary outflow tract by the fibrous nodules prevents these high pressures from being transmitted into the pulmonary circulation (Grigg, 1989; Shelton and Jones, 1991).

Blood flow between the LAo and RAo results from pressure differences across the foramen of Panizza and from the timing of the opening and closing of the aortic valves. Normally, when there is no cardiac shunting, the pressures in the LAo and RAo are very similar in timing but differ in their absolute values (Axelsson et al., 1989; Shelton and Jones, 1991). The peak systolic pressures in the LAo are lower than in the RAo. At the end of phase L3 of the cardiac cycle, a notch develops in the LAo pressure trace. This has been termed the foramen spike (Grigg and Johansen, 1987) and is correlated with the closure of the aortic valves. The size of the foramen spike may be altered by downstream resistance offered in the LAo (Shelton and Jones, 1991). Two types of flow patterns are observed in the LAo. During the rising phase of pressure in the RAo, flow in the LAo reverses (i.e., the blood flows toward the heart). After closure of the aortic valves, flow reverts to being forward (i.e., away from the heart). During systole, flow from the RAo to the LAo is prevented by the cusp of the RAo valve (Shelton and Jones, 1991). The reverse flow in the LAo results from RAo blood "charging" the elastic reservoir of the LAo via the anastomoses between the RAo and LAo.

During diastole, the closure of the RAo valve causes the medial cusp to uncover the foramen of Panizza. This allows flow from the RAo to the LAo; thus, forward flow occurs in the LAo.

A R-L shunt develops from a pressure mechanism and occurs when the second phase of the RV pressure exceeds the diastolic pressure in the LAo. Under these conditions, the LAo valve will open, and a fraction of RV blood will be ejected into the LAo. There are four hemodynamic conditions that result in R-L shunting, summarized by Shelton and Jones (1991). These include a selective increase in the contractility of the RV (probably from sympathetic stimulation), an increase in the preload of the RV, an increase the pulmonary outflow resistance, and a reduction of systemic pressures by vasodilation. Experimental evidence has shown that R-L shunting can result from all these conditions (White, 1956; Axelsson et al., 1989; Shelton and Jones, 1991; Jones and Shelton, 1993; Franklin and Axelsson, 1994).

During R-L shunting, resulting from acetylcholine-induced constriction of the pulmonary blood vessels, the reverse flow in the LAo stops and there is a monophasic forward flow pulse in systole (Axelsson et al., 1989; Jones and Shelton, 1993). If the R-L shunt results from a systemic hypotension, then the LAo flow pulse remains biphasic (Jones and Shelton, 1993). Blood-flow patterns through the foramen during cardiac shunting have also been deduced by injecting an indicator substance in the left and right atrium (Malvin et al., 1995). During cardiac shunting, there can be unidirectional flow (LAo to RAo; Pattern 3, Fig. 5.6) or bidirectional flow (Pattern 4, Fig. 5.6) through the foramen of Panizza (Malvin et al., 1995). However, in the latter, injected indicator substances cannot distinguish during which phase of the cardiac cycle the flow through the foramen occurs. Blood-flow across the foramen of Panizza may be influenced by kinetic factors (Malvin et al., 1995). Echocardiography demonstrates turbulent flow in the foramen of Panizza and at the base of the LAo (Malvin et al., 1995); however, the quantitative contribution of kinetic energy to the blood flow through the foramen is unknown.

C. Testudines and Squamates

Although both R-L and L-R cardiac shunts occur in testudines and squamates, the precise mechanisms that account for cardiac shunting have not been well understood (Heisler et al., 1983; Heisler and Glass, 1985; White et al.,1989; Hicks and Malvin, 1992; Hicks and Comeau, 1994). Two principal mechanisms may be responsible for cardiac shunts. These include pressure shunting and washout shunting (Heisler and Glass, 1985). The critical difference between these two mechanisms is the ability of the muscular ridge to separate the CP from the CV and CA during systole.

Blood Pressures in the Reptilia

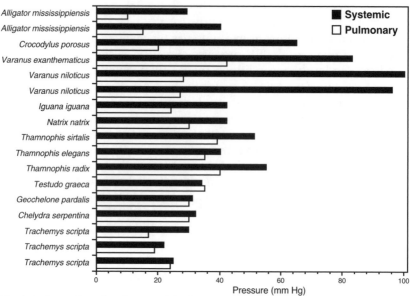

Fig. 5.8. Systemic and pulmonary blood pressures in the Reptilia. Solid bars indicate systemic arterial pressure and open bars indicate pulmonary arterial pressure in *Trachemys scripta* (White and Ross, 1966; Comeau and Hicks, 1994; Shelton and Burggren, 1976), *Chelydra serpentina* (Steggarda and Essex, 1957), *Testudo graeca* (Shelton and Burggren, 1976), *Geochelone pardalis* (Burggren et al., 1977), *Thamnophis* spp. (Burggren, 1977b), *Natrix natrix* (Johansen, 1959), *Iguana iguana* (White, 1959), *Varanus niloticus* (Millard and Johansen, 1973; Ishimatsu et al., 1988), *V. exanthematicus* (Burggren and Johansen, 1982), *Crocodylus porosus* (Grigg and Johansen, 1987), and *Alligator mississippiensis* (Greenfield and Morrow, 1961; White, 1959).

1. PRESSURE SHUNTING

In contrast to the situation in crocodylians, the ventricle of most testudines and some squamates functions as a single pressure pump. This concept is supported by measurements of pulmonary and systemic arterial pressures in a variety of species (Fig. 5.8) as well as intraventricular pressure measurements. For example, in *Trachemys scripta*, ventricular systole is characterized by an almost simultaneous rise in the blood pressure of the CP and CA (Fig. 5.9). This overlap of pressure suggests that the ventricular cava are interconnected during all phases of the cardiac cycle (Burggren, 1985).

In its simplest form, the pressure mechanism predicts that the direction and size of the cardiac shunt depends on the intraventricular pressure gradients during diastole and/or systole, the size of the communication between the ventricular compartments, and the outflow resistance of the pulmonary and systemic circulations. For example, in many testudines and squamates, the diastolic pressure in the pulmonary artery can be up to 15 mmHg lower than the diastolic pressure in the LAo and RAo (Steggarda and Essex, 1957; Johansen, 1959; White and Ross, 1966; Shelton and Burggren, 1976; Burggren, 1977b). Therefore, during systole, the opening of the pulmonary valve precedes that of the aortic valves, leads it to an earlier ejection of blood into the pulmonary than into the systemic arteries, and thus favors the development of a L-R shunt (Johansen, 1959; White and Ross, 1966; Shelton and Burggren, 1976; Burggren, 1977b). In contrast, if the pulmonary arterial diastolic pressure is higher than the aortic pressure, the reverse occurs. The opening of the aortic valves then precedes the opening of the valve of the pulmonary artery, and blood from all three compartments (CP and CV/CA) will be ejected into the systemic circuit, resulting in a R-L shunt.

Based on the simplified concepts presented above, the following hemodynamic relationships should exist. First, the timing of ejection into the pulmonary and systemic arteries will be a function of the diastolic pressures in the two respective circuits. Experiments with *Trachemys scripta* (Hicks et al., 1996) support this hypothesis (Fig. 5.10A). This study found that an increase of the diastolic pressure difference between the pulmonary and systemic circulations allows ejection of blood into the pulmonary artery to precede ejection of blood into the systemic circulation. Second, the size and direction of the net cardiac shunt will be correlated with the timing of ejection into the pulmonary and systemic arteries. Specifically, if the ejection of blood into the pulmonary circuit precedes ejection of blood into the systemic circuit, then a net L-R shunt will develop; the size of this shunt will be correlated with the difference in the ejection timing, i.e., the greater the timing differential, the larger the net L-R shunt. In contrast, if ejection of blood into the systemic circuit precedes the pulmonary ejection, then a net R-L shunt will develop. Measurements of net intracardiac shunting and the timing of ejection into the pulmonary and systemic circuits of *Trachemys scripta* support this prediction (Fig. 5.10B) (Hicks et al., 1996). Third, as the vascular resistances of the pulmonary

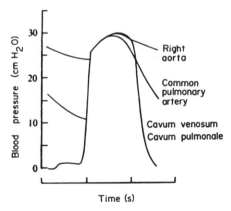

Fig. 5.9. Cardiac cycle of *Trachemys scripta*. Tracing is from Burggren (1987), redrawn from original study by Shelton and Burggren (1976).

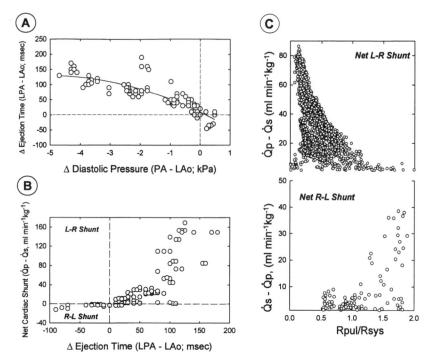

Fig. 5.10. Pressure shunting in *Trachemys scripta*. A. The relationship between the diastolic pressure difference in the pulmonary and systemic circulation and the difference in the timing of blood ejection into these respective circulations. (Graph redrawn from Hicks et al., 1996). B. The relationship between the ejection timing into the pulmonary and systemic circulations and the size of the net cardiac shunt. (From Hicks et al., 1996.) C. The effects of changing the relative resistances in the pulmonary and systemic circulations (Rp/Rs) on the size of cardiac shunting. Upper panel. The net shunt is indicated by the difference between the pulmonary and systemic blood flows ($\dot{Q}p - \dot{Q}s$). Values above zero indicate a net left-to-right (L-R) shunt. Lower panel. The net shunt is indicated by the difference between systemic and pulmonary blood flows ($\dot{Q}s - \dot{Q}p$). Values above zero indicate a net right-to-left shunt (R-L) (From Hicks, 1994.)

and systemic circulations partially determine the diastolic pressures within these circuits, the size and direction of the net shunt is correlated with the relative resistances between the pulmonary and systemic circuits (Fig. 5.10C) (Burggren, 1985; Hicks, 1994; Hicks et al., 1996). Experimental support for these hemodynamic relationships supports the hypothesis that the pressure mechanism contributes to intracardiac shunting in turtles. In addition, these experiments support the idea that the regulation of pulmonary and systemic vascular resistance is an important causative factor in controlling the direction and size of the intracardiac shunt.

2. WASHOUT SHUNTING

The unique anatomical relationships of the ventricular cava suggest an alternative mechanism for cardiac shunting, the washout model. A "washout-like" mechanism was first proposed by Khalil and Zaki (1964). However, the mechanism was fully developed, refined, and experimental evidence supporting it was provided by Heisler and co-workers (1983). Basically, the washout model suggests that, during systole, tight adpression of the muscular ridge against the dorsal ventricular wall prevents translocation of systemic venous blood from CP into the RAo or LAo. Conversely, blood from the CV and CA is prevented from flowing into the CP during systole. Cardiac shunting results from the residual volume of blood within the CV and its mixing within the pulmonary or systemic circuit during the cardiac cycle. To understand this, it is best to trace the movement through the heart of deoxygenated, systemic venous blood during the cardiac cycle. During diastole, blood from the right atrium fills both the CP and CV (Fig. 5.11). However, during

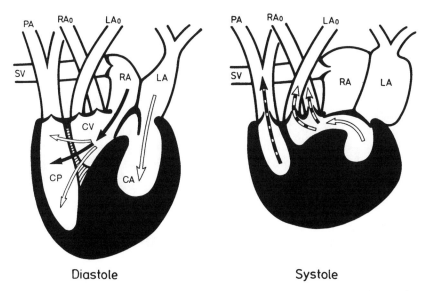

Diastole   Systole

Fig. 5.11. Schematic representation of intracardiac shunting due to the washout of the cavum venosum (CV). Diastole. Oxygenated blood (open arrows) remaining in the CV from the preceding systole is washed into the cavum pulmonale (CP) by deoxygenated blood returning from the body via the right atrium (RA). Systole. Deoxygenated blood remaining in the CV at the end of diastole is washed into the systemic arches (RAo and LAo) from blood ejected from the cavum arteriosum (CA). Blood within the CP, which contains a mixture of oxygenated and deoxygenated blood, is ejected into the pulmonary artery (PA). Note the separation of the CP from the CA/CV via the muscular ridge, during systole. Other abbreviations: LA, left atrium; SV, sinus venosus. (Redrawn from Heisler and Glass, 1985.)

ventricular systole, blood within the CA is ejected through the CV to enter the aortic arches (Fig. 5.11). Consequently, the degree of R-L shunt is dependent on the volume of deoxygenated blood in the CV at end-diastole (Vcv_{ED}) and the volume of blood ejected from the CA during systole (Vca_S). At the end of systole, the CV is filled with residual blood from the CA. This end-systolic blood is pulmonary venous in origin (oxygenated) and is *washed* from the CV into the CP during the subsequent diastole. This mixing increases the O_2 level of pulmonary arterial blood and accounts for the L-R shunt. Thus, the size of the L-R shunt will be determined by the end-systolic volume of oxygenated blood in the CV (Vcv_{ESV}) and the systemic venous return. Variability in intracardiac shunting between individuals and during different physiological states can be accounted for by the ratio of stroke volume to the volumes of the CV during the cardiac cycle (Heisler et al., 1983). These volumes may be subject to modulation by changes in preload, afterload, or contractility of the heart (Heisler and Glass, 1985).

The washout model is based on hemodynamic studies on varanid lizards. The cardiovascular dynamics of these lizards are considered unique among non-crocodylian reptiles. As in other squamates, the ventricular chambers in the varanids are interconnected during diastole. Thus, there is the possibility of intracardiac mixing during the diastolic phase of the cardiac cycle. However, during systole, the pressures generated in the CA and CV are three- to four-fold higher than those in the CP (Fig. 5.12) (Millard and Johansen, 1973; Burggren and Johansen, 1982; Heisler et al., 1983; Ishimatsu et al., 1988). Unlike testudines and other squamates, the pressures in the ventricular cava of varanids never become superimposable during systole. Therefore, blood probably does not flow around the muscular ridge during systole (Millard and Johansen,1973; Burggren and Johansen, 1982; Heisler et al., 1983; Johansen and Burggren, 1984). Clearly, these lizards are approaching an avian and mammalian-like ventricular pressure separation (Burggren and Johansen, 1982) and, consequently, the washout hypothesis has not been generally accepted for most squamates or testudines.

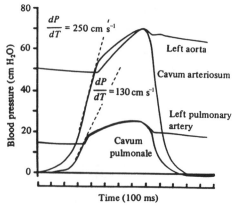

Fig. 5.12. Cardiac cycle in the monitor lizard, *Varanus exanthematicus*. (Redrawn from Burggren and Johansen, 1982.)

A direct test of the washout hypothesis requires visualizing or tracing blood flow patterns through the ventricle. One such method to deduce blood flow patterns is the indicator dilution technique. This technique is well defined and can be used to detect, localize, and quantify intracardiac shunts (Grossman, 1986). An indicator is any substance that is easily and accurately detected because of its chemical, electrical, optical, or thermal properties. The application of this technique to detect intracardiac shunting is simple. Assuming minor pulmonary recirculation, detection of the indicator in the systemic arches following injection into the right atrium demonstrates a R-L shunt. Detection of indicator in the pulmonary artery following injection into the left atrium will demonstrate a L-R shunt. The mechanism of R-L shunting is directly tested by injection of indicator into the CP. Detection of the indicator in the systemic arches after injection into the CP supports the pressure shunting hypothesis. In contrast, absence of the indicator in the systemic arch following its injection into CP supports the washout hypothesis. The indicator method cannot be used to determine the mechanism of L-R shunting.

Hicks and Malvin (1992) have used a mass spectrometer to monitor central vascular blood gases and to detect an inert tracer gas following its injection into the cardiac chambers of *Trachemys scripta*. These experiments pharmacologically manipulated the level of R-L intracardiac shunting by the infusion of epinephrine (EPI) or acetylcholine (ACh) into the venous circulation. Injection of ACh results in an intensification of the R-L shunt, as indicated by reductions in the systemic arch PO_2 from control values (Fig. 5.13). During this period, injection of He-saline into the right atrium is always detected in the systemic arches (Hicks and Malvin, 1992). In contrast, injection of He-saline into the CP is never detected in the systemic arches (Fig. 5.13). These He tracer patterns suggest that the muscular ridge effectively separates the CP and CV during systole (Hicks and Malvin, 1992). Interestingly, following administration of EPI, He-saline injected into the right atrium is never detected in the systemic outflow tracts. This absence provides evidence that adrenergic stimulation eliminates R-L shunting (Fig. 5.13). The results following ACh administration are inconsistent with the pressure shunting hypothesis and strongly support the washout mechanism for R-L intracardiac shunting, because blood from the CP is not detected in the systemic arches (Hicks and Malvin, 1992).

An alternative to the mass spectrometry system described above is the use of platinum electrodes to detect hydrogen and localize intracardiac shunts (Clark et al., 1960). Basically, a small platinum wire (30 g) can be non-occlusively inserted into central vascular sites and, based on the cardiac anatomy, blood flow patterns can be deduced. The

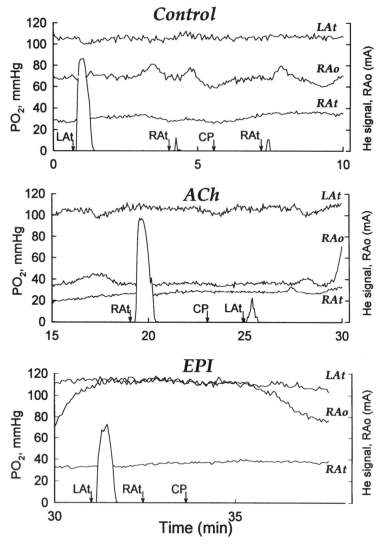

Fig. 5.13. Blood gases and He tracer signal in cardiac chambers and systemic vessel in *Trachemys scripta* as continuously monitored utilizing a mass spectrometer. Top panel. Control conditions. Injection of He-saline (downward arrows) into the right atrium (RAt) and left atrium (LAt) were detected in right aortic arch (RAo). Injection of He-saline into cavum pulmonale (CP) was not detected in the RAo. Middle panel. Central vascular PO_2 measurements following injection of acetylcholine (ACh; 0.1 mg kg^{-1}). Injection of He-saline into RAt and LAt was detected in the RAo, but was not detected following injection into the CP. Bottom panel. Central vascular PO_2 measurements following injection of epinephrine (EPI 1mg kg^{-1}). Injection of He-saline into RAt and CP was not detected in RAo. Injection of He-saline into LAt was detected in the RAo. Solid line represents continuous PO_2 measurements. (Redrawn from Hicks and Malvin, 1992.)

advantage of this technique is that the hydrogen electrodes are small, inexpensive, and exhibit a very fast response time (<100 ms; Clark et al., 1960). In addition, the small size and flexibility of the platinum wire allow the animal also to be instrumented for the measurement of additional physiological parameters, i.e., blood flow and pressure. Platinum electrodes have been used to investigate the effects of vagal nerve stimulation on central vascular blood gases and blood flow patterns in *Trachemys scripta* (Hicks and Comeau, 1994). These experiments used a very similar experimental preparation to that described by Hicks and Malvin (1992), the primary difference being the use of vagal nerve stimulation to modulate intracardiac shunt levels. During control conditions, injection of H_2 in either the left atrium or jugular vein is detected in the RAo, the LAo, and the PA (Fig. 5.14). Infusion of H_2 into CP is never detected in LAo or RAo during control (Fig. 5.14). This detection pattern suggests bi-directional shunting during control. Stimulation of the right vagal efferent nerve elicits a 70% reduction in both heart rate and pulmonary blood flow, and the pulmonary vascular resistance doubles. The R-L intracardiac shunt also increases as indicated by a reduction in the PO_2 of both RAo and LAo. During these conditions, infusion of H_2 into the jugular vein and left atrium is detected in both RAo and LAo (Fig. 5.15). However, infusion of H_2 into the CP is detected in the systemic arches in only two of seven animals, suggesting that the translocation of blood from the CP into the systemic arches does not account for desaturation of arterial blood (Hicks and Comeau, 1994). It should be noted that, during these conditions, H_2 injected into left atrium is simultaneously detected in the pulmonary artery, thereby demonstrating the presence of bi-directional intracardiac shunting during vagal stimulation (Fig. 5.14).

D. Washout and Pressure Shunting: Are the Mechanisms Mutually Exclusive?

The precise mechanism of cardiac shunting has been studied directly in only two non-crocodylians, *Varanus* and *Trachemys*. Given the degree of variability that exists in the ventricular anatomy, differences in the size of the muscular ridge, and the various physiological characteristics of these reptiles, it would not be surprising to discover that both the washout and pressure mechanisms can contribute to cardiac shunting. In the varanid lizards, the washout of the CV is the primary mechanism responsible for cardiac shunting. This mechanism reflects the well-developed muscular ridge that is capable of completely separating the ventricular chambers during the early phases of systole, preventing the movement of blood between the ventricular cava. In turtles, both washout and pressure mechanisms appear to contribute to the development of cardiac shunts.

The contribution of these two mechanisms in turtles can be summarized as follows. Washout appears to occur during the diastolic phase of the cardiac cycle. The CP receives a mixture of pulmonary venous blood (oxygen rich) and systemic venous blood (oxygen poor). During systole, the mechanisms that determine the size and direction of shunting result from the dynamic events that occur during the cardiac cycle. These include the rate of ventricular pressure development, the time it takes for the muscular ridge

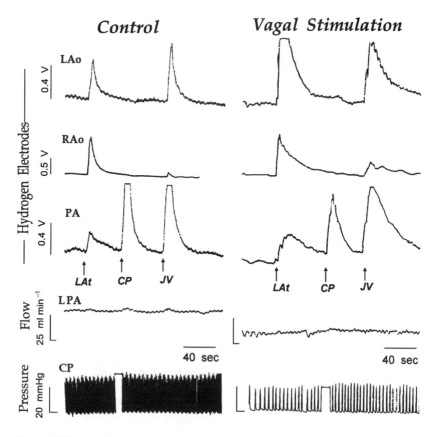

Fig. 5.14. Washout shunting in *Trachemys scripta*. The H_2 signals (V) are measured in the left aortic arch (LAo), right aortic arch (RAo) and pulmonary artery (PA) during control and during conditions that promote R-L cardiac shunting (electrical stimulation of the vagus nerve). In this figure, the mean blood flow in the left pulmonary artery (LPA) and blood pressure in the cavum pulmonale (CP) are shown. Recordings are from a 1.8 kg animal under control conditions, and during stimulation of the right vagal efferent nerve. Infusion of H_2-saline into the left atrium (LAt), CP, or jugular vein (JV) is indicated by an upward arrow. For all the injections into the CP, note the disruption of the pressure trace as the catheter is switched from a pressure port to an infusion port. Also note the reduction in LPA blood flow and heart rate during RVEF. (Redrawn from Hicks and Comeau, 1994.)

to separate the CP from the CV and CA, and the diastolic pressures in the pulmonary and systemic arteries. Whenever the pulmonary diastolic pressure is lower than the systemic diastolic pressure, then the ejection of blood into the pulmonary artery precedes the ejection of blood into the systemic artery. During this early phase of systole, the muscular ridge does not initially separate the CP from the CV/CA. Therefore, a fraction of blood from the CV and CA is translocated around the muscular ridge into the CP and pulmonary circulation. Under these conditions, a L-R shunt occurs, and a portion of this L-R shunt results from the pressure mechanism. During the subsequent diastole, oxygen rich blood left in the CV is "washed" into the CP, and thus, at end-diastole, the CP contains a mixture of oxygen rich and oxygen poor blood. In contrast, if the diastolic pressure of the pulmonary circulation approaches the diastolic pressures in the systemic circulation, the ejection of blood into the great vessels occurs almost simultaneously, and little if any blood flows between the CP and CV or CA. As systole progresses, the muscular ridge effectively separates the two sides of the heart, and blood from the CP is prevented from being ejected into the systemic vessels. Under these hemodynamic conditions, the R-L shunt results from the mixing of blood in the CV and CA during the systolic phase of the cardiac cycle.

The contribution of these mechanisms to the overall shunting patterns in other representative squamates and testudines is unknown. These mechanisms need to be determined in multiple reptiles, especially in species that exhibit varying degrees of pressure separation and/or development of the muscular ridge, in order to provide insights into the phylogeny of the reptilian heart.

V. REGULATION OF CARDIAC SHUNTING
A. Overview
The size and direction of intracardiac shunting are determined by factors that control cardiac function (HR and myocardial contractility) and the vascular resistance of the pulmonary and systemic circulations. These factors include adrenergic and cholinergic mechanisms (Berger and Burnstock, 1979; Nilsson, 1983). In addition, non-adrenergic, non-cholinergic systems (NANC) may play an important role in controlling cardiovascular function in reptiles (Lillywhite and Donald, 1989; Conlon et al., 1990; Comeau et al., 1992).

B. Cholinergic Regulation
In reptiles, the right and left atria and the ventricle are innervated by the vagus nerve, which runs in a common vagosympathetic trunk (see Berger and Burnstock,1979, for review). As in most vertebrates, the vagus exerts an inhibitory cholinergic influence on the heart rate. Injection of ACh re-

duces the heart rate in testudines (White, 1976; Hicks, 1994), lizards (Kirby and Burnstock, 1969), and in crocodylians (Axelsson et al., 1989; Jones and Shelton, 1993). Similarly, injection of atropine results in a tachycardia in snakes (Burggren, 1977a), testudines (J. W. Hicks, unpublished), and lizards (Kirby and Burnstock, 1969). Furthermore, in *Trachemys scripta*, electrical stimulation of the vagus nerve results in a bradycardia that is eliminated by atropine (Hicks and Comeau, 1994; Comeau and Hicks, 1994).

The pulmonary vasculature of reptiles exhibits a cholinergic vasoconstrictor innervation. Electrical stimulation of the vagus nerve or injection of acetylcholine results in an increase in the pulmonary vasculature resistance in testudines (Luckhardt and Carlson, 1921; Milsom et al., 1977; Burggren, 1977a; Hicks and Comeau, 1994; Comeau and Hicks, 1994), lizards, (Berger, 1972, 1973; D. G. Smith and Macintyre, 1979), snakes (Donald et al., 1990), and crocodylians (White, 1956; Axelsson et al., 1989; Jones and Shelton, 1993). The resulting increase in pulmonary vascular resistance is abolished by atropine.

As previously discussed (Section IV), an increase in the pulmonary vascular resistance can promote the development of a R-L shunt. Thus, a R-L shunt is said to be under cholinergic control (White, 1976, 1978). Electrical stimulation of the vagus efferent nerves of testudines results in the development of a net R-L shunt (Comeau and Hicks, 1994; Hicks, 1994). In addition, electrical stimulation of the vagus nerves reduces the blood PO_2 of both the LAo and RAo (Burggren, 1978; Hicks and Comeau, 1994) without changes in the pulmonary venous and systemic venous PO_2. The systemic arterial PO_2 is also decreased by the intravenous infusion of acetylcholine (ACh) (Hicks and Malvin, 1992). In the crocodylians, injection of ACh (White, 1969; Axelsson et al., 1989; Jones and Shelton, 1993) or electrical stimulation of the vagus (Malvin et al., 1995) promotes the development of a R-L shunt. The R-L shunt is abolished following the administration of atropine (White, 1956).

C. Adrenergic Regulation

The cardiac sympathetic nerves of turtles leave the spinal cord at the level of the tenth spinal nerve, run forward through three ganglia of the sympathetic chain, and extend toward the heart (Gaskell and Gadow, 1884). Sympathetic fibers innervate the atrium, and ultrastructural observations confirm that fibers containing vesicles typical of adrenergic nerves occur in the ventricular myocardium of testudines (Yamauchi and Chiba 1973). Stimulation of these fibers results in tachycardia. This effect is blocked by bretylium (an adrenergic neurone-blocking agent) (see Berger and Burnstock, 1979, for review). Tachycardia occurs after intravenous administration of epinephrine and norepinephrine (Berger and Burnstock, 1979; Comeau and Hicks, 1994).

Histochemical studies show adrenergic nerves in the pulmonary vasculature of *Tiliqua rugosa* (McLean and Burnstock, 1967; Furness and Moore, 1970), *Acrochordus granulatus* (Lillywhite and Donald, 1989), and *Chelodina longicollis* (R. V. Smith and Satchell, 1987a). *Elaphe obsoleta* has adrenergic innervation of the pulmonary artery, the smaller pulmonary arteries and veins, and the main pulmonary vein (Donald et al., 1990). The evidence for adrenergic regulation of the pulmonary vasculature is contradictory. Luckhardt and Carlson (1921) reported a differential effect of epinephrine; in turtles, small doses of epinephrine produce vasodilation, whereas larger doses produce vasoconstriction. Injection of the adrenergic agonists norepinephrine, isoprenaline or phenylephrine have no effect on the pulmonary arterial tone in *Malaclemys* (Berger, 1972). In *Trachemys scripta*, infusion of epinephrine, in a dose range from 1–100 µg, does not affect the pulmonary artery pressure (Milsom et al., 1977). In contrast, a marked pulmonary vasodilation results from the injection of epinephrine into the pulmonary artery of rat snakes (Donald et al., 1990). Administration of propranolol eliminates this response. In caimans, an intravenous injection of epinephrine does not affect the pulmonary vascular resistance (Axelsson et al., 1989). However, the study of Axelsson et al. did not measure pulmonary blood flow following epinephrine administration. Therefore, conclusions regarding adrenergic affect on the pulmonary vascular resistance in caimans are tenuous (Badeer and Hicks, 1994).

Electrical stimulation of sympathetic nerves also produces contradictory effects on the pulmonary circulation. In *Trachemys scripta*, electrical stimulation of the cervical sympathetic nerves produce no change in the pulmonary perfusion pressure (Milsom et al., 1977). In contrast, electrical stimulation of the vagus nerve produces a biphasic response in *Elaphe*; during the stimulation, there is a pulmonary vasoconstriction followed by a post-stimulatory pulmonary vasodilation (Donald et al., 1990). The administration of bretylium or propranolol eliminates this post-stimulatory vasodilation, suggesting that the vasodilation is under adrenergic control.

In *Trachemys scripta*, electrical stimulation of cardiac vagal afferent fibers results in an increase of HR, a reduction of Rp, and an increase of systemic vascular resistance (Rs). These changes result in an increase in $\dot{Q}p$ and a decrease in $\dot{Q}s$ (Comeau and Hicks, 1994). Infusion of epinephrine produces similar changes in these cardiovascular variables (Comeau and Hicks, 1994). Administration of bretylium tosylate virtually eliminates the circulatory changes that occurred during vagal afferent nerve stimulation. It appears that electrical stimulation of vagal afferents results in general adrenergic outflow, albeit indirectly (Comeau and Hicks, 1994).

Adrenergic control of intracardiac shunting is not well studied. Analysis of blood PO_2 from the systemic arteries and from cardiac sites shows that adrenergic stimulation may abolish the R-L shunt. An intravenous infusion of epinephrine eliminates the systemic venous admixture in the aortic arches of *Trachemys scripta* (Hicks and Malvin, 1992). A similar result is obtained during electrical stimulation of vagal afferent nerves in this species (Hicks and Comeau, 1994). Finally, vagal afferent nerve stimulation or the injection of epinephrine produces a net L-R shunt in testudines (Comeau and Hicks, 1994).

D. Non-Adrenergic Non-Cholinergic Regulation

In addition to the "classical" control exerted by cholinergic and adrenergic neurones, there is a growing body of evidence that non-adrenergic non-cholinergic (NANC) control of the cardiovascular system may be important in reptiles. A vagal NANC inhibitory innervation of the smooth muscles of the lung have been reported in *Thamnophis* spp. (D. G. Smith and Macintyre, 1979) and in testudines (R. V. Smith and Satchell, 1987b). *Acrochordus granulatus* shows extensive distribution of vasoactive intestinal polypeptide (VIP) immunoreactivity in the pulmonary arterial and venous vessels (Donald and Lillywhite, 1989). This distribution is distinctly different from that of the adrenergic neurons that innervate the pulmonary vasculature (Donald and Lillywhite, 1989). In mammals, VIP is a potent pulmonary vasodilator (Barnes et al., 1986), but its role in the pulmonary vasculature of *Acrochordus* has not yet been determined.

Additional vasoactive peptides have been shown to have an effect on the circulatory system of reptiles. Intravenous injections of [Thr][6] bradykinin increase the blood flow in the LAo of *Trachemys scripta* (Conlon et al., 1990) and may produce a R-L shunt (J. W. Hicks, unpublished observation). In alligators, [Thr][6] bradykinin results in a reduction in the systemic blood pressure (Comeau et al., 1992). However, no changes were reported in blood flow in the aortic arches. Bombesine has been shown to increase the pulmonary vascular resistance in *Crocodylus porosus* and *Caiman crocodilus* (Holmgren et al., 1989). Intravenous injections of Substance P, a potent vasodilator in mammals (Dahlström et al., 1988), produce an increase in the LAo blood flow, and a reduction in the coelic vascular resistance, which may result in a R-L shunt in *Crocodylus porosus* (Axelsson et al., 1991; Karila et al., 1995).

E. Summary

In summary, cardiac shunting in reptiles is determined by the specific cardiac anatomy and caval volumes and by factors that affect heart rate, myocardial contractility, and the vascular resistances in the pulmonary and systemic circulations. These factors include both cholinergic and adrenergic mechanisms. Cholinergic stimulation results in a bradycardia, an increase in pulmonary vascular resistance, a reduction in cardiac output, and the development of a R-L shunt. In contrast, adrenergic stimulation results in a tachycardia, a reduction in pulmonary vascular resistance, an increase in cardiac output, and the development of a L-R shunt (in non-crocodylian reptiles). In addition, there is growing evidence that NANC factors, by affecting systemic and pulmonary vascular resistances, may influence cardiac shunting.

VI. PHYSIOLOGICAL STATES AND CARDIAC SHUNTS
A. General

The physiological state of reptiles, like that of most animals, is influenced by many behaviors. These include thermoregulation, exploration of the local environment, escape from predators, feeding, and reproduction. Over the past several decades, information on the relationship between the physiological states and cardiac shunting has been reported. The vast majority of these reports have focused on the relationship between ventilatory state and cardiac shunts, particularly on the effects of diving. In addition, there have been a few reports on the effects of activity, thermoregulation, hypoxia, and hypercapnia. Below is a brief summary of the major findings.

B. Effects of Ventilation on Cardiac Shunting

1. OVERALL Many reptiles, particularly testudines and crocodylians, are intermittent lung breathers. In these animals, brief ventilatory periods are interspersed among apneas of variable duration (Shelton et al., 1986). These apneic periods can be associated with quiet breathing or with diving in semi-aquatic species. The cardiovascular changes associated with intermittent lung ventilation have received much attention (Belkin, 1964; White and Ross, 1966; Burggren, 1975; Burggren et al., 1977; Shelton and Burggren, 1976; White et al., 1989; Johansen, 1959; Johansen et al., 1987; White, 1956; E. N. Smith and De Carvalho, 1985; Lillywhite and Donald, 1989; Pough, 1973; Moberly, 1968; Seymour and Webster, 1975).

2. TESTUDINES AND SQUAMATES
Quantitative measures of pulmonary and systemic blood flows during apnea have been made in only a few studies and are summarized in Table 5.2. Generally in testudines, apnea is associated with a cholinergically mediated bradycardia, an increase in pulmonary vascular resistance (Rp) leading to a reduction in $\dot{Q}p$. For example in freely diving *Trachemys scripta*, the heart rate (HR) decreases by 80% and the

Table 5.2. Blood flows in the pulmonary and systemic circulations during ventilation and apnea.

Species	Respiratory State	$\dot{Q}p$	$\dot{Q}s$	$\dot{Q}shunt$	$\dot{Q}p/\dot{Q}s$	HR	Tb	Reference
Trachemys	Ventilation	46.2	25.1	21.1	1.84	23	19	Shelton and
scripta	Apnea	14.8	18.5	−3.7	0.8	11		Burggren, 1976
Trachemys	Ventilation	50.1	71.5	−23.1	0.76	41	25	Wang and
scripta	Apnea	18.9	54.9	−35.2	0.36	23		Hicks, 1996
Chrysemys	Ventilation	30.0	41.6	−11.6	0.72	—	15	Heisler and
picta	Apnea	6.3	13.2	−6.9	0.48	—		Glass, 1985
Chrysemys	Ventilation	80.7	85.7	−5.0	0.94	—	30	Heisler and
picta	Apnea	61.6	65.0	−3.4	0.95	—		Glass, 1985
Varanus	Ventilation	26.9	35.3	−8.4	0.76	—	30	Heisler and
exanthematicus	Apnea	26.9	35.3	−8.4	0.76	—		Glass, 1985
Acrochordus	Ventilation	36	~0	36	>36	26	27	Lillywhite and
granulatus	Apnea	~3	—	—	—	—		Donald, 1989

$\dot{Q}p$ = pulmonary blood flow, $\dot{Q}s$ = systemic blood flow, $\dot{Q}shunt$ = net shunt flow ($\dot{Q}p - \dot{Q}s$). Note that blood flows are in ml min^{-1} kg^{-1}, heart rate (HR) is in beats min^{-1}, and body temperature (Tb) is in °C. Values for *Acrochordus* are estimated from original publication.

Rp increases by 150%, resulting in an 80% reduction in the $\dot{Q}p$ (Shelton and Burggren, 1976). These circulatory changes promote the development of a R-L shunt (Millen et al., 1964; White and Ross, 1966; Shelton and Burggren, 1976; Wang and Hicks, 1996). In *Chrysemys picta*, the total R-L shunt is 18 ml min^{-1} kg^{-1}, or approximately 61% of the $\dot{Q}s$ during apnea (Heisler and Glass, 1985). In addition, analyses of blood PO_2 measurements from arterial and cardiac sites indicate a R-L intracardiac shunt that may approach 90% of the systemic output in *Trachemys scripta* (Fig. 5.15; Burggren and Shelton, 1979; White et al., 1989).

In squamates, the non-ventilatory periods are also associated with a R-L shunt. For example, in *Varanus exanthematicus*, the total R-L shunt flow is 11 ml min^{-1} kg^{-1}, or approximately 31% of the $\dot{Q}s$ (Heisler and Glass, 1985). It must be emphasized that in neither testudines nor squamates does the development of R-L shunt mean that the $\dot{Q}s$ is maintained at pre-apnea or pre-dive levels. On the contrary, during apnea or diving, the total cardiac output can be reduced by 80%, and the $\dot{Q}s$ is consequently reduced by a similar amount (Shelton and Burggren, 1976; Wang and Hicks, 1996). Thus, the shunt fraction can be very large (>90%), but the total R-L shunt flow is relatively small. This distinction is important, as it has been implied that reductions in $\dot{Q}p$, resulting from a R-L shunt, will result in the maintainance of a $\dot{Q}s$ at pre-apnea or pre-dive levels.

A L-R shunt also occurs during apnea. During apnea in *Varanus exanthematicus* and *Chrysemys picta*, a fractional L-R shunt of 11–20% occurs (Heisler and Glass, 1985). Measurements of blood PO_2 from the pulmonary artery and the left and right atrium indicate a similar-sized L-R shunt fraction in *Trachemys scripta* during apnea (White et al., 1989). During ventilatory periods, the cardiovascular changes are the reciprocals of those occurring during apnea. For example, in *Trachemys scripta*, the HR doubles, and the Rp decreases by more than 50%, leading to a threefold increase in the Qp (Shelton and Burggren, 1976). Blood flow measurements from selected arteries indicate that a net L-R shunt develops during ventilation (White and Ross, 1966; Shelton and Burggren, 1976). However, in a study in *Trachemys scripta*, the Qp never exceeded Qs during ventilation (Wang and Hicks, 1996). Nevertheless, the Qp increased relatively more than the Qs and the Qp/Qs increased from 0.29 during apnea to 0.8 during ventilation. Analysis of the blood PO_2 from the left atrium, right atrium, and pulmonary artery confirms a L-R intracardiac shunt during ventilation in *Trachemys scripta* (White et

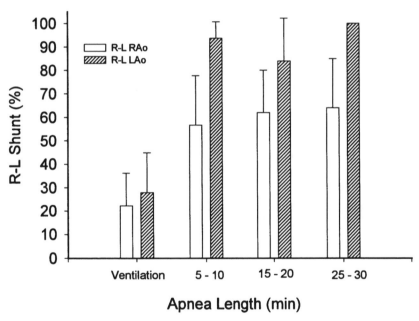

Apnea Length (min)

Fig. 5.15. Relationship between ventilatory state and magnitude of right-to-left (R-L) intracardiac shunt in *Trachemys scripta* at 15°C, as determined from measurements of blood oxygen levels. The difference between the fractional R-L shunt calculated from values of the RAo or LAo, represent the differences in shunt distribution to these two aortic arches. Based on the three-vessel shunt model (see text), the total R-L shunt value must reside within the ranges shown. (Redrawn from White et al., 1989.)

al., 1989). In this species, the fractional L-R shunt is 24% during ventilation (White et al., 1989). The magnitude of the total L-R shunt flow during ventilation has also been estimated in *Varanus exanthematicus* and *Chrysemys picta*. In the former, the total L-R shunt flow is 3 ml⁻¹ kg⁻¹ and is 11% of the $\dot{Q}$p. In the latter, the total L-R shunt flow is 5.5 ml⁻¹ kg⁻¹, representing 18% of the $\dot{Q}$p (Heisler and Glass, 1985). In *Acrochordus granulatus*, the $\dot{Q}$p is estimated to be tenfold higher than $\dot{Q}$s during ventilation (Lillywhite and Donald, 1989). This may be the largest net L-R shunt reported for an intermittently breathing reptile.

A R-L intracardiac shunt also occurs during ventilation. In *Varanus exanthematicus* and *Chrysemys picta*, the R-L shunt is 10–25% of the $\dot{Q}$s during ventilation (Heisler and Glass, 1985). In *Trachemys scripta*, measurements of blood PO_2 from cardiac and arterial sites suggest a 20–30% fractional R-L during ventilation (White et al., 1989). The possible mechanisms responsible for bidirectional cardiac shunting have been discussed (Section IV.B.1–2).

3. CROCODYLIANS

In the crocodylians, a bradycardia is often associated with diving (Andersen, 1961; White, 1956; Gaunt and Gans, 1969). In *Alligator mississippiensis*, forced submersion results in an increase in the second-stage RV pressure after 10 min (White, 1956). This increase is sufficient to cause a R-L shunt. The increase in RV pressure results from a cholinergically mediated increase in the resistance of the pulmonary outflow tract. Jones and Shelton (1993) have conducted forced submersion experiments on two American alligators. After 10 min, a R-L shunt did not develop in either animal according to blood flow measurements in the LAo. In one alligator, the systemic and pulmonary pressures increased, but the second-stage PA pressure was always well below the LAo pressure. In the other animal, a severe bradycardia developed (HR was 10% of the surface value), and the systemic pressure increased by 25% (Jones and Shelton, 1993).

A severe bradycardia and the development of a R-L shunt may not always be correlated with voluntary diving in crocodylians (Smith et al., 1974; Grigg and Johansen, 1987; Jones and Shelton, 1993). In unrestrained, freely diving *Crocodylus porosus*, a R-L shunt frequently shows, but this is not always correlated with diving (Grigg and Johansen, 1987). Based on measurements of blood oxygen levels and hemodynamic analysis of central vascular pressure, the R-L shunt probably never exceeds 10% of the cardiac output (Grigg and Johansen, 1987). Undisturbed *Alligator mississippiensis* frequently develop a R-L shunt (Jones and Shelton, 1993). These shunts are observed in undisturbed alligators quietly resting on the surface or during diving. The development of the shunt is positively correlated with lower systemic blood pressures. Under these conditions, the second-stage RV pressure is suffcient to eject blood into the LAo. The R-L shunt lasts up to 13 min and is 5.5 ml min^{-1} kg^{-1}, which is only 14% of the cardiac output (Jones and Shelton, 1993).

C. Activity

During periods of increased oxygen demand, for exmple during aerobic activity, systemic oxygen transport or the product of arterial oxygen content (CaO$_2$) and cardiac output must be increased. Consequently, a R-L shunt, with the resulting reduction in CaO$_2$, can limit oxygen transport during such periods.

The $\dot{Q}$s can increase 3–4 fold with activity (Gleeson et al., 1980); however, the effects of activity on the magnitude of cardiac shunting remain unclear. In *Trachemys scripta* and *Terrapene ornata*, activity results in a significant reduction in the oxygen saturation of LAo blood, from 90% at rest to 50% during activity (Gatten, 1975). These results are probably relevant only to highly stressful conditions, because the activity was induced by electric shock to the shoulder and thigh musculature. In contrast, in *Varanus exanthematicus* and *Iguana iguana*, O$_2$ and PO$_2$

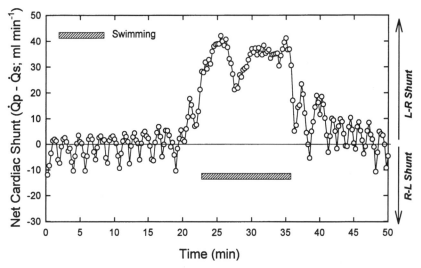

Fig. 5.16. Effects of spontaneous locomotion on the net cardiac shunt in *Trachemys scripta*. Negative values indicate a net right-to-left (R-L) shunt and positive values represent a net left-to-right (L-R) shunt. Blood flows were recorded continously, individual points (○) represent the mean values for 30 seconds. A 1.5 kg turtle has been instrumented with minature ultrasonic blood flow probes (Transonic Systems Inc.) and tested at 22°C. The period of locomotion (cross-hatched bar) represents spontaneous exploratory behavior within a 1 × 1 meter space. Note the development of a net L-R shunt with the onset of activity and the termination of activity. (Data from E. Krosniunas and J. W. Hicks, unpublished observation.)

content of the RAo remains constant during treadmill exercise, up to $\dot{V}O_2$ max (Gleeson et al., 1980). This result indirectly suggests that, during exercise, shunt fraction may decrease or, at least, remain constant (Mitchell et al., 1981). West et al.(1992) measured left pulmonary artery blood flow ($\dot{Q}Lpul$) and left aortic arch blood flow ($\dot{Q}LAo$) during rest and swimming in *Chelonia mydas*. During swimming, HR increases and Rp decreases leading to an increase in the $\dot{Q}Lpul$. The total increase in cardiac output ($\dot{Q}p + \dot{Q}s$) is accounted for, primarily, by an increase in $\dot{Q}Lpul$ (i.e., during exercise, $\dot{Q}Lpul$ increases more than $\dot{Q}LAo$). These results suggest that a net L-R shunt develops during exercise. Preliminary experiments on other turtles also indicate that a net L-R shunt may develop during activity. Total systemic and pulmonary blood flows have been measured using miniature ultrasonic blood flow probes in chronically instrumented *Trachemys scripta*. Spontaneous activity leads to a net L-R shunt (Fig. 5.16). These changes in pulmonary and LAo blood flow in *Trachemys* are very similar to the changes in blood flow observed during swimming in *Chelonia mydas* (West et al., 1992). Clearly, further studies are required to assess the importance of L-R shunting during exercise in testudines.

D. Thermoregulation

The physiological control of heat exchange rates has been shown in many reptiles (Templeton, 1970). Reptiles exhibit differential rates of heating and cooling, generally showing faster rates during warming and lower rates during cooling. Such hysteresis enables reptiles to remain at or near their preferred body temperature for longer periods of time (Templeton, 1970). The differential rates of heating and cooling result from changes in the cutaneous, deep muscle, and visceral blood flow in response to elevation of core body temperature or in response to local heating of the skin (see White, 1976). For example, measurements of cutaneous blood flow using xenon clearance have shown a cutaneous vasodilation during heating and a vasoconstriction during cooling in *Iguana iguana* (Baker et al., 1972), *Amblyrhynchus* (Morgareidge and White, 1969), *Ctenosaura hemilopha* (Weathers and Morgareidge, 1971), and testudines (Weathers and White, 1971).

Peripheral vasodilation during heating results in the development of a R-L intracardiac shunt (Baker and White, 1970). In *Iguana iguana* and *Tupinambis teguixin*, the arterial O_2 decreases, and there is a narrowing of the arterial-venous O_2 difference during heating. These changes in blood oxygen levels reflect a R-L shunt of approximately 20% of the ventricular systemic output during heating in *Iguana*. In *Tupinambis*, the results are less consistent, but R-L shunts as large as 8% of the ventricular systemic output have been estimated. In contrast, in *Varanus niloticus*, the level of R-L shunting decreases as the animals are warmed from 25° to 35°C (Ishimatsu et al., 1988). At 25°C, the R-L shunt is 33% of the cardiac output and decreases to 8.5% at 35°C. It should be noted that these values represent steady state (the animals were at 35°C for at least 12 hours before measurements). In varanids, the response of shunting to transient changes in body temperature is unknown. Recently, preliminary data obtained with *Trachemys scripta* confirm that a net R-L shunt develops during heating (Fig. 5.17). This net R-L shunt may be as large as 60% of the systemic output. A net L-R shunt develops during cooling.

E. Other Physiological States or Environmental Challenges
The ventilatory response of reptiles to hypoxia and hypercapnia has been well studied (see Shelton et al., 1986). However, the effects of inspiratory gases on the direction and size of the shunt are virtually unknown.

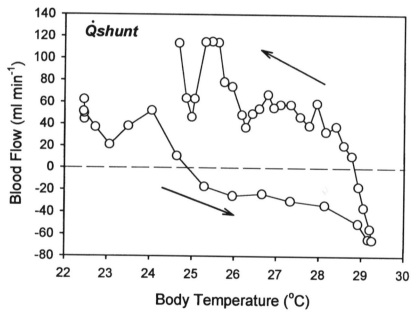

Body Temperature (°C)

Fig. 5.17. The effects of changes in body temperature on net cardiac shunting in *Trachemys scripta*. Negative values represent net right-to-left (R-L) shunts and positive values represent net left-to-right (L-R) shunts. A 1.85 kg animal has been instrumented with ultrasonic blood flow probes on the RAo, LAo, and pulmonary artery. A temperature probe has been inserted into the cloaca and the animal placed under an infrared heat lamp (40 cm above the animal). Movement was restricted. Blood flow and body temperature were recorded continuously. Individual values represent means for 3-min intervals. Note the development of a R-L shunt during heating and a reversal of this trend during cooling. Q̇shunt = net cardiac shunt.

Whenever *Varanus niloticus* are exposed to hypoxia and hypercapnia, their pulmonary and systemic blood pressures increase but are never superimposable (Millard and Johansen, 1973). It has been concluded that intracardiac shunting is small and does not change in response either to hypoxia or hypercapnia.

The cardiac shunting patterns during the post-prandial period have not been directly measured. The LAo is the primary source of blood for the splanchnic circulation. During digestion, a R-L shunt may develop (Jones and Shelton, 1993). In *Crocodylus porosus*, blood flow in the LAo and the coeliac artery increases following feeding (Axelsson et al., 1991). However, the development of a R-L shunt was not determined. In *Python molurus*, blood PO_2 is reduced during the postprandial period (Secor and Diamond, 1995). However, as the blood samples on which this conclusion is based were acquired by cardiac puncture, and because no other cardiopulmonary measurements were made, it is difficult to determine whether the reduction in blood PO_2 is due to cardiac shunt, hypoventilation, changes in $\dot{V}/\dot{Q}p$ distributions, or results from the mixing of blood at the sampling site.

F. Summary

The cardiovascular events that occur during intermittent ventilation in reptiles have been well described. In contrast, the effects of other physiological states on cardiac shunting remain relatively unknown in reptiles. In particular, the cardiac shunting patterns that occur during thermoregulation, voluntary diving, activity, prey capture, feeding, and digestion remain to be determined directly. The absence of such basic information does not reflect a lack of interest by comparative physiologists and zoologists; rather, it probably reflects the inherent difficulty in measuring cardiac shunts. The development of miniature blood flow probes and computer-assisted data acquisition systems makes on-line collection and analysis of net shunting patterns increasingly possible. The effects of various physiological states on cardiac shunting remains an important and fruitful area for future research.

VII. THE PHYSIOLOGICAL SIGNIFICANCE OF CARDIAC SHUNTING IN REPTILES
A. Overview

The reptilian cardiovascular system provides these vertebrates with a potential flexibility in blood flow that cannot be achieved in mammals or birds. The differential distributions of the pulmonary and systemic blood flow have prompted comparative physiologists to postulate the functional significance of such a circulatory design. These hypotheses are summarized in Table 5.3 and are briefly discussed below. It should

Table 5.2: Potential physiological functions of intracardiac shunting in reptiles.

Physiological Function	Type of Shunt	Reference
Saves cardiac energy	R-L	Burggren, 1987
"Meters" lung oxygen stores	R-L	Burggren and Shelton, 1979; Burggren et al., 1989
Reduces CO_2 flux into the lungs	R-L	White, 1985
Reduces plasma filtration into the lungs	R-L	Burggren, 1982
Facilitates warming	R-L	Tucker, 1966; Baker and White, 1970
Facilitates CO_2 elimination into the lung	L-R	Ackerman and White, 1979; White, 1985
Minimizes $\dot{V}/\dot{Q}$ mismatching	L-R	Wood, 1984; West et al., 1992
Improves systemic O_2 transport	L-R	Hicks, 1994

be noted that, whereas the physiological benefits of a R-L shunt apply to both crocodylian and non-crocodylian reptiles, the physiological benefits of a L-R shunt are specific to non-crocodylian reptiles.

B. Right-to-Left Shunt "Meters" Lung Oxygen Stores

Gas exchange in the lungs of most vertebrates is primarily perfusion-limited (Burggren et al., 1989); thus, the rate of pulmonary perfusion determines the rate of O_2 transfer from lung gas to pulmonary capillary blood. Consequently, the reduction in pulmonary blood flow associated with apnea may act to conserve lung O_2 (Burggren et al., 1989). In addition, periodic increases of pulmonary blood flow during apnea will increase arterial O_2 levels and effectively "meter" O_2 out from the lung, thus contributing to overall homeostasis of arterial O_2 (Burggren et al., 1989; Wang and Hicks, 1996). Several studies have supported this general pattern of pulmonary blood flow during apnea (Burggren and Shelton, 1979; Burggren et al., 1989). However, the importance of the R-L shunt to this perfusion pattern remains unclear (Hicks and Wang, 1996; Wang and Hicks, 1996).

In comparison with diving mammals, blood volume and blood oxygen carrying capacity in reptiles (except sea snakes) are relatively small, whereas lung volumes are relatively large (Perry,1983; Burggren, 1988). Therefore, in contrast to the situation in mammals, the lungs of reptiles serve as the primary oxygen store. The majority of voluntary dives or breath holds in reptiles are well within the aerobic limits, without significant increases in plasma or muscle lactate and without exhausting oxygen stores (Grigg and Johansen, 1987; Hicks and White, 1992; Ackerman and White, 1979). Consequently, the present discussion will emphasize the functional significance of R-L shunting during dives and breath holds that occur within the aerobic limit.

During breath hold, the total oxygen stores (lung and blood O_2 stores) are depleted at a rate determined by the oxygen uptake of the tissue. Whenever lung PO_2 is high enough to complete HbO_2 saturation of pulmonary venous blood, the oxygen content of the vascular system remains intact, and only lung oxygen stores are depleted. As lung PO_2 is reduced, the pulmonary venous blood can no longer be completely saturated. Thus, the delivery of oxygen to the tissues is maintained by reductions in both lung and blood oxygen stores. It must be emphasized that this pattern of oxygen depletion is unaffected by cardiac shunts. This point is illustrated in Figure 5.18. In this figure, pulmonary venous (Cpv), systemic arterial (Ca), and mixed venous (Cv) oxygen content levels are depicted on the oxygen dissociation curve in the absence (A) and presence (B) of a R-L shunt. Systemic and pulmonary blood flows

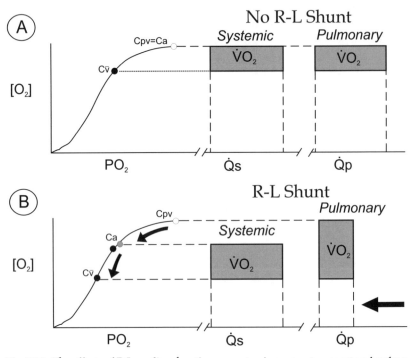

Fig. 5.18. The effects of R-L cardiac shunting on systemic oxygen transport and pulmonary oxygen uptake. A. Graphical solution of the Fick principle in the absence of a R-L shunt. Note that Ca = Cpv, where Ca = arterial oxygen content and Cpv = pulmonary venous oxygen content. B. Graphical solution of the Fick principle whenever $\dot{Q}p$ is reduced due to the R-L shunt. Note that Ca is less than Cpv and that Cv (mixed venous oxygen content) has been shifted downwards. Also note that the product, $\dot{Q}s$ (Ca – Cv)O_2, is equal to $\dot{Q}p$ (Cpv – Cv), where $\dot{Q}s$ = systemic blood flow and $\dot{Q}p$ = pulmonary blood flow. See text for detailed description.

($\dot{Q}$s and $\dot{Q}$p, respectively) are presented in the right portion of the figure. Pulmonary oxygen uptake (the product of $\dot{Q}$p and (a-v)O_2 difference across the lung) and the systemic oxygen uptake (the product of $\dot{Q}$s and (a-v)O_2 difference across the tissues) are depicted as stippled areas. As shown, a R-L shunt reduces CaO_2, which, for a given $\dot{Q}$s, results in a reduction in CvO_2. Therefore, systemic oxygen uptake remains constant, albeit at lower levels of systemic blood O_2 than in the absence of a shunt. Because a R-L shunt reduces the CvO_2, blood returning to the lungs takes up more O_2 and oxygen uptake at the lungs remains constant in spite of the lower pulmonary blood flow (note that the shaded areas in Figure 5.18A and Figure 5.18B are equivalent in area). This pattern of pulmonary O_2 uptake results from the increase in O_2 capacitance coefficient (βO_2; $[O_2]/PO_2$) of blood induced by R-L shunt. The increase in βO_2 offsets the reduction in $\dot{Q}$p, such that the pulmonary oxygen conductance ($\dot{Q}$p × βO_2) remains constant. Experiments determining the effects of cardiac shunting on pulmonary gas exchange in *Trachemys scripta* support this conclusion (Hopkins et al., 1996).

In the description above, the level of R-L shunting has been kept constant throughout a breath hold. However, in testudines, transient increases in $\dot{Q}$p, and presumably transient reductions in R-L shunt, have been observed during long-lasting breath holds (Burggren and Shelton, 1979; Burggren, 1988; Burggren et al., 1989). Brief reductions of R-L shunt (not just the increase in $\dot{Q}$p, as commonly stated) oxygenates the blood (increase blood oxygen store) and causes a simultaneous reduction of lung oxygen stores. The discontinuous depletion of lung oxygen has led to the notion that oxygen is metered out from the lungs and represents a possible role of the shunt in the regulation of arterial blood oxygen (Burggren et al., 1989). It must be emphasized that the development of a R-L shunt does not prolong the use of oxygen stores in the lung during a breath hold. For example, in the extreme condition of complete pulmonary bypass (R-L = 100%), the rate of oxygen uptake from the lung is zero. However, the systemic tissues continue to use oxygen and, thus, blood oxygen stores decline at a rate equal to the tissue metabolic rate. Upon transient reperfusion of the lungs (by elimination of R-L shunt), the blood oxygen stores are rapidly replenished; this results in a large decrease in oxygen stores of the lung. This decrease must equal the amount of oxygen given up by the blood prior to reperfusion. This process can be repeated continually throughout the breath hold until lung oxygen stores can no longer adequately replenish blood oxygen stores. At this point, oxygen delivery to the tissues is insufficient for meeting aerobic metabolic requirements. A large R-L shunt temporarily shifts the burden of oxygen delivery to the blood oxygen stores. However, periodic shifts of this burden between lung and blood stores does not reduce the rate of total oxygen depletion and, thus, cannot prolong the length of an aerobic breath hold (Hicks and Wang, 1996).

The aerobic limit of a breath hold or dive is determined by the total oxygen stores and the delivery of oxygen to the metabolizing tissue. Severe reductions in systemic oxygen delivery, induced by a large R-L shunt, could promote reliance on anaerobic pathways with the subsequent production of lactic acid. This strategy does not appear to provide any advantage during aerobic dives or breath holds. On the other hand, a R-L shunt, through its reduction of systemic oxygen delivery, may induce a hypometabolic state. Under these conditions, the prolonged aerobic dive time would result from the reduction in tissue metabolic rate, possibly triggered by a R-L cardiac shunt. Under severe stress conditions, such as anoxia or "fright" dives, such hypometabolic states may develop, and, thus, the development of a large R-L shunt may provide certain survival advantages.

In summary, during quiet intermittent breathing, in which the periods of apnea are within aerobic limits, the development of a R-L shunt does not provide a unique functional advantage in terms of systemic or pulmonary oxygen transport. The important characteristic is that reptiles possess the mechanisms to alter pulmonary blood flow so as to match lung ventilation. Such mechanisms do not necessarily require the development of a R-L shunt.

C. Right-to-Left Shunt Reduces Carbon Dioxide Flux to Lungs

It has been suggested that an important consequence of R-L shunting during apnea results from its combined effects on CO_2 and O_2 (White, 1978, 1985; Grigg and Johansen, 1987). Specifically, the sequestration of CO_2 away from the lung facilitates efficient oxygen uptake as the apnea progresses, because it prevents or decreases acidification of the blood in the pulmonary circulation (White, 1978). This ensures high blood oxygen affinity as the pulmonary PO_2 declines (White, 1978; Grigg and Johansen, 1987). In addition, a R-L shunt promotes an increase in tissue CO_2, right-shifts the oxygen equilibrium curve (Bohr effect) in the systemic circulation and thus augments O_2 delivery (White, 1978; Grigg and Johansen, 1987).

It is not entirely clear why a R-L shunt is needed to sequester CO_2 away from lung. In all air breathing vertebrates, the majority of CO_2 produced during a breath hold is stored away from the lungs. In those vertebrates that lack cardiac shunts (mammals), voluntary breath holding results in changes in the pulmonary CO_2 and gas exchange ratio (R) that are qualitatively similar to those observed in reptiles (Douglas and Haldane, 1922; Otis et al., 1948; Mithoefer, 1959). For example, in humans, voluntary breath hold at normoxia results in an R of 0.1 to 0.16, and the O_2 uptake during apnea remains normal (Otis et al., 1948). The capacity to store CO_2 in tissues and blood is simply higher than the storage capacity of the lung gas; consequently, the majority of CO_2 produced during a breath hold is not eliminated into the lung. That R-L shunting is important for the pattern of CO_2 exchange during breath holding is simply an incorrect notion. The pattern of CO_2 exchange during breath hold is the result of the physicochemical properties of tissue, blood, and air and does not result from a R-L cardiac shunt.

The second argument, that R-L shunt promotes CO_2 storage in the tissues, thereby facilitating oxygen delivery to the tissues, is tautological. Undoubtedly, increasing the CO_2 of tissues will acidify the blood perfusing them, and thereby right-shift the oxygen equilibrium curve. However, the R-L shunt also decreases the systemic arterial oxygen levels; thus, the benefit of tissue CO_2 retention is apparent only when the reduction in blood oxygen affinity is greater than the reduction of arterial PO_2 resulting from R-L shunt (Hicks and Wang, 1996). Based on the changes in blood pH during aerobic breath holding (White et al., 1989; Hicks and White, 1992), the magnitude of the Bohr shift is not large enough to offset the reductions in arterial O_2 content and PO_2 due to the shunting. It is difficult to reconcile the notion that regulation of R-L shunting evolved to depress arterial oxygen levels in order to improve arterial oxygen delivery.

In summary, cardiac shunts affect the levels of oxygen and carbon dioxide in the blood. The effects of cardiac shunting on blood gases are thought to provide unique physiological advantages to reptiles. In the case of oxygen transport, the advantages of a R-L shunt during a breath hold may be, at first, intuitively appealing. Upon closer examination, these physiological advantages probably do not exist. Simply stated, oxygen transport does not benefit from mechanisms that impair oxygen transport. In the case of CO_2, its distribution between lung, blood, and tissues is virtually independent of the shunt. Rather, the changes in CO_2 that are observed during a breath hold result, primarily, from the buffering capacities of these compartments.

D. Right-to-Left Shunt Reduces Plasma Filtration

In reptilian lungs, the Starling forces are greatly unbalanced such that filtration is favored, generating plasma filtration rates two orders of magnitude higher than in similar-sized mammals (Burggren, 1982; Levin, 1988; Smits, 1989). Based on hematocrit differences of blood drawn simultaneously from the pulmonary artery and vein in testudines, Burggren (1982) demonstrated that plasma filtration increases linearly with pulmonary blood flow and constitutes 15-20% of blood entering the lungs whenever the pulmonary blood flow is higher than 15 ml kg^{-1}. At lower rates of blood flow, both the relative and absolute levels of plasma filtration decrease, and at very low rates of pulmonary blood flow (7 ml kg^{-1}), the direction of fluid movement reverses and plasma is reabsorbed. Levin (1988) has shown that administration of atropine results in a three-fold increase in the net fluid filtration into the lungs. Accordingly, if the lymphatic system is unable to remove the filtrated plasma, high pulmonary blood flows would result in pulmonary edemas, which, in turn, could reduce the gas exchange efficacy of the lung. In intermittent lung breathers, the high plasma fluxes associated with the increase in pulmonary blood flow during ventilation are offset by a lower blood flow and reduced filtration during apnea. Because these animals spend 85% of the time in apnea, they remain in a state of fluid balance (Burggren, 1982). It has been suggested that the reduction in pulmonary blood flow is accomplished through the development of cardiac R-L shunt. However, taken to its extreme, this suggestion argues that blood oxygen transport needs to be impaired (remember that R-L shunt reduces arterial oxygen content) because of leaky, hence "poorly performing," lungs.

There are relatively few studies on fluid balance in the reptilian lung; however, a study on *Bufo marinus* does not support the functions described above (Smits, 1994). This study compared the lung water content in toads with "normal" pulmonary blood flows and pressure with that of toads in which pulmonary blood flow was elevated through pulmocutaneous baroreceptor denervation. In spite of a four-fold increase in pulmonary blood flow and a two-fold increase in the blood pressure, the water content of the denervated lungs of the toads remains constant. Therefore, at least in this toad, the lymphatic system is able to effectively remove the filtrated plasma, even at high pulmonary blood flows. If the lymphatic system is equally effective in reptiles, it seems unlikely that R-L shunts are needed to prevent pulmonary edemas. It should be noted that chronic denervation of the pulmocutaneous baroreceptors of *B. marinus* elicits higher mortality (Van Vliet and West, 1989). Initially, this finding has been interpreted to result from pulmonary edemas; it may instead, as suggested by Smits (1994), result from high pressure induced rupture of pulmonary capillies.

In summary, additional experiments are needed to test the hypothesis that reductions in pulmonary blood flow protect lung function in amphibians and reptiles. In particular, it seems essential to resolve whether pulmonary gas transfer actually is impaired in animals with high pulmonary blood flow. If gas exchange is impaired, a widening of the PO$_2$ gradient between pulmonary venous blood and faveolar gas would be expected. It should be noted that, in crocodylians, the filtration of plasma into the lungs does not pose a serious problem. As discussed in an earlier section, the pulmonary pressures of crocodylians are maintained at very low levels.

E. Right-to-Left Shunt Affects Heating and Cooling

The respiratory membranes can be an important route for heat loss. Tucker (1966) suggested that the development of a R-L shunt during heating would reduce the rate of heat loss across the lungs and, subsequently, increase the rate of heating. During heating, a R-L shunt develops in *Iguana iguana* and *Tupinambis* (Baker and White, 1970). In testudines, preliminary experiments suggest that a net R-L shunt develops during heating, and a large net L-R shunt develops during cooling (Fig. 5.17). The presence of a L-R shunt should facilitate the transfer of heat from the core to the environment, a result that appears paradoxical. The role of shunting during thermoregulation requires further experimental testing.

F. Right-to-Left Shunt Saves Cardiac Energy

Lung oxygen levels are reduced during apnea. As the lung PO_2 declines toward the pulmonary arterial levels, the "benefit" of continued perfusion of the lung is outweighed by the energetic "cost" of pulmonary perfusion. In other words, it is cheaper to pump the blood once than to pump it twice.

It has been suggested that the energetic benefits of a R-L shunt are probably not very important (Burggren, 1987). Assuming a muscular efficiency of 10%, the estimated cost of perfusing the pulmonary circulation during lung ventilation is 5% of that of the total aerobic metabolism at rest (Burggren, 1987). Consequently, during apnea, the energetic savings that result from a R-L shunt is approximately 0.5% of the aerobic metabolic rate (see Burggren, 1987, for details). In contrast, it should be noted that, although the short term energetic savings are relatively small, the cumulative savings over the lifetime of an individual could be significant.

G. Left-to-Right Shunting Facilitates CO_2 Elimination

The pulsatile nature of CO_2 elimination in reptiles may provide an important clue into the functional significance of L-R shunting. Computer model analysis suggests that, at the onset of ventilation, lung PCO_2 is rapidly lowered; however, the pulmonary arterial PCO_2 remains unaffected, representing a "hinge point" from which progressively larger extraction of CO_2 proceeds (White and Hicks, 1987). The amount of CO_2 eliminated depends on the shape of the CO_2 dissociation curve, clearance of CO_2 from the lung with each breath, and the level of pulmonary perfusion ($\dot{Q}p$). In addition, the presence of L-R shunting promotes oxygenation of pulmonary arterial blood and reduces the Haldane effect, thereby promoting the offloading of CO_2. This "CO_2-hinge" eliminates progressively larger amounts of CO_2 from pulmonary arterial blood (Fig.

5.19) and, theoretically, accounts for the characteristic changes in R (increasing) during a ventilatory bout following a long apnea (White and Hicks, 1987). However, as with many of the proposed physiological functions of cardiac shunting, this hypothesis requires experimental testing.

H. Left-to-Right Shunt Improves Ventilation-Perfusion Matching

The physiological factors that influence the O_2 transport efficacy of the lung include, (1) incomplete diffusion equilibration, (2) spatial matching of pulmonary ventilation and pulmonary perfusion ($\dot{V}/\dot{Q}p$), and (3) intrapulmonary and intracardiac shunt. The development of a large L-R shunt associated with an increase in $\dot{Q}p$ may increase the efficacy of the

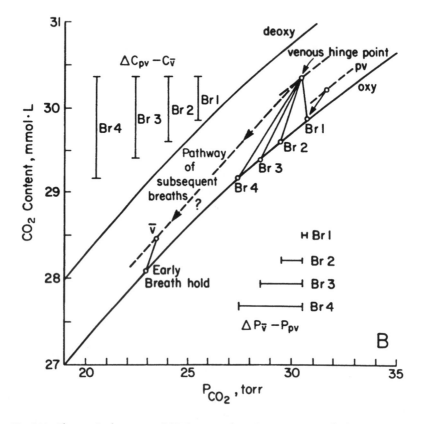

Fig. 5.19. Changes in the course of CO_2 between the pulmonary venous (pv) and mixed venous blood ($\bar{v}$) during a theoretical four-breath sequence following a simulated 21-minute breath hold at 25°C in *Trachemys scripta*. The graph shows a CO_2 dissociation curve at 25°C. Individual breaths are indicated by Br_1, Br_2, Br_3, and Br_4. The venous hinge point is unaffected during the early phase of a ventilatory period. Each successive breath (Br) results in a progressively larger extraction of CO_2 by the lung ($\Delta Cpv - C\bar{v}$). (From White and Hicks, 1987.)

lung by reducing physiological shunting due to $\dot{V}/\dot{Q}p$ mismatching in the lung (Wood, 1984; West et al., 1992) and thus lead to an improvement in the level of oxygenation of pulmonary venous blood.

The $\dot{V}/\dot{Q}p$ heterogeneity within the reptilian lung has been described for only a few reptiles including *Trachemys scripta* (Hopkins et al., 1996), *Tupinambis teguixin* (Hlastala et al., 1985), *Varanus exanthematicus* (Hopkins et al., 1995), and *Alligator mississippiensis* (Powell and Gray, 1989). Two of these studies (Hopkins et al., 1995, 1996) are particularly relevant because they determined the effects of increasing $\dot{Q}p$ on $\dot{V}/\dot{Q}p$. In *Trachemys scripta*, $\dot{Q}p$ is varied over a 12-fold range by reducing $\dot{Q}p$ through partial occlusion of the pulmonary artery or increasing $\dot{Q}p$ by bolus injections of epinephrine (Hopkins et al., 1996). At high $\dot{Q}p$, there is a significant net L-R shunt, and at low $\dot{Q}p$, there is a net R-L shunt. In this study, the $\dot{V}/\dot{Q}p$ heterogeneity is significantly correlated with $\dot{Q}p$. Consistent with these changes, the blood PO_2 in the left atrium increases from 88 mmHg at low $\dot{Q}p$ to 120 mmHg at the higher $\dot{Q}p$. These data indicate that increases in $\dot{Q}p$ result in both temporal and spatial matching of ventilation and perfusion (Hopkins et al., 1996). In contrast, in varanid lizards, treadmill exercise at levels that are at least 80% of $\dot{V}O_2max$ increases the $\dot{Q}p$ three-fold above resting values and results in a significant increase in the $\dot{V}/\dot{Q}p$ heterogeneity (Hopkins et al., 1995). Although $\dot{V}/\dot{Q}p$ heterogeneity worsens during exercise in these animals, the left atrial blood PO_2 is maintained or even increased (Hopkins et al., 1995). This results from a reduction in perfusion to areas of low $\dot{V}/\dot{Q}p$, reductions in the intrapulmonary shunt and by increasing the lung PO_2 through hyperventilation (Hopkins et al., 1995).

The potential benefit of a L-R shunt during periods of ventilation remains unclear. Paradoxically, an increase in the level of the L-R shunt may adversely affect O_2 exchange. The mixing of pulmonary venous and systemic venous blood would increase the pulmonary arterial PO_2 ($PpaO_2$). This increase will reduce the PO_2 gradient from lung gas to blood and may offset any benefit that results from the resulting increase in $\dot{Q}p$.

I. Left-to-Right Shunting Facilitates Systemic O_2 Transport

A consequence of an increase in the L-R shunt may be an improvement in systemic oxygen transport ($CaO_2 \times \dot{Q}s$), particularly in testudines (Hicks, 1994). During periods of increased oxygen demand, the systemic oxygen transport can be improved by increasing CaO_2, $\dot{Q}s$, or both. In testudines, the capacity to increase $\dot{Q}s$ during exercise may be constrained as there develops a large L-R shunt (West et al., 1992; Krosniunas and Hicks, 1995). This probably results from the vasodilation of the pulmonary circulation, making the pulmonary circuit the favored route for blood flow. An adrenergically induced L-R shunt completely eliminates the R-L shunt

(Hicks and Malvin, 1992; Hicks and Comeau, 1994; Ishimatsu et al., 1996). This subsequently raises the systemic arterial oxygen saturation to levels that are equal to pulmonary venous values (Fig. 5.20; Hicks and Comeau, 1994; Hicks and Malvin, 1992; Ishimatsu et al., 1996). Thus, total systemic oxygen transport is improved. However, the development of a L-R shunt potentially "steals" blood flow from the systemic circulation. The improvement of systemic oxygen transport, through the development of a L-R shunt, may simply be a consequence of the ventricular anatomy and the hemodynamic events that occur during exercise, and it may not result in a significant physiological advantage.

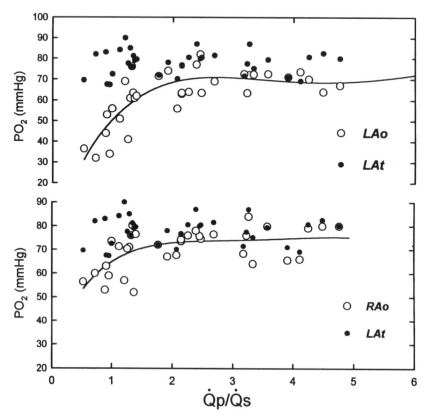

Fig. 5.20. The effects of changing the level of net cardiac shunting ($\dot{Q}p/\dot{Q}s$) on the blood PO_2 in the left atrium (LAt), right aortic arch (RAo) (lower panel), and left aortic arch (LAo) (upper panel) in the turtle, *Trachemys scripta*. The L-R shunt was increased by administration of epinephrine or the electrical stimulation of vagal afferent nerves. A R-L shunt was induced by electrical stimulation of vagal efferent fibers. $\dot{Q}p/\dot{Q}s$ values greater than 1 indicate a L-R shunt and values less than 1 indicate a R-L shunt. (Redrawn from Ishimatsu et al.,1996.)

VIII. CARDIAC SHUNT:
ADAPTATION OR ATAVISTIC RELIC?

The role of cardiac shunting remains undetermined in comparative physiology. The persistence of cardiac shunts in reptiles combined with the evidence that suggests shunts are regulated leads to the notion that the structure of the heart is not an atavistic relic, but rather, represents a highly derived, successful cardiovascular adaptation in extant reptiles (White, 1976; Johansen and Burggren, 1980; Burggren, 1985; White, 1985; Jones and Shelton, 1993; Burggren and Warburton, 1994). Although this opinion is intuitively appealing, the question still remains whether the reptilian circulatory system is a derived condition that conveys important physiological functions. Most proposed functions for cardiac shunts have focused on their roles in pulmonary gas exchange. However, given the absence of experimental support for such a role, it is premature to support the idea that cardiac shunts represent a important adaptation for pulmonary gas exchange.

Inferring adaptive significance to cardiac shunts may also be premature for other reasons. To date, all published studies on cardiac shunts have focused on their role in adult or sub-adult animals. There is little, if any, information on the regulation of cardiac shunts during development. It is possible that cardiac shunts may be physiologcially important during embryonic development but do not represent an important adaptation in adults. For example, during embryonic development, many vertebrate embryos possess cardiac and central vascular shunts. In the Amniota, these shunts bypass the non-functional lungs and provide a pathway for gas exchange via the chorioallantoic membrane or placenta. These shunt pathways are no longer required after birth or hatching. In endothermic vertebrates (mammals and birds), the continued presence of R-L cardiac shunting is maladaptive because of its pronounced effects on systemic oxygen transport. However, ectotherms have significantly lower (five- to ten-fold) tissue oxygen demands, and the persistence of a R-L cardiac shunt may not be detrimental to systemic oxygen transport. Consequently, there may not have been strong selection pressures for eliminating the cardiac shunt pathways, and their continued presence in adult reptiles would not be considered adaptations.

Obviously, cardiac shunts provide reptiles with a flexibile blood flow that is not found in birds and mammals; such flexibility may eventually prove to be physiologically important. However, before this idea is accepted, more information is needed. For example, little is known about the extent of cardiac shunting in most species of squamates and testudines. The vast majority of studies have concentrated on two testudines (*Trachemys* and *Chrysemys*), a single lizard (*Varanus*), and two crocodylians (*Alligator* and *Crocodylus*). More importantly, there is little information on the cardiac shunting patterns associated with basic physiological states, other than the detailed descriptions of cardiovascular changes occurring during intermittent ventilation in testudines and a few observations in crocodylians. Consequently, interpretations of the physiological function of cardiac shunts have been limited to the events that occur during pulmonary gas exchange. The cardiac shunting patterns during voluntary locomotion (aquatic or terrestrial), voluntary diving, feeding, digestion, or thermoregulation are virtually unknown. Ultimately, a full understanding of the functional significance of cardiac shunting will require measurements of the various shunting patterns that occur in fully recovered animals under a wide variety of behavioral states and physiological challenges, all within the natural environment or in a laboratory setting that elicits a variety of behaviors that are appropriate for reptiles. Recent advances in blood flow measuring devices, computer assisted data acquisition systems, and the potential advances in telemetry devices are making these types of measurements increasingly possible; thus, there remain many exciting possibilites for advancing our fundamental understanding of the cardiovascular system of these unique and important vertebrates.

ACKNOWLEDGMENTS

The author would like to express his gratitude to Tobias Wang and Egle Krosniunas. The author is indebted to Fred N. White, Norbert Heisler, and Atsushi Ishimatsu for their many insightful and fruitful discussions on cardiac shunts in reptiles. Finally, the author thanks the anonymous referees for their helpful suggestions. Preparation of this manuscript was partially supported by NSF Grant IBN–928936.

APPENDIX: REPTILIAN SPECIES DISCUSSED

TESTUDINES

Chelodina longicollis
  McLean and Burnstock, 1967
  Smith and Satchell, 1987
Chelonia mydas
  Van Mierop and Kutsche, 1985
  West et al., 1992
Chelydra serpentina
  Steggarda and Essex, 1957
Chrysemys picta
  Milsom et al., 1977
  Heisler and Glass, 1985

Geochelone pardalis
  Burggren et al., 1977
Kinosternon sp.
  Van Mierop and Kutsche, 1985
Malaclemys sp.
  Luckhardt and Carlson, 1921
Pseudemys floridana
  Van Mierop and Kutsche, 1985
Terrapene ornata
  Gatten, 1975
Testudo graeca
  Shelton and Burggren, 1976

Testudo lethii (=*T. kleinmanni*)
  Khalil and Zaki, 1964
Trachemys scripta
  White and Ross, 1966
  Shelton and Burggren, 1976
  Burggren, 1977b
  White et al., 1989

Hicks and Malvin, 1992
Comeau and Hicks, 1994
Hicks, 1994
Hicks and Comeau, 1994
Hicks et al., 1996
Hopkins et al., 1996
Ishimatsu et al., 1996

SQUAMATES

Acrochordus granulatus
  Pough, 1973
  Lillywhite and Donald, 1989
Boa constrictor
  Van Mierop and Kutsche, 1985
Crotalus sp.
  Van Mierop and Kutsche, 1985
Elaphe obsoleta
  Donald et al., 1990
Iguana iguana
  White, 1959
  Baker and White, 1970
  Gleeson et al., 1980
  Mitchell et al., 1981
  Van Mierop and Kutsche, 1985
Natrix (as *Tropidonotus*) *natrix*
  Johansen, 1959
Python molurus
  Secor and Diamond, 1995

Thamnophis sp.
  Burggren, 1977b
Tiliqua rugosa
  McLean and Burnstock, 1967
  Furness and Moore, 1970
Tupinambis nigropunctatus (=*T. teguixin*)
  Baker and White, 1970
Varanus exanthematicus
  Gleeson et al., 1980
  Mitchell et al., 1981
  Burggren and Johansen, 1982
  Heisler et al., 1983
  Johansen and Burggren, 1984
  Heisler and Glass, 1985
Varanus niloticus
  Millard and Johansen, 1973
  Ishimatsu et al., 1988
  Ishimatsu et al., 1996

CROCODYLIA

Alligator mississippiensis
  White, 1956
  White, 1959
  Greenfield and Morrow, 1961
  Powell and Gray, 1990
  Shelton and Jones, 1991

Jones and Shelton, 1993
Malvin et al., 1995
Crocodylus porosus
  Grigg and Johansen, 1987
  Axelsson et al., 1991

REFERENCES

Ackerman, R. A., and White, F. N. (1979). Cyclic carbon dioxide exchange in the turtle, *Trachemys scripta*. *Physiol. Zool.* 52, 378–389.

Andersen, H. T. (1961). Physiological adjustments to prolonged diving in the American alligator, *Alligator mississippiensis*. *Acta Physiol. Scand.* 53, 23–45.

Axelsson, M., Holm, S., and Nilsson, S. (1989). Flow dynamics in the crocodylian heart. *Am. J. Physiol.* 256, R875–R879.

Axelsson, M., Fritsche, R., Holgren, S., Grove, D. J., and Nilsson, S. (1991). Gut blood flow in the estuarine crocodile, *Crocodylus porosus*. *Acta Physiol. Scand.* 142, 509–516.

Axelsson, M., Franklin, C. E., Lofman, C. O., Grigg, G. C., and Nilsson, S. (1996). Dynamic anatomical study of cardiac shunting in crocodiles using high resolution angioscopy. *J. Exp. Biol.* 199, 359–365.

Badeer, H. S., and Hicks, J. W. (1994). Pitfalls of assessment of vascular resistance. *Cardiology* 85, 23–27.

Baker, L. A., and White, F. N. (1970). Redistribution of cardiac output in response to heating in *Iguana iguana*. *Comp. Biochem. Physiol.* 35, 253–262.

Baker, L. A., Weathers, W. W., and White, F. N. (1972). Temperature induced peripheral blood flow changes in lizards. *J. Comp. Physiol.* 80, 313–323.

Barnes, P. J., Cadieux, A., Carstairs, J. R., Greenberg, B., Polak, J. M., and Rhoden, K. (1986). VIP in bovine pulmonary artery: localisation, function, and receptor autoradiography. *Br. J. Pharmacol.* 89, 157–162.

Belkin, D. A. (1964). Variations in heart rate during voluntary diving in the turtle *Pseudemys concinna*. *Copeia* 1964, 321–330.

Berger, P. J. (1972). The vagal and sympathetic innervation of the isolated pulmonary artery of a lizard and a tortoise. *Comp. Gen. Pharmacol.* 3, 13–124.

Berger, P. J. (1973). Autonomic innervation of the visceral and vascular smooth muscle of the lizard lung. *Comp. Gen. Pharmacol.* 4, 1–10.

Berger, P. J., and Burnstock, G. (1979). Autonomic nervous system. In *Biology of the Reptilia* (C. Gans, R. G. Northcutt, and P. Ulinski, eds.). Academic Press, New York, vol. 10, pp. 1–47.

Berggren, S. (1942). The oxgen deficit of arterial blood caused by nonventilating parts of the lung. *Acta. Physiol. Scand.* Suppl. 4, 5–91.

Berman, W. (1985). The hemodynamics of shunts in congenital heart disease. In *Cardiovascular Shunts: Phylogenetic, Ontogenetic, and Clinical Aspects* (K. Johansen and W. W. Burggren, eds.) Munksgaard, Copenhagen, pp. 399–410.

Bojanus, L. H. (1821). *Anatome Testudinis Europaeae*. J. Zawadsky, Vilna. [Reprinted in 1970. Society for the Study of Amphibians and Reptiles. Facsimile Reprints in Herpetology. No. 26].

Brücke, E. (1852). Beiträge zur vergleichenden Anatomie und Physiologie des Gefässsystems. *Denkschr. Akad. Wien* 3, 335–367.

Burggren, W. W. (1975). A quantitative analysis of ventilation tachycardia and its control in two chelonians, *Trachemys scripta* and *Testudo graeca*. *J. Exp. Biol.* 63, 367–380.

Burggren, W. W. (1977a). The pulmonary circulation of the chelonian reptile: morphology, pharmacology, and hemodynamics. *J. Comp. Physiol.*, ser. B, 116, 303–324.

Burggren, W. W. (1977b). Circulation during intermittent lung ventilation in the garter snake *Thamnophis*. *Can. J. Zool.* 55, 1720–1725.

Burggren, W. W. (1978). Influence of intermittent breathing on ventricular depolarization patterns in chelonian reptiles. *J. Physiol.* 378, 349–364.

Burggren, W. W. (1982). Pulmonary plasma filtration in the turtle: a wet vertebrate lung? *Science* 215, 77–78.

Burggren, W. W. (1985). Hemodynamics and regulation of central cardiovascular shunts in reptiles. In *Cardiovascular Shunts: Phylogenetic, Ontogenetic, and Clinical Aspects* (K. Johansen and W. W. Burggren, eds.). Munksgaard, Copenhagen, pp. 121–142.

Burggren, W. W. (1987). Form and function in reptilian circulation. *Amer. Zool.* 27, 5–20.

Burggren, W. W. (1988). Cardiovascular responses to diving and their relation to lung and blood oxygen stores in vertebrates. *Can. J. Zool.* 66, 20–28.

Burggren, W. W., and Johansen, K. (1982). Ventricular hemodynamics in the monitor lizard, *Varanus exanthematicus*; pulmonary and systemic pressure separation. *J. Exp. Biol.* 96, 343–354.

Burggren, W. W., and Shelton, G. (1979). Gas exchange and transport during intermittent breathing in chelonian reptiles. *J. Exp. Biol.* 82, 75–92.

Burggren W. W., and Warburton, S. J. (1994). Patterns of form and function in developing hearts: contributions from non-mammalian vertebrates. *Cardioscience* 5, 183–191.

Burggren, W. W., Glass, M. L., and Johansen, K. (1977). Pulmonary ventilation: perfusion relationships in terrestrial and aquatic chelonian reptiles. *Can. J. Zool.* 55, 2024–2034.

Burggren, W. W., Smits, A., and Evans, B. (1989). Arterial O_2 homeostasis during diving in the turtle *Chelodina longicollis*. *Physiol. Zool.* 62, 668–686.

Clark, L. C., Bargeron, L. M., Lyons, C., Bradley, M. N., and McArthur, K. T. (1960). Detection of right-to-left shunts with an arterial potentiometric electrode. *Circulation* 22, 949–955.

Comeau, S. G, and Hicks, J. W. (1994). Regulation of central vascular blood flow in the turtle. *Am. J. Physiol.* 267, R569–R578.

Comeau, S., Lance, V. A., Hicks, J. W., and Conlon, J. M. (1992). Purification and biological activity of alligator bradykinin. *Am. J. Physiol.* 263, R400–R404.

Conlon, J. M., Hicks, J. W., and Smith, D. D. (1990). Isolation and biological activity of a novel kinin ([Thr[6]] bradykinin) from the turtle, *Pseudemys scripta*. *Endocrinology* 126, 985–991.

Dahlström, A., Nilsson, O., Lundgren, O., and Ahlman, H. (1988). Nonadrenergic, noncholinergic innervation of gastrointestinal vessels, morphological, and physiological aspects. In *Nonadrenergic Innervation of Blood Vessels* (G. Burnstock, and S. G. Griffith, eds.). CRC Press, Boca Raton, vol. 2, pp. 143–172.

Donald, J. A., and Lillywhite, H. B. (1989). Vasoactive intestinal polypeptide-immunoreactive nerves in the pulmonary vasculature of the aquatic file snake *Acrochordus granulatus*. *Cell Tissue Res.* 255, 585–588.

Donald, J. A., O'Shea, J. E., and Lillywhite, H. B. (1990). Neural regulation of the pulmonary vasculature in a semi-arboreal snake, *Elaphe obsoleta*. *J. Comp. Physiol.*, ser. B, 159, 677–685.

Douglas, C. G., and Haldane, J. S. (1922). The regulation of the general circulation rate in man. *J. Physiol., Lond.* 56, 69–100.

Faber, J. J., Anderson, D. F., Morton, M. J., Parks, C. M., Pinson, C. W., and Thornburg, K. L. (1985). Hemodynamics of shunts in the fetal lamb. In *Cardio-*

vascular Shunts: Phylogenetic, Ontogenetic and Clinical Aspects (K. Johansen and W. W. Burggren, eds.). Munksgaard, Copenhagen, pp. 216–225.

Foxon, G. E. H. (1955). Problems of the double circulation in vertebrates. *Biol. Rev.* 30, 196–228.

Franklin, C. E., and Axelsson, M. (1994). The intrinsic properties of an *in situ* perfused crocodile heart. *J. Exp. Biol.* 186, 269–288.

Fritsch, G. (1869). Zur vergleichenden Anatomie des Amphibienherzens. *Arch. Anat. Physiol.* 6, 654–758.

Furness, J. B., and Moore, J. (1970). The adrenergic innervation of the cardiovascular system of the lizard, *Trachysaurus rugosus*. *Z. Zellforsch. Mikrosk. Anat.* 108, 150–176.

Gaskell, W. H. and Gadow, H. (1884). On the anatomy of the cardiac nerves in certain cold-blooded vertebrates. *J. Physiol., Lond.* 5, 362–372.

Gatten, R. E., Jr. (1975). Effects of activity on blood oxygen saturation, lactate, and pH in the turtles *Pseudemys scripta* and *Terrapene ornata*. *Physiol. Zool.* 48, 24–35.

Gaunt, A. S., and Gans, C. (1969). Diving bradycardia and withdrawal bradycardia in *Caiman crocodilus*. *Nature* 223, 207–208.

Gleeson, T. T., Mitchell, G. S., and Bennett, A. F. (1980). Cardiovascular responses to graded activity in the lizards *Varanus* and *Iguana*. *Am. J. Physiol.* 239, R174–R179.

Goodrich, E. S. (1916). On the classification of the Reptilia. *Proc. R. Soc. Lond.*, ser. B, 89, 261–276.

Goodrich, E. S. (1919). Note on the reptilian heart. *J. Anat., Lond.* 53, 298–304.

Greenfield, L. J., and Morrow, A. G. (1961). The cardiovascular hemodynamics of crocodila. *J. Surg. Res.* 1, 97–103.

Griel, A. (1903). Beiträge zur vergleichenden Anatomie und Entwicklungsgeschichte des Herzens und des Truncus Arteriosis der Wirbelthiere. *Morph. Jb.* 31, 123–310.

Grigg, G. C. (1989). The heart and flow patterns of cardiac outflow in Crocodilia. *Proc. Aust. Physiol. Pharmac. Soc.* 20, 43–57.

Grigg, G. C., and Johansen, K. (1987). Cardiovascular dynamics in *Crocodylus porosus* breathing air and during voluntary aerobic dives. *J. Comp. Physiol.*, ser. B, 157, 381–392.

Grossman, W. (1986). Shunt detection and measurement. In *Cardiac Catheterization and Angiography* (W. Grossman, ed.). Lea and Febiger, Philadelphia, pp. 155–169.

Heisler, N., and Glass, M. L. (1985). Mechanisms and regulation of central vascular shunts in reptiles. In *Cardiovascular Shunts: Phylogenetic, Ontogenetic and Clinical Aspects* (K. Johansen and W. W. Burggren, eds.). Munksgaard, Copenhagen, pp. 334–353.

Heisler, N., Neumann, P., and Maloiy, G. M. O. (1983). The mechanism of intracardiac shunting in the lizard *Varanus exanthematicus J. Exp. Biol.* 105, 15–31.

Hicks, J. W. (1993). Mechanism of intracardiac shunting in reptiles. In *Respiration in Health and Disease, Lessons from Comparative Physiology, Bochum, 16 to 20 August 1992* (P. Scheid, ed.). Akademie der Wissenschaften und der Literatur, Gustav Fischer Verlag, Stuttgart, pp. 249–260.

Hicks, J. W. (1994). Adrenergic and cholinergic regulation of intracardiac shunting in chelonians. *Physiol. Zool.* 67, 1325–1346.

Hicks, J. W., and Comeau, S. G. (1994). Vagal regulation of intracardiac shunting in turtles. *J. Exp. Biol.* 186, 109–126.

Hicks, J. W., and Malvin, G. M. (1992). Mechanism of intracardiac shunting in the turtle *Pseudemys scripta*. *Am. J. Physiol.* 262, R986–R992.

Hicks, J. W., and Wang, T. (1996). Functional role of cardiac shunts in reptiles. *J. Exp. Zool.* 275, 204–216.

Hicks, J. W., and White, F. N. (1992). Ventilation and gas exchange during intermittent ventilation in the American alligator, *Alligator mississippiensis*. *Respir. Physiol.* 88, 23–36.

Hicks, J. W., Ishimatsu, A., Molloi, S., Erashin, A., and Heisler, N. (1996). The mechanism of cardiac shunting in reptiles: a new synthesis. *J. Exp. Biol.* 199, 1435–1446.

Hlastala, M. P., Standaert, T. A., Pierson, D. J., and Luchtel, D. L. (1985). The matching of ventilation and perfusion in the lung of the tegu lizard, *Tupinambis nigropunctatus*. *Respir. Physiol.* 60, 277–294.

Holmgren, S., Axelsson, M., Jensen, J., Aldman, G., Sundell, K., Jönsson, A.-C. (1989). Bombesin-like immunoreactivity and the effect of bombesin in the gut, circulatory system and lung of the caiman, *Caiman crocodylus* and the crocodile, *Crocodylus porosus*. *Exp. Biol.* 48, 261–271.

Holmes, E. B. (1975). A reconsideration of the phylogeny of the tetrapod heart. *J. Morphol.* 147, 209–228.

Hopkins, S. R., Hicks, J. W., Cooper, T. K., and Powell, F. L. (1995). Ventilation and pulmonary gas exchange in the savannah monitor lizard (*Varanus exanthematicus*). *J. Exp. Biol.* 198, 1783–1789.

Hopkins, S. R., Wang, T., and Hicks, J. W. (1996). The effect of altering pulmonary blood flow on pulmonary gas exchange in turtle *Trachemys (Pseudemys) scripta*. *J. Exp. Biol.* 199, 2207–2214.

Ishimatsu, A., Hicks, J. W., and Heisler, N. (1988). Analysis of intracardiac shunting in the lizard, *Varanus niloticus*: a new model based on blood oxygen levels and microsphere distribution. *Respir. Physiol.* 71, 83–100.

Ishimatsu, A., Hicks, J. W., and Heisler, N. (1996), Analysis of intracardiac shunting in the turtle, *Trachemys (Pseudemys) scripta*: application of the three outflow vessel model. *J. Exp. Biol.* 199, 2667–2677.

Johansen, K. (1959). Circulation in the three-chambered snake heart. *Circ. Res.* 7, 828–832.

Johansen, K., and Burggren, W. W. (1980). Cardiovascular function in lower vertebrates. In *Hearts and Heart-like Organs* (G. Bourne, ed.). Academic Press, New York, vol. 1, pp. 61–117.

Johansen, K., and Burggren, W. W. (1984). Venous return and cardiac filling in varanid lizards. *J. Exp. Biol.* 113, 389–400.

Johansen, K., Abe, A. S., and Andresen, J. H. (1987). Intracardiac shunting revealed by angiocardiography in the lizard *Tupinambis teguixin*. *J. Exp. Biol.* 130, 1–12.

Jones, D. R., and Shelton, G. (1993). The physiology of the alligator heart: left aortic flow patterns and right-to-left shunts. *J. Exp. Biol.* 176, 247–269.

Karila, P., Axelsson, M., Franklin, C. E., Fritsche, R., Gibbins, I. L., Grigg, G. C., Nilsson, S., and Holmgren, S. (1995). Neuropeptide immunoreactivity and co-existence in cardiovascular nerves and autonomic ganglia of the estuarine crocodile, *Crocodylus porosus*, and cardiovascular effects of neuropeptides. *Regulatory Peptides*, 58, 25–39.

Khalil, F., and Zaki, K. (1964). Distribution of blood in the ventricle and aortic arches in Reptilia. *Z. vergl. Physiol.* 48, 663–689.

Kirby, S., and Burnstock, G. (1969). Pharmacological studies on the cardiovascular system in the anaesthetized sleepy lizard (*Tiliqua rugosa*) and toad (*Bufo marinus*). *Comp. Biochem. Physiol.* 28, 321–331.

Krosniunas, E., and Hicks, J. W. (1995). Intracardiac shunts during voluntary activity and rest in the turtle. *Am. Zool.* 35, A35.

Leene, J. E., and Vorstman, A. G. (1930). Note on the structure of the heart of *Varanus* as compared with other reptilian hearts. *Tijdschr. Ned. Dierkd. Ver.* 2, 62–66.

Levin, D. L. (1988). "Studies on the movement of fluid and protein across the pulmonary microvascular endothelium in a freshwater turtle." Ph.D. dissertation, University of California, San Diego.

Lillywhite, H. B., and Donald, J. A. (1989). Pulmonary blood flow regulation in an aquatic snake. *Science* 245, 293–295.

Luckhardt, A. B., and Carlson, A. J. (1921). Studies on the visceral sensory nervous system. VIII. On the presence of vasomotor fibres in the vagus nerve to the pulmonary vessels of the amphibian and reptilian lung. *Am. J. Physiol.* 56, 72–112.

Malvin, G. M., Hicks, J. W., and Greene, D. (1995). Central vascular blood flow patterns in the alligator, *Alligator mississippiensis. Am. J. Physiol.* 269, R1133–R1139.

Mathur, P. N. (1946). The anatomy of the reptilian heart. Part II. Serpentes, Testudinata, and Loricata. *Proc. Indian Acad. Sci.* 20, 1–29.

McLean, J. R., and Burnstock, G. (1967). Innervation of the lungs of the sleepy lizard (*Trachysaurus rugosus*). Fluorescent histochemistry of catecholamines. *Comp. Biochem. Physiol.* 22, 809–813.

Millard, R. W., and Johansen, K. (1973). Ventricular outflow dynamics in the lizard, *Varanus niloticus:* responses to hypoxia, hypercarbia, and diving. *J. Exp. Biol.* 60, 871–880.

Millen, J. E., Murdaugh, H. V., Bauer, C. B., and Robin, D. (1964). Circulatory adaptation to diving in the freshwater turtle. *Science* 145, 591–593.

Milsom, W. K., Langille, B. L., and Jones, D. R. (1977). Vagal control of pulmonary vascular resistance in the turtle, *Chrysemys scripta. Can. J. Zool.* 55, 359–367.

Mitchell, G. S., Gleeson, T. T., and Bennett, A. F. (1981). Pulmonary oxygen transport during activity in lizards. *Respir. Physiol.* 43, 365–375.

Mithoefer, J. C. (1959). Mechanism of pulmonary gas exchange and CO_2 transport during breath holding. *J. Appl. Physiol.* 14, 706–710.

Moberly, W. (1968). The metabolic responses of the common iguana, *Iguana iguana*, to walking and diving. *Comp. Biochem. Physiol.* 27, 21–32.

Morgareidge, K. R., and White, F. N. (1969). Cutaneous vascular changes during heating and cooling in the Galapagos marine iguana. *Nature* 223, 587–591.

Nilsson, S. (1983). *Autonomic Nerve Function in the Vertebrates*. Springer Verlag, New York.

O'Donoghue, C. H. (1918). The heart of the leathery turtle, *Dermochelys* (*Sphargis*) *coriacea*. With a note on the septum ventriculorum in the Reptilia. *J. Anat., Lond.* 52, 823–890.

Otis, A. B., Rahn, H., and Fenn, W. O. (1948). Alveolar gas exchange during breath holding. *Am. J. Physiol.* 152, 674–686.

Panizza, B. (1833). Sulla struttura del cuore e sulla circolazione del sangue del *Crocodilus lucius*. *Bibl. Ital.* 70, 87–91.

Perry, S. F. (1983). Reptilian lungs: functional anatomy and evolution. In *Advances in Anatomy, Embryology and Cell Biology* (F. Beck, W. Hild, J. van Limborgh, R. Ortmann, J. E. Pauly, and T. H. Schiebler, eds.). Springer-Verlag, Berlin, vol. 79, 1–81.

Pough, F. H. (1973). Heart rate, breathing and voluntary diving of the elephant trunk snake, *Acrochordus javanicus*. *Comp. Biochem. Physiol.* 44A, 183–189.

Powell, F. L., and Gray, A. T. (1989). Ventilation-perfusion relationships in alligators. *Respir. Physiol.* 78, 83–94.

Rau, A. S. (1924). Observations of the anatomy of the heart of *Tiliqua scincoides* and *Eunectes murinus*. *J. Anat., Lond.* 59, 60–71.

Rudolf, A. M. (1974). *Congenital Diseases of the Heart: Clinical-Physiologic Considerations in Diagnosis and Management*. Year Book Medical Publishers Inc., Chicago.

Secor, S. M., and Diamond, J. (1995). Adaptive responses to feeding in Burmese pythons: pay before pumping. *J. Exp. Biol.* 198, 1313–1325.

Seymour, R. S., and Webster, M. E. D. (1975). Gas transport and blood acid–base balance in diving sea snakes. *J. Exp. Zool.* 191, 169–181.

Shelton, G., and Burggren, W. W. (1976). Cardiovascular dynamics of the Chelonia during apnea and lung ventilation. *J. Exp. Biol.* 64, 323–343.

Shelton, G., and Jones, D. R. (1991). The physiology of the alligator heart: the cardiac cycle. *J. Exp. Biol.* 158, 539–564.

Shelton, G., Jones, D. R., and Milsom, W. K. (1986). Control of breathing in ectothermic vertebrates. In *Handbook of Physiology, Section 3: The Respiratory System* (A. P. Fishman, ed.). American Physiological Society, Bethesda, vol. 2, pp. 857–909.

Smith, D. G., and Macintyre, D. H. (1979). Autonomic innervation of the visceral and vascular smooth muscle of a snake lung (Ophidia: Colubridae). *Comp. Biochem. Physiol.* 62C, 187–191.

Smith, E. N., and De Carvalho, M. C. (1985). Heart rate response to threat and diving in the ornate box turtle, *Terrapene ornata*. *Physiol. Zool.* 58, 236–241.

Smith, E. N., Allison, R. D., and Crowder, W. E. (1974). Bradycardia in a free ranging American alligator. *Copeia* 1974, 770–772.

Smith, R. V., and Satchell, D. G. (1987a). Histochemistry of the lung of the Australian snake-necked tortoise, *Chelodina longicollis*. *J. Morphol.* 192, 257–268.

Smith, R. V., and Satchell, D. G. (1987b). Innervation of the lung of the Australian snake-necked tortoise, *Chelodina longicollis*. *Comp. Biochem. Physiol.* 87, 439–444.

Smits, A. W. (1989). Fluid balance in vertebrate lungs. In *Comparative Pulmonary Physiology: Current Concepts*, (Lung Biol. Health Dis. Ser.) (S. C. Wood, ed.). Dekker, New York, vol. 39, pp. 503–537.

Smits, A. W. (1994). Lack of edema in toad lungs after pulmonary hypertension. *Am. J. Physiol.* 266, R1338–1344.

Steggerda F. R., and Essex, H. E. (1957). Circulation and blood pressure in the great vessels and heart of the turtle *Chelydra serpentina. Am. J. Physiol.* 190, 320–326.

Templeton, J. R. (1970). Reptiles. In *Comparative Physiology of Thermoregulation* (G. C. Whittow, ed.). New York, Academic Press, pp. 205–209.

Tucker, V. A. (1966). Oxygen transport by the circulatory system of the green iguana (*Iguana iguana*) at different body temperatures. *J. Exp. Biol.* 44, 77–92.

Van Mierop, L. H. S., and Kutsche, L. M. (1981). Comparative anatomy of the ventricular septum. In *The Ventricular Septum of the Heart*. (A. C. G. Wenink, ed.). Martinus Nijhoff, The Hague, Boston, London, pp. 35–46.

Van Mierop, L. H. S., and Kutsche, L. M. (1985). Some aspects of comparative anatomy of the heart. In *Cardiovascular Shunts: Phylogenetic, Ontogenetic, and Clinical Aspects* (K. Johansen and W. W. Burggren, eds.). Munksgaard, Copenhagen, pp. 38–56.

Van Vliet, B. N., and West, N. H. (1989). Cardiovascular responses to denervation of pulmocutaneous baroreceptors in toads. *Am. J. Physiol.* 256, R946–R954.

Wang, T., and Hicks, J. W. (1996). Cardiorespiratory synchrony in turtles. *J. Exp. Biol.* 199, 2121–2129.

Weathers, W. W., and Morgareidge, K. R. (1971). Cutaneous vascular responses to temperature change in the spiny-tailed iguana, *Ctenosaura hemilopha. Copeia* 1971, 546–551.

Weathers, W. W., and White, F. N. (1971). Physiological thermoregulation in turtles. *Am. J. Physiol.* 221, 704–710.

Webb, G. J. W. (1979). Comparative cardiac anatomy of the Reptilia. III. The heart of crocodylians and an hypothesis on the completion of the interventricular septum of crocodylians and birds. *J. Morph.* 161, 221–240.

Webb, G. J. W., Heatwole, H., and de Bavay, J. (1971). Comparative cardiac anatomy of the Reptilia. I. The chambers and septa of the varanid ventricle. *J. Morphol.* 134, 335–350.

Webb, G. J. W., Heatwole, H., de Bavay, J. (1974). Comparative cardiac anatomy of the Reptilia. II. A critique of the literature on the Squamata and Rhynchocephalia. *J. Morph.* 142, 1–20.

West, N., Butler, P. J., and Bevan, R. M. (1992). Pulmonary blood flow at rest and during swimming in the green turtle, *Chelonia mydas. Physiol. Zool.* 65, 287–310.

White, F. N. (1956). Circulation in the reptilian heart (*Caiman sclerops*) *Anat. Rec.* 125, 417–432.

White, F. N. (1959). Circulation in the reptilian heart (Squamata). *Anat. Rec.* 135, 129–134.

White, F. N. (1968). Functional anatomy of the heart of reptiles. *Am. Zool.* 8, 211–219.

White, F. N. (1969). Redistribution of cardiac output in the diving alligator. *Copeia* 1969, 567–570.

White, F. N. (1970). Central vascular shunts and their control in reptiles. *Fedn. Proc. Fedn. Socs. Exp. Biol.* 29, 1149–1153.

White, F. N. (1976). Circulation. In *Biology of the Reptilia* (W. R. Dawson and C. Gans, eds.). Academic Press, New York, vol. 5, pp. 275–334.

White, F. N. (1978). Circulation: a comparison of reptiles, mammals and birds. In *Respiratory Function in Birds, Adult and Embryonic* (J. Piiper, ed.). Springer, Berlin, Heidelberg, New York, pp. 51–60.

White, F. N. (1985). Role of intracardiac shunts in pulmonary gas exchange in chelonian reptiles. In *Cardiovascular Shunts: Phylogenetic, Ontogenetic, and Clinical Aspects* (K. Johansen and W. Burggren, eds.). Munksgaard, Copenhagen, pp. 296–309.

White, F. N., and Hicks, J. W. (1987). Cardiovascular implications of the transition from aquatic to aerial respiration. In *Comparative Physiology: Life in Water and on Land* (P. Dejours, L. Bolis, C. R. Taylor, and E. R. Weibel, eds.). Fidia Research Series, Liviana Press, Padova, pp. 93–106.

White, F. N., and Ross, G. (1966). Circulatory changes during experimental diving in the turtle. *Am. J. Physiol.* 211, 15–18.

White, F. N., Hicks, J. W., and Ishimatsu, A. (1989). Respiratory states and intracardiac shunts in turtles. *Am. J. Physiol.* 256, R240–R247.

Wood, S. C. (1984). Cardiovascular shunts and oxygen transport in lower vertebrates. *Am. J. Physiol.* 247, R3–R14.

Yamauchi, A., and Chiba, T. (1973). Adrenergic and cholinergic innervation of the turtle heart ventricle. *Z. Zellforsch. Mikrosk. Anat.* 143, 485–493.

Yoshida, H., Manasek, F., and Arcilla, R.A. (1983). Intracardiac flow patterns in early embryonic life. *Circ. Res.* 53, 363–371.

Hicks, J. W. (1998). Cardiac Shunting in Reptiles: Mechanisms, Regulation, and Physiological Functions. In *Biology of the Reptilia*, vol. 19 (Morphology G) (C. Gans and A. S. Gaunt, eds.). Society for the Study of Amphibians and Reptiles, Ithaca, New York, Contrib. Herpetol., vol. 14, pp. 425–483.

6

The Liver

FENTON SCHAFFNER

CONTENTS

I. INTRODUCTION

The reptilian liver is similar in structure and function to that of other vertebrates. It is the largest single visceral organ, and its most unusual feature is its shape, which conforms to the shape of the visceral cavity so that the liver may be long and slender in snakes and some lizards, whereas it is transverse in testudines and other lizards. The cells of the reptilian liver are equivalent to those in the livers of other vertebrates except for the melanomacrophages, discussed later, which are absent in birds and mammals. The organelles in the various cells of the liver have counterparts in all eukaryotic cells. Specific function and organ structure depend on gene expression rather than on differences in organelle content or structure. The livers of only a few of the various reptiles have been studied, generally in response to specific questions, in contrast to the systematic and extensive studies of human or rat liver. Therefore, terms such as "typical" and "usual" are inappropriate (Beresford and Henninger, 1986). The data available on the biology of the reptilian liver are truly inadequate. Consequently, this chapter relies heavily on observations in mammals. Whether the morphologic and enzymatic conditions found are also applicable to reptiles needs to be checked. Also, the roles of the reptilian liver in shifting to prolonged anaerobiosis, tolerance of hypothermy, and general conformity to environmental circumstances remain to be determined. Such analyses are likely to be critical in understanding the factors that have permitted long survival of these animals, as well as whether aspects of the physiology of their liver could benefit mankind.

The two main aspects of investigation of the reptilian liver have been its metabolic functions, particularly energy production, in an air breathing, but sometimes hibernating and sometimes diving, poikilothermic or ectothermic animal, and the place of the reptilian liver in the evolution of the structure of the organ in vertebrates.

II. STRUCTURE
A. Location

The liver is a dark brown to almost black mass of cells comprising about 3–4% of body weight in some snakes and lizards, seemingly regardless of the season of the year (Abdel-Raheem et al., 1989). The liver tends to weigh more in the fall before hibernation, at which time the glycogen stores are maximal; however, great variation has been noted in different species (Gregory, 1982). The relative mass of the liver of a male *Vipera aspis* remains fairly constant throughout the year, although its weight decreases in May when the animals are sexually active (Saint Girons and Duguy, 1994). The snakes are emaciated at this time, and body fat stores are at their lowest. The livers of both sexes of the snake *Thamnophis sirtalis parietalis* are largest at the end of the summer feeding period; they decrease a little in the fall, more during the prolonged hibernation, and at the beginning of spring (Aleksiuk and Stewart, 1971).

The liver of testudines is large and bridges the upper abdomen (Pritchard, 1979). The left lobe is connected to the concave side of the stomach by the gastrohepatic ligament, and the right lobe is attached to the duodenum by the hepatoduodenal ligament. The coronary ligament connects the testudine liver to the transverse septum (which may be only a membrane between the heart and the liver) (Hyman, 1942). The snake liver lies alongside the right lung or is retroperitoneal along the posterior body wall; the heart is cranial to the liver and the stomach caudal (Davies, 1981; Knobel et al., 1976). The liver of *Calotes versicolor* lies mainly on the right side of the abdomen, ventral to the stomach; a long tongue-like extension reaches from the lateral portion of the right lobe along the right abdominal wall dorsally to the right gonad (Paranjape, 1974). By contrast, the liver of *Sceloporus occidentalis biseriatus* is almost triangular and extends the entire width of the body cavity (Ells, 1954). It has a large middle lobe and may have several small accessory lobes. The right lobe extends caudally into a long, slender, triangularly shaped tailpiece that encases the inferior or post vena cava and part of the right adrenal gland.

In crocodylians, the liver occupies a large portion of the pleuro-peritoneal or coelomic cavity, more so on the right side. During inspiration, the liver is pulled caudally, allowing the lung to expand (Hubert, 1985). It is nestled under the posthepatic septum, which is not homologous to the mammalian diaphragm (Gans and Clark, 1976), but may be to a similar structure in birds (Goodrich, 1986). This septum shuts off the pleural and hepatic cavities from the intestinal chamber and participates in expiration but not inspiration (Gans and Clark, 1976). Lizards lack a septum but have a deep nephric fold that may be attached to the liver and to the body wall, partially separating the pleural and peritoneal spaces.

The liver in all vertebrates is covered by Glisson's capsule, a thin capsule of connective tissue that extends into the substance of the liver at its hilum and from its surface. A sparse collagen network surrounds blood vessels and bile ducts (Ells, 1954). The mass of the liver is divided into variable lobes; most often into two lobes, that of the right side being larger. The pericardial sac of testudines rests in a depression between the two lobes (Hyman, 1942). A very short mesentery, equivalent to the falciform ligament of other vertebrates, attaches the testudine liver to the parietal peritoneum (Hyman, 1942). This mesentery contains ventral abdominal veins that carry blood from the peritoneal cavity to the portal vein. The two lobes of the liver may be widely separated in some pythons (Frye, 1991). The liver of *Calotes* is attached to the ventral body wall and is also joined to the stomach by a mesentery (Paranjape, 1974).

B. Development

The liver originates from the endodermal gut in most reptiles. It arises from the foregut of alligators (Elias, 1965) and from the midgut immediately behind the foregut of *Chelydra serpentina* (Ewert, 1985). The human liver arises from the ventral wall of the foregut (Desmet and van Eyken, 1995). The liver diverticulum branches as it advances, giving rise to the bile ducts and gallbladder (Elias, 1965). However, in crocodylians a separate bud of the gut may give rise to a portion of the bile duct in association with the pancreatic duct (Ferguson, 1985). Hepatocytes sprout from the terminal portions of the diverticulum to form the main portions of the liver. These early developmental structures have been recognized in the embryos of testudines (Yntema stages 8 and 9 or 4–5 mm) (Ewert, 1985) and of crocodylians (stage 9 of Ferguson, 1985). During embryogenesis, some of the blood cells are formed in the liver. Granulopoiesis, but not erythropoiesis, occurs in the peripheral parts of the testudine liver (Ewert, 1985). By contrast, erythropoiesis is prominent in the human fetal liver, where it persists for a few weeks after birth.

C. Blood Supply

The reptilian liver receives blood from the portal vein and from the hepatic artery, as does the liver in other vertebrates. The hepatic portal vein is formed by junction of the gastric and the lienogastric and intestinal veins that join the ventral abdominal vein in *Calotes* (Ells, 1954; Paranjape, 1974)(Fig. 6.1). The ventral abdominal vein in *Sceloporus biseriatus* joins the intestinal vein along the pancreas to form the main trunk of the portal vein, which enters the liver between the middle and left lobes (Ells, 1954). A large branch supplies the left lobe, whereas the rest of the vessel supplies the remainder of the liver. The liver also receives blood from a large gastroesophageal vein on its dorsal surface and from two dorsal parietohepatic veins from the vertebral veins; these vessels are independent of the portal vein and drain into sinusoids soon after entering the liver. The anterior mesenteric artery of *Calotes* supplies most of the arterial blood, but some also comes to the left lobe from the lienogastric (Paranjape, 1974). Intrahepatic ramifications of the arteries and veins in reptiles differ from those found in human and rat livers, in which the vessels usually run alongside one another to the level of

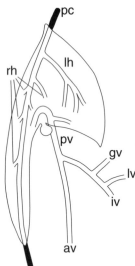

Fig. 6.1. *Calotes versicolor*, ventral view of the major veins supplying and draining the liver. The post caval vein (pc) receives several hepatic veins (rh) from the right lobe while drainage from the left lobe is by a single vein (lh). The portal vein (pv) is formed by the junction of the anterior abdominal vein (av) and the gastric (gv), lienogastric (lv), and intestinal (iv) veins. (Modified and redrawn from Paranjape, 1974.)

the portal tracts, where they enter the sinusoidal network to perfuse the hepatocellular parenchyma (Ekataksin et al., 1994). Systematic study of the vessels has been carried out in the rainbow trout (*Onchorhynchus mykiss*) (Hampton et al., 1989; Schär et al., 1985). The vessels in these fish branch independently into the liver with few portal tracts containing portal vein, bile duct, and hepatic artery branches. A similar arrangement has been found in *Terrapene carolina* (Henninger, 1982) and *Alligator mississippiensis* (Fig. 6.2). The proportion of blood entering the reptilian liver by way of the portal vein and hepatic artery has not been studied. About two-thirds of the blood, carrying almost all of the absorbed nutrients, enters the mammalian liver via the portal vein, whereas the hepatic artery supplies much of the oxygen. The flow of portal blood into the liver is controlled by smooth muscle sphincters in the intrahepatic branches of the hepatic artery in the monitors *Varanus salvator* and *V. flavescens* (Beresford and Henninger, 1986). The portal vein branch in the portal tracts of terrapins is usually accompanied by a bile ductule (Henninger, 1982); in the rainbow trout, this association may also be missing (Hampton et al., 1989). Blood is drained from the liver by the hepatic vein, which may be short and multiple as in testudines, or long and single, as in most snakes. Up to four hepatic veins drain the right lobe and at least two the left lobe of *Calotes* (Paranjape, 1974)(Fig. 6.1), whereas up to 60 enter the cava from the right lobe but only one from the left lobe in *Sceloporus occidentalis biseriatus* (Ells, 1954). Humans have five hepatic veins, two each from the right and left lobes that enter the vena cava just below the diaphragm and one from the caudate lobe that enters more caudally. Flow in the largest hepatic veins is regulated by spiral sphincters in reptiles (Beresford and Henninger, 1986). Dogs and diving mammals have similar hepatic vein sphincters, but rats and humans do not. The tributaries of the hepatic vein are everywhere separated by parenchyma from the terminal twigs of the portal veins and hepatic arteries. Consequently, the blood entering the liver must traverse the parenchyma to leave the organ. This spatial relationship guarantees efficient perfusion and filtration.

D. Parenchymal Organization

Although the parenchyma is one continuous mass of cells, it is not functionally homogeneous. Mammalian hepatocytes nearest the portal tract receive more oxygen, release glucose, make urea, store more iron, and secrete more bile than those around the terminal hepatic venule. The latter take up more glucose and are more involved in fat metabolism. The organization of the reptilian liver into lobules is less apparent than for the liver of mammals (Frye, 1991; Gabe and Saint Girons, 1964)(Fig. 6.2). Fish liver has no lobular organization (Hampton et al., 1988; Schär

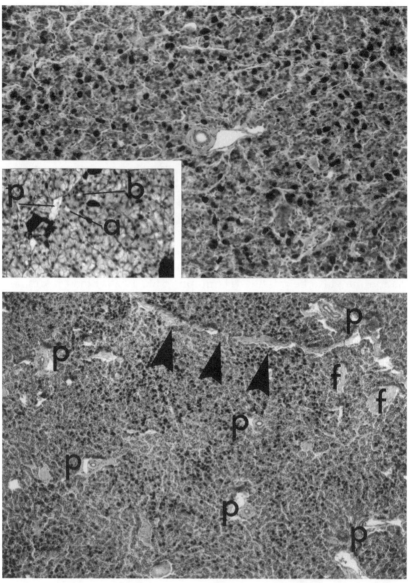

Fig. 6.2. *Alligator mississippiensis.* Top. Section of normal liver showing portal tract in center with no hepatic artery branch but with bile duct on left and portal vein on right (Trichrome stain, ×36). Bottom. Higher power of same section as above showing long band of fibrous connective tissue (arrowheads) extending from portal tract and other nearby bundles of collagen (f). Also note numerous portal tracts (p) without evidence of lobular arrangement (×90). *Terrapene carolina.* Inset, lower left corner of top panel. Complete portal tract containing portal vein (p), bile duct (b) and hepatic artery (a) branches. (Hematoxylin and eosin stain, ×90). (Sections provided by William Beresford.)

et al., 1985). Metabolic zonation, readily seen in mammalian liver (Gumucio and Miller, 1982), is difficult to recognize in reptiles, even with histochemical methods. As mentioned in the preceding paragraph, portal tracts may consist of a bile duct and a portal vein branch surrounded by a small amount of connective tissue; the distribution of the portal tracts is not uniform (Henninger, 1982). The liver of the alligator has fibrous trabeculae extending from portal tracts and from the capsule (Beresford, 1993)(Fig. 6.2). These trabeculae are not septa and may function to prevent injury to the organ during thrashing of the body.

Cross sections suggest that the hepatocytes are arranged in a tubular or trabecular fashion, but in three dimensions, most of these cords are sheets or plates (Elias and Sherrick, 1969). Most of the snake liver is composed of two-cell-thick plates, but some tubules are recognized (Hruban and Maschgan, 1982) also in *Terrapene carolina* (Fig. 6.3). Tubules or plates are two cells thick in most vertebrates, including reptiles (Storch et al., 1989), although in human adults they are only one cell thick (Elias, 1965). Occasional lizards have one-cell-thick plates (Elias and Bengelsdorf, 1952). By contrast, fish hepatocytes are arranged as glands surrounding a bile canaliculus (Hampton et al., 1988). The arrangement of the cells in the liver of various reptiles appears to be intermediate between that of fish and mammals, with some gland formation and some tubule and plate formation (Henninger, 1982; Beresford, 1987). The liver of the crocodylian *Osteolaemus* is said to be to be composed of branching and anastomosing tubules (Storch et al., 1989). Tubules or plates converge toward the terminal hepatic venule (Frye, 1991). This vessel may be difficult to distinguish from an isolated branch of the portal vein.

The appearance of the fetal and infantile or regenerating human liver suggests developmental recapitulation of phylogeny in that glands, tubules, two-cell-thick plates, and single cell plates probably all develop sequentially. These observations lend support to the idea that the internal configuration of the liver parenchyma evolved as its metabolic functions became more complex with increased blood-liver exchanges. The internal configuration has been suggested to be determined by the arrangement and shape of the sinusoids that form a network in a solid mass of hepatocytes (Elias and Bengelsdorf, 1952). Two forms of sinusoids can be distinguished, a tubulosinusoidal type and a sacculosinusoidal one. The channels of the former are narrow and cylindrical, whereas those of the latter are wide and irregular. The sinusoids of tortoises, turtles, and lizards are sacculosinusoidal, like those of humans; the sinusoids of alligators are intermediate. Congestion, which may be a terminal event in any animal, may mask the normal hepatocellular-sinusoidal relationship and probably is responsible for some of the conflicting descriptions of the internal arrangement of the liver.

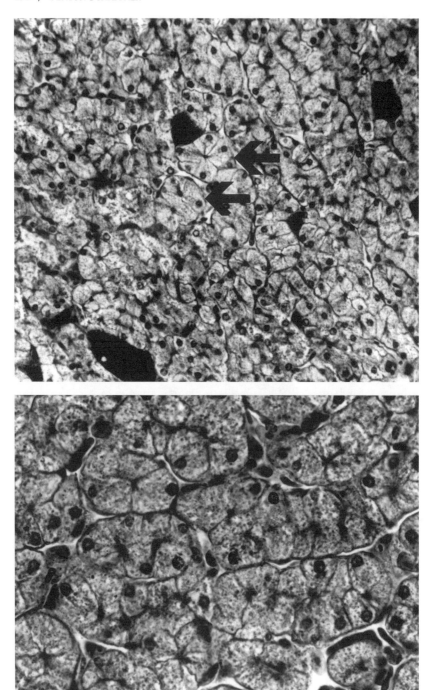

E. The Hepatocyte

Most of the details of the ultrastructure of hepatocytes have been learned from mammalian liver (Jones and Aggeler, 1994). The few studies available indicate that the features are similar in reptiles, and, indeed, in all vertebrates. The hepatocyte is multifaceted and polar, and is up to 60 microns in greatest diameter, when the cell is rich in glycogen (Gabe and Saint Girons, 1964). Some variation in cell size has been noted among different species over 100 years ago (Shore and Jones, 1889). The tortoise hepatocyte was said to be larger than that of vipers, but the conditions of the animals may not have been the same. For instance, the hepatocytes of hibernating testudines are smaller than those of the non-hibernating animal (Ferrer et al., 1987). The hepatocyte is most often of a polyhedral shape. Usually two of its surfaces face sinusoids; in tubular or gland-like formations, the hepatocytes are wedge-shaped or pyramidal in cross section (Henninger, 1982)(Fig. 6.3). Similarly shaped human hepatocytes are seen in cholestasis and in regenerating liver (Nagore and Scheuer, 1990).

The cell is surrounded by a phospholipid bilayered plasma membrane. Almost all standard textbooks of histology, molecular biology, pathology, and diseases of the liver include descriptions of the ultrastructure of the hepatocyte. Therefore, references are given only for details that apply specifically to reptiles. A few illustrations are provided for orientation (Fig. 6.4 and 6.5) The surface of the hepatocyte facing the sinusoid is termed the basilar portion; that containing the bile canaliculus is the apical portion (Table 6.1). These two surfaces are responsible for the polarity of the cell. The surfaces of adjacent cells are the lateral ones, and a portion is merely an extension of the sinusoidal surface for a short distance as a recess between neighboring cells. This gives the basal surface a dome-like shape, termed the basolateral surface. The sinusoidal blood-liver exchange occurs along the basolateral portion of the hepatocyte plasma membrane. The plasma membranes of the various surfaces differ in structure as well as function. The basolateral surface is covered by irregular microvilli, each less than a micron in length and about 0.1 micron in diameter. The microvilli extend to but rarely touch the sinusoidal endothelium.

The lateral cell borders are straight but contain occasional peg and groove arrangements. Two specialized areas of lateral membranes are seen. The first are short segments called gap junctions through which

---

Fig. 6.3. *Terrapene carolina.* Top. Liver with some hepatocytes arranged as tubules (arrows). Most of the hepatocytes are in two-cell-thick plates (Hematoxylin and eosin stain, ×250). Bottom. Parenchyma of same liver showing some hepatocytes in two-cell-thick plates, some in tubules, and some in transitions between the two forms. (Section provided by William Beresford.)

Fig. 6.4. Diagram of a hepatocyte showing spatial relations and examples of some of the organelles. The nucleus (N) is in the center of the cell and 1–4 nucleoli (n) are usually seen; the dense chromatin is distributed along the nuclear membrane, which contains small pores (arrowheads) between the chromatin clumps. The sinusoidal lumen (S) is at the top, and an endothelial lining cell (L) separates the lumen from the sinusoidal surface of the hepatocyte, which has several microvilli of varying length and shapes extending into the pericellular space of Dissé. The lining cell has clusters of fenestrae (arrow) called a

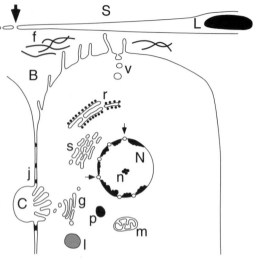

sieve plate. The space of Dissé contains small bundles of collagen (f), the reticulum framework, and the space extends for a variable distance between adjacent cells. The cell surface facing the sinusoid and the extensions of the space of Dissé constitute the basolateral membrane (B). The bile canaliculus (C) is made up of a specialized portion of two adjacent hepatocytes, and the adjacent cell membranes of neighboring cells are joined by a tight junction (j) next to the canaliculus, whereas gap junctions are between the tight junction and the extension of the Dissé space. Various organelles are rough (r) and smooth (s) endoplasmic reticulum, Golgi apparatus (g), lysosome (l), peroxisome (p), and a mitochondrion (m). Vesicles (v) come from pits on the cell surface by pinocytosis.

cells communicate with one another. The second are tight junctions that lie near the bile canaliculi, sealing them and fastening the neighboring cells together. The tight junctions contain an obscure zone, in which ad-

Table 6.1. Regions and functions of hepatocyte plasma membrane.

Basolateral membrane	Microvilli	Aid in absorption of soluble (sinusoidal) material
	Glycoprotein coat	Receptors and signal transducers
	Intrinsic proteins	Ion channels, pumps, transporters
	Clathrin pits	Endocytosis
	Vesicles	Endocytosis, exocytosis
Apposing membrane	Gap junction	Cell to cell communication
	Tight junction	Cell to cell adherance, seal for canaliculus and sinusoid
Apical membrane	Microvilli	Aid in secretion of soluble (canalicular) material, movement of bile
	Intrinsic proteins	Bile acid and other transporters
	Vesicles	Exocytosis

jacent cell borders are indistinct, and an occluded zone, in which the cell borders appear to merge. On scanning electron microscopy, the occluded zone is a network of concentric pericanalicular ridges, roughly paralleling one another. The normal hepatocellular tight junction has 3 or 4 such ridges; it is considered a moderately leaky tight junction because water, inorganic ions, and small organic solutes may enter the bile canaliculus from the tissue space or bloodstream without traversing the hepatocyte. Connected to the tight junction within the cell is an occasional fan-shaped array of microfilaments composed of smooth muscle actin fibrils, often attached to a single mitochondrion.

The bile canaliculus or apical part of the cell comprises less than 10% of the surface area of the hepatocytes. The number of canaliculi in testudines decreases during hibernation (Ferrer et al., 1987). Adenosine triphosphatase and 5'-nucleotidase activity can be demonstrated histochemically on the canalicular membranes. The canalicular lumen, normally about one micron in diameter or less, is filled with slender and uniform microvilli. One such microvillus always extends from the corner where the lateral and canalicular borders meet.

The basolateral portion of the plasma membrane of the hepatocyte is like a complex keyboard in that the outer surface has an array of various receptors, each with a mossy coat of different polysaccharides. The binding polysaccharides are lectins, and some are calcium-dependent or C-type. They have been studied in alligators and are specific for mannose/l-fucose (Lee et al. 1994). Bird and mammalian hepatic lectins are mainly hexameric, but they are monomers in alligators. These sugars are anchored to proteins inserted into the plasma membrane. The protein-carbohydrate complexes are not only receptors; they also are pumps, ion channels, and carriers for material to be taken up or extruded by hepatocytes. The receptors also serve as signal transducers, with specific cell functions directed by second messengers, often in the form of kinases activated by inositol phosphates and guanosine-containing G-proteins attached to the cytoplasmic end of the transmembrane protein receptors. Material may enter the hepatocyte via protein carriers in a molecular fashion, as inorganic cations and anions through channels, and as small particles by endo- or pinocytosis. The last occurs by invagination of coated pits on the cell surface between microvilli; the coating is clathrin, a protein to which the particle adheres. Endocytosis results in the formation of vesicles within the cell. The vesicles are transported to the endoplasmic reticulum, lysosomes, and directly to bile canaliculi depending on their contents. The portion of the cytoplasm between the basolateral plasma membrane and the nucleus contains most of the rough endoplasmic reticulum, peroxisomes, and fat and glycogen stores, described later.

The canalicular plasma membrane also has proteins in the phospholipid bilayer. Only a few of the proteins have been identified in man and the rat, including the one that is a major transporter of bile salts and, hence, the principal determinant of bile flow. The microvilli contain microfilaments, part of the cytoskeleton, connected to a

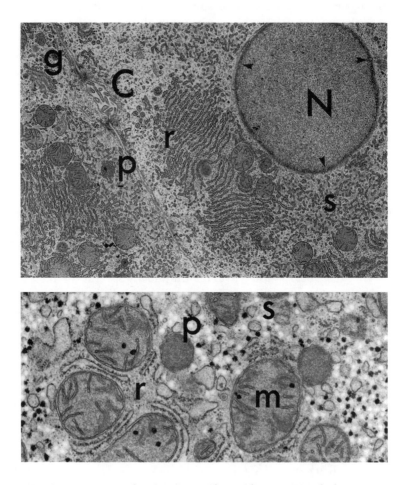

Fig. 6.5. Electron micrographs of portions of human hepatocytes, which are similar to those in reptiles (Glutaraldehyde/osmium fixed, uranyl/lead stained). Top. Pores (arrowheads) penetrate the membrane surrounding the nucleus (N). Stacks of parallel profiles of rough endoplasmic reticulum (r) and clusters of vesicles of smooth endoplasmic reticulum (s) lie around the nucleus. The bile canaliculus (C) is between two hepatocytes and a Golgi zone (g) is nearby. A peroxisome (p) is also in the vicinity (×6000). Bottom. Mitochondria (m) with rough (r) and smooth (s) endoplasmic reticulum. Peroxisomes (p) are interspersed. The black dots in the mitochondria are calcium-containing dense bodies, whereas those scattered outside of the mitochondria are glycogen granules (×24,000).

Table 6.2. Cytoplasmic components of hepatocyte and some functions.

Cytosol	Internal milieu; homeostasis, movement of solutes
Endoplasmic reticulum	Rough - protein synthesis Smooth - detoxification, conjugation, glycogenolysis
Mitochondria	Energy formation, oxidative phosphorylation
Golgi zone	Packaging of material for export to blood or bile
Cytoskeleton	Microfilaments - contractility, peristalsis Intermediate filaments - maintain shape of cell Microtubules - mitosis, movement of material in cell
Lysosomes	Digesting macromolecules; storing residues, Fe, Cu
Vesicles	Transporting large molecules
Nucleus	Gene expression; synthesis of DNA, RNA; mitosis

pericanalicular filamentous network containing mainly actin fibrils, similar to the terminal web of the small intestinal epithelial cell. The pericanalicular area contains the Golgi apparatus and lysosomes, described later.

The hepatocellular cytoplasm contains a complex array of organelles within an aqueous medium, the cytosol (Table 6.2). They are held in place or moved around by a cytoskeleton comprised of microfilaments (actin and myosin fibrils), intermediate filaments (mainly cytokeratin in the hepatocyte), and microtubules (polymerized tubulin). The cytoplasm is acidophilic and stains red with eosin. Cytokeratin filaments give the cell a permanent shape, and actin fibrils move parts of membranes, organelles and vesicles. Soluble material may move through microtubules from one area to another.

Human or murine hepatocytes contain about 800 mitochondria, whereas fewer have been seen in reptiles, such as *Terrapene carolina* (Henninger, 1982). Each mitochondrion is round to oval in cross section and averages about half to three quarters of a micron in diameter. Their number and, to a lesser extent, their shape in reptiles depend on the oxygen consumption of the animal; they increase during hibernation in *Testudo graeca* (Ferrer et al., 1987). These organelles are responsible for aerobic metabolism of all cells, in which the stored energy ultimately derived from the sun is converted to biologic energy, mainly by the process of oxidative phosphorylation. The basic architecture of mitochondria is remarkably similar throughout the plant and animal kingdoms. Each is surrounded by a double layer of phospholipid membrane, the inner one of which has deep, narrow invaginations or cristae into the mitochondrial matrix. Small knob-like projections line the inner surfaces of the cristae; these are the site of the chain of respiratory cytochromes responsible for oxidative phosphorylation. Mitochondria of the liver of hibernating testudines have fewer cristae than in non-hibernating animals even though the number of organelles is greater (Ferrer et al., 1987) The mitochondrial matrix contains numerous other enzyme complexes of the basic metabolic processes of the cell, like those of the citric or tricarboxylic acid cycle, and the urea forming cycle. Most of the hepatocellular glutamine synthetase, ornithine transcarbamylase, and carbamyl phosphate synthetase are in the mitochondria of *Gopherus agassizii* and *G. berlandieri* (Campbell et al., 1985). The mitochondrial pattern of these animals seems to have changed little since their origin from the stem reptiles. Certainly these mitochondrial enzymes are similar to those in fish, birds, and mammals. The tortoises make urea (ureotelic), but they make more uric acid (uricotelic) (Campbell et al., 1985).

Mitochondrial membranes contain transfer enzymes to move various metabolic building blocks and substrates in and out of the organelles. The matrix also contains DNA, different from the main genetic material in the nucleus. The mitochondrial matrix has one or more dense bodies measuring 0.01–0.02 microns in diameter; these may be storage sites for calcium. Their number increases during hibernation (Ferrer et al., 1987). The matrix, in rare instances in reptiles and mammals, including man, may display crystalline formation, in addition to which the organelle may be much larger than normal (megamitochondria), up to several microns in length (Knobel et al., 1976). The significances of crystal formation and large size are unknown. The effect of aging on mitochondrial enzyme behavior has been studied in *Calotes versicolor* (Gena and Patnaik, 1990). Here, the activity of succinic dehydrogenase is inhibited moreso in older animals by malonate and p-chlorophenoxy acetic acid than in younger lizards.

Filling much of the space between mitochondria are parallel profiles of membrane pairs arranged in stacks and membrane vesicles or intermediary forms. These membranes constitute the endoplasmic reticulum, in which occur most of the specific synthetic and conjugating functions of the hepatocytes. Each membrane pair surrounds a narrow, flat lumen. Alongside the outer surface of each pair is a covering of ribosomes, small particles containing RNA. The combination of membranes and particles constitutes the rough form of the endoplasmic reticulum, in which protein synthesis takes place. The amount of rough endoplasmic reticulum decreases in hibernating testudines, indicating reduced protein synthesis (Ferrer et al., 1987). The genetic template for peptide synthesis is in the form of a thin filament of transfer RNA, delivered into the cytosol from the nucleus. Each filament picks up several (20 or so) ribosomes and can be seen as a beaded spiral or polyribosome. The polyribosome attaches to and becomes part of the endoplasmic reticulum or remains free in the cytosol.

Ribosomes receive amino acids attached to small RNA molecules (soluble RNA). As the peptide chain is formed, the ribosome moves along the filament of transfer RNA until the peptide chain is complete. Free polyribosomes probably synthesize protein for intracellular use, whereas ribosomes attached to endoplasmic reticulum membranes make protein for export. As much as half or more of the endoplasmic reticulum lacks attached ribosomes. This is the smooth endoplasmic reticulum, and it is more likely to be in the form of small vesicles rather than long profiles. Here occurs glucose–6–phosphatase, the enzyme responsible for release of glucose from the hepatocyte. The amount of smooth endoplasmic reticulum increases during hibernation (Ferrer et al., 1987). Surrounding the membranes of smooth endoplasmic reticulum is glycogen in the form of rosettes that are clusters of monoparticulates, the form found in muscle cells. Glycogen rosettes are most numerous in the postprandial state and whenever the smooth endoplasmic reticulum is not hypertrophic. They are absent during hibernation. The smooth endoplasmic reticulum is also the site of many conjugation reactions, particularly glucuronidation. The proportion of the endoplasmic reticulum that is rough or smooth depends on the activities of the cell; rough abounds with rapid or extensive protein synthesis, whereas smooth is hypertrophied whenever detoxification is a main function. Changes in the amount of rough or smooth endoplasmic reticulum occur within hours along with the amounts of the accompanying enzymes, such as the various cytochrome P450s, during the process of adaptation to any new or altered task the liver has to perform.

Lysosomes are identified histochemically by their acid phosphatase activity. They are vesicles containing acid hydrolases, which digest effete organelles or portions of cytoplasm and exogenous material that cannot enter specific metabolic pathways. Some of the digested material is secreted in bile, whereas the indigestible residue remains in the form of pigment granules. The organelles may be either preformed structures (primary lysosomes) or secondary, formed from the endogenous cytoplasm or exogenous engulfed material. Lysosomes are most numerous toward the biliary pole of the hepatocyte and vary in diameter from 0.2 micron to more than a micron. During hibernation of *Testudo graeca*, the number of lysosomes increases (Ferrer et al., 1987). Cells continue to accumulate indigestible material as they get older and pigment increases, particularly in the hepatocytes around the terminal hepatic venule. This pigment is lipofuscin or "wear and tear" pigment, so called because small variably sized fat droplets are intermixed within it. The lysosomes stain positively in the periodic acid Schiff (PAS) reaction. They also are the site of storage of iron. The

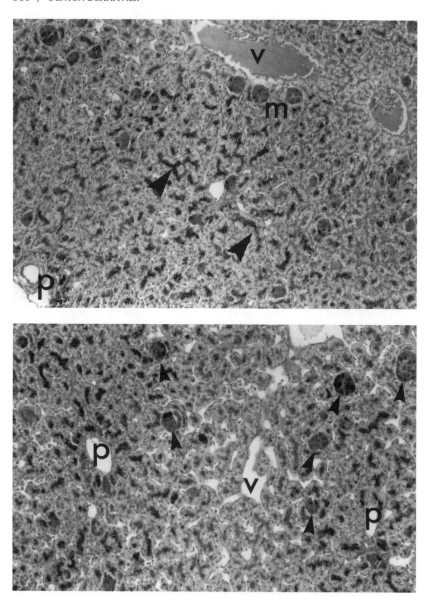

Fig. 6.6. *Caiman crocodilus.* Top. Liver with much hepatocellular iron in a pericanalicular position (arrowheads) and iron-containing melanomacrophages (m) near hepatic vein tributary (v). Note that iron is present throughout the parenchyma with no accentuation around the portal tract (p) (Prussian blue stain, ×90). (Section provided by William Beresford.) Bottom. Another area of same section with semblance of lobular arrangement of portal tracts (p) and hepatic vein tributary (v). Note that more iron is in periportal hepatocytes than perivenular ones. The iron-containing melanomacrophages (arrowheads) seem to be randomly distributed.

hepatocytes of some reptiles contain large amounts of stainable iron in pericanalicular granules (Fig. 6.6 and 6.7). These granules can also be recognized in thin histologic sections stained with hematoxylin and eosin. Periportal cells have somewhat more iron than those around the terminal hepatic venule, but the difference in lobular distribution is not as striking as in humans with an iron overload (hemochromatosis). No evidence can be found that the hepatocellular iron in reptiles is as injurious as a similar amount would be in mammals with an iron overload. Another difference is that the bile ductules do not contain excess iron (Fig. 6.7B), as they do in hemochromatosis, and that no iron occurs in endothelial cells.

Peroxisomes, discovered by electron microscopy, are slightly smaller than and scattered among the mitochondria (Fig. 6.5); they are outnumbered by mitochondria by about 10:1. Each is about half a micron in diameter and is surrounded by a single membrane. Its matrix is more dense than that of mitochondria, and it sometimes contains a nucleoid that is shaped differently in each species, although it is absent in man and in *Geochelone carbonaria* during thermal adaptation (De Brito Gitirana and Gorgas, 1986). The number, size, and catalase content of peroxisomes vary during such thermal adaptation. The main function of peroxisomes concerns fatty acid oxidation, but it is also involved in purine metabolism.

The Golgi apparatus was known for decades before its function was understood. It is identified histochemically by its thiamin pyrophosphatase activity. Electron microscopy shows it to be a complex of membrane profiles and vesicles near the bile canaliculus. The number of profiles and vesicles and their sizes varies among cells. The main function of this organelle is the packaging of material for export from the cell. Its location adjacent to the bile canaliculus suggests that most of its activity is directed towards bile formation, but, in fact, protein made in the endoplasmic reticulum to be delivered to the bloodstream passes through here. Transport to or from the Golgi complex can be vesicular or by microtubules or by carriers in the cytosol. The close functional as well as spatial relation of the Golgi apparatus, the endoplasmic reticulum, and lysosomes led to the acronym GERL for the entire complex.

Small fat droplets normally may be found in cytoplasm. These are not surrounded by membranes and vary in size up to several microns in diameter. The liver of *Sphenodon punctatus* contains 8.8% fat in terms of wet weight, which is similar to that of other reptiles (Body and Newman, 1989). Neutral fat, mainly triacylglycerol, accounts for two-thirds, whereas the remaining polar lipids are 70% choline and ethanolamine. The pattern of lipid distribution appears to be similar in frogs, testudines, and mammals. The liver of the male *Gekko japonicus*

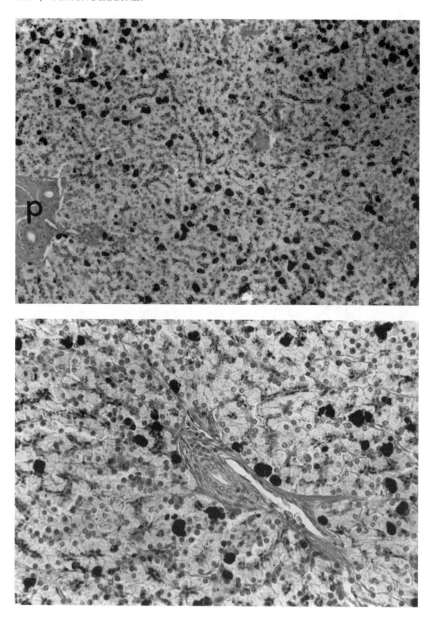

Fig. 6.7. *Alligator mississippiensis.* Top. This liver shows less hepatocellular iron than that of the caiman. The iron content around a large portal tract (p) is not greater than elsewhere in the section. The melanomacrophages are smaller and more numerous than in the caiman liver. (Prussian blue stain, ×90). (Section provided by William Beresford.) Bottom. Higher magnification of portal tract in same section showing no iron deposition (×225).

has more fat than that of the female; fat accumulation is greatest prior to hibernation and least near its end and during vitellogenesis (Ji and Wang, 1990). Macrosteatosis occurs whenever droplets coalesce into a single drop, pushing the nucleus to one side, and giving the cell a "signet ring"-like appearance in paraffin embedded histologic sections. The liver is the main site of lipogenesis in *Phrynops hilarii* (Da Silva and Migliorini, 1990). The fatty acids in adipose tissue come from the liver.

The nucleus of the hepatocyte is found in the center of the polyhe-dral cell but is more in the basal portion of the pyramidal hepatocyte as seen in *Osteolaemus* (Storch et al., 1989). It is about 7 microns in di-ameter and is round to slightly ovoid. The ratio of nucleus-to-cyto-plasm area is higher in reptiles than it is in fish or mammals (Storch et al., 1989). During hibernation of *Testudo graeca*, the nuclear volume increases, but the amount of chromatin decreases (Ferrer et al., 1987). The nucleus is surrounded by a double membrane, the outer one be-ing connected in places with the endoplasmic reticulum and often hav-ing attached ribosomes. The double nuclear membrane is perforated by many small pores, about 0.01 microns in diameter (Fig. 6.5). Each pore contains a fine web that probably acts as a valve. The matrix of the nucleus, the nucleoplasm, contains DNA in chromatin granules, mainly packed around the inner circumference except around the pores. The more active a cell is in protein synthesis, the thinner the rim of chromatin granules, with more of the DNA free in the nucleoplasm. The nucleus also contains RNA, histones, and usually four nucleoli, only two of which are seen in sections. The DNA and the histones are basophilic and are responsible for the deep blue color seen in hematoxylin and eosin stains in histologic sections. The hepatocytic nucleus of *Trachemys scripta elegans* is rich in the histone found in the nucleated erythrocytes that is homologous to the H1° of mammals (Rutledge et al., 1981). Some, but not all the tissue specific histones in erythrocytes of some testudines may be found in the hepatocytic nu-clei (Tsai and Huilica, 1975). Nuclei contain estrogen receptors as dem-onstrated in *Thamnophis sirtalis parietalis* (Whittier et al., 1991) and *Chrysemys picta* (Riley and Callard, 1988). These receptors are also found in the cytosolic fraction of the hepatocyte and are homologous with receptors in other vertebrates. The amount in reptiles is similar to that in amphibians but lower than that in fish, birds and mammals. Some receptors in the liver are activated or transformed, whereas others are nontransformed or multimeric.

Nucleoli are up to a micron in diameter, are composed of dense mate-rial with interspersed lighter areas, and are rich in RNA. During mito-sis, nuclear chromatin granules cluster together to form chromosomes; when the nuclear membrane disappears, the chromosomes become attached to microtubules that extend in a ray-like fashion from the centriole. As nuclear division progresses, the microtubules shorten and separate the chromosomes into pairs; one member goes to each daughter cell. The nuclei reform before cell division is complete. Sometimes cell division fails to occur after mitosis and cells become binucleated or even multinucleated. During embryonal growth and in early life, hepatocytes are diploid but become tetraploid in mammals as these become adults. This shift does not occur in fish, amphibians, or birds; however the crocodylian liver does have small numbers of tetraploid cells (Gahan and Middleton, 1982). The life span of the adult hepatocyte is normally as long as that of the animal.

F. Bile Ductules and Ducts

The bile canaliculi form a chicken-wire-like network throughout the parenchyma. This network is drained primarily near the portal tracts. One or two cells 10–15 microns in diameter are found alongside hepatocytes, sharing a canalicular lumen. These cells have no glycogen rosettes, scanty endoplasmic reticulum, and a few scattered small mitochondria. The basal surfaces of duct and ductular epithelial cells rest on a thin basement membrane that hepatocytes normally lack. This hepatocyte-ductular cell junction has been called the canal of Hering. Its lumen becomes completely surrounded by ductular cells, and the basement membrane envelopes the entire structure. A few small lysosomes lie scattered in the ductular cytoplasm. The ductular cell nucleus is smaller than that of the hepatocyte and the chromatin denser.

A single microscopic field of the reptilian liver may contain several bile ductules (Frye, 1991). Short and irregular microvilli line the ductular lumen, and occasional cilia arising from the centriole protrude into it. Junctional complexes seal the ductular lumen, and the lateral cell borders are straight or interdigitate with each other. The basal border rests on a continuous basement membrane. Varying numbers of collagen fibrils in bundles are on the other side of the basement membrane. The surrounding collagen may be denser, and the ductules have more cells surrounding a larger lumen. Gradually the cells change from cuboidal to columnar. Structures with more than six cells in circumference are considered ducts. These are also surrounded by a basement membrane. Whenever the cells are columnar, the nucleus occupies a basal position and the luminal surface is covered by long, uniform microvilli. This configuration of the epithelial cells continues to the duodenum. The extrahepatic portion of the bile duct also has occasional mucus producing goblet cells. These cells may be clustered in small glands in the adventitia. Smooth muscle fibers surround the inner epithelial layer, and the entire structure is encased in a collagenous extension of Glisson's capsule.

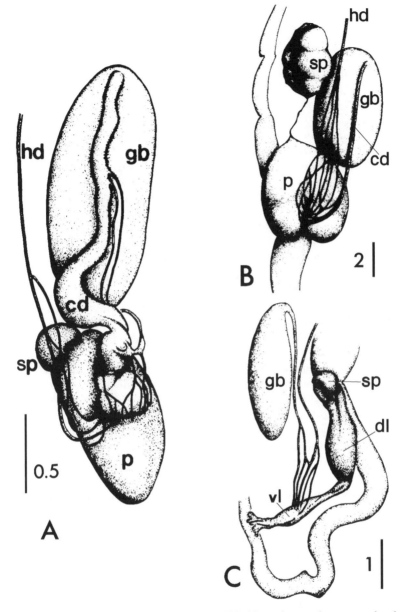

Fig. 6.8. Anatomic arrangement of bile ducts, gallbladder, spleen and pancreas of snakes. A. Colubrid type, B. *Eryx jaculus*, C. *Malpolon monspessulana*. Abbreviations: hd, hepatic duct; gb, gallbladder; cd, common duct; sp, spleen; p, pancreas; dl and vl, dorsal and ventral lobes of pancreas. The bars and numbers represent the scale in centimeters. Note the variations in the distribution of the bile ducts. (Modified from Moscona, 1980, with permission.)

G. The Gallbladder

Most reptiles have a gallbladder; in many, it lies in a bed on or in the liver, as in those mammals with a gallbladder. However, in snakes it is caudal to the liver (Frye, 1991; Knobel et al., 1976; Moscona, 1980), and in testudines, it is dorsal to the right border of the liver (Pritchard, 1979). The gallbladder of *Calotes* is embedded in the posterior margin of the right lobe; here begins the fissure between the right and left lobes (Paranjape, 1974). The organ is covered by a thin serosa. The mucosa of the gallbladder is composed of simple or pseudostratified columnar epithelial cells, but collapse of the organ when it is empty throws the mucosa into irregular folds. The adventitia contains more collagen and smooth muscle bundles as well as numerous lymphatic channels. Local goblet cells are more numerous and clustered than in the ductal epithelium. They form mucus glands (Frye, 1991), although *Sceloporus occidentalis* lacks goblet cells (Ells, 1954). Lectins have been used for the histochemical demonstration of glycogen in the gallbladders of the *Tarentola mauritanica* and *Elaphe scalaris*, whereas only small amounts of sialic acid occur in the gecko (Madrid et al., 1989). More glycoconjugates are found in mammalian livers.

Peristaltic contractions have been noted in the gallbladder and common duct of testudines, beginning at the fundus and proceeding down to the duodenum (Higgins, 1928). These contractions are stimulated by fat in the duodenum. The terminus of the biliary system differs in various reptiles as it enters the duodenum. The gallbladder of colubrid snakes splits into many branches, forming a biliary plexus that joins the cystic duct (Moscona, 1980)(Fig. 6.8). The common bile duct passes to the right of a small spherical gallbladder and through the pancreas to the ampulla of Vater where it is joined by the pancreatic duct before entering the intestine. The common bile duct in some lizards does not go through the pancreas but enters directly into the ampulla (Moscona, 1980)(Fig. 6.9). *Calotes versicolor* has two main bile ducts that are closely applied and parallel to the portal vein (Paranjape, 1974). Each enters the duodenum independently, and the cystic duct from the gallbladder joins the duct from the right lobe. A similar dual arrangement of common bile ducts occurs in *Sceloporus* bile ducts (Ells, 1954). A basement membrane begins around the hepatocytic-ductular cell junction and may also be seen over the pyramidal cells of the glandular or tubular hepatocytes. A few collagen fibrils may also be seen in the space (Figs. 6.4 and 6.5). No information is available about neural control of gallbladder function in reptiles (Berger and Burnstock, 1979).

H. Sinusoidal Mesenchymal Cells

Three main types of cells that are part of the hepatic sinusoid are the endothelial cells, macrophages including Kupffer cells, and stellate or Ito cells.

The sinusoids are lined by a thin layer of endothelial cells. This endothelium does not have a discrete basement membrane, although laminin and matrix proteins fill the narrow space of Dissé between the epithelium and the hepatocyte. Fuzzy, filamentous material can be seen in the Dissé space of *Osteolaemus* (Storch et al., 1989). Dolichols, long-chain polyprenols, are part of the liver matrix in reptiles and are closely associated with the hepatocytic plasma membrane (Tosheva et al., 1991). They may play an insulating role in ectotherms, maintaining metabolism despite variations in body temperature.

The endothelial cells are very flat, and the flat area contains holes or fenestrae, usually in clusters (sieve plates). These have been described in many vertebrates, from fish to man, and vary in size from 0.05–1.0 micron in diameter (Arias, 1990). They are less numerous in crocodylians than in rats (Storch et al., 1989). The fenestrae are not fixed; instead, they open and close depending on the functional state of the liver. They permit plasma to bathe the basolateral surface of the hepatocytes and may prevent formation of an unstirred layer along the sinusoidal lumen.

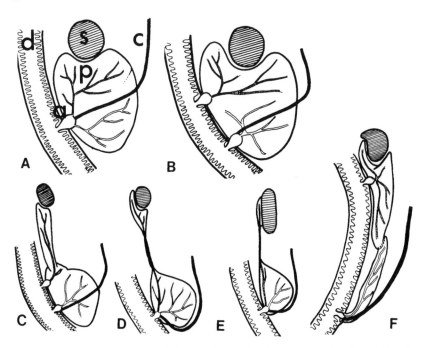

Fig. 6.9. Diagrams of location of ducts and ampullae in pancreas of snakes. Abbreviations: s, spleen; c, common duct; d, duodenum; p, pancreas; a, ampulla of Vater. Note that in some species two ampullae are present, the upper one serving the pancreatic duct of Wirsung, the lower one serving the duct of Santorini. A. *Coluber*; B. *Vipera*; C. *Typhlops*; D. *Eryx*; E. *Leptotyphlops*; F. *Malpolon*. (From Moscona, 1980, with permission.)

Rotation of erythrocytes around an axis perpendicular to the sinusoidal wall in larger sinusoids and bending of erythrocytes in narrower lumens also effectively mixes the sinusoidal contents.

The second sinusoidal cell is the macrophage. The Kupffer cell is an intraluminal macrophage, being attached to the endothelium in one or more places but with no junctional complexes. Kupffer cells are numerous in the crocodylian liver (Storch et al., 1989) and may be resident macrophages or may be recruited from circulating monocytes. The plasma membrane is ruffled, and the cytoplasm contains numerous phagosomes or lysosomes, the size and content of which depend on what the cell had previously phagocytosed. Clearing the portal blood of endotoxin of intestinal origin is an important function. The Kupffer cell, probably in all vertebrates, is both the source and target of several cytokines, including some interleukins, tumor necrosis factors, and transforming growth factors. A second macrophage is perisinusoidal and is variably pigmented. Clusters of these macrophages or melanomacrophages are numerous in a parasinusoidal position in amphibians and reptiles (Frye, 1991) and fewer in fish (Herráez and Zapata, 1986). Snakes have the fewest pigment cells among reptiles (Hack and Helmy, 1964), but the amount varies greatly from animal to animal, and even within the same species (Ells, 1954)(Figs. 6.10 and 6.11 top). The pigment is black, and has been called melanin. Whether it is the same as the melanin in the skin is unclear. Reptilian melanomacrophages are apparently not of neural crest origin, unlike skin melanophores, but incorporate l-tyrosine and l-DOPA or dihydroxyphenylalanine (Scalia et al., 1988). Iron is present in many of these pigmented cells, which are also PAS-positive (Figs. 6.6 and 6.7), suggesting a role as a scavenger of free radicals (Henninger and Beresford, 1990). The melanin content of the liver is inversely related to the activity of superoxide dismutase (SOD). This enzyme, in many animals, is mainly responsible for removal of free radicals (Sichel et al., 1987). SOD is low in testudine livers, which contain a lot of melanin, and is twice as high in lizards, which have much less liver melanin. Animals that have starved for a month have engorged macrophages with extensive pigmentation, and even some hepatocytes have many pigment granules (Ells, 1954).

The third sinusoidal cell is the stellate or Ito cell (Ito and Nemoto, 1952) or lipocyte (Bronfenmajer et al., 1966). The stellate cell was originally described by Kupffer and has been well studied in various reptiles. It lies between the endothelium and the sinusoidal surface of the hepatocyte (Taira and Mutch, 1981). Stellate cells are numerous in crocodylians (Storch et al., 1989) but are less numerous in testudines (Ferrer et al., 1987). The cells are irregularly shaped and exist in a resting form or an activated one. The cytoplasm of the resting form contains

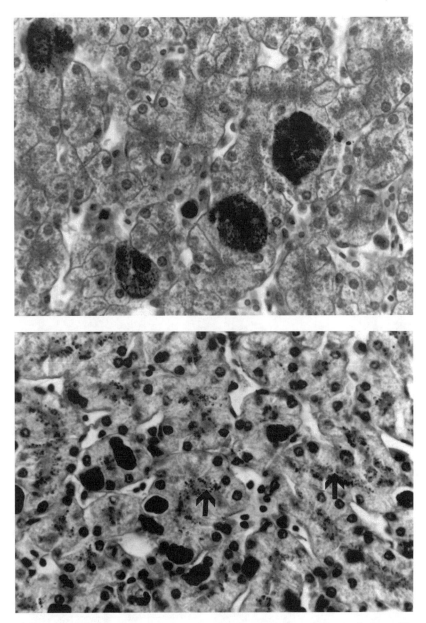

Fig. 6.10. Top. *Terrapene carolina*. Four clusters of melanomacrophages in the liver. The cells are strongly PAS positive (PAS stain, ×320). Bottom. *Alligator mississippiensis*. View of liver at same magnification as in top panel. Note that bile canaliculi are outlined by small, iron-containing granules (lysosomes)(arrows). The melanomacrophages are smaller but more numerous than in the *Terrapene* (Diastase-PAS stain, ×320). (Both sections provided by William Beresford.)

several round fat droplets, ranging from 0.1 to 2.0 microns in diameter
(Fig. 6.11 bottom). The fat is rich in vitamin A ester and is the main site
at which vitamin A is stored in the body. The number and size of the fat
droplets vary among species of reptiles (Beresford and Henninger, 1986).

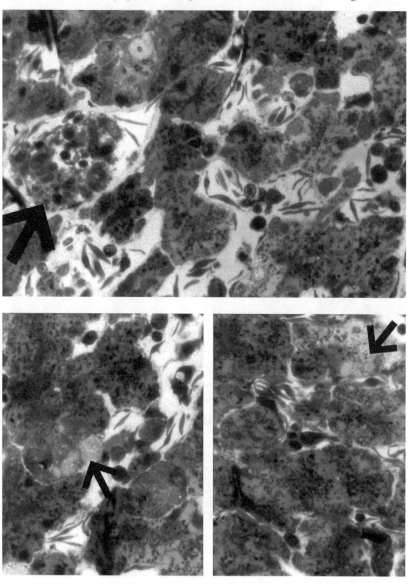

Fig. 6.11. *Terrapene carolina.* Thin sections of resin-embedded specimen of normal liver (Tolu-
idine blue stain, ×360). Top. Melanomacrophage cluster (arrow). Bottom left & right. Fat-
storing Ito or stellate cells (arrows). (Stained sections provided by William Beresford.)

Many stellate cells in *Eumeces algeriensis* and *Tropidurus torquatus* contain little or no fat (De Brito Gitirana, 1988). The cytoplasm contains rough endoplasmic reticulum, peroxisomes and a few mitochondria but no phagosomes. The stellate cells become activated during any injury to the liver. They then lose their vitamin A, the lipid droplets disappear, smooth muscle fibrils appear, and the cell starts to form extracellular matrixes and collagen. The activated cell form is called the myofibroblast; it is responsible for formation of basement membrane collagen (types IV and V) as well as collagen type I, probably in all vertebrates. The stellate cells are also the source of several cytokines regulating hepatocellular growth and immune responses.

Other components of the immune system, including lymphocytes, pit cells, and plasma cells may lie in and around sinusoids in the liver. Clusters of lymphoid cells occur in the livers of testudines and snakes (Beresford and Henninger, 1986). Nerve cells are notable for their absence from the hepatic parenchyma, although some twigs may be found in portal tracts (Berthoud et al., 1992).

III. PHYSIOLOGY
A. General

Metabolism in reptilian liver changes as the animals develop from egg to hatchling to adult (Snell and Tracy, 1985). During each year it changes in those animals that hibernate (Agid et al., 1961). The rate of metabolism in tissues of various reptiles, measured most recently in *Chelonia mydas*, a warm water sea turtle that is a regional endotherm, is dependent upon the ambient temperature (Penick et al., 1996). The metabolic rate in the liver in this species is about the same as that of the kidney and only slightly less than that of the heart. Liver functon is very sensitive to changes in temperature and decreases sharply in a linear fashion when the temperature drops.

B. Carbohydrate Metabolism

The most important of the many functions of the liver is to supply glucose. Whenever a liver is removed from a rat or a dog, death from hypoglycemia occurs in hours. The normal precursor of glucose in the hepatocyte under aerobic conditions is glycogen. Glycogenolysis is a multi-step enzymatic process. It begins in the cytosol and finishes in the smooth endoplasmic reticulum; here, glucose-6-phosphatase releases free glucose. The liver can synthesize glucose from pyruvate or lactate. The liver can also convert some amino acids and fats to glucose by gluconeogenesis, with pyruvate or acetate being the main intermediaries. Ectothermic animals tend to have lower blood sugar levels than do endothermic ones, but also show much greater fluctuations, especially upon variations in temperature (Agid et al., 1961; Coulson and Hernandez, 1964). The average reptilian blood sugar levels normally tend to be between 40 and 50 mg dl^{-1} but can be lower than 10 mg dl^{-1} or >100 mg dl^{-1}. By contrast, fasting human blood sugar values average between 80 and 90 mg dl^{-1}; symptoms develop if they fall below 50 mg dl^{-1}, and permanent cerebral cortical damage occurs whenever the level remains at less than 40 mg dl^{-1}. Reptiles do not incur cortical damage at the very low blood glucose levels that have been measured during hibernation (Agid et al., 1961) nor at the end of prolonged dives. *Phrynops hilarii* maintains blood glucose during prolonged fasting as well as glycogen stores, mainly derived by gluconeogenesis from protein (Da Silva and Migliorini, 1990). Thus metabolic reserves are depleted and insulin levels also drop. The hepatic glycogen stores reach a maximum in the fall in those animals that hibernate (Marcus, 1981; Gregory, 1982). Hepatic glycogen is used up quickly during hibernation (Ferrer et al., 1987).

Glycolysis switches from aerobic to anaerobic, being no longer dependent on adenosine triphosphate (ATP) (Gatten, 1985). The glycolytic and tricarboxylic acid pathways are less active (Gregory, 1982). A result of anaerobic glycolysis is the production by the liver of lactate, which tends to be taken up from the blood under aerobic conditions and converted to pyruvate. The resulting lactic acidosis causes a drop in blood pH (Gatten, 1985). The heart rate slows dramatically even if the animal is active, for instance, during a dive, the heart rate of *Caiman* may be as slow as 10 per minute (Gaunt and Gans, 1969). Awakening from hibernation or surfacing after a prolonged dive of a few days is often followed by a further drop in blood sugar. As aerobic conditions are restored and eating resumes, the blood glucose level returns to normal, and lactic acid is reconstituted by the liver into glycogen or glucose, the glucose being distributed to muscle to restore the depleted glycogen.

C. Fat Metabolism

Homeothermic animals use stored fat in subcutaneous tissue as insulation, but reptiles have less need for such insulation and, hence, less subcutaneous fat. However, fat is stored in abdominal fat bodies (Saint Girons and Duguy, 1992). The main purpose of this fat is to supply material for vitellogenesis during the reproductive cycle. It also serves as stored energy during hibernation, prolonged fasting, and in hatchlings (Gatten, 1985). The fat content of the liver is highest just before hibernation and lowest late in hibernation (Ferrer et al., 1987; Ji and Wang, 1990). The liver of female geckos has more fat than that of males, but this is depleted during vitellogenesis. Fat is transported to the liver in the form of unesterified fatty acids from the gut or from fat depots. Whenever the fat leaves the liver, it is esterified; it is bound to protein as lipoproteins. The liver also exports phospholipids and cholesterol. The liver recycles lipoproteins that left the hepatocytes as very low-density lipoproteins and returned as low-density lipoprotein remnants. Diets high in fat and carbohydrates increase the fat content of the hepatocytes to more than 30%; the intracellular lipid is visible as large fat drops displacing the nuclei. The liver can break down fatty acids to two carbon fragments by omega oxidation and can synthesize fat from these small molecules. The liver also uses fatty acids to make its own phospholipid membranes and cholesterol. The liver probably contains different pools of cholesterol. One provides the sterol for structural needs, one for export purposes, and one for conversion to bile salts.

D. Bile Acid Metabolism

Bile acids are formed from cholesterol only in hepatocytes, in which they serve as the driving force of bile secretion. They are also important in lipid digestion and absorption in which they function as emulsifying agents and detergents. The bile acids of reptiles have been extensively studied as evolutionary markers (Hagey, 1992; Haslewood, 1965)(Table 6.3). The most primitive bile acid, $3\alpha,7\alpha$-dihydroxy-5β-cholestan-27-oic acid or trihydroxycoprostanoic acid, is found in crocodylians. Testudines show another hydroxyl group on carbon 22 of the side chain, forming sterocholanic acid, and the tuatara and lizards added one at carbon 24. Some testudines and lizards also show a hydroxyl group in the 12α position on the ring.

Table 6.3. Most common bile acids found in Reptilia. (Data derived from Haslewood, 1965; Hagey, 1992).

Order/ Family	Total C atoms	3a	7a	12a	16a	22	23	24	Common name
Turtles									
Cheloniidae	27	x	x	x		x			Sterocholanic
		x		x		x			*
Emydidae	27	x	x	x		x			Sterocholanic
Sphenodon	27	x	x	x				x	Varanic
Lizards									
Varanidae	27	x	x	x				x	Varanic
Snakes									
Pythoninae	24	x		x	x				Pythocholic
Viperidae	24	x	x	x			x		Bitocholic
Crotalidae	24	x	x	x					Cholic
Crocodylians	27	x	x	x					Coprostanoic

*Probably secondary bile acid.

The 3α,7α,12α,24R-tetrahydroxy-5β-cholestan-27-oic acid of lizards has been called varanic acid because it was first found in the monitor *Varanus niloticus*. This bile acid is an intermediate in the formation of cholic acid in snakes and mammals. Boas and pythons show a shorter side chain that lacks three carbon atoms, and the ring is also hydroxylated at position 16, as is that of birds, forming 3α,12α,16α-trihydroxy-5β-cholan-24-oic acid or pythocholic acid. These snakes cannot form 7α bile acid, but they can hydroxylate chenodeoxycholic acid at the 12α position and deoxycholic acid at the 16α position. Some vipers and other snakes also can shorten the side chain by three carbon atoms as well as hydroxylate it to form 3α,12α,23R-trihydroxy-5β-cholan-24-oic acid or bitocholic acid. These snakes can also hydroxylate at the 7α position, forming a tetrahydroxy bile acid. Still other snakes, notably the Crotalidae, synthesize cholic acid, 3α,7α,12α trihydroxy bile acid, as do many mammals, including man. Bacteria in the intestinal tract of these snakes remove the 7α hydroxyl group to form deoxycholic acid, which is reabsorbed in the enterohepatic circulation re-excreted in the bile. Removal of the 7α hydroxyl group can occur in all reptiles that have one at this position; levels of the appropriate secondary bile acid may be found in serum. Most of the bile acids in all reptiles are secreted as taurine conjugates.

The evolutionary implications of bile acid metabolism in reptiles suggest that changes in side chains and hydroxylation may have been selected as they improved efficiency of bile flow on one hand and lipid absorption from the gut on the other.

E. Protein Metabolism

The liver is central in protein metabolism. It processes alimentary amino acids and peptides so that the organism can make its own distinctive proteins. Most of this synthesis occurs in the endoplasmic reticulum of the hepatocytes, with the help of transfer RNA to transport the amino acids, ribosomal RNA to serve as the site of synthesis, and messenger RNA to provide the protein blueprint. During the winter, when the animal is hibernating, protein metabolism increases with formation of more amino acids and amides (Gregory, 1982).

The liver is the sole source of serum albumin, the carrier of many endogenous and exogenous substances and a main factor in providing the colloid osmotic pressure of plasma. The liver also makes clotting proteins, including fibrinogen, prothrombin, and factors V, VII, IX and XI. The hepatic endothelial cells contribute to the pool of factor VIII in the plasma.

Carrier proteins for various substances transported in the blood are synthesized and usually also degraded in the liver. These include transferrin as well as ferritin for iron storage and various hormone transporting proteins for secretions of the thyroid, adrenal cortex, pituitary, and others. During liver injury, especially when acute, the level of carrier proteins rises in plasma; they behave like acute phase reactants. Fibrinogen may also participate in this rise, as do enzymes in serum that are at least partly of hepatocellular origin. This is the basis for the widely used measurement of alanine or aspartate aminotransferase activity as a means of assessing hepatic injury. The range of normal activities of the aminotransferases have been determined in a few reptilian species and are similar to those measured in birds and mammals (Ramsay and Dotson, 1995). Enzymes related to bile secretion are alkaline phosphatase, gamma glutamyl transferase, 5'-nucleotidase and leucine aminopeptidase. Only alkaline phosphatase has been studied in various tissues and serum of a few reptiles. The level of activity is normally low, and no gamma glutamyl transferase activity could be found in *Elaphe obsoleta quadrivittata* (Ramsay and Dotson, 1995).

Vitellogenins, the yolk protein precursors, are formed exclusively in the liver (Hubert, 1985) and are transported to the ovaries by the general circulation. Estradiol is the stimulus for production of vitellogenin (Ferguson, 1985).

The liver processes proteins prior to recycling or removal from the body. The amino groups may be used in transamination or may be converted to urea by the ornithine-citrulline-arginine cycle.

Urea is formed in hepatocellular mitochondria and occurs even in fish (Campbell et al., 1985). Most of the urea is excreted by the kidneys, but some enters the intestinal tract, either in bile or by direct diffusion. Nucleic acids are degraded to uric acid, which is also secreted by the kidneys. This uricotelic process is present in some testudines (Campbell et al., 1985). Most mammals and birds carry nucleotide metabolism a step further, to allantoin, but humans and some dogs are uricotelic like testudines and stop at uric acid formation (Campbell et al., 1985).

F. Bile Pigment Metabolism

Little is known about bile pigment metabolism in lower vertebrates (Berk and Noyer, 1994). Reptiles can develop hyperbilirubinemia with jaundice owing to impairment of bile flow or liver damage described later (section on Pathology). Whereas fish can form bilirubin from the breakdown of heme as well as conjugate it with glucuronide and, to a lesser extent, with other sugars, at least some reptiles lack biliverdin reductase and have been reported to be unable to reduce the biliverdin to bilirubin (Calkran and O'Carra, 1970, 1977). However, snake plasma contains bilirubin, and not biliverdin, but biliverdin may be the predominant pigment in the bile (Schmid and Lester, 1966). The situation is equivalent to that in frogs and chickens. The activity of uridyl diphosphate glucuronyl transferase, the enzyme responsible for conjugation of bilirubin with glucuronic acid, is less in snakes than in mammals, and the hepatic uptake of injected unconjugated bilirubin is much slower than in mammals, which have much greater glucuronyl transferase activity (Schmid and Lester, 1966). The plasma of normal Eastern, Texan, and Mexican *Drymarchon corais* contains 10 times more unconjugated bilirubin in the absence of hemolysis than does that of other species of snakes (Noonan et al. 1979). Also, the bile of these snakes contains over 95 percent biliverdin (Cornelius et al., 1975). When unconjugated bilirubin is injected into indigo snakes, initial plasma clearance is slower than it is in rat snakes used as controls, and the second phase of clearance is extremely slow (Noonan et al. 1979). Similarly, the clearance of injected sulfobromophthalien (BSP) is slower in indigo snakes than in control snakes. *Drymarchon corais* can be considered another animal model of unconjugated hyperbilirubinemia, similar to the Gunn rat or human Crigler-Najjar syndrome (Berk and Noyer, 1994).

G. Hormone Metabolism

The liver removes many hormones from the circulation, a process that may require oxidation, reduction, and conjugation. The metabolism of progesterone has been examined in the liver of *Tiliqua rugosa* and was found to be the same as in mammals (Bourne, 1984). Estrogen receptors have been found in the hepatocellular nuclei and cytosol of *Chrysemys picta* (Riley and Callard, 1988). The levels of these receptors in the liver vary during the year, but significant changes occur only in the nuclear compartment. A large peak occurs in the spring, the animal then being preovulatory with high levels of blood estrogen. A smaller peak develops in the fall during vitellogenesis. The levels are modulated by pituitary growth hormone. The seasonal variations in the hepatic metabolism of adrenal hormones have been studied in *Calotes* (Gupta and Thaplial, 1983). Levels are greatest in April and lowest in October. Epinephrine and thyroidectomy have opposite effects on metabolism, whereas corticosterone has little effect unless it is combined with thyroidectomy, in which case it depresses hormone metabolism.

IV. PATHOLOGY
A. General

The liver and biliary tree are sites of diseases similar to those found in mammals (including man), including toxic injuries, infections, tumors, and metabolic disturbances. None of these has been studied systematically in reptiles, and most of the information is anecdotal. Reptiles in their natural habitat are exposed to different injuries than those in captivity, making generalization difficult. Furthermore, few experimental studies have been performed in reptilian liver. Nonspecific pathological changes appear, including focal necrosis and hydropic degeneration, but they are not common, and their significance is unknown (Frye, 1991). Portal fibrosis and ductular proliferation may also be found (Fig. 6.12).

B. Toxic Injury

Environmental pollutants can affect the livers of all exposed species, although different species, even closely related ones, differ greatly in their responses to these substances. Toxic chemicals include pesticides, herbicides, polychlorinated or polybrominated biphenyls, byproducts of chemical and petrochemical industries, dioxin and other defoliants, as well as accidental spills of various noxious substances. Natural poisons such as amanita mushrooms, crotalaria, and other plants containing pyrrolizidine alkaloids, and foods containing molds that produce mycotoxins, may be ingested.

Toxic injury can be acute or chronic. Acute injury causes hepatocellular necrosis with or without a fatty liver. The injury is usually most severe around the terminal hepatic venule, although all hepatocytes can be destroyed. The extent of the injury is generally dose related, but this can vary depending on nutrition and age. If the injury is not extensive, recovery is rapid with restitution to normal. Chronic injury usually leads to fibrosis.

Radiation damage is a special form of toxic injury rarely occurring in reptiles under natural conditions (Cosgrove, 1971). Exposure to large doses of ionizing radiation usually kills reptiles at the time that hematopoietic depression is fatal. Foci of necrosis appear in the liver, and these become abscesses if the animal survives long enough.

C. Infection

The infections reported in the livers of reptiles are the same as those in other vertebrates and are caused by viral and bacterial agents and protozoan infestations.

Several viruses can infect the reptilian liver (Clarke and Lunger, 1981). Herpes hepatitis is often recognized in testudinians and iguanas (Frye et al., 1977). The histologic features include hepatocellular necrosis and characteristic viral inclusions producing "owl eyed" nuclei in affected hepatocytes. The virions are readily recognized under the electron microscope. Adenovirus-like hepatitis has been found in a group of captive-bred Rankin's dragon lizards (*Pogona henrylawsoni*) (Frye et al., 1994).

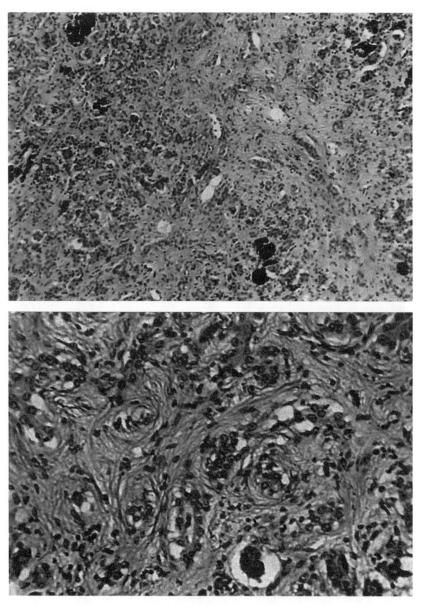

Fig. 6.12. *Iguana iguana.* Top. Portal fibrosis in the liver. The numerous melanomacrophages are randomly distributed in the surrounding parenchyma (Hematoxylin and eosin stain, original magnification ×24). (From Kodachrome provided by Fredric L. Frye.) Bottom. Higher magnification of same specimen as above showing that some of the fibrosis encircles ducts and ductules, the number of which may indicate proliferation of biliary cells. Such an appearnce suggests chronic or past abnormalities in the biliary tree (original magnification ×60). (From Kodachrome provided by Fredric L. Frye.)

The brief illness involved lack of appetite, lethargy, and limb paresis. The light microscopic appearance of the liver was that of typical viral hepatitis with large eosinophilic inclusions in the nuclei and occasionally in the cytoplasm of hepatocytes (Fig. 6.13). Under the electron microscope, the inclusions proved to be crystalline arrays of virus particles (Fig. 6.14). This virus may be similar to one reported for *Pogona barbata* (Julian and Dunham, 1990), and in *Boa constrictor* (Jacobson et al., 1985), *Varanus* (Jacobson and Kollias, 1986) and two specimens of *Crocodylus niloticus* (Jacobson et al., 1984), and also *Pogona henrylawsoni* (Frye et al., 1994). Other viruses undoubtedly infect various reptiles because these also show chronic hepatitis and cirrhosis, as do mammals. Diagnosis can be made in life with fine needle or wedge biopsies; therapy of chronic hepatitis with corticosteroids and antibiotics has been said to be helpful if started early before fibrosis becomes extensive (Frye, 1991) despite the fact that steroids are immunosuppressive.

Bacterial infections are common and have been described in several species of reptiles (Cooper, 1981; Frye, 1991). Such infections are frequently associated with septicemia, which leads to congestion and discolors the liver because it accumulates hemosiderin (Cooper, 1981).

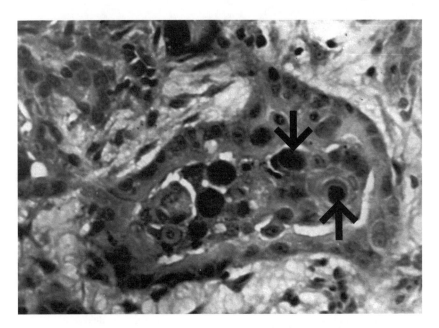

Fig. 6.13. *Pogona henrylawsoni.* Nuclear inclusions (arrows) in hepatocytes due to adenoviral hepatitis (Hematoxylin and eosin stain, original magnification ×120). (From Kodachrome provided by Fredric L. Frye.)

Often bacterial infections lead to formation of abscesses; the contents of these are usually caseous rather than purulent. Coliform bacteria are the most common cause of non-amoebic abscess and give the abscess contents an unpleasant odor. The wall of the abscess is thick and contains leukocytes and fibrous tissue; the amount of the latter depends on the age of the abscess. If the animal survives and the abscess heals, a scar remains. However, some abscess do not heal and remain chronic; scar formation in the wall increases, whereas softer contents diminish. Diffuse bacterial hepatitis can precede abscess formation; it

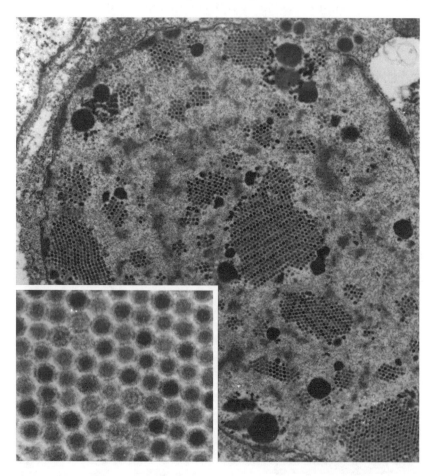

Fig. 6.14. Electron photomicrograph of liver of *Pogona henrylawsoni* in Fig. 6.13, with showing clusters of viral particles in a nucleus of a hepatocyte (Paraformaldehyde-glutaraldehyde fixed, uranyl and lead stained, ×12,000). Inset. High magnification of one cluster of viral particles, some of which are only empty capsids, but a hexagonal shape of the capsid is seen (×100,000). (Pictures provided by Fredric L. Frye and R. J. Munn.)

can develop without ever leading to abscess formation, or it can be spread from an abscess. The acute hepatitis may be sub-clinical or fulminant. Whenever severe, it is usually accompanied by jaundice, renal failure, and central nervous system manifestations (Frye, 1991). Scar formation, chronic hepatitis, and cirrhosis may eventually develop. Miliary tuberculosis has been reported in lizards (Elkan and Reichenbach-Klinke, 1974).

Fungal infections frequently involve the liver with formation of granulomas (Frye, 1991). The organisms most often identified are species of *Candida* and actinomycetes (Austwick and Keymer, 1981).

The protozoan infestation most frequently encountered is amoebiasis, often with formation of an amoebic abscess, which may or may not be preceded by amoebic hepatitis (Keymer, 1981; Marcus, 1981). Snakes, especially in warm climates, seem to be frequently affected (Marcus, 1981), but amoebiasis is uncommon in other species of reptiles (Keymer, 1981). Infected snakes in captivity have high morbidity and mortality rates; these rates are less in lizards, and very low in testudines, although these are frequent carriers (Marcus, 1981). The species of amoeba most often identified is *Entamoeba invadens*, which is similar to *E. histolytica*, the common cause of human amoebiasis (Elkan and Reichenbach-Klinke, 1974; Marcus, 1981). However, reptiles may also be infected by other amoebas. The parasites secrete proteolytic enzymes that cause hepatocellular necrosis. The areas of necrosis become confluent (Keymer, 1981), and the amoebic enzymes lyse all the cells in the area, including erythrocytes and sometimes even the amoebas themselves. The lysate is brown and odorless unless secondarily infected with coliform bacteria. Very little inflammatory exudate or fibrosis is present in the wall of the abscess (Elkan and Reichenbach-Klinke, 1974), but scattered amoebas can be identified, although not in the liquid center of the abscess. The abscess is most often in the cephalad portion of the liver, and the entire organ has a swollen and mottled appearance (Keymer, 1981). Portal vein thrombosis has been associated with amoebic abscesses in a few cases (Marcus, 1981). If the animal survives and the abscess heals, no scar remains. Therapy for reptilian amoebiasis is similar to that in humans.

Malaria has been reported in testudines and snakes. Focal necrosis appears in the liver secondary to clotting of blood in the sinusoids resulting from large collections of schizonts in macrophages (Keymer, 1981). Microsporidia have been found in *Sphenodon* (Liu and King, 1971). Nematode and cestode infestations have been reported in various reptiles, but little is known of the functional consequences of these parasitic diseases (Telford, 1977); the liver capsule of such animals is thickened and covered with fibrin and macrophages, and sinusoids are congested. Pseudophyllidian tapeworms have been found in various reptiles with occasional liver granulomas (Marcus, 1981). Autoinfection of the liver with pentastomes from the lung can also produce granulomas.

Infection of the bile ducts or cholangitis develops when the flow of bile is interrupted owing to the presence of stones or parasites in the biliary tree. This may also occur in the gallbladder, or be due to tumors anywhere in the biliary tree or in the head of the pancreas (Frye, 1991). Gallstones tend to be soft and friable and to contain inspissated bile. Stones can be diagnosed in larger animals using ultrasound (Frye, 1991). Parasitic biliary tract disease, sometimes with obstructive jaundice, occurs in larger terrestrial testudinians, iguanas, and snakes. Cholecystitis has also been reported in various species. The gallbladder may be inspissated with cellular debris often from parasites. Coccidiosis due to infestation with *Isospora* species has been found in the gallbladder and the bile ducts; it causes inflammation in their walls (Keymer, 1981). Granulomatous infiltration and thickening of the walls of the gallbladder and bile ducts are noted in cases in which the parasitic infestations of the biliary tree become chronic (Frye, 1991).

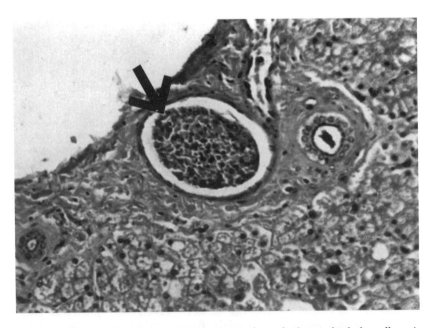

Fig. 6.15. *Boa constrictor.* Intravascular metastasis (arrow) of a renal tubular cell carcinoma in the liver. (Hematoxylin and eosin stain, original magnification ×60). (From Kodachrome provided by Fredric L. Frye.)

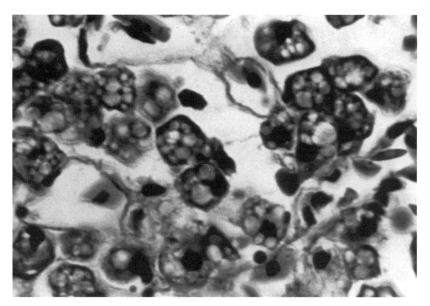

Fig. 6.16. *Boa constrictor.* Microsteatosis. Note the several small fat droplets per cell although some coalescence to larger drops may be starting (Hematoxylin and eosin stain, original magnification ×60). (From Kodachrome provided by Fredric L. Frye.)

D. Tumors

Although uncommon, several tumors have been reported in different species of reptiles (iguanas, tegus, skinks, chameleons, snakes; Lucké and Schlumberger, 1947; Jacobson, 1981; Marcus, 1981). These tumors include primary hepatocellular carcinoma reported in several species; it may or may not be associated with cirrhosis (Frye, 1991; Marcus, 1981). Cholangiocellular carcinoma seems to be more common and is an aggressive tumor (Frye, 1991). Carcinomas of the larger bile duct and the gallbladder have been reported in several snakes but are uncommon (Jacobson, 1981; Marcus, 1981), although bile duct adenomas are seen more frequently. Lymphosarcoma has been noted in snakes, with viral particles identified under the electron microscope (Jacobson, 1981), reminiscent of the lymphoproliferative disease caused in man by the Epstein-Barr virus. Metastatic tumors are uncommon (Lucké and Schlumberger, 1947), but have been noted in the liver, including melanomas (Elkan and Reichenbach-Klinke, 1974) and renal tubular cell carcinoma (Fig. 6.15). Benign adenomas have been found (Frye, 1991). One, reported from the liver of a captive *Sistrurus catenatus catenatus*, has been studied in detail (Hruban and Maschgan, 1982). This was well differentiated, with no melanomacrophages, portal tracts or ductular proliferation. Pre-malignant basophilic areas have been described.

E. Metabolic Abnormalities

Fatty liver or steatosis is a common finding in captive reptiles (Fig. 6.16). It is mainly the result of overfeeding and lack of exercise, just as in humans (Frye, 1991). Obesity and diabetes mellitus frequently accompany steatosis. Under some circumstances of captivity, deficiencies of vitamins A, D, and E develop along with low stores of iron and calcium (Wallach, 1971). Because uric acid is the end product of nucleotide metabolism in reptiles, gout can develop (Wallach, 1971).

F. Other Diseases

Little is known of vascular diseases in reptiles. Portal vein thrombosis has been described as have hepatic infarcts. Rarely have developmental anomalies been reported in reptiles.

V. EVOLUTION AND THE REPTILIAN LIVER

Liver structure and function have changed very little during the course of vertebrate evolution. Probably the main change has been an increase in effectiveness, with perfusion of blood improved due to the development of portal tracts and the switch from glandular to tubular to plate-like arrangement of hepatocytes. Effectiveness of bile secretion and lipid absorption also has improved with the development of bile acids with a shorter side chain and addition of more hydroxyl groups. The reptilian liver suggests a stage intermediate between fish and mammals; it retains some old characteristics mixed with new developments. Finally, some functions have become more effective, for instance, the development of a better system for removal of free radicals or toxic oxygen ions. The original system employed the melanin occurring in extrasinusoidal macrophages in the liver of fish, amphibians, and reptiles. This system has been replaced by superoxide dismutase in birds and mammals. Here again, the reptilian system is intermediate, the proportions varying with different species.

VI. ROLE OF THE LIVER IN HIBERNATION AND DIVING

Many terrestrial vertebrates experience long periods of deprivation of oxygen and food during hibernation; marine vertebrates experience these during protracted dives. During hibernation and diving, the animals shift from aerobic to anaerobic metabolism, causing minor structural changes in hepatocytes and little change in the metabolic rate of the organ. Once carbohydrate and fat stores in the liver and elsewhere are used up, gluconeogenesis provides energy at the expense of depletion of the body protein. The reverse shifts to aerobic metabolism, and resumption of breathing and eating do not change the appearance or function of hepatocytes except for those reflecting the repletion of glycogen stores.

APPENDIX: REPTILIAN SPECIES MENTIONED

TESTUDINES

Chelonia mydas
Pennick et al., 1996
Chelydra serpentina
Ewert, 1985
Chrysemys picta
Riley and Callard, 1988
Geochelone carbonaria
De Brito Gitirana and Gorgas, 1986
Gopherus agassizii
Campbell et al., 1985

Gopherus berlandieri
Campbell et al., 1985
Phrynops hilarii
Da Silva and Migliorini, 1990
Testudo graeca
Ferrer et al., 1987
Terrapene carolina
Henninger, 1982
Trachemys scripta
Rutledge et al., 1981

RHYNCHOCEPHALIA

Sphenodon punctatus
Liu and King, 1971
Body and Newman, 1989

SQUAMATA

Bitis arietans
Knobel et al., 1976
Boa constrictor
Jacobson et al., 1985
Calotes versicolor
Ells, 1954
Paranjape, 1974
Gupta and Thaplial, 1983
Gena and Patnaik, 1990
Conolophus subcristatus
Snell and Tracy, 1985
Drymarchon corais
Cornelius et al., 1975
Noonan et al., 1979
Elaphe obsoleta
Ramsay and Dotson, 1995
Elaphe scalaris
Madrid et al., 1989
Eryx colubrinus
Abdel-Raheem et al., 1989
Eryx jaculus
Moscona, 1980
Eumeces schneideri
Abdel-Raheem et al., 1989
Gekko japonicus
Ji and Wang, 1990
Malpolon monspessulana
Moscona, 1980

Pogona barbata
Julian and Dunham, 1990
Pogona henrylawsoni
Frye et al., 1994
Sceloporus occidentalis
Ells, 1954
Sistrurus catenatus
Hruban and Maschgan, 1982
Tarentola mauritanica
Madrid et al., 1989
Thamnophis sirtalis
Aleksiuk and Stewart, 1971
Whittier et al., 1991
Tiliqua rugosa
Bourne, 1984
Varanus exanthematicus
Jacobson and Kollias, 1986
Varanus flavescens
Beresford and Henninger, 1986
Varanus salvator
Beresford and Henninger, 1986
Vipera aspis
Agid et al., 1961
Saint Girons and Duguy, 1992
Saint Girons and Duguy, 1994

CROCODYLIA

Alligator mississippiensis
Coulson and Hernandez, 1964
Beresford, 1983
Caiman crocodilus
Gaunt and Gans, 1969
Beresford, 1987

Crocodylus niloticus
Jacobson et al., 1984
Osteolaemus tetraspis
Storch et al., 1989

REFERENCES

Abdel-Raheem, K., Okasha, S., El-Deib, S., Shalaan. S., and El Daly, E. (1989). Hibernation in reptiles, 3. Carbohydrate metabolism in *Eryx colubrinus* and *Eumeces schneideri*. *J. Thermal Biol.* 14, 133–137.

Agid, R., Duguy, R., and Saint Girons, H. (1961). Variations de la glycémie du glycogène hépatique et de l'aspect histologique du pancréas chez *Vipera aspis*, au cours du cycle annuel. *J. Physiol.* 153, 807–824.

Aleksiuk, M., and Stewart, K. W. (1971). Seasonal changes in the body composition of the garter snake (*Thamnophis sirtalis parietalis*) at northern latitudes. *Ecology* 52, 485–490.

Arias, I. M. (1990). The biology of hepatic endothelial fenestrae. In *Progress in Liver Diseases* (H. Popper and F. Schaffner, eds.). W. B. Saunders Co., Philadelphia, vol. 9, pp. 11–26.

Austwick, P. K. C., and Keymer, I. F. (1981). Fungi and actinomycetes. In *Diseases of Reptiles* (J. E. Cooper and O. F. Jackson, eds.). Academic Press, London, vol. 1, pp. 193–231.

Beresford, W. A. (1987). Some light microscopic histology of the liver in *Caiman crocodilus*. *Anat. Rec.* 218, 16A. (abstract)

Beresford, W. A. (1993). Fibrous trabeculae in the liver of alligator (*Alligator mississippiensis*). *Ann. Anat.* 175, 357–359.

Beresford, W. A., and Henninger, J. M. (1986). A tabular comparative histology of the liver. *Arch. Histol. Japon.* 49, 267–281.

Berger, P. J., and Burnstock, G. (1979). Autonomic nervous system. In *Biology of the Reptilia* (C. Gans, R. G. Northcutt, and P. Ulinski, eds.). Academic Press, New York, vol. 10, pp. 1–110.

Berk, P. D., and Noyer, C. (1994). Bilirubin metabolism and the hereditary hyperbilirubinemias. *Semin. Liver Dis.* 14, 323–394.

Berthoud, H.-R., Kressel, M., and Neuhuber, W. L. (1992). An antegrade tracing study of the vagal innervation of rat liver, portal vein and biliary system. *Anat. Embryol.* 186, 431–442.

Body, D. R., and Newman, D. G. (1989). The lipid composition of liver, lung and adipose tissue from tuatara (*Sphenodon punctatus*)(Reptilia, Sphenodontia). *Comp. Biochem. Physiol.* 93B, 223–227.

Bourne, A. R. (1984). Occurrence of 20β hydroxysteroid oxidoreductase in the kidney and liver of the lizard *Tiliqua rugosa*. *Comp. Biochem. Physiol.* 77B, 221–222.

Bronfenmajer, S., Schaffner, F., and Popper, H. (1966). Fat-storing cells (lipocytes) in human liver. *Arch. Pathol.* 82, 447–453.

Calkran, E., and O'Carra, P. (1970). Specificity of biliverdin reductase. *Biochem. J.* 119, 16–17.

Calkran, E., and O'Carra, P. (1977). Enzymology and comparative physiology of biliverdin reduction. In *Chemistry and Physiology of Bile Pigments* (P. D. Berk and N. I. Berlin, eds.). U.S. Dept. Health Environl. Welfare (Nat. Inst. Health) 77–110, Bethesda, pp. 69–80.

Campbell, J. W., Smith, D. D., Jr., and Vorhaben, J. E. (1985). Anions and mammalian mitochondrial ammonia-detoxyfying systems in tortoise liver. *Science* 228, 349–351.

Clarke, H. F., and Lunger, P. D. (1981). Viruses. In *Diseases of Reptiles* (J. E. Cooper and O. F. Jackson, eds.). Academic Press, London, vol. 1, pp. 135–164.

Cooper, J. E. (1981). Bacteria. In *Diseases of Reptiles* (J. E. Cooper and O. F. Jackson, eds.). Academic Press, London, vol. 1, pp. 165–191.

Cornelius, C. E., Kelley, K. C., and, Hines, J. A. (1975). Heterogeneity of bilirubin conjugates in several animal species. *Cornell Vet.* 65, 90–95.

Cosgrove, G. E. (1971). Reptilian radiobiology. *J. Am. Vet. Med. Assoc.* 159, 1678–1684.

Coulson, R. A., and Hernandez, T. (1964). *Biochemistry of the Alligator: A Study of Metabolism in Slow Motion.* Louisiana State University Press, Baton Rouge.

Da Silva, R. S. M., and Migliorini, R. H. (1990). Effects of starvation and refeeding on energy-linked metabolic processes in the turtle (*Phrynops hilarii*). *Comp. Biochem. Physiol.* 96A, 415–419.

Davies, P. M. C. (1981). Anatomy and physiology. In *Diseases of Reptiles* (J. E. Cooper and O. F. Jackson, eds.). Academic Press, London, vol. 1, pp. 9–73.

Desmet, V. J., and van Eyken, P. (1995). Embryology, malformations, and malpositions of the liver. In *Bockus Gastroenterology*, 5th ed. (W. S. Haubrich and F. Schaffner, eds.). W. B. Saunders, Philadelphia, vol. 3, pp. 1849–1857.

De Brito Gitirana, L. (1988). The fine structure of the fat-storing cell (Ito cell) in the liver of some reptiles. *Z. Mikrosk.-anat. Forsch.* 102, 143–149.

De Brito Gitirana, L., and Gorgas, K. (1986). The fine structure of peroxisomes in the liver of the Brazilian land tortoise (*Testudo carbonaria*, Spix) during thermal adaptation. *Eur. J. Cell Biol. Suppl.* 14, 8. (abstract)

Ekataksin, W., Zou, Z., Kawai, V., Wake, V., and McCuskey, R. S. (1994). Three dimensional cholangioarchitecture: biliary subunits conform with the hepatic microcirculatory subunits (HMS) in mammalian livers. *Hepatology* 20, 215A.

Elias, H. (1965). Embryology, histology and anatomy of the biliary system. In *The Biliary System. A Symposium of the NATO Advanced Study Institute* (W. Taylor, ed.). F. A. Davis, Philadelphia, pp. 1–14.

Elias, H., and Bengelsdorf, H. (1952). The structure of the liver of vertebrates. *Acta Anat.* 14, 297–337.

Elias, H., and Sherrick, J. L. (1969). *Morphology of the Liver.* Academic Press, New York.

Elkan, E., and Reichenbach-Klinke, H.-H. (1974). *Color Atlas of Diseases of Fishes, Amphibians and Reptiles.* TFH Publications, Neptune City, N.J.

Ells, H. A. (1954). The gross and microscopic anatomy of the liver and gall bladder of the lizard, *Sceloporus occidentalis biseriatus* (Hallowell). *Anat. Rec.* 119, 213–226.

Ewert, M. A. (1985). Embryology of turtles. In *Biology of the Reptilia* (C. Gans, F. Billett, and P. F. A. Maderson, eds.). Wiley, New York, vol. 14, pp. 75–268.

Ferguson, M. W. J. (1985). Reproductive biology and embryology of the crocodilians. In *Biology of the Reptilia* (C. Gans, F. Billett, and P. F. A. Maderson, eds.). Wiley, New York, vol. 14, pp. 329–492.

Ferrer, C., Zuasti, A., Bellesta, J., Fernandez, F., and Rastor, L. M. (1987). The liver of *Testudo graeca* (Chelonia), a comparative study of hibernating and non-hibernating animals. *J. Submicr. Cytol.* 19, 275–282.

Frye, F. L. (1991). *Reptile Care: An Atlas of Diseases and Treatments*, vols. 1–2. TFH Publications, Neptune City, N.J.

Frye, F. L., Oshiro, L. S., Dutra, F. R., and Carney, J. D. (1977). Herpesvirus-like infection in two Pacific pond turtles. *J. Am. Vet. Med. Assoc.* 171, 882–884.

Frye, F. L., Munn, R. J., Gardner, M., Barten, S. L., and Hadfy, L. B. (1994). Adenovirus-like hepatitis in a group of Rankin's dragon lizards (*Pogona henrylawsoni*). *J. Zoo Wildlife Med.* 25, 167–171.

Gabe, U., and Saint Girons, H. (1964). *Histologie de* Sphenodon punctatus. Editions du CNRS, Paris.

Gahan, P. B., and Middleton, J. (1982). Hepatocyte euploidization is a typical mammalian physiological specialization. *Comp. Biochem. Physiol.* 71A, 345–348.

Gans, C., and Clark, B. D. (1976). Studies on the ventilation of *Caiman crocodilus* (Crocodilia: Reptilia). *Respir. Physiol.* 26, 285–301.

Gatten, R. E., Jr. (1985). The uses of anaerobiosis by amphibians and reptiles. *Am. Zool.* 25, 945–954.

Gaunt, A. S., and Gans, C. (1969). Diving bradycardia and withdrawal bradycardia in *Caiman crocodilus*. *Nature* 223, 207–208.

Gena, B. S., and Patnaik, B. K. (1990). Effect of malonate and p-chlorophenoxy acetic acid on hepatic succinic dehydrogenase activity of ageing reptiles. *Gerontology* 36, 12–18.

Goodrich, E. S. (1986). *Studies on the Structure and Development of Vertebrates*. University of Chicago Press, Chicago.

Gregory, P. T. (1982). Reptilian hibernation. In *Biology of the Reptilia* (C. Gans and F. H. Pough, eds.). Academic Press, New York, vol. 13, pp. 53–154.

Gumucio, J. J., and Miller, D. L. (1982). Zonal hepatic function: Solute-hepatocyte interactions within the liver acinus. In *Progress in Liver Diseases* (H. Popper and F. Schaffner, eds.). Grune and Stratton, New York, vol. 7, pp. 17–30.

Gupta, B. B. D., and Thaplial, J. P. (1983). Adrenal hormones and oxidative metabolism of the garden lizard (*Calotes versicolor*). *J. Endocrinol.* 99, 211.

Hack, M. H., and Helmy, F. M. (1964). A comparative chemical study of the liver of various vertebrates. *Acta Histochem.* 19, 316–328.

Hagey, L. R. (1992). "Bile Acid Biodiversity in Vertebrates: Chemistry and Evolutionary Implications." Dissertation, University of California at San Diego.

Hampton, J. A., Lantz, R. C., and Hinton, D. E. (1989). Functional units in rainbow trout (*Salmo gairdneri* Richardson) liver: III. Morphometric analysis of parenchyma, stroma and component cell types. *Am. J. Anat.* 185, 58–73.

Haslewood, G. A. D. (1965). Comparative biochemistry of bile salts. In *The Biliary System: a Symposium of the NATO Advanced Study Institute* (W. Taylor, ed.). F.

A. Davis, Philadelphia, pp. 107–116.

Henninger, J. M. (1982) Histology of the liver in the box turtle. *Anat. Rec.* 202, 79A. (abstract)

Henninger, J. M., and Beresford, W. A. (1990). Is it coincidence that iron and melanin coexist in hepatic and other melanomacrophages? *Histol. Histopath.* 5, 457–459.

Herráez, M. P., and Zapata, A. G. (1986). Stucture and function of the melano-macrophage centers of the goldfish, *Carassius auratis. Vet. Immunol. Immunopathol.* 12, 117–126.

Higgins, G. M. (1928). Contractions of the gallbladder in the common bullhead (*Ameiurus nebulosus*). *Arch. Surg.* 26, 1021–1038.

Hruban, Z., and Maschgan, E. R. (1982). A hepatocellular adenoma in a rattle-snake. *J. Comp. Path.* 92, 429–435.

Hubert, J. (1985). The origin and development of oocytes. In *Biology of the Reptilia* (C. Gans, F. Billett, and P. F. A. Maderson, eds.). Wiley, New York, vol. 14, pp. 41–74.

Hyman, L. H. (1942) *Comparative Vertebrate Anatomy*, 2nd ed. University of Chicago Press, Chicago.

Ito, T., and Nemoto, M. (1952). Über die kupfferschen Sternzellen und die "Fettspeicherungzellen" in der Blutkapillarenwand der menschlichen Leber. *Okajima Folia Anat. Japan* 24, 243–258.

Jacobson, E. R. (1981). Neoplastic diseases. In *Diseases of Reptiles* (J. E. Cooper and O. F. Jackson, eds.). Academic Press, London, vol. 1, pp. 429–468.

Jacobson, E. R., and Kollias, G. V. (1986). Adenovirus-like infection in a savannah monitor. *J. Zoo Anim. Med.* 17, 149–151.

Jacobson, E. R., Gardiner, C. H., and Foggin, C. M. (1984). Adenovirus-like infection in two Nile crocodiles. *J. Am. Vet. Med. Assoc.* 185, 1421–1422.

Jacobson, E. R., Gaskin, J. M., and Gardiner, C. H. (1985). Adenovirus-like infection in a boa constrictor. *J. Am. Vet. Med. Assoc.* 187, 1226–1227.

Ji, X., and Wang, P. C. (1990). Annual cycle of lipid contents and caloric values of carcass and some organs of the gecko (*Gekko japonicus*). *Comp. Biochem. Physiol.* 96A, 267–271.

Jones, A. L., and Aggeler, J. (1995). Structure of the liver. In *Bockus Gastroenterology*, 5th ed. (W. S. Haubrich and F. Schaffner, eds.). W. B. Saunders, Philadelphia, vol. 3, pp. 1813–1831.

Julian, J. F., and Durham, P. J. K. (1990). Adenoviral hepatitis in a female bearded dragon (*Amphibolurus barbatus*). *New Zealand Vet. J.* 30, 59–60.

Keymer, I. F. (1981). Protozoa. In *Diseases of Reptiles* (J. E. Cooper and O. F. Jackson, eds.). Academic Press, London, vol. 1, pp. 233–290.

Knobel, D. P., Schoeman, J. H., and van Aawegen, G. (1976). The microscopic anatomy of the liver of *Bitis arietans. J. Anat.* 121, 430. (abstract)

Lee, R. T., Yang, G. C., Kiang, J., Bingham, J. B., Golgher, L., and Lee, Y. C. (1994). Major lectin of alligator liver is mannose/l-fucose dependent. *J. Biol. Chem.* 269, 19617–19625.

Liu, S.-K., and King, F. W. (1971). Microsporidiosis in the tuatara. *J. Am. Vet. Med. Assoc.* 159, 1578–1582.

Lucké, B., and Schlumberger, H. G. (1947). Neoplasia in cold blooded vertebrates. *Physiol. Rev.* 29, 91–126.

Madrid, J. F., Ballesta, J., Galera, T., Castells, M. T., and Perez-Tomas, R. (1989). Histochemistry of glycoconjugates in the gallbladder of ten animal species. *Histochemistry* 91, 437–443.

Marcus, L. C. (1981). *Veterinary Biology and Medicine of Captive Amphibians and Reptiles.* Lea and Febiger, Philadelphia.

Moscona, A. A. (1980). Anatomy of the pancreas and Langerhans islets in snakes and lizards. *Anat. Rec.* 227, 232–248.

Nagore, N., and Scheuer, P. J. (1990). The three-dimensional liver. In *Progress in Liver Diseases* (H. Popper and F. Schaffner, eds.). W. B. Saunders, Philadelphia, vol. 9, pp. 1–10.

Noonan, N. E., Olsen, G. A., and Cornelius, C. E. (1979). A new animal model with hyperbilirubinemia: the indigo snake. *Am. J. Dig. Dis.* 24, 521–524.

Paranjape, S. Y. (1974). *Anatomy of the Garden Lizard* (Calotes versicolor, Bouln.). University of Poona Press, Poona, India.

Penick, D. N., Paladino, F. V., Steyermark, A. C., and Spotila, J. R. (1996). Thermal dependence of tissue metabolism in the green turtle, *Chelonia mydas*. *Comp. Biochem. Physiol.* 113A, 293–296.

Pritchard, P. C. H. (1979). *Encyclopedia of Turtles.* THF Publications, Neptune, N. J., p. 53.

Ramsay, E. C., and Dotson, T. K. (1995). Tissue and serum enzyme activities in the yellow rat snake (*Elaphe obsoleta quadrivitatta*). *Am. J. Vet. Res.* 56, 423–428.

Riley, D., and Callard, I. P. (1988). Characterization of turtle liver nuclear estrogen receptors, seasonal changes, and pituitary dependence of the nuclear and cytoplasmic forms. *J. Exp. Zool.* 245, 277–285.

Rutledge, R. G., Shay, C. E., Brown, G. L., and Neelin, J. M. (1981). The similarities of histones from turtle erythrocytes and liver. *Can. J. Biochem.* 59, 273–279.

Saint Girons, H., and Duguy, R. (1992). Evolution de las masse corporelle et de la masse relative des corps gras, des ovaries et des oeufs au cours des cycles reproducteurs chez *Vipera aspis*. *Amphibia-Reptilia* 13, 351–364.

Saint Girons, H., and Duguy, R. (1994). Evolution de la masse corporelle et de la masse relative de quelques organes au cours du cycle annuel les mâles matures de *Vipera aspis*. *Amphibia-Reptilia* 15, 123–133.

Scalia, M., Geremia, E., Corsaro, C., Santoro, C., Sciuto, S., and Sichel, G. (1988). The extracutaneous pigmentary system: Evidence for the melanosynthesis in Amphibia and Reptilia liver. *Comp. Biochem. Physiol.* 89B, 715–717.

Schär, M., Maly, I. P., and Sasse, D. (1985). Histochemical studies on zonation of the liver in the trout (*Salmo gairdneri*). *Histochemistry* 83, 147–151.

Schmid, R., and Lester, R. (1966). Implication of conjugation of endogenous compounds-bilirubin. In *Glucuronic Acid: Free and Combined* (G. J. Dutton, ed.) Academic Press, New York, pp. 500–501.

Shore, T. W., and Jones, H. L. (1889). On the structure of the vertebrate liver. *J. Physiol.* 10, 408–428.

Sichel, G., Corsaro, C., Scalia, M., Sciuto, S., and Geremia, E. (1987). Relationship between melanin contents and superoxide dismutase (SOD) in the liver of various species of animals. *Cell Biochem. Funct.* 5, 123–128.

Snell, H. L., and Tracy, C. R. (1985). Behavioral and morphological adaptations by Galapagos land iguanas (*Conolophus subcristatus*) to water and energy requirements of eggs and neonates. *Am. Zool.* 25, 1009–1018.

Storch, V., Braunbeck, T., and Waitkuwait, W. E. (1989) The liver of the West African crocodile *Osteolaemus tetraspis*. An ultrastructural study. *J. Submicr. Cytol. Pathol.* 21, 317–327.

Taira, K., and Mutch, H. (1981). Comparative ultrastructural study of the Ito cells in the liver of some reptiles. *Arch. Histol. Japon.* 44, 373–384.

Telford, S. R., Jr. (1977) Parasitic diseases of reptiles. *J. Am. Vet. Med. Assoc.* 159, 1644–1661.

Tosheva, R. T., Jankowski, W. A., Stoychova, L. I., and Chojnacki, T. (1991). Dolichols in the liver of some poikilothermic animals and birds. *Comp. Biochem. Physiol.* 98B, 397–402.

Tsai, Y. H., and Huilica, L. S. (1975). Tissue-specific histones in the erythrocytes of chicken and turtle. *Exp. Cell. Res.* 91, 109–112.

Wallach, J. D. (1971). Environmental and nutritional diseases of captive reptiles. *J. Am. Vet. Med. Assoc.* 159, 1632–1643.

Whittier, J. M., West, M. B., and Brenner, R. M. (1991). Immunorecognition of estrogen receptors by monoclonal antibody H222 in reproductive tissue of the red-sided garter snake. *Gen. Comp. Endocrinol.* 81, 1–6.

Schaffner, F. (1998). The Liver. In *Biology of the Reptilia*, vol. 19 (Morphology G) (C. Gans and A. S. Gaunt, eds.). Society for the Study of Amphibians and Reptiles, Ithaca, New York, Contrib. Herpetol., vol. 14, pp. 485–531.

7

Structure of the Reptilian Spleen

YASUKAZU TANAKA

I. INTRODUCTION

The spleen is an organ present exclusively in vertebrates and is lacking in invertebrates. It lies within the abdominal cavity in the close vicinity of the stomach or upper intestine, but in a position independent from other abdominal organs. Its variegated morphology and function have caused biologists to refer to it as an enigmatic organ. The mechanism for establishing this unique state remains to be presented. Problems relating to the spleen are vaguely named as "Milzprobleme" (Tischendorf, 1969). Most previous anatomical studies on the spleen concern its morphology in particular species. We lack phylogenetic approaches to the origin and evolution of the spleen throughout vertebrate species (see Section V.A).

Most morphological studies of reptilian spleens have been restricted. Because reptiles represent a sister group to mammals, a morphological study of reptilian spleens may be interesting as it may disclose characteristics shares of mammalian spleens. The absence of intermediate characteristics would raise other questions.

The variegated morphology of the spleen suggests that its histo-anatomy be documented initially. Unless recent progress in splenic morphology is understood, the significance of the reptile spleen in vertebrate phylogeny cannot be fully understood. The structural characteristics of the spleen in all vertebrate groups will next be summarized; following is the description of the splenic structure of each reptilian group and splenic embryology.

This approach clarifies the significance of the reptilian spleen in phylogeny and permits analysis of problems relating to its origin and evolution. Also discussed is the vascular remodelling theory, as it explains variegated splenic morphology during evolution. The information here presented is restricted to the structure of the spleen, and the topics of both subcellular and molecular levels are not included.

II. GENERAL MORPHOLOGY OF THE SPLEEN
A. Descriptions of the Spleen in the Literature

The morphology and function of the human spleen are well documented in histo-anatomical textbooks of medical sciences (Tischendorf, 1969; Fawcett, 1994). The spleens of some mammalian groups, rodents for examples, are commonly studied in modern medical science. The best example may be the enormous encyclopedia of the spleen by Tischendorf (1969), now outdated for function. In contrast, there are far fewer comparative descriptions of the spleen in diverse animals. The best comparative study is in the three volume monograph by Starck (1978–1982), which devotes only three pages to the spleen. This level of attention is also common in handbooks and texts of comparative anatomy (Bolk et al., 1931–1939; Romer and Parsons, 1977). Descriptions of nonmammalian spleens are nearly absent or extremely limited in these treatments. Although more attention recently has been paid to the splenic lymphoid tissue of reptiles and birds, their splenic structure is still insufficiently analyzed. This inattention probably reflects the absence of a characteristic splenic morphology. As important is the discovery of the immune functions of this organ, a major non-morphological aspect that must be treated elsewhere (Cooper et al., 1985).

B. Anatomy of the Spleen

1. LOCATION AND NUMBERS OF THE SPLEEN The spleen is a mesenchymal organ found in the abdominal cavity with the digestive canal and liver. In most mammals, the spleen lies at the upper abdominal cavity within the dorsal mesentery closely associated with the stomach. In nonmammalian vertebrates, the spleen commonly lies along the small intestine.

In lungfishes (*Neoceratodus, Lepidosiren, Protopterus*), the hemopoietic nest (intestinal spleen) homologous to the spleen lies in the intestinal wall closely adjacent with large intestinal vessels, particularly the vein. The spleen of all other vertebrates lies at an extra-intestinal position near the stomach within the ventral (ventral spleen), the dorsal (dorsal spleen), or both mesenteries (ventral and dorsal spleen) (Fig. 7.1). Under nonpathological conditions, most species have a single spleen. However, some sharks (Chondrichthyes) and the gar pike (Osteichthyes) (see Section IV) have two independent spleens. In general, the spleen always lies close to a large intestinal vein, the hepatic portal vein or its distal segment.

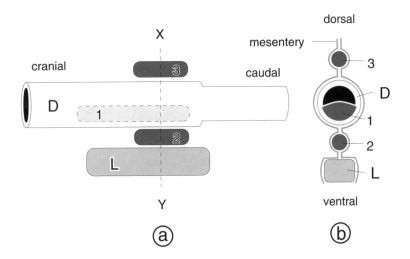

Fig. 7.1. A schema illustrating the general location of the spleen. a. A longitudinal plane of the intestinal tract (D) showing the cranial side on the left and the caudal side on the right; 1, the intestinal spleen; 2, the ventral spleen; 3, the dorsal spleen; L, the liver. b. A frontal plane cut at the x-y position in a.

2. Extrasplenic Vasculature

a. Arteries In most vertebrates, the splenic artery is a major branch of the coeliac artery that originates from the dorsal aorta. The splenic artery frequently supplies such other organs as the pancreas, stomach, and omentum. Earlier, Schabadasch (1935) classified the splenic artery by its distributional pattern into two major types, simple (einfache A. lienalis) and complicated (komplizierte A. lienalis) (Fig. 7.2). The simple type occurs only in nonmammals (fishes, amphibians, reptiles and birds). It originates from a stem artery as an independent branch and distributes exclusively to the spleen. The complicated type occurs only in mammals, and is further classified into two subtypes, dispersed (zerstreuter Typus) and uniaxial (magistral). In the former subtype, multiple small branches (rami lienales) originate segmentally from a stem artery and distribute to the spleen along its largest axis.

Simple type	Complicated type	
fishes amphibans reptiles birds	mammals uniaxial type (horses, pigs)	dispersed type (hedgehogs, dogs)

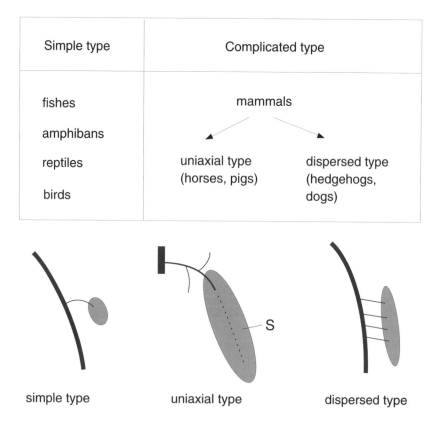

simple type   uniaxial type   dispersed type

Fig. 7.2. Classification of the splenic artery after Schabadasch (1935). Schemata at bottom illustrate types of the splenic artery described in the above table.

Practically, this classification is questionable. For example, the dispersed subtype of the complicated type frequently occurs in spleens of Chondrichthyes and Amphibia (particularly Urodela). The uniaxial subtype of a horse's spleen actually represents the dispersed subtype as the splenic artery runs outside of the spleen along its largest axis and provides multiple branches to the stomach and omentum. The distal segment of this artery distributes to and ends in the omentum. It is likely that the dispersed subtype represents the prototype, and both uniaxial subtype and simple type may have been modified by involution of the spleen during evolution.

b. VEINS

There are few descriptions of the splenic vein. Its architecture tends to be complicated; however, it is important to understand it as a basis for analyzing of splenic evolution, because splenogenesis relates closely to vasculogenesis of the intestine (Miki, 1965). The splenic vein itself represents a major distal segment of the hepatic portal vein. As evolution progressed, the spleens appear to have separated from the intestinal vein but maintained communication by segmental drainage veins (splenic veins). The multiple segmental drainage veins that run along arterial branches of the dispersed subtype are probably a vestige of these veins. The spleen displays two independent drainage routes, the capsular and that via the hilus. The capsular route is the major drainage pathway of primitive spleens and is frequently noted in spleens of Chondrichthyes, Amphibia, Reptilia, and Aves. Especially in Chondrichtyes, it forms either a complicated vascular net or a set of accessory veins. Some of these veins eventually join the hilus route, which joins directly to the splenic vein (usually multiple at the splenic hilus), a distal segment of the hepatic portal vein. It is the major venous pathway of mammalian spleens.

3. ORGAN WEIGHTS

The weight of organs may directly or indirectly reflect the importance of the organ in bodily activity. Comparison of organ weights among different groups of animals commonly uses weight ratios of either body or brain. This method minimizes the influences of factors, such as age, sex, and the physical condition of the subject.

It is possible to compare the weight ratio of spleen to body (S/B ratio) among the vertebrate classes (Fig. 7.3). The S/B ratios of Elasmobranchii are high, about 1/25–1,000 (Fänge and Nilsson, 1985). The S/B ratio of *Chimaera* is 1/55–240 (Fänge and Sundell, 1969) and 1/300–2,000 in teleosts (Tischendorf, 1969). In Amphibia, the S/B ratio is highest in the Urodela (1/200–860) and lowest in the Anura (1/690–5,000) (Murata, 1959a). The S/B ratio of the reptiles is 1/460–1,050 in *Chinemys reevesii*

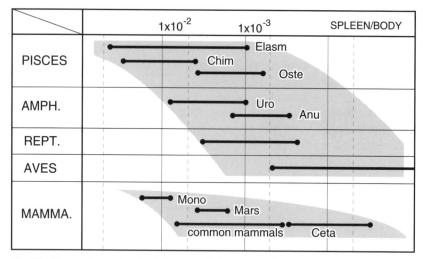

Fig. 7.3. Figure illustrating the Spleen weight/Body weight ratio of each vertebrate class. Ratios are plotted on a logarithmic scale. The vertical scale is arbitrary. Note the absence of continuity in the S/B ratios for the nonmammalian and mammalian groups. Abbeviations: Elasm, Elasmobranchii; Chim, Chimaera; Oste, Osteichthyes; Uro, Urodela; Anu, Anura; Mono, Monotremata; Mars, Marsupialia; Ceta, Cetacea.

(Murata, 1959a) and 1/940–4,350 in *Elaphe quadrivirgata* (Murata, 1959a). The S/B ratio is significantly lower in Aves, particularly for larger species being 1/200 to 1/over 100,000 (Tischendorf, 1969). Apparently, the S/B ratio decreases with derived state in vertebrates; it is lowest in Reptilia and Aves.

As seen in Figure 7.3, the distributional pattern of the S/B ratio in mammals is distinct. The S/B ratio of the platypus is as high as about 1/100 (Tanaka, 1986b). The S/B ratio is also high in rodents (1/150–300). The S/B ratio is high in the spleen of horses (1/250–400). The S/B ratio of man is about 1/500. The S/B ratio is low in guinea pigs (1/1,300) and rabbits (1/2,500–3,000). The lowest S/B ratio is reported in whales (Cetacea), 1/5,000–10,000 for Odontoceti and 1/10,000–50,000 for Mysticeti. The change of the mammalian S/B ratio suggests that the splenic evolution of mammals took a path different from that noted in nonmammalian phylogeny; thus, the mammalian spleen can hardly be regarded as directly derived from modern nonmammalian spleens.

4. STRUCTURES

a. OVERVIEW The spleen is exclusively composed of mesenchymal tissue enclosed in a fibrous capsule. Arteries and veins enter or leave the spleen through the hilus on its visceral face. The hilus is obvious in the spleens of the larger mammals, but it is obscure in most nonmammals and small mammals. This reflects the absence of a thick fibrous capsule and the complicated distribution of the vasculatures in the latter group. Nonmammals normally have accessory arteries and veins that frequently enter (or leave) the spleens directly through the capsule. This feature makes identification of the hilus difficult. In small mammals, the dispersed subtype of the splenic artery enters the spleen from multiple sites along the spleen's largest axis without forming a distinctive port of entry. This feature also complicates identification of the hilus.

Histologically, the spleen is divided into the capsule/trabeculae and the splenic pulp (Fig. 7.4). It should be stressed that structural details of these units are primarily derived mostly from studies of human spleen; thus, some anatomical terms may not be suitable for the description of reptilian spleen.

b. THE CAPSULE AND TRABECULAE

The spleen is supported by the capsule and trabeculae, which reinforce the soft splenic pulp. Trabeculae are commonly noted in the mammalian spleen. In nonmammals, the trabeculae appear in the spleen of some reptiles (Testudines, *Alligator*) and birds (*Gallus*).

In spleens of small mammals and most nonmammals, the capsule is comprised of a thin layer of connective tissue consisting of collagen and

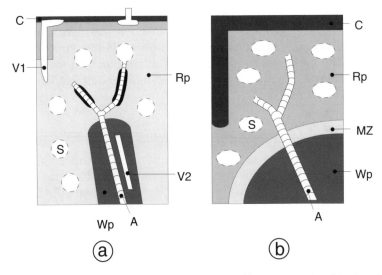

Fig. 7.4. Structural characteristics of the nonmammalian (a) and mammalian (b) spleen. The red pulp of the nonmammalian spleen corresponds to the marginal zone of the mammalian spleen. Abbreviations: A, artery; C, capsule; MZ, marginal (or intermediate) zone; Rp, the red pulp; S, venous sinus; V1, primary vein; V2, secondary vein; and Wp, white pulp.

elastic fibers. A mesothelial layer covers the surface. In the the spleen of larger mammals, the capsule is definitively double-layered. The outer layer is thin and comprised of a layer of tissues similar to that of nonmammalian spleens. The inner layer is thick and collagenous, containing elastic fibers and leiomyocytes. Large mammalian spleens show trabeculae, projections of the connective tissue with similar histological constituents. Trabeculae are said to occur only in mammals; however, poorly developed ones also appear in spleens of some reptiles and birds. Trabeculae provide passage for "trabecular arteries or veins" and nerves. Veins are more commonly associated with trabeculae than are arteries. As true trabeculae occur mainly in mammalian spleens, they are discussed below (Section IV.F). In most nonmammalian spleens, the larger intrasplenic vasculature is surrounded by a fibrous connective tissue capsule. Although, this structure lacks leiomyocytes, it is frequently referred to as the trabecula. In mammalian spleens, those pulp arteries that run independently from the trabeculae have a connective tissue coat lacking leiomyocytes. This coat clearly differs from the trabeculae; thus, the periarterial connective tissue of nonmammalian spleens is not homologous to the trabeculae of mammalian spleens.

c. THE SPLENIC PULP

i. General The splenic pulp may be divided into two zones, arterial and venous. The arterial zone or white pulp is composed of arteries and surrounding lymphoid tissue. The development of the latter tissue differs considerably among species; it may be lacking in some nonmammalian groups. The dark red venous zone or red pulp includes sinusoidal vessels (usually congested with peripheral blood) and an intervascular space. For detailed morphology of the white and red pulp see Tischendorf (1969) and Fawcett (1994).

ii. The White Pulp
The structure of white pulp shows little interspecific difference. The lymphoreticular tissues differ little from those noted universally in the body. The lymphoid tissue usually lies around distal segments of the intrasplenic artery creating a "periarterial lymphoid sheath (PALS)." The PALS of mammals is made of two layers, an inner loose layer that includes T-lymphocytes (T-cell zone) and an outer reticulated layer that includes both T- and B-lymphocytes (T·B-cell zone). The deep lymphatics may be seen in the inner layer. In nonmammals, the accumulation of thymus-independent lymphocytes in the white pulp of *Xenopus* (Obara, 1982; Obara et al., 1982) and bursa-dependent B cells in the PALS of *Gallus* (Mori and Hoshi, 1971) has been reported. Nodular structures (lymphoid nodules or follicles) may develop within the PALS. In spleens

of larger mammals, the PALS develops poorly in contrast to lymphoid nodules, which are developed around terminal arteries. Thus, the white pulp contains multiple nodules known as the Malpighian corpuscle. The lymphoid nodules may or may not contain germinal centers. Lymphoid tissue is absent or poorly developed in the spleen of some fish and amphibians, but is well developed in spleens of most reptiles and birds. The white and red pulp of mammalian spleens are separated by a distinctive border but are indistinctive in nonmammalian spleens. An arterial (capillary) net (perilymphatic arterial net, PLAN: Tanaka, 1990) may be noted around the white pulp of small mammals. Vasculatures of this arterial net dilate into a "marginal sinus" in some mammalian spleens (Snook, 1964).

iii. The Red Pulp
As stated earlier, the red pulp is the venous zone of the spleen, and consists of vasculatures (splenic or pulp sinus) and the intervascular space (splenic or pulp cord). The pulp sinus is frequently referred to as "venous sinus" or "sinusoidal vein" based on its a unique appearance. The pulp sinus of the human spleen has been regarded as either the venous capillary, specialized vein (Tischendorf, 1969; Fawcett, 1994), or specialized venule. In addition, sinusal and nonsinusal types are distinguished in the pulp sinus of the mammalian spleen (Snook, 1950). This characteristic is used as one of morphological parameters in the type-classification of the mammalian spleen (Von Herrath, 1935, 1958). The recently proposed vascular remodelling theory of the intrasplenic vasculature (see Section V.E) suggests that the pulp sinus of mammalian spleens represents the venule rather than the capillary/venule of nonmammalian spleens. Generally, the pulp cord is narrow in mammalian spleens; it composes the reticular tissue, which includes many macrophages and blood cells. However, spleens of large terrestrial mammals with a nonsinusal vessel have a wide pulp cord including frequently developed either leiomyocytes or myofibroblasts, elements that may expel stored blood. In nonmammalian spleens, the pulp cord also comprises reticular tissue; however, no special contractile element has been described. Structural differences of the red pulp are responsible for creation of pleomorphism in the spleen. Most Milzprobleme relate to the complicated structure of the red pulp, mostly of mammalian spleens. Hence, discussion is restricted to topics important for understanding of splenic morphology.

A critical topic in splenic morphology is the pattern of the arteriovenous (a-v) communication of the intrasplenic vasculature. Three patterns, closed, open, and coexistence of both patterns, have been considered (Chen, 1978). Recent SEM studies of perfused spleens have allowed conclusions. At present, many agree that a-v communications of most mammalian spleens are open (Suzuki et al., 1977, 1989; Hataba, 1986), whereas those of nonmammalian spleens (Miyamoto et al., 1980; Oláh and Glick, 1982; Hataba et al., 1990) and a few mammalian ones (Tanaka, 1990) are closed. The coexistence of both types has been suggested (Chen, 1978); however, it has not yet been morphologically demonstrated.

Other discussions deal with a unique structure lying around terminal segments of intrasplenic arteries juxta oral of anastomoses with venous vessels. The ellipsoids comprise loose reticular tissues that include residential macrophages. "Sheathed capillaries" are arteries included within the ellipsoid. These capillaries lack a basement membrane, i.e., the vasculature is open within the ellipsoid. In general, the development of the ellipsoid is significant in nonmammalian spleens. Amphibians and mammals lack them or have them poorly devleoped. No similar structures are known in any other organ. The size and shape of the ellipsoid have been described (Tischendorf, 1969; Fawcett, 1994); they differ significantly in spleens of different species. Due to significant elimination of particulate matter from circulation by phagocytic activity of residential macrophages, ellipsoids are named as "periarteriolar macrophage center (PAMC)" in the spleen of cats (Blue and Weiss, 1981). The origin of this unique structure remains unknown, however, the ellipsoid might be a response to the advantage of a significantly lower draining capacity by vascular remodelling. This might produce a notable increase in the back pressure at the a-v junction and induce a loosening of endothelial junction and stimulation of the local connective tissues.

The last and only recently discovered Milzprobleme is the double-layered architecture of the red pulp. Early spleens might involve a triple-layered architecture; a central arterial zone (i.e., the white pulp) and a double-layered outer venous zone (i.e., the red pulp of broad sense) (see Section V.C). Analysis discloses that histogenesis of the red pulp may differ in nonmammals and mammals (Fig. 7.5). The red pulp of mammalian spleens apparently corresponds to the outer venous layer of early spleens. The outer venous layer is either absent or observed only as a subcapsular zone of tissue including larger drainage veins. In contrast, the red pulp of nonmammals corresponds to the inner venous layer of early spleens. In mammals, the inner venous layer is observed as either intermediate (IZ) or marginal (MZ) zone (Tanaka, 1990). Thus, the red pulp of nonmammalian spleens is a tissue zone homologous to the MZ (or IZ) of mammalian spleens. This conclusion does not support a notion that nonmammalian spleens show the MZ (Zapata and Cooper, 1990).

d. THE INTRASPLENIC DRAINAGE ROUTE

The spleen shows two drainage routes, hilus and capsular. These routes may not coexist in differentiated mammalian spleens such as human spleen; however, they commonly coexist in nonmammalian spleens. The best example may be seen in the spleen of Chondrichthyes (see Section IV.B). The hilus route involves the collateral vein(s) found around intrasplenic arteries. These veins are the secondary vein(s) formed lately during vascular remodelling. The capsular route does not involve the artery and drains splenic blood through the capsule via a complicated vascular net outside of the spleen.

e. THE MELANOMACROPHAGE CENTER

The melanomacrophage center(s) is a nodular nest made of aggregated macrophages containing heterogeneous cytoplasmic inclusions, such as melanin, hemosiderin, and lipofuscin (Agius and Agbede, 1984). It is common in the spleen of teleosts; however, similar structures occur in amphibians and reptiles (*Eumeces*). Certainly the structure is not specific for the spleen as it also occurs in kidneys and liver (see Zapata

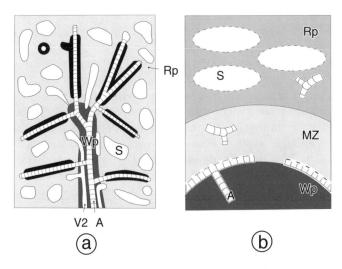

Fig. 7.5. Schemata illustrating the architectural difference of the splenic pulp between nonmammalian (a) and mammalian (b) spleens. The splenic pulp of most nonmammalian spleens (a) consists of a double-layered architecture made of the inner arterial (Wp) and single-layered venous zone (Rp). Ellipsoids are well developed and the arterio-venous communication is closed. The splenic pulp of common mammalian spleens (b) consists of a triple-layered architecture made of the inner arterial (Wp) and outer double-layered venous zone (MZ and Rp). Ellipsoids are poorly developed and the arterio-venous communication is of an open type. Abbreviations: A, artery; MZ, marginal zone; s, pulp sinus; Rp, red pulp; V2, secondary vein; Wp, white pulp.

and Cooper, 1990, for additional information). No such structures occur in mammalian spleens or in bone marrow.

C. Functions of the Spleen

Although the spleen is significant in the defense activity of the body, the human spleen is considered dispensable; surgical splenectomy in cases of abdominal traumas or advanced gastric carcinomas does not produce serious complications. This is may also be the case for lizards (*Calotes, Scincus*) (Kanakambika and Muthukkaruppan, 1972; Hussein et al., 1979c); after all, the spleen as an organ does not show specific functions vital for life. The hemopoietic activity in some groups may be the exception (see Section IV.D).

The classic literature repeatedly stressed the hemopoietic activity in spleens of fishes and amphibians (Jordan, 1932, 1938; Jordan and Speidel, 1923, 1925, 1930a; Ohuye, 1928; Tooze and Davis, 1967, 1968). In the spleen of reptiles, and also in other nonmammals, accumulated granulocytes are commonly noted in the red pulp near the arterial terminal. They may or may not be produced in the spleen. Hemopoietic activity has also been reported in spleens of human embryos (Ono, 1930). However, more recent ontogenic studies deny this (Ishikawa, 1985; Fukuda, 1990). Most adult mammals show little splenic hemopoiesis. Instead, recent comparative anatomical studies suggest that the spleen of reptiles as well as other nonmammals is primarily lymphopoietic (Osogoe, 1954; Kanesada, 1956; Zapata and Cooper, 1990). The spleen contributes to immunological activity by producing antibodies and immunologically competent cells in the lymphoid tissue. Textbooks of comparative anatomy always classify the spleen as an organ of the reticuloendothelial system. Mammalian spleens with such activity are known as the Abwehrmilz (defense spleen, Von Herrath, 1935, 1958).

Another important function of the spleen is blood storage. Larger terrestrial mammals store a large volume of peripheral blood. Spleens with this characteristic are named the Speichermilz (storage spleen) (Von Herrath, 1935, 1958) and may act as a reservoir of extra peripheral blood for specific physical requirement. Similar activity has been reported in spleens of *Onchorhynchus mykiss* (Kita and Itazawa, 1994) but has not been reported in reptiles.

III. ANATOMY OF THE REPTILIAN SPLEEN
A. General

As seen in the appendix, morphological studies of the spleen have been made on only a few (less than 30) of the 6,600 species of the Reptilia. Some reports are too old to deal with recent topics. Few studies report on spleens of amphisbaenians or crocodilians.

B. General Appearance, Position, and Vasculature

The reptilian spleen is a small organ of elliptical, spherical or tubular shape. As stated earlier, its S/B ratio is lower than that of all but birds. The reptilian spleen lies in the abdominal cavity within the dorsal mesentery. The splenic artery is reported as the simple type (einfache A. lienalis; Schabadasch, 1935). This conclusion may be incorrect. The distributional pattern of the splenic artery in each group is schematically illustrated in Figures 6 through 10. In *Emys europea* and *E. caspica* [presently *E. orbicularis* and *Mauremys caspica*] (Fig. 7.6) (Schabadasch, 1935), the splenic artery originates from an lienointestinalis ramus, a branch of the anterior mesenteric artery. The spleen of *Sphenodon punctatus* is nourished by the coeliac artery (Fig. 7.7) (Klaatsch, 1892). In *Lacerta viridis* (Fig. 7.8) (Schabadasch, 1935), the splenic artery originates from the coeliac artery and shares its stem with the pancreas. In *Vipera berus* (Fig. 7.9) (Schabadasch, 1935), a splenic branch originated from the third gastric artery nourishes the gallblader and pancreas simultaneously. In

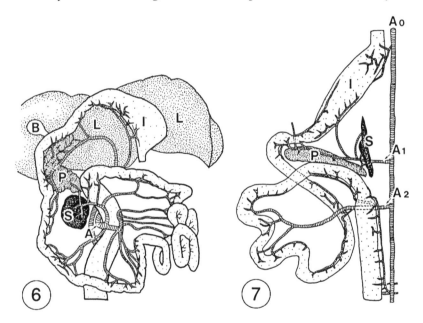

Fig. 7.6. Schema illustrating the gross anatomy of the spleen and its related artery in *Emys europea* and *E. caspica* [presently *E. orbicularis* and *Mauremys caspica*] (redrawn from Schabadasch, 1935). A, artery; B, gallbladder; I, digestive canal; L, liver; P, pancreas; S, spleen.

Fig. 7.7. Schema illustrating the gross anatomy of the spleen and its related artery of *Sphenodon punctatus* (redrawn from Hochstetter, 1898). A$_0$, dorsal aorta; A$_1$, coeliac artery; A$_2$, superior mesenteric artery; I, digestive canal; P, pancreas; S, spleen.

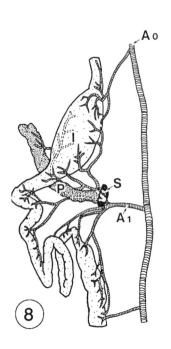

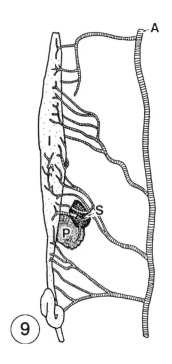

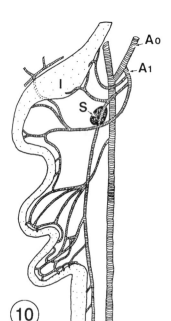

Fig. 7.8. Schema illustrating the gross anatomy of the spleen and its related artery in *Lacerta viridis* (redrawn from Schabadasch, 1935). A_0, dorsal aorta; A_1, coeliac artery; I, digestive canal; P, pancreas; S, spleen.

Fig. 7.9. Schema illustrating the gross anatomy of the spleen and its related artery in *Vipera berus* (redrawn from Schabadasch, 1935). A, dorsal aorta; I, digestive canal; P, pancreas; S, spleen.

Fig. 7.10. Schema illustrating the gross anatomy of the spleen and its related artery in *Crocodylus niloticus* (redrawn from Bolk et al., 1933). A_0, dorsal aorta; A_1, coeliacomesenteric artery; I, digestive canal; S, spleen.

amphisbaenians, the splenic artery originates from the coeliac artery, distributes to the spleen, and nourishes the posterior segment of the stomach (Crook and Parsons, 1980). The spleen of *Crocodylus niloticus* (Fig. 7.10) (Bolk et al., 1935) is nourished by a splenic artery originating from the gastro-lieno-intestinalis (the 2nd branch of the coeliaco-mesenteric artery).

This summary, which is derived from old studies, needs further reconfirmation.

C. Structure

1. GENERAL Histologically, the reptilian spleen contains a capsule/ trabecula, plus white and red pulp. In general, the white pulp is well developed and shows seasonal variations whereas the red pulp is modestly developed. Details of the white pulp are given by Zapata and Cooper (1991). Ellipsoids form around the terminal arteries in most species except for some lizards (*Eumeces kishinouyei, Iguana iguana*) and snakes (*Elaphe climacophora, E. quadrivirgata*). A-v communications of the reptilian spleen are of a closed type. In general, the trabeculae are homologous to those of mammalian spleens, except in the spleens of the crocodilians.

2. TESTUDINES (Figs. 7.11a–d)
Histological studies are available for *Pelodiscus sinensis* (Murata, 1959b), *Chelydra serpentina* (Borysenko and Cooper, 1972; Borysenko, 1976a, 1976b), *Trachemys scripta elegans* (Kroese and Rooijen, 1982, 1983), *Cuora flavomarginata* (Tanaka, 1993), *Mauremys japonica* (Murata, 1959b; Tanaka, 1993), and *Mauremys caspica* (Zapata et al., 1981; Leceta and Zapata, 1985, 1991).

The reddish brown turtle spleen is either spherical (Zapata et al., 1981) or elliptical (Tanaka, 1993). In *Cuora flavomarginata*, the capsule is irregularly thickened particularly at the site where vasculatures, mostly the veins, appear. In *Mauremys japonica*, the connective tissue capsule is thin, double-layered and of uniform thickness. The thin outer layer includes few cells. It is covered by mesothelium. The irregularly thick inner layer comprises collagen and elastic fibers. Leiomyocytes may be noted in the capsule of *Trachemys scripta elegans* (Kroese and Rooijen, 1982). *Mauremys japonica* and *Cuora* lack trabeculae projecting from the capsule into the parenchyma; however, *Mauremys caspica* (Zapata et al., 1981) and *Trachemys scripta elegans* (Kroese and Rooijen, 1982) have them. This difference may relate to the size of the spleens studied. Both arteries and veins lie closely adjacent to the hilus. Arteries divide immediately into proximal branches. Their wall comprises a single-layered endothelium, an internal elastic layer, a multi-cellular muscle layer, and a collagenous

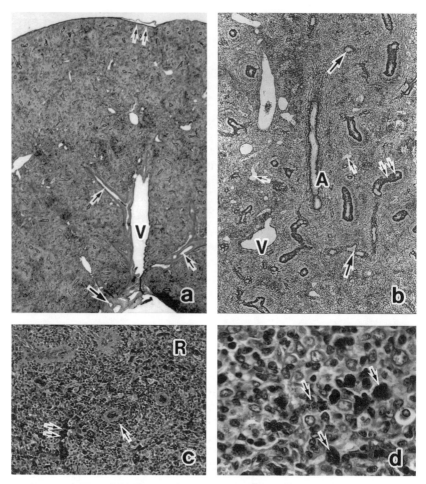

Fig. 7.11. Spleens of *Mauremys japonica* (a, b) and *Cuora flavomarginata* (c, d). a. Low power view of a silver impregnated specimen (SI) showing the architecture of the spleen. The visceral face (the hilus) at bottom. An artery (large arrow) is observed at the hilus closely relating to a large vein (V). It divides and sends peripheral branches (small arrow) to the capsular side. The splenic pulp is wide and includes many sheathed capillaries. Drainage veins (double arrows) are observed at the subcapsular site and splenic pulp unrelated to the artery. ×15. b. A peripheral arterial branch (at the center, A) and its terminal branch (large arrows), which gives off sheathed capillaries. The lymphoid tissue (white pulp) appears as a nodular zone around sheathed capillaries (double arrows). The red pulp is relatively wide and extends between ellipsoids. A coarse reticulin network develops in the pulp cord. Vascular structures in the pulp cord are sinusoids (small arrows) that eventually join to drainage veins (V). These veins do not take a collateral position with the artery. SI, ×50. c. Hematoxylin and eosin (HE) stained cross sections of four sheathed capillaries (arrow) surrounded by the lymphoid tissue. The red pulp (R) is a fibrous zone rich in venous vessels around ellipsoids. Double arrows, collecting venules. ×125. d. Elastic Masson stained (e-Masson) granulocytes (arrows) noted around the distal area of the ellipsoid. ×500.

outer layer. Veins take a collateral position at the hilus, but separate earlier from arteries (Fig. 7.11a). Nerves occasionally pass around larger arteries; however, no lymphoid tissue is observed around arteries of this level. Arteries run to the organ center and divide into peripheral branches that are made of an internal elastic lamina and single-layered leiomyocytes (Fig. 7.11a). Thus, they are arteriolar in nature and surrounded by a thin layer of collagen fibers. Arterioles initially run straight and then give off terminal branches that lack a definitive muscle coat but are enveloped by ellipsoids comprising homogenous collagen tissue (Fig. 7.11b). The swollen endothelial cells of the sheathed capillaries nearly close the lumina. The silver impregnated method does not disclose internal structures in the ellipsoids (Fig. 7.11b). Sheathed capillaries run straight and give off short end branches. The distal ellipsoids are somewhat thinner than those of proximal segments. End branches communicate directly with the vasculature of the red pulp in a closed manner. The splenic structure of two species examined is essentially similar to that of *Mauremys caspica* (Zapata et al., 1981; Leceta and Zapata, 1985, 1991).

The lymphoid tissue (white pulp) lies around arterial branches (Murata, 1959b; Borysenko, 1976a, 1976b; Zapata et al., 1981; Kroese et al., 1985). Lymphocytes may be developed around arteries, transforming proximal of terminal arteries to ellipsoids. The zone noted around the terminal artery may correspond to the PALS described in *Mauremys caspica* (Zapata et al., 1981). The lymphoid tissue lies most significantly around sheathed capillaries and is named as the periellipsoidal lymphoid sheath (PELS) (Murata, 1959b; Kroese and Rooijen, 1982) (Fig. 7.11c). In routine histological sections, the border between the white and red pulp is obscured by the occurrence of many lymphoid cells and granulocytes in the red pulp. However, silver impregnated specimens show the two layers more clearly (Fig. 7.11b). The white pulp then appears as a lighter zone around ellipsoids due to the presence of lymphoid tissue with insignificant reticulin fibers (Fig. 7.11c). Electron microscopy displays lymphoblasts, plasma cells and dendritic macrophages, as well as proliferating lymphocytes (Zapata et al., 1981) on a frame of reticular cells and connective tissue. Dendritic macrophages occur more commonly in the lymphoid tissue around the ellipsoid. No germinal centers are formed even after antigenic stimulation (paratyphoid vaccine). Antigen trapping cells, nonphagocytic dendritic cells with a large lobulated nucleus, occur exclusively in the PELS (Kroese and Rooijen, 1983). In *Mauremys caspica*, the marginal zone develops between the white and red pulp, clearly bordering these two structures (Zapata et al., 1981). The marginal zone here described is simply a layer of reticular cells; it differs from that of mammalian spleens.

The red pulp is a blood-congested zone around the white pulp. Its extent may vary in location and is wider in the organ center near the larger veins. The red pulp is comprised of slit-like veins (pulp sinus) and the intervascular tissue (pulp cord). Pulp sinuses are made of flattened endothelial cells surrounded by a thin collagen layer. In silver impregnated specimens, the vascular architecture is clearly distinguished within the reticulin net that appears in the pulp cord (Fig. 7.11b). Venous vessels anastomose to form collecting venules around the white pulp. The pulp cord contains lymphocytes, macrophages, plasma cells, granulocytes (Fig. 7.11d) and interstitial cells. However, there is no contribution of the spleen to the hemopoietic activity (Murata, 1959b). Collecting veins join to drainage veins that run independently from the arteries (Fig. 7.11a). Drainage veins anastomose to form larger veins and lead splenic blood to either the capsular or hilus side. The capsular veins are well developed and form an independent drainage route from the hilus route and have no associated arteries. Hilus drainage veins run either collateral to or independent from intrasplenic arteries. Veins leave the spleen close by the artery at the hilus.

3. RHYNCHOCEPHALIANS (Fig. 7.8)
The small elliptical spleen of *Sphenodon punctatus* lies near the stomach (Klaatsch, 1892; Hochstetter, 1898) (Fig. 7.8). Marchalonis et al. (1969) briefly describe the morphology of the spleen of this species in relation to its immunological response. There is a white and a red pulp. Central arteries and nodular structures occur in the white pulp, but there are neither germinal centers nor a marginal zone. No lymphoid tissue other than the splenic white pulp occurs in other sites of the body. An illustration (Marchalonis et al., 1969, fig. 7b) indicates that the histology of the spleen of *Sphenodon punctatus* resembles that of lizards.

4. LIZARDS (Figs. 7.12a–e and 7.13a–e)
The spleen of various lizards and its histology has been reported in *Agama agama* (Tanaka, 1993), *A. stellio* (Saad and Bassiouni, 1993), *Calotes versicolor* (Kanakambika and Muthukkaruppan, 1973), *Chalcides ocellatus* (Hussein et al., 1978a; El Deeb et al., 1985; Saad and Bassiouni, 1993), *Eumeces latiscutatus* (Kanesada, 1956; Murata, 1959b), *E. kishinouyei* (Tanaka, 1993), *Mabuya quinquetaeniata* (Hussein et al., 1978b), *Phrynosoma solare* (Jordan and Speidel, 1929), *Scincus scincus* (Hussein et al., 1979b), *Tiliqua rugosa* (Wetherall and Turner, 1972), and *Uromastyx aegyptius* (Hussein et al., 1978b).

The small lizard spleen is either elliptical (*Phrynosoma solare*, Jordan and Speidel, 1929; *Calotes versicolor*, Kanakambika and Muthukkaruppan, 1973; *Mabuya quinquetaeniata*, Hussein et al., 1978b; *Agama agama* and

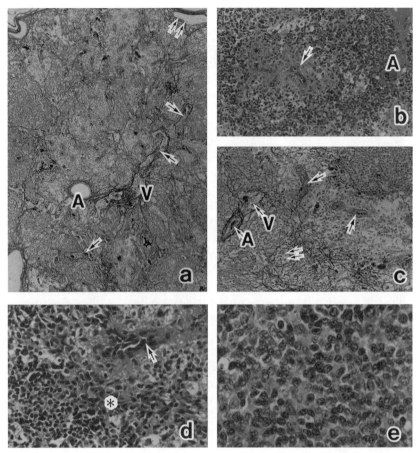

Fig. 7.12. Spleen of *Agama agama*. a. A low power picture of the spleen in a silver-impreg-nated section. The spleen is covered by a thin fibrous capsule. No trabeculae may be dis-tinguished. A large artery at the left lower corner is the proximal segment of the intrasplenic artery whose distal segment is shown near the center (A). The intrasplenic artery of this spleen runs near the splenic center. Veins (V) associate closely with the artery particularly at the hilus region. However, it is unclear whether they are in a collateral position or not. The lymphoid tissue develops around the artery; thus, it lies near the splenic center. Ellip-soids appear as light nodular zones easily recongnized in silver impregnated specimens. The red pulp is very narrow and is noted only around ellipsoids. Pulp sinuses form col-lecting venules (arrows) that join to drainage veins. The capsular vein is evident (double arrows). SI, ×60. b. The lymphoid tissue around a peripheral artery (A) and sheathed capillaries (arrow). Ellipsoids are developed moderately and the red pulp is indistinctive. HE, ×125. c. Ellipsoids and their surrounding area in a silver impregnated specimen. The ellipsoids appear as a light nodular area including sheathed capillaries (arrows). A mar-ginal area of the ellipsoid is lighter and includes blood cells. Venous vessels of the red pulp lie adjacent to ellipsoids (double arrows) in a coarse reticulin net. A, artery; V, vein; SI, ×125. d. A higher magnification of an ellipsoid with an arterial capillary (arrow) and their surrou nding area. The red pulp (*) is observed around the ellipsoid as a narrow layer including slit-like venous sinuses. HE, ×250. e. A higher magnification of the lymphoid tissue developed around a peripheral artery. HE, ×500.

Eumeces kishinouyei, Tanaka, 1993) or tubular (*Tiliqua rugosa*, Wetherall and Turner, 1972; *Calotes versicolor*, Kanakambika and Muthukkaruppan, 1973; *Mabuya quinquetaeniata*, Hussein et al., 1978b). Its color is reddish, reddish brown, and dark brown. *Uromastyx aegyptius* has a large spleen (Hussein et al., 1978b), but the size of the spleen may vary considerably within a single species (Jordan and Speidel, 1929; Kanakambika and Muthukkaruppan, 1973).

The spleen is covered with a thin fibrous capsule. The spleens of *Phrynosoma solare* (Jordan and Speidel, 1929), *Chalcides ocellatus* (Hussein et al., 1978a), *Mabuya quinquetaeniata* (Hussein et al., 1978b), and *Uromastyx aegyptius* (Hussein et al., 1978b) have trabeculae, whereas those of *Agama agama* and *Eumeces kishinouyei* (Tanaka, 1993) lack them. Fibrous trabeculae separate the parenchyma into lobules (Jordan and Speidel, 1929). Both arteries and veins enter the organ from the hilus (Jordan and Speidel, 1929). Arteries at the hilus have a wall made of leiomyocytes and collagen fibers. They divide into proximal branches that pass the parenchyma independently from veins in *Eumeces kishinouyei*. In *Agama agama* (Fig. 7.12a), large arteries and veins are closely positioned, probably due to lack of a pulp space to include vasculatures; thus, the arterio-venous relationship is unclear. In *Iguana iguana*, arteries and veins lie in a close position at the hilus, but run independently in the parenchyma (Fig. 7.13a). In spleens of both lizards, the arteries divide a few times and give off short terminal arteries (Fig. 7.13b) that soon become sheathed capillaries. Ellipsoids around end arterial branches are well developed in the spleen of *Agama* (Figs. 7.12b, c, e), but insignificant in those of *Iguana iguana* (Figs. 7.13b, c, d). In *Agama agama*, they appear as fibrous nodules that occupy most of the splenic pulp (Fig. 7.12a), whereas in *Eumeces kishinouyei* they appear as fibrous zones of a modest size and irregular shape lying between the white and red pulp. *Phrynosoma solare* has relatively few ellipsoids lying near the center of the organ along a stem artery (Jordan and Speidel, 1929). End branches communicate with venous vessels of the red pulp in a closed manner.

The lymphoid tissue (the white pulp) forms around arteries (Murata, 1959b; Wetherall and Turner, 1972; Hussein et al., 1978b) (Figs. 7.12b, c, 7.13b). Most species have a nodular white pulp around arteries (Murata, 1959b; Wetherall and Turner, 1972; Hussein et al., 1978b). In *Eumeces kishinouyei*, the lymphoid tissue develops well along the stem artery reaching to the periphery around arterial capillaries. Both PALS and PELS occur in this species; the former is well developed. In *Agama agama* and *Iguana iguana*, the lymphoid tissue lies along both arteries and veins (Figs. 7.12a, 7.13a), but sometimes shows closest relation to the vein. The lymphoid tissue also occurs at the subcapsular area of the *Iguana* spleen adjacent to the venous vessels. Because the production of

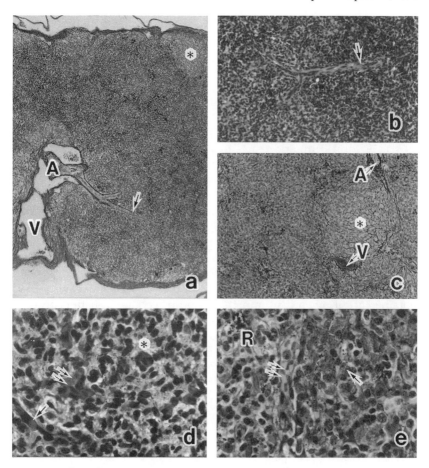

Fig. 7.13. Spleen of *Iguana iguana*. a. A low power view of the spleen in a silver impregnated section. An artery (A) near the hilus and its associated vein (V). A peripheral arterial branch (arrow) extends into the splenic pulp which is embedded by diffusely distributed small free cells and interstitial elements. Light nodular structures are noted in the parenchyma and subcapsular area (*). They comprise of lymphoid cells and are found around vasculatures, particularly veins. Note the capsular drainage veins. SI, ×50. b. Part of the splenic pulp showing a peripheral artery (arrow). The artery is only traceable as a fibrous streak that includes peripheral erythrocytes. The vascular architecture of the artery is difficult to demonstrate at the periphery. HE, ×125. c. Part of the spleen in a silver impregnated section. Ellipsoids and a reticulin network of the pulp cord are not distinguished. A coarse reticulin network contains the lymphoid nodule (*), which is found around veins (V) and arteries (A). SI, ×125. d. Higher magnification of a fibrous zone (*) near the arterial terminal (arrow). This zone may be an immature ellipsoid. The zone contains many dark pigments either diffusely in the connective tissue or aggregated in interstitial cells. HE, ×500. e. Part of a light nodular tissue showing developed granulated cells. The nodular structure is distinguished by venous vessels (double arrows) from the red pulp (R). HE, ×600.

granulocytes is associated with the veins, myelopoietic activity could be expected in these lymphoid nests. Saad and Bassiouni (1993) note that the lymphoid tissue is poorly developed in spleens of *Agama* studied during the summer. Nodular structures (probably germinal centers) occasionally appear in *Phrynosoma solare* (Jordan and Speidel, 1929). In *Eumeces kishinouyei*, the PALS frequently contains small nodular structures made of large lymphoid cells, structures that also resemble germinal centers. The white pulp shows seasonal variations (Hussein et al., 1978a, 1978b, 1979b) and reacts to various immunologial stimulations (Wetherall and Turner, 1972).

The red pulp is poorly developed in *Agama* and *Iguana* examined (Figs. 7.12a, 7.13a). It forms a narrow vasculated zone lying between ellipsoids or terminal arteries. Slit-like veins congested with peripheral erythrocytes appear. The narrow pulp cord is formed of primarily reticular cells with a large pale nucleus. Macrophages, pigment-laden cells, plasma cells, and lymphocytes also occur, as does a coarse net of reticulin fibers (Fig. 7.13c). The slit-like veins are short; they do not form a complicated plexus pattern but join to form collecting veins. In *Mabuya quinquetaeniata* obtained at spring and autumn, the red pulp becomes indistinct because of the infiltrating lymphocytes (Hussein et al., 1978b).

Collecting veins drain blood from corresponding areas and anastomose with drainage veins. Drainage veins run either toward a capsular or hilus direction. In the latter case, they lie close to the artery. Capsular veins are the independent venous route from the collateral vein and drain splenic blood from the capsule of the non-hilus region.

5. SNAKES (Fig. 7.14a–e)

The spleens of about seven species of snakes have been reported, namely *Elaphe climacophora* (Tanaka and Hirahara, 1995), *E. quadrivirgata* (Murata, 1959b), *Natrix natrix* (Hartmann, 1930), *Psammophis schokari* (El Ridi et al., 1981), *Python reticulatus* (Kroese et al., 1985), and *Spalerosophis diadema* (Hussein et al., 1979a).

The snake spleen is unique because it has almost no red pulp and resembles a lymph node (Hartmann, 1930; Murata, 1959b). The reddish or brown spleen is either oval or spherical (Hussein et al., 1979a; Tanaka and Hirahara, 1995). In *Elaphe climacophora*, three tissue zones, the capsule/septum, perilymphoid fibrous zone (PLFZ), and lymphoid tissue (the white pulp), may be distinguished histologically (Tanaka and Hirahara, 1995). The PLFZ corresponds to the red pulp of common spleens, and the spleen is covered by a fibrous capsule (Hussein et al., 1979a; Kroese et al., 1985; Tanaka and Hirahara, 1995). In *Spalerosophis diadema* (Hussein et al., 1979a) and *Python reticulatus* (Kroese et al., 1985), trabeculae project into the parenchyma from the capsule. The spleen of *Elaphe climacophora* lacks trabeculae (Tanaka and Hirahara, 1995).

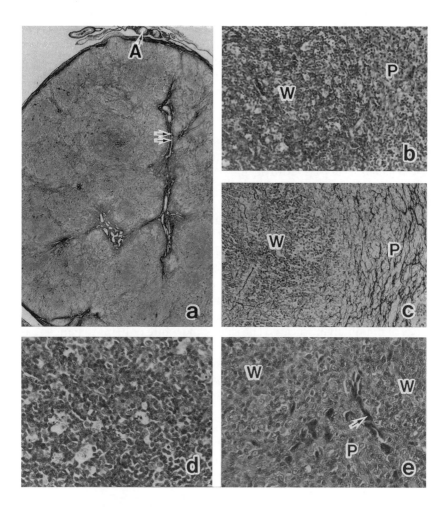

Fig. 7.14. Spleen of *Elaphe climacophora*. a. A low power view of the spleen, which is covered by a thin capsule and is divided into nodular zones by fibrous septa (double arrows) that include vasculatures. The splenic pulp is nearly occupied by the lymphoid tissue. SI, ×15. Abbreviation: A, artery. b. A part of the nodular lymphoid tissue (W) at left and its surrounding area (P), the perilymphoid fibrous zone, at right. The latter includes many venous vessels; however, is difficult to distinguish it by routine histological stains due to diffuse infiltration of lymphocytes. HE, ×125. c. An area similar to "b" and impregnated with silver. The border between the lymphoid tissue (W) and PLFZ (P) is distinguished clearly. SI, ×125. d. Lymphoid tissue at higher magnification reminding one of a starry sky due to the presence of scattered macrophages with light cytoplasm in densely-packed lymphocytes. HE, ×250. e. A border between the lymphoid tissue (W) and PLFZ (P) shows many venous vessels (arrow) in the latter. e-Masson, ×250.

In *Elaphe climacophora*, arteries enter the spleen independent from the veins. These arteries have a wall composed of single-layered leiomyocytes; thus, they are arteriolar in nature. They run in the fibrous septa to the center of the organ (Fig. 7.14a), leave the septum, enter the PLFZ for a distance, and divide into terminal arteries about 20–30 μm in diameter. They are surrounded by a non-muscular wall, being arterial capillaries that lack ellipsoids, run within the white pulp, and give off end branches.

The lymphoid tissue lies around terminal arteries in a nodular form (Fig. 7.14a). No PALS appears around septal arterioles. However, the lymphoid tissue is interpreted as present around central arterioles in *Psammophis schokari* (El Ridi et al., 1981) and *Python reticulatus* (Kroese et al., 1985). The spleen is divided by septa and the PLFZ into multiple nodular lymphoid tissues (Fig. 7.15b, d). These lymphoid nodules contain round lighter zones resembling germinal centers. The lymphoid tissue is made of an aggregation of lymphocytes, reticular cells, and macrophages (Hussein et al., 1979a). In a TEM study, three types of non-lymphoid cells; reticular cells, macrophages, and dendritic cells at the white pulp periphery, are distinguished in the lymphoid tissue (Kroese et al., 1985). Only the dendritic cells can trap the immune-complex. They are assumed to be phylogenetic precursors of the follicular dendritic cells of mammalian spleens. The size of the white pulp may change seasonally (El Ridi et al., 1981) and under immunological stimulations (Kroese et al., 1985). Terminal arteries divide into end branches near the nodular center and become small arterial capillaries (transitional vessels, Tanaka and Hirahara, 1995). They run toward peripheries of the lymphoid tissue and communicate to venous vessels of the PLFZ.

The PLFZ, the red pulp, is a fibrous zone rich in small venous vessels (Fig. 7.14e) (Tanaka and Hirahara, 1995). The zone is not clearly distinguished from the white pulp due to the presence of many infiltrating lymphocytes and interstitial cells including macrophages (Fig. 7.14b). However, it is clearly distinguished in silver impregnated specimens by the presence of fine reticulin fibers in the PLFZ (Fig. 7.14c). In *Psammophis schokari*, studied during the winter, the distinctive red pulp consists of sheets and cords of reticular cells and encloses blood sinusoids (El Ridi et al., 1981). In active seasons, many lymphocytes migrate from the white pulp, obscuring the red pulp. The latter is nearly absent in the spleen of *Elaphe quadrivirgata* (Murata, 1959b). These vessels anastomose into drainage veins for splenic blood from the capsular drainage.

6. Amphisbaenians

The splenic structure of amphisbaenians has yet to be studied histologically. The gross anatomy of their spleen has been described by Crook and Parsons (1980), who reported on 41 specimens from 13 genera. The smooth, dark, globular spleen is either grayish or mottled brown and lies in the dorsal mesentery slightly dorsal to the apex of the pancreas (*Amphisbaena alba, A. darwini, Anops, Blanus, Chirindia, Cynisca,* and *Leposternon*). In some groups (*Amphisbaena darwini, Bipes, Rhineura*), the spleen is embedded in the right side of the pancreas. Two equal sized globular structures, either or both of which could be the spleen, are found in *Trogonophis* and *Rhineura*. The spleen may also be of an elongated spindle-shape (*Zygaspis*), or U-shaped (*Agamodon, Diplometopon*). In some specimens (*Chirindia, Monopeltis*), the spleen is not distinguishable.

7. CROCODYLIANS (Figs. 7.15a–d)

Earlier, Kanesada (1956) stated that he examined two samples of *Alligator sinensis*; however, no data were included in his report. A histological report on two spleens from juvenile *Alligator mississippiensis* (whole length, 1.01 m and 0.78 m respectively) is available (Dittmann, 1969). The following observation is made on the spleen of *Alligator mississippiensis* and is supplementary to the earlier report. For this study, ten spleens provided through the courtesy of Ruth M. Elsey, the Rockefeller Wildlife Refuge, Louisiana, were used. Four of these spleens derive from male adults (2.0–3.2 m in total length) and 6 spleens from juveniles (4 females, 2 possible males; 0.8–0.9 m in total length; splenic weight 1.1– 1.4 g). The S/B ratio of the juvenile group was 1/1,310–1,630 (no data are available for the adults due to unknown body weights). These values are lower than those (1/959 and 1/567) reported by Dittmann (1969).

The spleens of *Alligator mississippiensis* are bean or sausage-shaped, and have one extremity larger than the other. The spleen lies within the dorsal mesentery, being covered by the stomach and duodenum. Its caudal end lies close to the mesenteric root (Dittmann, 1969). Its ventral side is slightly convex and its dorsal side is concave (Dittmann, 1969). The lienointestinal artery (the post-gastric segment of the gastro-lieno-intestinal artery, see Section III.A and Fig. 7.10) enters the spleen from its oral extremity and leaves it from the anal end. Apparently the spleen is formed around a stem segment of the gastro-lieno-intestinal artery. No collateral veins parallel the splenic artery; however, many larger capsular veins lie on the splenic surface. They tend to gather from the convex margin to the concave side and then join to larger extrasplenic veins. On the ventral convex surface, a venous plexus consisting of v. lienalis and its three ventral and two dorsal branches is observed (Dittmann, 1969).

Histologically, the capsule/trabecula and the white and red pulp are distinguished (Fig. 7.15a). The capsule is thick and is made of irregularly developing leiomyocytes, collagen, and elastic fibers. Many venous

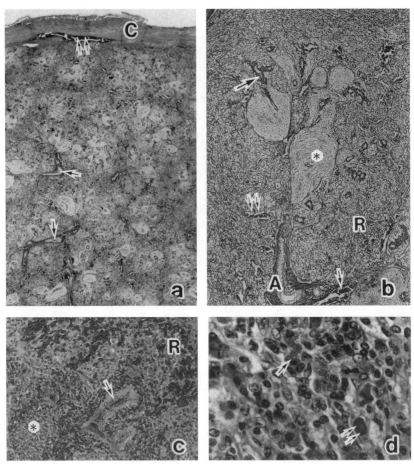

Fig. 7.15. Spleen of *Alligator mississippiensis*. a. A low power view of a SI spleen showing the capsule (C) and the splenic pulp. No trabeculae appear in this picture. Arrows indicate peripheral arteries and accompanying veins. Light nodular areas around peripheral arterial branches are the lymphoid tissue (the white pulp). The red pulp is wide, and is made of pulp sinus and a wider pulp cord. Note the capsular vein (double arrows). ×15. b. The peripheral artery (A) and an associating vein (small arrow) at bottom. Veins are noted along the artery of this level. The artery runs straight upwards and gives off terminal branches that further divide into sheathed capillaries (large arrow). Nodular lymphoid tissue develops around terminal arteries. No collateral veins are noted around arteries of this level. The lymphoid tissue around ellipsoids is made up of small lymphocytes and distributes rather uniformly around the vasculature without forming a nodular structure. The red pulp is wide and includes many venous sinuses (double arrows). A coarse network of reticulin fiber develops in the pulp cord. SI, ×50. c. Two ellipsoids surrounded by small lymphocytes and a part of a nodular lymphoid tissue (*) made of medium lymphocytes appear in this section. As stated earlier, the latter is the lymphoid tissue which develops around the terminal artery. A fibrous zone rich in venous vessels (R) is the red pulp. HE, ×125. d. Granulocytes (arrow) found around terminals of the ellipsoid and collecting venules. Double arrows indicate a degenerated erythrocyte in the pulp cord. This picture does not show macrophages with iron-positive granules. HE, ×500.

vessels are noted in the capsule (Fig. 7.15a). The capsular tissue extends into the splenic parenchyma along vasculatures, particularly veins, and forms trabeculae in adult samples, but are not noted in juvenile spleens. This result is agreeable with the Dittmann's observation (1969). The artery enters in the spleen obliquely from the lateral face of the larger extremity, reaches to the splenic center, runs along the splenic axis toward the smaller opposite extremity, and leaves the spleen from there. Nerves associate closely with the artery. Large capsular veins appear to envelop the artery at the entry site, run along its stem, and branch toward the periphery (Fig. 7.15b). The capsular tissue (trabeculae) lies peripheral to these veins, and reinforces the vasculature. The artery divides and sends peripheral branches toward the capsule. These arterial segments have a definitive wall comprising single-layered endothelial cells, an internal elastic lamina, leiomyocytic media, and a well-developed external elastic lamina. Collagenous tissue forms around the arteries, and nerve fibers commonly occur here. Branches of the peripheral arteries divide a few times, abruptly loose both leiomyocytic media and external elastic lamina, and become terminal arteries (arterial capillaries). Lymphoid tissue sheathes both terminal arteries and ellipsoids (Fig. 7.15c). It appears nodular around terminal arteries and uniform in thickness around the ellipsoids (Fig. 7.15b, c). Collecting venules leave the artery at this level and pass the lymphoid tissue (Fig. 7.15b). Terminal arteries are usually short; they divide into end branches, which are surrounded by ellipsoids (Fig. 7.15b). Sheathed arteries communicate with the venous vessels of the red pulp in a closed manner. According to Dittmann (1969), the arterial terminals end in the pulp cord.

The wide red pulp includes many small veins (Fig. 7.15b). The pulp cord is comprised of a coarse network of reticulin fibers and interstitial cells. Extravasated erythrocytes, macrophages with iron-positive cytoplasmic inclusions, and granulocytes commonly occur (Fig. 7.15d). Venous vessels anastomose to form collecting venules that run along arterial branches and join to drainage veins. This venous route drains splenic blood to the hilus side. Drainage veins independent from the arterial route are also present. These veins lead splenic blood directly to capsular drainage veins. Two drainage routes observed in the alligator spleen eventually join at the hilus. Because the splenic artery lacks collateral veins, the splenic blood must be drained by the capsular drainage vein to the splenic vein(s).

D. Embryology of the Reptilian Spleen

The embryology of reptilian spleens has been reported by a few authors (Tonkoff, 1900, 1903; Dantchakoff, 1916; Evans, 1934; Kanakambika and Muthukkaruppan, 1973; El Deeb et al., 1985).

Tonkoff (1900, 1903) studied splenic ontogeny in *Lacerta agilis, Natrix natrix,* and *Crocodylus porosus.* One specimen from each three different stages of development was analyzed in *Lacerta* and *Crocodylus,* but no stage classification was given. The splenic anlage appears in the dorsal mesentery at the dorsum of the pancreas close to the vitelline vessels. The descriptions are poor and difficult to use for reference.

In *Natrix natrix,* the splenic anlage first appears in the embryos of 5–6 mm in length (Dantchakoff, 1916). The pancreatic anlage appears simultaneously being clearly separated from the splenic one. After 5–10 incubation days, mesenchymal cells are distinguished in the splenic anlage. The numbers of these cells increase as the embryos develop, and granulocytes and their immature forms become distinguishable. The oral side of the anlage faces the pancreas. The anal side is round and smooth. In 15 day samples, there are many spaces between developing cells, as if these were forming an aggregate of tubular glands. Later, many blood capillaries appear and form a vascular network among cells. Mature erythrocytes and immature blood cells appear in the vascular lumen. These vascular nets communicate occasionally with pancreatic vessels. Many free cells also occur in the splenic stroma.

Splenic ontogeny has been studied in 46 individuals of *Gymnodactylus kotschysi* (Evans, 1934) using the staging table for *Lacerta agilis* (Peter, 1904) for estimation of development. Thirteen individuals of Stages 14–20 lack any splenic anlage. Splenogenesis occurs in materials between Stage 21 (corresponds to the 8-hour incubation stage of chicken eggs) and 34 (right before hatching). They were divided into four groups. In the first group (Stages 21–23, 2.25–3.5 mm in length), the splenic anlage appears at the dorsum of the gastric anlage as a cellular layer on the peritoneal surface. The layer becomes distinctive in materials of the second group (Stages 24–28). Vessels (probably arterial) appear in the anlage. Blood in the anlage is drained via the pancreatic dorsum to the ductus venosus. The splenic anlage becomes oval at Stages 27–30. Many capillaries (mostly arterial) are then noted. One can then distinguish whether vessels are arterial or venous. All venous blood drains directly by the ductus venosus. The pancreatic route observed in earlier developmental stages disappears.

The ontogeny of *Calotes versicolor* at the 28–42 developmental stages has been studied using over 100 embryos (Kanakambika and Muthukkaruppan, 1973). The splenic premordium appears at Stage 30 as a small protuberance consisting of loose mesenchymal cells that project into the body cavity close to the anlage of the dorsal pancreas. An increase in numbers, both of mesenchymal cells and blood spaces, is observed as embryos develop. Numerous blood spaces that contain erythrocytes are formed in mesenchymal cells from Stage 30 onwards.

Sinusoids become prominent during Stage 33–34 accompanying widespread erythrocytes. The anlage is well established at Stages 34–35, at Stage 35, it forms primarily erythroid cells. A few granulocytes appear around Stage 30. Numbers of granulocytes increase from Stage 36, and definitive granulocytic nests appear by Stage 38. Most of the granulocytes are eosinophils. Lymphocytopoiesis begins at Stage 40, followed by an increase in lymphocytes during successive developmental stages. The lymphoid tissue lacks lymphoid nodules.

The splenic anlage of *Chalcides ocellatus* is observed at Stage 31 as a cell nest in the dorsal mesogastrium (El Deeb et al., 1985). At Stage 32, the splenic anlage protrudes into the abdominal cavity and vascular development occur in the mesenchymal nest. By Stages 34–35, the anlage is covered by a capsule and shows a distinctive form. The splenic anlage is occupied by many mesenchymal cells, but no hemopoietic activity is seen up to Stage 36. A few erythroblastic islands and granulocytes may be noted by Stage 37 and lymphoid tissue has now developed. By Stage 37, the red and white pulp are clearly distinguished.

IV. COMPARATIVE ANATOMY OF THE SPLEEN
A. Agnatha

Modern Agnatha include Myxiniformes (hagfish) and Petromyzontiformes (lampreys). Intestinal hemopoiesis noted in both groups has been interpreted as an ancestral condition (Jordan and Speidel, 1930; Jordan, 1938). However, location and distribution of the hemopoietic nest(s) in these two groups differ (Jordan and Speidel, 1930b; Tanaka et al., 1981).

Hemopoietic nests of the hagfish are small and dispersed along the wall of the intestinal vein. They consist mostly of granulocytes and their immature forms. In lampeys, an intestinal hemopoietic nest appears transiently in the typhlosole at the larval stage (ammocoete). It is an aggregated cellular nest that develops around the intestinal artery along the axis of the typhlosole (Percy and Potter, 1976; Tanaka et al., 1981; Potter et al., 1982). The hemopoietic nest comprises mature/immature nucleated erythrocytes, granulocytes, macrophages and lymphoid cells (probably immature granulocytes). In small ammocoetes, the hemopoietic nest is solid around the intestinal artery and contains many sinusoidal veins that have a fenestrated endothelial layer in and around it.

Neither metamorphosis nor drastic change is noted in the intestine and its hemopoietic nests during development of the hagfish. However, significant metamorphoic changes occur in the intestinal circulation and the hemopoietic nest of the lamprey intestine. As ammocoetes grow, the hemopoietic nest is gradually eroded by the development of sinusoidal veins; in larger ammocoetes, especially before metamorphosis, hemopoietic activity occurs in slender tissue cords between sinusoidal veins. The hemopoietic nest disappears during and/or after metamorphosis, leaving completed veins along the intestinal artery (Yamada, 1951). After metamorphosis, hemopoiesis occur in the perineural fatty tissue in adult lampreys (George and Beamish, 1974).

B. Chondrichthyes

The chondrichthyan spleen is expected to show a primitive structure because of its phylogenetic position. However, there are no rudiments directly suggesting structural transition between the intestinal spleen of lungfishes and extra-enteral spleens of actinopterans in the chondrichthyan spleen. Primitive splenic structures analogous to those of lungfishes (see Sections IV.C and V.C) are no longer present in the spleen of *Chlamydoselachus*, the most primitive form of living Chondrichthyes (Tanaka and Goto, 1992). No significant differences appear between the splenic structure of Elasmobranchii and Holocephalii.

The dorsal spleen (shark group), the ventral spleen (ray group), and both splenic forms (dorsal and ventral spleen) may be noted in one individual of Elasmobranchii (*Centrophorus calceus*, Woodland, 1906; *Hexanchus cornius*, O'Donoghue, 1926; *Notorhynchus maculatus*, Daniel, 1928; *Squatina squatina*, Marples, 1936; *Etomopterus spinax*, Mattison and Fänge, 1982; *Chlamydoselachus anguineus*, Tanaka and Goto, 1990). This feature is unusal and not observed in other vertebrate groups except gar pikes (Osteichthyes) (see Section IV.C). In general, the S/B ratio (see Section II.B.3) of this group is high among vertebrates suggesting that the spleen is still an important organ for the body activity. It commonly has deep incisions or incomplete lobulations. The surface of the organ is usually smooth, but a granular or lobulated appearance formed by an aggregated small lobules is seen in some groups (*Alopias*, Hemmeter, 1926: *Triaks*, Tanaka, 1993).

Histologically, the spleen contains distinctive white and red pulp. The white pulp comprises lymphoid tissue forming around terminal arteries. The border between white and red pulp is usually unclear. The wide red pulp consists of venous vessels (pulp sinus) and a reticulin-rich intervascular space (pulp cord). Significant fenestrations of venous endothelia complicate delineation of the vascular architecture in the red pulp. Thus, the structure of the red pulp is vaguely referred as the reticular meshwork. Developed ellipsoids commonly appear around distal segments of the terminal artery. A-v communications are of a closed type (see Section II.B). Two venous routes occur in the chondrichthyan spleen.

Hemopoietic activity has been repeatedly claimed for the chondrichthyan spleen (Maximow, 1923; Hemmeter, 1926; Yoffey, 1928/29; Jordan, 1938; Zapata, 1980). The lymphopoietic activity and antibody production have also been claimed (Tomonaga et al., 1986; Zapata and Cooper, 1990). Chondrichthyan spleens lack melanomacrophage centers. In sections stained for tissue iron, iron-positive macrophages appear diffusely in the red pulp but do not form nodular structures.

C. Osteichthyes

1. GENERAL Two fish groups, archaic and modern, may be distinguished in living Osteichthyes. By their phylogenetic position, two subgroups are further distinguished in the archaic group; one group includes Brachiopterygii, Chondrostei, Crossopterygii, and Dipneustei, and the other Holostei. Splenic structures of the former subgroup differ considerably among species (Tanaka, 1985a, 1985b, 1985c).

2. BICHIRS (*POLYPTERUS*, BRACHIOPTERYGII)
Polypterus (Tanaka, 1985b) and *Calamoichthyes* (Purser, 1926) have an elongated spleen resembling that of lungfishes. The spleen of *Polypterus* lies extra-intestinally along the lower intestine. As it associates closely with the liver and lungs, it is likely the ventral spleen. An independent splenic artery originates from the truncus coeliacomesentericus at the oral end of the midgut, enters the spleen and runs via its axial center to the caudal end. The histology of *Polypterus* spleen differs considerably from that of lungfishes by showing signs of vascular differentiation. A collateral (secondary) vein appears along the axial artery but in an incomplete (segmental) manner. Each venous segment has an independent drainage vein that communicates directly with the hepatic vein (V. cava inferior). This unique vascular architecture in turn divides the elongated spleen into several segments and keeps the vascular architecture of each segment under the primary venous type.

The spleen shows two histologically distinctive zones, a central arterial and outer venous zone. The arterial zone is wide and consists of an aggregated nest of granulocytes and lymphoid cells. Lymphoid cells, which probably are immature granulocytes and lymphocytes, lie close to the arterial branches. The proportion of these cells may vary seasonally; granulocytes are probably most common. The venous zone is narrow and includes poorly developed sinusal veins and the intervascular space. The zone lies at the outermost splenic margin and along drainage veins. This layer must correspond to the inner venous layer of lungfish spleen. The area corresponding to the outer venous layer is not seen. Ellipsoids develop poorly around terminal arteries. A-v communications are of a closed type. Intrasplenic veins begin from the venous zone, extend toward the splenic center and eventually join to a segmentally formed drainage vein.

3. LUNGFISHES (DIPNEUSTEI)

Three genera are distinguished in living lungfishes, *Neoceratodus* (Australian), *Protopterus* (African), and *Lepidosiren* (South American). Among them, *Neoceratodus* is considered to be the least derived. Structurally, the spleens of lungfishes appear essentially similar (Jordan and Speidel, 1931; Rafn and Wingstrand, 1984; Tanaka, 1985a). They are intestinal spleens with the primitive morphology representing an early splenic form. Two spleens, one each in the fore- and midgut, occur along major branches (coeliac and mesenteric) of the intestinal artery (the distal segment of truncus coeliacomesentericus). The midgut spleen in *Neoceratodus* and the foregut spleen in both *Protopterus* and *Lepidosiren* are well developed.

Histologically, two zones, the central arterial and outer double-layered venous zones, are distinguished. The lymphoid tissue (white pulp) appears around the axial artery of both *Proptopterus* and *Lepidosiren* spleens (Jordan and Speidel, 1931; Tanaka, 1985a), however, it is not found in the spleen of *Neoceratodus* (Rafn and Wingstrand, 1984). Only scattered foci of lymphoid tissue occur in the spleen of adult *Neoceratodus*. The double-layered venous zone is comprised of an inner layer of sinusoidal vessels and an outer layer of plexiform drainage veins of the axial artery. The outer layer simultaneously receives blood from the intestinal wall (the splenic portal veins). At the margin of the lymphoid tissue, all arterial branches end anastomosing with sinusoidal vessels of the inner venous layer. Ellipsoids are unclear or absent. Many immature/mature nucleated erythrocytes lie in the vascular lumina of the inner layer. Active granulopoiesis occurs in the intervascular space of the outer venous layer. Structurally, lungfish spleen appears as a hemopoietic organ.

The outer venous layers of the fore- and midgut spleens form intestinal veins of the corresponding area and join to form the hepatic portal vein within the ventral mesentery (Tanaka, 1985a).

4. COELACANTH (*LATIMERIA*, CROSSOPTERYGII)

The small elongated spleen of *Latimeria* lies within the dorsal mesentery at the proximal segment of the intestine close to the pancreas (Millot et al., 1978; Tanaka, 1985a). It is supplied by the lienopancreatic artery from the dorsal intestinal artery. Grossly, segmental veins form in the capsule.

Histologically, the adult spleen is formed mostly of the red pulp. The white pulp is indistinctive. There are cellular nests along intrasplenic vessels, mostly venous; however, it is still unclear whether these comprise lymphoid or myeloid cells. Ellipsoids develop poorly or are nearly absent. It appears that the spleen of *Latimeria* resembles that of amphibians rather than of teleosts. The adult spleen may not be important organ for this species because it has a low S/B ratio (see Section II.B.3) (about 1/3,200; Tanaka, 1985a).

The difficulty of obtaining well-fixed specimens for histological analysis, has left details of the splenic structure unknown.

5. STURGEONS (*ACIPENSER*, CHONDROSTEI)

The spleen of *Acipenser* lies at the foregut end within the dorsal mesentery. In general appearance, the spleen resembles that of Chondrichthyes (Tanaka, 1985b). Incomplete lobulations give the surface a granulated appearance. The arterial supply to the spleen has not been studied thoroughly, but it is postulated that arterial branches originate from the truncus coeliacomesentericus. The status of a splenic artery from the dorsal aorta is uncertain.

Histologically, the *Acipenser* spleen resembles that of Chondrichthyes. In *Acipenser*, the spleen is formed of a central arterial (white pulp) and outer double-layered venous zone (red pulp of the broad sense). The lymphoid tissue (white pulp) develops well around intrasplenic arteries. A coarse reticulin net develops in the white pulp. The border between the white and red pulp (broad sense) is distinctive because the latter lacks a reticulin net. The venous zone is wide. The inner layer forms the red pulp (narrow sense) consisting of the pulp sinus and cord. The pulp sinus shows a definitive vascular architecture. Its outer layer is formed of subcapsular lymphoid tissue resembling the white pulp and includes larger drainage veins that are continuous with capsular veins and pass splenic blood from the capsule. Collateral veins lie in the white pulp along intrasplenic arteries. Thus, the spleen of *Acipenser* has two independent drainage routes. Ellipsoids are noted around distal segments of terminal arteries in the red pulp.

6. THE BOWFIN (*AMIA*) AND GAR PIKE (HOLOSTEI)

There are a few reports on the structure of the spleen of *Amia* (Robeson, 1932; Finstad et al., 1964; Tanaka, 1993). Two previous reports of the splenic structure are inadequate. The pyramidal spleen of *Amia* has a smooth unlobulated surface and lies at the junction of the fore and midgut (Tanaka, 1993). It is supplied by an artery originating from the coeliac artery; however, this requires future confirmation. Histologically, the white and red pulp are distinguished clearly. The white pulp develops poorly. The wide red pulp consists of poorly developed venous vessels and a pulp cord with developed reticulin fibers. Ellipsoids are modestly developed. Collateral veins occur along intrasplenic arteries. There are no capsular drainage veins.

Two elliptic spleens occur in the gar pike (Tanaka, 1995c). One is found at the fore-midgut junction and the other at the mesenteric root. Both are similar in size and shape. The abdominal artery of this species is the mesenteric (inferior?) artery, differing considerably from that of other fishes. It originates from the dorsal aorta at the level of the lower intestine and runs orally to the liver. This unique feature is probably created by the presence of developed air-bladders (or lungs) that change development of abdominal arteries from the dorsal aorta. The relation of the spleens to the mesentery is unclear. Histologically, the structure of the gar pike spleen is essentially similar to that of *Amia* except that it has distinctive ellipsoids and sinusoidal veins in the red pulp. The red pulp contains immature nucleated erythrocytes and thrombocytes. Granulocytes are rare. Melano-macrophage centers are absent; however, iron-positive macrophages correspond to ellipsoids. Collateral veins of intrasplenic arteries are present, but no capsular drainage veins develop. In conclusion, the spleens of both *Amia* and gar pikes resemble those of teleosts.

7. Teleosts

The spleen of teleosts lies in the dorsal mesentery at the junction of the fore- and midgut. In some groups, the spleen lies on the dorsal surface of the intestine. Spleens are supplied by an artery originating from either the coeliac or mesenteric artery. Teleost spleens may be classified into four groups (Tanaka, 1993). The first group contains the spleens of various marine fishes, such as *Lateolabrax japonicus*, in which the white pulp is poorly developed or nearly absent. Most of the splenic pulp consists of wide red pulp which includes many ellipsoids and clear vasculature. Collateral veins run along intrasplenic arteries, but there are no capsular veins. There may be hemopoietic activity. Melano-macrophage centers occur around the proximal segments of terminal arteries.

The second group may be represented by the spleens of *Arothron mappa* (Tetraodontiformes) and *Synanceia verucosa* (Scorpaeniformes). The red pulp is poorly developed. Its venous vessels show a distinctive vascular architecture and surround nearby ellipsoids. Consequently, there is a subdivision into ellipsoids and their related vessels. Septal structures surround each unit.

The third group may be represented by the spleens of *Sardinops melanosticta* (Clupeiformes). Splenic structures of this group resemble those of *Amia* and the gar pike described above. The lymphoid tissue is poorly developed. The red pulp is wide, ellipsoids develop poorly, and no melanomacrophage centers are present. The spleen can probably store a large volume of peripheral blood.

The fourth group is comprised of *Anguilla japonica* (Anguilliformes). This spleen has a wide red pulp consisting of developed venous vessels. Ellipsoids develop poorly or are absent. No lymphoid tissue or melanomacrophage centers appear, but there are both collateral and capsular veins. The splenic structure of this group resembles that of Amphibia, particularly Urodela.

D. Amphibia

1. GENERAL Modern Amphibia include three groups, but studies on the spleen are known mostly for Urodela and Anura. In general, amphibian spleens are less specialized than those of Teleostei. This phenomenon may be related, at least in part, to the trend to paedogenesis.

2. APODA

A few reports are available for Apoda (Weilacher, 1993; Zapata et al., 1982; Welsch and Storch, 1982). Their spleen is a small elliptic organ in the dorsal mesentery. It is mainly comprised of the red pulp and resembles that of Urodela (Zapata et al., 1982) described below.

3. URODELA

Urodelan spleens are elliptical and flat organs positioned close to the stomach within the dorsal mesentery. In *Siren lacertina*, the elongate spleen extends along nearly the entire intestine (Klaatsch, 1892).The oral segment of the organ is supplied by a branch of the coeliac artery originating from the dorsal aorta. The lower segment is nourished by mesenteric branches that originate segmentally from the dorsal aorta. Klemperer (1938) speculated that the spleen of *Siren* may represent an early form of the extra-intestinal spleen.

The urodelan spleen has a wide red pulp with well-formed venous vessels. The white pulp is poorly formed and contains no ellipsoids. The spleen contains both hilus and capsular drainage veins. A histological study has characterized the spleens of 21 species of 19 urodele genera into three types (Barrett, 1936). In the first type, the spleen has a distinctive white pulp and a red pulp comprised of venous vessels with clear vascular architecture. This group is most common and shows active erythropoiesis in the red pulp. The second type is less common. The spleens are comprised of diffuse lymphoid tissue and poorly developed red pulp. The third type consists of two patterns; the first spleen has indistinct white and red pulp, the second has developed reticular tissue probably formed by the involution of the lymphoid tissue. These patterns are noted rarely in *Gyrinophilus porphyriticus*. However, the third type is similar to the spleen of reptiles.

In general, the urodelan spleen shows active hemopoiesis, particularly erythropoiesis (Jordan, 1932, 1938; Osogoe, 1954; Tooze and Davis, 1967, 1968). Experimental splenectomy does not kill urodeles (Jordan and Speidel, 1930a; Ohuye, 1928). This probably reflects the fact that erythropoiesis is not solely operated by the spleen in Urodela; rather, intravascular erythropoiesis in other organs contributes to recovery from the severe anemia caused by splenectomy.

3. ANURA

Anuran spleens are either elliptical or spherical and lie within the dorsal mesentery close to the intestine. They are supplied by arteries branching from the truncus coeliacomesentericus.

A thin capsule encloses these spleens, and there are well-formed capsular veins. In *Bombina variegata* (Dulak, 1990), the spleen consists of the centrally located white pulp and surrounding red pulp. The splenic artery enters the spleen, reaching the white pulp via the septum. No collateral relation occurs between artery and vein. The white pulp contains arterial branches, a boundary zone, and sinuses. The boundary zone is a peripheral part of the white pulp facing to the red pulp; sinuses that are probably dilated lymphatics distinguish it from the other splenic parts. Lymphoid tissue that has been considered to be analogous to the marginal zone of mammalian spleens lies outside of the boundary zone. The red pulp consists of sinusoidal vessels and cellular cords, and its expression varies among materials examined. Nodular structures formed from macrophages containing melanin pigments appear at the subendothelial space of the larger veins. Ellipsoids are not obvious but may be poorly developed. The spleen of *Xenopus laevis* (Sterba, 1950) resembles that of *Bombina* except for having lymphoid tissue dispersed around the peripheral arteries to form cellular islands. An experimental study using labeled lymphocytes has revealed thymus-independent lymphocytes in the white pulp and thymus-dependent lymphocytes in the red pulp (Obara, 1982; Obara et al., 1982). The red pulp of *Xenopus* is much wider than it is in *Bombina*, being formed of developed venous vessels. No ellipsoids are noted.

In *Rana* and *Bufo*, the white pulp develops poorly whereas the red pulp is wide and includes many venous vessels and no ellipsoids. Both collateral veins and capsular drainage veins occur. The vascular lumina contain many erythrocytes, granulocytes, and thrombocytes as well as iron-positive macrophages, but no nodular structures resembling melanomacrophage centers. Blood cells also occur in the pulp cord. *Rana pipiens* die after experimental splenectomy unless there is compensatory erythropoiesis in the bone marrow or regeneration of the spleen from the residual tissue within 50 days (Jordan and Speidel, 1923, 1925).

E. Aves

Most morphological studies of the avian spleen have been made on chickens (*Gallus gallus*). Their elliptical spleen lies within the dorsal mesentery closely associated with the stomach. It is supplied by two major splenic branches, lienalis cranialis and caudalis arteries, originating from the coeliac artery (Fukuta et al., 1969). The right gastric glandular and right hepatic arteries also furnish the accessory branches. The distributional pattern of accessory arteries varies considerably in each animal. Most blood is drained by the large splenic vein. Several small accessory veins drain blood from the capsular side and anastomose directly to the gastric glandular lienal vein in a segmental pattern.

The spleen is covered by a thin capsule formed of collagen/elastic fibers and a few leiomyocytes. Arteries enter the spleen from the hilus being surrounded by the trabecula for a short distance, then runs in the splenic pulp to become the central artery. The central artery is surrounded by the lymphoid tissue (PALS) (Oláh and Glick, 1982). Lymphocytes in the PALS may be bursa-dependent B cells (Mori and Hoshi, 1971). Central arteries divide and send rectangularly peripheral branches, sheathed arteries. The PALS usually disappears at this level. Nodular structures resembling the lymphoid nodule appear in the PALS as a distal arterial segment involving a part of the ellipsoid (Murata, 1959b) or as an area between a proximal arterial segment and trabecula (Oláh and Glick, 1982). A capsule-like structure frequently encloses the nodules.

Ellipsoids are well developed and consist of double-layered reticular fibers. No basement structure appears around the endothelial cells of sheathed capillaries. A periellipsoidal white pulp (PWP) consisting of reticular tissue and a few lymphocytes, macrophages, and plasma cells has been characterized (Oláh and Glick, 1982). The PWP is probably the equivalent to the PELS described in the reptilian spleen. A-v communications of chicken spleen are reported as a closed type (Miyamoto et al., 1980; Oláh and Glick, 1982; Hataba et al., 1990). The red pulp is comprising of venous vessels of a simple architecture, interpreted as primitive veins. Two independent drainage routes, hilus and capsular, also occur in the chicken spleen.

F. Mammals

The spleen of mammals has a wide red pulp and well formed lymphoid tissue. The latter appears in a sheath form around intrasplenic arteries (PALS) in small mammals and in a nodular form around terminal arteries in larger ones. Structural differences from those of nonmammalian spleens are mainly in the red pulp. Three types are distinguished; primitive and common types, and the cetacean spleen.

The primitive type is the spleen with the IZ (see Section II.B.4), i.e., the spleen with a-v communications of a closed type. This type has been described in *Ornithorhynchus anatinus* (Monotremata) (Tanaka et al., 1989) and two insectivores, *Suncus murinus* (Tanaka, 1986b) and *Talpa wogura*

(Tanaka, 1987). The architecture of the intrasplenic vasculature resembles that of lungfish spleens. Active hemopoiesis is present in the red pulp and this type probably acts a major hemopoietic organ.

The common type is the spleen with the MZ and a wide red pulp. A-v communications are of an open type. Spleens of this type are regarded to have remodelled intrasplenic veins. Three groups are distinguished. The first group is found in small to medium-sized mammals that include man. This spleen corresponds to the defense spleen (die Abwehrmilz, Herrath, 1935, 1958); a wide red pulp with developed sinusoids and a developed white pulp. The body defense activity is considered for the function. The second group is the spleens of large terrestrial mammals and corresponds to the storage spleen (die Speichermilz, Herrath, 1935, 1958); a wide red pulp with poorly developed venous vessels, thick capsule / trabeculae and moderately developed white pulp. The spleen of carnivorans may also belong to this group. In the wide pulp cord, contractile elements, such as leiomyocytes (in cattle, sheep, pigs, and deer) or myofibroblasts (in giraffes and horses), develop. They contribute in expelling stored blood into the circulation. The last group is spleens of small mammals as represented by mice and rats. The group is difficult to classify by the Herrath's criteria due to the presence of structures characteristic to both splenic types (Speicher- and Abwehrmilz). Active hemopoiesis is present in the red pulp of this group.

Whale spleen is known for its extremely low S/B ratio (see Section II.B.3; Fig. 7.2). The architecture of this spleen is unique; i.e., the red pulp is made of a venous zone corresponding to the IZ (Nakamine et al., 1991; Tanaka, 1994). The outer venous layer that corresponds to the red pulp of other mammalian spleens is involuted, suggesting the involutional pattern of the venous zone of nonmammalian spleens (Tanaka, 1994).

V. EVOLUTION OF THE SPLEEN
A. Survey of Phylogenetic Studies in the Literature

Few attempts have been made to overview splenic evolution in vertebrates. Some attempts have involved comparison of the morphological states in vertebrate classes (Osogoe, 1954; Herrath, 1958; Pitchappan, 1980; Fänge and Nilsson, 1985; Tischendorf, 1985; Zapata and Cooper, 1990). Unfortunately, most of these attempts limited the range of discussion to a specific vertebrate group (fishes in Fänge and Nilsson, 1985; nonmammals in Osogoe, 1954, Zapata and Cooper, 1990; mammals in Herrath, 1959), or to a certain specific structure, such as the lymphoid tissue (Pitchappan, 1980; Zapata and Cooper, 1990). No discussion on splenic evolution is included in a recent edited monograph (Bowdler, 1990). Tischendorf's report (1985), "On the evolution of the spleen," fails to illustrate the process of splenic evolution and remains a résumé of his earlier monograph (Tischendorf, 1969). Thus, splenic evolution has been largely ignored.

Very recently, there has been introduced an hypothesis of intrasplenic vascular remodelling (vascular remodelling theory) (Tanaka, 1990, 1993, 1994; Nakamine et al., 1992; Tanaka and Hirahara, 1995) intended to explain most enigmas in splenic morphology.

B. Origin of the Spleen

The histology of the hemopoietic nests of the two agnathan groups suggests an analogy (or homology) of the bone marrow / spleen for the hagfish to the spleen for the lamprey. It has been similarly speculated that dispersed hemopoietic nests of the hagfish intestine may be an immature form and subsequently may develop (or differentiate) to an aggregated form observed in the ammocoete typhlosole. Intestinal hemopoiesis of both agnathan groups may be regarded as primitive spleens; a dispersed form for the hagfish and an aggregated one for the lamprey (Jordan and Speidel, 1930b). This popular conclusion has been accepted by many anatomists.

An analysis on the intestinal hemopoietic nest(s) of Agnatha invalidated the above conclusion based on morphology of the venous vessels relating to the hemopoietic nest(s) (Tanaka and Saito, 1982). Venous vessels adjacent to hemopoietic nests of the hagfish intestine are probably homologous to the intestinal veins, whereas the fenestrated venous vessels of the ammocoete typhlosole are apomorphies associated with generation of large intestinal veins. Because the hemopoietic nest(s) formed during intestinal vasculogenesis may be regarded as a progenitor of the later spleen (Miki, 1965), the nests of the hagfish developed around the original intestinal veins are probably unrelated to splenogenesis and cannot represent the primitive spleen. However, the basic structure of highly vasculated structure of the hemopoietic nest in the ammocoete typhlosole is essentially similar to that of the spleens, although its general appearance dissimilar. Hemopoietic tissue appears in the typhlosole only transiently at the larval stage; it disappears in the adult lamprey. This phenomenon may not allow definition of the structure as a hemopoietic organ. The ammocoete typholosole contains neither ellipsoids nor lymphoid tissue although lymphocytes may be present.

C. An Early Splenic Form: the Lungfish Spleen

The digestive canal of three dipnoan genera contains a structure resembling the hemopoietic nest(s) of the ammocoete typhlosole. The nest(s) of the lungfish intestine remains in adults, thus, it can be interpreted as an hemopoietic organ. This triple-layered structure lies within the intestinal wall, has a closed circulation and generates blood cells. Accumulation of pigment cells is noted in the hemopoietic space. This configuration may recapitulate the earliest vertebrate condition. As the lungfish spleen lies within the intestinal wall, it is an "intestinal spleen." The spleen of lungfishes resembles the hemopoietic nest of the ammocoete typhlosole in terms of its relation to the intestinal circulation and a histology rich in sinusoidal vessels.

This putatively ancestral splenic form of the lungfish type occurs neither in living Chondrichthyes (including *Chlamydoselachus*, the most primitive extant shark) nor in *Latimeria*. It is curious that this morphologically simplest spleen occurs in a fish group phylogenetically close to Amphibia. Perhaps the evolution of the pulmonary circulation that had started in ancestors of the lungfish have interfered with development (differentiation) of the intestine and the intestinal circulation retained in a primitive condition (Tanaka, 1985a). This would have led to preserving a primitive form of the spleen in ancestors of modern Amphibia, Reptilia, and Mammalia (Tanaka, 1985a).

D. Establishment of the Extra-enteral Spleen

The hemopoietic nest of the ammocoete typhlosole, analogous to the original spleen, and the lungfish spleen lie within the intestinal wall. In other living vertebrates, the spleen is enclosed by a mesentery at the outside of the intestinal tract; consequently it is extra-intestinal. The spleen is partly separated from the intestine at the oral segment of the foregut spleen of some lungfishes (*Lepidosiren paradoxa, Protopterus dolloi, Protopterus amphibius*) involving separation of its vasculature from the intestine. In evolution, the intestinal vasculatures might have become separated from the intestinal wall forming an extra-intestinal spleens, as splenogenesis follows vasculogenesis of the intestine. The earliest extra-intestinal spleens might have resembled those of lungfishes, minor modifications then separating this organ from the vasculature.

The extra-intestinal spleens of living vertebrates may lie ventrally or dorsally to the intestine. Ventral spleens occur in a few Chondrichthyes. In contrast, dorsal spleens occur in all vertebrate classes. Both ventral and dorsal spleens occur in one individual of some Chondrichthyes (see Section IV.B) and in the gar pike (Tanaka, 1985c). Locations, numbers, and sizes of the extra-intestinal spleen(s) may reflect remodelling patterns of the intestinal vasculature. Variegated distributional patterns of the intestinal and splenic arteries of living Chondrichthyes may provide analogues for illustrating the process involved in formation of extra-intestinal spleens. Variability in numbers / locations of the spleen and its circulation reflects a "trial and error" process that might be tested during the formation of extra-intestinal spleens in ancestral fishes.

E. Vascular Remodelling Theory

In ancestral vertebrates, the spleen might be formed within the intestinal wall, as still occurs in lungfish. These spleens comprise the primary vein favorable for generation of blood cells and served as hemopoietic organs. As in the lungfish spleen, the ancestral structure of the spleen

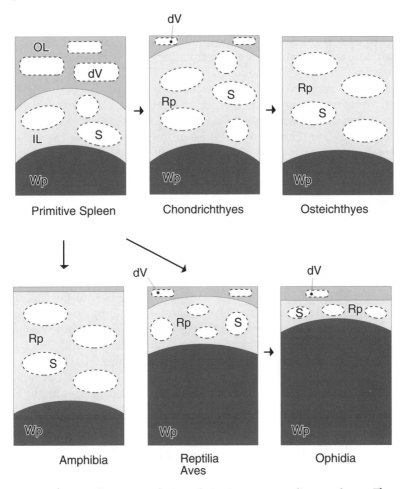

Fig. 7.16. Schemata illustrating splenic evolution in nonmammalian vertebrates. The architecture of primitive spleens expected in ancestral fishes is shown at left in the upper row. The architecture of the spleen in Chondrichthyes at the center upper row, the spleen of Osteichthyes at right upper row, the spleen of Amphibia at left lower row, the spleen of Reptilia/Aves at center lower row and the spleen of snakes at right lower row. Arrows indicate a possible evolutionary sequence. Abbreviations: dV, drainage veins; IL, the inner venous layer of the primitive spleen; OL, the outer venous layer of the primitive spleen; Rp, red pulp (common term); S, sinusoidal vessels; Wp, white pulp. Note the evolutionary changes in the proportion of each tissue layer.

might have been triple-layered; an inner arterial layer and a double-layered venous zone, namely the inner sinusoidal and outer drainage veins. Lymphoid tissue was either absent or developed poorly in the arterial zone (white pulp). The double-layered venous zone corresponded to the red pulp (broad sense). In evolution, the remodelling of the intrasplenic vasculature might have led to the secondary vein formation of intrasplenic arteries (vascular remodelling theory). Whereas the process is modelled on intestinal vasculogenesis of the lamprey typhlosole, the pattern and extent of vascular remodelling vary considerablly among species, ultimately leading to formation of pleomorphic spleens of modern vertebrates.

In nonmammalian spleens, vascular remodelling started by involution of the outer venous layer (Tanaka, 1990, 1993; Tanaka and Hirahara, 1995) (Fig. 7.16). The uninvolved inner venous layer has been transformed into a major venous zone (red pulp in the common term), whereas the outer layer disappears, leaving only the capsular drainage veins. The capsular veins have also disappeared in some nonmammalian spleens. Sites of a-v communication lying at the border of the white and red pulp remain unaffected by this process, thus, a closed type of a-v communications has been preserved. In mammalian spleens, the remodelling of the intrasplenic vasculature seems to have started from the inner venous layer (Fig. 7.17). This probably kept the hemopoietic outer venous layer active and allowed the veins eventually to be lost from the inner venous layer. This process transformed the IZ into the MZ. The process involved the site of a-v communication leading an open type of a-v communications in the spleen. Cetaceans and *Tupaia* show vascular remodelling of the nonmammalian type (Tanaka, 1993, 1994) (Fig. 7.17).

The mechanism by which the vascular remodelling started in the primitive ancestral spleens remains unclear; however, it has been proposed that the mechanism operative on the intestinal vasculatures might also act on the spleen at the time at which vasculatures became separated from the intestine.

F. Splenic Evolution in Phylogeny

A schema of the process by which the enigmatic organ, the spleen, changed in vertebrate phylogeny is shown in Figure 7.18.

The spleen originated from an activated mesenchyme of the intestinal wall that became induced during the formation of large intestinal vessels (such as the hepatic portal vein) in ancestral Agnatha. The earliest phase of splenogenesis probably involved vasculated mesenchyme during vasculogenesis as the site of hemopoiesis. This hemopoietic nest disappeared after establishment of large intestinal veins. Analogy of this process may be sought to the hemopoietic nest of the ammocoete typhlosole and could be interpreted as the "prespleen" (Tanaka, 1993). Early splenogenesis likely occurred prior to the origin of lymphoid tissue, thus, the spleen was only later related to the immune function.

A transient hemopoietic nest of the intestine (prespleen) differentiated and became an hemopoietic center operative throughout ontogeny (intestinal spleen). An intestinal spleen resembling the spleen of the lungfish appeared first in ancestors of jawed fishes. Drainage vessels of

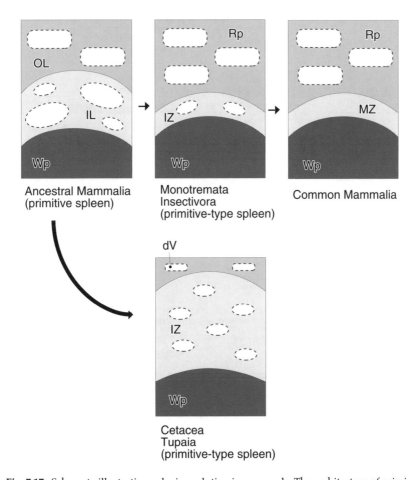

Fig. 7.17. Schemata illustrating splenic evolution in mammals. The architecture of primitive spleens in ancestral mammals at left in the upper row, primitive-type spleens of Monotremata/Insectivora at middle upper row, common mammalians spleens at right upper row and Cetacea spleens in lower row. Abbreviations: dV, drainage veins; IL, inner venous layer of the primitive spleen; IZ, intermediate zone; MZ, marginal zone; OL, outer venous layer of the primitive spleen; Rp, red pulp; S, sinusoidal vessels; Wp, white pulp. The architecture of the Cetacea spleen resembles that of nonmammalian spleens.

the intestinal spleen represented a distal segment of the hepatic portal vein. Because the intestinal spleen is present in living lungfishes, it is reasonable to speculate that intestinal spleens occurred in the ancestors of both Chondrichthyes and Osteichthyes.

Evolution of the intestine led dislocation of vasculatures from its wall. As splenogenesis follows intestinal vasculogenesis, intestinal spleens likely left the digestive canal to occupy an extra-intestinal position. Early the extra-enteral spleen(s) may have been formed within the ventral mesentery closely associated with larger intestinal veins. In fishes, intestinal vascular supply differentiated from the type seen in Chondrichthyes to that observed in Osteichthyes. During this process,

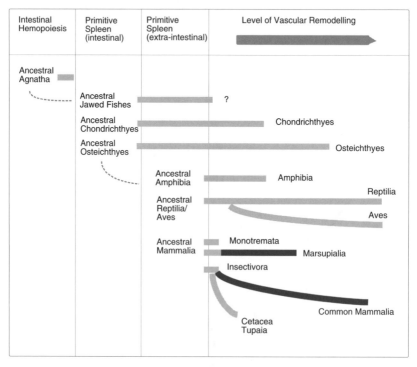

Fig. 7.18. A figure illustrating splenic evolution in the vertebrates. The spleen appeared as hemopoietic nest(s) in the intestine of ancestral Agnatha. In ancestral jawed fishes it became established as a hemopoietic organ within the intestine (the intestinal spleen). This condition characterizes ancestors of both Chondrichthyes and Osteichthyes. In ancestors of modern Amphibia, primitive spleens of the extra-intestinal type might have formed in association with the mesenteric vein (distal segment of the hepatic portal vein). In ancestors of Reptilia / Mammalia through the insectivoran level, primitive spleens were apparently extra-intestinal. The intrasplenic vasculature is assumed to be remodelled in primitive spleens of each vertebrate class; this created variegated morphology in the spleen of modern vertebrates.

the dorsal spleen was formed and the ventral spleen disappeared. Unfortunately, structural alterations occurring in evolution are unable to be traced by an analysis on living Chondrichthyes because their spleens show an advanced state of vascular remodelling, and these animals are not ancestral to Osteichthyes or tetrapods. The vascular remodelling progressed further in modern Teleostei spleens. The spleen is an hemopoietic organ in Chondrichthyes and archaic Osteichthyes, and it shows the reticuloendothelial function in modern teleosts. The involvement of lymphoid tissue in the fish spleen is poor. The immune activity is rather insignificant.

Primitive spleens of ancestral Amphibia might be formed in the dorsal mesentery relating to the establishment of the mesenteric vein, thus it might primarily be the dorsal spleen. In general, the spleens of Amphibia have a wide red pulp, and the white pulp is poorly developed or nearly absent. The spleen mostly contributes in hemopoiesis and less significantly in the lymphoreticular activity.

In Reptilia, the vascular remodelling of the spleen involved both inner and outer venous layers. The spleens of Crocodylians and Testudines retain the histological characteristics of fishes and amphibians, a wider red pulp. However, the white pulp also develops. Spleens of other reptiles show signs of advanced states of vascular remodelling. An extreme example may be seen in snake spleen. Involvement of the lymphoid tissue is now significant. This phenomenon is further enhanced by advanced involution of the venous zone. The reptilian spleen is apparently an organ of the lymphoreticular function. Hemopoietic activity is difficult to evaluate. Morphological characteristics of the reptilian spleen are extended and modified in the spleen of Aves.

Spleens with a simple (seemingly primitive) architecture are noted in the platypus (Monotremata) and modern insectivores. The phenomenon suggests that such spleens had been retained in direct ancestors of Insectivora (Therians). In modern mammalian spleen, the structural changes probably modified this level under the influence of physiological factors specific for each group; this led to pleomorphic spleens.

VI. CONCLUSION

The reptilian spleen plays an important role in the body defense function by developing lymphoid tissue in this organ. The present report provides a summary of the structure of the reptilian spleen based on recent knowledge in the splenic morphology extending to all vertebrate classes. The vascular remodelling theory, which has been introduced to explicate Milzprobleme, is also presented.

Morphological studies on the reptilian spleen are scarce. The reptilian spleen is small in size (indicated by lowest S/B ratios among vertebrates) due to an advanced state of involution in the venous zone, which is needed for generation of blood cells. In contrast, an insignificant change of the volume of the lymphoid tissue succeeded to keep the immunological activity in this organ. In general, the reptilian spleen shows structural characteristics pleomorphic and intermediate between amphibian and avian spleens; some types resemble amphibian spleens (crocodylians, testudines), others resemble avian spleens (lizards, snakes).

Although the reptilian spleen generally shows advanced structural characteristics, the vascular architecture of the *Alligator* spleen appears to form a primitive type, perhaps worthy of comment. In this spleen, the axial artery is the stem of the intestinal artery itself. Such a vascular architecture is unusual in extra-intestinal spleens, but is similar only to the spleen of the lungfish. The crocodylian spleen may represent an early form of extra-intestinal spleens in ancestral vertebrates.

Obviously, additional studies are necessary to determine which functions appear to effect reptiles in hemopoiesis and the importance of immunological roles of the spleen. It is also important to determine how these functional effects change splenic morphology in ontogeny. As is clear from the present report, both gross and microscopic morphology of the spleen remain unfortunately unknown for most reptilian families.

APPENDIX: REPTILIAN SPECIES DISCUSSED

TESTUDINES

Chinemys reevesii
  Murata, 1959a
Chelydra serpentina
  Borysenko and Cooper, 1971
  Borysenko, 1976a
  Borysenko, 1976b
Cuora flavomarginata
  Tanaka, 1993
Emys europea [=*E. orbicularis*] and *E.*
  caspica [=*Mauremys caspica*]
  Schabadasch, 1935
Mauremys caspica
  Zapata et al., 1981

Leceta and Zapata, 1985
Leceta and Zapata, 1991
Mauremys japonica
  Murata, 1959a
  Murata, 1959b
  Tanaka, 1993
Pelodiscus sinensis
  Murata, 1959b
Trachemys scripta elegans
  Kroese and Rooijen, 1982
  Kroese and Rooijen, 1983

Note: The spleens of both *Pelodiscus sinensis* (Kanesada, 1956) and *Chinemys reevesii* (Osogoe, 1954; Kanesada, 1956) have been studied. However, the studies reported only a general condition pertinent to the reptilian spleen rather than specific details for individual species; thus the species are not listed above. Schabadasch (1935) described only the splenic artery.

RHYNCHOCEPHALIA

Sphenodon punctatus
    Marchalonis et al., 1969
Note: Klaatsch (1892) and Hochstetter (1898) described the gross appearance of the spleen and its vasculature.

SAURIA

Agama caucasica
    Schabadasch, 1935
Agama stellio
    Saad and Bassiouni, 1993
Calotes versicolor
    Kanakambika and Muthukkaruppan, 1973
Chalcides ocellatus
    Hussein et al., 1978a
    El Deeb et al., 1985
    Saad and Bassiouni, 1993
Eumeces kishinouyei
    Tanaka, 1993

Eumeces latiscutatus
    Murata, 1959b
Lacerta viridis
    Schabadasch, 1935
Mabuya quinquetaeniata
    Hussein et al., 1978b
Phrynosoma solare
    Jordan and Speidel, 1929
Scincus scincus
    Hussein et al., 1979b
Tiliqua rugosa
    Wetherall and Turner, 1972
Uromastyx aegyptius
    Hussein et al., 1978b

Note: Hochstetter (1898) described the gross appearance of the spleen and its vasculature in 88 species of lizards. Schabadasch (1935) described only the splenic artery. Osogoe (1954) and Kanesada (1956) studied some lizards; however, the description was made as characteristics of a group, not individual species, and is not included in here.

AMPHISBAENIA

Amphisbaena alba
    Crook and Parsons, 1980
Note: Hochstetter (1898) examined the gross anatomy of the spleen and its vasculatures in four species of amphisbaenians; however, practically no description of its details was given. Crook and Parsons (1980) described the visceral anatomy of 16 species of amphisbaenians. Gross anatomy of the spleen and its vasculatures were stated; however, no histological data were given.

SERPENTES

Elaphe climacophora
    Tanaka, 1993
    Tanaka and Hirahara, 1995
Elaphe quadrivirgata
    Murata, 1959b
Psammophis schokari
    El Ridi et al., 1981
Python reticulatus
    Kroese et al., 1985

Natrix natrix
    Hartmann, 1930
    Schabadasch, 1935
Spalerosophis diadema
    Hussein et al., 1979a
Vipera berus
    Schabadasch, 1935

Note: Osogoe (1954) and Kanesada (1956) studied the spleen of *Elaphe quadrivirgata*; however, the description was not specific for individual species and is not included here. Schabadasch (1935) described only the splenic artery.

CROCODYLIA

Alligator mississippiensis
Dittmann, 1969
Tanaka, 1995

Note: Tonkoff (1900, 1903) studied splenic ontogeny of *Crocodylus porosus*. Bolk et al. (1933) described the gross appearance and vascular supply of the spleen in *Crocodylus niloticus*. Kanesada (1956) reported that the spleen of *Alligator sinensis* had been studied; they provided neither reference to it in the text nor illustrations.

REFERENCES

Agius, C., and Agbede, S. A. (1984). An electron microscopical study on the genesis of lipofuscin, melanin and haemosiderin in haematopoietic tissues of fish. *J. Fish Biol.* 24, 471–488.

Barrett, W. C., Jr. (1936). A comparative survey of hemopoietic foci in urodele Amphibia, with especial reference to the bone marrow of the Plethodontidae. *Folia Haemat.* 64, 165–192.

Blue, J., and Weiss, L. (1981). Periarterial macrophage sheaths (ellipsoids) in cat spleen — an electron microscope study. *Am. J. Anat.* 161, 115–134.

Bolk, L., Göppert, E., Kallius, E., and Lubosch, W., eds. (1931–1939). *Handbuch der vergleichenden Anatomie der Wirbeltiere*, vols. 1–6. Urban und Schwarzenberg, Berlin, Vienna.

Borysenko, M. (1976a). Changes in spleen histology in response to antigenic stimulation in the snapping turtle *Chelydra serpentina*. *J. Morph.* 149, 223–241.

Borysenko, M. (1976b). Ultrastructural analysis of normal and immunized spleens of the snapping turtle *Chelydra serpentina*. *J. Morph.* 149, 243–264.

Borysenko, M., and Cooper, E. L. (1972). Lymphoid tissue in the snapping turtle, *Chelydra serpentina*. *J. Morph.* 138, 487–498.

Bowdler, A. J., ed. (1990). *The Spleen, Structure, Function and Clinical Significance*. Chapmann and Hall, London.

Chen, L. T. (1978). Microcirculation of the spleen: An open or closed circulation? *Science* 201, 157–159.

Cooper, E. L., Klempau, A. E., and Zapata, A. G. (1985). Reptilian Immunity. In *Biology of the Reptilia* (C. Gans, F. A. Billett, and P. F. A. Maderson, eds.). John Wiley & Sons, New York, vol. 14, pp. 599–678.

Crook, J. M., and Parsons, T. S. (1980). Visceral anatomy of the Amphisbaenia. *J. Morph.* 163, 99–133.

Dantchakoff, W. (1916). Ueber die Entwicklung des Blutes in den Blutbildungsorganen (Area vasculosa, Dottersacksanhänge, Knochenmark, Thymus, Milz, und lockeres Bindegewebe) bei *Tropidonotus natrix*. *Arch. Mikrosk. Anat.* 87, 497–584.

Daniel, J. F. (1928). *The Elasmobranch Fishes*. University of California Press, Berkeley.

Dittmann, M. (1969). "Die Milz des *Alligator mississippiensis* (Daudin)." Doctoral thesis, Anat. Inst. Frei. Univ., Berlin.

Dulak, J. (1990). The architecture of the spleen of the yellow-bellied toad, *Bombina variegata*. *J. Zool., Lond.* 221, 489–498.

El Deeb, S., Zada, S., and El Ridi, R. (1985). Ontogeny of hemopoietic and lymphoietic tissue in the lizard *Chalcides ocellatus* (Reptilia, Sauria, Scincidae). *J. Morph.* 185, 241–253.

El Ridi, R., Badir, N., and El Rouby, S. (1981). Effect of seasonal variations of the immune system of the snake, *Psammophis schokari. J. Exp. Zool.* 216, 357–365.

Evans, L. T. (1934). The development of the spleen in the gecko, *Gymnodactylus kotschyi. Z. Anat. EntwGesch.* 103, 402–408.

Fänge, R., and Nilsson, R. (1985). The fish spleen: structure and function. *Experientia* 41, 152–158.

Fänge, R., and Sundell, G. (1969). Lymphoid tissues, blood cells and plasma proteins in *Chimaera monstrosa* (Pisces, Holocephali). *Acta. Zool., Stockh.* 50, 155–168.

Fawcett, D. W. (1994). *A Textbook of Histology,* 12th ed. Chapman & Hall, New York, London.

Finstad, J., Papermaster, B. W., and Good, R. A. (1964). Evolution of the immune response. II. Morphologic studies on the origin of the thymus and organized lymphoid tissue. *Lab. Invest.* 13, 490–512.

Fukuda, T. (1990). The Spleen C: Ontogeny of the Human Spleen. In *New Handbook of Hematology,* Japan Haemat. Soc. (S. Watanabe and M. Koizumi, eds.). Maruzen, Tokyo, vol. 2, pp. 257–277 [in Japanese].

Fukuta, K., Nishida, T., and Yasuda, M. (1969). Comparative and topographical anatomy of the fowl. LVI. Blood vascular system of the spleen in the fowl. *Japan. J. Vet. Sci.* 31, 179–185 [in Japanese with English abstract].

George, J. C., and Beamish, F. W. H. (1974). Haemocytology of the supraneural myeloid body in the sea lamprey during several phases of life cycle. *Can. J. Zool.* 52, 1585–1589.

Hartmann, A. (1930). Die Milz. In *Handbuch der mikroskopischen Anatomie des Menschen* (W. v. Möllendorff, ed.). Springer, Berlin, vol. 6(1), pp. 397–563.

Hataba, Y. (1986). A comparative scanning electron microscopy on the red pulp of the mouse, mole, rat, guinea-pig, rabbit, and cat spleens. *Tokyo Jikeikai Med. J.* 101, 199–214 [in Japanese with English abstract].

Hataba, Y., Misawa, T., and Suzuki, T. (1990). Scanning electron microscopy of the red pulp of chicken spleens. *J. Electron Microsc.* 39, 343.

Hemmeter, J. H. (1926). The special histology of the spleen of *Alopias vulpes,* its relation to hemolysis and hematopoiesis. *Z. Zellforsch. Mikrosk. Anat.* 3, 328–345.

Hochstetter, F. (1898). Über die Arterien des Darmkanals der Saurier. *Morph. Jb.* 26, 213–273.

Hussein, M. F., Badir, N., El Ridi, R., and Akef, M. (1978a). Differential effect of seasonal variation on lymphoid tissue of the lizard, *Chalcides ocellatus. Devl. Comp. Immunol.* 2, 797–311.

Hussein, M. F., Badir, N., El Ridi, R., and Akef, M. (1978b). Effect of seasonal variation on lymphoid tissues of the lizards, *Mabuya quinquetaeniata* Lich. and *Uromastyx aegyptia* Forsk. *Devl. Comp. Immunol.* 2, 469–479.

Hussein, M. F., Badir, N., El Ridi, R., and Akef, M. (1979a). Lymphoid tissues of the snake, *Spalerosophis diadema,* in the different seasons. *Devl. Comp. Immunol.* 3, 77–88.

Hussein, M. F., Badir, N., El Ridi, R., and El Deeb, S. (1979b). Effect of seasonal variation on immune system of the lizard, *Scincus scincus*. *J. exp. Zool.* 209, 91–96.

Hussein, M. F., Badir, N., El Ridi, R., and El Deeb, S. (1979c). Effects of splenectomy on the humoral immune response in the lizard, *Scincus scincus*. *Experientia* 35, 869–870.

Ishikawa, H. (1985). Differentiation of red pulp and evaluation of hemopoietic role of human prenatal spleen. *Arch. Histol. Japonica* 48, 183–197.

Jordan, H. E. (1932). The blood and blood-forming organs of the salamander, *Plethodon cinereus*. *Anat. Rec.* 54, 45–46. (abstract)

Jordan, H. E. (1938). Comparative Hematology. In *Handbook of Hematology* (H. Downey, ed.). Huber, New York, vol. 2, pp. 699–862.

Jordan, H. E., and Speidel, C. C. (1923). Studies on lymphocytes. I. Effect of splenectomy, experimental hemorrhage and a hemolytic toxin in the frog. *Am. J. Anat.* 32, 155–187.

Jordan, H. E., and Speidel, C. C. (1925). Studies on lymphocytes. IV. Further observations upon the hemopoietic effects of splenectomy in frogs. *J. Morph. Physiol.* 40, 461–477.

Jordan, H. E., and Speidel, C. C. (1929). Blood-cell formation in the horned toad, *Phrynosoma solare*. *Am. J. Anat.* 43, 77–101.

Jordan, H. E., and Speidel, C. C. (1930a). The hemocytopoietic effect of splenectomy in the salamander, *Triturus viridescens*. *Am. J. Anat.* 46, 33–90.

Jordan, H. E., and Speidel, C. C. (1930b). Blood formation in cyclostomes. *Am. J. Anat.* 46, 355–391.

Jordan, H. E., and Speidel, C. C. (1931). Blood formation in the African lungfish, under normal conditions and under conditions of prolonged estivation and recovery. *J. Morph. Physiol.* 51, 319–371.

Kanakambika, P., and Muthukkaruppan, V. R. (1972). Effect of splenectomy on the humoral response of the lizard, *Calotes vesicolor*. *Experientia* 28, 1225–1226.

Kanakambika, P., and Muthukkaruppan, V. R. (1973). Lymphoid differentiation and organization of the spleen in the lizard, *Calotes versicolor*. *Proc. Indian Acad. Sci.* B 78, 37–44.

Kanesada, A. (1956). A phylogenetical survey of hemocytopoietic tisssues in submammalian vertebrates, with special reference to the differentiation of the lymphocyte and lymphoid tissue. *Bull. Yamaguchi Med. School* 4, 1–35.

Kita, J., and Itazawa, Y. (1994). Scanning electron microscope study of rainbow trout spleen with special reference to the role of the reticular meshwork in erythrocyte release. *Japan. J. Ichthyol.* 4, 287–293.

Klaatsch, H. (1892). Zur Morphologie der Mesenterialbildungen am Darmkanal der Wirbelthiere. 1. Amphibien und Reptilien. *Morph. Jb.* 18, 385–448.

Klemperer, P. (1938). The Spleen. In *Handbook of Hematology* (H. Downey, ed.). Huber, New York, vol. 3, pp. 1591–1754.

Kroese, F. G. M., and Rooijen, N. van (1982). The architecture of the spleen of the red-eared slider, *Chrysemys scripta elegans* (Reptilia, Testudines). *J. Morph.* 173, 279–284.

Kroese, F. G. M., and Rooijen, N. van (1983). Antigen trapping in the spleen of the turtle, *Chrysemys scripta elegans*. *Immunology* 49, 61–68.

Kroese, F. G. M., Leceta, J., Döpp, E. A., Herráez, M. P., Nieuwenhuis, P., and Zapata, A. G. (1985). Dendritic immune complex trapping cells in the spleen of the snake, *Python reticulatus*. *Devl. Comp. Immunol.* 9, 641–652.

Leceta, J., and Zapata, A. G. (1985). Seasonal changes in the thymus and spleen of the turtle *Mauremys caspica*. A morphometrical, light microscopical study. *Devl. Comp. Immunol.* 9, 653–668.

Leceta, J., and Zapata, A. G. (1991). White pulp compartments in the spleen of the turtle *Mauremys caspica*. A light-microscopic, electron microscopic and immuno-histochemical study. *Cell Tissue Res.* 266, 605–613.

Marchalonis, J. J., Ealey, E. H. M., and Diener, E. (1969). Immune response of the tuatara, *Sphenodon punctatum*. *Aust. J. Exp. Biol. Med. Sci.* 47, 367–380.

Marples, B. J. (1936). The blood vascular system of the elasmobranch fish *Squatina squatina* (Linné). *Trans. Roy. Soc., Edinb.* 58, 817–840.

Mattison, A., and Fänge, R. (1982). The cellular structure of the Leydig organ in the shark *Etmopterus spinax* (L.). *Biol. Bull.* 162, 182–194.

Maximow, A. (1923). Untersuchung über Blut und Bindegewebe. X. Ueber die Blutbildung bei den Selachiern im erwachsenen und embryonalen Zustande. *Arch. Mikr. Anat.* 97, 623–717.

Miki, S. (1965). The genetic relation of the spleen to the secondary gastro-intestinal veins in chick embryo. *Acta Anat. Nippon.* 40, 329–341 [in Japanese with English abstract].

Millot, J., Anthony, J., and Robineau, D. (1978). *Anatomie de* Latimeria chalumnae. III. *Appareil digestif - Appareil respiratorie - Appareil urogénital - Glands endocrine - Appareil circulatoire - Tegments - Ecalilles - Conclusions générale.* Centre Natl. Rech. Scient., Paris.

Miyamoto, M., Seguchi, H., and Ogawa, K. (1980). Electron microscopic studies of the Schweigger-Seidel sheath in hen spleen with special reference to the existence of "closed" microcirculation. *J. Electron Microsc.* 29, 158–172.

Mori, T., and Hoshi, H. (1971). The periellipsoidal lymphoid tissue in chick spleen: A bursa-dependent area of the white pulp. *Tohoku J. exp. Med.* 104, 201–202.

Murata, H. (1959a). Comparative studies of the spleen in submammalian vertebrates. 1. Topographical anatomy and relative weight of the spleen. *Okajima Folia Anat. Japan* 33, 1–9.

Murata, H. (1959b). Comparative studies of the spleen in submammalisn vertebrates. 2. Minute structure of the spleen, with special reference to the periarterial lymphoid sheath. *Bull. Yamaguchi Med. School* 6, 83–106.

Nakamine, H., Nagata, S., Yonezawa, M., and Tanaka, Y. (1992). The whale (Odontoceti) spleen: A type of primitive mammalian spleen. *Acta Anat. Nippon.* 67, 69–82.

O'Donoghue, C. H. (1926). Observations on the anatomy of *Hexanchus corinus*. *J. Anat.* 61, 40–63.

Obara, N. (1982). Autoradiographic study on the distribution of thymus-derived and thymus-independent lymphocytes in the spleen of *Xenopus laevis*. *Devl. Comp. Immunol.* 6, 95–104.

Obara, N., Tochinai, S., and Katagiri, C. (1982). Splenic white pulp as a thymus-independent area in African clawed toad, *Xenopus laevis*. *Cell Tiss. Res.* 226, 372–335.

Ohuye, T. (1928). On the changes in the blood, the liver and the bone of the newt following splenctomy. *Sci. Rep. Tohoku Imp. Univ.* (*Biol.*) 3, 71–86.

Oláh, I., and Glick, B. (1982). Splenic white pulp and associated vascular channel in chicken spleen. *Am. J. Anat.* 165, 445–480

Ono, K. (1930). Untersuchungen über die Entwicklung der menschlichen Milz. *Z. Zellforsch. Mikrosk. Anat.* 10, 573–603.

Osogoe, B. (1954). Phylogenetic evolution of the spleen. *Proc. Japan. Hematologist Conference* 7, 1–35 [in Japanese].

Percy, R., and Potter, I. C. (1976). Blood cell formation in the river lamprey, *Lampetra fluviatilis. J. Zool., Lond.* 178, 319–340.

Peter, K. (1904). Normentafeln zur Entwicklungsgeschichte der Zauneidechse (*Lacerta agilis*). In *Normentafeln zur Entwicklungs geschichte der Wirbeltiere* (F. Keibel, ed.). Gustav Fischer, Jena, part 4, pp. 1–165.

Pitchappan, R. M. (1980). On the phylogeny of splenic structure and function. *Devl. Comp. Immunol.* 4, 395–416.

Potter, I. C., Percy, R., Barber, D. L., and Macey, D. J. (1982). The morphology, development, and physiology of blood cells. In *The Biology of Lampreys* (M. W. Hardisty and I. C. Potter, eds.). Academic Press, London, New York, vol. 4A, pp. 233–292.

Purser, G. L. (1926). *Calamoichthyes calabarius* J.A. Smith. Part 1. The alimentary and respiratory systems. *Trans. Roy. Soc. Edinb.* 54, 767–784.

Rafn, S., and Wingstrand, K. G. (1984). Structure of intestine, pancreas and spleen of the Australian lungfish, *Neoceratodus forsteri* (Krefft). *Zool. Scripta* 10, 223–239.

Robeson, J. M., Jr. (1932). Hemopoiesis in *Amia calva* (Linnaeus). *Z. Zellforsch. Mikrosk. Anat.* 16, 305–313.

Romer, A. S., and Parsons, T. S. (1977). *The Vertebrate Body*, 5th ed. Saunders, translated into Japanese by R. Hirakow (1983), Housei University Press, Tokyo.

Saad, A. H., and Bassiouni, W. M. (1993). Structure and histochemical organization of the spleen of *Agama stellio* (Sauria: Agamidae) and *Chalcides ocellatus* (Sauria: Scincidae). *J. Morph.* 216, 115–120.

Schabadasch, A. (1935). Beiträge zur vergleichenden Anatomie der Milzarterien. Versuch einer Analyse der Evolutionsbahnen des peripherischen Gefäßsystems. *Z. Anat. EntwGesch.* 104, 502–570.

Snook, T. (1950). A comparative study of the vascular arrangements in mammalians spleens. *Am. J. Anat.* 57, 31–77.

Snook, T. (1964). Studies on the perifollicular region of the rat's spleen. *Anat. Rec.* 148, 149–159.

Starck, D. (1982). Die sekundären lymphatischen Organen (Lymphknoten, Tonsillen, lymphatische Gebilde des Schleimhäute, Milz). In *Vergleichende Anatomie der Wirbeltiere*. Springer, Berlin, vol. 3, pp. 1074–1079.

Sterba,G. (1950). Untersuchungen an der Milz des Krallenforsches (*Xenopus laevis*). *Morph. Jb.* 90, 221–248.

Suzuki, T., Furusato, M., Takassaki, M., Shimizu, S., and Hataba, Y. (1977). Stereoscopic scanning electron microscopy of the red pulp of dog spleen with special reference to the terminal structure of the cordal capillaries. *Cell Tiss. Res.* 182, 441–453.

Suzuki, T., Hataba, Y., and Sasaki, H. (1989). Fine architecture of the splenic terminal vascular bed as revealed by arterial and venous pressure-loading perfusion fixation. *J. Electron Microsc. Tech.* 12, 132–145.

Tanaka, Y. (1985a). An anatomical study on the spleen of archaic fishes. 1. Coelacanthiformes and Dipneustei. *Acta Haematol. Japon.* 48, 710–723 [in Japanese with English abstract].

Tanaka, Y. (1985b). An anatomical study on the spleen of archaic fishes. 2. Brachiopterygii and Chondrostei. *Acta Haematol. Japon.* 48, 1131–1144 [in Japanese with English abstract].

Tanaka, Y. (1985c). An anatomical study on the spleen of archaic fishes. 3. Lepidostei. *Acta Haematol. Japon.* 48, 1145–1153 [in Japanese with English abstract].

Tanaka, Y. (1986a). Vascular architecture of the spleen of the musk shrew, *Suncus murinus. Acta Haematol. Japon.* 49, 627–633 [in Japanese with English abstract].

Tanaka, Y. (1986b). A morphological study of hematopoietic organs of the platypus, *Ornithorhynchus anatinus. J. Kyushu Haemat. Soc.* 34, 82–91 [in Japanese with English abstract].

Tanaka, Y. (1987). A morphological study of the spleen of the mole, with special reference to its vascular architecture. *Acta Haematol. Japon.* 50, 939–948 [in Japanese with English abstract].

Tanaka, Y. (1990). "Intermediate zone" of mammalian spleens: Light and electron microscopic study of three primitive mammalian species (platypus, shrew, and mole) with special reference to intrasplenic arterio-venous communication. *Am. J. Anat.* 187, 313–337.

Tanaka, Y. (1993). *The Spleen: Origin and Evolution.* Private publication [in Japanese].

Tanaka, Y. (1994). Microscopy of vascular architecture and arteriovenous communications in the spleen of two odontocetes. *J. Morph.* 221, 211–233.

Tanaka, Y., and Goto, M. (1992). A histo-anatomical study on the spleen of a frilled shark (*Chlamydoselachus anguineus*). *Acta Anat. Nippon.* 66, 20–26 [in Japanese with English abstract].

Tanaka, Y., and Hirahara, Y. (1995). Spleen of the snake (*Elaphe climacophora*) and intrasplenic vascular architecture. *J. Morph.* 226, 223–235.

Tanaka, Y., and Saito, Y. (1982). A comparative anatomical study of three different intestinal spleens and their significances in vertebrate hematopoiesis. *Acta Haematol. Japon.* 45, 1,017–1,030. [in Japanese with English abstract].

Tanaka, Y., Saito, Y., and Gotoh, H. (1981). Vascular architecture and intestinal hematopoietic nests of two cyclostomes, *Eptatretus burgeri* and ammocoetes of *Entosphenus reissneri*: A comparative morphological study. *J. Morph.* 170, 71–93.

Tischendorf, F. (1969). Die Milz. In *Handbuch der mikroskopischen Anatomie des Menschen* (W. Bargmann, ed.). Springer, Berlin, vol. 6(6).

Tischendorf, F. (1985) On the evolution of the spleen. *Experientia* 41, 145–151.

Tomonaga, S., Kobayashi, K., and Kajii, T. (1986). Two populations of immunoglobulin-forming cells in the skate *Raja kanojei*: Their distribution and characterization. *Devl. Comp. Immunol.* 8, 803–812.

Tonkoff, W. (1900). Die Entwickelung der Milz bei den Amnioten. *Arch. Mikros. Anat.* 56, 392–458.

Tonkoff, W. (1903). Ueber die Entwickelung der Milz bei *Tropidonotus natrix*. *Anat. Anz.* 23, 214–216.

Tooze, J., and Davis, H. G. (1967). Light- and electron-microscopic studies on the newt *Triturus cristatus*: The fine structure of erythropoietic cells. *J. Cell Sci.* 2, 617–640.

Tooze, J., and Davis, H. G. (1968). Light and electron microscopic observations on the spleen and the splenic leukocytes of the newt *Triturus cristatus*. *Am. J. Anat.* 123, 521–556.

Von Herrath, E. (1935). Bau und Funktion der Milz. *Z. Zellforsch. Mikrosk. Anat.* 23, 375–430.

Von Herrath, E. (1958). *Bau und Funktion der normalen Milz*. Walter de Gruyter, Berlin.

Weilacher, S. (1933). Die Milz der Gymnophionen. Beitrag zur Kenntnis der Gymnophionen Nr. XVII. *Morph. Jb.* 72, 469–498.

Welsch, U., and Storch, V. (1982). Light and electron microscopical observations on the caecilian spleen. A contribution to the evolution of lymphatic organs. *Devl. Comp. Immunol.* 6, 293–302.

Wetherall, J. D., and Turner, K. J. (1972). Immune response of the lizard, *Tiliqua rugosa*. *Aust. J. Exp. Biol. Med. Sci.* 50, 79–95.

Woodland, W. (1906). On the anatomy of *Centrophorus calceus* (*crepidalbus* Bocage and Capello) Günther. *Proc. Zool. Soc. Lond.* 2, 865–886.

Yamada, H. (1951). The post-branchial intestine of the lamprey, with special reference to its vascular system. *Okayama Ishi* (Medical Journal) 63, 1–52 [in Japanese].

Yoffey, J. M. (1928–1929). A contribution to the study of the comparative histology and physiology of the spleen, with reference chiefly to its cellular consistuents. 1. In fishes. *J. Anat.* 63, 314–344.

Zapata, A. G. (1980). Splenic erythropoiesis and thrombopoiesis in elasmobrachs: An ultrastructural study. *Acta Zool., Stockh.* 61, 59–64.

Zapata, A. G., and Cooper, E. L. (1990). *The Immune System, Comparative Histophysiology*. Wiley-Liss, New York.

Zapata, A. G., Leceta, J., and Barrutia, M. G. (1981). Ultrastructure of splenic white pulp of the turtle, *Mauremys caspica*. *Cell Tiss. Res.* 220, 845–855.

Zapata, A. G., Gomariz, R. P., Garrido, E., and Cooper, E. L. (1982). Lymphoid organs and blood cells of the caecilian *Ichthyophis kohtaoensis*. *Acta Zool., Stockh.* 63, 11–16.

Tanaka, Y. (1998). Structure of the Reptilian Spleen. In *Biology of the Reptilia*, vol. 19 (Morphology G) (C. Gans and A. S. Gaunt, eds.). Society for the Study of Amphibians and Reptiles, Ithaca, New York, Contrib. Herpetol., vol. 14, pp. 533–586.

Author Index

Entries in **bold** are to citations in the reference sections of the chapters.

Subject Index

Previous Volumes of
Biology of the Reptilia

Note: None of the above volumes is available for sale from the Society for the Study of Amphibians and Reptiles; inquiries should be addressed to the original publisher. Paperback copies of volumes 17 and 18 are available from the University of Chicago Press. Volume 16 was reprinted by Branta Books and is available from Carl Gans, Department of Zoology, Patterson Building, University of Texas, Austin, Texas 78712, USA.

PUBLICATIONS OF THE
SOCIETY FOR THE STUDY OF AMPHIBIANS AND REPTILES

SOCIETY PUPLICATIONS may be purchased from:
Dr. Robert D. Aldridge, Publications Secretary, Department of Biology, Saint Louis University, Saint Louis, Missouri 63103-2010, USA.

Telephone: area code 314, 977-3916 or 977-1710.
Fax: area code 314, 977-3658.
E-mail: ssar@slu.edu
URL: http://falcon.cc.ukans.edu/~gpisani/SSAR.html

Prices are effective through December 1998. Make checks payable to "SSAR." Overseas customers must make payment in USA funds using a draft drawn on American banks or by International Money Order. All persons may charge to MasterCard or VISA (provide account number and expiration date); items marked "out-of-print" are no longer available from the Society.

Shipping and Handling Costs

• *Shipments inside the USA*: Shipping costs are in addition to the price of publications. Add an amount for shipping of the first item ($3.00 for a book costing $10.00 or more or $2.00 if the item costs less than $10.00) plus an amount for any additional items ($2.00 each for books costing over $10.00 and $1.00 for each item costing less than $10.00).
• *Shipments outside the USA*: Determine the cost for shipments inside USA (above) and then add 5% of the total cost of the order.
• *Large prints* (marked *): For shipments inside the USA, add $3.00 for any quantity; outside the USA, instead add $7.00 for any quantity.

CONTRIBUTIONS TO HERPETOLOGY
Book-length monographs, comprising taxonomic revisions, results of symposia, and other major works. Prepublication discount to Society members.

Vol. 1. *Reproductive Biology and Diseases of Captive Reptiles,* by James B. Murphy and Joseph T. Collins (eds.). 1980. Results of a Society-sponsored symposium, including papers by 37 leading specialists. 287 p., illus. Out-of-print.
Vol. 2. *The Turtles of Venezuela,* by Peter C. H. Pritchard and Pedro Trebbau. 1984. An exhaustive natural history covering half of the turtle species of South America. 414 p., 48 color plates (25 watercolor portraits by Giorgio Voltolina and 165 photographs of turtles and habitats) measuring 8½ × 11 inches, keys, 16 maps. Regular edition, clothbound $45.00; patron's edition, two leatherbound volumes in cloth-covered box, signed and numbered by authors and artist $300.00. (*Also*: set of 25 color prints of turtle portraits on heavy paper stock, in protective wrapper $30.00.)
Vol. 3. *Introduction to the Herpetofauna of Costa Rica / Introducción a la Herpetofauna de Costa Rica,* by Jay M. Savage and Jaime Villa R. 1986. Bilingual edition in English and Spanish, with distribution checklist, bibliographies, and extensive illustrated keys. 220 p., map. Clothbound $30.00.

Vol. 4. *Studies on Chinese Salamanders,* by Ermi Zhao, Qixiong Hu, Yaoming Jiang, and Yuhua Yang. 1988. Evolutionary review of all Chinese species with keys, diagnostic figures, and distribution maps. 80 p., 7 plates (including 10 color photographs of salamanders and habitats). Clothbound $12.00.
Vol. 5. *Contributions to the History of Herpetology,* by Kraig Adler, John S. Applegarth, and Ronald Altig. 1989. Biographies of 152 prominent herpetologists (with portraits and signatures), index to 2500 authors in taxonomic herpetology, and academic lineages of 1450 herpetologists. International coverage. 202 p., 148 photographs, 1 color plate. Clothbound $20.00.
Vol. 6. *Snakes of the* Agkistrodon *Complex: A Monographic Review,* by Howard K. Gloyd and Roger Conant. 1990. Comprehensive treatment of 33 taxa of pitvipers included in four genera: *Agkistrodon, Calloselasma, Deinagkistrodon,* and *Hypnale.* Also includes nine supplementary chapters by leading specialists. 620 p., 33 color plates (247 photographs of snakes and habitats), 20 uncolored plates, 60 text figures, checklist and keys, 6 charts, 28 maps. Clothbound $75.00. (*Also*: separate set of the 247 color photographs of snakes and habitats [on 32 plates], in protective wrapper. $30.00; limited-edition print of the book's frontispiece illustrating snakes of all four genera, from watercolor by David M. Dennis. Signed individually by Roger Conant and the artist $25.00.)
Vol. 7. *The Snakes of Iran,* by Mahmoud Latifi. 1991. Review of the 60 species of Iranian snakes, covering general biology, venoms, and snake bite. Appendix and supplemental bibliography by Alan E. Leviton and George R. Zug. 167 p., 22 color plates of snakes (66 figures), 2 color relief maps, 44 species range maps. Clothbound $22.00.
Vol. 8. *Handbook to Middle East Amphibians and Reptiles,* by Alan E. Leviton, Steven C. Anderson, Kraig Adler, and Sherman A. Minton. 1992. Annotated checklist, illustrated key, and identification manual covering 148 species and subspecies found in region from Turkish border south through the Arabian Peninsula (including Bahrain, Qatar, and United Arab Emirates) and the Arabian (Persian) Gulf. Chapters on venomous snakes and snakebite treatment plus extensive bibliography. 264 p., 32 color plates (220 photographs), maps, text figures. Clothbound $30.00.
Vol. 9. *Herpetology: Current Research on the Biology of Amphibians and Reptiles.* 1992. Proceedings of the First World Congress of Herpetology (Canterbury, 1989), edited by Kraig Adler and with a foreword by H.R.H. Prince Philip, Duke of Edinburgh. Includes the plenary lectures, a summary of the congress, and a list of delegates with their current addresses. 225 p., 28 photographs. Clothbound $28.00.
Vol. 10. *Herpetology of China,* by Ermi Zhao and Kraig Adler. 1993. Comprehensive review of Chinese amphibians and reptiles, including Hong Kong and Taiwan. 522 p., 48 color plates (371 photographs illustrating all 164 genera and half of the 661 species), portraits, text figures, maps, indices. Clothbound $60.00.
Vol. 11. *Captive Management and Conservation of Amphibians and Reptiles,* by James B. Murphy, Kraig Adler, and Joseph T. Collins (eds.). 1994. Results of a Society-sponsored

symposium, including chapters by 70 leading specialists. Foreword by Gerald Durrell. 408 p., 35 photographs, 1 color plate. Clothbound $58.00.

Vol. 12. *Contributions to West Indian Herpetology*, by Robert Powell and Robert W. Henderson (eds.). 1996. Results of a Society-sponsored symposium, including research chapters by 59 authors and a checklist of species with complete citations. Foreword by Thomas W. Schoener. 457 p., 28 photographs, 70 color photographs, index. Clothbound $60.00.

Vol. 13. *Gecko Fauna of the USSR and Contiguous Regions*, by Nikolai N. Szczerbak and Michael L. Golubev. 1996. Covers the systematics, natural history, and conservation of the gecko fauna of the former Soviet Union and related species in surrounding regions from Mongolia through Pakistan, the Middle East, and northern Africa. 245 p., 32 colored and 60 black-and-white photographs, spot distribution maps, bibliography, index. Clothbound $48.00.

Vol. 14. *Biology of the Reptilia, vol. 19 (Morphology G)*, by Carl Gans and Abbot S. Gaunt (eds.). 1998. Chapters by 11 authors cover the major organs situated in the coelom: lungs, heart, liver, and spleen. 660 p., 145 figures, indices. Clothbound $58.00. (A complete list of the earlier volumes in this series [vols. 1–18], with names of publishers, is given in the book.)

FACSIMILE REPRINTS IN HERPETOLOGY

Exact reprints of classic and important books and papers. Most titles have extensive new introductions by leading authorities. Prepublication discount to Society members. Missing volumes are out-of-print and no longer available from the Society.

ANDERSON, J. 1896. *Contribution to the Herpetology of Arabia*. Introduction and new checklist of Arabian amphibians and reptiles by Alan E. Leviton and Michele L. Aldrich. 160 p., illus. (one plate in color), map. Clothbound $25.00.

BOGERT, C. M., and R. MARTÍN DEL CAMPO. 1956. *The Gila Monster and Its Allies*. The standard work on lizards of the family Helodermatidae. New preface by Charles M. Bogert and retrospective essay by Daniel D. Beck. 262 p., color plate, 62 photographs, 35 text figures, index. Clothbound $38.00.

BOULENGER, G. A. 1877–1920. *Contributions to American Herpetology*. A collection of papers (from various journals) covering North, Central, and South American species, with an introduction by James C. Battersby. Complete in 18 parts totalling 880 p., numerous illustrations, index. Paperbound. Complete set: 18 parts plus index and two tables of contents (for binding in two volumes), in parts as issued $55.00.

COPE, E. D. 1864. *Papers on the Higher Classification of Frogs*. Reprinted from Proceedings of the Academy of Natural Sciences of Philadelphia and Natural History Review. 32 p. Paperbound $3.00.

COPE, E. D. 1871. *Catalogue of Batrachia and Reptilia Obtained by McNiel in Nicaragua; Catalogue of Reptilia and Batrachia Obtained by Maynard in Florida*. 8 p. Paperbound $1.00.

COPE, E. D. 1892. *The Osteology of the Lacertilia*. An important contribution to lizard anatomy, reprinted from Proceedings of the American Philosophical Society. 44 p., 6 plates. Paperbound $4.00.

COWLES, R. B., and C. M. BOGERT. 1944. *A Preliminary Study of the Thermal Requirements of Desert Reptiles*. The foundation of thermoregulation biology, with extensive review of recent studies by F. Harvey Pough. Reprinted from Bulletin of American Museum of Natural History. 52 p., 11 plates. Paperbound $5.00.

ESCHSCHOLTZ, F. 1829–1833. *Zoologischer Atlas* (herpetological sections). Descriptions of new reptiles and amphibians from California and the Pacific. Introduction by

Kraig Adler. 32 p., 4 plates (measuring 8½ × 11 inches). Paperbound $3.00.

ESPADA, M. JIMÉNEZ DE LA. 1875. *Vertebrados del Viaje al Pacifico: Batracios*. A major taxonomic work on South American frogs. Introduction by Jay M. Savage. 208 p., 6 plates, maps. Clothbound $20.00.

FAUVEL, A.-A. 1879. *Alligators in China*. Original description of *Alligator sinensis*, including classical and natural history. 42 p., 3 plates. Paperbound $5.00.

FITZINGER, L. 1826 & 1835. *Neue Classification der Reptilien* and *Systematische Anordnung der Schildkröten*. Important nomenclatural landmarks for herpetology, including Amphibia as well as reptiles; world-wide in scope. Introduction by Robert Mertens. 110 p., folding chart. Clothbound $30.00.

GRAY, J. E. 1825. *A Synopsis of the Genera of Reptiles and Amphibia*. Reprinted from Annals of Philosophy. 32 p. Paperbound $3.00.

GRAY, J. E. 1831–1844. *Zoological Miscellany*. A privately printed journal, devoted mostly to descriptions of amphibians, reptiles, and birds from throughout the world. Introduction by Arnold G. Kluge. 86 p., 4 plates. Paperbound $6.00.

GRAY, J. E., and A. GÜNTHER. 1845–1875. *Lizards of Australia and New Zealand*. The reptile section from "Voyage of H.M.S. Erebus and Terror," together with Gray's 1867 related book on Australian lizards. Introduction by Glenn M. Shea. 82 p., 20 plates (measuring 8½ × 11 inches). Clothbound $20.00. (*Also*: set of the 20 plates in protective wrapper $12.00.)

GÜNTHER, A. 1885–1902. *Biologia Centrali-Americana. Reptilia and Batrachia*. The standard work on Middle American herpetology with 76 full-page plates measuring 8½ × 11 inches (12 in color). Introductions by Hobart M. Smith, A. E. Gunther, and Kraig Adler. 575 p., photographs, maps. Clothbound $50.00. (*Also*: separate set of the 12 color plates, in protective wrapper $18.00.)

HOLBROOK, J. E. 1842. *North American Herpetology*. Five volumes bound in one. The classic work by the father of North American herpetology. Exact facsimile of the definitive second edition, including all 147 plates, measuring 8½ × 11 inches (20 reproduced in full color). Introduction and checklists by Richard and Patricia Worthington and by Kraig Adler. 1032 p. Leatherbound patron's edition, out-of-print; regular edition, clothbound $60.00.

JUNIOR SOCIETY OF NATURAL SCIENCES (CINCINNATI, OHIO). 1930–1932. Herpetological papers from the society's Proceedings, with articles by Weller, Walker, Dury, and others. 56 p. Paperbound $3.00.

KIRTLAND, J. P. 1838. *Zoology of Ohio* (herpetological portion). 8 p. Paperbound $1.00.

LeCONTE, J. E. 1824–1828. *Three Papers on Amphibians*, from the Annals of the Lyceum of Natural History, New York. 16 p. Paperbound $2.00.

McILHENNY, E. A. 1935. *The Alligator's Life History*. The most complete natural history of the American alligator. Introduction by Archie Carr and a review of recent literature by Jeffrey W. Lang. 125 p., 18 photographs and a portrait. Clothbound $20.00.

McLAIN, R. B. 1899. *Contributions to North American Herpetology* (three parts). 28 p., index. Paperbound $2.00.

ORBIGNY, A. D' [and G. BIBRON]. 1847. *Voyage dans l'Amérique Méridionale*. This extract comprises the complete section on reptiles and amphibians from this voyage to South America. 14 p., 9 plates measuring 8½ × 11 inches. Paperbound $3.00.

PETERS, W. 1838–1883. *The Herpetological Contributions of Wilhelm C. H. Peters (1815–1883)*. A collection of 174 titles, world-wide in scope, and including the herpetological volume in Peters' series, "Reise nach Mossambique." Biography, annotated bibliography, and synopsis of species by Aaron M. Bauer, Rainer

Günther, and Meghan Klipfel. 714 pages, 114 plates, 9 photographs, maps, index. Clothbound $75.00.

RAFINESQUE, C. S. 1820. *Annals of Nature* (herpetological and ichthyological sections), 4 p. Paperbound $1.00.

RAFINESQUE, C. S. 1822. *On Two New Salamanders of Kentucky.* 2 p. Paperbound $1.00.

RAFINESQUE, C. S. 1832–1833. *Five Herpetological Papers from the Atlantic Journal.* 4 p. Paperbound $1.00.

SCHMIDT, K. P., and G. K. NOBLE. 1919–1923. *Contributions to the Herpetology of the Belgian Congo.* An essential reference for the Congo rain forest and the Sudanese savanna. Introductions by Donald G. Broadley and John C. Poynton. 780 pages, 141 photographs, maps, indices. Clothbound $65.00.

SOWERBY, J. DEC., E. LEAR, and J. E. GRAY. 1872. *Tortoises, Terrapins, and Turtles Drawn From Life.* The finest atlas of turtle illustrations ever produced. Introduction by Ernest E. Williams. 26 p., 61 full-page plates (measuring 8½ × 11 inches). Clothbound $25.00.

SPIX, J. B. VON, and J. G. WAGLER. 1824–1825. *Herpetology of Brazil.* The most comprehensive and important early survey of Brazilian herpetology. Introduction by P. E. Vanzolini. 400 p., 98 plates, one in color (each measuring 8½ × 11 inches), map. Clothbound $36.00.

STEJNEGER, L. 1907. *Herpetology of Japan and Adjacent Territory.* Introduction by Masafumi Matsui. Also covers Taiwan, Korea, and adjacent China and Siberia. 684 pages, 35 plates, 409 text figures, keys, index. Clothbound $58.00.

TROSCHEL, F. H. 1850 [1852]. Cophosaurus texanus, *neue Eidechsengattung aus Texas.* 8 p. Paperbound $1.00.

TSCHUDI, J. J. VON. 1838. *Classification der Batrachier.* A major work in systematic herpetology, with introduction by Robert Mertens. 118 p., 6 plates. Paperbound $18.00.

TSCHUDI, J. J. VON. 1845. *Reptilium Conspectus.* New reptiles and amphibians from Peru. 24 p. Paperbound $2.00.

VANDENBURGH, J. 1895–1896. *Herpetology of Lower California.* Herpetology of Baja California, Mexico (collected papers). 101 p., 11 plates, index. Paperbound $8.00.

VANDENBURGH, J. 1914. *The Giant Land Tortoises of the Galapagos Archipelago.* The most extensive review of Galapagos tortoises. Foreword by Peter C. H. Pritchard. 290 pages, 205 photographs, map, index. Clothbound $55.00.

WAITE, E. R. 1929. *The Reptiles and Amphibians of South Australia.* Introduction by Michael J. Tyler and Mark Hutchinson. 282 p., color plate, portrait, 192 text figures including numerous photographs. Clothbound $35.00.

WILCOX, E. V. 1891. *Notes on Ohio Batrachians.* 3 p. Paperbound $1.00.

WRIGHT, A. H., and A. A. WRIGHT. 1962. *Handbook of Snakes of the United States and Canada, Volume 3, Bibliography.* Cross-indexed bibliography to Volumes 1 and 2. 187 p. Clothbound $18.00.

JOURNAL OF HERPETOLOGY

The Society's official scientific journal, international in scope. Issued quarterly as part of Society membership. All numbers are paperbound as issued, measuring 7 × 10 inches.

Volume 1 (1968), numbers 1–4 combined.

Volumes 2–5 (1968–1971), numbers 1–2 and 3–4 combined, $8.00 per double number.

Volume 6 (1972), numbers 1, 2, and double number 3–4.

Volumes 7–31 (1973–1997), four numbers in each volume, $8.00 per single number.

The following volumes and numbers are out-of-print and are *no longer available*: Volume 1, 2, 3, 4, 5(3, 4), 6, 7(1), 8(1), 9(1, 2, 4), 10(1, 4), 11(4), and 12(1, 2).

Cumulative Index for Volumes 1–10 (1968–1976), 72 pages, $8.00.

HERPETOLOGICAL REVIEW AND H.I.S.S. PUBLICATIONS

The Society's official newsletter, international in coverage. In addition to news notes and feature articles, regular departments include regional societies, techniques, husbandry, life history, geographic distribution, and book reviews. Issued quarterly as part of Society membership or separately by subscription. All numbers are paperbound as issued and measure 8½ × 11 inches. In 1973, publications of the Herpetological Information Search Systems (*News-Journal* and *Titles and Reviews*) were substituted for *Herpetological Review*; content and format are the same.

Volume 1 (1967–1969), numbers 1–9, $5.00 per number.

Volumes 2–28 (1970–1997), four numbers in each volume (except volumes 3–4, with 6 numbers each), $5.00 per number.

The following numbers are out-of-print and *no longer available*: Volume 1 (number 7), 3(2), 4(1), 5(1, 2), 6(1, 2, 4), 7(3, 4), and 10(2).

Cumulative Index for Volumes 1–7 (1967–1976), 60 pages, $5.00.

Cumulative Index for Volumes 1–17 (1967–1986), 90 pages, $8.00.

H.I.S.S. Publications: News-Journal, volume 1, numbers 1–6, and Titles and Reviews, volume 1, numbers 1–2 (all of 1973–1974), complete set, $10.00.

Index to Geographic Distribution Records for Volumes 1–17 (1967–1986), including H.I.S.S. publications, 44 pages, $6.00.

CATALOGUE OF AMERICAN AMPHIBIANS AND REPTILES

Loose-leaf accounts of taxa (measuring 8½ × 11 inches) prepared by specialists, including synonymy, definition, description, distribution map, and comprehensive list of literature for each taxon. Covers amphibians and reptiles of the entire Western Hemisphere. Issued by subscription. Individual accounts are not sold separately.

CATALOGUE ACCOUNTS:

Complete set: Numbers 1–660, $360.00.

Partial sets: Numbers 1–190, $75.00.
　　　　　　 Numbers 191–410, $85.00.
　　　　　　 Numbers 411–660, $230.00.

INDEX TO ACCOUNTS 1–400: Cross-referenced, 64 pages, $6.00; accounts 401–600: Cross-referenced, 32 pages, $6.00.

IMPRINTED POST BINDER: $35.00. (*Note:* one binder holds about 200 accounts.)

SYSTEMATIC TABS: Ten printed tabs for binder, such as "Class Amphibia," "Order Caudata," etc., $6.00 per set.

HERPETOLOGICAL CONSERVATION

A new series of book-length monographs, including symposia, devoted to all aspects of the conservation of amphibian and reptiles. Prepublication discount to Society members.

Vol. 1. *Amphibians in Decline: Canadian Studies of a Global Problem,* by David M. Green (ed.). Chapters by 52 authors dealing with population dispersal and fluctuations, genetic diversity, monitoring of natural populations, as well as effects of temperature, acidity, pesticides, UV light, forestry practices, and disease. 351 p., numerous photographs, figures, and tables, index. Paperbound $40.00.

Vol. 2. *Amphibian and Reptilian Ecotoxicology: Papers from the Third World Congress of Herpetology,* by Michael R. K. Lambert (ed.), in preparation.

HERPETOLOGICAL CIRCULARS

Miscellaneous publications of general interest to the herpetological community. All numbers are paperbound, as issued. Prepublication discount to Society members.

No. 1. *A Guide to Preservation Techniques for Amphibians and Reptiles* by George R. Pisani. 1973. 22 p., illus. $3.00.

No. 2. *Guía de Técnicas de Preservación de Anfibios y Reptiles* por George R. Pisani y Jaime Villa. 1974. 28 p., illus. $3.00.

No. 3. *Collections of Preserved Amphibians and Reptiles in the United States* compiled by David Wake (chair) and the Committee on Resources in Herpetology. 1975. 22 p. Out-of-print.

No. 4. *A Brief Outline of Suggested Treatments for Diseases of Captive Reptiles* by James Murphy. 1975. 13 p. Out-of-print.

No. 5. *Endangered and Threatened Amphibians and Reptiles in the United States* compiled by Ray E. Ashton, Jr. (chair) and 1973–74 SSAR Regional Herpetological Societies Liaison Committee. 1976. 65 p. Out-of-print.

No. 6. *Longevity of Reptiles and Amphibians in North American Collections* by J. Kevin Bowler. 1977. 32 p. Out-of-print. (see also number 21.)

No. 7. *Standard Common and Current Scientific Names for North American Amphibians and Reptiles* (1st ed.) by Joseph T. Collins, James E. Huheey, James L. Knight, and Hobart M. Smith. 1978. 36 p. $3.00. (See also numbers 12, 19, and 25.)

No. 8. *A Brief History of Herpetology in North America Before 1900* by Kraig Adler. 1979. 40 p., 24 photographs, 1 map. $3.00.

No. 9. *A Review of Marking Techniques for Amphibians and Reptiles* by John W. Ferner. 1979. 42 p., illus. $3.00.

No. 10. *Vernacular Names of South American Turtles* by Russell A. Mittermeier, Federico Medem and Anders G. J. Rhodin. 1980. 44 p. $3.00.

No. 11. *Recent Instances of Albinism in North American Amphibians and Reptiles* by Stanley Dyrkacz. 1981. 36 p. $3.00.

No. 12. *Standard Common and Current Scientific Names for North American Amphibians and Reptiles* (2nd ed.) by Joseph T. Collins, Roger Conant, James E. Huheey, James L. Knight, Eric M. Rundquist, and Hobart M. Smith. 1982. 32 p. $3.00. (See also numbers 7, 19, and 25.)

No. 13. *Silver Anniversary Membership Directory*, including addresses of all SSAR members, addresses and publications of the herpetological societies of the world, and a brief history of the Society. 1983. 56 p., 4 photographs. $3.00.

No. 14. *Checklist of the Turtles of the World with English Common Names* by John Iverson. 1985. 14 p. $3.00.

No. 15. *Cannibalism in Reptiles: A World-Wide Review* by Joseph C. Mitchell. 1986. 37 p. $4.00.

No. 16. *Herpetological Collecting and Collections Management* by John E. Simmons. 1987. 72 p., 6 photographs. $6.00.

No. 17. *An Annotated List and Guide to the Amphibians and Reptiles of Monteverde, Costa Rica* by Marc P. Hayes, J. Alan Pounds, and Walter W. Timmerman. 1989. 70 p., 32 figures. $5.00.

No. 18. *Type Catalogues of Herpetological Collections: An Annotated List of Lists* by Charles R. Crumly. 1990. 50 p. $5.00.

No. 19. *Standard Common and Current Scientific Names for North American Amphibians and Reptiles* (3rd ed.) compiled by Joseph T. Collins (coordinator for SSAR Common and Scientific Names List). 1990. 45 p. Out-of-print. (See also numbers 7, 12, and 25.)

No. 20. *Age Determination in Turtles* by George R. Zug. 1991. 32 p., 6 figures. $5.00.

No. 21. *Longevity of Reptiles and Amphibians in North American Collections* (2nd ed.) by Andrew T. Snider and J. Kevin Bowler. 1992. 44 p. $5.00.

No. 22. *Biology, Status, and Management of the Timber Rattlesnake* (Crotalus horridus): *A Guide for Conservation* by William S. Brown. 1993. 84 p., 16 color photographs. $12.00.

No. 23. *Scientific and Common Names for the Amphibians and Reptiles of Mexico in English and Spanish / Nombres Científicos y Comunes en Ingles y Español de los Anfibios y los Reptiles de México* by Ernest A. Liner. Spanish translation by José L. Camarillo R. 1994. 118 p. $12.00.

No. 24. *Citations for the Original Descriptions of North American Amphibians and Reptiles*, by Ellin Beltz. 1995. 48 p. $7.00.

No. 25. *Standard Common and Scientific Names for North American Amphibians and Reptiles* (4th ed.) compiled by Joseph T. Collins (coordinator for SSAR Common and Scientific Names List). 1997. 44 p. $9.00. (see also numbers 7, 12, and 19.)

No. 26. *Venomous Snakes: a Safety Guide for Keepers*, by William Altimari. In press.

PUBLICATIONS OF THE OHIO HERPETOLOGICAL SOCIETY

OHS was the predecessor to the Society for the Study of Amphibians and Reptiles. All publications international in scope. Paperbound as issued.

Volume 1 numbers 1–4, plus Special Publications 1–2 (all 1958), facsimile reprint, out-of-print.

Volume 2 (1959–1960), four numbers, $2.00 per number; numbers 3 and 4 out-of-print.

Volume 3 (1961–1962), four numbers, $1.00 per number; numbers 1 and 3 out-of-print.

Volume 4 (1963–1964), four numbers; double number 1–2, $4.00, numbers 3 and 4 $2.00 each.

Volume 5 (1965–1966), four numbers, $2.00 per number.

Special Publications 3–4 (1961–1962), $2.00 per number; number 3 out-of-print.

OTHER MATERIALS AVAILABLE FROM THE SOCIETY

The following color prints and brochures may be purchased from the Society. (*Extra postage required; see "Shipping and Handling Costs.")

*SILVER ANNIVERSARY COMMEMORATIVE PRINT. Full-color print (11½ × 15¼ inches) of a Gila Monster (*Heloderma suspectum*) on natural background, from a watercolor by David M. Dennis. Issued as part of Society's 25th Anniversary in 1982. Edition limited to 1000. $6.00 each or $5.00 in quantities of 10 or more.

*WORLD CONGRESS COMMEMORATIVE PRINT. Full-color print (11½ × 15 inches) of an Eastern Box Turtle (*Terrapene carolina*) in a natural setting, from a watercolor by David M. Dennis. Issued as part of SSAR's salute to the First World Congress of Herpetology, held at Canterbury, United Kingdom, in 1989. Edition limited to 1500. $6.00 each or $5.00 in quantities of 10 or more.

*WATER SNAKE PRINT. Full-color print (9½ × 12 inches) of endangered water snakes (*Nerodia erythrogaster neglecta* and *N. sipedon insularum*) described by Roger Conant. Edition limited to 450 copies, each individually signed and numbered by Dr. Conant and the artist, David M. Dennis. $25.00.

GUIDELINES FOR THE USE OF LIVE AMPHIBIANS AND REPTILES IN FIELD RESEARCH, by George R. Pisani, Stephen D. Busack, Herbert C. Dessauer, and Victor H. Hutchison, representing a joint committee of ASIH, HL, and SSAR. 1987. Brochure covers animal care, regulations, collecting, restraint and handling, marking, housing and maintenance in field, and final disposition of specimens. 16 p. $4.00 ($3.00 each in quantities of five or more copies).

GRANTS AND AWARDS FOR HERPETOLOGISTS, by Joan C. Milam. 1997. A detailed listing, with descriptions and addresses, for about 100 research award programs. 106 p. $8.00.

Production Specifications

WORD PROCESSING AND FORMATTING OF TEXT: Cornell University, Ithaca, New York, USA. Type was set in Palatino face, using Adobe PageMaker 5.0 on a Macintosh IIci computer, and was provided to the printer on 200 Mb Syquest disks.

PRINTING OF TEXT AND BINDING: Thomson-Shore, Inc., Dexter, Michigan, USA (Ned Thomson, Lana Paton, Rebecca Dawson). The text is printed on 60-pound Domtar Windsor Smooth (Joy) White Offset paper, a recycled stock. The book is covered in Roxite C-1 cloth (vellum finish) with Multicolor Antique endpapers.

PAPER: All paper in this book is acid- and groundwood-free. It meets the guidelines for permanence and durability of the Committee on Publication Guidelines for Book Longevity of the Council on Library Resources.

DATE OF PUBLICATION: 10 July 1998.

PLACE OF PUBLICATION: Ithaca, New York, USA.

NUMBER OF COPIES: 1000.